ORGANIC CHEMISTRY I

CHEM 313

Author

Solomons

ISBN 9781118978887

Cover Image: Suzanne W. Slayden

Printed in the United States of America 10 9 8 7 6 5 4 3 2 1

List of Titles

Organic Chemistry, 11th edition
by T.W. Graham Solomons, Craig B. Fryhle, and Scott A. Snyder
Copyright © 2014, ISBN: 978-1-118-13357-6

Table of Contents

Originally from *Organic Chemistry, 11th edition*

CHAPTER

1

The Basics

BONDING AND MOLECULAR STRUCTURE

Organic chemistry plays a role in all aspects of our lives, from the clothing we wear, to the pixels of our television and computer screens, to preservatives in food, to the inks that color the pages of this book. If you take the time to understand organic chemistry, to learn its overall logic, then you will truly have the power to change society. Indeed, organic chemistry provides the power to synthesize new drugs, to engineer molecules that can make computer processors run more quickly, to understand why grilled meat can cause cancer and how its effects can be combated, and to design ways to knock the calories out of sugar while still making food taste deliciously sweet. It can explain biochemical processes like aging, neural functioning, and cardiac arrest, and show how we can prolong and improve life. It can do almost anything.

IN THIS CHAPTER WE WILL CONSIDER:

- what kinds of atoms make up organic molecules
- the principles that determine how the atoms in organic molecules are bound together
- how best to depict organic molecules

[**WHY** DO THESE TOPICS MATTER?] At the end of the chapter, we will see how some of the unique organic structures that nature has woven together possess amazing properties that we can harness to aid human health.

1

1.1 LIFE AND THE CHEMISTRY OF CARBON COMPOUNDS—WE ARE STARDUST

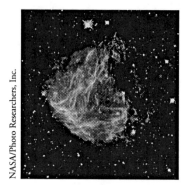

Supernovae were the crucibles in which the heavy elements were formed.

Organic chemistry is the chemistry of compounds that contain the element carbon. If a compound does not contain the element carbon, it is said to be *inorganic*.

Look for a moment at the periodic table inside the front cover of this book. More than a hundred elements are listed there. The question that comes to mind is this: why should an entire field of chemistry be based on the chemistry of compounds that contain this one element, carbon? There are several reasons, the primary one being this: **carbon compounds are central to the structure of living organisms and therefore to the existence of life on Earth. We exist because of carbon compounds.**

What is it about carbon that makes it the element that nature has chosen for living organisms? There are two important reasons: carbon atoms can form strong bonds to other carbon atoms to form rings and chains of carbon atoms, and carbon atoms can also form strong bonds to elements such as hydrogen, nitrogen, oxygen, and sulfur. Because of these bond-forming properties, carbon can be the basis for the huge diversity of compounds necessary for the emergence of living organisms.

From time to time, writers of science fiction have speculated about the possibility of life on other planets being based on the compounds of another element—for example, silicon, the element most like carbon. However, the bonds that silicon atoms form to each other are not nearly as strong as those formed by carbon, and therefore it is very unlikely that silicon could be the basis for anything equivalent to life as we know it.

1.1A What Is the Origin of the Element Carbon?

Through the efforts of physicists and cosmologists, we now understand much of how the elements came into being. The light elements hydrogen and helium were formed at the beginning, in the Big Bang. Lithium, beryllium, and boron, the next three elements, were formed shortly thereafter when the universe had cooled somewhat. All of the heavier elements were formed millions of years later in the interiors of stars through reactions in which the nuclei of lighter elements fuse to form heavier elements.

The energy of stars comes primarily from the fusion of hydrogen nuclei to produce helium nuclei. This nuclear reaction explains why stars shine. Eventually some stars begin to run out of hydrogen, collapse, and explode—they become supernovae. Supernovae explosions scatter heavy elements throughout space. Eventually, some of these heavy elements drawn by the force of gravity became part of the mass of planets like the Earth.

1.1B How Did Living Organisms Arise?

This question is one for which an adequate answer cannot be given now because there are many things about the emergence of life that we do not understand. However, we do know this. Organic compounds, some of considerable complexity, are detected in outer space, and meteorites containing organic compounds have rained down on Earth since it was formed. A meteorite that fell near Murchison, Victoria, Australia, in 1969 was found to contain over 90 different amino acids, 19 of which are found in living organisms on Earth. While this does not mean that life arose in outer space, it does suggest that events in outer space may have contributed to the emergence of life on Earth.

In 1924 Alexander Oparin, a biochemist at the Moscow State University, postulated that life on Earth may have developed through the gradual evolution of carbon-based molecules in a "primordial soup" of the compounds that were thought to exist on a prebiotic Earth: methane, hydrogen, water, and ammonia. This idea was tested by experiments carried out at the University of Chicago in 1952 by Stanley Miller and Harold Urey. They showed that amino acids and other complex organic compounds are synthesized when an electric spark (think of lightning) passes through a flask containing a mixture of these four compounds (think of the early atmosphere). Miller and Urey in their 1953 publication reported that five amino acids (essential constituents of proteins) were formed. In 2008, examination of archived solutions from Miller and Urey's original

NASA/Photo Researchers, Inc.

experiments have shown that 22 amino acids, rather than the 5 amino acids originally reported, were actually formed.

Similar experiments have shown that other precursors of biomolecules can also arise in this way—compounds such as ribose and adenine, two components of RNA. Some RNA molecules can not only store genetic information as DNA does, they can also act as catalysts, as enzymes do.

There is much to be discovered to explain exactly how the compounds in this soup became living organisms, but one thing seems certain. The carbon atoms that make up our bodies were formed in stars, so, in a sense, we are stardust.

An RNA molecule

1.1C Development of the Science of Organic Chemistry

The science of organic chemistry began to flower with the demise of a nineteenth century theory called vitalism. According to vitalism, organic compounds were only those that came from living organisms, and only living things could synthesize organic compounds through intervention of a vital force. Inorganic compounds were considered those compounds that came from nonliving sources. Friedrich Wöhler, however, discovered in 1828 that an organic compound called urea (a constituent of urine) could be made by evaporating an aqueous solution of the inorganic compound ammonium cyanate. With this discovery, the synthesis of an organic compound, began the evolution of organic chemistry as a scientific discipline.

$$NH_4{}^+NCO^- \xrightarrow{\text{heat}} \underset{\substack{\\ H_2N \qquad NH_2 \\ \textbf{Urea}}}{\overset{\substack{O \\ \| \\ C}}{}}$$

Ammonium cyanate   **Urea**

THE CHEMISTRY OF... Natural Products

Despite the demise of vitalism in science, the word "organic" is still used today by some people to mean "coming from living organisms" as in the terms "organic vitamins" and "organic fertilizers." The commonly used term "organic food" means that the food was grown without the use of synthetic fertilizers and pesticides. An "organic vitamin" means to these people that the vitamin was isolated from a natural source and not synthesized by a chemist. While there are sound arguments to be made against using food contaminated with certain pesticides, while there may be environmental benefits to be obtained from organic farming, and while "natural" vitamins may contain beneficial substances not present in synthetic vitamins, it is impossible to argue that pure "natural" vitamin C, for example, is healthier than pure "synthetic" vitamin C, since the two substances are identical in all respects. In science today, the study of compounds from living organisms is called natural products chemistry. In the closer to this chapter we will consider more about why natural products chemistry is important.

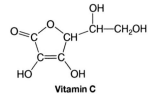

Vitamin C

Vitamin C is found in various citrus fruits.

FOODCOLLECTION/Image Source

1.2 ATOMIC STRUCTURE

Before we begin our study of the compounds of carbon we need to review some basic but familiar ideas about the chemical elements and their structure.

- The **compounds** we encounter in chemistry are made up of **elements** combined in different proportions.

- **Elements** are made up of **atoms.** An atom (Fig. 1.1) consists of a dense, positively charged *nucleus* containing **protons** and **neutrons** and a surrounding cloud of **electrons.**

Each proton of the nucleus bears one positive charge; electrons bear one negative charge. Neutrons are electrically neutral; they bear no charge. Protons and neutrons have

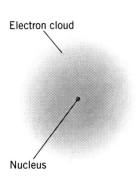

Electron cloud

Nucleus

FIGURE 1.1 An atom is composed of a tiny nucleus containing protons and neutrons and a large surrounding volume containing electrons. The diameter of a typical atom is about 10,000 times the diameter of its nucleus.

nearly equal masses (approximately 1 atomic mass unit each) and are about 1800 times as heavy as electrons. Most of the **mass** of an atom, therefore, comes from the mass of the nucleus; the atomic mass contributed by the electrons is negligible. Most of the **volume** of an atom, however, comes from the electrons; the volume of an atom occupied by the electrons is about 10,000 times larger than that of the nucleus.

The elements commonly found in organic molecules are carbon, hydrogen, nitrogen, oxygen, phosphorus, and sulfur, as well as the halogens: fluorine, chlorine, bromine, and iodine.

Each **element** is distinguished by its **atomic number (Z)**, a **number equal to the number of protons in its nucleus**. Because an atom is electrically neutral, **the atomic number also equals the number of electrons surrounding the nucleus**.

1.2A Isotopes

Before we leave the subject of atomic structure and the periodic table, we need to examine one other observation: **the existence of atoms of the same element that have different masses**.

For example, the element carbon has six protons in its nucleus giving it an atomic number of 6. Most carbon atoms also have six neutrons in their nuclei, and because each proton and each neutron contributes one atomic mass unit (1 amu) to the mass of the atom, carbon atoms of this kind have a mass number of 12 and are written as ^{12}C.

• **Although all the nuclei of all atoms of the same element will have the same number of protons**, some atoms of the same element **may have different masses** because they have **different numbers of neutrons**. Such atoms are called isotopes.

For example, about 1% of the atoms of elemental carbon have nuclei containing 7 neutrons, and thus have a mass number of 13. Such atoms are written ^{13}C. A tiny fraction of carbon atoms have 8 neutrons in their nucleus and a mass number of 14. Unlike atoms of carbon-12 and carbon-13, atoms of carbon-14 are radioactive. The ^{14}C isotope is used in *carbon dating*. The three forms of carbon, ^{12}C, ^{13}C, and ^{14}C, are isotopes of one another.

Most atoms of the element hydrogen have one proton in their nucleus and have no neutron. They have a mass number of 1 and are written ^{1}H. A very small percentage (0.015%) of the hydrogen atoms that occur naturally, however, have one neutron in their nucleus. These atoms, called *deuterium* atoms, have a mass number of 2 and are written ^{2}H. An unstable (and radioactive) isotope of hydrogen, called *tritium* (^{3}H), has two neutrons in its nucleus.

PRACTICE PROBLEM 1.1   There are two stable isotopes of nitrogen, ^{14}N and ^{15}N. How many protons and neutrons does each isotope have?

1.2B Valence Electrons

We discuss the electron configurations of atoms in more detail in Section 1.10. For the moment we need only to point out that the electrons that surround the nucleus exist in **shells** of increasing energy and at increasing distances from the nucleus. The most important shell, called the **valence shell**, is the outermost shell because the electrons of this shell are the ones that an atom uses in making chemical bonds with other atoms to form compounds.

• How do we know how many electrons an atom has in its valence shell? We look at the periodic table. The number of electrons in the valence shell (called **valence electrons**) is equal to the group number of the atom. For example, carbon is in group **IVA** and carbon has *four* valence electrons; oxygen is in group **VIA** and oxygen has *six* valence electrons. The halogens of group **VIIA** all have *seven* electrons.

PRACTICE PROBLEM 1.2   How many valence electrons does each of the following atoms have?

    (a) Na   **(b)** Cl   **(c)** Si   **(d)** B   **(e)** Ne   **(f)** N

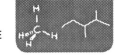

1.3 CHEMICAL BONDS: THE OCTET RULE

The first explanations of the nature of chemical bonds were advanced by G. N. Lewis (of the University of California, Berkeley) and W. Kössel (of the University of Munich) in 1916. Two major types of chemical bonds were proposed:

1. **Ionic** (or electrovalent) bonds are formed by the transfer of one or more electrons from one atom to another to create ions.
2. **Covalent** bonds result when atoms share electrons.

The central idea in their work on bonding is that atoms without the electronic configuration of a noble gas generally react to produce such a configuration because these configurations are known to be highly stable. For all of the noble gases except helium, this means achieving an octet of electrons in the valence shell.

- The **valence shell** is the outermost shell of electrons in an atom.
- The tendency for an atom to achieve a configuration where its valence shell contains eight electrons is called the **octet rule**.

The concepts and explanations that arise from the original propositions of Lewis and Kössel are satisfactory for explanations of many of the problems we deal with in organic chemistry today. For this reason we shall review these two types of bonds in more modern terms.

1.3A Ionic Bonds

Atoms may gain or lose electrons and form charged particles called **ions**.

- An **ionic bond** is an attractive force between oppositely charged ions.

One source of such ions is a reaction between atoms of widely differing electronegativities (Table 1.1).

- **Electronegativity** *is a measure of the ability of an atom to attract electrons.*
- Electronegativity increases as we go across a horizontal row of the periodic table from left to right and it increases as we go up a vertical column (Table 1.1).

An example of the formation of an ionic bond is the reaction of lithium and fluorine atoms:

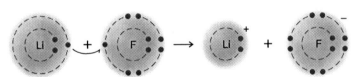

Lithium, a typical metal, has a very low electronegativity; fluorine, a nonmetal, is the most electronegative element of all. The loss of an electron (a negatively charged species)

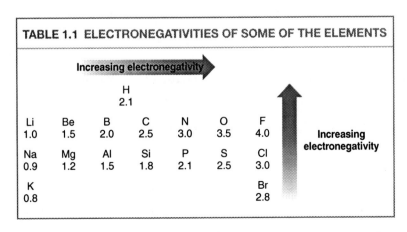

TABLE 1.1 ELECTRONEGATIVITIES OF SOME OF THE ELEMENTS

Increasing electronegativity →

			H 2.1				
Li 1.0	Be 1.5	B 2.0	C 2.5	N 3.0	O 3.5	F 4.0	Increasing electronegativity
Na 0.9	Mg 1.2	Al 1.5	Si 1.8	P 2.1	S 2.5	Cl 3.0	
K 0.8						Br 2.8	

by the lithium atom leaves a lithium cation (Li^+); the gain of an electron by the fluorine atom gives a fluoride anion (F^-).

- Ions form because atoms can achieve the electronic configuration of a noble gas by gaining or losing electrons.

The lithium cation with two electrons in its valence shell is like an atom of the noble gas helium, and the fluoride anion with eight electrons in its valence shell is like an atom of the noble gas neon. Moreover, crystalline lithium fluoride forms from the individual lithium and fluoride ions. In this process negative fluoride ions become surrounded by positive lithium ions, and positive lithium ions by negative fluoride ions. In this crystalline state, the ions have substantially lower energies than the atoms from which they have been formed. Lithium and fluorine are thus "stabilized" when they react to form crystalline lithium fluoride.

We represent the formula for lithium fluoride as LiF, because that is the simplest formula for this ionic compound.

Ionic substances, because of their strong internal electrostatic forces, are usually very high melting solids, often having melting points above 1000 °C. In polar solvents, such as water, the ions are solvated (see Section 2.13D), and such solutions usually conduct an electric current.

- Ionic compounds, often called salts, form only when atoms of very different electronegativities transfer electrons to become ions.

PRACTICE PROBLEM 1.3   Using the periodic table, which element in each pair is more electronegative?
(a) Si, O   **(b)** N, C   **(c)** Cl, Br   **(d)** S, P

1.3B Covalent Bonds and Lewis Structures

When two or more atoms of the same or similar electronegativities react, a complete transfer of electrons does not occur. In these instances the atoms achieve noble gas configurations by *sharing electrons.*

- Covalent bonds form by sharing of electrons between atoms of similar electronegativities to achieve the configuration of a noble gas.
- Molecules are composed of atoms joined exclusively or predominantly by covalent bonds.

Molecules may be represented by electron-dot formulas or, more conveniently, by formulas where each pair of electrons shared by two atoms is represented by a line.

- A dash structural formula has lines that show bonding electron pairs and includes elemental symbols for the atoms in a molecule.

Some examples are shown here:

1. Hydrogen, being in group IA of the periodic table, has one valence electron. Two hydrogen atoms share electrons to form a hydrogen molecule, H_2.

$$H_2 \qquad H\cdot \ + \ \cdot H \ \longrightarrow \ H{:}H \qquad \text{usually written} \qquad H{-}H$$

2. Because chlorine is in group VIIA, its atoms have seven valence electrons. Two chlorine atoms can share electrons (one electron from each) to form a molecule of Cl_2.

$$Cl_2 \qquad :\!\ddot{C}\!l\cdot \ + \ \cdot\ddot{C}\!l\!: \ \longrightarrow \ :\!\ddot{C}\!l\!:\!\ddot{C}\!l\!: \qquad \text{usually written} \qquad :\!\ddot{C}\!l\!-\!\ddot{C}\!l\!:$$

3. And a carbon atom (group IVA) with four valence electrons can share each of these electrons with four hydrogen atoms to form a molecule of methane, CH_4.

$$CH_4 \qquad \cdot\overset{\displaystyle\cdot}{\underset{\displaystyle\cdot}{C}}\cdot \ + \ 4\,H\cdot \ \longrightarrow \ H\!:\!\overset{\displaystyle H}{\underset{\displaystyle H}{\ddot{C}}}\!:\!H \qquad \text{usually written} \qquad H\!-\!\overset{\displaystyle H}{\underset{\displaystyle H}{\overset{\displaystyle |}{\underset{\displaystyle |}{C}}}}\!-\!H$$

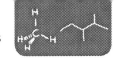

Two carbon atoms can use one electron pair between them to form a carbon–carbon single bond while also bonding hydrogen atoms or other groups to achieve an octet of valence electrons. Consider the example of ethane below.

C_2H_6 H:C:C:H   and as a dash formula   H—C—C—H

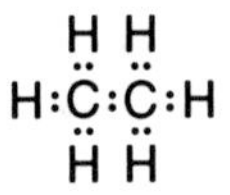

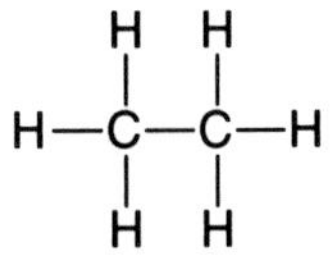

Ethane

These formulas are often called **Lewis structures**; in writing them we show all of the valence electrons. Unshared electron pairs are shown as dots, and in dash structural formulas, bonding electron pairs are shown as lines.

4. Atoms can share *two or more pairs of electrons* to form **multiple covalent bonds**. For example, two nitrogen atoms possessing five valence electrons each (because nitrogen is in group VA) can share electrons to form a **triple bond** between them.

N_2 :N⋮⋮N: and as a dash formula   :N≡N:

Carbon atoms can also share more than one electron pair with another atom to form a multiple covalent bond. Consider the examples of a carbon–carbon double bond in ethene (ethylene) and a carbon–carbon triple bond in ethyne (acetylene).

C_2H_4 C::C   and as a dash formula

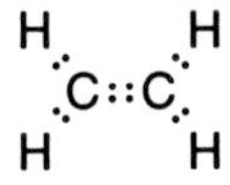

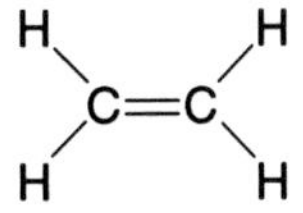

Ethene

C_2H_2 H:C⋮⋮C:H   and as a dash formula   H—C≡C—H

Ethyne

5. Ions, themselves, may contain covalent bonds. Consider, as an example, the ammonium ion.

NH_4 H:N:H   and as a dash formula   H—N—H

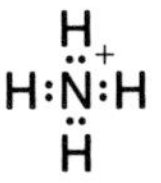

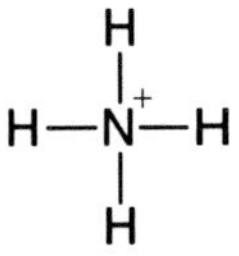

PRACTICE PROBLEM 1.4

Consider the following compounds and decide whether the bond in them would be ionic or covalent.

(a) KCl   (b) F_2 (c) PH_3 (d) CBr_4

1.4 HOW TO WRITE LEWIS STRUCTURES

Several simple rules allow us to draw proper Lewis structures:

1. **Lewis structures show the connections between atoms in a molecule or ion using only the valence electrons of the atoms involved.** Valence electrons are those of an atom's outermost shell.

2. **For main group elements, the number of valence electrons a neutral atom brings to a Lewis structure is the same as its group number in the periodic table.**

Helpful Hint

The ability to write proper **Lewis structures** is one of the most important tools for learning organic chemistry.

Carbon, for example, is in group IVA and has four valence electrons; the halogens (e.g., fluorine) are in group VIIA and each has seven valence electrons; hydrogen is in group IA and has one valence electron.

3. **If the structure we are drawing is a negative ion (an anion), we add one electron for each negative charge to the original count of valence electrons. If the structure is a positive ion (a cation), we subtract one electron for each positive charge.**

4. **In drawing Lewis structures we try to give each atom the electron configuration of a noble gas.** To do so, we draw structures where atoms share electrons to form covalent bonds or transfer electrons to form ions.

   a. Hydrogen forms one covalent bond by sharing its electron with an electron of another atom so that it can have two valence electrons, the same number as in the noble gas helium.

   b. Carbon forms four covalent bonds by sharing its four valence electrons with four valence electrons from other atoms, so that it can have eight electrons (the same as the electron configuration of neon, satisfying the octet rule).

   c. To achieve an octet of valence electrons, elements such as nitrogen, oxygen, and the halogens typically share only some of their valence electrons through covalent bonding, leaving others as unshared electron pairs.

The following problems illustrate the rules above.

●●● SOLVED PROBLEM 1.1

Write the Lewis structure of CH_3F.

STRATEGY AND ANSWER:

1. We find the total number of valence electrons of all the atoms:

$$4 + 3(1) + 7 = 14$$
$$\uparrow \qquad \uparrow \qquad \uparrow$$
$$C \quad 3H \quad F$$

2. We use pairs of electrons to form bonds between all atoms that are bonded to each other. We represent these bonding pairs with lines. In our example this requires four pairs of electrons (8 of the 14 valence electrons).

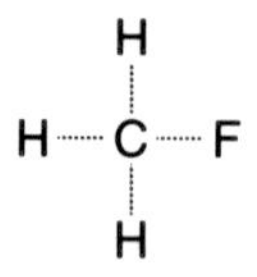

$$
\begin{array}{c}
H \\
| \\
H - C - F \\
| \\
H
\end{array}
$$

3. We then add the remaining electrons in pairs so as to give each hydrogen 2 electrons (a duet) and every other atom 8 electrons (an octet). In our example, we assign the remaining 6 valence electrons to the fluorine atom in three nonbonding pairs.

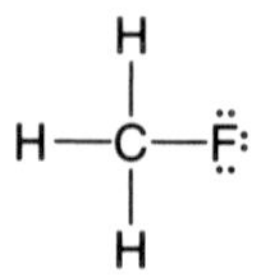

$$
\begin{array}{c}
H \\
| \\
H - C - \ddot{F}: \\
| \\
H
\end{array}
$$

......●●●

PRACTICE PROBLEM 1.5 Write the Lewis structure of (a) CH_2Fl_2 (difluoromethane) and (b) $CHCl_3$ (chloroform).

Write a Lewis structure for methylamine (CH_3NH_2).

STRATEGY AND ANSWER:

1. We find the total number of valence electrons for all the atoms.

$$
\begin{array}{ccc}
4 & 5 & 5(1) = 14 = 7 \text{ pairs} \\
\uparrow & \uparrow & \uparrow \\
\text{C} & \text{N} & \text{5H}
\end{array}
$$

2. We use one electron pair to join the carbon and nitrogen.

$$\text{C—N}$$

3. We use three pairs to form single bonds between the carbon and three hydrogen atoms.

4. We use two pairs to form single bonds between the nitrogen atom and two hydrogen atoms.

5. This leaves one electron pair, which we use as a lone pair on the nitrogen atom.

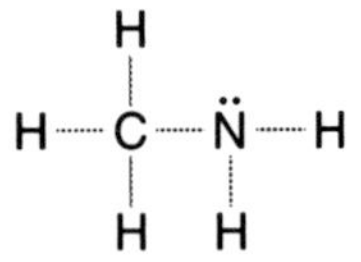

$$
\begin{array}{c}
\quad\quad\;\; \text{H} \\
\quad\quad\;\; | \\
\text{H—C—}\ddot{\text{N}}\text{—H} \\
\quad\quad\;\; | \quad\; | \\
\quad\quad\;\; \text{H} \quad \text{H}
\end{array}
$$

Write the Lewis structure of CH_3OH.

5. If necessary, we use multiple bonds to satisfy the octet rule (i.e., give atoms the noble gas configuration). The carbonate ion (CO_3^{2-}) illustrates this:

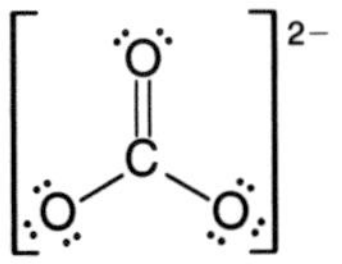

$$
\left[
\begin{array}{c}
\;\;\ddot{\ddot{\text{O}}} \\
\;\;\| \\
\;\;\text{C} \\
:\ddot{\text{O}}\diagdown\;\;\diagup\ddot{\text{O}}:
\end{array}
\right]^{2-}
$$

The organic molecules ethene (C_2H_4) and ethyne (C_2H_2), as mentioned earlier, have a double and triple bond, respectively:

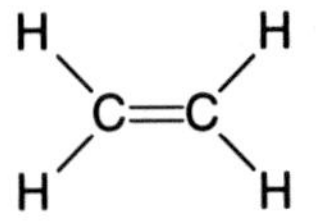

$$
\begin{array}{c}
\text{H}\diagdown\quad\quad\diagup\text{H} \\
\quad\text{C}{=}\text{C} \\
\text{H}\diagup\quad\quad\diagdown\text{H}
\end{array}
\quad \text{and} \quad \text{H—C}{\equiv}\text{C—H}
$$

Write the Lewis structure of CH_2O (formaldehyde).

STRATEGY AND ANSWER:

1. Find the total number of valence electrons of all the atoms:

$$
\begin{array}{ccc}
2(1) & + 1(4) & + 1(6) = 12 \\
\uparrow & \uparrow & \uparrow \\
\text{2H} & \text{1C} & \text{1O}
\end{array}
$$

2. (a) Use pairs of electrons to form single bonds.

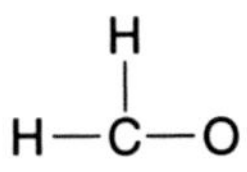

$$
\begin{array}{c}
\;\;\text{H} \\
\;\;| \\
\text{H—C—O}
\end{array}
$$

(continues on next page)

(b) Determine which atoms already have a full valence shell and which ones do not, and how many valence electrons we have used so far. In this case, we have used 6 valence electrons, and the valence shell is full for the hydrogen atoms but not for the carbon and oxygen.

(c) We use the remaining electrons as bonds or unshared electron pairs, to fill the valence shell of any atoms whose valence shell is not yet full, taking care not to exceed the octet rule. In this case 6 of the initial 12 valence electrons are left to use. We use 2 electrons to fill the valence shell of the carbon by another bond to the oxygen, and the remaining 4 electrons as two unshared electron pairs with the oxygen, filling its valence shell.

$$
\begin{array}{c}
\text{H} \\
| \\
\text{H}\!-\!\text{C}\!=\!\ddot{\text{O}}\!:
\end{array}
$$

● ● ●

PRACTICE PROBLEM 1.7 Write a dash structural formula showing all valence electrons for CH_3CHO (acetaldehyde).

6. **Before we can write some Lewis structures, _we must know how the atoms are connected to each other_**. Consider nitric acid, for example. Even though the formula for nitric acid is often written HNO_3, the hydrogen is actually connected to an oxygen, not to the nitrogen. The structure is $HONO_2$ and not HNO_3. Thus the correct Lewis structure is:

$$
\text{H}\!-\!\ddot{\text{O}}\!-\!\text{N}\!\!\begin{array}{c} \nearrow^{\ddot{\text{O}}:} \\ \searrow_{\cdot\ddot{\text{O}}:} \end{array} \qquad \text{and not} \qquad \text{H}\!-\!\text{N}\!-\!\ddot{\text{O}}\!-\!\ddot{\text{O}}\!: \\ \qquad\qquad\qquad\qquad\qquad \underset{\cdot\text{O}\cdot}{\overset{\|}{}}
$$

Helpful Hint

Check your progress by doing each Practice Problem as you come to it in the text.

This knowledge comes ultimately from experiments. If you have forgotten the structures of some of the common inorganic molecules and ions (such as those listed in Practice Problem 1.8), this may be a good time for a review of the relevant portions of your general chemistry text.

● ● ● **SOLVED PROBLEM 1.4**

Assume that the atoms are connected in the same way they are written in the formula, and write a Lewis structure for the toxic gas hydrogen cyanide (HCN).

STRATEGY AND ANSWER:

1. We find the total number of valence electrons on all of the atoms:

$$
\begin{array}{ccc}
1 + & 4 + & 5 = 10 \\
\uparrow & \uparrow & \uparrow \\
\text{H} & \text{C} & \text{N}
\end{array}
$$

2. We use one pair of electrons to form a single bond between the hydrogen atom and the carbon atom (see below), and we use three pairs to form a triple bond between the carbon atom and the nitrogen atom. This leaves two electrons. We use these as an unshared pair on the nitrogen atom. Now each atom has the electronic structure of a noble gas. The hydrogen atom has two electrons (like helium) and the carbon and nitrogen atoms each have eight electrons (like neon).

$$
\text{H}\!-\!\text{C}\!\equiv\!\text{N}\!:
$$

PRACTICE PROBLEM 1.8

Write a Lewis structure for each of the following:

(a) HF   **(c)** CH_3F **(e)** H_2SO_3 **(g)** H_3PO_4

(b) F_2 **(d)** HNO_2 **(f)** BH_4^- **(h)** H_2CO_3

1.4A Exceptions to the Octet Rule

Atoms share electrons, not just to obtain the configuration of an inert gas, but because sharing electrons produces increased electron density between the positive nuclei. The resulting attractive forces of nuclei for electrons is the "glue" that holds the atoms together (cf. Section 1.11).

- Elements of the second period of the periodic table can have a maximum of four bonds (i.e., have eight electrons around them) because these elements have only one $2s$ and three $2p$ orbitals available for bonding.

Each orbital can contain two electrons, and a total of eight electrons fills these orbitals (Section 1.10A). The octet rule, therefore, only applies to these elements, and even here, as we shall see in compounds of beryllium and boron, fewer than eight electrons are possible.

- Elements of the third period and beyond have d orbitals that can be used for bonding.

These elements can accommodate more than eight electrons in their valence shells and therefore can form more than four covalent bonds. Examples are compounds such as PCl_5 and SF_6. Bonds written as ⫽ (dashed wedges) project behind the plane of the paper. Bonds written as ⟋ (solid wedges) project in front of the paper.

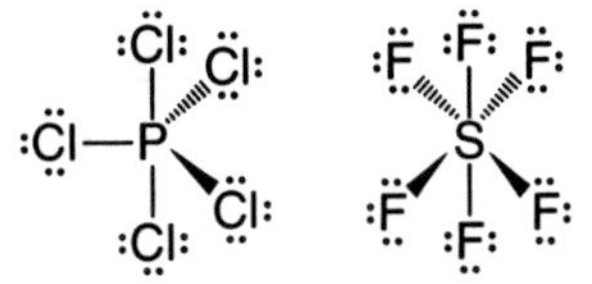

●●● SOLVED PROBLEM 1.5

Write a Lewis structure for the sulfate ion (SO_4^{2-}). (*Note*: The sulfur atom is bonded to all four oxygen atoms.)

STRATEGY AND ANSWER:

1. We find the total number of valence electrons including the extra 2 electrons needed to give the ion the double negative charge:

$$6 + 4(6) + 2 = 32$$
$$\uparrow \qquad \uparrow \qquad \uparrow$$
$$S \qquad 4O \quad 2e^-$$

2. We use four pairs of electrons to form bonds between the sulfur atom and the four oxygen atoms:

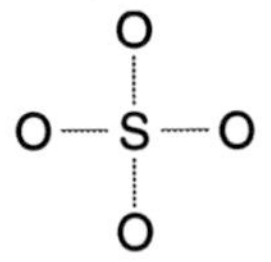

3. We add the remaining 24 electrons as unshared pairs on oxygen atoms and as double bonds between the sulfur atom and two oxygen atoms. This gives each oxygen 8 electrons and the sulfur atom 12:

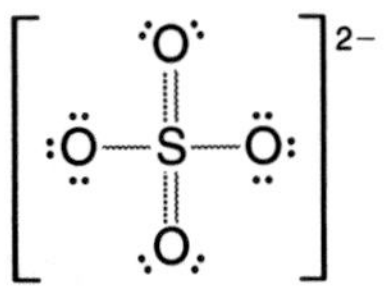

●●● PRACTICE PROBLEM 1.9

Write a Lewis structure for the phosphate ion (PO_4^{3-}).

Some highly reactive molecules or ions have atoms with fewer than eight electrons in their outer shell. An example is boron trifluoride (BF_3). In a BF_3 molecule the central boron atom has only six electrons around it:

1.5 FORMAL CHARGES AND **HOW TO** CALCULATE THEM

Helpful Hint

Proper assignment of **formal charges** is another essential tool for learning organic chemistry.

Many **Lewis structures** are incomplete until we decide whether any of their atoms have a formal charge. Calculating the formal charge on an atom in a Lewis structure is simply a bookkeeping method for its valence electrons.

* First, we examine each atom and, using the periodic table, we determine how many **valence electrons** it would have if it were an atom not bonded to any other atoms. **This is equal to the group number of the atom in the periodic table.** For hydrogen this number equals 1, for carbon it equals 4, for nitrogen it equals 5, and for oxygen it equals 6.

Next, we examine the atom in the Lewis structure and we assign the valence electrons in the following way:

* **We assign to each atom half of the electrons it is sharing with another atom and all of its unshared (lone) electron pairs.**

Then we do the following calculation for the atom:

Formal charge = number of valence electrons − 1/2 number of shared electrons − number of unshared electrons

or

$$F = Z - (1/2)S - U$$

where F is the formal charge, Z is the group number of the element, S equals the number of shared electrons, and U is the number of unshared electrons.

* It is important to note, too, that **the arithmetic sum of all the formal charges in a molecule or ion will equal the overall charge on the molecule or ion.**

Let us consider several examples showing how this is done.

The Ammonium Ion (NH_4^+) As we see below, the ammonium ion has no unshared electron pairs. We divide all of the electrons in bonds equally between the atoms that share them. Thus, each hydrogen is assigned one electron. We subtract this from one (the number of valence electrons in a hydrogen atom) to give each hydrogen atom a formal charge of zero. The nitrogen atom is assigned four electrons (one from each bond). We subtract four from five (the number of valence electrons in a nitrogen atom) to give the nitrogen a formal charge of +1.

$$
\begin{array}{c}
\text{H} \quad + \\
\ddot{} \\
\text{H}\!:\!\ddot{\text{N}}\!:\!\text{H} \\
\ddot{} \\
\text{H}
\end{array}
$$

For hydrogen:	valence electrons of free atom	=	1
	subtract assigned electrons	=	− 1
	Formal charge on each hydrogen	=	0
For nitrogen:	valence electrons of free atom	=	5
	subtract assigned electrons	=	− $(1/2)8$
	Formal charge on nitrogen	=	+1

Overall charge on ion = 4(0) + 1 = +1

The Nitrate Ion (NO_3^-) Let us next consider the nitrate ion (NO_3^-), an ion that has oxygen atoms with unshared electron pairs. Here we find that the nitrogen atom has a formal charge of +1, that two oxygen atoms have formal charges of −1, and that one oxygen has a formal charge equal to 0.

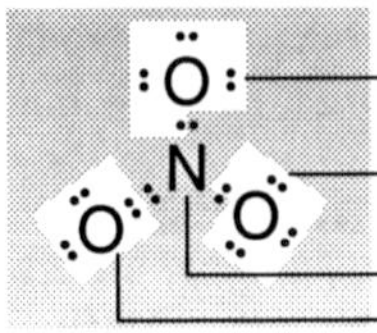

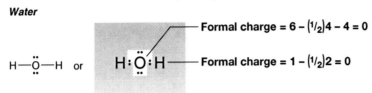

Formal charge = $6 - (1/2)2 - 6 = -1$

Formal charge = $6 - (1/2)2 - 6 = -1$

Formal charge = $5 - (1/2)8 = +1$

Formal charge = $6 - (1/2)4 - 4 = 0$

Charge on ion = $2(-1) + 1 + 0 = -1$

Water and Ammonia The sum of the formal charges on each atom making up a molecule must be zero. Consider the following examples:

Water

H—Ö—H   or   H:Ö:H

Formal charge = $6 - (1/2)4 - 4 = 0$

Formal charge = $1 - (1/2)2 = 0$

Charge on molecule = $0 + 2(0) = 0$

Ammonia

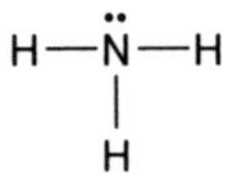

H—N̈—H   or   H:N̈:H
    | H
    H

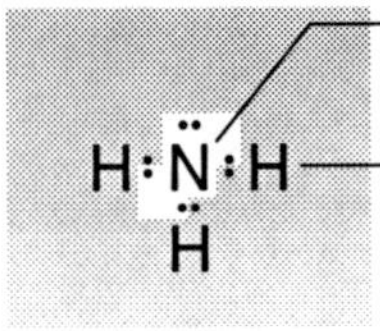

Formal charge = $5 - (1/2)6 - 2 = 0$

Formal charge = $1 - (1/2)2 = 0$

Charge on molecule = $0 + 3(0) = 0$

PRACTICE PROBLEM 1.10

Write a Lewis structure for each of the following negative ions, and assign the formal negative charge to the correct atom:

(a) CH_3O^- **(b)** NH_2^- **(c)** CN^- **(d)** HCO_2^- **(e)** HCO_3^- **(f)** HC_2^-

1.5A A Summary of Formal Charges

With this background, it should now be clear that each time an oxygen atom of the type —Ö: appears in a molecule or ion, it will have a formal charge of -1, and that each time an oxygen atom of the type $=Ö$ or —Ö— appears, it will have a formal charge of 0. Similarly, —N̶— will be $+1$, and —N̈— will be zero. These and other common structures are summarized in Table 1.2.

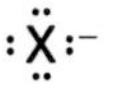

Helpful Hint

In later chapters, when you are evaluating how reactions proceed and what products form, you will find it essential to keep track of formal charges.

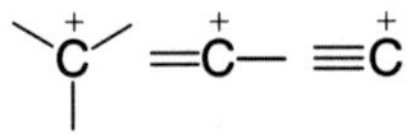

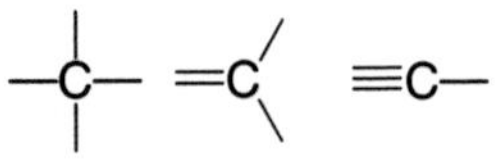

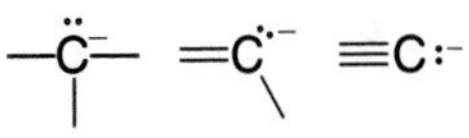

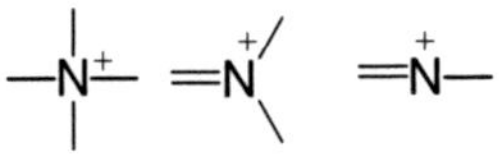

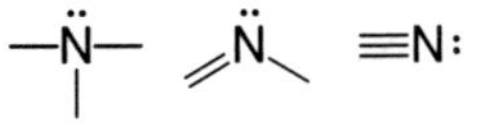

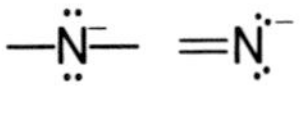

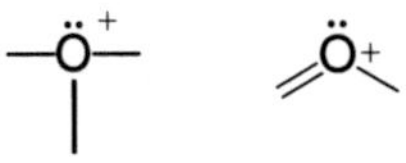

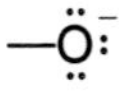

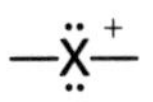

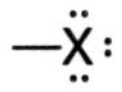

TABLE 1.2 A SUMMARY OF FORMAL CHARGES			
Group	**Formal Charge of +1**	**Formal Charge of 0**	**Formal Charge of −1**
IIIA		⟍B⟋	—B̄—
IVA	⟍C⟋⁺ =C̈—⁺ ≡C⁺	—C̈— =C⟍ ≡C—	—C̈⁻— =C̈⁻⟍ ≡C̈:⁻
VA	—N̶⁺— =N̈⁺⟋ =N⁺—	—N̈— ⟍N̈⟋ ≡N:	—N̈⁻— =N̈⁻⟋
VIA	—Ö⁺— ⟍⟍Ö⁺⟋	—Ö— =Ö̈	—Ö̈:⁻
VIIA	—Ẍ⁺—	—Ẍ: (X = F, Cl, Br, or I)	:Ẍ:⁻

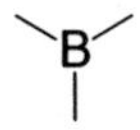

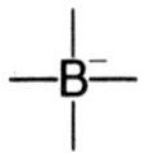

PRACTICE PROBLEM 1.11 Assign the proper formal charge to the colored atom in each of the following structures:

(a) H–C–C with H atoms around each carbon

(b) H–Ö–H with H below (water, lone pairs on O)

(c) formic acid structure: C with double bond O on top, H on left, Ö on lower right

(d) H–C–H with :Ö: on top and H below

(e) H–C–N–H with H atoms around C and N

(f) H–C–H with H–Ö–H on top and H below

(g) CH_3–C≡N:

(h) CH_3–N≡N:

1.6 ISOMERS: DIFFERENT COMPOUNDS THAT HAVE THE SAME MOLECULAR FORMULA

Now that we have had an introduction to Lewis structures, it is time to discuss isomers.

* Isomers are compounds that have the same **molecular formula** but different structures.

We will learn about several kinds of isomers during the course of our study. For now, let us consider a type called constitutional isomers.

* **Constitutional isomers** are different compounds that have the same molecular formula but differ in the sequence in which their atoms are bonded—that is, their **connectivity**.

Acetone, used in nail polish remover and as a paint solvent, and propylene oxide, used with seaweed extracts to make food-grade thickeners and foam stabilizers for beer (among other applications) are isomers. Both of these compounds have the molecular formula C_3H_6O and therefore the same molecular weight. Yet acetone and propylene oxide have distinctly different boiling points and chemical reactivity that, as a result, lend themselves to distinctly different practical applications. Their shared molecular formula simply gives us no basis for understanding the differences between them. We must, therefore, move to a consideration of their structural formulas.

On examining the structures of acetone and propylene oxide several key aspects are clearly different (Fig. 1.2). Acetone contains a double bond between the oxygen atom and the central carbon atom. Propylene oxide does not contain a double bond, but has three atoms joined in a ring. The connectivity of the atoms is clearly different in acetone

Acetone is used in some nailpolish removers.

Propylene oxide alginates, made from propylene oxide and seaweed extracts, are used as food thickeners.

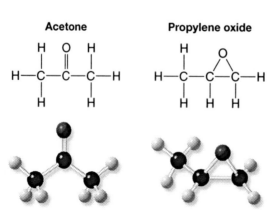

Acetone

Propylene oxide

FIGURE 1.2 Ball-and-stick models and chemical formulas show the different structures of acetone and propylene oxide.

> **Helpful Hint**
> Build handheld models of these compounds and compare their structures.

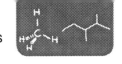

and propylene oxide. Their structures have the same molecular formula but a different constitution. They are constitutional isomers.*

- Constitutional isomers usually have different physical properties (e.g., melting point, boiling point, and density) and different chemical properties (reactivity).

●●● **SOLVED PROBLEM 1.6**

There are two constitutional isomers with the formula C_2H_6O. Write structural formulas for these isomers.

STRATEGY AND ANSWER: If we recall that carbon can form four covalent bonds, oxygen can form two, and hydrogen only one, we can arrive at the following constitutional isomers.

Dimethyl ether   **Ethanol**

It should be noted that these two isomers are clearly different in their physical properties. At room temperature and 1 atm pressure, dimethyl ether is a gas. Ethanol is a liquid.

●●● **SOLVED PROBLEM 1.7**

Which of the following compounds are constitutional isomers of one another?

A   B   C   D   E

ANSWER: First determine the molecular formula for each compound. You will then see that **B** and **D** have the same molecular formula (C_4H_8O) but have different connectivities. They are, therefore, constitutional isomers of each other. **A**, **C**, and **E** also have the same molecular formula (C_3H_6O) and are constitutional isomers of one another.

1.7 HOW TO WRITE AND INTERPRET STRUCTURAL FORMULAS

Organic chemists use a variety of formats to write **structural formulas**. We have already used electron-dot formulas and dash formulas in previous sections. Two other important types of formulas are condensed formulas and bond-line (skeletal) formulas. Examples of these four types of structural formulas are shown in Fig. 1.3 using propyl alcohol as an example.

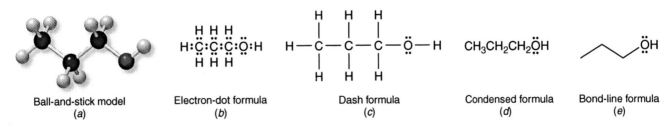

Ball-and-stick model (a)   Electron-dot formula (b)   Dash formula (c)   Condensed formula (d)   Bond-line formula (e)

FIGURE 1.3 Structural formulas for propyl alcohol.

*An older term for isomers of this type was **structural isomers**. The International Union of Pure and Applied Chemistry (IUPAC) now recommends that use of the term "structural" when applied to constitutional isomers be abandoned.

Although electron-dot formulas account explicitly for all of the valence electrons in a molecule, they are tedious and time-consuming to write. Dash, condensed, and bond-line formulas are therefore used more often.

Generally it is best to draw unshared electron pairs in chemical formulas, though sometimes they are omitted if we are not considering the chemical properties or reactivity of a compound. When we write chemical reactions, however, we shall see that it is necessary to include the unshared electron pairs when they participate in a reaction. It is a good idea, therefore, to be in the habit of writing unshared electrons pairs.

1.7A More About Dash Structural Formulas

* **Dash structural formulas** have lines that show bonding electron pairs, and include elemental symbols for all of the atoms in a molecule.

If we look at the ball-and-stick model for propyl alcohol given in Fig. 1.3*a* and compare it with the electron-dot, dash, and condensed formulas in Figs. 1.3*b–d* we find that the chain of atoms is straight in those formulas. In the model, which corresponds more accurately to the actual shape of the molecule, the chain of atoms is not at all straight. Also of importance is this: ***Atoms joined by single bonds can rotate relatively freely with respect to one another.*** (We shall discuss the reason for this in Section 1.12B.) This relatively free rotation means that the chain of atoms in propyl alcohol can assume a variety of arrangements like these:

Equivalent dash formulas for propyl alcohol

> **Helpful Hint**
>
> It is important that you be able to recognize when a set of structural formulas has the same connectivity versus when they are constitutional isomers.

It also means that all of the structural formulas above are *equivalent* and all represent propyl alcohol. Dash structural formulas such as these indicate the way in which the atoms are attached to each other and *are not* representations of the actual shapes of the molecule. (Propyl alcohol does not have 90° bond angles. It has tetrahedral bond angles.) Dash structural formulas show what is called the **connectivity** of the atoms. *Constitutional isomers (Section 1.6A) have different connectivities and, therefore, must have different structural formulas.*

Consider the compound called isopropyl alcohol, whose formula we might write in a variety of ways:

Equivalent dash formulas for isopropyl alcohol

Isopropyl alcohol is a constitutional isomer (Section 1.6A) of propyl alcohol because its atoms are connected in a different order and both compounds have the same molecular formula, C_3H_8O. In isopropyl alcohol the OH group is attached to the central carbon; in propyl alcohol it is attached to an end carbon.

* In problems you will often be asked to write structural formulas for all the isomers that have a given molecular formula. Do not make the error of writing several equivalent formulas, like those that we have just shown, mistaking them for different constitutional isomers.

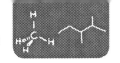

● ● ●

There are actually three constitutional isomers with the molecular formula C_3H_8O. We have seen two of them in propyl alcohol and isopropyl alcohol. Write a dash formula for the third isomer. **PRACTICE PROBLEM 1.12**

1.7B Condensed Structural Formulas

Condensed structural formulas are somewhat faster to write than dash formulas and, when we become familiar with them, they will impart all the information that is contained in the dash structure. In condensed formulas all of the hydrogen atoms that are attached to a particular carbon are usually written immediately after the carbon. In fully condensed formulas, all of the atoms that are attached to the carbon are usually written immediately after that carbon, listing hydrogens first. For example,

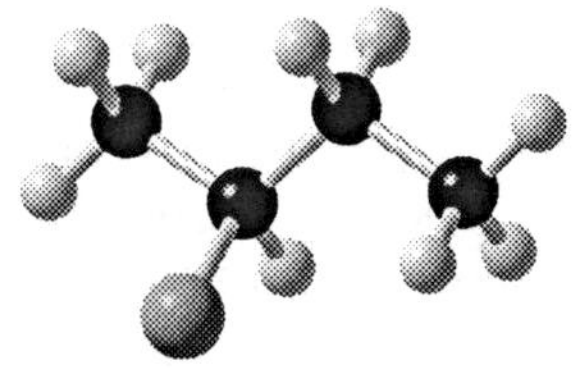

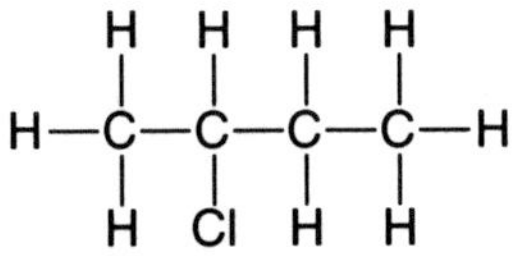

$$CH_3CHCH_2CH_3 \text{ or } CH_3CHClCH_2CH_3$$
$$| \atop Cl$$

Dash formula   **Condensed formulas**

The condensed formula for isopropyl alcohol can be written in four different ways:

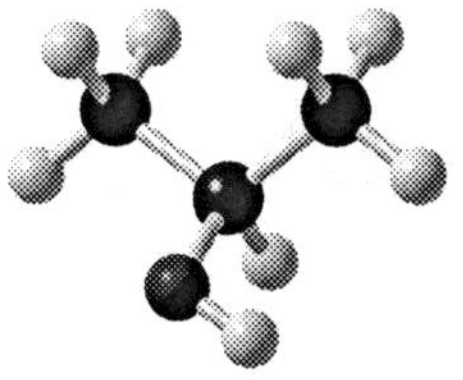

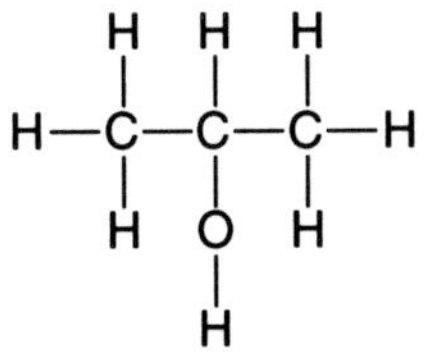

$$CH_3CHCH_3 \text{ or } CH_3CH(OH)CH_3$$
$$| \atop OH$$
$$CH_3CHOHCH_3 \text{ or } (CH_3)_2CHOH$$

Dash formula   **Condensed formulas**

● ● ● SOLVED PROBLEM 1.8

Write a condensed structural formula for the compound that follows:

ANSWER:

$$CH_3CHCH_2CH_3 \text{ or } CH_3CH(CH_3)CH_2CH_3 \text{ or } (CH_3)_2CHCH_2CH_3$$
$$| \atop CH_3$$
$$\text{or } CH_3CH_2CH(CH_3)_2 \text{ or } CH_3CH_2CHCH_3$$
$$| \atop CH_3$$

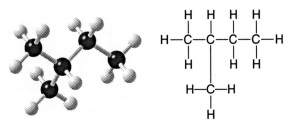

PRACTICE PROBLEM 1.13 Write a condensed structural formula for the following compound.

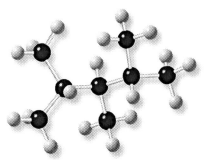

1.7C Bond-Line Formulas

The most common type of structural formula used by organic chemists, and the fastest to draw, is the bond-line formula. (Some chemists call these skeletal formulas.) The formula in Fig. 1.3e is a bond-line formula for propyl alcohol. The sooner you master the use of bond-line formulas, the more quickly you will be able to draw molecules when you take notes and work problems. And, lacking all of the symbols that are explicitly shown in dash and condensed structural formulas, bond-line formulas allow you to more quickly interpret molecular connectivity and compare one molecular formula with another.

HOW TO DRAW BOND-LINE FORMULAS

We apply the following rules when we draw bond-line formulas:

- Each line represents a bond.
- Each **bend** in a line or **terminus** of a line represents a carbon atom, unless another group is shown explicitly.
- No Cs are written for carbon atoms, except optionally for CH_3 groups at the end of a chain or branch.
- No Hs are shown for hydrogen atoms, unless they are needed to give a three-dimensional perspective, in which case we use dashed or solid wedges (as explained in the next section).
- The number of hydrogen atoms bonded to each carbon is inferred by assuming that as many hydrogen atoms are present as needed to fill the valence shell of the carbon, unless a charge is indicated.
- When an atom other than carbon or hydrogen is present, the symbol for that element is written at the appropriate location (i.e., in place of a bend or at the terminus of the line leading to the atom).
- Hydrogen atoms bonded to atoms other than carbon (e.g., oxygen or nitrogen) are written explicitly.

Consider the following examples of molecules depicted by bond-line formulas.

$$CH_3CHClCH_2CH_3 = \begin{matrix} CH_3 \ \ CH_2 \\ CH \ \ \ \ CH_3 \\ | \\ Cl \end{matrix} = \underbrace{\quad}_{\substack{\text{Bond-line}\\\text{formulas}}}$$

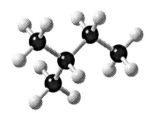

$CH_3CH(CH_3)CH_2CH_3 =$

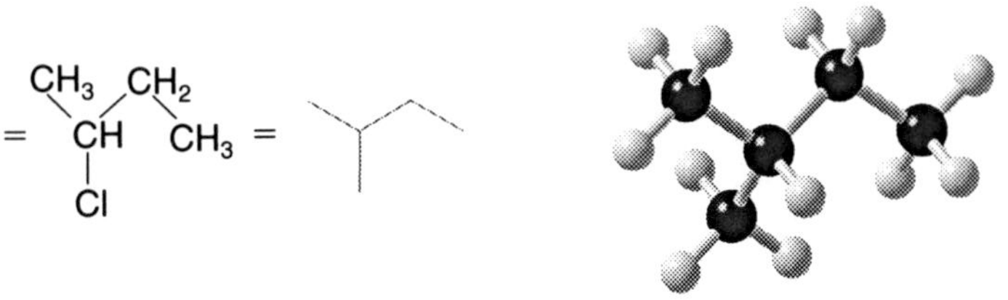

$$\begin{array}{cc} CH_3 & CH_2 \\ CH & CH_3 \\ Cl & \end{array}$$

=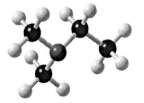

$(CH_3)_2NCH_2CH_3 =$

$$\begin{array}{cc} CH_3 & CH_2 \\ N & CH_3 \\ CH_3 & \end{array}$$

=

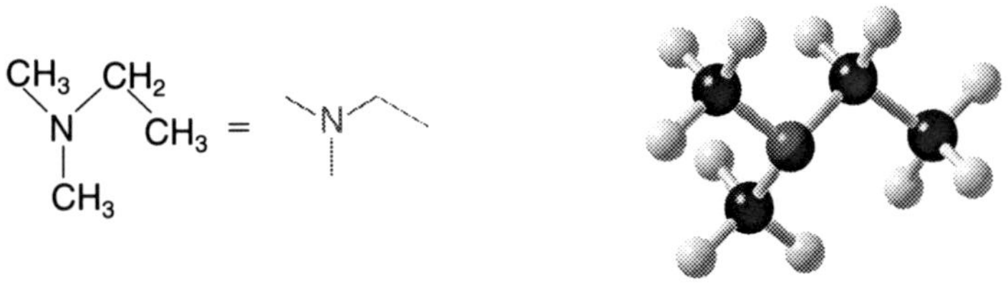

Helpful Hint

As you become more familiar with organic molecules, you will find bond-line formulas to be very useful tools for representing structures.

Bond-line formulas are easy to draw for molecules with multiple bonds and for cyclic molecules, as well. The following are some examples.

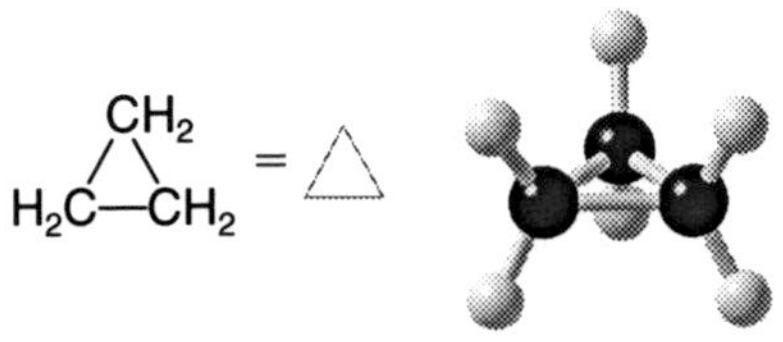

$$\begin{array}{c} CH_2 \\ H_2C{-}CH_2 \end{array} = \triangle$$

and

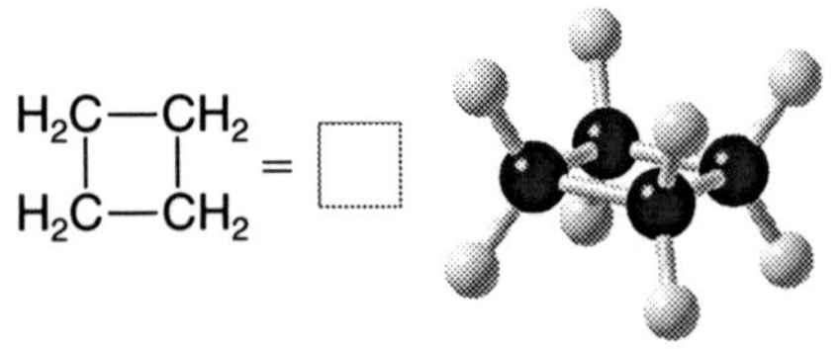

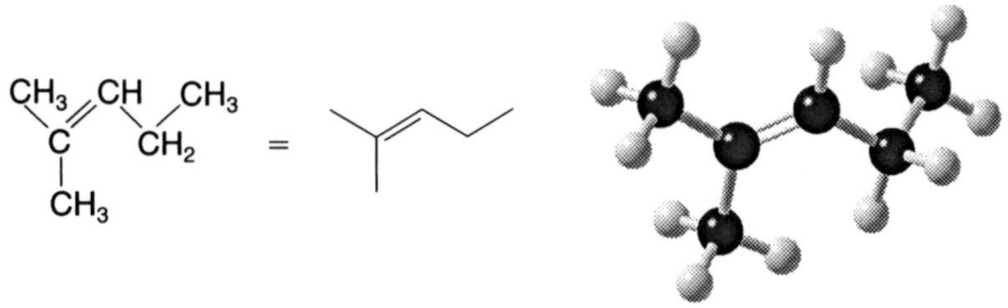

$$\begin{array}{c} H_2C{-}CH_2 \\ H_2C{-}CH_2 \end{array} = \square$$

$$\begin{array}{ccc} CH_3 & CH & CH_3 \\ C & CH_2 & \\ CH_3 & & \end{array} =$$

$CH_2{=}CHCH_2OH =$ ⟍⟍⟋OH

⟍⟋≡⟍

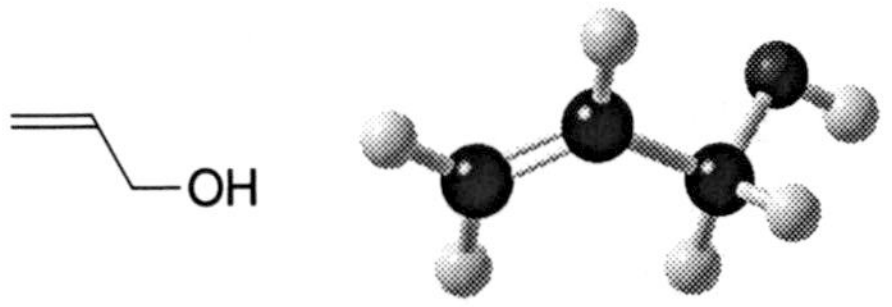

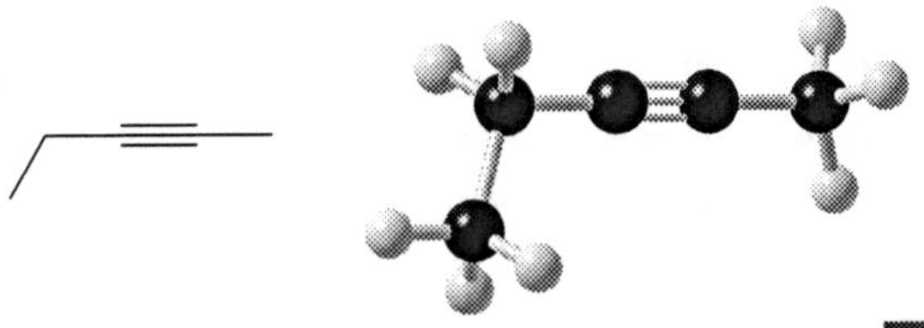

●●● SOLVED PROBLEM 1.9

Write the bond-line formula for

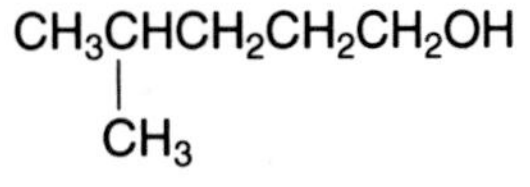

$$\begin{array}{c} CH_3CHCH_2CH_2CH_2OH \\ | \\ CH_3 \end{array}$$

STRATEGY AND ANSWER: First, for the sake of practice, we outline the carbon skeleton, including the **OH** group, as follows:

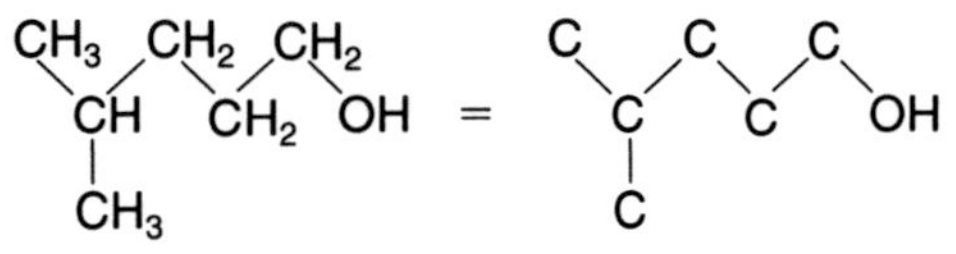

$$\begin{array}{ccc} CH_3 & CH_2 & CH_2 \\ CH & CH_2 & OH \\ CH_3 & & \end{array} = \begin{array}{ccc} C & C & C \\ C & C & OH \\ C & & \end{array}$$

Then we write the bond-line formula as ⟍⟋⟍⟋OH. As you gain experience you will likely skip the intermediate steps shown above and proceed directly to writing bond-line formulas.

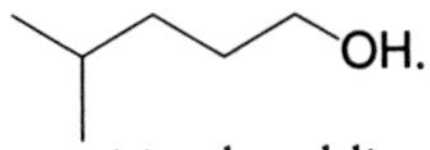

PRACTICE PROBLEM 1.14 Write each of the following condensed structural formulas as a bond-line formula:

(a) $(CH_3)_2CHCH_2CH_3$

(b) $(CH_3)_2CHCH_2CH_2OH$

(c) $(CH_3)_2C{=}CHCH_2CH_3$

(d) $CH_3CH_2CH_2CH_2CH_3$

(e) $CH_3CH_2CH(OH)CH_2CH_3$

(f) $CH_2{=}C(CH_2CH_3)_2$

(g) $CH_3\overset{\overset{\displaystyle O}{\|}}{C}CH_2CH_2CH_2CH_3$

(h) $CH_3CHClCH_2CH(CH_3)_2$

PRACTICE PROBLEM 1.15 Which molecules in Practice Problem 1.14 form sets of constitutional isomers?

PRACTICE PROBLEM 1.16 Write a dash formula for each of the following bond-line formulas:

(a) (b) (c)

1.7D Three-Dimensional Formulas

None of the formulas that we have described so far convey any information about how the atoms of a molecule are arranged in space. Molecules exist in three dimensions. We can depict three-dimensional geometry in molecules using bonds represented by dashed wedges, solid wedges, and lines.

- A dashed wedge (⠿) represents a bond that projects behind the plane of the paper.
- A solid wedge (◄) represents a bond that projects out of the plane of the paper.
- An ordinary line (—) represents a bond that lies in the plane of the paper.

For example, the four C—H bonds of methane (CH_4) are oriented toward the corners of a regular tetrahedron, with the carbon in the center and an approximately 109° angle between each C—H bond, as was originally postulated by J. H. van't Hoff and L. A. Le Bel in 1874. Figure 1.4 shows the tetrahedral structure of methane.

We will discuss the physical basis for the geometries of carbon when it has only single bonds, a double bond, or a triple bond in Sections 1.12–14. For now, let us consider some guidelines for representing these bonding patterns in three dimensions using dashed and solid wedge bonds.

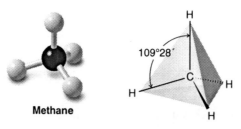

Methane

FIGURE 1.4 The tetrahedral structure of methane.

In general for carbon atoms that have only single bonds:

● A carbon atom with **four single bonds** has tetrahedral geometry (Section 1.12) and can be drawn with two bonds in the plane of the paper separated by approximately 109°, one bond behind the plane using a dashed wedge, and one bond in front of the plane using a solid wedge.

● The dashed wedge and solid wedge bonds in tetrahedral geometry nearly eclipse each other when drawn in proper three-dimensional perspective.

For carbon atoms with a double or a triple bond:

● A carbon atom with a **double bond** has trigonal planar geometry (Section 1.13) and can be depicted with bonds that are all in the plane of the paper and separated by 120°.

● A carbon atom with a **triple bond** has linear geometry (Section 1.14) and can be depicted with its bonds in the plane of the paper and separated by a 180° angle.

Last, when drawing three-dimensional formulas for molecules:

● Draw as many carbon atoms in the plane of the paper as possible using ordinary lines, then use dashed or solid wedge bonds for substituent groups or hydrogen atoms that are needed to show three dimensions.

Some examples of three-dimensional formulas are shown below.

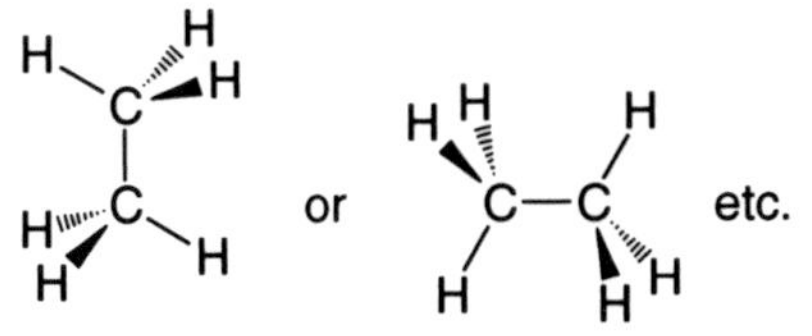

Ethane 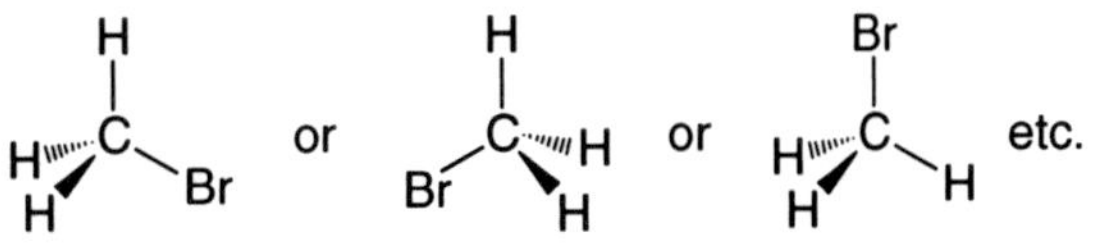   **Bromomethane**

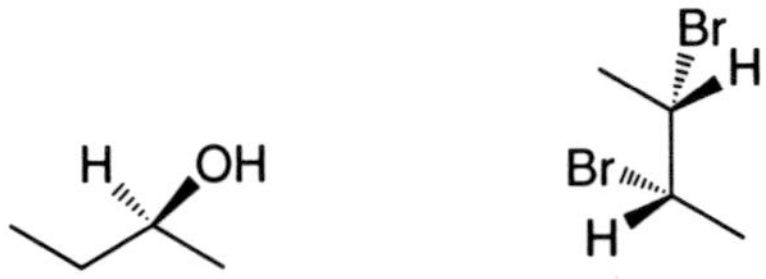

Examples of bond-line formulas that include three-dimensional representations

The carbon chains are shown in the plane of the paper. The dashed and solid wedge bonds nearly eclipse each other.

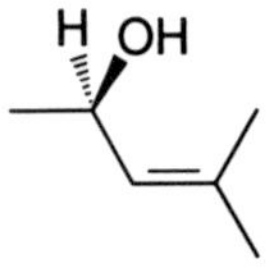

An example involving trigonal planar geometry

Bonds to the carbon with the double bond are in the plane of the paper and separated by 120°.

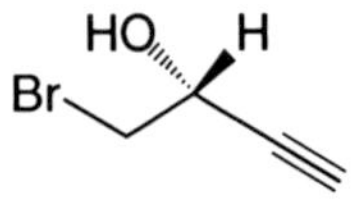

An example involving linear geometry

Bonds to the carbon with the triple bond are in the plane of the paper and separated by 180°.

●●● SOLVED PROBLEM 1.10

Write a bond-line formula for the following compound showing three dimensions at the carbon bearing the chlorine atom.

$$CH_3CH_2CHCH_2CH_3$$
$$|$$
$$Cl$$

STRATEGY AND ANSWER: First draw the carbon skeleton, placing as many carbon atoms in the plane of the paper as possible (which is all of them, in this case).

Then add the chlorine atom at the appropriate carbon using a three-dimensional representation.

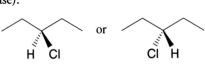

●●●

Write three-dimensional (wedge–dashed wedge–line) representations for each of the following:

PRACTICE PROBLEM 1.17

(a) CH_3Cl **(b)** CH_2Cl_2 **(c)** CH_2BrCl **(d)** CH_3CH_2Cl

1.8 RESONANCE THEORY

Often more than one *equivalent* Lewis structure can be written for a molecule or ion. Consider, for example, the carbonate ion ($CO_3{}^{2-}$). We can write three *different* but *equivalent* structures, **1–3**:

Notice two important features of these structures. First, each atom has the noble gas configuration. Second, *and this is especially important*, we can convert one structure into any other by *changing only the positions of the electrons*. We do not need to change the relative positions of the atomic nuclei. For example, if we move the electron pairs in the manner indicated by the **curved arrows** in structure **1**, we change structure **1** into structure **2**:

In a similar way we can change structure **2** into structure **3**:

Helpful Hint

Curved arrows (Section 3.2) show movement of electron pairs, not atoms. The tail of the arrow begins at the current position of the electron pair. The *head* of the arrow points to the location where the electron pair will be in the next structure. Curved-arrow notation is one of the most important tools that you will use to understand organic reactions.

Structures **1–3**, although not identical on paper, *are equivalent*. None of them alone, however, fits important data about the carbonate ion.

X-ray studies have shown that carbon–oxygen double bonds are shorter than single bonds. The same kind of study of the carbonate ion shows, however, that all of its carbon–oxygen bonds *are of equal length*. One is not shorter than the others as would be expected from representations **1**, **2**, and **3**. Clearly none of the three structures agrees with this evidence. In each structure, **1–3**, one carbon–oxygen bond is a double bond and the other two are single bonds. None of the structures, therefore, is correct. How, then, should we represent the carbonate ion?

One way is through a theory called **resonance theory**. This theory states that whenever a molecule or ion can be represented by two or more Lewis structures *that differ only in the positions of the electrons*, two things will be true:

1. None of these structures, which we call **resonance structures** or **resonance contributors**, will be a realistic representation for the molecule or ion. None will be in complete accord with the physical or chemical properties of the substance.

2. The actual molecule or ion will be better represented by a *hybrid (average) of these structures.*

   • *Resonance structures, then, are not real structures for the actual molecule or ion; they exist only on paper.* As such, they can never be isolated. No single contributor adequately represents the molecule or ion. In resonance theory we view the carbonate ion, which is, of course, a real entity, as having a structure that is a **hybrid** of the three **hypothetical** resonance structures.

What would a hybrid of structures **1–3** be like? Look at the structures and look especially at a particular carbon–oxygen bond, say, the one at the top. This carbon–oxygen bond is a double bond in one structure (**1**) and a single bond in the other two (**2** and **3**). The actual carbon–oxygen bond, since it is a hybrid, must be something in between a double bond and a single bond. Because the carbon–oxygen bond is a single bond in two of the structures and a double bond in only one, it must be more like a single bond than a double bond. It must be like a one and one-third bond. We could call it a partial double bond. And, of course, what we have just said about any one carbon–oxygen bond will be equally true of the other two. Thus all of the carbon–oxygen bonds of the carbonate ion are partial double bonds, and *all are equivalent.* All of them *should be* the same length, and this is exactly what experiments tell us. The bonds are all 1.28 Å long, a distance which is intermediate between that of a carbon–oxygen single bond (1.43 Å) and that of a carbon–oxygen double bond (1.20 Å). One angstrom equals 1×10^{-10} meter.

- One other important point: by convention, when we draw resonance structures, we connect them by double-headed arrows ($\leftrightarrow$) to indicate clearly that they are hypothetical, not real. For the carbonate ion we write them this way:

We should not let these arrows, or the word "resonance," mislead us into thinking that the carbonate ion fluctuates between one structure and another. These structures individually do not represent reality and exist only on paper; therefore, the carbonate ion cannot fluctuate among them because it is a hybrid of them.

- Resonance structures do not represent an **equilibrium.**

In an equilibrium between two or more species, it is quite correct to think of different structures and moving (or fluctuating) atoms, *but not in the case of resonance* (as in the carbonate ion). Here the atoms do not move, and the "structures" exist only on paper. **An equilibrium is indicated by $\rightleftharpoons$ and resonance by $\leftrightarrow$.**

How can we write the structure of the carbonate ion in a way that will indicate its actual structure? We may do two things: we may write all of the resonance structures as we have just done and let the reader mentally fashion the hybrid, or we may write a non-Lewis structure that attempts to represent the hybrid. For the carbonate ion we might do the following:

Hybrid   **Contributing resonance structures**

The bonds in the structure on the left are indicated by a combination of a solid line and a dashed line. This is to indicate that the bonds are something in between a single bond and a double bond. As a rule, we use a solid line whenever a bond appears in all structures, and a dashed line when a bond exists in one or more but not all. We also place a $\delta-$ (read partial minus) beside each oxygen to indicate that something less than a full negative charge resides on each oxygen atom. In this instance, each oxygen atom has two-thirds of a full negative charge.

Calculations from theory show the equal charge density at each oxygen in the carbonate anion. Figure 1.5 shows a calculated **electrostatic potential map** of the electron density in the carbonate ion. In an electrostatic potential map, regions of relatively more negative charge are red, while more positive regions (i.e., less negative regions) are indicated by colors trending toward blue. Equality of the bond lengths in the carbonate anion (partial double bonds as shown in the resonance hybrid above) is also evident in this model.

> ## Helpful Hint
>
> Each type of arrow in organic chemistry (e.g., ⌒, $\rightleftharpoons$, and $\leftrightarrow$) has a specific meaning. It is important that you use each type of arrow only for the purpose for which it is defined.

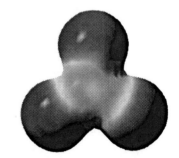

FIGURE 1.5 A calculated electrostatic potential map for the carbonate anion, showing the equal charge distribution at the three oxygen atoms. In electrostatic potential maps like this one, colors trending toward red mean increasing concentration of negative charge, while those trending toward blue mean less negative (or more positive) charge.

1.8A The Use of Curved Arrows: HOW TO Write Resonance Structures

As we have mentioned earlier, curved arrows are often used in writing **resonance structures**, and as we shall see in Section 3.2 they are essential in writing reaction mechanisms. Let us now point out several important things to remember about their use.

* Curved arrows are used to show the movement of both **bonding** and **unshared** electrons.

* A double-barbed curved arrow (⌢) shows the movement of **two** electrons (an electron pair). [Later, we will see that a single-barbed arrow (⌢) can be used to show the movement of a single electron.]

* A curved arrow should originate precisely at the location of the relevant electrons in the initial formula and point precisely to where those electrons will be drawn in the new formula.

* A new formula should be drawn to show the result of the electron shift(s). All formulas should be proper Lewis structures and should include formal charges as appropriate. The maximum number of valence electrons should not be exceeded for any atom in a formula.

1.8B Rules for Writing Resonance Structures

1. **Resonance structures exist only on paper.** Although they have no real existence of their own, **resonance structures** are useful because they allow us to describe molecules and ions for which a single Lewis structure is inadequate. We write two or more Lewis structures, calling them resonance structures or resonance contributors. We connect these structures by double-headed arrows (↔), and we say that the real molecule or ion is a hybrid of all of them.

2. **We are only allowed to move electrons in writing resonance structures.** The positions of the nuclei of the atoms must remain the same in all of the structures. Structure **3** is not a resonance structure of **1** or **2**, for example, because in order to form it we would have to move a hydrogen atom and this is not permitted:

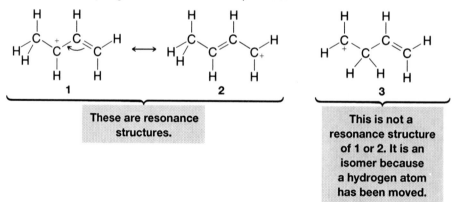

Generally speaking, when we move electrons, we move only those of **multiple bonds** (as in the example above) and those of **nonbonding electron pairs**.

3. **All of the structures must be proper Lewis structures.** We should not write structures in which carbon has five bonds, for example:

$$H-\overset{\underset{|}{H}}{\underset{|}{C}}=\overset{+}{O}-H$$

> This is not a proper resonance structure for methanol because carbon has five bonds. Elements of the first major row of the periodic table cannot have more than eight electrons in their valence shell.

4. **The energy of the resonance hybrid is lower than the energy of any contributing structure.** Resonance stabilizes a molecule or ion. This is especially true when the resonance structures are equivalent. Chemists call this stabilization *resonance stabilization*. **If the resonance structures are equivalent, then the resonance stabilization is large.**

In Chapter 14 we shall find that benzene is highly resonance stabilized because it is a hybrid of the two equivalent forms that follow:

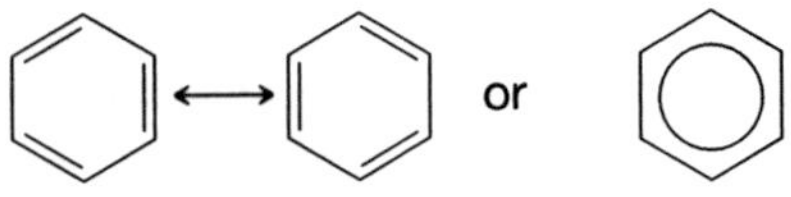

Resonance structures
for benzene

Representation
of hybrid

5. **The more stable a structure is (when taken by itself), the greater is its contribution to the hybrid.**

1.8C How Do We Decide When One Resonance Structure Contributes More to the Hybrid Than Another?

The following rules will help us:

1. **The more covalent bonds a structure has, the more stable it is.** Consider the resonance structures for formaldehyde below. (Formaldehyde is a chemical used to preserve biological specimens.) Structure **A** has more covalent bonds, and therefore makes a larger contribution to the hybrid. In other words, the hybrid is more like structure **A** than structure **B**.

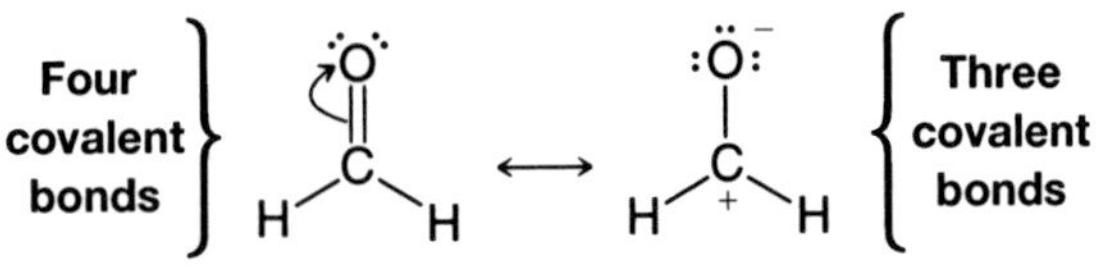

Resonance structures for formaldehyde

These structures also illustrate two other considerations:

2. **Charge separation decreases stability.** It takes energy to separate opposite charges, and therefore a structure with separated charges is less stable. Structure **B** for formaldehyde has separated plus and minus charges; therefore, on this basis, too, it is the less stable contributor and makes a smaller contribution to the hybrid.

3. **Structures in which all the atoms have a complete valence shell of electrons (i.e., the noble gas structure) are more stable.** Look again at structure **B**. The carbon atom has only six electrons around it, whereas in **A** it has eight. On this basis we can conclude that **A** is more stable and makes a larger contribution.

●●● SOLVED PROBLEM 1.11

The following is one way of writing the structure of the nitrate ion:

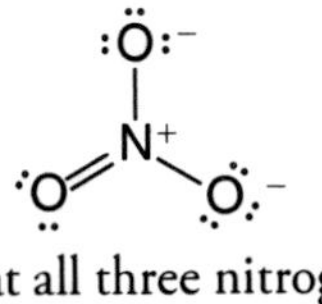

However, considerable physical evidence indicates that all three nitrogen–oxygen bonds are equivalent and that they have the same length, a bond distance between that expected for a nitrogen–oxygen single bond and a nitrogen–oxygen double bond. Explain this in terms of resonance theory.

STRATEGY AND ANSWER: We recognize that if we move the electron pairs in the following way, we can write three *different* but *equivalent* structures for the nitrate ion:

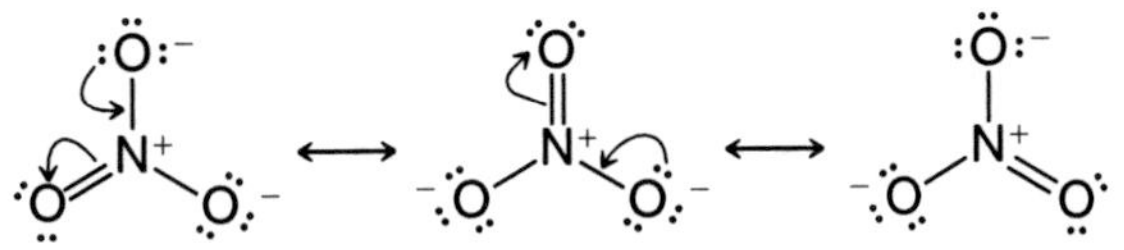

(continues on the next page)

Since these structures differ from one another *only in the positions of their electrons*, they are *resonance structures* or *resonance contributors*. As such, no single structure taken alone will adequately represent the nitrate ion. The actual molecule will be best represented by a *hybrid of these three structures*. We might write this hybrid in the following way to indicate that all of the bonds are equivalent and that they are more than single bonds and less than double bonds. We also indicate that each oxygen atom bears an equal partial negative charge. This charge distribution corresponds to what we find experimentally.

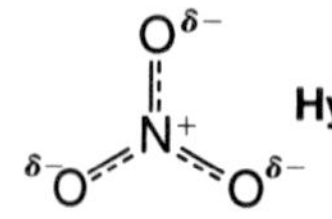

Hybrid structure for the nitrate ion

PRACTICE PROBLEM 1.18 **(a)** Write two resonance structures for the formate ion HCO_2^-. (*Note*: The hydrogen and oxygen atoms are bonded to the carbon.) **(b)** Explain what these structures predict for the carbon–oxygen bond lengths of the formate ion, and **(c)**, for the electrical charge on the oxygen atoms.

PRACTICE PROBLEM 1.19 Write the resonance structure that would result from moving the electrons as the curved arrows indicate. Be sure to include formal charges if needed.

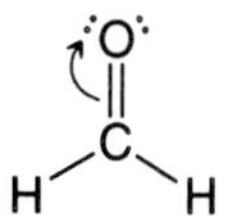

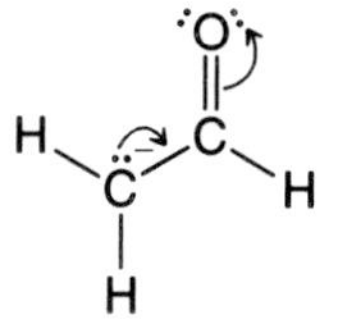

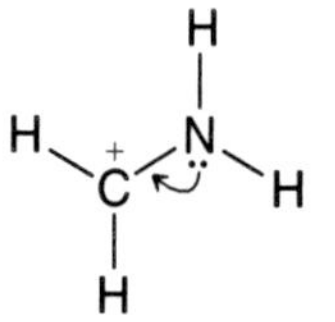

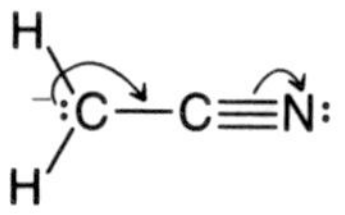

PRACTICE PROBLEM 1.20 Add any missing unshared electron pairs (if any), then, using curved arrows to show the shifts in electrons, write the contributing resonance structures and resonance hybrid for each of the following:

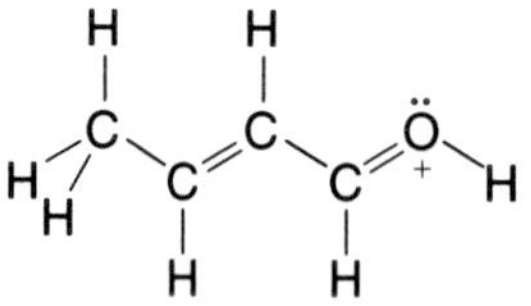

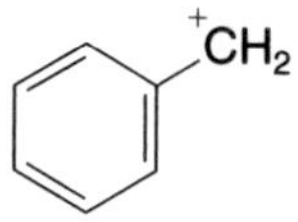

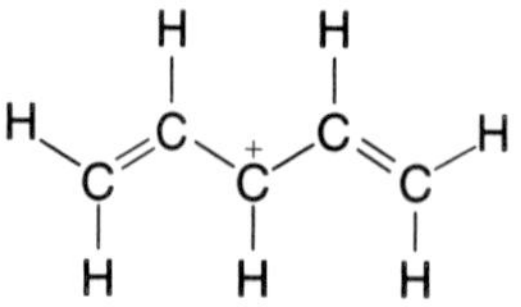

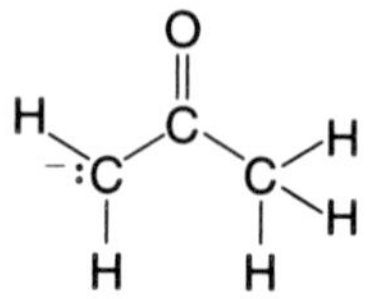

(g) $CH_3\overset{+}{S}CH_2$

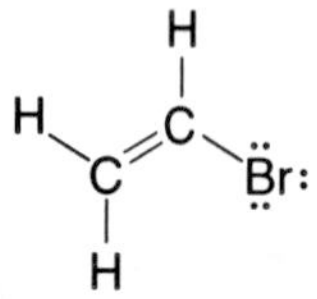

(h) CH_3NO_2

For each set of resonance structures that follow, add a curved arrow that shows how electrons in the left formula shift to become the right formula, and designate the formula that would contribute most to the hybrid. Explain your choice:

(a)

(b) CH_3-C ⟷ CH_3-C

(c) :NH$_2$—C≡N: ⟷ $\overset{+}{N}H_2$=C=$\ddot{N}$ $^-$

1.9 QUANTUM MECHANICS AND ATOMIC STRUCTURE

A theory of atomic and molecular structure was advanced independently and almost simultaneously by three people in 1926: Erwin Schrödinger, Werner Heisenberg, and Paul Dirac. This theory, called **wave mechanics** by Schrödinger and **quantum mechanics** by Heisenberg, has become the basis from which we derive our modern understanding of bonding in molecules. At the heart of quantum mechanics are equations called wave functions (denoted by the Greek letter psi, ψ).

- Each **wave function** (ψ) corresponds to a different *energy state* for an electron.
- Each *energy state* is a sublevel where one or two electrons can reside.
- The **energy** associated with the state of an electron can be calculated from the wave function.
- The **relative probability** of finding an electron in a given region of space can be calculated from the wave function (Section 1.10).
- The solution to a wave function can be positive, negative, or zero (Fig. 1.6).
- The **phase sign** of a wave equation indicates whether the solution is positive or negative when calculated for a given point in space relative to the nucleus.

Wave functions, whether they are for sound waves, lake waves, or the energy of an electron, have the possibility of constructive interference and destructive interference.

- **Constructive interference** occurs when wave functions with the same phase sign interact. There is a *reinforcing effect* and the amplitude of the wave function increases.
- **Destructive interference** occurs when wave functions with opposite phase signs interact. There is a *subtractive effect* and the amplitude of the wave function goes to zero or changes sign.

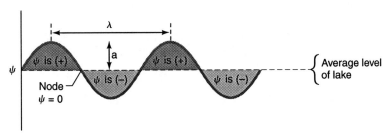

FIGURE 1.6 A wave moving across a lake is viewed along a slice through the lake. For this wave the wave function, ψ, is plus (+) in crests and minus (−) in troughs. At the average level of the lake it is zero; these places are called nodes. The magnitude of the crests and troughs is the amplitude (a) of the wave. The distance from the crest of one wave to the crest of the next is the wavelength (λ, or lambda).

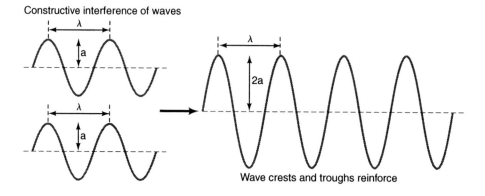

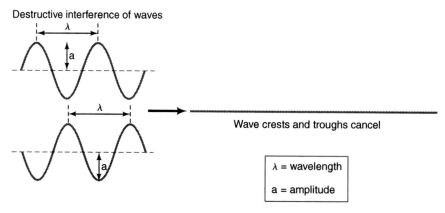

Experiments have shown that electrons have properties of waves and particles, which was an idea first put forth by Louis de Broglie in 1923. Our discussion focuses on the wavelike properties of electrons, however.

1.10 ATOMIC ORBITALS AND ELECTRON CONFIGURATION

A physical interpretation related to the electron wave function was put forth by Max Born in 1926:

- The square of a wave function (ψ^2) for a particular x, y, z location expresses the probability of finding an electron at that location in space.

If the value of ψ^2 is large in a unit volume of space, the probability of finding an electron in that volume is high—we say that the **electron probability density** is large. Conversely, if ψ^2 for some other volume of space is small, the probability of finding an electron there is low.* This leads to the general definition of an orbital and, by extension, to the familiar shapes of atomic orbitals.

- An **orbital** is a region of space where the probability of finding an electron is high.
- **Atomic orbitals** are plots of ψ^2 in three dimensions. These plots generate the familiar s, p, and d orbital shapes.

The volumes that we show are those that would contain the electron 90–95% of the time. There is a finite, but very small, probability of finding an electron at greater distance from the nucleus than shown in the plots.

The shapes of s and p orbitals are shown in Fig. 1.7.

All s orbitals are spheres. A $1s$ orbital is a simple sphere. A $2s$ orbital is a sphere with an inner nodal surface ($\psi^2 = 0$). The inner portion of the $2s$ orbital, ψ_{2s}, has a negative phase sign.

---

*Integration of ψ^2 over all space must equal 1; that is, the probability of finding an electron somewhere in all of space is 100%.

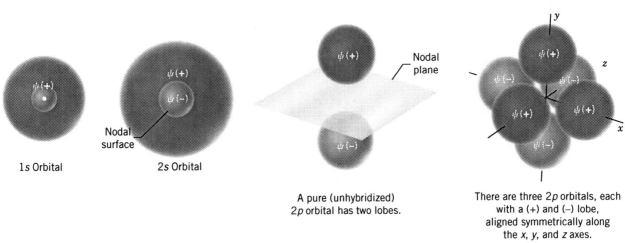

FIGURE 1.7 The shapes of some *s* and *p* orbitals. Pure, unhybridized *p* orbitals are almost-touching spheres. The *p* orbitals in hybridized atoms are lobe-shaped (Section 1.13).

The shape of a *p* orbital is like that of almost-touching spheres or lobes. The phase sign of a 2*p* wave function, ψ_{2p}, is positive in one lobe and negative in the other. A nodal plane separates the two lobes of a *p* orbital, and the three *p* orbitals of a given energy level are arranged in space along the *x*, *y*, and *z* axes in a Cartesian coordinate system.

* The + and − signs of wave functions do not imply positive or negative charge or greater or lesser probability of finding an electron.
* ψ^2 (the probability of finding an electron) is always positive, because squaring either a positive or negative solution to ψ leads to a positive value.

Thus, the probability of finding an electron in either lobe of a *p* orbital is the same. We shall see the significance of the + and − signs later when we see how atomic orbitals combine to form molecular orbitals.

1.10A Electron Configurations

The relative energies of atomic orbitals in the first and second principal shells are as follows:

* Electrons in 1*s* orbitals have the lowest energy because they are closest to the positive nucleus.
* Electrons in 2*s* orbitals are next lowest in energy.
* Electrons of the three 2*p* orbitals have equal but higher energy than the 2*s* orbital.
* Orbitals of equal energy (such as the three 2*p* orbitals) are called **degenerate orbitals**.

We can use these relative energies to arrive at the electron configuration of any atom in the first two rows of the periodic table. We need follow only a few simple rules.

1. **Aufbau principle:** Orbitals are filled so that those of lowest energy are filled first. (*Aufbau* is German for "building up.")

2. **Pauli exclusion principle:** A maximum of two electrons may be placed in each orbital *but only when the spins of the electrons are paired.* An electron spins about its own axis. For reasons that we cannot develop here, an electron is permitted only one or the other of just two possible spin orientations. We usually show these orientations by arrows, either ↑ or ↓. Thus two spin-paired electrons would be designated ↓↑. Unpaired electrons, which are not permitted in the same orbital, are designated ↑↑ (or ↓↓).

3. **Hund's rule:** When we come to orbitals of equal energy (degenerate orbitals) such as the three *p* orbitals, we add one electron to each *with their spins unpaired* until each of the degenerate orbitals contains one electron. (This allows the electrons, which repel each other, to be farther apart.) Then we begin adding a second electron to each degenerate orbital so that the spins are paired.

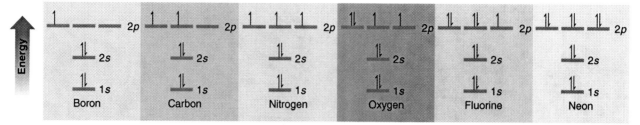

FIGURE 1.8 The ground state electron configurations of some second-row elements.

If we apply these rules to some of the second-row elements of the periodic table, we get the results shown in Fig. 1.8.

1.11 MOLECULAR ORBITALS

Atomic orbitals provide a means for understanding how atoms form covalent bonds. Let us consider a very simple case—formation of a bond between two hydrogen atoms to form a hydrogen molecule (Fig. 1.9).

When two hydrogen atoms are relatively far apart their total energy is simply that of two isolated hydrogen atoms (**I**). Formation of a covalent bond reduces the overall energy of the system, however. As the two hydrogen atoms move closer together (**II**), each nucleus increasingly attracts the other's electron. This attraction more than compensates for the repulsive force between the two nuclei (or the two electrons). The result is a covalent bond (**III**), such that the internuclear distance is an ideal balance that allows the two electrons to be shared between both atoms while at the same time avoiding repulsive interactions between their nuclei. This ideal internuclear distance between hydrogen atoms is 0.74 Å, and we call this the bond length in a hydrogen molecule. If the nuclei are moved closer together (**IV**) the repulsion of the two positively charged nuclei predominates, and the energy of the system rises.

Notice that each H· has a shaded area around it, indicating that its precise position is uncertain. Electrons are constantly moving.

- According to the Heisenberg uncertainty principle, we cannot simultaneously know the position and momentum of an electron.

These shaded areas in our diagram represent orbitals, and they result from applying the principles of quantum mechanics. Plotting the square of the wave function (ψ^2) gives us a three-dimensional region called an orbital where finding an electron is highly probable.

- An atomic orbital represents the region of space where one or two electrons of an isolated atom are likely to be found.

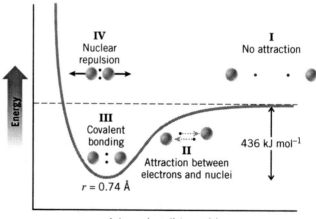

FIGURE 1.9 The potential energy of the hydrogen molecule as a function of internuclear distance.

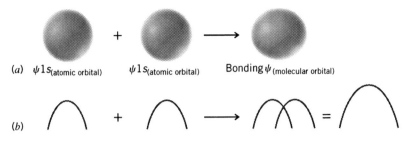

FIGURE 1.10 (a) The overlapping of two hydrogen 1s atomic orbitals with the same phase sign (indicated by their identical color) to form a bonding molecular orbital. (b) The analogous overlapping of two waves with the same phase, resulting in constructive interference and enhanced amplitude.

In the case of our hydrogen model above, the shaded spheres represent the $1s$ orbital of each hydrogen atom. As the two hydrogen atoms approach each other their $1s$ orbitals begin to overlap until their atomic orbitals combine to form molecular orbitals.

- A **molecular orbital (MO)** represents the region of space where one or two electrons of a molecule are likely to be found.
- An orbital (atomic or molecular) can contain a maximum of two spin-paired electrons (Pauli exclusion principle).
- When atomic orbitals combine to form molecular orbitals, **the number of molecular orbitals that result always equals the number of atomic orbitals that combine.**

Thus, in the formation of a hydrogen molecule the two ψ_{1s} atomic orbitals combine to produce two molecular orbitals. Two orbitals result because the mathematical properties of wave functions permit them to be combined by either addition or subtraction. That is, they can combine either in or out of phase.

- A **bonding molecular orbital** (ψ_{molec}) results when two orbitals of the same phase overlap (Fig. 1.10).
- An **antibonding molecular orbital** (ψ^*_{molec}) results when two orbitals of opposite phase overlap (Fig. 1.11).

The bonding molecular orbital of a hydrogen molecule in its lowest energy (ground) state contains both electrons from the individual hydrogen atoms. The value of ψ (and therefore also ψ^2) is large between the nuclei, precisely as expected since the electrons are shared by both nuclei to form the covalent bond.

The antibonding molecular orbital contains no electrons in the ground state of a hydrogen molecule. Furthermore, the value of ψ (and therefore also ψ^2) goes to zero between the nuclei, creating a node ($\psi = 0$). The antibonding orbital does not provide for electron density between the atoms, and thus it is not involved in bonding.

What we have just described has its counterpart in a mathematical treatment called the **LCAO (linear combination of atomic orbitals)** method. In the LCAO treatment, wave functions for the atomic orbitals are combined in a linear fashion (by addition or subtraction) in order to obtain new wave functions for the molecular orbitals.

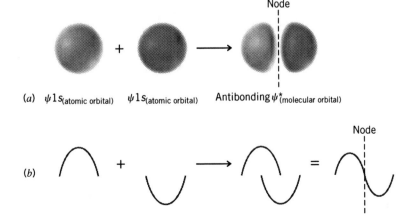

FIGURE 1.11 (a) The overlapping of two hydrogen 1s atomic orbitals with opposite phase signs (indicated by their different colors) to form an antibonding molecular orbital. (b) The analogous overlapping of two waves with the opposite sign, resulting in destructive interference and decreased amplitude. A node exists where complete cancellation by opposite phases makes the value of the combined wave function zero.

FIGURE 1.12 Energy diagram for the hydrogen molecule. Combination of two atomic orbitals, ψ_{1s}, gives two molecular orbitals, ψ_{molec} and ψ^*_{molec}. The energy of ψ_{molec} is lower than that of the separate atomic orbitals, and in the lowest electronic energy state of molecular hydrogen the bonding MO contains both electrons.

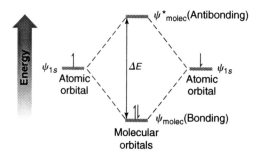

Molecular orbitals, like atomic orbitals, correspond to particular energy states for an electron. Calculations show that the relative energy of an electron in the bonding molecular orbital of the hydrogen molecule is substantially less than its energy in a ψ_{1s} atomic orbital. These calculations also show that the energy of an electron in the antibonding molecular orbital is substantially greater than its energy in a ψ_{1s} atomic orbital.

An energy diagram for the molecular orbitals of the hydrogen molecule is shown in Fig. 1.12. Notice that electrons are placed in molecular orbitals in the same way that they are in atomic orbitals. Two electrons (with their spins opposed) occupy the bonding molecular orbital, where their total energy is less than in the separate atomic orbitals. This is, as we have said, the *lowest electronic state* or *ground state* of the hydrogen molecule. An electron may occupy the antibonding molecular orbital in what is called an *excited state* for the molecule. This state forms when the molecule in the ground state (Fig. 1.12) absorbs a photon of light having the proper energy (ΔE).

1.12 THE STRUCTURE OF METHANE AND ETHANE: sp^3 HYBRIDIZATION

The s and p orbitals used in the quantum mechanical description of the carbon atom, given in Section 1.10, were based on calculations for hydrogen atoms. These simple s and p orbitals do not, when taken alone, provide a satisfactory model for the *tetravalent–tetrahedral* carbon of methane (CH_4, see Practice Problem 1.22). However, a satisfactory model of methane's structure that is based on quantum mechanics *can* be obtained through an approach called orbital hybridization. Orbital hybridization, in its simplest terms, is nothing more than a mathematical approach that involves the combining of individual wave functions for s and p orbitals to obtain wave functions for new orbitals. The new orbitals have, *in varying proportions*, the properties of the original orbitals taken separately. These new orbitals are called hybrid atomic orbitals.

According to quantum mechanics, the electronic configuration of a carbon atom in its lowest energy state—called the ground state—is that given here:

$$\text{C} \quad \underline{\uparrow\downarrow} \quad \underline{\uparrow\downarrow} \quad \underline{\uparrow} \quad \underline{\uparrow} \quad \underline{}$$
$$\quad \quad 1s \quad 2s \quad 2p_x \; 2p_y \; 2p_z$$

Ground state of a carbon atom

The valence electrons of a carbon atom (those used in bonding) are those of the *outer level*, that is, the $2s$ and $2p$ electrons.

1.12A The Structure of Methane

Hybrid atomic orbitals that account for the structure of methane can be derived from carbon's second-shell s and p orbitals as follows (Fig. 1.13):

• Wave functions for the $2s$, $2p_x$, $2p_y$, and $2p_z$ orbitals of ground state carbon are mixed to form four new and equivalent $2sp^3$ hybrid orbitals.

• The designation sp^3 signifies that the hybrid orbital has one part s orbital character and three parts p orbital character.

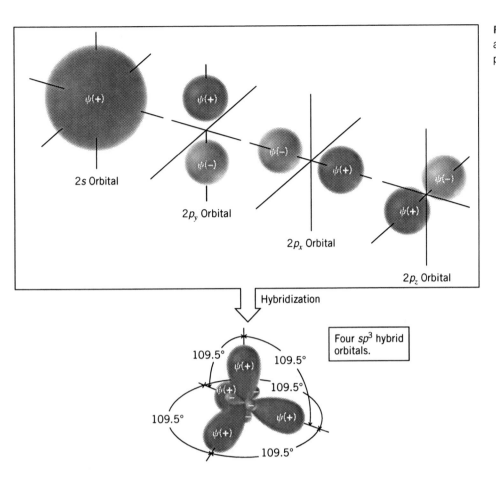

FIGURE 1.13 Hybridization of pure atomic orbitals of a carbon atom to produce sp^3 hybrid orbitals.

- The mathematical result is that the four $2sp^3$ orbitals are oriented at angles of 109.5° with respect to each other. This is precisely the orientation of the four hydrogen atoms of methane. Each **H—C—H** bond angle is 109.5°.

If, in our imagination, we visualize the hypothetical formation of methane from an sp^3-hybridized carbon atom and four hydrogen atoms, the process might be like that shown in Fig. 1.14. For simplicity we show only the formation of the **bonding molecular orbital** for each carbon–hydrogen bond. We see that an sp^3-hybridized carbon gives a *tetrahedral structure for methane, and one with four equivalent C—H bonds.*

In addition to accounting properly for the shape of methane, the orbital hybridization model also explains the very strong bonds that are formed between carbon and

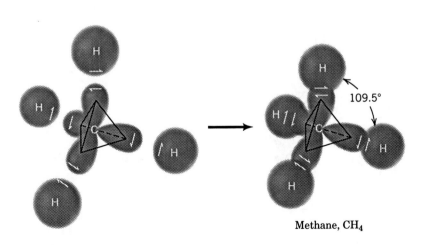

Methane, CH_4

FIGURE 1.14 The hypothetical formation of methane from an sp^3-hybridized carbon atom and four hydrogen atoms. In orbital hybridization we combine orbitals, *not* electrons. The electrons can then be placed in the hybrid orbitals as necessary for bond formation, but always in accordance with the Pauli principle of no more than two electrons (with opposite spin) in each orbital. In this illustration we have placed one electron in each of the hybrid carbon orbitals. In addition, we have shown only the bonding molecular orbital of each C—H bond because these are the orbitals that contain the electrons in the lowest energy state of the molecule.

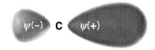

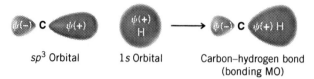

FIGURE 1.15 The shape of an sp^3 orbital.

hydrogen. To see how this is so, consider the shape of an individual sp^3 orbital shown in Fig. 1.15. Because an sp^3 orbital has the character of a p orbital, the positive lobe of an sp^3 orbital is large and extends relatively far from the carbon nucleus.

It is the positive lobe of an sp^3 orbital that overlaps with the positive $1s$ orbital of hydrogen to form the bonding molecular orbital of a carbon–hydrogen bond (Fig. 1.16).

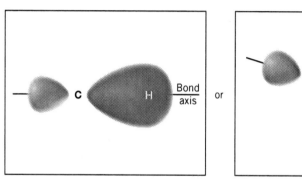

| sp^3 Orbital | $1s$ Orbital | Carbon–hydrogen bond (bonding MO) |

FIGURE 1.16 Formation of a C—H bond.

Because the positive lobe of the sp^3 orbital is large and is extended into space, the overlap between it and the $1s$ orbital of hydrogen is also large, and the resulting carbon–hydrogen bond is quite strong.

The bond formed from the overlap of an sp^3 orbital and a $1s$ orbital is an example of a **sigma (σ) bond** (Fig. 1.17).

FIGURE 1.17 A σ (sigma) bond.

- A sigma (σ) bond has a circularly symmetrical orbital cross section when viewed along the bond between two atoms.
- All purely single bonds are sigma bonds.

From this point on we shall often show only the bonding molecular orbitals because they are the ones that contain the electrons when the molecule is in its lowest energy state. Consideration of antibonding orbitals is important when a molecule absorbs light and in explaining certain reactions. We shall point out these instances later.

In Fig. 1.18 we show a calculated structure for methane where the tetrahedral geometry derived from orbital hybridization is clearly apparent.

FIGURE 1.18 (a) In this structure of methane, based on quantum mechanical calculations, the inner solid surface represents a region of high electron density. High electron density is found in each bonding region. The outer mesh surface represents approximately the furthest extent of overall electron density for the molecule. (b) This ball-and-stick model of methane is like the kind you might build with a molecular model kit. (c) This structure is how you would draw methane. Ordinary lines are used to show the two bonds that are in the plane of the paper, a solid wedge is used to show the bond that is in front of the paper, and a dashed wedge is used to show the bond that is behind the plane of the paper.

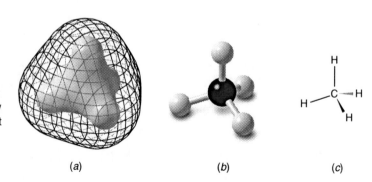

(a) (b) (c)

1.12B The Structure of Ethane

The bond angles at the carbon atoms of ethane, and of all alkanes, are also tetrahedral like those in methane. A satisfactory model for ethane can be provided by sp^3-hybridized carbon atoms. Figure 1.19 shows how we might imagine the bonding molecular orbitals of an ethane molecule being constructed from two sp^3-hybridized carbon atoms and six hydrogen atoms.

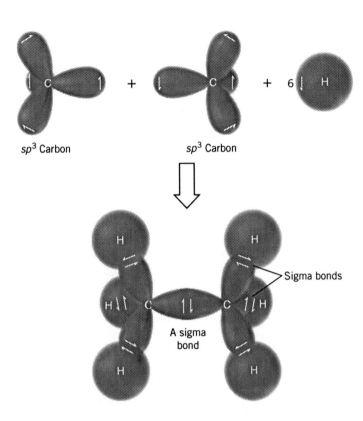

sp³ Carbon   *sp³* Carbon

A sigma bond

Sigma bonds

FIGURE 1.19 The hypothetical formation of the bonding molecular orbitals of ethane from two sp^3-hybridized carbon atoms and six hydrogen atoms. All of the bonds are sigma bonds. (Antibonding sigma molecular orbitals—called σ^* orbitals—are formed in each instance as well, but for simplicity these are not shown.)

The carbon–carbon bond of ethane is a *sigma bond* with cylindrical symmetry, formed by two overlapping sp^3 orbitals. (The carbon–hydrogen bonds are also sigma bonds. They are formed from overlapping carbon sp^3 orbitals and hydrogen s orbitals.)

● Rotation of groups joined by a single bond does not usually require a large amount of energy.

Consequently, groups joined by single bonds rotate relatively freely with respect to one another. (We discuss this point further in Section 4.8.) In Fig. 1.20 we show a calculated structure for ethane in which the tetrahedral geometry derived from orbital hybridization is clearly apparent.

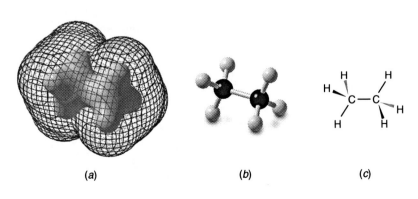

(a)   *(b)*   *(c)*

FIGURE 1.20 (a) In this structure of ethane, based on quantum mechanical calculations, the inner solid surface represents a region of high electron density. High electron density is found in each bonding region. The outer mesh surface represents approximately the furthest extent of overall electron density for the molecule. (b) A ball-and-stick model of ethane, like the kind you might build with a molecular model kit. (c) A structural formula for ethane as you would draw it using lines, wedges, and dashed wedges to show in three dimensions its tetrahedral geometry at each carbon.

● THE CHEMISTRY OF... Calculated Molecular Models: Electron Density Surfaces

In this book we make frequent use of molecular models derived from quantum mechanical calculations. These models will help us visualize the shapes of molecules as well as understand their properties and reactivity. A useful type of model is one that shows a calculated three-dimensional surface at which a chosen value of electron density is the same all around a molecule, called an **electron density surface**. If we make a plot where the value chosen is for low electron density, the result is a van der Waals surface, the surface that represents approximately the overall shape of a molecule as determined by the furthest extent of its electron cloud. On the other hand, if we make a plot where the value of electron density is relatively high, the resulting surface is one that approximately represents the region of covalent bonding in a molecule. Surfaces of low and high electron density are shown in this box for dimethyl ether. Similar models are shown for methane and ethane in Figs. 1.18 and 1.20.

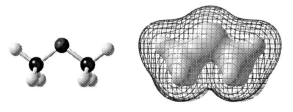

Dimethyl ether

1.13 THE STRUCTURE OF ETHENE (ETHYLENE): sp^2 HYBRIDIZATION

The carbon atoms of many of the molecules that we have considered so far have used their four valence electrons to form four single covalent (sigma) bonds to four other atoms. We find, however, that many important organic compounds exist in which carbon atoms share more than two electrons with another atom. In molecules of these compounds some bonds that are formed are multiple covalent bonds. When two carbon atoms share two pairs of electrons, for example, the result is a carbon–carbon double bond:

$$ \ddot{C}::\ddot{C} \quad \text{or} \quad \overset{\diagdown}{\underset{\diagup}{C}}=\overset{\diagup}{\underset{\diagdown}{C}} $$

Hydrocarbons whose molecules contain a carbon–carbon double bond are called **alkenes**. Ethene (C_2H_4) and propene (C_3H_6) are both alkenes. Ethene is also called ethylene, and propene is sometimes called propylene.

$$
\begin{array}{cc}
\overset{H}{\underset{H}{\diagdown}}C=C\overset{\diagup H}{\underset{\diagdown H}{}} & \overset{H}{\underset{H_3C}{\diagdown}}C=C\overset{\diagup H}{\underset{\diagdown H}{}} \\
\textbf{Ethene} & \textbf{Propene}
\end{array}
$$

In ethene the only carbon–carbon bond is a double bond. Propene has one carbon–carbon single bond and one carbon–carbon double bond.

The spatial arrangement of the atoms of alkenes is different from that of alkanes. The six atoms of ethene are coplanar, and the arrangement of atoms around each carbon atom is triangular (Fig. 1.21).

● Carbon–carbon double bonds are comprised of sp^2-hybridized carbon atoms.

The mathematical mixing of orbitals that furnish the sp^2 orbitals for our model can be visualized in the way shown in Fig. 1.22. The $2s$ orbital is mathematically mixed (or hybridized) with two of the $2p$ orbitals. (The hybridization procedure applies only to the

FIGURE 1.21 The structure and bond angles of ethene. The plane of the atoms is perpendicular to the paper. The dashed wedge bonds project behind the plane of the paper, and the solid wedge bonds project in front of the paper.

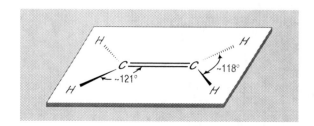

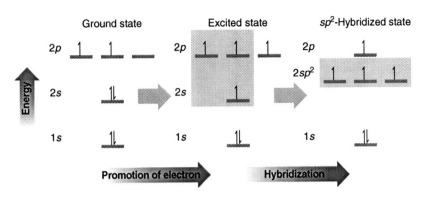

Ground state   Excited state sp^2-Hybridized state

FIGURE 1.22 A process for deriving sp^2-hybridized carbon atoms.

Promotion of electron   Hybridization

orbitals, not to the electrons.) One $2p$ orbital is left unhybridized. One electron is then placed in each of the sp^2 hybrid orbitals and one electron remains in the $2p$ orbital.

The three sp^2 orbitals that result from hybridization are directed toward the corners of a regular triangle (with angles of 120° between them). The carbon p orbital that is not hybridized is perpendicular to the plane of the triangle formed by the hybrid sp^2 orbitals (Fig. 1.23).

In our model for ethene (Fig. 1.24) we see the following:

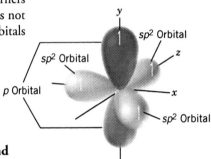

FIGURE 1.23 An sp^2-hybridized carbon atom.

- Two sp^2-hybridized carbon atoms form a sigma (σ) bond between them by overlap of one sp^2 orbital from each carbon. The remaining carbon sp^2 orbitals form σ bonds to four hydrogens through overlap with the hydrogen $1s$ orbitals. These five σ bonds account for 10 of the 12 valence electrons contributed by the two carbons and four hydrogens, and comprise the **σ-bond framework** of the molecule.

- The remaining two bonding electrons are each located in an unhybridized p orbital of each carbon. Sideways overlap of these p orbitals and sharing of the two electrons between the carbons leads to a **pi (π) bond**. The overlap of these orbitals is shown schematically in Fig. 1.25.

The bond angles that we would predict on the basis of sp^2-hybridized carbon atoms (120° all around) are quite close to the bond angles that are actually found (Fig. 1.21).

We can better visualize how these p orbitals interact with each other if we view a structure showing calculated molecular orbitals for ethene (Fig. 1.25). We see that the parallel p orbitals *overlap above and below the plane of the σ framework*.

Note the difference in shape of the bonding molecular orbital of a π bond as contrasted to that of a σ bond. A σ bond has cylindrical symmetry about a line connecting the two bonded nuclei. A π bond has a nodal plane passing through the two bonded nuclei and between the π molecular orbital lobes.

- When two p atomic orbitals combine to form a π bond, two π molecular orbital molecular orbitals form: one is a bonding molecular orbital and the other is an **antibonding molecular orbital.**

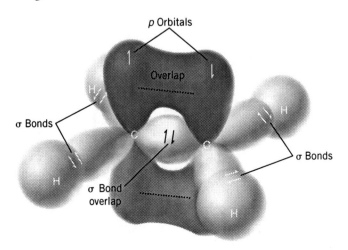

FIGURE 1.24 A model for the bonding molecular orbitals of ethene formed from two sp^2-hybridized carbon atoms and four hydrogen atoms.

FIGURE 1.25 (a) A wedge–dashed wedge formula for the sigma bonds in ethene and a schematic depiction of the overlapping of adjacent p orbitals that form the π bond. (b) A calculated structure for ethene. The blue and red colors indicate opposite phase signs in each lobe of the π molecular orbital. A ball-and-stick model for the σ bonds in ethene can be seen through the mesh that indicates the π bond.

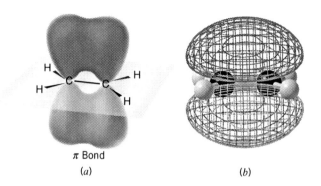

π Bond

(a)   (b)

The bonding π molecular orbital results when p-orbital lobes of like signs overlap; the antibonding π molecular orbital results when opposite signs overlap (Fig. 1.26).

The bonding π orbital is the lower energy orbital and contains both π electrons (with opposite spins) in the ground state of the molecule. The region of greatest probability of finding the electrons in the bonding π orbital is a region generally situated above and below the plane of the σ-bond framework between the two carbon atoms. The antibonding π* orbital is of higher energy, and it is not occupied by electrons when the molecule is in the ground state. It can become occupied, however, if the molecule absorbs light of the right frequency and an electron is promoted from the lower energy level to the higher one. The antibonding π* orbital has a nodal plane between the two carbon atoms.

- To summarize, a carbon–carbon double bond consists of one σ bond and one π bond.

The σ bond results from two sp^2 orbitals overlapping end to end and is symmetrical about an axis linking the two carbon atoms. The π bond results from a sideways overlap of two p orbitals; it has a nodal plane like a p orbital. In the ground state the electrons of the π bond are located between the two carbon atoms but generally above and below the plane of the σ-bond framework.

Electrons of the π bond have greater energy than electrons of the σ bond. The relative energies of the σ and π molecular orbitals (with the electrons in the ground state) are shown in the margin diagram. The σ* orbital is the antibonding **sigma orbital**.

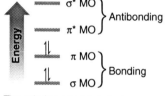

The relative energies of electrons involved in σ and π bonds

FIGURE 1.26 How two isolated carbon p orbitals combine to form two π (pi) molecular orbitals. The bonding MO is of lower energy. The higher energy antibonding MO contains an additional node. Both orbitals have a node in the plane containing the C and H atoms.

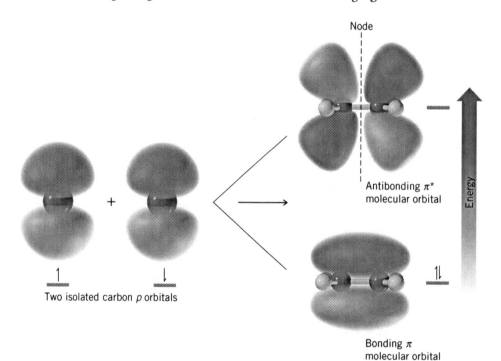

Node

Antibonding π* molecular orbital

Two isolated carbon p orbitals

Bonding π molecular orbital

1.13A Restricted Rotation and the Double Bond

The σ–π model for the carbon–carbon double bond also accounts for an important property of the double bond:

- There is a large energy barrier to rotation associated with groups joined by a double bond.

Maximum overlap between the p orbitals of a π bond occurs when the axes of the p orbitals are exactly parallel. Rotating one carbon of the double bond 90° (Fig. 1.27) breaks the π bond, for then the axes of the p orbitals are perpendicular and there is no net overlap between them. Estimates based on thermochemical calculations indicate that the strength of the π bond is 264 kJ mol^{-1}. This, then, is the barrier to rotation of the double bond. It is markedly higher than the rotational barrier of groups joined by carbon–carbon single bonds (13–26 kJ mol^{-1}). While groups joined by single bonds rotate relatively freely at room temperature, those joined by double bonds do not.

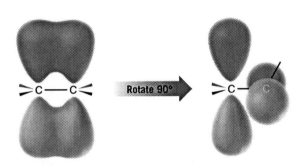

FIGURE 1.27 A stylized depiction of how rotation of a carbon atom of a double bond through an angle of 90° results in breaking of the π bond.

1.13B Cis–Trans Isomerism

Restricted rotation of groups joined by a double bond causes a new type of isomerism that we illustrate with the two dichloroethenes written as the following structures:

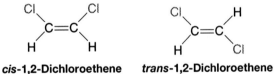

cis-1,2-Dichloroethene   *trans*-1,2-Dichloroethene

- These two compounds are isomers; they are different compounds that have the same molecular formula.

We can tell that they are different compounds by trying to place a model of one compound on a model of the other so that all parts coincide, that is, to try to **superpose** one on the other. We find that it cannot be done. Had one been superposable on the other, all parts of one model would correspond in three dimensions exactly with the other model. (*The notion of superposition is different from simply superimposing one thing on another.* The latter means only to lay one on the other without the necessary condition that all parts coincide.)

- We indicate that they are different isomers by attaching the prefix cis or trans to their names (*cis*, Latin: on this side; *trans*, Latin: across).

cis-1,2-Dichloroethene and *trans*-1,2-dichloroethene are not constitutional isomers because the connectivity of the atoms is the same in each. The two compounds *differ only in the arrangement of their atoms in space*. Isomers of this kind are classified formally as stereoisomers, but often they are called simply cis–trans isomers. (We shall study stereoisomerism in detail in Chapters 4 and 5.)

The structural requirements for *cis–trans isomerism* will become clear if we consider a few additional examples. 1,1-Dichloroethene and 1,1,2-trichloroethene do not show this type of isomerism.

1,1-Dichloroethene
(no cis-trans isomerism)

1,1,2-Trichloroethene
(no cis-trans isomerism)

1,2-Difluoroethene and 1,2-dichloro-1,2-difluoroethene do exist as cis–trans isomers. Notice that we designate the isomer with two identical groups on the same side as being cis:

cis-**1,2-Difluoroethene**   *trans*-**1,2-Difluoroethene**

cis-**1,2-Dichloro-1,2-difluoroethene**   *trans*-**1,2-Dichloro-1,2-difluoroethene**

Clearly, then, ***cis–trans isomerism of this type is not possible if one carbon atom of the double bond bears two identical groups.***

●●● SOLVED PROBLEM 1.12

Write structures of all the isomers of C_2H_5F.

ANSWER: Taking into account cis–trans isomerism and the possibility of a ring we have the following four possibilities.

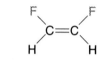

●●●

PRACTICE PROBLEM 1.22 Which of the following alkenes can exist as cis–trans isomers? Write their structures. Build hand-held models to prove that one isomer is not superposable on the other.

(a) $CH_2{=}CHCH_2CH_3$ (c) $CH_2{=}C(CH_3)_2$

(b) $CH_3CH{=}CHCH_3$ (d) $CH_3CH_2CH{=}CHCl$

1.14 THE STRUCTURE OF ETHYNE (ACETYLENE): *sp* HYBRIDIZATION

Hydrocarbons in which two carbon atoms share three pairs of electrons between them, and are thus bonded by a triple bond, are called **alkynes**. The two simplest alkynes are ethyne and propyne.

$H{-}C{\equiv}C{-}H$ $CH_3{-}C{\equiv}C{-}H$
Ethyne   **Propyne**
(acetylene)   **(C_3H_4)**
(C_2H_2)

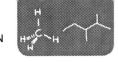

Ethyne, a compound that is also called acetylene, consists of a linear arrangement of atoms. The H—C≡C bond angles of ethyne molecules are 180°:

$$H \overbrace{} C \overline{\overline{\overline{}}} C \overbrace{} H$$
180° 180°

We can account for the structure of ethyne on the basis of orbital hybridization as we did for ethane and ethene. In our model for ethane (Section 1.12B) we saw that the carbon orbitals are sp^3 hybridized, and in our model for ethene (Section 1.13) we saw that they are sp^2 hybridized. In our model for ethyne we shall see that the carbon atoms are *sp hybridized.*

The mathematical process for obtaining the *sp* hybrid orbitals of ethyne can be visualized in the following way (Fig. 1.28).

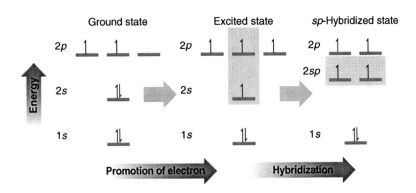

FIGURE 1.28 A process for deriving *sp*-hybridized carbon atoms.

- The 2*s* orbital and one 2*p* orbital of carbon are hybridized to form two *sp* orbitals.
- The remaining two 2*p* orbitals are not hybridized.

Calculations show that the *sp* hybrid orbitals have their large positive lobes oriented at an angle of 180° with respect to each other. The two 2*p* orbitals that were not hybridized are each perpendicular to the axis that passes through the center of the two *sp* orbitals (Fig. 1.29). We place one electron in each orbital.

We envision the bonding molecular orbitals of ethyne being formed in the following way (Fig. 1.30).

- Two carbon atoms overlap *sp* orbitals to form a sigma bond between them (this is one bond of the triple bond). The remaining two *sp* orbitals at each carbon atom overlap with *s* orbitals from hydrogen atoms to produce two sigma C—H bonds.

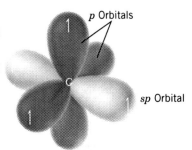

FIGURE 1.29 An *sp*-hybridized carbon atom.

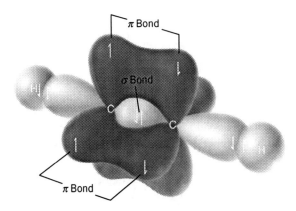

FIGURE 1.30 Formation of the bonding molecular orbitals of ethyne from two *sp*-hybridized carbon atoms and two hydrogen atoms. (Antibonding orbitals are formed as well, but these have been omitted for simplicity.)

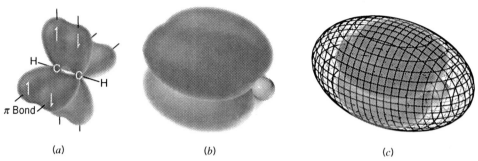

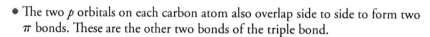

(a) (b) (c)

FIGURE 1.31 (a) The structure of ethyne (acetylene) showing the sigma-bond framework and a schematic depiction of the two pairs of *p* orbitals that overlap to form the two π bonds in ethyne. (b) A structure of ethyne showing calculated π molecular orbitals. Two pairs of π molecular orbital lobes are present, one pair for each π bond. The red and blue lobes in each π bond represent opposite phase signs. The hydrogen atoms of ethyne (white spheres) can be seen at each end of the structure (the carbon atoms are hidden by the molecular orbitals). (c) The mesh surface in this structure represents approximately the furthest extent of overall electron density in ethyne. Note that the overall electron density (but not the π-bonding electrons) extends over both hydrogen atoms.

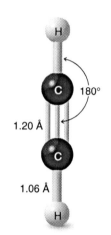

- The two *p* orbitals on each carbon atom also overlap side to side to form two π bonds. These are the other two bonds of the triple bond.

- The carbon–carbon triple bond consists of two π bonds and one σ bond.

Structures for ethyne based on calculated molecular orbitals and electron density are shown in Fig. 1.31. Circular symmetry exists along the length of a triple bond (Fig. 1.31*b*). As a result, there is no restriction of rotation for groups joined by a triple bond (as compared with alkenes), and if rotation would occur, no new compound would form.

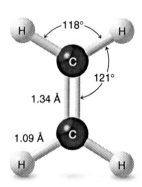

1.14A Bond Lengths of Ethyne, Ethene, and Ethane

The carbon–carbon triple bond of ethyne is shorter than the carbon–carbon double bond of ethene, which in turn is shorter than the carbon–carbon single bond of ethane. The reason is that bond lengths are affected by the hybridization states of the carbon atoms involved.

- The greater the *s* orbital character in one or both atoms, the shorter is the bond. This is because *s* orbitals are spherical and have more electron density closer to the nucleus than do *p* orbitals.

- The greater the *p* orbital character in one or both atoms, the longer is the bond. This is because *p* orbitals are lobe-shaped with electron density extending away from the nucleus.

In terms of hybrid orbitals, an *sp* hybrid orbital has 50% *s* character and 50% *p* character. An *sp²* hybrid orbital has 33% *s* character and 67% *p* character. An *sp³* hybrid orbital has 25% *s* character and 75% *p* character. The overall trend, therefore, is as follows:

- Bonds involving *sp* hybrids are shorter than those involving *sp²* hybrids, which are shorter than those involving *sp³* hybrids. This trend holds true for both C—C and C—H bonds.

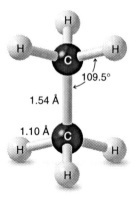

FIGURE 1.32 Bond angles and bond lengths of ethyne, ethene, and ethane.

The bond lengths and bond angles of ethyne, ethene, and ethane are summarized in Fig. 1.32.

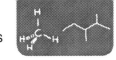

1.15 A SUMMARY OF IMPORTANT CONCEPTS THAT COME FROM QUANTUM MECHANICS

1. An **atomic orbital (AO)** corresponds to a region of space about the nucleus of a single atom where there is a high probability of finding an electron. Atomic orbitals called *s* orbitals are spherical; those called *p* orbitals are like two almost-tangent spheres. Orbitals can hold a maximum of two electrons when their spins are paired. Orbitals are described by the square of a wave function, ψ^2, and each orbital has a characteristic energy. The phase signs associated with an orbital may be + or −.

2. When atomic orbitals overlap, they combine to form **molecular orbitals (MOs)**. Molecular orbitals correspond to regions of space encompassing two (or more) nuclei where electrons are to be found. Like atomic orbitals, molecular orbitals can hold up to two electrons if their spins are paired.

3. When atomic orbitals with the same phase sign interact, they combine to form a **bonding molecular orbital**:

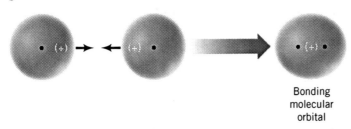

Bonding
molecular
orbital

The electron probability density of a bonding molecular orbital is large in the region of space between the two nuclei where the negative electrons hold the positive nuclei together.

4. An **antibonding molecular orbital** forms when orbitals of opposite phase sign overlap:

Node

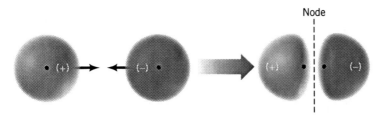

An antibonding orbital has higher energy than a bonding orbital. The electron probability density of the region between the nuclei is small and it contains a **node**—a region where $\psi = 0$. Thus, having electrons in an antibonding orbital does not help hold the nuclei together. The internuclear repulsions tend to make them fly apart.

5. The **energy of electrons** in a bonding *molecular* orbital is less than the energy of the electrons in their separate *atomic* orbitals. The energy of electrons in an antibonding orbital is greater than that of electrons in their separate atomic orbitals.

6. The **number of molecular orbitals** always equals the number of atomic orbitals from which they are formed. Combining two atomic orbitals will always yield two molecular orbitals—one bonding and one antibonding.

7. **Hybrid atomic orbitals** are obtained by mixing (hybridizing) the wave functions for orbitals of different types (i.e., *s* and *p* orbitals) but from the same atom.

8. Hybridizing three *p* orbitals with one *s* orbital yields four *sp³* **orbitals**. Atoms that are *sp³* hybridized direct the axes of their four *sp³* orbitals toward the corners of a tetrahedron. The carbon of methane is *sp³* hybridized and **tetrahedral**.

9. Hybridizing two *p* orbitals with one *s* orbital yields three *sp²* **orbitals**. Atoms that are *sp²* hybridized point the axes of their three *sp²* orbitals toward the corners of an equilateral triangle. The carbon atoms of ethene are *sp²* hybridized and **trigonal planar**.

Helpful Hint

A summary of *sp³*, *sp²*, and *sp* hybrid orbital geometries.

10. Hybridizing one *p* orbital with one *s* orbital yields two **sp orbitals**. Atoms that are *sp* hybridized orient the axes of their two *sp* orbitals in opposite directions (at an angle of 180°). The carbon atoms of ethyne are *sp* hybridized and ethyne is a **linear** molecule.

11. A **sigma (σ) bond** (a type of single bond) is one in which the electron density has circular symmetry when viewed along the bond axis. In general, the skeletons of organic molecules are constructed of atoms linked by sigma bonds.

12. A **pi (π) bond**, part of double and triple carbon–carbon bonds, is one in which the electron densities of two adjacent parallel *p* orbitals overlap sideways to form a bonding pi molecular orbital.

1.16 HOW TO PREDICT MOLECULAR GEOMETRY: THE VALENCE SHELL ELECTRON PAIR REPULSION MODEL

We can predict the arrangement of atoms in molecules and ions on the basis of a relatively simple idea called the **valence shell electron pair repulsion (VSEPR) model**.

We apply the **VSEPR** model in the following way:

1. We consider molecules (or ions) in which the central atom is covalently bonded to two or more atoms or groups.

2. We consider all of the valence electron pairs of the central atom—both those that are shared in covalent bonds, called **bonding pairs**, and those that are unshared, called **nonbonding pairs** or **unshared pairs** or **lone pairs**.

3. Because electron pairs repel each other, the electron pairs of the valence shell tend to stay as far apart as possible. The repulsion between nonbonding pairs is generally greater than that between bonding pairs.

4. We arrive at the *geometry* of the molecule by considering all of the electron pairs, bonding and nonbonding, but we describe the *shape* of the molecule or ion by referring to the positions of the nuclei (or atoms) and not by the positions of the electron pairs.

In the following sections we consider several examples.

1.16A Methane

The valence shell of methane contains four pairs of bonding electrons. Only a tetrahedral orientation will allow four pairs of electrons to have equal and maximum possible separation from each other (Fig. 1.33). Any other orientation, for example, a square planar arrangement, places some electron pairs closer together than others. Thus, methane has a tetrahedral shape.

The bond angles for any atom that has a regular tetrahedral structure are 109.5°. A representation of these angles in methane is shown in Fig. 1.34.

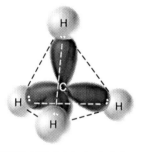

FIGURE 1.33 A tetrahedral shape for methane allows the maximum separation of the four bonding electron pairs.

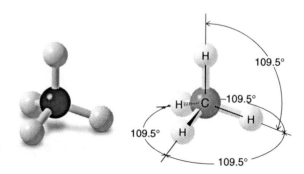

FIGURE 1.34 The bond angles of methane are 109.5°.

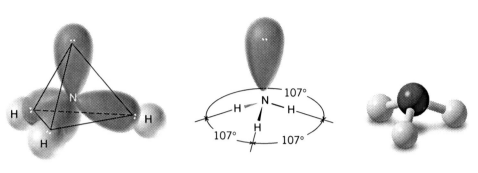

1.16B Ammonia

The shape of a molecule of ammonia (NH_3) is a **trigonal pyramid**. There are three bonding pairs of electrons and one nonbonding pair. The bond angles in a molecule of ammonia are 107°, a value very close to the tetrahedral angle (109.5°). We can write a general tetrahedral structure for the electron pairs of ammonia by placing the nonbonding pair at one corner (Fig. 1.35). A *tetrahedral arrangement* of the electron pairs explains the *trigonal pyramidal* arrangement of the four atoms. The bond angles are 107° (not 109.5°) because the nonbonding pair occupies more space than the bonding pairs.

What do the bond angles of ammonia suggest about the hybridization state of the nitrogen atom of ammonia?

PRACTICE PROBLEM 1.23

1.16C Water

A molecule of water has an **angular** or **bent** shape. The H—O—H bond angle in a molecule of water is 104.5°, an angle that is also quite close to the 109.5° bond angles of methane.

We can write a general tetrahedral structure for the electron pairs of a molecule of water *if we place the two bonding pairs of electrons and the two nonbonding electron pairs at the corners of the tetrahedron*. Such a structure is shown in Fig. 1.36. A *tetrahedral arrangement* of the electron pairs accounts for the *angular arrangement* of the three atoms. The bond angle is less than 109.5° because the nonbonding pairs are effectively "larger" than the bonding pairs and, therefore, the structure is not perfectly tetrahedral.

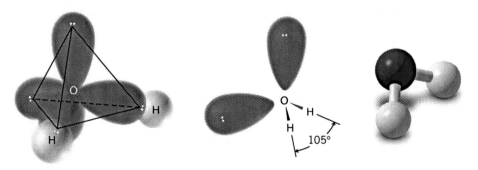

FIGURE 1.36 An approximately tetrahedral arrangement of the electron pairs of a molecule of water that results when the pairs of nonbonding electrons are considered to occupy corners. This arrangement accounts for the angular shape of the H_2O molecule.

What do the bond angles of water suggest about the hybridization state of the oxygen atom of water?

PRACTICE PROBLEM 1.24

1.16D Boron Trifluoride

Boron, a group IIIA element, has only three valence electrons. In the compound boron trifluoride (BF_3) these three electrons are shared with three fluorine atoms. As a result, the boron atom in BF_3 has only six electrons (three bonding pairs) around it. Maximum separation of three bonding pairs occurs when they occupy the corners of an equilateral

FIGURE 1.37 The triangular (trigonal planar) shape of boron trifluoride maximally separates the three bonding pairs.

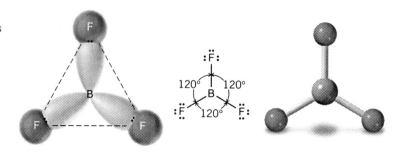

triangle. Consequently, in the boron trifluoride molecule the three fluorine atoms lie in a plane at the corners of an equilateral triangle (Fig. 1.37). Boron trifluoride is said to have a *trigonal planar structure*. The bond angles are 120°.

PRACTICE PROBLEM 1.25 What do the bond angles of boron trifluoride suggest about the hybridization state of the boron atom?

1.16E Beryllium Hydride

The central beryllium atom of BeH_2 has only two electron pairs around it; both electron pairs are bonding pairs. These two pairs are maximally separated when they are on opposite sides of the central atom, as shown in the following structures. This arrangement of the electron pairs accounts for the *linear geometry* of the BeH_2 molecule and its bond angle of 180°.

$$H : Be : H \quad \text{or} \quad H \overset{180°}{\longleftarrow} Be \longrightarrow H$$

Linear geometry of BeH_2

PRACTICE PROBLEM 1.26 What do the bond angles of beryllium hydride suggest about the hybridization state of the beryllium atom?

PRACTICE PROBLEM 1.27 Use VSEPR theory to predict the geometry of each of the following molecules and ions:

(a) $\bar{B}H_4$ (c) $\overset{+}{N}H_4$ (e) BH_3 (g) SiF_4

(b) BeF_2 (d) H_2S (f) CF_4 (h) $\bar{:}CCl_3$

1.16F Carbon Dioxide

The VSEPR method can also be used to predict the shapes of molecules containing multiple bonds if we assume that *all of the electrons of a multiple bond act as though they were a single unit* and, therefore, are located in the region of space between the two atoms joined by a multiple bond.

This principle can be illustrated with the structure of a molecule of carbon dioxide (CO_2). The central carbon atom of carbon dioxide is bonded to each oxygen atom by a double bond. Carbon dioxide is known to have a linear shape; the bond angle is 180°.

$$:O \overset{180°}{=} C = O: \quad \text{or} \quad :O :: C :: O:$$

The four electrons of each double bond act as a single unit and are maximally separated from each other.

Such a structure is consistent with a maximum separation of the two groups of four bonding electrons. The nonbonding pairs associated with the oxygen atoms have no effect on the shape.

TABLE 1.3 SHAPES OF MOLECULES AND IONS FROM VSEPR THEORY

Number of Electron Pairs at Central Atom			Hybridization State of Central Atom	Shape of Molecule or Ion[a]	Examples
Bonding	Nonbonding	Total			
2	0	2	sp	Linear	BeH_2
3	0	3	sp^2	Trigonal planar	BF_3, $\overset{+}{C}H_3$
4	0	4	sp^3	Tetrahedral	CH_4, $\overset{+}{N}H_4$
3	1	4	$\sim sp^3$	Trigonal pyramidal	NH_3, $\bar{C}H_3$
2	2	4	$\sim sp^3$	Angular	H_2O

[a]Referring to positions of atoms and excluding nonbonding pairs.

PRACTICE PROBLEM 1.28

Predict the bond angles of

(a) $F_2C=CF_2$ (b) $CH_3C\equiv CCH_3$ (c) $HC\equiv N$

The shapes of several simple molecules and ions as predicted by VSEPR theory are shown in Table 1.3. In this table we have also included the hybridization state of the central atom.

1.17 APPLICATIONS OF BASIC PRINCIPLES

Throughout the early chapters of this book we review certain basic principles that underlie and explain much of the chemistry we shall be studying. Consider the following principles and how they apply in this chapter.

Opposite Charges Attract We see this principle operating in our explanations for covalent and ionic bonds (Section 1.3A). It is the attraction of the *positively* charged nuclei for the *negatively* charged electrons that underlies our explanation for the covalent bond. It is the attraction of the oppositely charged ions in crystals that explains the ionic bond.

Like Charges Repel It is the repulsion of the electrons in covalent bonds of the valence shell of a molecule that is central to the valence shell electron pair repulsion model for explaining molecular geometry. And, although it is not so obvious, this same factor underlies the explanations of molecular geometry that come from orbital hybridization because these repulsions are taken into account in calculating the orientations of the hybrid orbitals.

Nature Tends toward States of Lower Potential Energy This principle explains so much of the world around us. It explains why water flows downhill: the potential energy of the water at the bottom of the hill is lower than that at the top. (We say that water is in a more stable state at the bottom.) This principle underlies the aufbau principle (Section 1.10A): in its lowest energy state, the electrons of an atom occupy the lowest energy orbitals available [but Hund's rule still applies, as well as the Pauli exclusion principle (Section 1.10A), allowing only two electrons per orbital]. Similarly in molecular orbital theory (Section 1.11), electrons fill lower energy bonding molecular orbitals first because this gives the molecule lower potential energy (or greater stability). Energy has to be provided to move an electron to a higher orbital and provide an excited (less stable) state.

Orbital Overlap Stabilizes Molecules This principle is part of our explanation for covalent bonds. When orbitals of the same phase from different nuclei overlap, the electrons in these orbitals can be shared by both nuclei, resulting in stabilization. The result is a covalent bond.

WHY Do These Topics Matter?]

NATURAL PRODUCTS THAT CAN TREAT DISEASE

Everywhere on Earth, organisms make organic molecules comprised almost exclusively of carbon, hydrogen, nitrogen, and oxygen. Sometimes a few slightly more exotic atoms, such as halogens and sulfur, are present. Globally, these compounds aid in day-to-day functioning of these organisms and/or their survival against predators. Organic molecules include the chlorophyll in green plants, which harnesses the energy of sunlight; vitamin C is synthesized by citrus trees, protecting them against oxidative stress; capsaicin, a molecule synthesized by pepper plants (and makes peppers taste hot), serves to ward off insects and birds that might try to eat them; salicylic acid, made by willow trees, is a signaling hormone; lovastatin, found in oyster mushrooms, protects against bacterial attacks.

Image Source

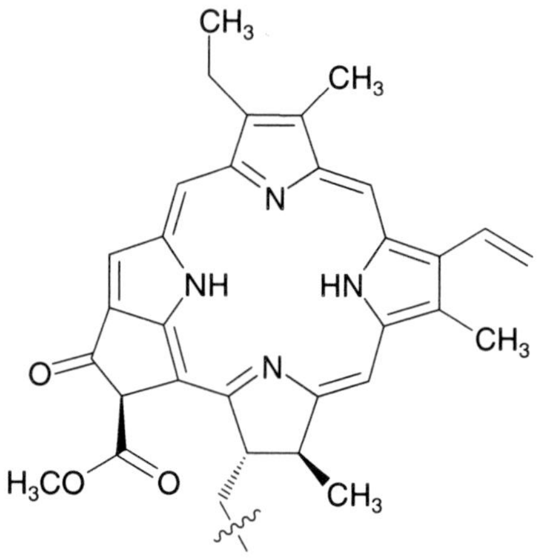

Capsaicin

Chlorophyll core

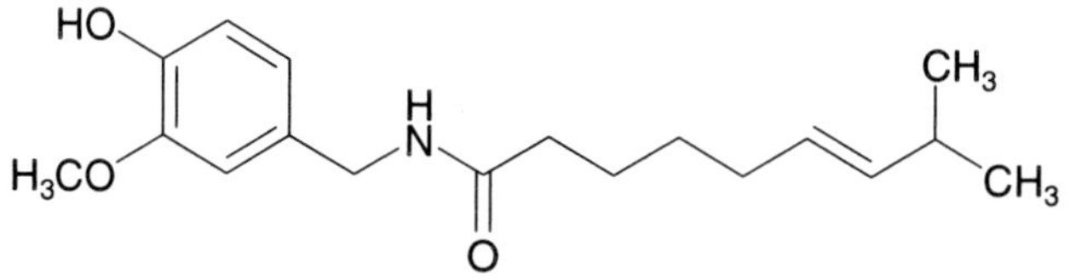

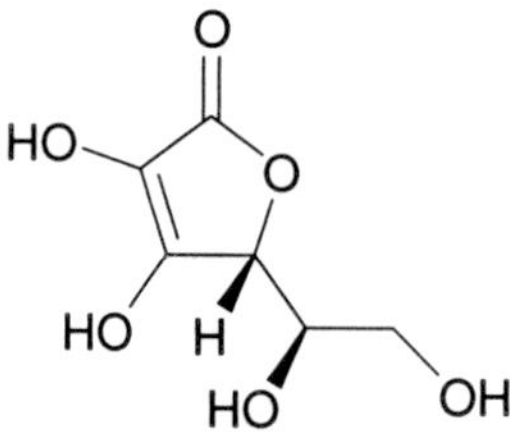

Vitamin C

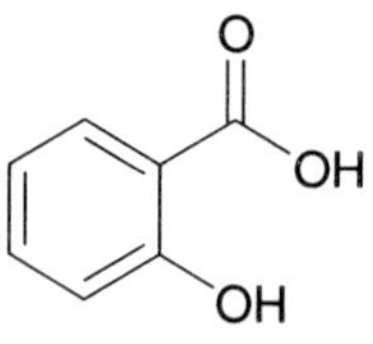

Salicylic acid

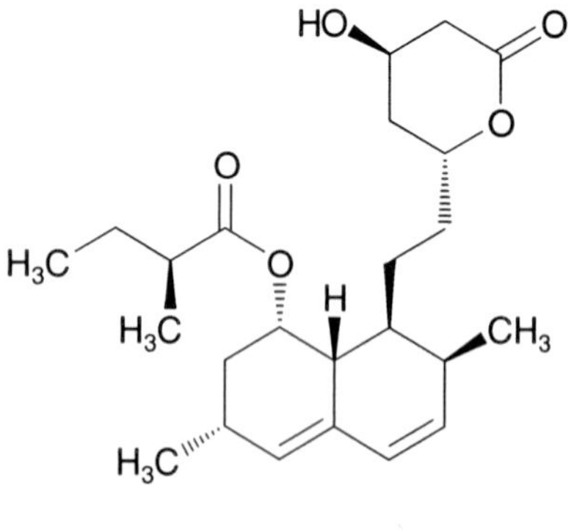

Lovastatin

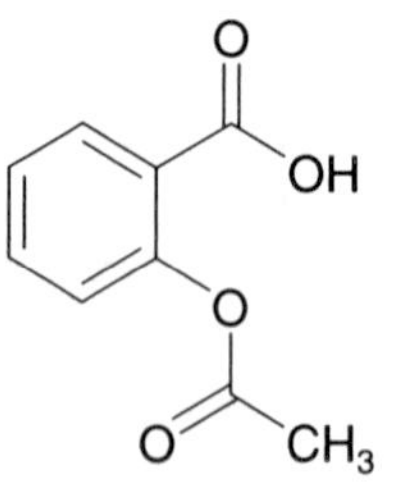

Aspirin

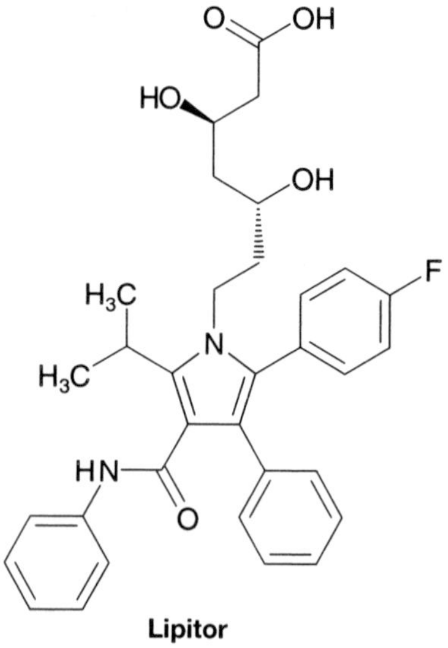

Lipitor

These compounds are all natural products, and many advances in modern society are the result of their study and use. Capsaicin, it turns out, is an effective analgesic. It can modulate pain when applied to the skin and is currently sold under the tradename Capzacin. Salicylic acid is a painkiller as well as an anti-acne medication, while lovastatin is used as a drug to decrease levels of cholesterol in human blood. The power of modern organic chemistry lies in the ability to take such molecules, sometimes found in trace quantities in nature, and make them from readily available and inexpensive starting materials on a large scale so that all members of society can benefit from them. For instance, although we can obtain vitamin C from eating certain fruits, chemists can make large quantities in the laboratory for use in daily supplements; while some may think that "natural" vitamin C is healthier, the "synthetic" compound is equally effective since they are exactly the same chemically.

Perhaps more important, organic chemistry also provides the opportunity to change the structures of these and other natural products to make molecules with different, and potentially even more impressive, properties. For example, the addition of a few atoms to salicylic acid through a chemical reaction is what led to the discovery of aspirin (see Chapter 17), a molecule with far greater potency as a painkiller and fewer side effects than nature's compound. Similarly, scientists at Parke–Davis Warner–Lambert (now Pfizer) used the structure and activity of lovastatin as inspiration to develop Lipitor, a molecule that has saved countless lives by lowering levels of cholesterol in human serum. In fact, of the top 20 drugs based on gross sales, slightly over half are either natural products or their derivatives.

To learn more about these topics, see:

1. Nicolaou, K. C.; Montagnon, T. *Molecules that Changed the World*. Wiley-VCH: Weinheim, **2008**, p. 366.
2. Nicolaou, K. C.; Sorensen, E. J.; Winssinger, N, "The Art and Science of Organic and Natural Products Synthesis" in *J. Chem. Educ.* **1998**, 75, 1225–1258.

SUMMARY AND REVIEW TOOLS

In Chapter 1 you have studied concepts and skills that are absolutely essential to your success in organic chemistry. You should now be able to use the periodic table to determine the number of valence electrons an atom has in its neutral state or as an ion. You should be able to use the periodic table to compare the relative electronegativity of one element with another, and determine the formal charge of an atom or ion. Electronegativity and formal charge are key concepts in organic chemistry.

You should be able to draw chemical formulas that show all of the valence electrons in a molecule (Lewis structures), using lines for bonds and dots to show unshared electrons. You should be proficient in representing structures as dash structural formulas, condensed structural formulas, and bond-line structural formulas. In particular, the more quickly you become skilled at using and interpreting bond-line formulas, the faster you will be able to process structural information in organic chemistry. You have also learned about resonance structures, the use of which will help us in understanding a variety of concepts in later chapters.

Last, you have learned to predict the three-dimensional structure of molecules using the valence shell electron pair repulsion (VSEPR) model and molecular orbital (MO) theory. An ability to predict three-dimensional structure is critical to understanding the properties and reactivity of molecules.

We encourage you to do all of the problems that your instructor has assigned. We also recommend that you use the summary and review tools in each chapter, such as the concept map that follows. Concept maps can help you see the flow of concepts in a chapter and also help remind you of key points. In fact, we encourage you to build your own concept maps for review when the opportunity arises.

Work especially hard to solidify your knowledge from this and other early chapters in the book. These chapters have everything to do with helping you learn basic tools you need for success throughout organic chemistry.

The study aids for this chapter include key terms and concepts (which are hyperlinked to the glossary from the bold, blue terms in the *WileyPLUS* version of the book at wileyplus.com) and a Concept Map after the end-of-chapter problems.

KEY TERMS AND CONCEPTS PLUS

The key terms and concepts that are highlighted in bold, blue text within the chapter are defined in the glossary (at the back of the book) and have hyperlinked definitions in the accompanying *WileyPLUS* course (www.wileyplus.com).

PROBLEMS PLUS

Note to Instructors: Many of the homework problems are available for assignment via *WileyPlus*, an online teaching and learning solution.

ELECTRON CONFIGURATION

1.29 Which of the following ions possess the electron configuration of a noble gas?

(a) Na^+ (b) Cl^- (c) F^+ (d) H^- (e) Ca^{2+} (f) S^{2-} (g) O^{2-} (h) Br^+

LEWIS STRUCTURES

1.30 Write a Lewis structure for each of the following:

(a) $SOCl_2$ (b) $POCl_3$ (c) PCl_5 (d) $HONO_2$ (HNO_3)

1.31 Give the formal charge (if one exists) on each atom of the following:

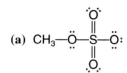

(a) 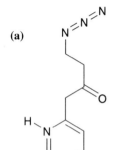   (b) 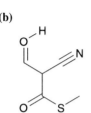   (c) 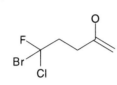   (d)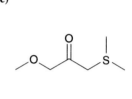

1.32 Add any unshared electrons to give each element an octet in its valence shell in the formulas below and indicate any formal charges. Note that all of the hydrogen atoms that are attached to heteroatoms have been drawn if they are present.

(a) 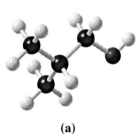   (b) 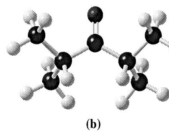   (c)    (d) 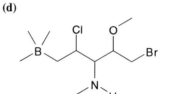   (e)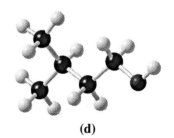

STRUCTURAL FORMULAS AND ISOMERISM

1.33 Write a condensed structural formula for each compound given here.

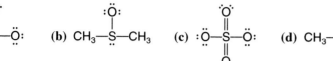

(a)   (b)   (c)   (d)

1.34 What is the molecular formula for each of the compounds given in Exercise 1.33?

1.35 Consider each pair of structural formulas that follow and state whether the two formulas represent the same compound, whether they represent different compounds that are constitutional isomers of each other, or whether they represent different compounds that are not isomeric.

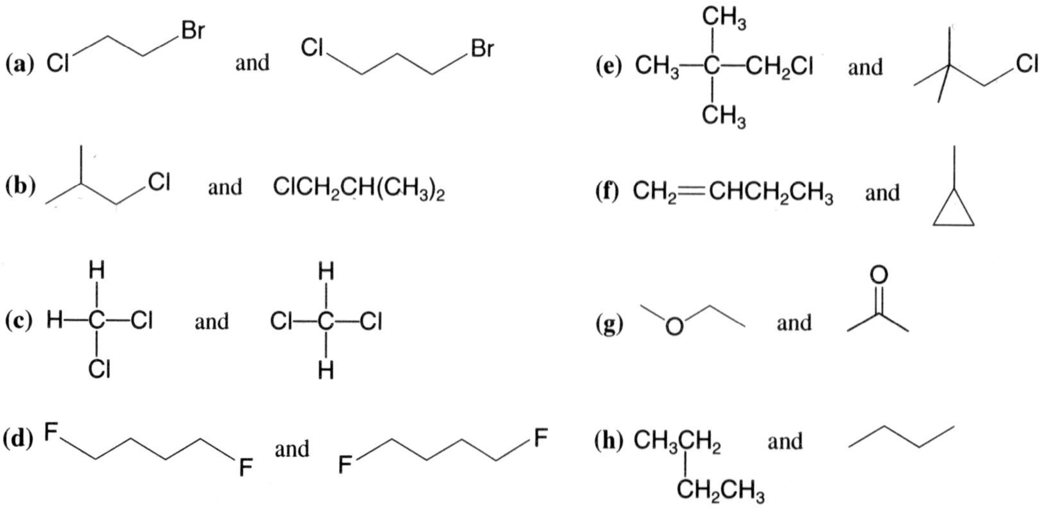

(a) Cl⌒⌒Br   and   Cl⌒⌒⌒Br

(e) $CH_3\!-\!\overset{\displaystyle CH_3}{\underset{\displaystyle CH_3}{C}}\!-\!CH_2Cl$ and   ⤳Cl

(b) ⤳Cl   and $ClCH_2CH(CH_3)_2$

(f) $CH_2\!=\!CHCH_2CH_3$ and   △

(c) $H\!-\!\overset{\displaystyle H}{\underset{\displaystyle Cl}{C}}\!-\!Cl$ and $Cl\!-\!\overset{\displaystyle H}{\underset{\displaystyle H}{C}}\!-\!Cl$

(g) ⌒O⌒   and

(d) F⌒⌒⌒⌒F   and   F⌒⌒⌒⌒F

(h) CH_3CH_2 and   ⌒⌒⌒
       $\quad\ \ \underset{\displaystyle CH_2CH_3}{|}$

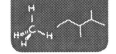

(i) $CH_3OCH_2CH_3$ and

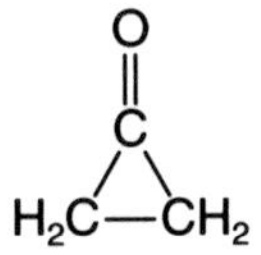

(j) $CH_2ClCHClCH_3$ and $CH_3CHClCH_2Cl$

(k) $CH_3CH_2CHClCH_2Cl$ and CH_3CHCH_2Cl
CH_2Cl

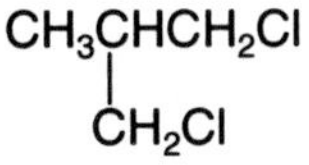

(l) 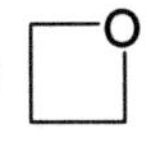 and

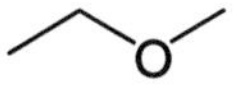

(m) 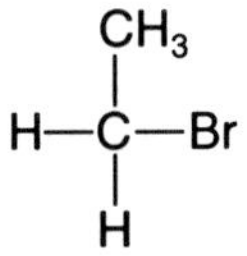 H—C—Br and CH_3—C—Br

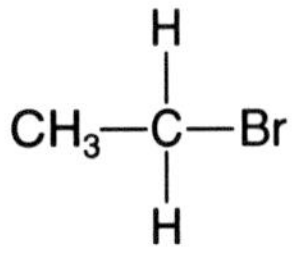

(n) 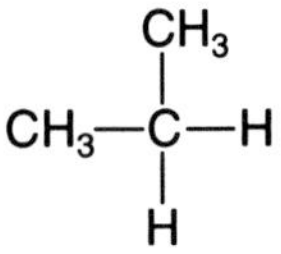 CH_3—C—H and CH_3—C—CH_3

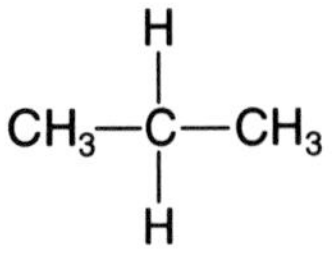

(o) 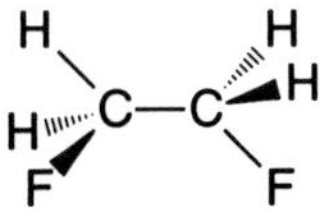 and

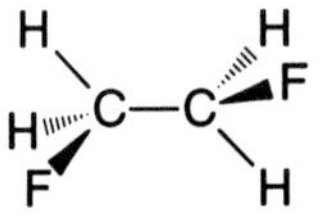

(p) 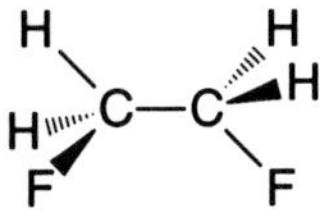 and

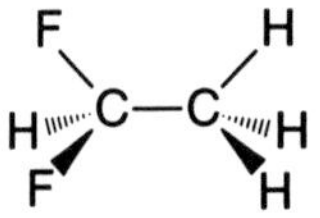

1.36 Rewrite each of the following using bond-line formulas:

(a) 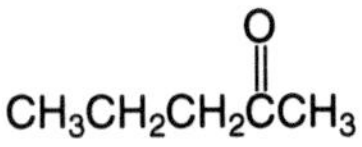 $CH_3CH_2CH_2CCH_3$

(b) 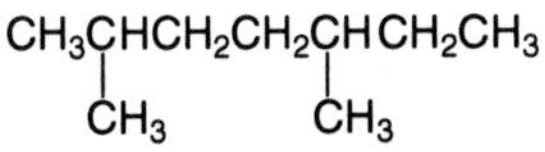 $CH_3CHCH_2CH_2CHCH_2CH_3$
$CH_3 CH_3$

(c) $(CH_3)_3CCH_2CH_2CH_2OH$

(d) 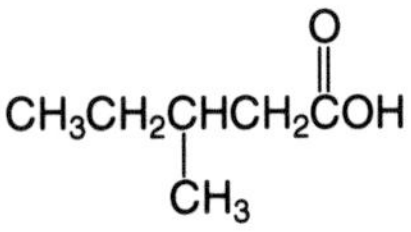 $CH_3CH_2CHCH_2COH$
CH_3

(e) $CH_2{=}CHCH_2CH_2CH{=}CHCH_3$

(f)

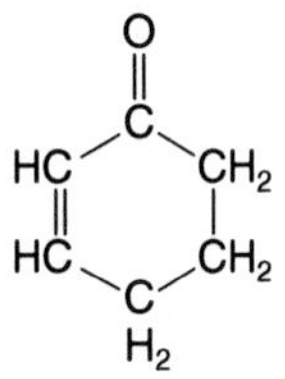

1.37 Write bond-line formulas for all of the constitutional isomers with the molecular formula C_4H_8.

1.38 Write structural formulas for at least three constitutional isomers with the molecular formula CH_3NO_2. (In answering this question you should assign a formal charge to any atom that bears one.)

RESONANCE STRUCTURES

1.39 Write the resonance structure that would result from moving the electrons in the way indicated by the curved arrows.

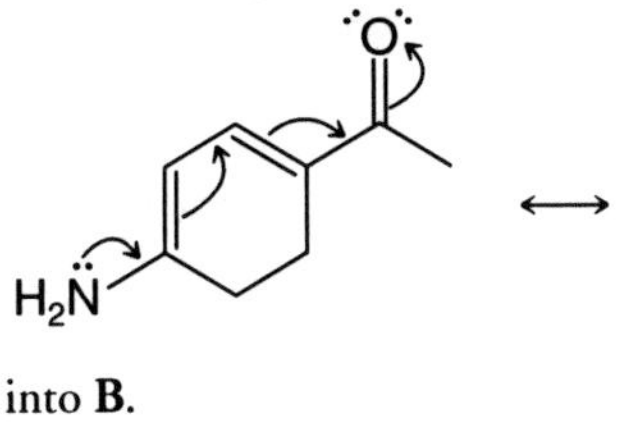

1.40 Show the curved arrows that would convert **A** into **B**.

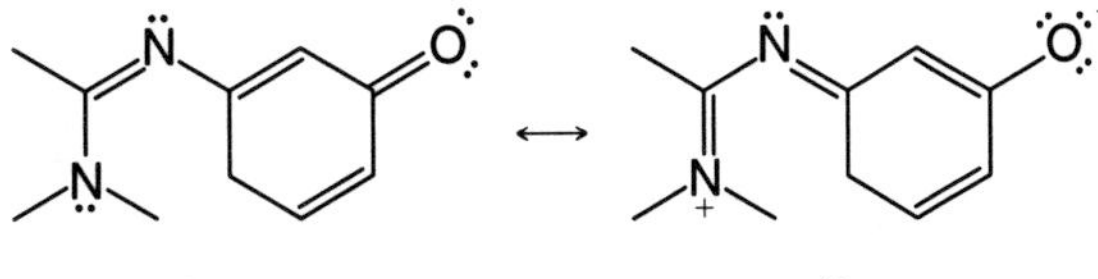

A   **B**

1.41 For the following write all possible resonance structures. Be sure to include formal charges where appropriate.

(a) 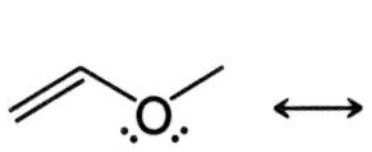   ⟷   **(d)** 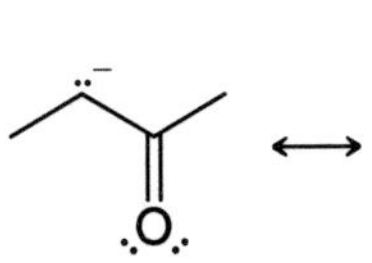   ⟷   **(g)** 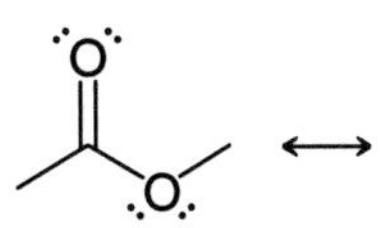   ⟷

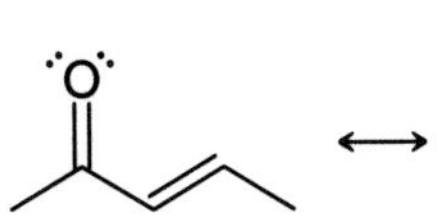

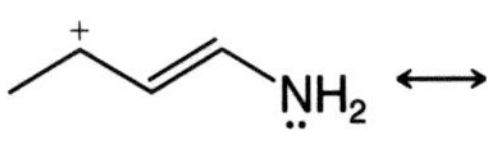

(b)   ⟷   **(e)**   ⟷   **(h)** 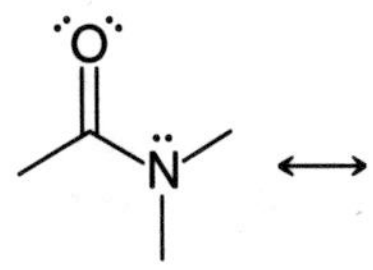   ⟷

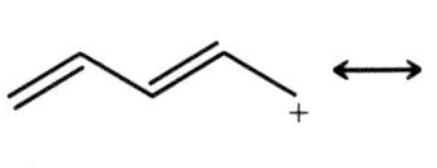

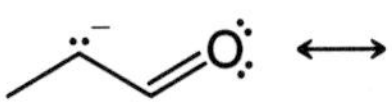

(c)   ⟷   **(f)**   ⟷   **(i)**

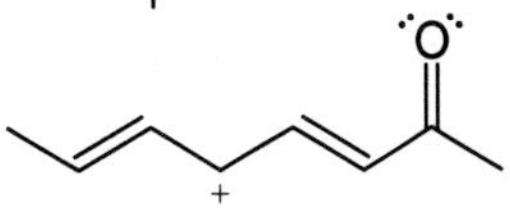

1.42 **(a)** Cyanic acid (H—O—C≡N) and isocyanic acid (H—N=C=O) differ in the positions of their electrons but their structures do not represent resonance structures. Explain. **(b)** Loss of a proton from cyanic acid yields the same anion as that obtained by loss of a proton from isocyanic acid. Explain.

1.43 Consider a chemical species (either a molecule or an ion) in which a carbon atom forms three single bonds to three hydrogen atoms and in which the carbon atom possesses no other valence electrons. **(a)** What formal charge would the carbon atom have? **(b)** What total charge would the species have? **(c)** What shape would you expect this species to have? **(d)** What would you expect the hybridization state of the carbon atom to be?

1.44 Consider a chemical species like the one in the previous problem in which a carbon atom forms three single bonds to three hydrogen atoms, but in which the carbon atom possesses an unshared electron pair. **(a)** What formal charge would the carbon atom have? **(b)** What total charge would the species have? **(c)** What shape would you expect this species to have? **(d)** What would you expect the hybridization state of the carbon atom to be?

1.45 Consider another chemical species like the ones in the previous problems in which a carbon atom forms three single bonds to three hydrogen atoms but in which the carbon atom possesses a single unpaired electron. **(a)** What formal charge would the carbon atom have? **(b)** What total charge would the species have? **(c)** Given that the shape of this species is trigonal planar, what would you expect the hybridization state of the carbon atom to be?

1.46 Draw a three-dimensional orbital representation for each of the following molecules, indicate whether each bond in it is a σ or π bond, and provide the hybridization for each non-hydrogen atom.

(a) CH_2O **(b)** $H_2C=CHCH=CH_2$ **(c)** $H_2C=C=C=CH_2$

1.47 Ozone (O_3) is found in the upper atmosphere where it absorbs highly energetic ultraviolet (UV) radiation and thereby provides the surface of Earth with a protective screen (cf. Section 10.11E). One possible resonance structure for ozone is the following:

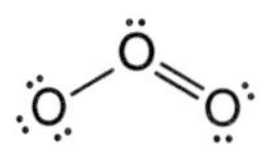

(a) Assign any necessary formal charges to the atoms in this structure. **(b)** Write another equivalent resonance structure for ozone. **(c)** What do these resonance structures predict about the relative lengths of the two oxygen–oxygen bonds of ozone? **(d)** In the structure above, and the one you have written, assume an angular shape for the ozone molecule. Is this shape consistent with VSEPR theory? Explain your answer.

1.48 Write resonance structures for the azide ion, N_3^-. Explain how these resonance structures account for the fact that both bonds of the azide ion have the same length.

1.49 Write structural formulas of the type indicated: **(a)** bond-line formulas for seven constitutional isomers with the formula $C_4H_{10}O$; **(b)** condensed structural formulas for two constitutional isomers with the formula C_2H_7N; **(c)** condensed structural formulas for four constitutional isomers with the formula C_3H_9N; **(d)** bond-line formulas for three constitutional isomers with the formula C_5H_{12}.

1.50 What is the relationship between the members of the following pairs? That is, are they constitutional isomers, the same, or something else (specify)?

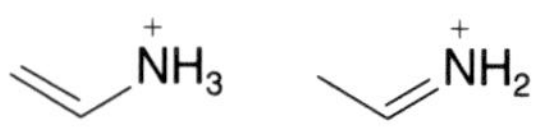

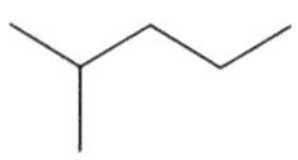

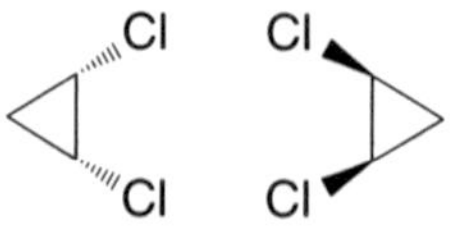

CHALLENGE PROBLEMS

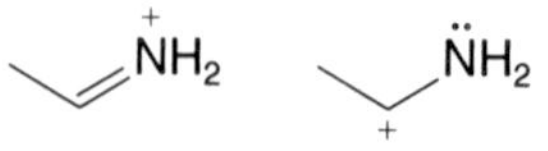

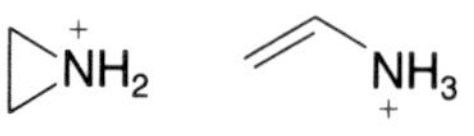

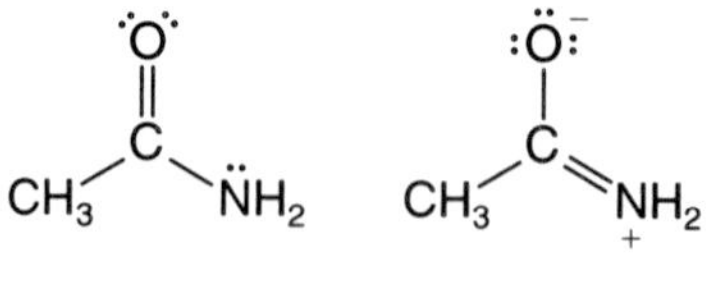

1.51 In Chapter 15 we shall learn how the nitronium ion, NO_2^+, forms when concentrated nitric and sulfuric acids are mixed. **(a)** Write a Lewis structure for the nitronium ion. **(b)** What geometry does VSEPR theory predict for the NO_2^+ ion? **(c)** Give a species that has the same number of electrons as NO_2^+.

1.52 Given the following sets of atoms, write bond-line formulas for all of the possible constitutionally isomeric compounds or ions that could be made from them. Show all unshared electron pairs and all formal charges, if any.

Set	C atoms	H atoms	Other
A	3	6	2 Br atoms
B	3	9	1 N atom and 1 O atom (not on same C)
C	3	4	1 O atom
D	2	7	1 N atom and 1 proton
E	3	7	1 extra electron

1.53 **(a)** Consider a carbon atom in its ground state. Would such an atom offer a satisfactory model for the carbon of methane? If not, why not? (*Hint:* Consider whether a ground state carbon atom could be tetravalent, and consider the bond angles that would result if it were to combine with hydrogen atoms.)

(b) Consider a carbon atom in the excited state:

$$C \; \underline{\uparrow\downarrow} \; \underline{\uparrow} \; \underline{\uparrow} \; \underline{\uparrow} \; \underline{\uparrow}$$
$$\quad 1s \; 2s \; 2p_x \; 2p_y \; 2p_z$$

Excited state of a carbon atom

Would such an atom offer a satisfactory model for the carbon of methane? If not, why not?

1.54 Open computer molecular models for dimethyl ether, dimethylacetylene, and *cis*-1,2-dichloro-1,2-difluoroethene from the 3D Molecular Models section of the book's website. By interpreting the computer molecular model for each one, draw **(a)** a dash formula, **(b)** a bond-line formula, and **(c)** a three-dimensional dashed-wedge formula. Draw the models in whatever perspective is most convenient—generally the perspective in which the most atoms in the chain of a molecule can be in the plane of the paper.

1.55 Boron is a group IIIA element. Open the molecular model for boron trifluoride from the 3D Molecular Models section of the book's website. Near the boron atom, above and below the plane of the atoms in BF_3, are two relatively large lobes. Considering the position of boron in the periodic table and the three-dimensional and electronic structure of BF_3, what type of orbital does this lobe represent? Is it a hybridized orbital or not?

1.56 There are two contributing resonance structures for an anion called acetaldehyde enolate, whose condensed molecular formula is CH_2CHO^-. Draw the two resonance contributors and the resonance hybrid, then consider the map of electrostatic potential (MEP) shown below for this anion. Comment on whether the MEP is consistent or not with predominance of the resonance contributor you would have predicted to be represented most strongly in the hybrid.

LEARNING GROUP PROBLEMS

Consider the compound with the following condensed molecular formula:

$$CH_3CHOHCH = CH_2$$

1. Write a full dash structural formula for the compound.

2. Show all nonbonding electron pairs on your dash structural formula.

3. Indicate any formal charges that may be present in the molecule.

4. Label the hybridization state at every carbon atom and the oxygen.

5. Draw a three-dimensional perspective representation for the compound showing approximate bond angles as clearly as possible. Use ordinary lines to indicate bonds in the plane of the paper, solid wedges for bonds in front of the paper, and dashed wedges for bonds behind the paper.

6. Label all the bond angles in your three-dimensional structure.

7. Draw a bond-line formula for the compound.

8. Devise two structures, each having two *sp*-hybridized carbons and the molecular formula C_4H_6O. Create one of these structures such that it is linear with respect to all carbon atoms. Repeat parts 1–7 above for both structures.

> **Helpful Hint**
>
> Your instructor will tell you how to work these problems as a Learning Group.

[C O N C E P T   M A P]

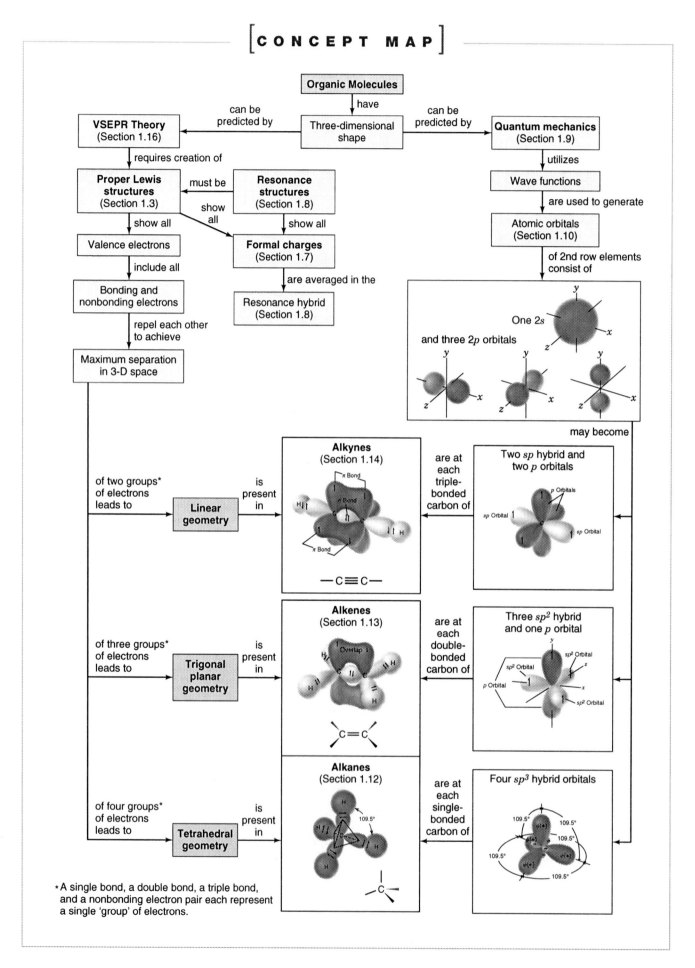

*A single bond, a double bond, a triple bond, and a nonbonding electron pair each represent a single 'group' of electrons.

C H A P T E R

2

Families of Carbon Compounds

FUNCTIONAL GROUPS, INTERMOLECULAR
FORCES, AND INFRARED (IR) SPECTROSCOPY

In this chapter we introduce one of the great simplifying concepts of organic chemistry—the functional group. Functional groups are common and specific arrangements of atoms that impart predictable reactivity and properties to a molecule. Even though there are millions of organic compounds, you may be relieved to know that we can readily understand much about whole families of compounds simply by learning about the properties of the common functional groups.

For example, all alcohols contain an —OH (hydroxyl) functional group attached to a saturated carbon bearing nothing else but carbon or hydrogen. Alcohols as simple as ethanol in alcoholic beverages and as complex as ethinyl estradiol (Section 2.1C) in birth control pills have this structural unit in common. All aldehydes have a —C(=O)— (carbonyl) group with one bond to a hydrogen and the other to one or more carbons, such as in benzaldehyde (which comes from almonds). All ketones include a carbonyl group bonded by its carbon to one or more other carbons on each side, as in the natural oil menthone, found in geraniums and spearmint.

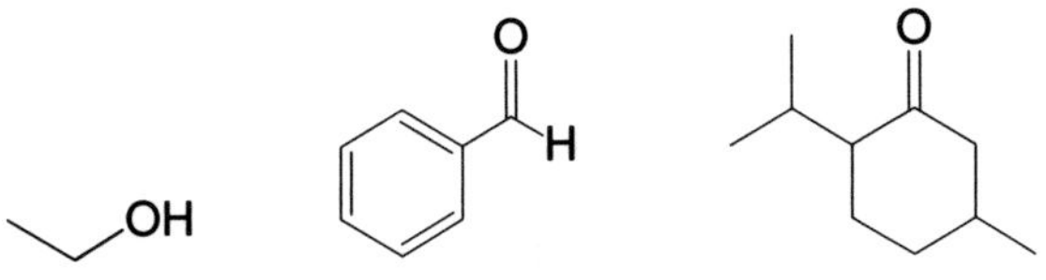

Ethanol **Benzaldehyde** **Menthone**

PHOTO CREDIT: © Valentyn Volkov/iStockphoto

55

Members of each functional group family share common chemical properties and reactivity, and this fact helps greatly in organizing our knowledge of organic chemistry. As you progress in this chapter it will serve you well to learn the arrangements of atoms that define the common functional groups. This knowledge will be invaluable to your study of organic chemistry.

IN THIS CHAPTER WE WILL CONSIDER:

- the major functional groups

- the correlation between properties of functional groups and molecules and intermolecular forces

- infrared (IR) spectroscopy, which can be used to determine what functional groups are present in a molecule

[**WHY** DO THESE TOPICS MATTER?]   At the end of the chapter, we will see how these important concepts merge together to explain how the world's most powerful antibiotic behaves and how bacteria have evolved to escape its effects.

2.1 HYDROCARBONS: REPRESENTATIVE ALKANES, ALKENES, ALKYNES, AND AROMATIC COMPOUNDS

We begin this chapter by introducing the class of compounds that contains only carbon and hydrogen, and we shall see how the -ane, -ene, or -yne ending in a name tells us what kinds of carbon–carbon bonds are present.

- Hydrocarbons are compounds that contain only carbon and hydrogen atoms.

Methane (CH_4) and ethane (C_2H_6) are hydrocarbons, for example. They also belong to a subgroup of compounds called alkanes.

 Propane (an alkane)

- Alkanes are hydrocarbons that do not have multiple bonds between carbon atoms, and we can indicate this in the family name and in names for specific compounds by the **-ane** ending.

Other hydrocarbons may contain double or triple bonds between their carbon atoms.

 Propene (an alkene)

 Propyne (an alkyne)

- Alkenes contain at least one carbon–carbon double bond, and this is indicated in the family name and in names for specific compounds by an **-ene** ending.

- Alkynes contain at least one carbon–carbon triple bond, and this is indicated in the family name and in names for specific compounds by an **-yne** ending.

 Benzene (an aromatic compound)

- Aromatic compounds contain a special type of ring, the most common example of which is a benzene ring. There is no special ending for the general family of aromatic compounds.

We shall introduce representative examples of each of these classes of hydrocarbons in the following sections.

Generally speaking, compounds such as alkanes, whose molecules contain only single bonds, are referred to as **saturated compounds** because these compounds contain the maximum number of hydrogen atoms that the carbon compound can possess. Compounds with multiple bonds, such as alkenes, alkynes, and aromatic hydrocarbons, are called **unsaturated compounds** because they possess fewer than the maximum number of hydrogen atoms, and they are capable of reacting with hydrogen under the proper conditions. We shall have more to say about this in Chapter 7.

2.1A Alkanes

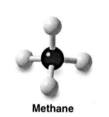

Methane

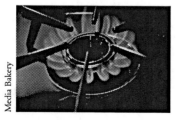

The primary sources of alkanes are natural gas and petroleum. The smaller alkanes (methane through butane) are gases under ambient conditions. Methane is the principal component of natural gas. Higher molecular weight alkanes are obtained largely by refining petroleum. Methane, the simplest alkane, was one major component of the early atmosphere of this planet. Methane is still found in Earth's atmosphere, but no longer in appreciable amounts. It is, however, a major component of the atmospheres of Jupiter, Saturn, Uranus, and Neptune.

Some living organisms produce methane from carbon dioxide and hydrogen. These very primitive creatures, called *methanogens*, may be Earth's oldest organisms, and they may represent a separate form of evolutionary development. Methanogens can survive only in an anaerobic (i.e., oxygen-free) environment. They have been found in ocean trenches, in mud, in sewage, and in cows' stomachs.

2.1B Alkenes

Ethene and propene, the two simplest alkenes, are among the most important industrial chemicals produced in the United States. Each year, the chemical industry produces more than 30 billion pounds of ethene and about 15 billion pounds of propene. Ethene is used as a starting material for the synthesis of many industrial compounds, including ethanol, ethylene oxide, ethanal, and the polymer polyethylene (Section 10.10). Propene is used in making the polymer polypropylene (Section 10.10 and Special Topic B*), and, in addition to other uses, propene is the starting material for a synthesis of acetone and cumene (Section 21.4B).

Ethene also occurs in nature as a plant hormone. It is produced naturally by fruits such as tomatoes and bananas and is involved in the ripening process of these fruits. Much use is now made of ethene in the commercial fruit industry to bring about the ripening of tomatoes and bananas picked green because the green fruits are less susceptible to damage during shipping.

There are many naturally occurring alkenes. Two examples are the following:

Ethene

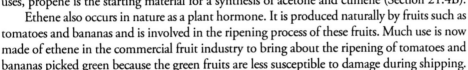

β-Pinene
(a component of
turpentine)

An aphid alarm pheromone

●●● SOLVED PROBLEM 2.1

Propene, $CH_3CH=CH_2$, is an alkene. Write the structure of a constitutional isomer of propene that is not an alkene. (*Hint*: It does not have a double bond.)

STRATEGY AND ANSWER: A compound with a ring of *n* carbon atoms will have the same molecular formula as an alkene with the same number of carbons.

     is a constitutional
             isomer of

Cyclopropane   **Propene**
C₃H₆   **C₃H₆**

$Cyclopropane$ has
anesthetic properties.

2.1C Alkynes

The simplest alkyne is ethyne (also called acetylene). Alkynes occur in nature and can be synthesized in the laboratory.

Two examples of alkynes among thousands that have a biosynthetic origin are capillin, an antifungal agent, and dactylyne, a marine natural product that is an inhibitor of pentobarbital metabolism. Ethinyl estradiol is a synthetic alkyne whose estrogen-like properties have found use in oral contraceptives.

Ethyne

Capillin   **Dactylyne**   **Ethinyl estradiol**
                                                 [17α-ethynyl-1,3,5(10)-estratriene-3,17β-diol]

*Special Topics A–F and H are in *WileyPLUS*; Special Topic G can be found later in this volume.

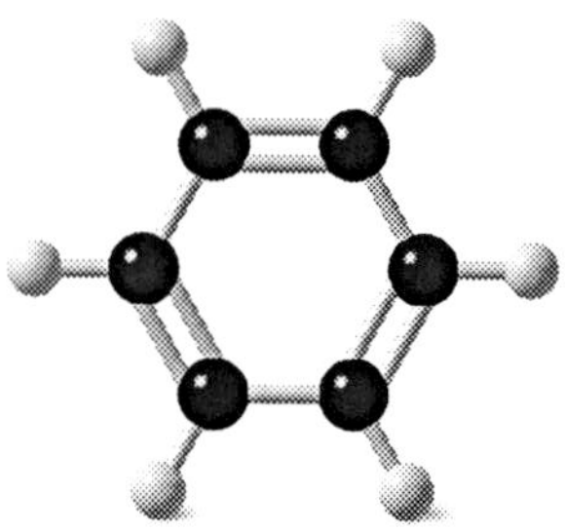

2.1D Benzene: A Representative Aromatic Hydrocarbon

In Chapter 14 we shall study in detail a group of unsaturated cyclic hydrocarbons known as **aromatic compounds**. The compound known as **benzene** is the prototypical aromatic compound. Benzene can be written as a six-membered ring with alternating single and double bonds, called a **Kekulé structure** after August Kekulé, who first conceived of this representation:

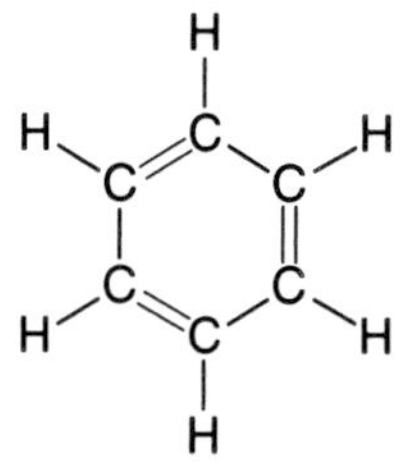

Benzene

Kekulé structure for benzene   or   **Bond-line representation of Kekulé structure**

Even though the Kekulé structure is frequently used for benzene compounds, there is much evidence that this representation is inadequate and incorrect. For example, if benzene had alternating single and double bonds as the Kekulé structure indicates, we would expect the lengths of the carbon–carbon bonds around the ring to be alternately longer and shorter, as we typically find with carbon–carbon single and double bonds (Fig. 1.31). In fact, the carbon–carbon bonds of benzene are all the same length (1.39 Å), a value in between that of a carbon–carbon single bond and a carbon–carbon double bond. There are two ways of dealing with this problem: with resonance theory or with molecular orbital theory.

If we use resonance theory, we visualize benzene as being represented by either of two equivalent Kekulé structures:

Two contributing Kekulé structures for benzene   **A representation of the resonance hybrid**

Based on the principles of resonance theory (Section 1.8) we recognize that benzene cannot be represented adequately by either structure, but that, instead, *it should be visualized as a hybrid of the two structures*. We represent this hybrid by a hexagon with a circle in the middle. Resonance theory, therefore, solves the problem we encountered in understanding how all of the carbon–carbon bonds are the same length. According to resonance theory, the bonds are not alternating single and double bonds, they are a resonance hybrid of the two. Any bond that is a single bond in the first contributor is a double bond in the second, and vice versa.

- All of the carbon–carbon bonds in benzene are one and one-half bonds, have a bond length in between that of a single bond and a double bond, and have bond angles of 120°.

In the molecular orbital explanation, which we shall describe in much more depth in Chapter 14, we begin by recognizing that the carbon atoms of the benzene ring are *sp*² hybridized. Therefore, each carbon has a *p* orbital that has one lobe above the plane of the ring and one lobe below, as shown on the next page in the schematic and calculated *p* orbital representations.

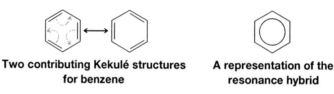

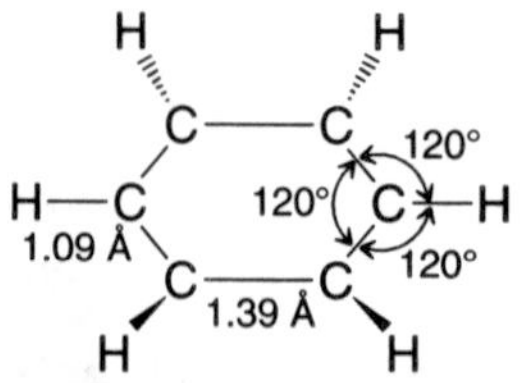

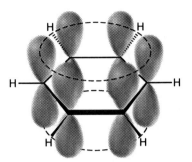

Schematic representation
of benzene *p* orbitals

Calculated *p* orbital
shapes in benzene

Calculated benzene molecular
orbital resulting from favorable
overlap of *p* orbitals above and
below plane of benzene ring

The lobes of each *p* orbital above and below the ring overlap with the lobes of *p* orbitals on the atoms to either side of it. This kind of overlap of *p* orbitals leads to a set of bonding molecular orbitals that encompass all of the carbon atoms of the ring, as shown in the calculated molecular orbital. Therefore, the six electrons associated with these *p* orbitals (one electron from each orbital) are **delocalized** about all six carbon atoms of the ring. This delocalization of electrons explains how all the carbon–carbon bonds are equivalent and have the same length. In Section 14.7B, when we study nuclear magnetic resonance spectroscopy, we shall present convincing physical evidence for this delocalization of the electrons.

●●●········

PRACTICE PROBLEM 2.1

Cyclobutadiene (below) is like benzene in that it has alternating single and double bonds in a ring. However, its bonds are not the same length, the double bonds being shorter than the single bonds; the molecule is rectangular, not square. Explain why it would be incorrect to write resonance structures as shown.

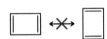

2.2 POLAR COVALENT BONDS

In our discussion of chemical bonds in Section 1.3, we examined compounds such as LiF in which the bond is between two atoms with very large electronegativity differences. In instances like these, a complete transfer of electrons occurs, giving the compound an **ionic bond:**

$$Li^+ \quad :\ddot{F}:^-$$

Lithium fluoride has an ionic bond.

We also described molecules in which electronegativity differences are not large, or in which they are the same, such as the carbon–carbon bond of ethane. Here the electrons are shared equally between the atoms.

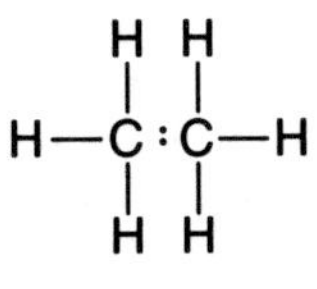

Ethane has a covalent bond.
The electrons are shared equally
between the carbon atoms.

Until now, we have not considered the possibility that the electrons of a covalent bond might be shared unequally.

Lithium fluoride crystal model

- If electronegativity differences exist between two bonded atoms, and they are not large, the electrons are not shared equally and a **polar covalent bond** is the result.
- Remember: one definition of electronegativity is *the ability of an atom to attract electrons that it is sharing in a covalent bond.*

An example of such a polar covalent bond is the one in hydrogen chloride. The chlorine atom, with its greater electronegativity, pulls the bonding electrons closer to it. This makes the hydrogen atom somewhat electron deficient and gives it a *partial* positive charge ($\delta+$). The chlorine atom becomes somewhat electron rich and bears a *partial* negative charge ($\delta-$):

$$\overset{\delta+}{H} : \overset{\delta-}{\ddot{\underset{..}{Cl}}} :$$

Because the hydrogen chloride molecule has a partially positive end and a partially negative end, it is a **dipole**, and it has a **dipole moment**.

The direction of polarity of a polar bond can be symbolized by a vector quantity $\longmapsto$. The crossed end of the arrow is the positive end and the arrowhead is the negative end:

$$(\text{positive end}) \longmapsto (\text{negative end})$$

In HCl, for example, we would indicate the direction of the dipole moment in the following way:

$$H—Cl$$
$$\longmapsto$$

The dipole moment is a physical property that can be measured experimentally. It is defined as the product of the magnitude of the charge in electrostatic units (esu) and the distance that separates them in centimeters (cm):

$$\text{Dipole moment} = \text{charge (in esu)} = \text{distance (in cm)}$$
$$\mu = e \times d$$

The charges are typically on the order of 10^{-10} esu and the distances are on the order of 10^{-8} cm. Dipole moments, therefore, are typically on the order of 10^{-18} esu cm. For convenience, this unit, 1×10^{-18} esu cm, is defined as one **debye** and is abbreviated D. (The unit is named after Peter J. W. Debye, a chemist born in the Netherlands and who taught at Cornell University from 1936 to 1966. Debye won the Nobel Prize in Chemistry in 1936.) In SI units $1 \text{ D} = 3.336 \times 10^{-30}$ coulomb meter (C · m).

If necessary, the length of the arrow can be used to indicate the magnitude of the dipole moment. Dipole moments, as we shall see in Section 2.3, are very useful quantities in accounting for physical properties of compounds.

PRACTICE PROBLEM 2.2 Write $\delta+$ and $\delta-$ by the appropriate atoms and draw a dipole moment vector for any of the following molecules that are polar:

(a) HF   **(b)** IBr   **(c)** Br_2 **(d)** F_2

Polar covalent bonds strongly influence the physical properties and reactivity of molecules. In many cases, these polar covalent bonds are part of **functional groups**, which we shall study shortly (Sections 2.5–2.13). Functional groups are defined groups of atoms in a molecule that give rise to the function (reactivity or physical properties) of the molecule. Functional groups often contain atoms having different electronegativity values and unshared electron pairs. (Atoms such as oxygen, nitrogen, and sulfur that form covalent bonds and have unshared electron pairs are called **heteroatoms**.)

2.2A Maps of Electrostatic Potential

One way to visualize the distribution of charge in a molecule is with a **map of electrostatic potential (MEP)**. Regions of an electron density surface that are more negative than others in an MEP are colored red. These regions would attract a positively charged species (or repel a negative charge). Regions in the MEP that are less negative (or are

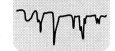

positive) are blue. Blue regions are likely to attract electrons from another molecule. The spectrum of colors from red to blue indicates the trend in charge from most negative to least negative (or most positive).

Figure 2.1 shows a map of electrostatic potential for the low-electron-density surface of hydrogen chloride. We can see clearly that negative charge is concentrated near the chlorine atom and that positive charge is localized near the hydrogen atom, as we predict based on the difference in their electronegativity values. Furthermore, because this MEP is plotted at the low-electron-density surface of the molecule (the van der Waals surface, Section 2.13B), it also gives an indication of the molecule's overall shape.

FIGURE 2.1 A calculated map of electrostatic potential for hydrogen chloride showing regions of relatively more negative charge in red and more positive charge in blue. Negative charge is clearly localized near the chlorine, resulting in a strong dipole moment for the molecule.

2.3 POLAR AND NONPOLAR MOLECULES

In the discussion of dipole moments in the previous section, our attention was restricted to simple diatomic molecules. Any *diatomic* molecule in which the two atoms are *different* (and thus have different electronegativities) will, of necessity, have a dipole moment. In general, a molecule with a dipole moment is a polar molecule. If we examine Table 2.1, however, we find that a number of molecules (e.g., CCl_4, CO_2) consist of more than two atoms, have *polar* bonds, *but have no dipole moment*. With our knowledge of the shapes of molecules (Sections 1.12–1.16) we can understand how this can occur.

TABLE 2.1 DIPOLE MOMENTS OF SOME SIMPLE MOLECULES

Formula	μ (D)	Formula	μ (D)
H_2	0	CH_4	0
Cl_2	0	CH_3Cl	1.87
HF	1.83	CH_2Cl_2	1.55
HCl	1.08	$CHCl_3$	1.02
HBr	0.80	CCl_4	0
HI	0.42	NH_3	1.47
BF_3	0	NF_3	0.24
CO_2	0	H_2O	1.85

Consider a molecule of carbon tetrachloride (CCl_4). Because the electronegativity of chlorine is greater than that of carbon, each of the carbon–chlorine bonds in CCl_4 is polar. Each chlorine atom has a partial negative charge, and the carbon atom is considerably positive. Because a molecule of carbon tetrachloride is tetrahedral (Fig. 2.2), however, *the center of positive charge and the center of negative charge coincide, and the molecule has no net dipole moment.*

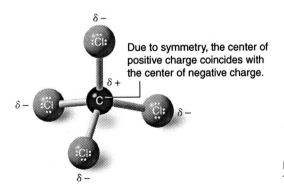

Due to symmetry, the center of positive charge coincides with the center of negative charge.

FIGURE 2.2 Charge distribution in carbon tetrachloride. The molecule has no net dipole moment.

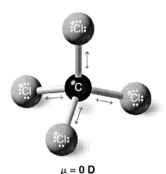

$\mu = 0$ D

FIGURE 2.3 A tetrahedral orientation of equal bond moments causes their effects to cancel.

This result can be illustrated in a slightly different way: if we use arrows ($\longmapsto$) to represent the direction of polarity of each bond, we get the arrangement of bond moments shown in Fig. 2.3. Since the bond moments are vectors of equal magnitude arranged tetrahedrally, their effects cancel. Their vector sum is zero. The molecule has *no net dipole moment.*

The chloromethane molecule (CH_3Cl) has a net dipole moment of 1.87 D. Since carbon and hydrogen have electronegativities (Table 1.1) that are nearly the same, the contribution of three C—H bonds to the net dipole is negligible. The electronegativity difference between carbon and chlorine is large, however, and the highly polar C—Cl bond accounts for most of the dipole moment of CH_3Cl (Fig. 2.4).

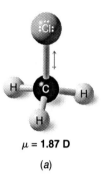

$\mu = 1.87$ D

(a)

(b)

FIGURE 2.4 (a) The dipole moment of chloromethane arises mainly from the highly polar carbon–chlorine bond. (b) A map of electrostatic potential illustrates the polarity of chloromethane.

●●● SOLVED PROBLEM 2.2

Although molecules of CO_2 have polar bonds (oxygen is more electronegative than carbon), carbon dioxide (Table 2.1) has no dipole moment. What can you conclude about the geometry of a carbon dioxide molecule?

STRATEGY AND ANSWER: For a CO_2 molecule to have a zero dipole moment, the bond moments of the two carbon–oxygen bonds must cancel each other. This can happen only if molecules of carbon dioxide are linear.

$$:\!O\!=\!C\!=\!O\!:$$
$$\longleftarrow \;\; \cdot \;\; \longrightarrow$$
$$\mu = 0 \text{ D}$$

●●●

PRACTICE PROBLEM 2.3 Boron trifluoride (BF_3) has no dipole moment ($\mu = 0$ D). Explain how this observation confirms the geometry of BF_3 predicted by VSEPR theory.

●●●

PRACTICE PROBLEM 2.4 Tetrachloroethene ($CCl_2\!=\!CCl_2$) does not have a dipole moment. Explain this fact on the basis of the shape of $CCl_2\!=\!CCl_2$.

●●◆

PRACTICE PROBLEM 2.5 Sulfur dioxide (SO_2) has a dipole moment ($\mu = 1.63$ D); on the other hand, carbon dioxide (see Solved Problem 2.2) has no dipole moment ($\mu = 0$ D). What do these facts indicate about the geometry of sulfur dioxide?

Unshared pairs of electrons make large contributions to the dipole moments of water and ammonia. Because an unshared pair has no other atom attached to it to partially neutralize its negative charge, an unshared electron pair contributes a large moment directed away from the central atom (Fig. 2.5). (The O—H and N—H moments are also appreciable.)

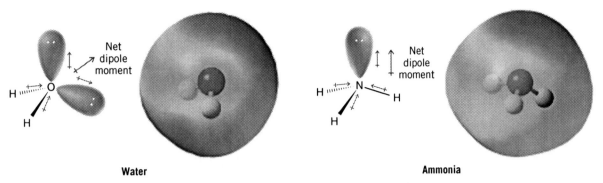

Water   Ammonia

FIGURE 2.5 Bond moments and the resulting dipole moments of water and ammonia.

Using a three-dimensional formula, show the direction of the dipole moment of CH_3OH. **PRACTICE PROBLEM 2.6**
Write $\delta+$ and $\delta-$ signs next to the appropriate atoms.

Trichloromethane ($CHCl_3$, also called *chloroform*) has a larger dipole moment than $CFCl_3$. **PRACTICE PROBLEM 2.7**
Use three-dimensional structures and bond moments to explain this fact.

2.3A Dipole Moments in Alkenes

Cis–trans isomers of alkenes (Section 1.13B) have different physical properties. They have different melting points and boiling points, and often cis–trans isomers differ markedly in the magnitude of their dipole moments. Table 2.2 summarizes some of the physical properties of two pairs of cis–trans isomers.

TABLE 2.2 PHYSICAL PROPERTIES OF SOME CIS–TRANS ISOMERS

Compound	Melting Point (°C)	Boiling Point (°C)	Dipole Moment (D)
cis-1,2-Dichloroethene	−80	60	1.90
trans-1,2-Dichloroethene	−50	48	0
cis-1,2-Dibromoethene	−53	112	1.35
trans-1,2-Dibromoethene	−6	108	0

••• SOLVED PROBLEM 2.3

Explain why *cis*-1,2-dichloroethene (Table 2.2) has a large dipole moment whereas *trans*-1,2-dichloroethene has a dipole moment equal to zero.

STRATEGY AND ANSWER: If we examine the net dipole moments (shown in red) for the bond moments (black), we see that in *trans*-1,2-dichloroethene the bond moments cancel each other, whereas in *cis*-1,2-dichloroethene they augment each other.

Bond moments (black) are in same general direction. Resultant dipole moment (red) is large.

Bond moments cancel each other. Net dipole is zero.

cis-1,2-Dichloroethene
μ = 1.9 D

trans-1,2-Dichloroethene
μ = 0 D

● ● ●

PRACTICE PROBLEM 2.8 Indicate the direction of the important bond moments in each of the following compounds (neglect C—H bonds). You should also give the direction of the net dipole moment for the molecule. If there is no net dipole moment, state that $\mu = 0$ D.

(a) *cis*-CHF=CHF   (b) *trans*-CHF=CHF   (c) CH_2=CF_2 (d) CF_2=CF_2

● ● ●

PRACTICE PROBLEM 2.9 Write structural formulas for all of the alkenes with (a) the formula $C_2H_2Br_2$ and (b) the formula $C_2Br_2Cl_2$. In each instance designate compounds that are cis–trans isomers of each other. Predict the dipole moment of each one.

2.4 FUNCTIONAL GROUPS

● **Functional groups** are common and specific arrangements of atoms that impart predictable reactivity and properties to a molecule.

The functional group of an alkene, for example, is its carbon–carbon double bond. When we study the reactions of alkenes in greater detail in Chapter 8, we shall find that most of the chemical reactions of alkenes are the chemical reactions of the carbon–carbon double bond.

The functional group of an alkyne is its carbon–carbon triple bond. Alkanes do not have a functional group. Their molecules have carbon–carbon single bonds and carbon–hydrogen bonds, but these bonds are present in molecules of almost all organic compounds, and C—C and C—H bonds are, in general, much less reactive than common functional groups. We shall introduce other common functional groups and their properties in Sections 2.5–2.11. Table 2.3 (Section 2.12) summarizes the most important functional groups. First, however, let us introduce some common alkyl groups, which are specific groups of carbon and hydrogen atoms that are not part of functional groups.

2.4A Alkyl Groups and the Symbol R

Alkyl groups are the groups that we identify for purposes of naming compounds. They are groups that would be obtained by removing a hydrogen atom from an alkane:

Alkane	Alkyl Group	Abbreviation	Bond-line	Model
CH_3—H **Methane**	H_3C—⁅ **Methyl**	Me-	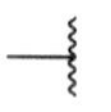	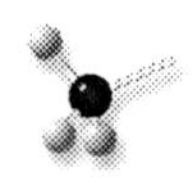
CH_3CH_2—H **Ethane**	CH_3CH_2—⁅ **Ethyl**	Et-		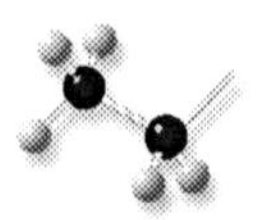
$CH_3CH_2CH_2$—H **Propane**	$CH_3CH_2CH_2$—⁅ **Propyl**	Pr-	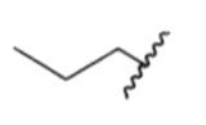	
$CH_3CH_2CH_2CH_2$—H **Butane**	$CH_3CH_2CH_2CH_2$—⁅ **Butyl**	Bu-		

While only one alkyl group can be derived from methane or ethane (the **methyl** and **ethyl** groups, respectively), two groups can be derived from propane. Removal of a hydrogen from one of the end carbon atoms gives a group that is called the **propyl** group; removal of a hydrogen from the middle carbon atom gives a group that is called the **isopropyl** group. The names and structures of these groups are used so frequently in organic chemistry that you should learn them now. See Section 4.3C for names and structures of branched alkyl groups derived from butane and other hydrocarbons.

We can simplify much of our future discussion if, at this point, we introduce a symbol that is widely used in designating general structures of organic molecules: the symbol R. R *is used as a general symbol to represent any alkyl group*. For example, R might be a methyl group, an ethyl group, a propyl group, or an isopropyl group:

$$CH_3—$$ Methyl
$$CH_3CH_2—$$ Ethyl
$$CH_3CH_2CH_2—$$ Propyl
$$CH_3CHCH_3$$ Isopropyl

} These and others can be designated by R.

Thus, the general formula for an alkane is R—H.

2.4B Phenyl and Benzyl Groups

When a benzene ring is attached to some other group of atoms in a molecule, it is called a **phenyl group**, and it is represented in several ways:

or   or $C_6H_5—$ or   Ph—

or ϕ—   or   Ar— (if ring substituents are present)

Ways of representing a phenyl group

The combination of a phenyl group and a **methylene group** ($—CH_2—$) is called a benzyl group:

CH$_2$—   or

or $C_6H_5CH_2—$ or   Bn—

Ways of representing a benzyl group

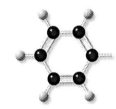

2-Chloropropane

2.5 ALKYL HALIDES OR HALOALKANES

Alkyl halides are compounds in which a halogen atom (fluorine, chlorine, bromine, or iodine) replaces a hydrogen atom of an alkane. For example, CH_3Cl and CH_3CH_2Br are alkyl halides. Alkyl halides are also called **haloalkanes**. The generic formula for an alkyl halide is R—$\ddot{X}$: where X = fluorine, chlorine, bromine, or iodine.

Alkyl halides are classified as being primary (1°), secondary (2°), or tertiary (3°). *This classification is based on the carbon atom to which the halogen is directly attached*. If the carbon atom that bears the halogen is directly attached to only one other carbon, the carbon atom is said to be a primary carbon atom and the alkyl halide is classified as a **primary alkyl halide**. If the carbon that bears the halogen is itself directly attached to two other carbon atoms, then the carbon is a secondary carbon and the alkyl halide is a **secondary alkyl halide**. If the carbon that bears the halogen is directly attached to three other carbon atoms, then the carbon is a tertiary

Helpful Hint

Although we use the symbols 1°, 2°, 3°, we do not say first degree, second degree, and third degree; we say *primary, secondary*, and *tertiary*.

carbon and the alkyl halide is a **tertiary alkyl halide**. Examples of primary, secondary, and tertiary alkyl halides are the following:

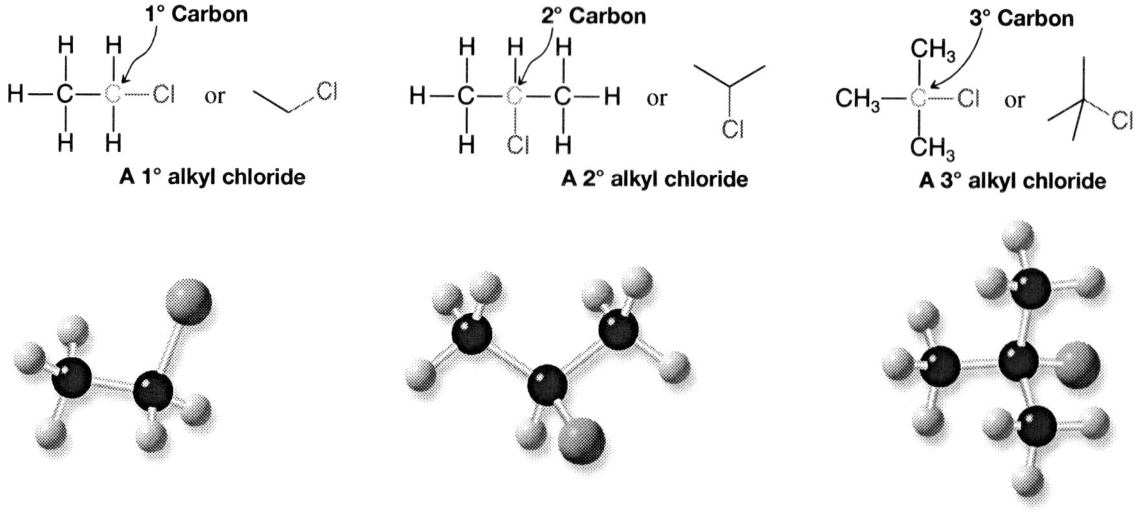

1° Carbon

H—C—C—Cl or ⌐Cl

A 1° alkyl chloride

2° Carbon

H—C—C—C—H or

A 2° alkyl chloride

3° Carbon

CH₃—C—Cl or

A 3° alkyl chloride

An **alkenyl halide** is a compound with a halogen atom bonded to an alkene carbon. In older nomenclature such compounds were sometimes referred to as vinyl halides. An **aryl halide** is a compound with a halogen atom bonded to an aromatic ring such as a benzene ring.

An alkenyl chloride   **A phenyl bromide**

●●● SOLVED PROBLEM 2.4

Write the structure of an alkane with the formula C_5H_{12} that has no secondary or tertiary carbon atoms. *Hint:* The compound has a quaternary (4°) carbon.

STRATEGY AND ANSWER: Following the pattern of designations for carbon atoms given above, a 4° carbon atom must be one that is directly attached to four other carbon atoms. If we start with this carbon atom, and then add four carbon atoms with their attached hydrogens, there is only one possible alkane. The other four carbons are all primary carbons; none is secondary or tertiary.

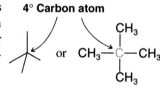

4° Carbon atom

●●◆

PRACTICE PROBLEM 2.10 Write bond-line structural formulas for **(a)** two constitutionally isomeric primary alkyl bromides with the formula C_4H_9Br, **(b)** a secondary alkyl bromide, and **(c)** a tertiary alkyl bromide with the same formula. Build handheld molecular models for each structure and examine the differences in their connectivity.

●●◆

PRACTICE PROBLEM 2.11 Although we shall discuss the naming of organic compounds later when we discuss the individual families in detail, one method of naming alkyl halides is so straightforward that it is worth describing here. We simply name the alkyl group attached to the halogen and add the word *fluoride, chloride, bromide,* or *iodide*. Write formulas for **(a)** ethyl fluoride and **(b)** isopropyl chloride.

What are the names for **(c)**  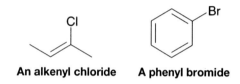 Br, **(d)** 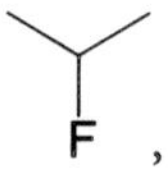 F , and **(e)** C_6H_5I?

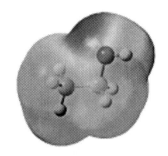

2.6 ALCOHOLS AND PHENOLS

Methyl alcohol (also called methanol) has the structural formula CH_3OH and is the simplest member of a family of organic compounds known as **alcohols**. The characteristic functional group of this family is the hydroxyl (—OH) group attached to an sp^3-hybridized carbon atom. Another example of an alcohol is ethyl alcohol, CH_3CH_2OH (also called ethanol).

$$-\overset{|}{\underset{|}{C}}-\ddot{O}-H$$

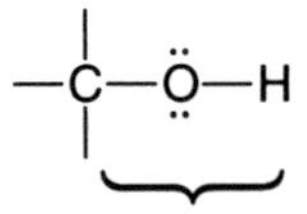

**This is the functional
group of an alcohol.**

Ethanol

Alcohols may be viewed structurally in two ways: (1) as hydroxyl derivatives of alkanes and (2) as alkyl derivatives of water. Ethyl alcohol, for example, can be seen as an ethane molecule in which one hydrogen has been replaced by a hydroxyl group or as a water molecule in which one hydrogen has been replaced by an ethyl group:

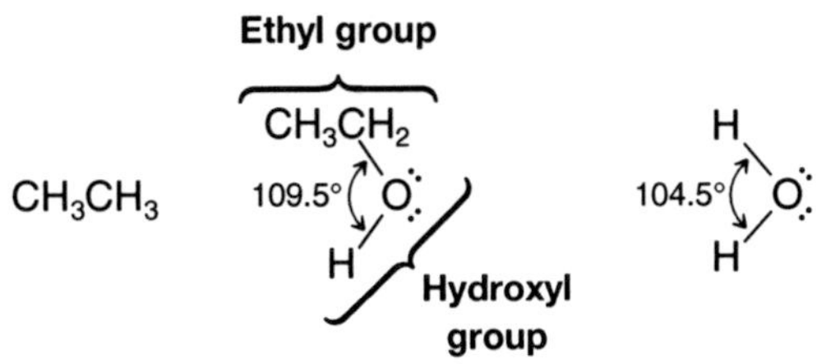

Ethyl group

CH_3CH_3 CH_3CH_2 109.5° $\ddot{O}$:
                        H   **Hydroxyl
                             group**

H   104.5° $\ddot{O}$:
                        H

Ethane   **Ethyl alcohol
(ethanol)**   **Water**

As with alkyl halides, alcohols are classified into three groups: primary (1°), secondary (2°), and tertiary (3°) alcohols. ***This classification is based on the degree of substitution of the carbon to which the hydroxyl group is directly attached.*** If the carbon has only one other carbon attached to it, the carbon is said to be a **primary carbon** and the alcohol is a **primary alcohol**:

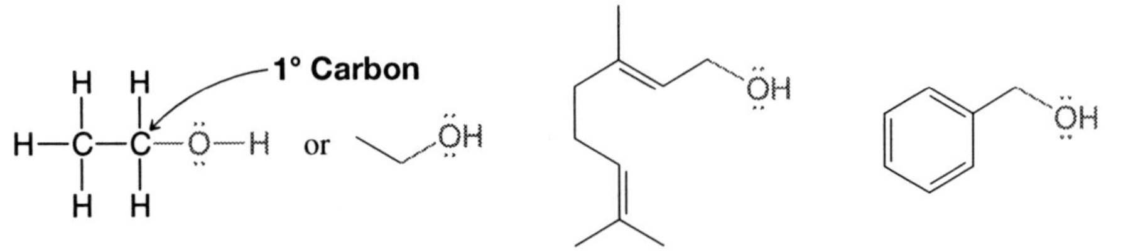

—1° Carbon

**Ethyl alcohol
(a 1° alcohol)**

**Geraniol
(a 1° alcohol)**

**Benzyl alcohol
(a 1° alcohol)**

If the carbon atom that bears the hydroxyl group also has two other carbon atoms attached to it, this carbon is called a secondary carbon, and the alcohol is a secondary alcohol:

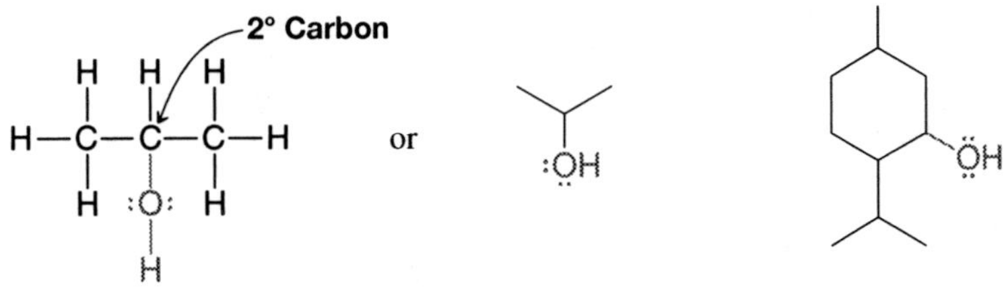

—2° Carbon

**Isopropyl alcohol
(a 2° alcohol)**

**Menthol
(a 2° alcohol found
in peppermint oil)**

If the carbon atom that bears the hydroxyl group has three other carbons attached to it, this carbon is called a tertiary carbon, and the alcohol is a tertiary alcohol:

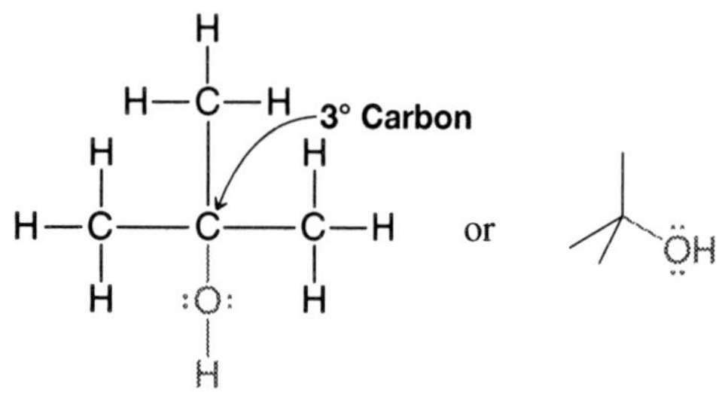

Helpful Hint

Practice with handheld molecular models by building models of as many of the compounds on this page as you can.

tert-Butyl alcohol
(a 3° alcohol)

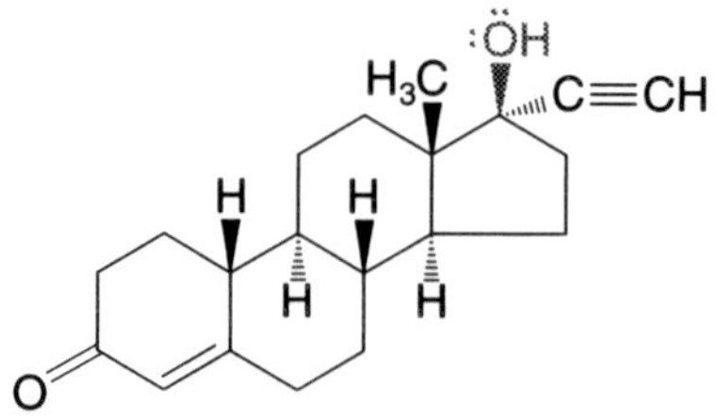

Norethindrone
(an oral contraceptive that contains a 3° alcohol
group as well as a ketone group and
carbon–carbon double and triple bonds)

PRACTICE PROBLEM 2.12 Write bond-line structural formulas for **(a)** two primary alcohols, **(b)** a secondary alcohol, and **(c)** a tertiary alcohol—all having the molecular formula $C_4H_{10}O$.

PRACTICE PROBLEM 2.13 One way of naming alcohols is to name the alkyl group that is attached to the —OH and add the word *alcohol*. Write bond-line formulas for **(a)** propyl alcohol and **(b)** isopropyl alcohol.

When a hydroxyl group is bonded to a benzene ring the combination of the ring and the hydroxyl is called a phenol. Phenols differ significantly from alcohols in terms of their relative acidity, as we shall see in Chapter 3, and thus they are considered a distinct functional group.

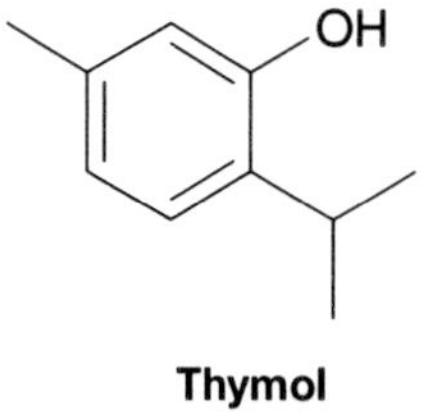

Thymol
(a phenol found in thyme)

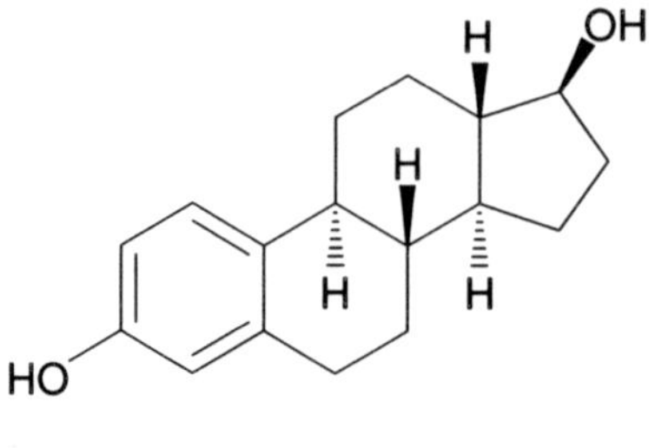

Estradiol
(a sex hormone that contains
both alcohol and phenol groups)

●●● SOLVED PROBLEM 2.5

Circle the atoms that comprise **(a)** the phenol and **(b)** the alcohol functional groups in estradiol. **(c)** What is the class of the alcohol?

STRATEGY AND ANSWER: (a) A phenol group consists of a benzene ring and a hydroxyl group, hence we circle these parts of the molecule together. **(b)** The alcohol group is found in the five-membered ring of estradiol. **(c)** The carbon bearing the alcohol hydroxyl group has two carbons directly bonded to it, thus it is a secondary alcohol.

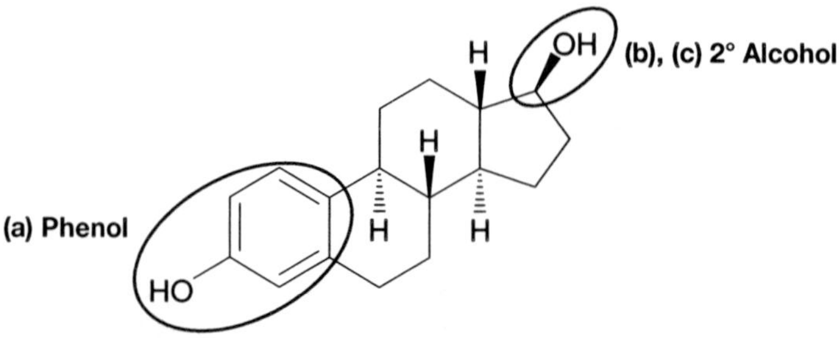

(b), (c) 2° Alcohol

(a) Phenol

2.7 ETHERS

Ethers have the general formula R—O—R or R—O—R′, where R′ may be an alkyl (or phenyl) group different from R. Ethers can be thought of as derivatives of water in which both hydrogen atoms have been replaced by alkyl groups. The bond angle at the oxygen atom of an ether is only slightly larger than that of water:

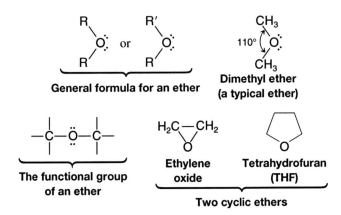

General formula for an ether

Dimethyl ether (a typical ether)

Dimethyl ether

The functional group of an ether

Ethylene oxide

Tetrahydrofuran (THF)

Two cyclic ethers

One way of naming ethers is to name the two alkyl groups attached to the oxygen atom in alphabetical order and add the word *ether*. If the two alkyl groups are the same, we use the prefix *di-*, for example, as in *dimethyl ether*. Write bond-line structural formulas for **(a)** diethyl ether, **(b)** ethyl propyl ether, and **(c)** ethyl isopropyl ether. What name would you give to **(d)** 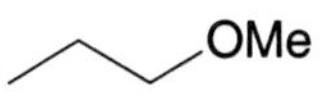 ⟨structure⟩OMe **(e)** 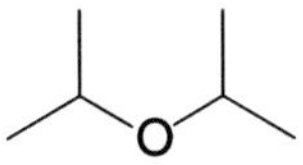 ⟨structure⟩ and **(f)** CH₃OC₆H₅ ?

PRACTICE PROBLEM 2.14

THE CHEMISTRY OF... Ethers as General Anesthetics

Nitrous oxide (N_2O), also called laughing gas, was first used as an anesthetic in 1799, and it is still in use today, even though when used alone it does not produce deep anesthesia. The first use of an ether, diethyl ether, to produce deep anesthesia occurred in 1842. In the years that have passed since then, several different ethers, usually with halogen substituents, have replaced diethyl ether as anesthetics of choice. One reason: unlike diethyl ether, which is highly flammable, the halogenated ethers are not. Two halogenated ethers that are currently used for inhalation anesthesia are desflurane and sevoflurane.

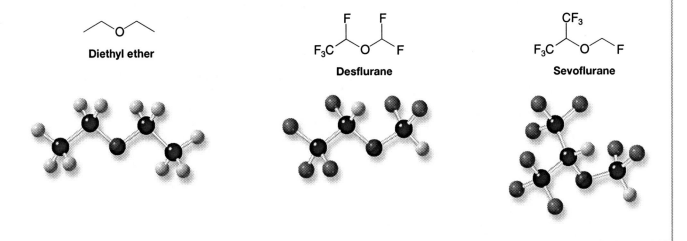

Diethyl ether

Desflurane

Sevoflurane

· · ·

PRACTICE PROBLEM 2.15 Eugenol is the main constituent of the natural oil from cloves. Circle and label all of the functional groups in eugenol.

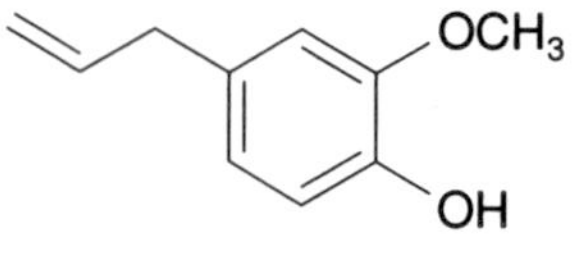

Eugenol (found in cloves)

2.8 AMINES

Ethylamine

Just as alcohols and ethers may be considered as organic derivatives of water, amines may be considered as organic derivatives of ammonia:

Ammonia    **An amine** 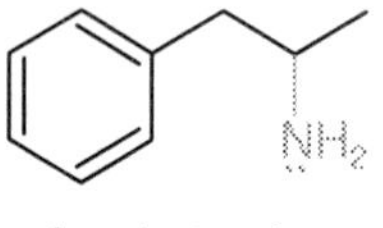   **Amphetamine**
(a dangerous stimulant) 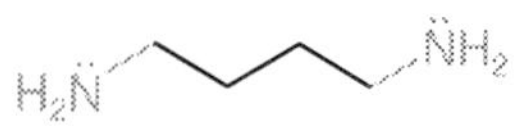   **Putrescine**
(found in decaying meat)

Amines are classified as primary, secondary, or tertiary amines. **This classification is based on** *the number of organic groups that are attached to the nitrogen atom*:

A primary (1°)
amine 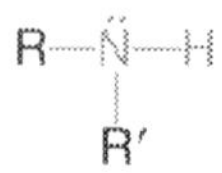   **A secondary (2°)**
amine 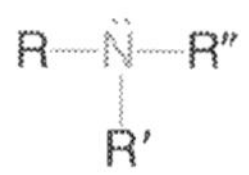   **A tertiary (3°)**
amine

Notice that this is quite different from the way alcohols and alkyl halides are classified. Isopropylamine, for example, is a primary amine even though its —NH_2 group is attached to a secondary carbon atom. It is a primary amine because only one organic group is attached to the nitrogen atom:

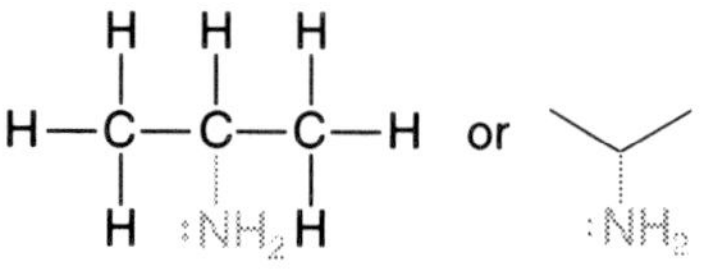

Isopropylamine
(a 1° amine) 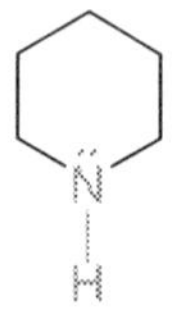   **Piperidine**
(a cyclic 2° amine)

Amphetamine (below), a powerful and dangerous stimulant, is a primary amine. Dopamine, an important neurotransmitter whose depletion is associated with Parkinson's disease, is also a primary amine. Nicotine, a toxic compound found in tobacco that makes smoking addictive, has a secondary amine group and a tertiary one.

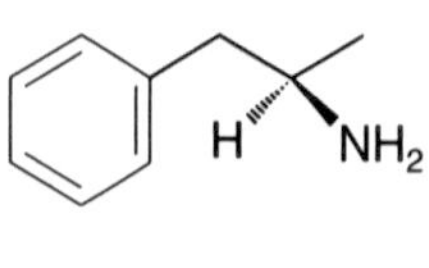

Amphetamine 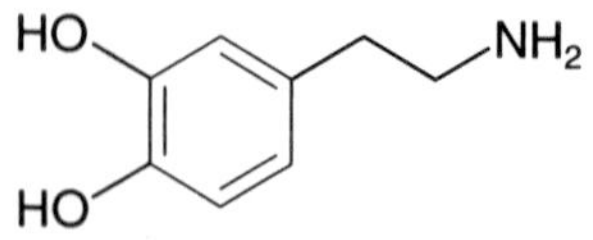   **Dopamine** 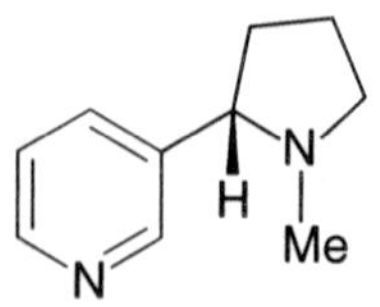   **Nicotine**

Amines are like ammonia (Section 1.16B) in having a trigonal pyramidal shape. The C—N—C bond angles of trimethylamine are 108.7°, a value very close to the

H—C—H bond angles of methane. Thus, for all practical purposes, the nitrogen atom of an amine can be considered to be sp^3 hybridized with the unshared electron pair occupying one orbital (see below). This means that the unshared pair is relatively exposed, and as we shall see this is important because it is involved in almost all of the reactions of amines.

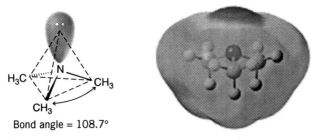

Bond angle = 108.7°

Trimethylamine

PRACTICE PROBLEM 2.16

One way of naming amines is to name in alphabetical order the alkyl groups attached to the nitrogen atom, using the prefixes *di-* and *tri-* if the groups are the same. An example is *isopropylamine*, whose formula is shown above. What are names for **(a)**, **(b)**, **(c)**, and **(d)**? Build hand-held molecular models for the compounds in parts **(a)**–**(d)**.

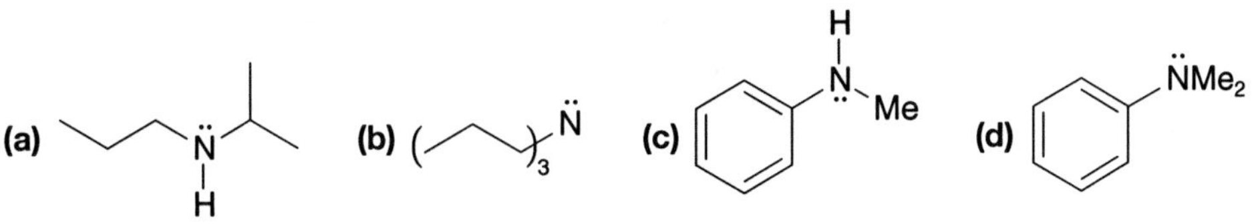

Write bond-line formulas for **(e)** propylamine, **(f)** trimethylamine, and **(g)** ethyliso-propylmethylamine.

PRACTICE PROBLEM 2.17

Which amines in Practice Problem 2.16 are **(a)** primary amines, **(b)** secondary amines, and **(c)** tertiary amines?

PRACTICE PROBLEM 2.18

Amines are like ammonia in being weak bases. They do this by using their unshared electron pair to accept a proton. **(a)** Show the reaction that would take place between trimethyl amine and HCl. **(b)** What hybridization state would you expect for the nitrogen atom in the product of this reaction?

2.9 ALDEHYDES AND KETONES

Aldehydes and ketones both contain the **carbonyl group**—a group in which a carbon atom has a double bond to oxygen:

The carbonyl group

The carbonyl group of an aldehyde is bonded to one hydrogen atom and one carbon atom (except for formaldehyde, which is the only aldehyde bearing two hydrogen atoms).

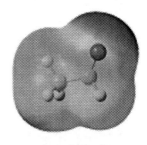

Acetaldehyde

The carbonyl group of a ketone is bonded to two carbon atoms. Using R, we can designate the general formulas for aldehydes and ketones as follows:

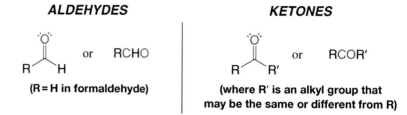

ALDEHYDES

or RCHO

(R = H in formaldehyde)

KETONES

or RCOR′

(where R′ is an alkyl group that may be the same or different from R)

Some specific examples of aldehydes and ketones are the following:

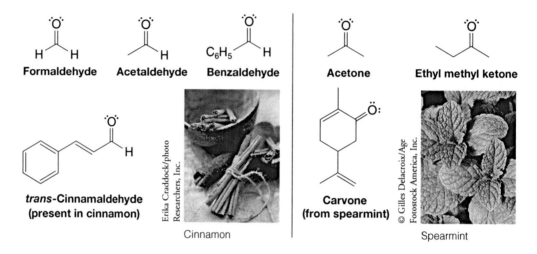

Formaldehyde   Acetaldehyde   Benzaldehyde   Acetone   Ethyl methyl ketone

trans-Cinnamaldehyde
(present in cinnamon)

Cinnamon

Carvone
(from spearmint)

Spearmint

Erika Craddock/photo Researchers, Inc.

© Gilles Delacroix/Age Fotostock America, Inc.

Helpful Hint

Computer molecular models can be found in the 3D Models section of the book's website for these and many other compounds we discuss in this book.

Aldehydes and ketones have a trigonal planar arrangement of groups around the carbonyl carbon atom. The carbon atom is *sp²* hybridized. In formaldehyde, for example, the bond angles are as follows:

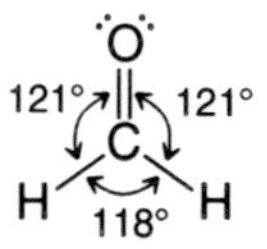

121°   121°

H   118°   H

Retinal (below) is an aldehyde made from vitamin A that plays a vital role in vision. We discuss this further in Chapter 13.

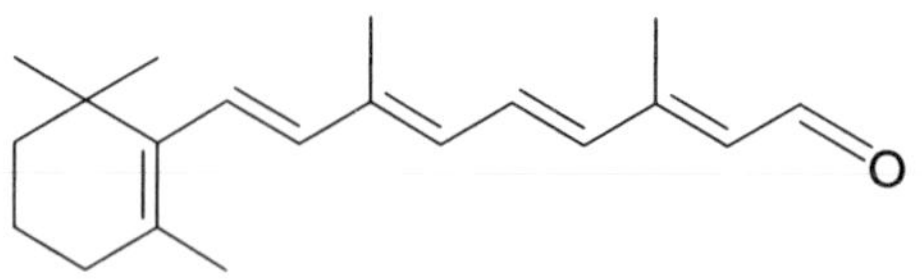

Retinal

PRACTICE PROBLEM 2.19 Write the resonance structure for carvone that results from moving the electrons as indicated. Include all formal charges.

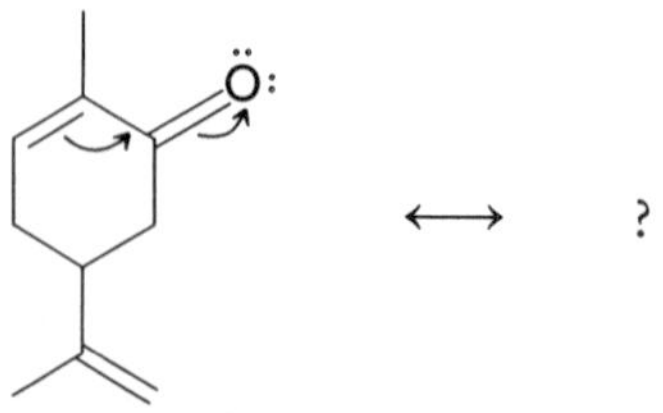

⟷   ?

PRACTICE PROBLEM 2.20

Write bond-line formulas for **(a)** four aldehydes and **(b)** three ketones that have the formula $C_5H_{10}O$.

2.10 CARBOXYLIC ACIDS, ESTERS, AND AMIDES

Carboxylic acids, esters, and amides all contain a carbonyl group that is bonded to an oxygen or nitrogen atom. As we shall learn in later chapters, all of these functional groups are interconvertible by appropriately chosen reactions.

2.10A Carboxylic Acids

Carboxylic acids have a carbonyl group bonded to a hydroxyl group, and they have the

general formula ![structure] . The functional group, ![structure], is called the **carboxyl group** (**carbo**nyl + hydro**xyl**):

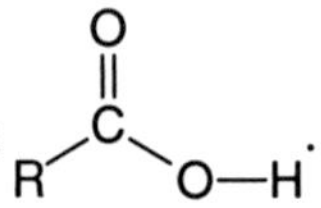

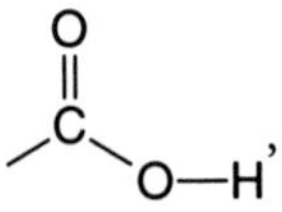

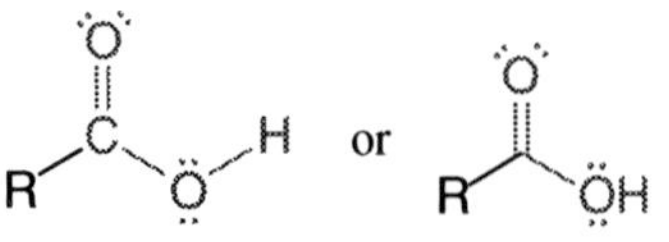

![A carboxylic acid structures: R—C(=O)—O—H or RCO2H or —CO2H or —COOH]

A carboxylic acid   **The carboxyl group**

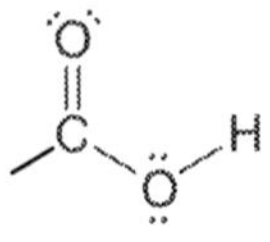

Examples of carboxylic acids are formic acid, acetic acid, and benzoic acid:

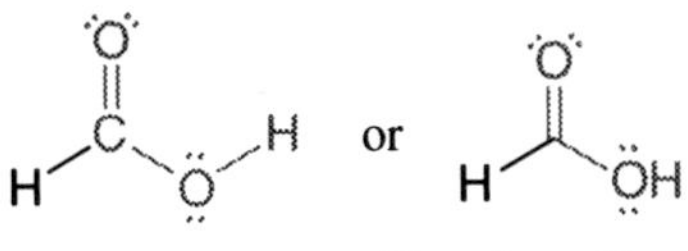

![Formic acid structures] or HCO_2H

Formic acid

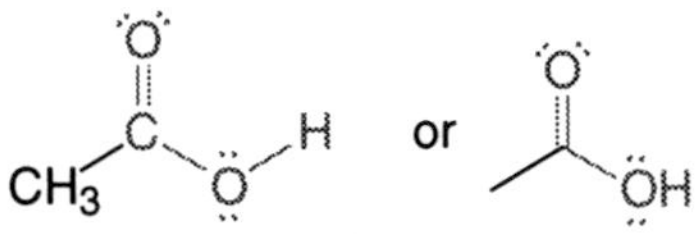

![Acetic acid structures] or CH_3CO_2H

Acetic acid

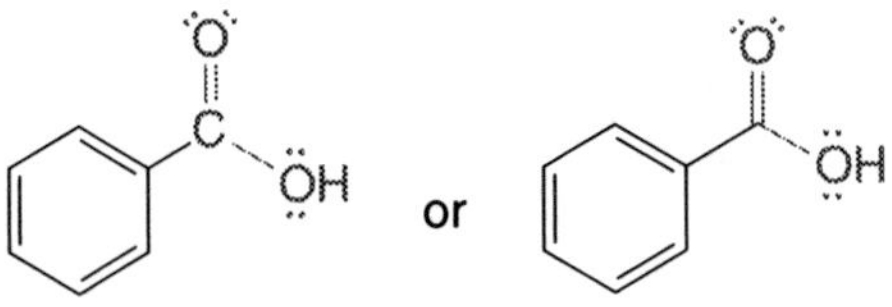

![Benzoic acid structures] or $C_6H_5CO_2H$

Benzoic acid

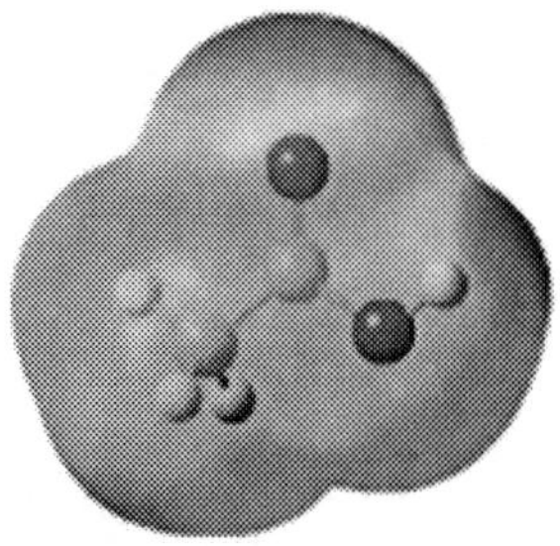

Acetic acid

Formic acid is an irritating liquid produced by ants. (The sting of the ant is caused, in part, by formic acid being injected under the skin. *Formic* is the Latin word for ant.) Acetic acid, the substance responsible for the sour taste of vinegar, is produced when certain bacteria act on the ethyl alcohol of wine and cause the ethyl alcohol to be oxidized by air.

●●● SOLVED PROBLEM 2.6

When formic acid (see above) donates a proton to a base, the result is the formation of a formate ion (HCO_2^-). **(a)** Write two resonance structures for the formate ion, and two resonance structures for formic acid. **(b)** Review the Rules for Resonance in Chapter 1, and identify which species, formate ion or formic acid, is most stabilized by resonance.

STRATEGY AND ANSWER: (a) We move the electron pairs as indicated below.

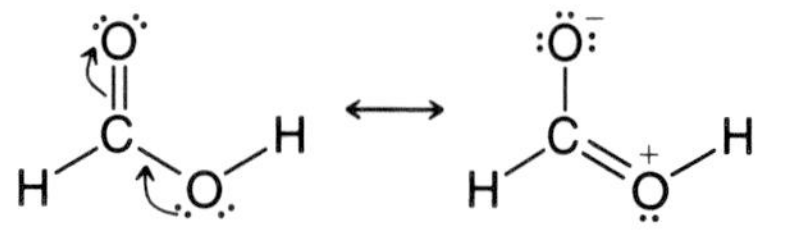

Formic acid 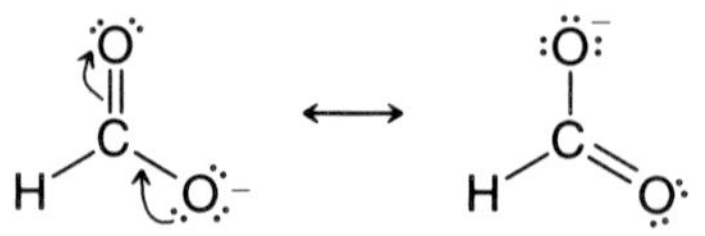   **Formate ion**

(b) The formate ion would be most stabilized because it does not have separated charges.

···●●●

PRACTICE PROBLEM 2.21   Write bond-line formulas for four carboxylic acids with the formula $C_5H_{10}O_2$.

2.10B Esters

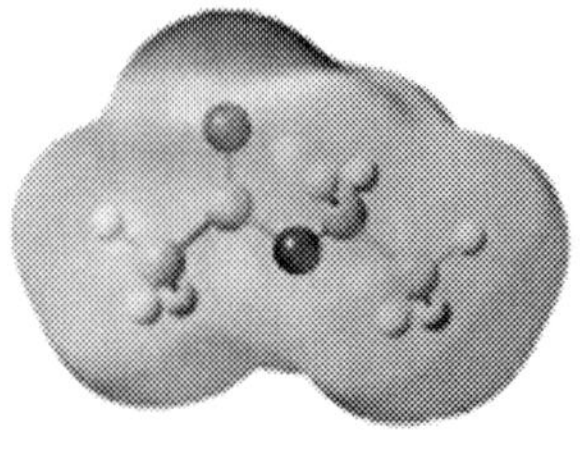

Esters have the general formula RCO_2R' (or $RCOOR'$), where a carbonyl group is bonded to an alkoxyl (—OR) group:

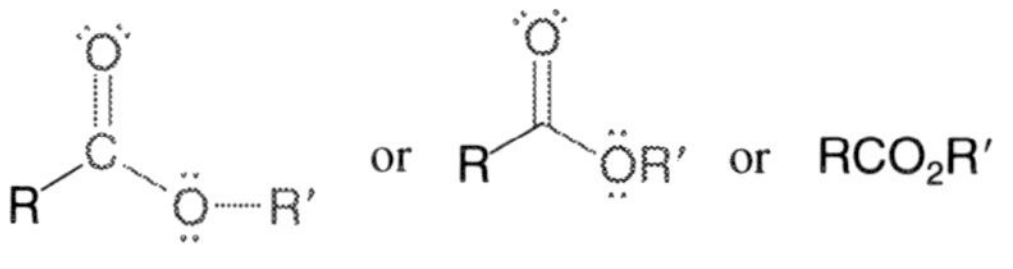

or   R $\overset{..}{O}R'$ or RCO_2R'

General formula for an ester

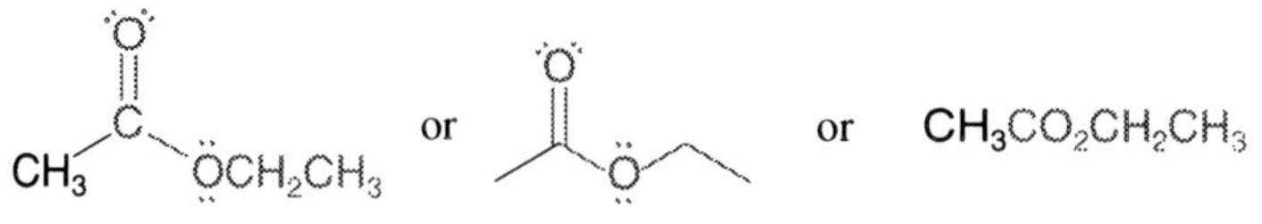

CH_3 $\overset{..}{O}CH_2CH_3$ or   or $CH_3CO_2CH_2CH_3$

Ethyl acetate is an important solvent.

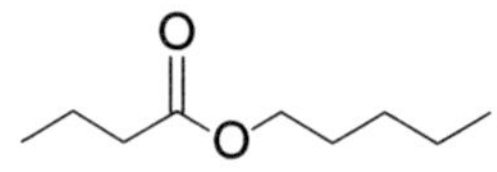

Pentyl butanoate has the odor of apricots and pears.

Ethyl acetate

The ester pentyl butanoate has the odor of apricots and pears.

···●●●

PRACTICE PROBLEM 2.22   Write bond-line formulas for three esters with the formula $C_5H_{10}O_2$.

···●●●

PRACTICE PROBLEM 2.23   Write another resonance structure for ethyl acetate. Include formal charges.

Esters can be made from a carboxylic acid and an alcohol through the acid-catalyzed loss of a molecule of water. For example:

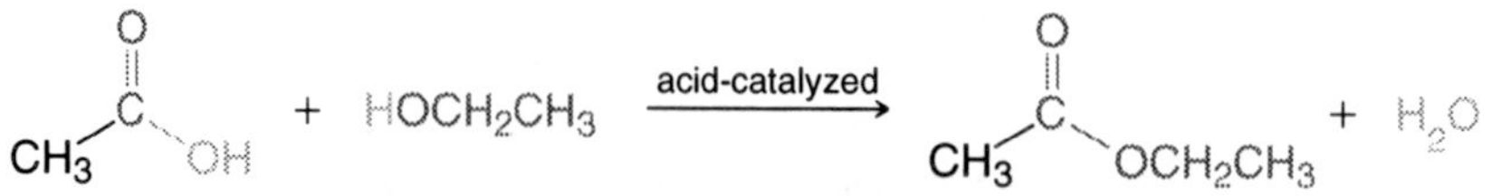

CH_3 OH   + $HOCH_2CH_3$ $\xrightarrow{\text{acid-catalyzed}}$ CH_3 OCH_2CH_3 + H_2O

Acetic acid   **Ethyl alcohol**   **Ethyl acetate**

Your body makes esters from long-chain carboxylic acids called "fatty acids" by combining them with glycerol. We discuss their chemistry in detail in Chapter 23.

2.10C Amides

Amides have the formulas $RCONH_2$, $RCONHR'$, or $RCONR'R''$ where a carbonyl group is bonded to a nitrogen atom bearing hydrogen and/or alkyl groups. General formulas and some specific examples are shown below.

An unsubstituted amide   An *N*-substituted amide   An *N,N*-disubstituted amide

General formulas for amides

Acetamide   *N*-Methylacetamide   *N,N*-Dimethylacetamide

Specific examples of amides

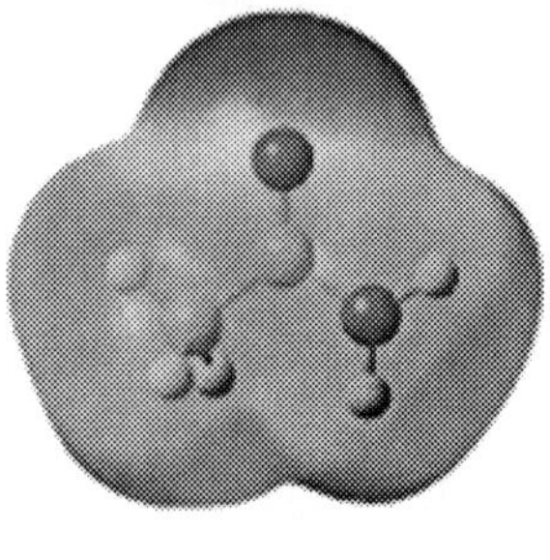

N- and *N,N*- indicate that the substituents are attached to the nitrogen atom.

Write another resonance structure for acetamide.

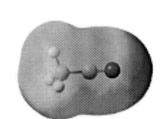

Nylon is a polymer comprised of regularly repeating amide groups.

Acetamide

••• ·········
PRACTICE PROBLEM 2.24

2.11 NITRILES

A nitrile has the formula $R—C≡N:$ (or $R—CN$). The carbon and the nitrogen of a nitrile are *sp* hybridized. In **IUPAC** systematic nomenclature, acyclic nitriles are named by adding the suffix *-nitrile* to the name of the corresponding hydrocarbon. The carbon atom of the $—C≡N$ group is assigned number 1. The name acetonitrile is an acceptable common name for CH_3CN, and acrylonitrile is an acceptable common name for $CH_2=CHCN$:

$$\overset{2}{C}H_3—\overset{1}{C}≡N:$$
Ethanenitrile
(acetonitrile)

$$\overset{4}{C}H_3\overset{3}{C}H_2\overset{2}{C}H_2—\overset{1}{C}≡N:$$
Butanenitrile

Propenenitrile
(acrylonitrile)

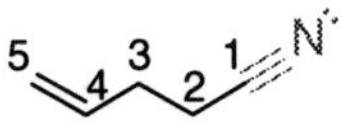

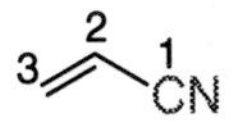

4-Pentenenitrile

Cyclic nitriles are named by adding the suffix *-carbonitrile* to the name of the ring system to which the $—CN$ group is attached. Benzonitrile is an acceptable common name for C_6H_5CN:

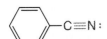

Benzenecarbonitrile   Cyclohexanecarbonitrile
(benzonitrile)

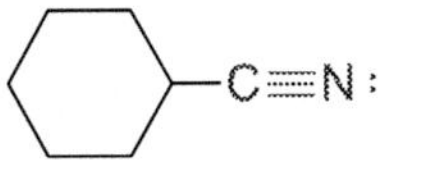

Acetonitrile

2.12 SUMMARY OF IMPORTANT FAMILIES OF ORGANIC COMPOUNDS

A summary of the important families of organic compounds is given in Table 2.3. You should learn to identify these common functional groups as they appear in other, more complicated molecules.

TABLE 2.3 IMPORTANT FAMILIES OF ORGANIC COMPOUNDS

	Alkane	Alkene	Alkyne	Aromatic	Haloalkane	Alcohol	Phenol	Ether
Functional group	$C-H$ and $C-C$ bonds	$>C=C<$	$-C\equiv C-$	Aromatic ring	$-\overset{\mid}{\underset{\mid}{C}}-\ddot{\ddot{X}}$	$-\overset{\mid}{\underset{\mid}{C}}-\ddot{O}H$	OH (on ring)	$-\overset{\mid}{\underset{\mid}{C}}-\ddot{O}-\overset{\mid}{\underset{\mid}{C}}-$
General formula	RH	$RCH=CH_2$ $RCH=CHR$ $R_2C=CHR$ $R_2C=CR_2$	$RC\equiv CH$ $RC\equiv CR$	ArH	RX	ROH	ArOH	ROR
Specific example	CH_3CH_3	$CH_2=CH_2$	$HC\equiv CH$	(benzene ring)	CH_3CH_2Cl	CH_3CH_2OH	(phenol OH)	CH_3OCH_3
IUPAC name	Ethane	Ethene	Ethyne	Benzene	Chloroethane	Ethanol	Phenol	Methoxymethane
Common name[a]	Ethane	Ethylene	Acetylene	Benzene	Ethyl chloride	Ethyl alcohol	Phenol	Dimethyl ether

	Amine	Aldehyde	Ketone	Carboxylic Acid	Ester	Amide	Nitrile
Functional group	$-\overset{\mid}{\underset{\mid}{C}}-\ddot{N}<$	$\overset{\ddot{O}}{\overset{\parallel}{C}}{-}H$	$-\overset{\mid}{\underset{\mid}{C}}-\overset{\ddot{O}}{\overset{\parallel}{C}}-\overset{\mid}{\underset{\mid}{C}}-$	$\overset{\ddot{O}}{\overset{\parallel}{C}}{-}\ddot{O}H$	$\overset{\ddot{O}}{\overset{\parallel}{C}}{-}\ddot{O}-\overset{\mid}{\underset{\mid}{C}}-$	$\overset{\ddot{O}}{\overset{\parallel}{C}}{-}\underset{\mid}{N}$	$-C\equiv N$
General formula	RNH_2 R_2NH R_3N	$\overset{O}{\overset{\parallel}{R}CH}$	$\overset{O}{\overset{\parallel}{R}CH'}$	$\overset{O}{\overset{\parallel}{R}COH}$	$\overset{O}{\overset{\parallel}{R}COR'}$	$\overset{O}{\overset{\parallel}{R}CNH_2}$ $\overset{O}{\overset{\parallel}{R}CNHR'}$ $\overset{O}{\overset{\parallel}{R}CNR'R''}$	RCN
Specific example	CH_3NH_2	$\overset{O}{\overset{\parallel}{CH_3CH}}$	$\overset{O}{\overset{\parallel}{CH_3CCH_3}}$	$\overset{O}{\overset{\parallel}{CH_3COH}}$	$\overset{O}{\overset{\parallel}{CH_3COCH_3}}$	$\overset{O}{\overset{\parallel}{CH_3CNH_2}}$	$CH_3C\equiv N$
IUPAC name	Methanamine	Ethanal	Propanone	Ethanoic acid	Methyl ethanoate	Ethanamide	Ethanenitrile
Common name	Methylamine	Acetaldehyde	Acetone	Acetic acid	Methyl acetate	Acetamide	Acetonitrile

[a]These names are also accepted by the IUPAC.

2.12A Functional Groups in Biologically Important Compounds

Many of the functional groups we have listed in Table 2.3 are central to the compounds of living organisms. A typical sugar, for example, is glucose. Glucose contains several alcohol hydroxyl groups (— OH) and in one of its forms contains an aldehyde group. Fats and oils contain ester groups, and proteins contain amide groups. See if you can identify alcohol, aldehyde, ester, and amide groups in the following examples.

Glucose

A typical fat

Part of a protein

2.13 PHYSICAL PROPERTIES AND MOLECULAR STRUCTURE

So far, we have said little about one of the most obvious characteristics of organic compounds—that is, *their physical state or phase*. Whether a particular substance is a solid, or a liquid, or a gas would certainly be one of the first observations that we would note in any experimental work. The temperatures at which transitions occur between phases— that is, melting points (mp) and boiling points (bp)—are also among the more easily measured physical properties. Melting points and boiling points are also useful in identifying and isolating organic compounds.

Suppose, for example, we have just carried out the synthesis of an organic compound that is known to be a liquid at room temperature and 1 atm pressure. If we know the boiling point of our desired product and the boiling points of by-products and solvents that may be present in the reaction mixture, we can decide whether or not simple distillation will be a feasible method for isolating our product.

In another instance our product might be a solid. In this case, in order to isolate the substance by crystallization, we need to know its melting point and its solubility in different solvents.

The physical constants of known organic substances are easily found in handbooks and other reference books.* Table 2.4 lists the melting and boiling points of some of the compounds that we have discussed in this chapter.

Often in the course of research, however, the product of a synthesis is a new compound—one that has never been described before. In these instances, success in isolating the new compound depends on making reasonably accurate estimates of its melting point, boiling point, and solubilities. Estimations of these macroscopic physical properties are based on the most likely structure of the substance and on the forces that act between molecules and ions. The temperatures at which phase changes occur are an indication of the strength of these intermolecular forces.

Helpful Hint

Understanding how molecular structure influences physical properties is very useful in practical organic chemistry.

*Two useful handbooks are *Handbook of Chemistry*, Lange, N. A., Ed., McGraw-Hill: New York; and *CRC Handbook of Chemistry and Physics*, CRC: Boca Raton, FL.

TABLE 2.4 PHYSICAL PROPERTIES OF REPRESENTATIVE COMPOUNDS

Compound	Structure	mp (°C)	bp (°C) (1 atm)[a]
Methane	CH_4	−182.6	−162
Ethane	CH_3CH_3	−172	−88.2
Ethene	$CH_2{=}CH_2$	−169	−102
Ethyne	$HC{\equiv}CH$	−82	−84 subl
Chloromethane	CH_3Cl	−97	−23.7
Chloroethane	CH_3CH_2Cl	−138.7	13.1
Ethyl alcohol	CH_3CH_2OH	−114	78.5
Acetaldehyde	CH_3CHO	−121	20
Acetic acid	CH_3CO_2H	16.6	118
Sodium acetate	CH_3CO_2Na	324	dec
Ethylamine	$CH_3CH_2NH_2$	−80	17
Diethyl ether	$(CH_3CH_2)_2O$	−116	34.6
Ethyl acetate	$CH_3CO_2CH_2CH_3$	−84	77

[a]In this table dec = decomposes and subl = sublimes.

2.13A Ionic Compounds: Ion–Ion Forces

- The melting point of a substance is the temperature at which an equilibrium exists between the well-ordered crystalline state and the more random liquid state.

If the substance is an ionic compound, such as sodium acetate (Table 2.4), the ion–ion forces that hold the ions together in the crystalline state are the strong electrostatic lattice forces that act between the positive and negative ions in the orderly crystalline structure. In Fig. 2.6 each sodium ion is surrounded by negatively charged acetate ions, and each acetate ion is surrounded by positive sodium ions. A large amount of thermal energy is required to break up the orderly structure of the crystal into the disorderly open structure of a liquid. As a result, the temperature at which sodium acetate melts is quite high, 324 °C. The boiling points of ionic compounds are higher still, so high that most ionic organic compounds decompose (are changed by undesirable chemical reactions) before they boil. Sodium acetate shows this behavior.

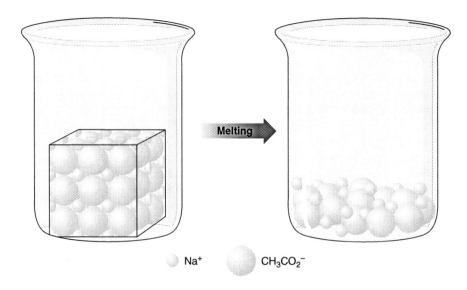

FIGURE 2.6 The melting of sodium acetate.

Na^+ $CH_3CO_2^-$

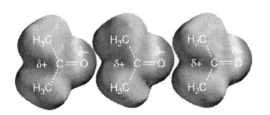

FIGURE 2.7 Electrostatic potential models for acetone molecules that show how acetone molecules might align according to attractions of their partially positive regions and partially negative regions (dipole–dipole interactions).

2.13B Intermolecular Forces (van der Waals Forces)

The forces that act between molecules are not as strong as those between ions, but they account for the fact that even completely nonpolar molecules can exist in liquid and solid states. These intermolecular forces, collectively called **van der Waals forces**, are all electrical in nature. We will focus our attention on three types:

1. Dipole–dipole forces
2. Hydrogen bonds
3. Dispersion forces

Dipole–Dipole Forces Most organic molecules are not fully ionic but have instead a *permanent dipole moment* resulting from a nonuniform distribution of the bonding electrons (Section 2.3). Acetone and acetaldehyde are examples of molecules with permanent dipoles because the carbonyl group that they contain is highly polarized. In these compounds, the attractive forces between molecules are much easier to visualize. In the liquid or solid state, dipole–dipole attractions cause the molecules to orient themselves so that the positive end of one molecule is directed toward the negative end of another (Fig. 2.7).

Hydrogen Bonds

- Very strong dipole–dipole attractions occur between hydrogen atoms bonded to small, strongly electronegative atoms (O, N, or F) and nonbonding electron pairs on other such electronegative atoms. This type of intermolecular force is called a hydrogen bond.

Hydrogen bonds (bond dissociation energies of about 4–38 kJ mol^{-1}) are weaker than ordinary covalent bonds but much stronger than the dipole–dipole interactions that occur above, for example, in acetone.

Hydrogen bonding explains why water, ammonia, and hydrogen fluoride all have far higher boiling points than methane (bp −161.6 °C), even though all four compounds have similar molecular weights.

bp 100 °C   bp 19.5 °C   bp −33.4 °C

Hydrogen bonds are shown by the red dots.

One of the most important consequences of hydrogen bonding is that it causes water to be a liquid rather than a gas at 25 °C. Calculations indicate that in the absence of hydrogen bonding, water would have a boiling point near −80 °C and would not exist as a liquid unless the temperature were lower than that temperature. Had this been the case, it is highly unlikely that life, as we know it, could have developed on the planet Earth.

Hydrogen bonds hold the base pairs of double-stranded DNA together (see Section 25.4). Thymine hydrogen bonds with adenine. Cytosine hydrogen bonds with guanine.

Water molecules associated by attraction of opposite partial charges.

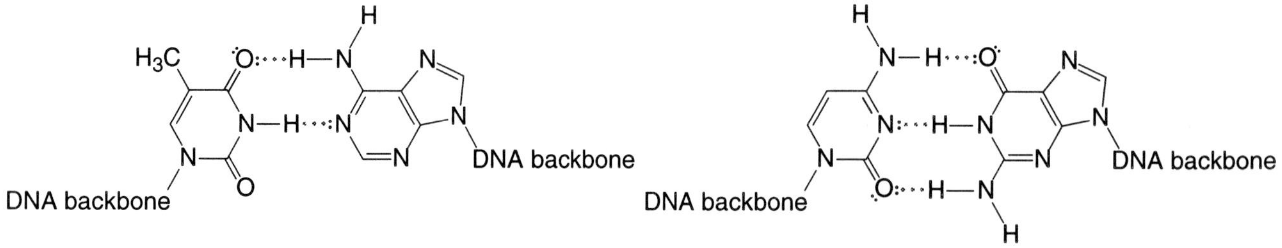

Thymine   **Adenine**   **Cytosine**   **Guanine**

Hydrogen bonding accounts for the fact that ethyl alcohol has a much higher boiling point (78.5 °C) than dimethyl ether (24.9 °C) even though the two compounds have the same molecular weight. Molecules of ethyl alcohol, because they have a hydrogen atom covalently bonded to an oxygen atom, can form strong hydrogen bonds to each other.

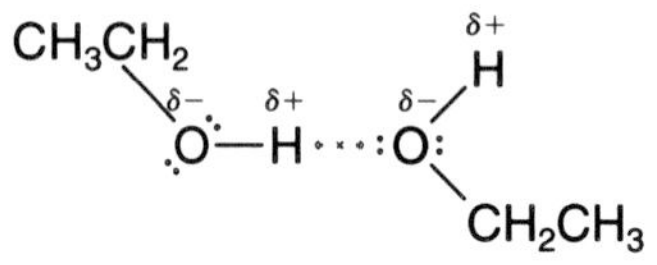

> **The red dots represent a hydrogen bond. Strong hydrogen bonding is limited to molecules having a hydrogen atom attached to an O, N, or F atom.**

Molecules of dimethyl ether, because they lack a hydrogen atom attached to a strongly electronegative atom, cannot form strong hydrogen bonds to each other. In dimethyl ether the intermolecular forces are weaker dipole–dipole interactions.

PRACTICE PROBLEM 2.25 The compounds in each part below have the same (or similar) molecular weights. Which compound in each part would you expect to have the higher boiling point? Explain your answers.

(a) 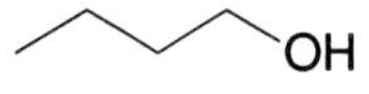 or   (c) or

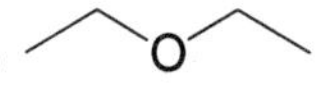

(b) $(CH_3)_3N$ or

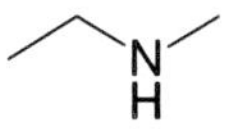

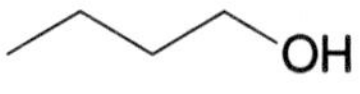

A factor (in addition to polarity and hydrogen bonding) that affects the *melting point* of many organic compounds is the compactness and rigidity of their individual molecules.

* Molecules that are symmetrical generally have abnormally high melting points. *tert*-Butyl alcohol, for example, has a much higher melting point than the other isomeric alcohols shown here:

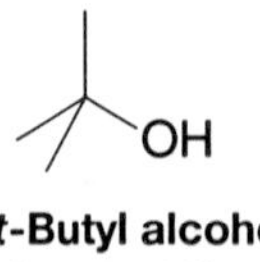

tert-Butyl alcohol   **Butyl alcohol**   **Isobutyl alcohol**   *sec*-Butyl alcohol
(mp 25 °C)   (mp −90 °C)   (mp −108 °C)   (mp −114 °C)

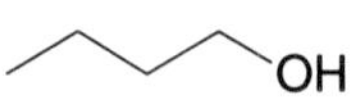

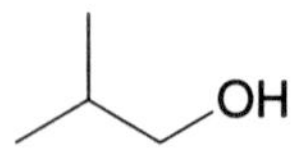

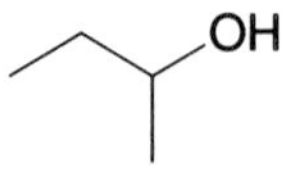

PRACTICE PROBLEM 2.26 Which compound would you expect to have the higher melting point, propane or cyclopropane? Explain your answer.

Dispersion Forces If we consider a substance like methane where the particles are nonpolar molecules, we find that the melting point and boiling point are very low: −182.6 °C and −162 °C, respectively. Instead of asking, "Why does methane melt and boil at low

FIGURE 2.8 Temporary dipoles and induced dipoles in nonpolar molecules resulting from an uneven distribution of electrons at a given instant.

temperatures?" a more appropriate question might be "Why does methane, a nonionic, nonpolar substance, become a liquid or a solid at all?" The answer to this question can be given in terms of attractive intermolecular forces called dispersion forces or London forces.

An accurate account of the nature of dispersion forces requires the use of quantum mechanics. We can, however, visualize the origin of these forces in the following way. The average distribution of charge in a nonpolar molecule (such as methane) over a period of time is uniform. At any given instant, however, *because electrons move*, the electrons and therefore the charge may not be uniformly distributed. Electrons may, in one instant, be slightly accumulated on one part of the molecule, and, as a consequence, *a small temporary dipole will occur* (Fig. 2.8). This temporary dipole in one molecule can induce opposite (attractive) dipoles in surrounding molecules. It does this because the negative (or positive) charge in a portion of one molecule will distort the electron cloud of an adjacent portion of another molecule, causing an opposite charge to develop there. These temporary dipoles change constantly, but the net result of their existence is to produce attractive forces between nonpolar molecules and thus make possible the existence of their liquid and solid states.

Two important factors determine the magnitude of dispersion forces.

1. **The relative polarizability of electrons of the atoms involved**. *By polarizability we mean how easily the electrons respond to a changing electric field*. The electrons of large atoms such as iodine are loosely held and are easily polarized, while the electrons of small atoms such as fluorine are more tightly held and are much less polarizable.

CF_4 and CI_4 are both nonpolar molecules. But if we were to consider the intermolecular forces between two CI_4 molecules, which contain polarizable iodine atoms, we would find that the dispersion forces are much larger than between two CF_4 molecules, which contains fluorine atoms that are not very polarizable.

2. **The relative surface area of the molecules involved**. The larger the surface area, the larger is the overall attraction between molecules caused by dispersion forces. Molecules that are generally longer, flatter, or cylindrical have a greater surface area available for intermolecular interactions than more spherical molecules, and consequently have greater attractive forces between them than the tangential interactions between branched molecules. This is evident when comparing pentane, the unbranched C_5H_{12} hydrocarbon, with neopentane, the most highly branched C_5H_{12} isomer (in which one carbon bears four methyl groups). Pentane has a boiling point of 36.1 °C. Neopentane has a boiling point of 9.5 °C. The difference in their boiling points indicates that the attractive forces between pentane molecules are stronger than between neopentane molecules.

For large molecules, the cumulative effect of these small and rapidly changing dispersion forces can lead to a large net attraction.

2.13C Boiling Points

- The boiling point of a liquid is the temperature at which the vapor pressure of the liquid equals the pressure of the atmosphere above it.

The boiling points of liquids are *pressure dependent*, and boiling points are always reported as occurring at a particular pressure, at 1 atm (or at 760 torr), for example. A substance that boils at 150 °C at 1 atm pressure will boil at a substantially lower temperature if the pressure is reduced to, for example, 0.01 torr (a pressure easily obtained with a vacuum pump). The normal boiling point given for a liquid is its boiling point at 1 atm.

In passing from a liquid to a gaseous state, the individual molecules (or ions) of the substance must separate. Because of this, we can understand why ionic organic compounds often decompose before they boil. The thermal energy required to completely separate (volatilize) the ions is so great that chemical reactions (decompositions) occur first.

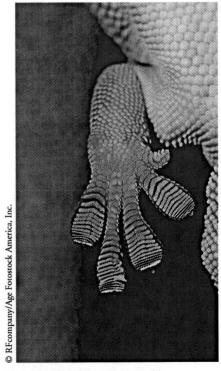

© RFcompany/Age Fotostock America, Inc.

Dispersion forces are what provides a gecko's grip to smooth surfaces.

THE CHEMISTRY OF... Fluorocarbons and Teflon

Fluorocarbons (compounds containing only carbon and fluorine) have extraordinarily low boiling points when compared to hydrocarbons of the same molecular weight. The fluorocarbon C_5F_{12} has a slightly lower boiling point than pentane (C_5H_{12}) even though it has a far higher molecular weight. The important factor in explaining this behavior is the very low polarizability of fluorine atoms that we mentioned earlier, resulting in very small dispersion forces.

The fluorocarbon called *Teflon* $[CF_2CF_2]_n$ (see Section 10.10) has self-lubricating properties that are exploited in making "nonstick" frying pans and lightweight bearings.

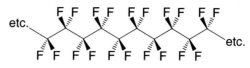

Teflon

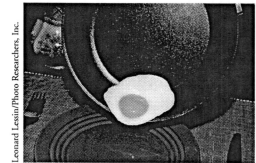

Leonard Lessin/Photo Researchers, Inc.

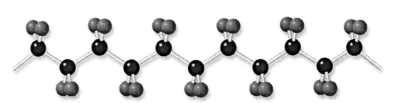

Nonpolar compounds, where the intermolecular forces are very weak, usually boil at low temperatures even at 1 atm pressure. This is not always true, however, because of other factors that we have not yet mentioned: the effects of molecular weight and molecular shape and surface area. Heavier molecules require greater thermal energy in order to acquire velocities sufficiently great to escape the liquid phase, and because the surface areas of larger molecules can be much greater, intermolecular dispersion attractions can also be much larger. These factors explain why nonpolar ethane (bp −88.2 °C) boils higher than methane (bp −162 °C) at a pressure of 1 atm. It also explains why, at 1 atm, the even heavier and larger nonpolar molecule decane ($C_{10}H_{22}$) boils at 174 °C. The relationship between dispersion forces and surface area helps us understand why neopentane (2,2-dimethylpropane) has a lower boiling point (9.5 °C) than pentane (36.1 °C), even though they have the same molecular weight. The branched structure of neopentane allows less surface interaction between neopentane molecules, hence lower dispersion forces, than does the linear structure of pentane.

●●● SOLVED PROBLEM 2.7

Arrange the following compounds according to their expected boiling points, with the lowest boiling point first, and explain your answer. Notice that the compounds have similar molecular weights.

Diethyl ether   **sec-Butyl alcohol**   **Pentane**

STRATEGY AND ANSWER:

pentane $<$ diethyl ether $<$ *sec*-butyl alcohol

Increasing boiling point

Pentane has no polar groups and has only dispersion forces holding its molecules together. It would have the lowest boiling point. Diethyl ether has the polar ether group that provides dipole–dipole forces which are greater than dispersion forces, meaning it would have a higher boiling point than pentane. *sec*-Butyl alcohol has an —OH group that can form strong hydrogen bonds; therefore, it would have the highest boiling point.

● ● ● · · · · · · · · · · · · · · · · · ·

Arrange the following compounds in order of increasing boiling point. Explain your answer in terms of the intermolecular forces in each compound.

PRACTICE PROBLEM 2.27

(a) (b) (c) (d)

2.13D Solubilities

Intermolecular forces are of primary importance in explaining the solubilities of substances. Dissolution of a solid in a liquid is, in many respects, like the melting of a solid. The orderly crystal structure of the solid is destroyed, and the result is the formation of the more disorderly arrangement of the molecules (or ions) in solution. In the process of dissolving, too, the molecules or ions must be separated from each other, and energy must be supplied for both changes. The energy required to overcome lattice energies and intermolecular or interionic attractions comes from the formation of new attractive forces between solute and solvent.

Consider the dissolution of an ionic substance as an example. Here both the lattice energy and interionic attractions are large. We find that water and only a few other very polar solvents are capable of dissolving ionic compounds. These solvents dissolve ionic compounds by **hydrating** or **solvating** the ions (Fig. 2.9).

Water molecules, by virtue of their great polarity as well as their very small, compact shape, can very effectively surround the individual ions as they are freed from the crystal surface. Positive ions are surrounded by water molecules with the negative end of the water dipole pointed toward the positive ion; negative ions are solvated in exactly the opposite way. Because water is highly polar, and because water is capable of forming strong hydrogen bonds, the ion–dipole forces of attraction are also large. The energy supplied by the formation of these forces is great enough to overcome both the lattice energy and interionic attractions of the crystal.

A general rule for solubility is that "like dissolves like" in terms of comparable polarities.

- Polar and ionic solids are usually soluble in polar solvents.
- Polar liquids are usually miscible.
- Nonpolar solids are usually soluble in nonpolar solvents.
- Nonpolar liquids are usually miscible.
- Polar and nonpolar liquids, like oil and water, are usually not soluble to large extents.

> **Helpful Hint**
>
> Your ability to make qualitative predictions regarding solubility will prove very useful in the organic chemistry laboratory.

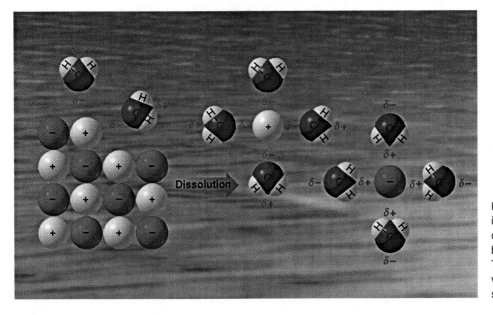

FIGURE 2.9 The dissolution of an ionic solid in water, showing the hydration of positive and negative ions by the very polar water molecules. The ions become surrounded by water molecules in all three dimensions, not just the two shown here.

Methanol and water are miscible in all proportions; so too are mixtures of ethanol and water and mixtures of both propyl alcohols and water. In these cases the alkyl groups of the alcohols are relatively small, and the molecules therefore resemble water more than they do an alkane. Another factor in understanding their solubility is that the molecules are capable of forming strong hydrogen bonds to each other:

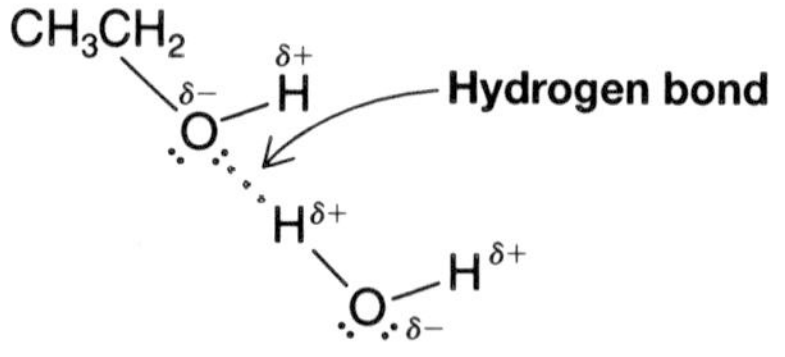

We often describe molecules or parts of molecules as being hydrophilic or hydrophobic. The alkyl groups of methanol, ethanol, and propanol are hydrophobic. Their hydroxyl groups are hydrophilic.

- *Hydrophobic* means incompatible with water (*hydro*, water; *phobic*, fearing or avoiding).
- *Hydrophilic* means compatible with water (*philic*, loving or seeking).

Decyl alcohol, with a chain of 10 carbon atoms, is a compound whose hydrophobic alkyl group overshadows its hydrophilic hydroxyl group in terms of water solubility.

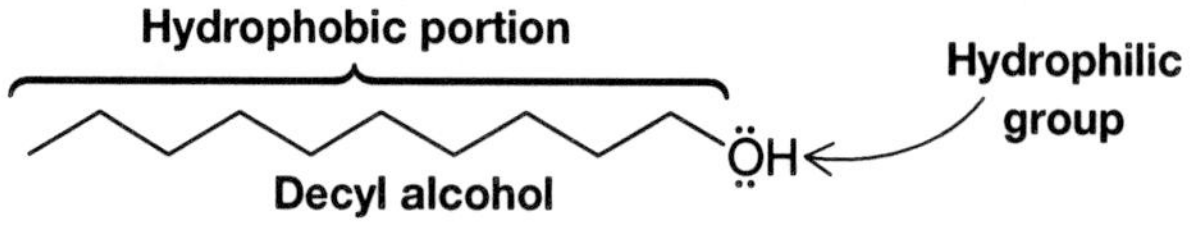

An explanation for why nonpolar groups such as long alkane chains avoid an aqueous environment—that is, for the so-called **hydrophobic effect**—is complex. The most important factor seems to involve an **unfavorable entropy change** in the water. Entropy changes (Section 3.10) have to do with changes from a relatively ordered state to a more disordered one or the reverse. Changes from order to disorder are favorable, whereas changes from disorder to order are unfavorable. For a nonpolar hydrocarbon chain to be accommodated by water, the water molecules have to form a more ordered structure around the chain, and for this, the entropy change is unfavorable.

We will see in Section 23.2C that the presence of a hydrophobic group and a hydrophilic group are essential components of soaps and detergents.

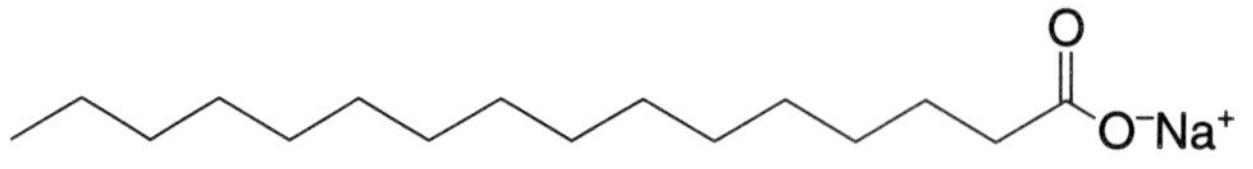

A typical soap molecule

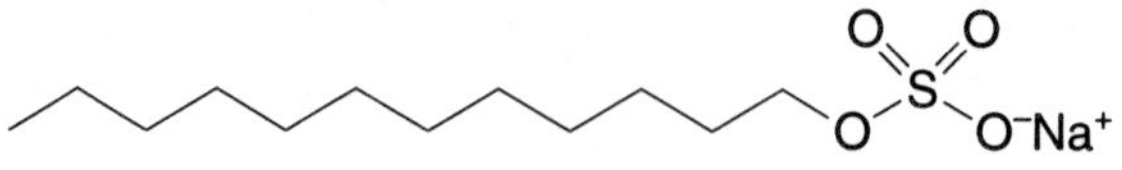

A typical detergent molecule

The hydrophobic long carbon chains of a soap or detergent embed themselves in the oily layer that typically surrounds the thing we want to wash away. The hydrophilic ionic groups at the ends of the chains are then left exposed on the surface and make the surface one that water molecules find attractive. Oil and water don't mix, but now the oily layer looks like something ionic and the water can take it "right down the drain."

2.13E Guidelines for Water Solubility

Organic chemists usually define a compound as water soluble if at least 3 g of the organic compound dissolves in 100 mL of water. We find that for compounds containing one hydrophilic group—and thus capable of forming strong hydrogen bonds—the following approximate guidelines hold: compounds with one to three carbon atoms are water

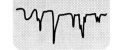

soluble, compounds with four or five carbon atoms are borderline, and compounds with six carbon atoms or more are insoluble.

When a compound contains more than one hydrophilic group, these guidelines do not apply. Polysaccharides (Chapter 22), proteins (Chapter 24), and nucleic acids (Chapter 25) all contain thousands of carbon atoms *and many are water soluble.* They dissolve in water because they also contain thousands of hydrophilic groups.

2.13F Intermolecular Forces in Biochemistry

Later, after we have had a chance to examine in detail the properties of the molecules that make up living organisms, we shall see how intermolecular forces are extremely important in the functioning of cells. Hydrogen bond formation, the hydration of polar groups, and the tendency of nonpolar groups to avoid a polar environment all cause complex protein molecules to fold in precise ways—ways that allow them to function as biological catalysts of incredible efficiency. The same factors allow molecules of hemoglobin to assume the shape needed to transport oxygen. They allow proteins and molecules called lipids to function as cell membranes. Hydrogen bonding gives certain carbohydrates a globular shape that makes them highly efficient food reserves in animals. It gives molecules of other carbohydrates a rigid linear shape that makes them perfectly suited to be structural components in plants.

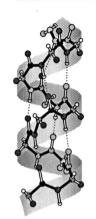

Hydrogen bonding
(red dotted lines) in
the α-helix structure
of proteins

(Illustration, Irving Geis. Image from the Irving Geis Collection, HHMI. Rights owned by Howard Hughes Medical Institute. Not to be reproduced without permission.)

2.14 SUMMARY OF ATTRACTIVE ELECTRIC FORCES

The attractive forces occurring between molecules and ions that we have studied so far are summarized in Table 2.5.

TABLE 2.5 ATTRACTIVE ELECTRIC FORCES			
Electric Force	**Relative Strength**	**Type**	**Example**
Cation–anion (in a crystal)	Very strong		Sodium chloride crystal lattice
Covalent bonds	Strong (140–523 kJ mol^{-1})	Shared electron pairs	H—H (436 kJ mol^{-1}) CH_3—CH_3 (378 kJ mol^{-1}) I—I (151 kJ mol^{-1})
Ion–dipole	Moderate		Na^+ in water (see Fig. 2.9)
Hydrogen bonds	Moderate to weak (4–38 kJ mol^{-1})	$-\overset{\delta-}{Z}:\cdots\overset{\delta+}{H}-$	
Dipole–dipole	Weak	$\overset{\delta+}{C}\overset{\delta-}{H_3Cl}\cdots\overset{\delta+}{C}\overset{\delta-}{H_3Cl}$	
Dispersion	Variable	Transient dipole	Interactions between methane molecules

THE CHEMISTRY OF... Organic Templates Engineered to Mimic Bone Growth

Intermolecular forces play a myriad of roles in life and in the world around us. Intermolecular forces hold together the strands of our DNA, provide structure to our cell membranes, cause the feet of gecko lizards to stick to walls and ceilings, keep water from boiling at room temperature and ordinary pressure, and literally provide the adhesive forces that hold our cells, bones, and tissues together. As these examples show, the world around us provides exquisite instruction in nanotechnology and bioengineering, and scientists throughout the ages have been inspired to create and innovate based on nature. One target of recent research in bioengineering is the development of synthetic materials that mimic nature's template for bone growth. A synthetic material with bone-promoting properties could be used to help repair broken bones, offset osteoporosis, and treat bone cancer.

Both natural bone growth and the synthetic system under development depend strongly on intermolecular forces. In living systems, bones grow by adhesion of specialized cells to a long fibrous natural template called collagen. Certain functional groups along the collagen promote the binding of bone-growing cells, while other functional groups facilitate calcium crystallization. Chemists at Northwestern University (led by S. I. Stupp) have engineered a molecule that can be made in the laboratory and that mimics this process. The molecule shown below spontaneously self-assembles into a long tubular aggregate, imitating the fibers of collagen. Dispersion forces between hydrophobic alkyl tails on the molecule cause self-assembly of the molecules into tubules. At the other end of the molecule, the researchers included functional groups that promote cell binding and still other functional groups that encourage calcium crystallization. Lastly, they included functional groups that allow one molecule to be covalently linked to its neighbors after the self-assembly process has occurred, thus adding further stabilization to the initially noncovalent structure. Designing all of these features into the molecular structure has paid off, because the self-assembled fiber promotes calcium crystallization along its axis, much like nature's collagen template. This example of molecular design is just one exciting development at the intersection of nanotechnology and bioengineering.

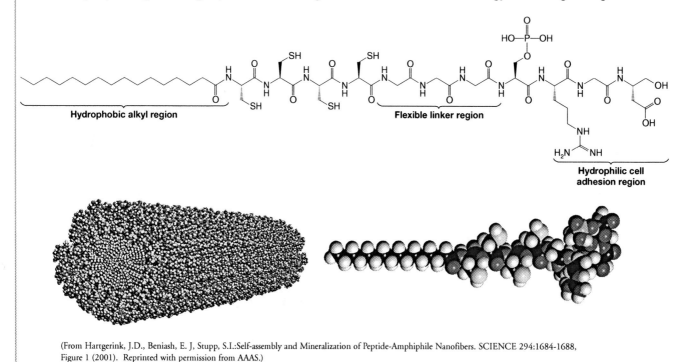

Hydrophobic alkyl region
Flexible linker region
Hydrophilic cell adhesion region

(From Hartgerink, J.D., Beniash, E. J, Stupp, S.I.:Self-assembly and Mineralization of Peptide-Amphiphile Nanofibers. SCIENCE 294:1684-1688, Figure 1 (2001). Reprinted with permission from AAAS.)

2.15 INFRARED SPECTROSCOPY: AN INSTRUMENTAL METHOD FOR DETECTING FUNCTIONAL GROUPS

Infrared (IR) spectroscopy is a simple, rapid, and nondestructive instrumental technique that can give evidence for the presence of various functional groups. If you had a sample of unknown identity, among the first things you would do is obtain an infrared spectrum, along with determining its solubility in common solvents and its melting and/or boiling point.

Infrared spectroscopy, as with all forms of spectroscopy, depends on the interaction of molecules or atoms with electromagnetic radiation. Infrared radiation causes atoms and groups of atoms of organic compounds to vibrate with increased amplitude about the

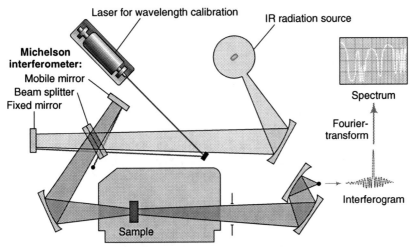

Laser for wavelength calibration   IR radiation source

Michelson interferometer:
Mobile mirror
Beam splitter
Fixed mirror

Spectrum

Fourier-transform

Interferogram

Sample

(Diagram adapted from the computer program IR Tutor, Columbia University.)

FIGURE 2.10 A diagram of a Fourier transform infrared (FTIR) spectrometer. FTIR spectrometers employ a Michelson interferometer, which splits the radiation beam from the IR source so that it reflects simultaneously from a moving mirror and a fixed mirror, leading to interference. After the beams recombine, they pass through the sample to the detector and are recorded as a plot of time versus signal intensity, called an interferogram. The overlapping wavelengths and the intensities of their respective absorptions are then converted to a spectrum by applying a mathematical operation called a Fourier transform.

The FTIR method eliminates the need to scan slowly over a range of wavelengths, as was the case with older types of instruments called dispersive IR spectrometers, and therefore FTIR spectra can be acquired very quickly. The FTIR method also allows greater throughput of IR energy. The combination of these factors gives FTIR spectra strong signals as compared to background noise (i.e., a high signal to noise ratio) because radiation throughput is high and rapid scanning allows multiple spectra to be averaged in a short period of time. The result is enhancement of real signals and cancellation of random noise.

covalent bonds that connect them. (Infrared radiation is not of sufficient energy to excite electrons, as is the case when some molecules interact with visible, ultraviolet, or higher energy forms of light.) Since the functional groups of organic molecules include specific arrangements of bonded atoms, absorption of IR radiation by an organic molecule will occur at specific frequencies characteristic of the types of bonds and atoms present in the specific functional groups of that molecule. These vibrations are *quantized*, and as they occur, the compounds absorb IR energy in particular regions of the IR portion of the spectrum.

An infrared spectrometer (Fig. 2.10) operates by passing a beam of IR radiation through a sample and comparing the radiation transmitted through the sample with that transmitted in the absence of the sample. Any frequencies absorbed by the sample will be apparent by the difference. The spectrometer plots the results as a graph showing absorbance versus frequency or wavelength.

● The position of an absorption band (peak) in an IR spectrum is specified in units of wavenumbers ($\bar{v}$).

Wavenumbers are the reciprocal of wavelength when wavelength is expressed in centimeters (the unit is cm^{-1}), and therefore give the number of wave cycles per centimeter. The larger the wavenumber, the higher is the frequency of the wave, and correspondingly the higher is the frequency of the bond absorption. IR absorptions are sometimes, though less commonly, reported in terms of wavelength (λ), in which case the units are micrometers (μm; old name micron, μ). Wavelength is the distance from crest to crest of a wave.

$$\bar{v} = \frac{1}{\lambda} \text{ (with } \lambda \text{ in cm)} \qquad \text{or} \qquad \bar{v} = \frac{10.000}{\lambda} \text{ (with } \lambda \text{ in } \mu\text{m)}$$

In their vibrations covalent bonds behave as if they were tiny springs connecting the atoms. When the atoms vibrate, they can do so only at certain frequencies, as if the bonds were "tuned." Because of this, covalently bonded atoms have only particular vibrational energy levels; that is, the levels are quantized.

The excitation of a molecule from one vibrational energy level to another occurs only when the compound absorbs IR radiation of a particular energy, meaning a particular wavelength or frequency. Note that the energy (E) of absorption is directly proportional to the frequency of radiation (v) because $\Delta E = hv$, and inversely proportional to the wavelength (λ) because $\dfrac{c}{\lambda}$, and therefore $\Delta E = \dfrac{hc}{\lambda}$.

Molecules can vibrate in a variety of ways. Two atoms joined by a covalent bond can undergo a stretching vibration where the atoms move back and forth as if joined by a spring. Three atoms can also undergo a variety of stretching and bending vibrations.

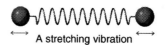

A stretching vibration

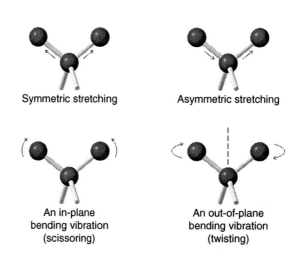

Symmetric stretching   Asymmetric stretching

An in-plane   An out-of-plane
bending vibration   bending vibration
(scissoring)   (twisting)

The *frequency* of a given stretching vibration *in an IR spectrum* can be related to two factors. These are *the masses of the bonded atoms*—light atoms vibrate at higher frequencies than heavier ones—*and the relative stiffness of the bond.* (These factors are accounted for in Hooke's law, a relationship you may study in introductory physics.) Triple bonds are stiffer (and vibrate at higher frequencies) than double bonds, and double bonds are stiffer (and vibrate at higher frequencies) than single bonds. We can see some of these effects in Table 2.6. Notice that stretching frequencies of groups involving hydrogen (a light atom) such as C—H, N—H, and O—H all occur at relatively high frequencies:

GROUP	BOND	FREQUENCY RANGE (cm^{-1})
Alkyl	C—H	2853–2962
Alcohol	O—H	3590–3650
Amine	N—H	3300–3500

Notice, too, that triple bonds vibrate at higher frequencies than double bonds:

GROUP	BOND	FREQUENCY RANGE (cm^{-1})
Alkyne	C≡C	2100–2260
Nitrile	C≡N	2220–2260
Alkene	C=C	1620–1680
Carbonyl	C=O	1630–1780

● Not all molecular vibrations result in the absorption of IR energy. *In order for a vibration to occur with the absorption of IR energy, the dipole moment of the molecule must change as the vibration occurs.*

TABLE 2.6 CHARACTERISTIC INFRARED ABSORPTIONS OF GROUPS

Group	Frequency Range (cm^{-1})		Intensity[a]
A. Alkyl			
C—H (stretching)		2853–2962	(m–s)
Isopropyl, —CH(CH$_3$)$_2$		1380–1385	(s)
	and	1365–1370	(s)
tert-Butyl, —C(CH$_3$)$_3$		1385–1395	(m)
	and	~1365	(s)
B. Alkenyl			
C—H (stretching)		3010–3095	(m)
C=C (stretching)		1620–1680	(v)
R—CH=CH$_2$		985–1000	(s)
	and	905–920	(s)
R$_2$C=CH$_2$ (out-of-plane C—H bendings)		880–900	(s)
cis-RCH=CHR		675–730	(s)
trans-RCH=CHR		960–975	(s)
C. Alkynyl			
≡C—H (stretching)		~3300	(s)
C≡C (stretching)		2100–2260	(v)
D. Aromatic			
Ar—H (stretching)		~3030	(v)
C=C (stretching)		1450–1600	(m)
Aromatic substitution type (C—H out-of-plane bendings)			
Monosubstituted		690–710	(very s)
	and	730–770	(very s)
o-Disubstituted		735–770	(s)
m-Disubstituted		680–725	(s)
	and	750–810	(very s)
p-Disubstituted		800–860	(very s)
E. Alcohols, Phenols, and Carboxylic Acids			
O—H (stretching)			
Alcohols, phenols (dilute solutions)		3590–3650	(sharp, v)
Alcohols, phenols (hydrogen bonded)		3200–3550	(broad, s)
Carboxylic acids (hydrogen bonded)		2500–3000	(broad, v)
F. Ethers, Alcohols, and Esters			
C—O (stretching)		1020–1275	(s)
G. Aldehydes, Ketones, Esters, Carboxylic Acids, and Amides			
C=O (stretching)		1630–1780	(s)
Aldehydes		1690–1740	(s)
Ketones		1680–1750	(s)
Esters		1735–1750	(s)
Carboxylic acids		1710–1780	(s)
Amides		1630–1690	(s)
H. Amines			
N—H		3300–3500	(m)
I. Nitriles			
C≡N		2220–2260	(m)

[a]Abbreviations: s = strong, m = medium, w = weak, v = variable, ~ = approximately.

Thus, methane does not absorb IR energy for symmetric streching of the four C—H bonds; asymmetric stretching, on the other hand, does lead to an IR absorption. Symmetrical vibrations of the carbon–carbon double and triple bonds of ethene and ethyne do not result in the absorption of IR radiation, either.

••• SOLVED PROBLEM 2.8

The infrared spectrum of l-hexyne shows a sharp absorption peak near 2100 cm^{-1} due to stretching of its triple bond. However, 3-hexyne shows no absorption in that region. Explain.

1-Hexyne   **3-Hexyne**

STRATEGY AND ANSWER: For an infrared absorption to occur there must be a change in the dipole moment of the molecule during the stretching process. Since 3-hexyne is symmetrical about its triple bond, there is no change in its dipole moment as stretching takes place, hence there is no IR absorption from the triple bond.

Vibrational absorption may occur outside the region measured by a particular IR spectrometer, and vibrational absorptions may occur so closely together that peaks fall on top of peaks.

Other factors bring about even more absorption peaks. Overtones (harmonics) of fundamental absorption bands may be seen in IR spectra even though these overtones occur with greatly reduced intensity. Bands called combination bands and difference bands also appear in IR spectra.

Because IR spectra of even relatively simple compounds contain so many peaks, the possibility that two different compounds will have the same IR spectrum is exceedingly small. It is because of this that an IR spectrum has been called the "fingerprint" of a molecule. Thus, with organic compounds, if two pure samples give different IR spectra, one can be certain that they are different compounds. If they give the same IR spectrum, then they are very likely to be the same compound.

2.16 INTERPRETING IR SPECTRA

IR spectra contain a wealth of information about the structures of compounds. We show some of the information that can be gathered from the spectra of octane and methylbenzene (commonly called toluene) in Figs. 2.11 and 2.12. In this section we shall learn how

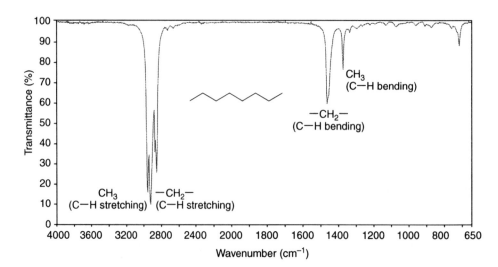

FIGURE 2.11 The IR spectrum of octane. (Notice that, in IR spectra, the peaks are usually measured in % transmittance. Thus, the peak at 2900 cm^{-1} has 10% transmittance—that is, an absorbance, A, of 0.90.)

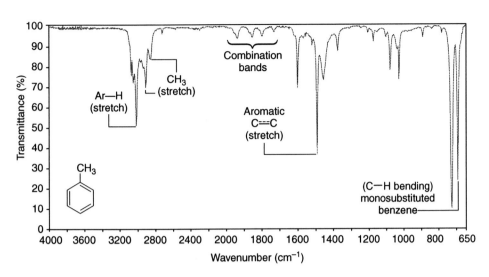

FIGURE 2.12 The IR spectrum of methylbenzene (toluene).

to recognize the presence of characteristic IR absorption peaks that result from vibrations of alkyl and functional groups. The data given in Table 2.6 will provide us with key information to use when correlating actual spectra with IR absorption frequencies that are typical for various groups.

2.16A Infrared Spectra of Hydrocarbons

- All hydrocarbons give absorption peaks in the 2800–3300-cm^{-1} region that are associated with carbon–hydrogen stretching vibrations.

We can use these peaks in interpreting IR spectra because the exact location of the peak depends on the strength (and stiffness) of the C—H bond, which in turn depends on the hybridization state of the carbon that bears the hydrogen. The C—H bonds involving sp-hybridized carbon are strongest and those involving sp^3-hybridized carbon are weakest. The order of bond strength is

$$sp > sp^2 > sp^3$$

This, too, is the order of the bond stiffness.

- The carbon–hydrogen stretching peaks of hydrogen atoms attached to sp-hybridized carbon atoms occur at highest frequencies, about 3300 cm^{-1}.

The carbon–hydrogen bond of a terminal alkyne ($\equiv$C—H) gives an absorption in the 3300-cm^{-1} region. We can see the absorption of the acetylenic (alkynyl) C—H bond of 1-heptyne at 3320 cm^{-1} in Fig. 2.13.

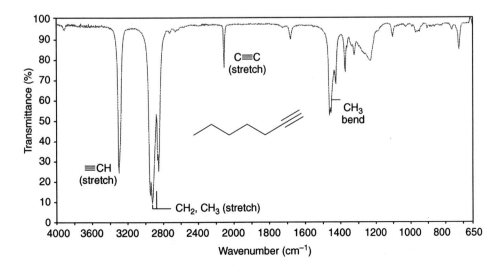

FIGURE 2.13 The IR spectrum of 1-heptyne.

FIGURE 2.14 The IR spectrum of 1-octene.

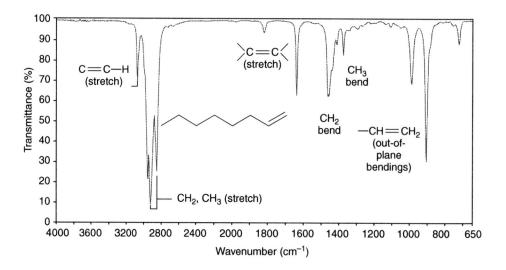

- The carbon–hydrogen stretching peaks of hydrogen atoms attached to sp^2-hybridized carbon atoms occur in the 3000–3100-cm^{-1} region.

Thus, alkenyl C—H bonds and the C—H groups of aromatic rings give absorption peaks in this region. We can see the alkenyl C—H absorption peak at 3080 cm^{-1} in the spectrum of 1-octene (Fig. 2.14), and we can see the C—H absorption of the aromatic hydrogen atoms at 3090 cm^{-1} in the spectrum of methylbenzene (Fig. 2.12).

- The carbon–hydrogen stretching bands of hydrogen atoms attached to sp^3-hybridized carbon atoms occur at lowest frequencies, in the 2800–3000-cm^{-1} region.

We can see methyl and methylene absorption peaks in the spectra of octane (Fig. 2.11), methylbenzene (Fig. 2.12), 1-heptyne (Fig. 2.13), and 1-octene (Fig. 2.14).

Hydrocarbons also give absorption peaks in their IR spectra that result from carbon–carbon bond stretchings. Carbon–carbon single bonds normally give rise to very weak peaks that are usually of little use in assigning structures. More useful peaks arise from carbon–carbon multiple bonds, however.

- Carbon–carbon double bonds give absorption peaks in the 1620–1680-cm^{-1} region, and carbon–carbon triple bonds give absorption peaks between 2100 and 2260 cm^{-1}.

These absorptions are not usually strong ones, and they are absent if the double or triple bond is symmetrically substituted. (No dipole moment change will be associated with the vibration.) The stretchings of the carbon–carbon bonds of benzene rings usually give a set of characteristic sharp peaks in the 1450–1600-cm^{-1} region.

- Absorptions arising from carbon–hydrogen bending vibrations of alkenes occur in the 600–1000-cm^{-1} region. With the aid of a spectroscopy handbook, the exact location of these peaks can often be used as evidence for the ***substitution pattern of the double bond and its configuration.***

Helpful Hint

IR spectroscopy is an exceedingly useful tool for detecting functional groups.

2.16B IR Spectra of Some Functional Groups Containing Heteroatoms

Infrared spectroscopy gives us an invaluable method for recognizing quickly and simply the presence of certain functional groups in a molecule.

Carbonyl Functional Groups One important functional group that gives a prominent absorption peak in IR spectra is the **carbonyl group**, C=O. This group is present in aldehydes, ketones, esters, carboxylic acids, amides, and others.

- The carbon–oxygen double-bond stretching frequency of carbonyl groups gives a strong peak between 1630 and 1780 cm^{-1}.

The exact location of the absorption depends on whether it arises from an aldehyde, ketone, ester, and so forth.

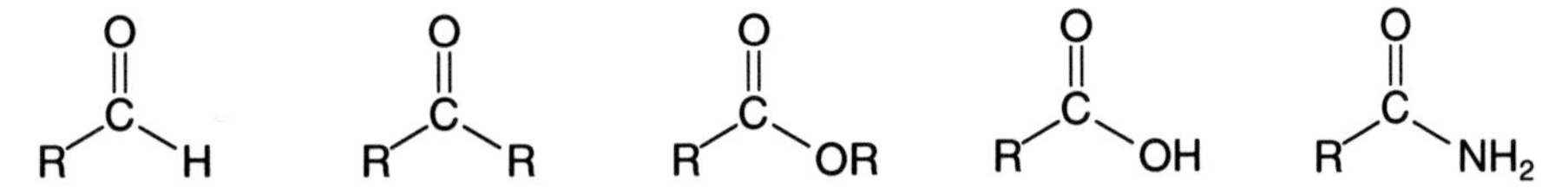

Aldehyde	Ketone	Ester	Carboxylic acid	Amide
$1690–1740\ cm^{-1}$	$1680–1750\ cm^{-1}$	$1735–1750\ cm^{-1}$	$1710–1780\ cm^{-1}$	$1630–1690\ cm^{-1}$

••• SOLVED PROBLEM 2.9

A compound with the molecular formula $C_4H_4O_2$ has a strong sharp absorbance near $3300\ cm^{-1}$, absorbances in the $2800–3000$-cm^{-1} region, and a sharp absorbance peak near $2200\ cm^{-1}$. It also has a strong broad absorbance in the $2500–3600$-cm^{-1} region and a strong peak in the $1710–1780$-cm^{-1} region. Propose a possible structure for the compound.

STRATEGY AND ANSWER: The sharp peak near $3300\ cm^{-1}$ is likely to arise from the stretching of a hydrogen attached to the sp-hybridized carbon of a triple bond. The sharp peak near $2200\ cm^{-1}$, where the triple bond of an alkyne stretches, is consistent with this. The peaks in the $2800–3000$-cm^{-1} region suggest stretchings of the C—H bonds of alkyl groups, either CH_2 or CH_3 groups. The strong, broad absorbance in the $2500–3600$-cm^{-1} region suggests a hydroxyl group arising from a carboxylic acid. The strong peak around $1710–1780\ cm^{-1}$ is consistent with this since it could arise from the carbonyl group of a carboxylic acid. Putting all this together with the molecular formula suggests the compound is as shown at the right.

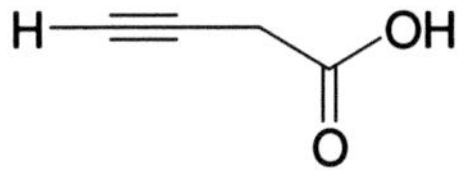

•••• PRACTICE PROBLEM 2.28

Use arguments based on resonance and electronegativity effects to explain the trend in carbonyl IR stretching frequencies from higher frequency for esters and carboxylic acids to lower frequencies for amides. (*Hint:* Use the range of carbonyl stretching frequencies for aldehydes and ketones as the "base" frequency range of an unsubstituted carbonyl group and consider the influence of electronegative atoms on the carbonyl group and/or atoms that alter the resonance hybrid of the carbonyl.) What does this suggest about the way the nitrogen atom influences the distribution of electrons in an amide carbonyl group?

Alcohols and Phenols The **hydroxyl groups** of alcohols and phenols are also easy to recognize in IR spectra by their O—H stretching absorptions. These bonds also give us direct evidence for hydrogen bonding (Section 2.13B).

- The IR absorption of an alcohol or phenol O—H group is in the $3200–3550$-cm^{-1} range, and most often it is broad.

The typical broadness of the peak is due to association of the molecules through hydrogen bonding (Section 2.13B), which causes a wider distribution of stretching frequencies for the O—H bond. If an alcohol or phenol is present as a very dilute solution in a solvent that cannot contribute to hydrogen bonding (e.g., CCl_4), O—H absorption occurs as a very sharp peak in the $3590–3650$-cm^{-1} region. In very dilute solution in such a solvent or in the gas phase, formation of intermolecular hydrogen bonds does not take place because molecules of the analyte are too widely separated. A sharp peak in the $3590–3650$-cm^{-1} region, therefore, is attributed to "free" (unassociated) hydroxyl groups. Increasing the concentration of the alcohol or phenol causes the sharp peak to be replaced by a broad band in the $3200–3550$-cm^{-1} region. Hydroxyl absorptions in IR spectra of cyclohexylcarbinol (cyclohexylmethanol) run in dilute and concentrated solutions (Fig. 2.15) exemplify these effects.

FIGURE 2.15 (a) The IR spectrum of an alcohol (cyclohexyl-carbinol) in a dilute solution shows the sharp absorption of a "free" (non-hydrogen-bonded) hydroxyl group at 3600 cm^{-1}. (b) The IR spectrum of the same alcohol as a concentrated solution shows a broad hydroxyl group absorption at 3300 cm^{-1} due to hydrogen bonding. (Reprinted with permission of John Wiley & Sons, Inc. From Silverstein, R., and Webster, F. X., *Spectrometric Identification of Organic Compounds*, Sixth Edition, p. 89. Copyright 1998.)

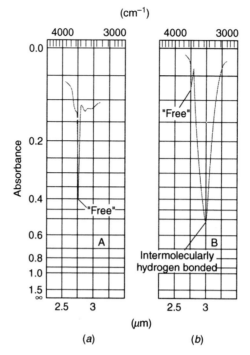

Carboxylic Acids The **carboxylic acid group** can also be detected by IR spectroscopy. If both carbonyl and hydroxyl stretching absorptions are present in an IR spectrum, there is good evidence for a carboxylic acid functional group (although it is possible that isolated carbonyl and hydroxyl groups could be present in the molecule).

* The hydroxyl absorption of a carboxylic acid is often very broad, extending from 3600 cm^{-1} to 2500 cm^{-1}.

Figure 2.16 shows the IR spectrum of propanoic acid.

Amines IR spectroscopy also gives evidence for N—H bonds (see Figure 2.17).

* Primary (1°) and secondary (2°) amines give absorptions of moderate strength in the 3300–3500-cm^{-1} region.
* Primary amines exhibit two peaks in this region due to symmetric and asymmetric stretching of the two N—H bonds.
* Secondary amines exhibit a single peak.
* Tertiary amines show no N—H absorption because they have no such bond.
* A basic pH is evidence for any class of amine.

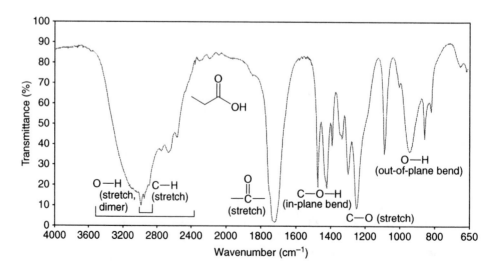

FIGURE 2.16 The IR spectrum of propanoic acid.

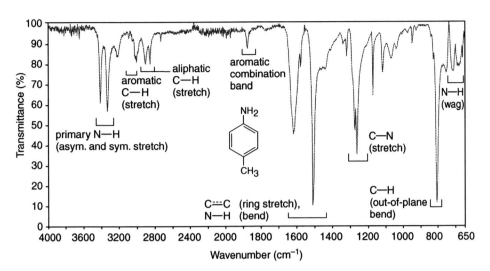

FIGURE 2.17 Annotated IR spectrum of 4-methylaniline.

 RNH₂ (1° Amine)

Two peaks in 3300–3500-cm⁻¹ region

Symmetric stretching   Asymmetric stretching

 R₂NH (2° Amine)

One peak in 3300–3500-cm⁻¹ region

Hydrogen bonding causes N—H stretching peaks of 1° and 2° amines to broaden. The NH groups of **amides** give similar absorption peaks and include a carbonyl absorption as well.

●●● SOLVED PROBLEM 2.10

What key peaks would you expect to find in the IR spectrum of the following compound?

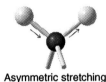

STRATEGY AND ANSWER: The compound is an amide. We should expect a strong peak in the 1630–1690 cm⁻¹ region arising from the carbonyl group and a single peak of moderate strength in the 3300–3500 cm⁻¹ region for the N—H group.

HOW TO INTERPRET AN IR SPECTRUM WITHOUT ANY KNOWLEDGE OF THE STRUCTURE

IR spectroscopy is an incredibly powerful tool for functional group identification, as we have seen in the preceding sections. However, in introducing this technique, we have explored IR spectra from the perspective of compounds of known structure, explaining the peaks observed in reference to each critical grouping of atoms that we know to be present. In the real world, one often encounters brand new materials of unknown structure. How IR can help in this scenario is something that a forensics scientist or natural products isolation chemist might need to worry about on a daily basis.

We certainly cannot use IR spectroscopy by itself to determine complete structure (techniques in Chapter 9 will help with that problem), but an IR spectrum can often point toward the presence of certain functional groups if one pays particular attention to signals whose peak positions are distinct from other groups and is consistently strong enough to be observed. The latter is an important consideration as there can be variations in signal strength for certain groups dependent on what other groups are in the molecule, and some signals overlap with others, making a definitive assignment impossible. For example, most organic molecules contain C—H bonds in one form or another, so peaks below 1450 cm^{-1} and signals in the range 2800–3000 cm^{-1} are not particularly definitive other than to indicate that the molecule is organic and contains C—H bonds.

Here are some examples of what one might consider in a first-pass assessment of any IR spectrum to generate what are likely to be correct answers about some of the functional groups that are present:

- Only C=O stretches tend to have a tight, strong absorbance in the 1630–1780 cm^{-1} range. We may not be able to identify what kind of carbonyl group is present, but we can tell that there is at least one carbonyl group.

- Only the stretches of nitrile or alkyne bonds tend to appear between 2000 and 2300 cm^{-1}, so these can be fairly readily assigned.

- Only hydroxyl groups as in alcohols or carboxylic acids tend to create a large and broad signal at about 3300 cm^{-1}; these groups are easy to identify assuming the sample is not contaminated with water.

- Only amines tend to produce broad but smaller peaks than hydroxyl peaks around 3300 cm^{-1}. The number of those peaks can sometimes tell if there is one or two hydrogens attached to that nitrogen atom.

The examples below allow us to put these general principles into practice.

The IR spectrum of Unknown 1 (Fig. 2.18) has broad signals centered around 3300 cm^{-1} and a medium absorption at 2250 cm^{-1}. Based on the information above, we can surmise that the molecule likely contains a hydroxyl group and a group with a triple bond. Most likely the triply-bonded group is a nitrile since nitriles tend to appear at about 2250 cm^{-1}, whereas alkynes appear slightly lower at around 2000 cm^{-1}. We cannot be strictly sure that it is a nitrile, but that would be a good hypothesis in the absence of any other chemical evidence. Indeed, this turns out to be correct, as the molecule is 3-hydroxypropionitrile in this case.

In the IR spectrum of Unknown 2 (Fig. 2.19) there is a hydroxyl absorption once again centered around 3300 cm^{-1}, as well as a carbonyl peak at 1705 cm^{-1}. And, although we cannot always tell what kind of carbonyl is present, when the hydroxyl peak is extremely broad and has a ragged appearance (due to overlap of the C—H absorptions that extend below it, in contrast to the first spectrum where the hydroxyl was smooth, it is usually safe to assume that this hydroxyl group is attached to the

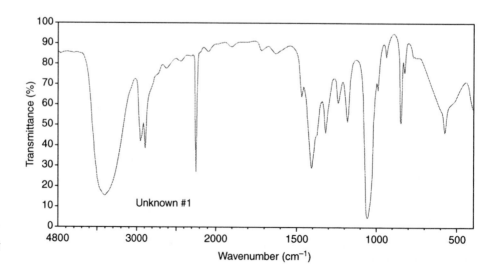

FIGURE 2.18 The IR Spectrum of Unknown 1. (SDBS, National Institute of Advanced Industrial Science and Technology)

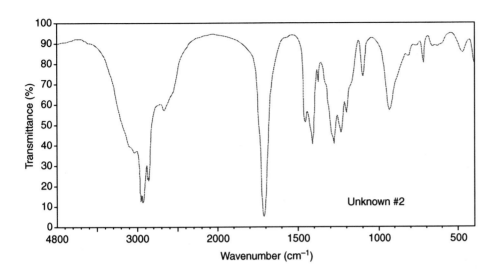

FIGURE 2.19 The IR Spectrum of Unknown 2. (SDBS, National Institute of Advanced Industrial Science and Technology)

carbonyl group; thus, these two groups are together part of a carboxylic acid functional group. Once again, we were able to identify the key functional group of the molecule since this is heptanoic acid.

2.17 APPLICATIONS OF BASIC PRINCIPLES

We now review how certain basic principles apply to phenomena that we have studied in this chapter.

Polar Bonds Are Caused by Electronegativity Differences We saw in Section 2.2 that when atoms with different electronegativities are covalently bonded, the more electronegative atom will be negatively charged and the less electronegative atom will be positively charged. The bond will be a *polar bond* and it will have a *dipole moment*.

Dipole moments are important in explaining physical properties of molecules (as we shall review below), and in explaining infrared spectra. For a vibration to occur with the absorption of IR energy, the dipole moment of the molecule must change during the course of the vibration.

Opposite Charges Attract This principle is central to understanding physical properties of organic compounds (Section 2.13). All of the forces that operate between individual molecules (and thereby affect boiling points, melting points, and solubilities) are between oppositely charged molecules (ions) or between oppositely charged portions of molecules. Examples are ion–ion forces (Section 2.13A) that exist between oppositely charged ions in crystals of ionic compounds, dipole–dipole forces (Section 2.13B) that exist between oppositely charged portions of polar molecules and that include the very strong dipole–dipole forces that we call *hydrogen bonds*, and the weak *dispersion* or *London forces* that exist between portions of molecules that bear small temporary opposite charges.

Molecular Structure Determines Properties We learned in Section 2.13 how physical properties are related to molecular structure.

[WHY Do These Topics Matter?

VANCOMYCIN AND ANTIBIOTIC RESISTANCE

Just as hydrogen bonds are critical in the pairing of nucleotides, they also play a major role in how one of the world's most powerful antibiotics kills bacteria. That antibiotic is vancomycin, a compound first isolated in 1956 by scientists at the Eli Lilly pharmaceutical company from the fermentation broth of a microbe found in the jungles of Borneo. Its name was derived from the verb "to vanquish," because it could kill every strain of gram-positive bacteria thrown at it, including the deadly strain known as MRSA (for methicillin-resistant *Staphylococcus aureus*), one of the so-called flesh-eating bacteria.

Vancomycin's success is due to its structure, a carefully designed arrangement of atoms that allows it to attack diverse bacterial strains. As bacteria move about their hosts, their cell walls are constantly being assembled and disassembled. Vancomycin targets one particular peptide sequence found on the surface of the cell walls, forming a network of five specific hydrogen bonds that allows it to lock onto the bacterium. These bonds are shown as dashed lines in the structures below. Once attached to vancomycin, bacteria can no longer build and strengthen their cell walls, leading to eventual lysis of the cell membrane and their death.

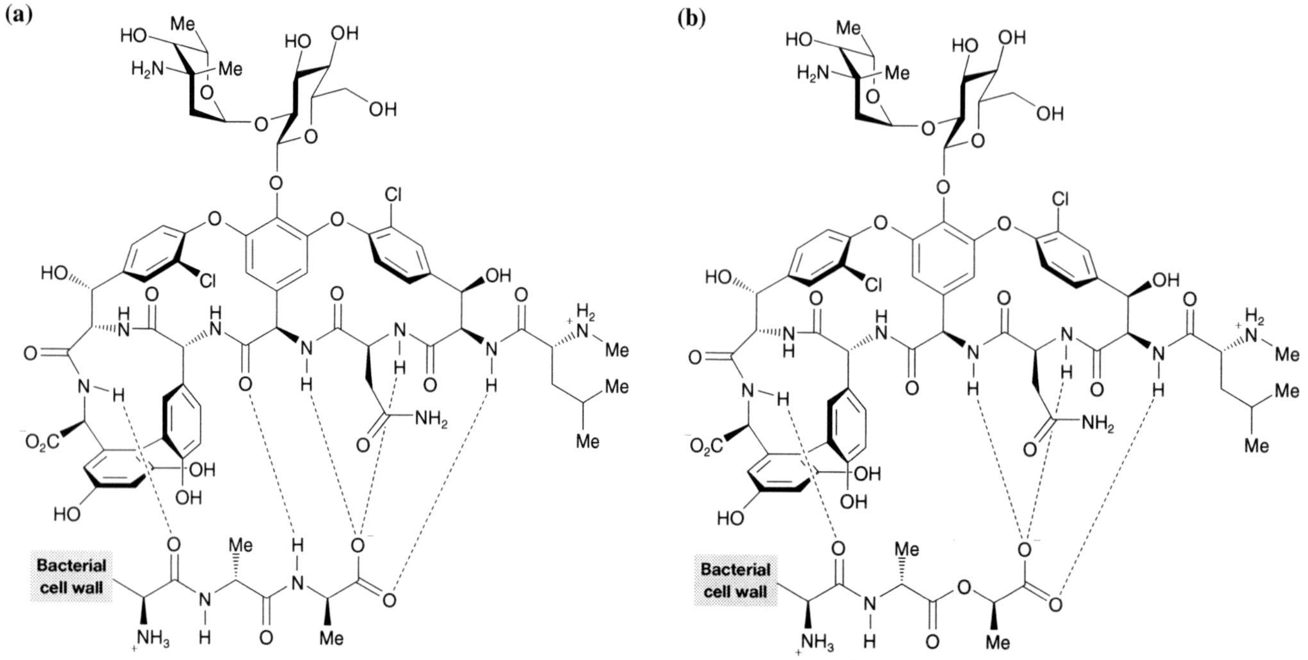

(a)

Vancomycin-susceptible bacteria

(b)

Vancomycin-resistant bacteria

Unfortunately, while vancomycin has proven effective for many decades in combating bacterial infections, in the past few years some bacteria have become resistant to it. These resistant bacteria have evolved a different set of peptides on their cell surface. The highlighted N—H group in (a) has been instead replaced with an O, as shown in (b). Although we will have much more to say about peptides and amino acids in Chapter 24, for now realize that this change has turned one hydrogen-bond donor (the N—H) into an atom that is a hydrogen-bond acceptor (O). As a result, vancomycin can form only four hydrogen bonds with the target. Although this constitutes a loss of just 20% of its hydrogen-bonding capacity, it turns out that its overall effectiveness in terms of its bacterial-killing ability is reduced by a factor of 1000. As a result, these bacteria are resistant to vancomycin, meaning that new chemical weapons are needed if patients infected with certain resistant gram-positive bacteria are to survive. Fortunately, there are several leads being explored in clinical trials, but given the ability of bacteria to constantly evolve and evade our therapies, we will need to keep developing new and better antibiotics.

Vancomycin was discovered in microbes from the jungles in Borneo.

To learn more about these topics, see:

1. Nicolaou, K. C.; Boddy, C. N. C., "Behind enemy lines" in *Scientific American*, May 2001, pp. 54–61.
2. Nicolaou, K. C.; Snyder, S. A. *Classics in Total Synthesis II*. Wiley-VCH: Weinheim, 2003, pp. 239–300.

SUMMARY AND REVIEW TOOLS

In Chapter 2 you learned about families of organic molecules, some of their physical properties, and how we can use an instrumental technique called infrared spectroscopy to study them.

You learned that functional groups define the families to which organic compounds belong. At this point you should be able to name functional groups when you see them in structural formulas, and, when given the name of a functional group, draw a general example of its structure.

You also built on your knowledge of how electronegativity influences charge distribution in a molecule and how, together with three-dimensional structure, charge distribution influences the overall polarity of a molecule. Based on polarity and three-dimensional structure, you should be able to predict the kind and relative strength of electrostatic forces between molecules. With this understanding you will be able to roughly estimate physical properties such as melting point, boiling point, and solubility.

Last, you learned to use IR spectroscopy as an indicator of the family to which an organic compound belongs. IR spectroscopy provides signatures (in the form of spectra) that suggest which functional groups are present in a molecule.

If you know the concepts in Chapters 1 and 2 well, you will be on your way to having the solid foundation you need for success in organic chemistry. Keep up the good work (including your diligent homework habits)!

The study aids for this chapter include key terms and concepts (which are hyperlinked to the glossary from the bold, blue terms in the *WileyPLUS* version of the book at wileyplus.com) and a Concept Map after the end-of-chapter problems.

KEY TERMS AND CONCEPTS PLUS

The key terms and concepts that are highlighted in bold, blue text within the chapter are defined in the glossary (at the back of the book) and have hyperlinked definitions in the accompanying *WileyPLUS* course (www.wileyplus.com).

PROBLEMS PLUS

Note to Instructors: Many of the homework problems are available for assignment via *WileyPLUS*, an online teaching and learning solution.

FUNCTIONAL GROUPS AND STRUCTURAL FORMULAS

2.29 Classify each of the following compounds as an alkane, alkene, alkyne, alcohol, aldehyde, amine, and so forth.

(a)

(c)

(e)

Obtained from oil of cloves

(b) $CH_3-C{\equiv}CH$

(d)

(f)

Sex attractant of the common housefly

2.30 Identify all of the functional groups in each of the following compounds:

(a)   **Vitamin D₃**

(d)   **Cholesterol**

(b)   **Aspartame**

(e)   **Demerol**

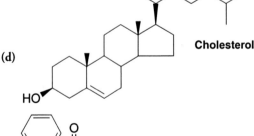

(c)   **Amphetamine**

(f)   **A cockroach repellent found in cucumbers**

(g)   **A synthetic cockroach repellent**

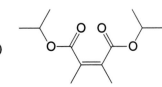

2.31 There are four alkyl bromides with the formula C_4H_9Br. Write their structural formulas and classify each as to whether it is a primary, secondary, or tertiary alkyl bromide.

2.32 There are seven isomeric compounds with the formula $C_4H_{10}O$. Write their structures and classify each compound according to its functional group.

2.33 Classify the following alcohols as primary, secondary, or tertiary:

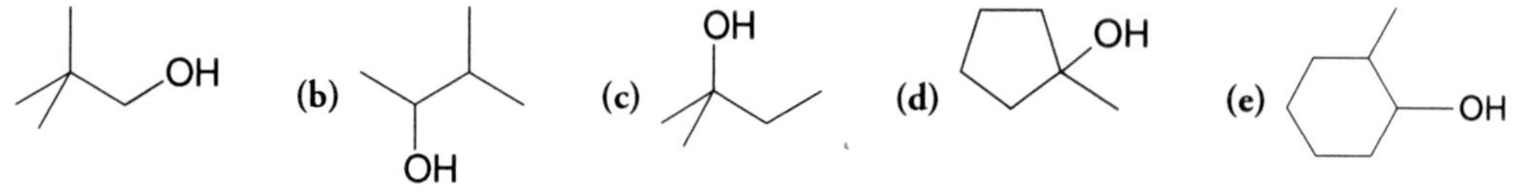

2.34 Classify the following amines as primary, secondary, or tertiary:

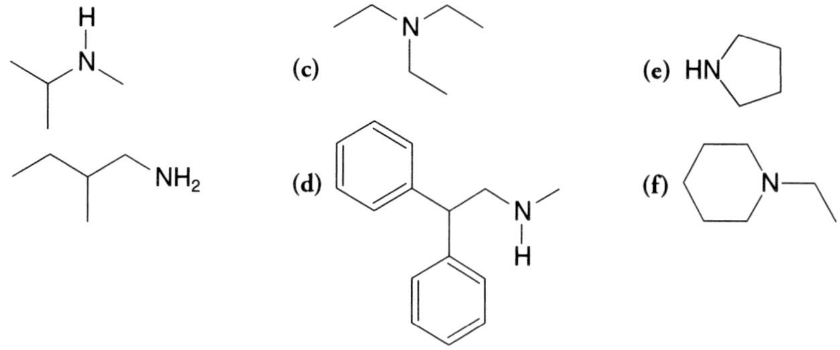

2.35 Write structural formulas for each of the following:

(a) Three ethers with the formula $C_4H_{10}O$.

(b) Three primary alcohols with the formula C_4H_8O.

(c) A secondary alcohol with the formula C_3H_6O.

(d) A tertiary alcohol with the formula C_4H_8O.

(e) Two esters with the formula $C_3H_6O_2$.

(f) Four primary alkyl halides with the formula $C_5H_{11}Br$.

(g) Three secondary alkyl halides with the formula $C_5H_{11}Br$.

(h) A tertiary alkyl halide with the formula $C_5H_{11}Br$.

(i) Three aldehydes with the formula $C_5H_{10}O$.

(j) Three ketones with the formula $C_5H_{10}O$.

(k) Two primary amines with the formula C_3H_9N.

(l) A secondary amine with the formula C_3H_9N.

(m) A tertiary amine with the formula C_3H_9N.

(n) Two amides with the formula C_2H_5NO.

2.36 Identify all of the functional groups in Crixivan, an important drug in the treatment of AIDS.

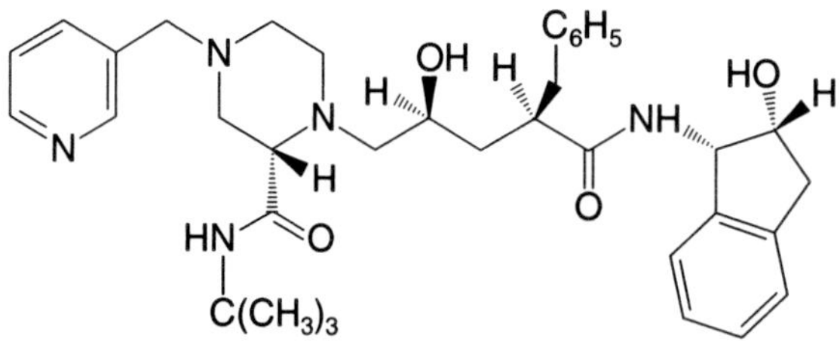

Crixivan (an HIV protease inhibitor)

2.37 Identify all of the functional groups in the following molecule.

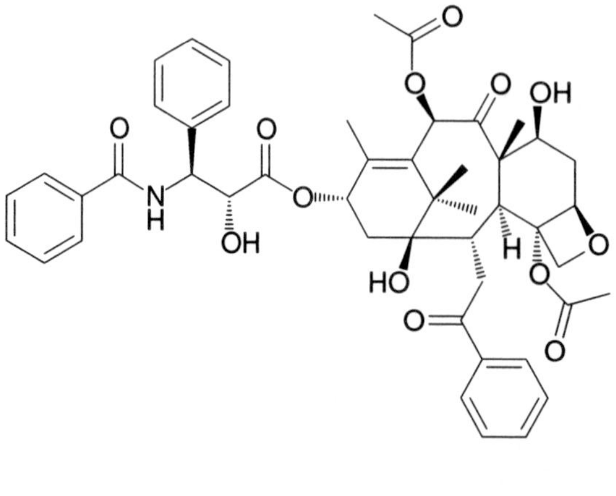

PHYSICAL PROPERTIES

2.38 **(a)** Indicate the hydrophobic and hydrophilic parts of vitamin A and comment on whether you would expect it to be soluble in water. **(b)** Do the same for vitamin B_3 (also called niacin).

Vitamin A   **Vitamin B$_3$ or niacin**

2.39 Hydrogen fluoride has a dipole moment of 1.83 D; its boiling point is 19.34 °C. Ethyl fluoride (CH_3CH_2F) has an almost identical dipole moment and has a larger molecular weight, yet its boiling point is −37.7 °C. Explain.

2.40 Why does one expect the cis isomer of an alkene to have a higher boiling point than the trans isomer?

2.41 Cetylethyldimethylammonium bromide is the common name for

, a compound with antiseptic properties. Predict its solubility behavior in water and in diethyl ether.

2.42 Which of the following solvents should be capable of dissolving ionic compounds?
(a) Liquid SO_2 **(b)** Liquid NH_3 **(c)** Benzene   **(d)** CCl_4

2.43 Write a three-dimensional formula for each of the following molecules using the wedge–dashed wedge–line formalism. If the molecule has a net dipole moment, indicate its direction with an arrow, ⟶. If the molecule has no net dipole moment, you should so state. (You may ignore the small polarity of $C-H$ bonds in working this and similar problems.)
(a) CH_3F **(c)** CHF_3 **(e)** CH_2FCl **(g)** BeF_2 **(i)** CH_3OH
(b) CH_2F_2 **(d)** CF_4 **(f)** BCl_3 **(h)** CH_3OCH_3 **(j)** CH_2O

2.44 Consider each of the following molecules in turn: **(a)** dimethyl ether, $(CH_3)_2O$; **(b)** trimethylamine, $(CH_3)_3N$; **(c)** trimethylboron, $(CH_3)_3B$; and **(d)** dimethylberyllium, $(CH_3)_2Be$. Describe the hybridization state of the central atom (i.e., O, N, B, or Be) of each molecule, tell what bond angles you would expect at the central atom, and state whether the molecule would have a dipole moment.

2.45 Analyze the statement: For a molecule to be polar, the presence of polar bonds is necessary, but it is not a sufficient requirement.

2.46 Which compound in each of the following pairs would have the higher boiling point? Explain your answers.

(a)   or

(b)   or

(c)   or

(d)   or

(e)   or

(f)   or

(g)   or

(h) Hexane, $CH_3(CH_2)_4CH_3$, or nonane, $CH_3(CH_2)_7CH_3$

(i)   or

IR SPECTROSCOPY

2.47 Predict the key IR absorption bands whose presence would allow each compound in pairs **(a)**, **(c)**, **(d)**, **(e)**, **(g)**, and **(i)** from Problem 2.46 to be distinguished from each other.

2.48 The IR spectrum of propanoic acid (Fig. 2.17) indicates that the absorption for the $O-H$ stretch of the carboxylic acid functional group is due to a hydrogen-bonded form. Draw the structure of two propanoic acid molecules showing how they could dimerize via hydrogen bonding.

2.49 In infrared spectra, the carbonyl group is usually indicated by a single strong and sharp absorption. However, in the case of carboxylic acid anhydrides, $R-\overset{\overset{\|}{O}}{C}-O-\overset{\overset{\|}{O}}{C}-R$, two peaks are observed even though the two carbonyl groups are chemically equivalent.

Explain this fact, considering what you know about the IR absorption of primary amines.

MULTICONCEPT PROBLEMS

2.50 Write structural formulas for four compounds with the formula C_3H_6O and classify each according to its functional group. Predict IR absorption frequencies for the functional groups you have drawn.

2.51 There are four amides with the formula C_3H_7NO. **(a)** Write their structures. **(b)** One of these amides has a melting and a boiling point that are substantially lower than those of the other three. Which amide is this? Explain your answer. **(c)** Explain how these amides could be differentiated on the basis of their IR spectra.

2.52 Write structures for all compounds with molecular formula C_4H_6O that would not be expected to exhibit infrared absorption in the 3200–3550-cm^{-1} and 1620–1780-cm^{-1} regions.

2.53 Cyclic compounds of the general type shown here are called lactones. What functional group does a lactone contain?

CHALLENGE PROBLEMS

2.54 Two constitutional isomers having molecular formula C_4H_6O are both symmetrical in structure. In their infrared spectra, neither isomer when in dilute solution in CCl_4 (used because it is nonpolar) has absorption in the 3600-cm^{-1} region. Isomer A has absorption bands at approximately 3080, 1620, and $700\ cm^{-1}$. Isomer B has bands in the 2900-cm^{-1} region and at $1780\ cm^{-1}$. Propose a structure for A and two possible structures for B.

2.55 When two substituents are on the same side of a ring skeleton, they are said to be cis, and when on opposite sides, trans (analogous to use of those terms with 1,2-disubstituted alkene isomers). Consider stereoisomeric forms of 1,2-cyclopentanediol (compounds having a five-membered ring and hydroxyl groups on two adjacent carbons that are cis in one isomer and trans in the other). At high dilution, both isomers have an infrared absorption band at approximately $3626\ cm^{-1}$ but only one isomer has a band at $3572\ cm^{-1}$.
(a) Assume for now that the cyclopentane ring is coplanar (the interesting actuality will be studied later) and then draw and label the two isomers using the wedge–dashed wedge method of depicting the OH groups. **(b)** Designate which isomer will have the 3572-cm^{-1} band and explain its origin.

2.56 Compound C is asymmetric, has molecular formula $C_5H_{10}O$, and contains two methyl groups and a 3° functional group. It has a broad infrared absorption band in the 3200–3550-cm^{-1} region and no absorption in the 1620–1680-cm^{-1} region. Propose a structure for C.

2.57 Examine the diagram showing an α-helical protein structure in Section 2.13E. Between what specific atoms and of what functional groups are the hydrogen bonds formed that give the molecule its helical structure?

LEARNING GROUP PROBLEMS

Consider the molecular formula $C_4H_8O_2$.

1. Write structures for at least 15 different compounds that all have the molecular formula $C_4H_8O_2$ and contain functional groups presented in this chapter.

2. Provide at least one example each of a structure written using the dash format, the condensed format, the bond-line format, and the full three-dimensional format. Use your choice of format for the remaining structures.

3. Identify four different functional groups from among your structures. Circle and name them on the representative structures.

4. Predict approximate frequencies for IR absorptions that could be used to distinguish the four compounds representing these functional groups.

5. If any of the 15 structures you drew have atoms where the formal charge is other than zero, indicate the formal charge on the appropriate atom(s) and the overall charge for the molecule.

6. Identify which types of intermolecular forces would be possible in pure samples of all 15 compounds.

7. Pick five formulas you have drawn that represent a diversity of structures, and predict their order with respect to trend in increasing boiling point.

8. Explain your order of predicted boiling points on the basis of intermolecular forces and polarity.

[CONCEPT MAP]

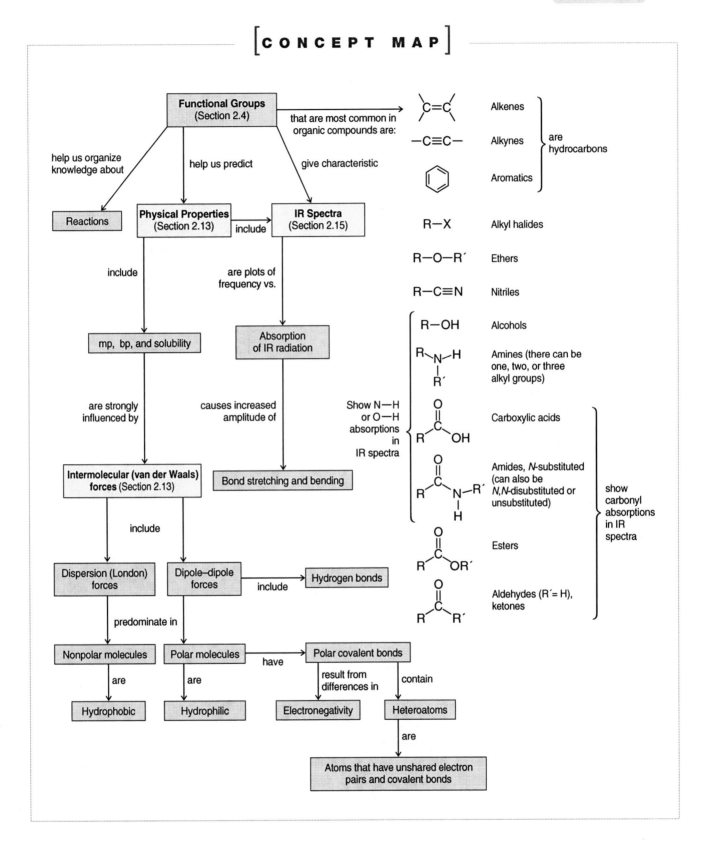

Acids and Bases

AN INTRODUCTION TO ORGANIC
REACTIONS AND THEIR MECHANISMS

To the uninitiated, a chemical reaction must seem like an act of magic. A chemist puts one or two reagents into a flask, waits for a time, and then takes from the flask one or more completely different compounds. It is, until we understand the details of the reaction, like a magician who puts apples and oranges in a hat, shakes it, and then pulls out rabbits and parakeets. We see a real-life example of this sort of "magic" in the photo above, where a strand of solid nylon is being pulled from a flask that contains two immiscible solutions. This synthesis of nylon is not magic, but it is indeed wonderful and amazing, and reactions like it have transformed our world.

One of our goals in this course will be, in fact, to try to understand how this chemical magic takes place. We will want to be able to explain *how the products of the reaction are formed*. This explanation will take the form of a reaction mechanism—**a description of the events that take place on a molecular level as reactants become products**. If, as is often the case, the reaction takes place in more than one step, we will want to know what chemical species, called intermediates, intervene between each step along the way.

One of the most important things about using mechanisms to learn organic chemistry is this: mechanisms help us organize what otherwise might be an overwhelmingly complex body of knowledge into a form that makes it understandable. There are millions of organic compounds now known, and there are millions of reactions that these compounds undergo. If we had to learn them all by rote memorization, then we would soon give up. But, we don't have to do this. In the same way

PHOTO CREDITS: (making nylon) Charles D. WInters/Photo Researchers, Inc.; (magician's hand) © AndyL/iStockphoto

104

that functional groups help us organize compounds in a comprehensible way, mechanisms help us organize reactions. Fortunately, too, there are a relatively small number of basic mechanisms.

IN THIS CHAPTER WE WILL CONSIDER:

- rules that show how to classify reactive groups within molecules from the standpoints of acids and bases as well as from electron-rich and electron-poor domains
- the step-by-step processes of a chemical reaction and how to codify these processes into a few specific, easy-to-understand types

[**WHY** DO THESE TOPICS MATTER?]   At the end of the chapter, we will show a rare case where an important discovery that truly changed the world was made without any knowledge of these principles. However, the rare occurrence of such events argues for why real advances require a core understanding of the topics in this chapter.

3.1 ACID-BASE REACTIONS

We begin our study of chemical reactions and mechanisms by examining some of the basic principles of acid–base chemistry. There are several reasons for doing this:

- Many of the reactions that occur in organic chemistry are either acid–base reactions themselves or they involve an acid–base reaction at some stage.
- Acid–base reactions are simple fundamental reactions that will enable you to see how chemists use curved arrows to represent mechanisms of reactions and how they depict the processes of bond breaking and bond making that occur as molecules react.

3.1A Brønsted–Lowry Acids and Bases

Two classes of acid–base reactions are fundamental in organic chemistry: Brønsted–Lowry and Lewis acid–base reactions. We start our discussion with Brønsted–Lowry acid–base reactions.

- Brønsted–Lowry acid–base reactions involve the transfer of protons.
- A **Brønsted–Lowry acid** is a substance that can donate (or lose) a proton.
- A **Brønsted–Lowry base** is a substance that can accept (or remove) a proton.

Let us consider some examples.

Hydrogen chloride (HCl), in its pure form, is a gas. When HCl gas is bubbled into water, the following reaction occurs.

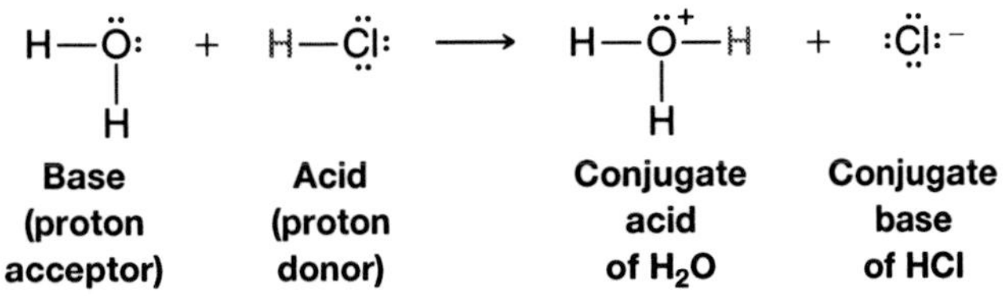

$$H-\overset{\cdot\cdot}{\underset{H}{O}}: \ + \ H-\overset{\cdot\cdot}{\underset{\cdot\cdot}{Cl}}: \ \longrightarrow \ H-\overset{\cdot\cdot}{\underset{H}{O}}\overset{+}{-}H \ + \ :\overset{\cdot\cdot}{\underset{\cdot\cdot}{Cl}}:^{-}$$

Base	Acid	Conjugate	Conjugate
(proton	(proton	acid	base
acceptor)	donor)	of H_2O	of HCl

The color of hydrangea flowers depends, in part, on the relative acidity of their soil.

In this reaction hydrogen chloride donates a proton; therefore it acts as a Brønsted–Lowry acid. Water accepts a proton from hydrogen chloride; thus water serves as a Brønsted–Lowry base. The products are a hydronium ion (H_3O^+) and chloride ion (Cl^-).

Just as we classified the reactants as either an acid or a base, we also classify the products in a specific way.

- The molecule or ion that forms when an acid loses its proton is called the conjugate base of that acid. In the above example, chloride ion is the conjugate base.
- The molecule or ion that forms when a base accepts a proton is called the conjugate acid. Hydronium ion is the conjugate acid of water.

Hydrogen chloride is considered a strong acid because transfer of its proton in water proceeds essentially to completion. Other strong acids that completely transfer a proton when dissolved in water are hydrogen iodide, hydrogen bromide, and sulfuric acid.

$$HI + H_2O \longrightarrow H_3O^+ + I^-$$
$$HBr + H_2O \longrightarrow H_3O^+ + Br^-$$
$$H_2SO_4 + H_2O \longrightarrow H_3O^+ + HSO_4^-$$
$$HSO_4^- + H_2O \rightleftharpoons H_3O^+ + SO_4^{2-}$$

* The extent to which an acid transfers protons to a base, such as water, is a measure of its strength as an acid. Acid strength is therefore a measure of the percentage of ionization and *not* of concentration.

Sulfuric acid is called a diprotic acid because it can transfer two protons. Transfer of the first proton occurs completely, while the second is transferred only to the extent of about 10% (hence the equilibrium arrows in the equation for the second proton transfer).

3.1B Acids and Bases in Water

* Hydronium ion is the strongest acid that can exist in water to any significant extent. Any acid stronger than hydronium ion will simply transfer its proton to a water molecule to form hydronium ions.

* Hydroxide ion is the strongest base that can exist in water to any significant extent. Any base stronger than hydroxide will remove a proton from water to form hydroxide ions.

When an ionic compound dissolves in water the ions are solvated. With sodium hydroxide, for example, the positive sodium ions are stabilized by interaction with unshared electron pairs of water molecules, and the hydroxide ions are stabilized by hydrogen bonding of their unshared electron pairs with the partially positive hydrogens of water molecules.

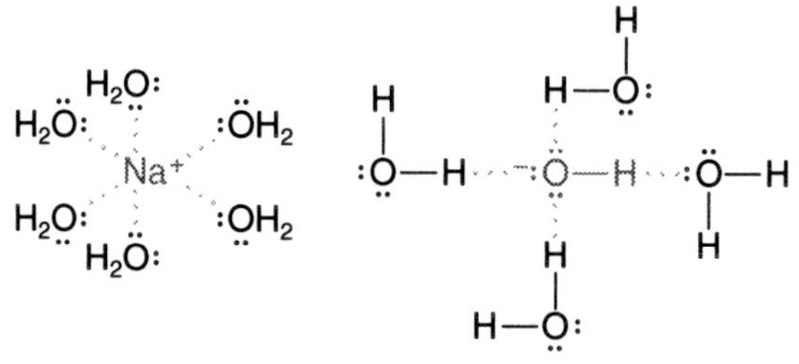

Solvated sodium ion   **Solvated hydroxide ion**

When an aqueous solution of sodium hydroxide is mixed with an aqueous solution of hydrogen chloride (hydrochloric acid), the reaction that occurs is between hydronium and hydroxide ions. The sodium and chloride ions are called **spectator ions** because they play no part in the acid–base reaction:

Total Ionic Reaction

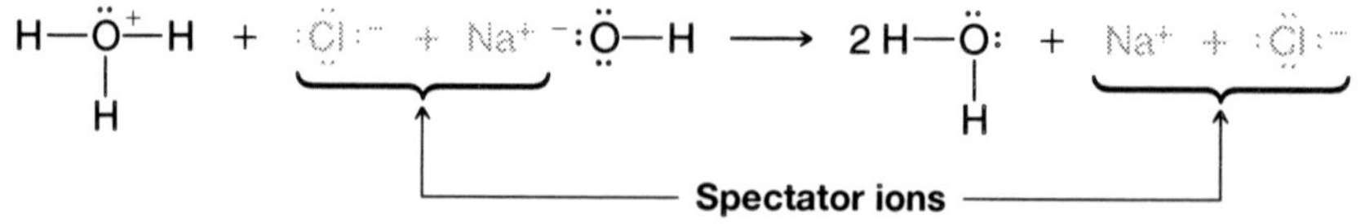

Net Reaction

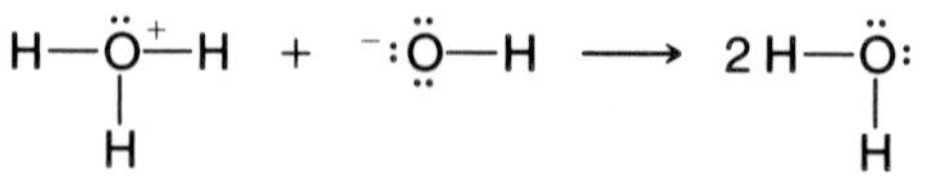

What we have just said about hydrochloric acid and aqueous sodium hydroxide is true when solutions of all aqueous strong acids and bases are mixed. The net ionic reaction is simply

$$H_3O^+ + HO^- \longrightarrow 2 H_2O$$

3.2 HOW TO USE CURVED ARROWS IN ILLUSTRATING REACTIONS

Up to this point we have not indicated how bonding changes occur in the reactions we have presented, but this can easily be done using curved-arrow notation. **Curved arrows** show the direction of electron flow in a reaction mechanism.

1. Draw the curved arrow so that it points from the source of an electron pair to the atom receiving the pair. (Curved arrows can also show the movement of single electrons. We shall discuss reactions of this type in a later chapter.)

2. Always show the flow of electrons from a site of higher electron density to a site of lower electron density.

3. **Never** use curved arrows to show the movement of atoms. Atoms are assumed to follow the flow of the electrons.

4. Make sure that the movement of electrons shown by the curved arrow does not violate the octet rule for elements in the second row of the periodic table.

The reaction of hydrogen chloride with water provides a simple example of how to use curved arrow notation. Here we invoke the first of many "A Mechanism for the Reaction" boxes, in which we show every key step in a mechanism using color-coded formulas accompanied by explanatory captions.

[**A MECHANISM FOR THE REACTION** ⸱⸱⸱ **Reaction of Water with Hydrogen Chloride: The Use of Curved Arrows**]

Reaction

$$H_2O \ + \ HCl \ \longrightarrow \ H_3O^+ \ + \ Cl^-$$

Mechanism

A water molecule uses one of the nonbonding electron pairs to form a bond to a proton of HCl. The bond between the hydrogen and chlorine breaks, and the electron pair goes to the chlorine atom.	**This leads to the formation of a hydronium ion and a chloride ion.**

Helpful Hint

Curved arrows point *from* electrons *to* the atom receiving the electrons.

The curved arrow begins with a covalent bond or unshared electron pair (a site of higher electron density) and points toward a site of electron deficiency. We see here that as the water molecule collides with a hydrogen chloride molecule, it uses one of its unshared electron pairs (shown in blue) to form a bond to the proton of HCl. This bond forms because the negatively charged electrons of the oxygen atom are attracted to the positively charged proton. As the bond between the oxygen and the proton forms, the hydrogen–chlorine bond of HCl breaks, and the chlorine of HCl departs with the electron pair that formerly bonded it to the proton. (If this did not happen, the proton would end up forming two covalent bonds, which, of course, a proton cannot do.) We, therefore, use a curved arrow to show the bond cleavage as well. By pointing from the bond to the chlorine, the arrow indicates that the bond breaks and the electron pair leaves with the chloride ion.

The following acid–base reactions give other examples of the use of the curved-arrow notation:

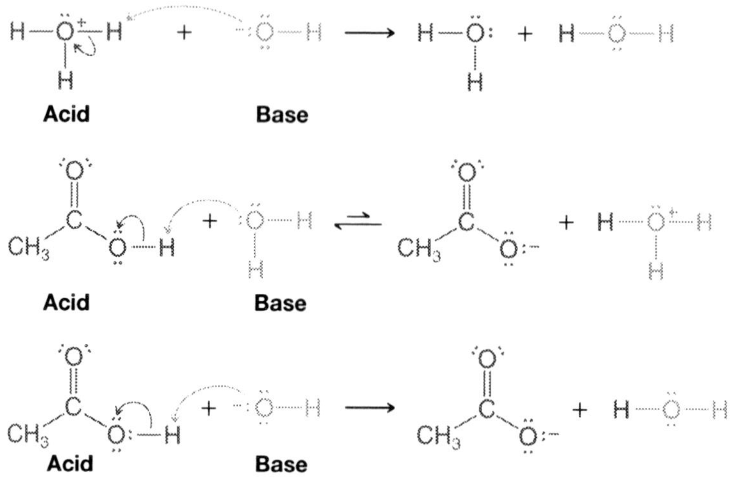

$$H-\overset{+}{\underset{|}{O}}-H \quad + \quad :\overset{..}{O}-H \longrightarrow H-\overset{..}{O}: \quad + \quad H-\overset{..}{O}-H$$

Acid   **Base**

Acid   **Base**

Acid   **Base**

••• SOLVED PROBLEM 3.1

Add curved arrows to the following reactions to indicate the flow of electrons for all of the bond-forming and bond-breaking steps.

(a)

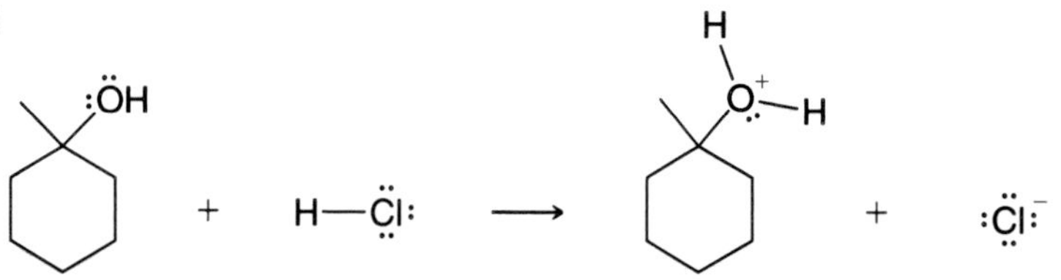

(b)

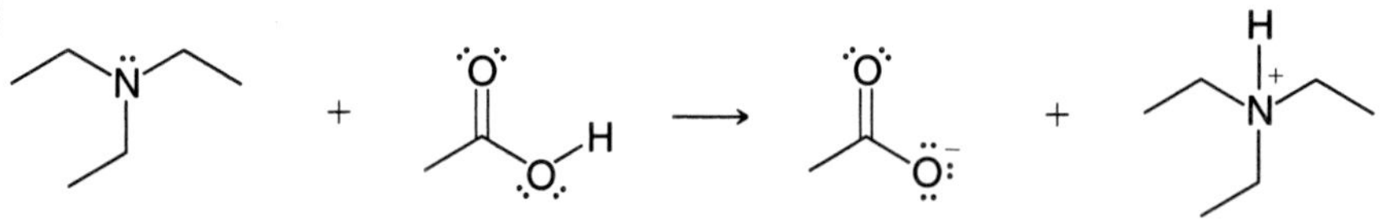

STRATEGY AND ANSWER: Recall the rules for use of curved arrows presented at the beginning of Section 3.2. Curved arrows point from the source of an electron pair to the atom receiving the pair, and always point from a site of higher electron density to a site of lower electron density. We must also not exceed two electrons for a hydrogen atom, or an octet of electrons for any elements in the second row of the periodic table. We must also account for the formal charges on atoms and write equations whose charges are balanced.

In (a), the hydrogen atom of **HCl** is partially positive (electrophilic) due to the electronegativity of the chlorine atom. The alcohol oxygen is a source of electrons (a Lewis base) that can be given to this partially positive proton. The proton must lose a pair of electrons as it gains a pair, however, and thus the chloride ion accepts a pair of electrons from the bond it had with the hydrogen atom as the hydrogen becomes bonded to the alcohol oxygen.

(a)

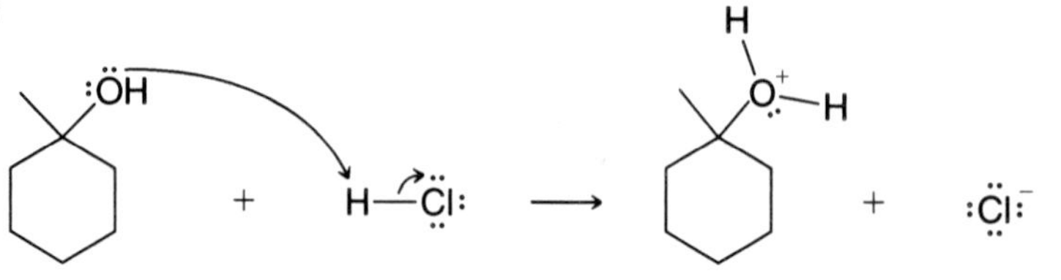

In (b), the carboxylic acid hydrogen is partially positive and therefore electrophilic, and the amine provides an unshared pair of electrons that forms a bond with the carboxylic acid hydrogen, causing departure of a carboxylate anion.

(b)

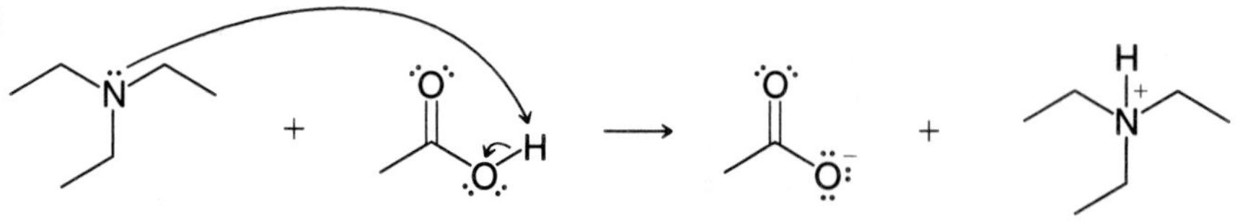

● ● ●

Add curved arrows to the following reactions to indicate the flow of electrons for all of the bond-forming and bond-breaking steps.

PRACTICE PROBLEM 3.1

(a)

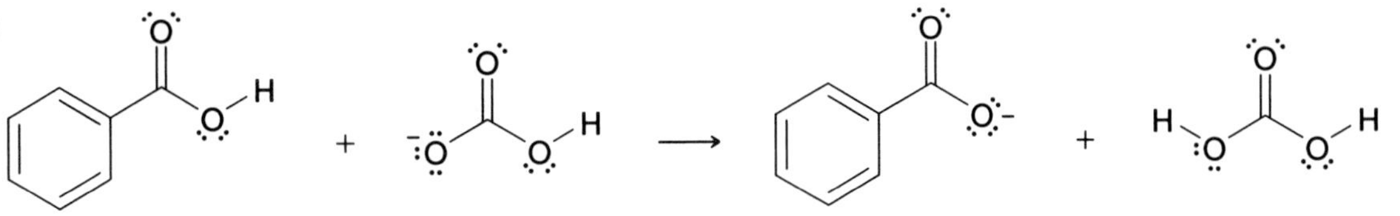

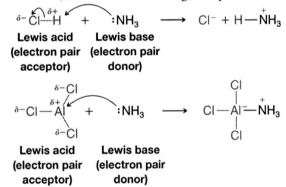

(b)

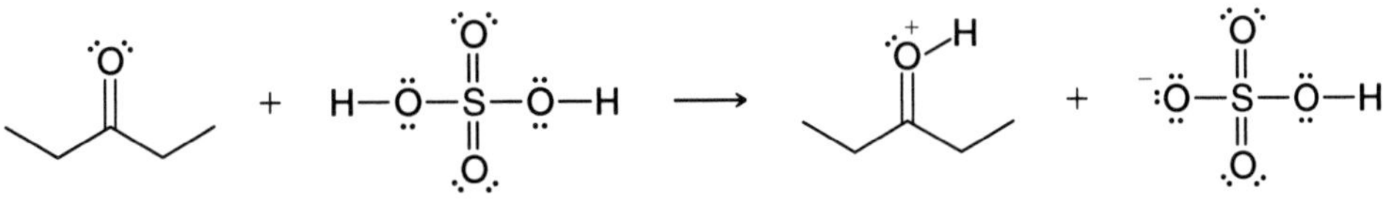

3.3 LEWIS ACIDS AND BASES

In 1923 G. N. Lewis proposed a theory that significantly broadened the understanding of acids and bases. As we go along we shall find that an understanding of **Lewis acid–base theory** is exceedingly helpful to understanding a variety of organic reactions. Lewis proposed the following definitions for acids and bases.

- Acids are electron pair acceptors.
- Bases are electron pair donors.

In Lewis acid–base theory, proton donors are not the only acids; many other species are acids as well. Aluminum chloride, for example, reacts with ammonia in the same way that a proton donor does. Using curved arrows to show the donation of the electron pair of ammonia (the Lewis base), we have the following examples:

$$\delta^- \overset{\curvearrowleft}{Cl} - \overset{\delta^+}{H} \quad + \quad :NH_3 \quad \longrightarrow \quad Cl^- + H - \overset{+}{N}H_3$$

Lewis acid
(electron pair acceptor)

Lewis base
(electron pair donor)

> **Helpful Hint**
>
> Verify for yourself that you can calculate the formal charges in these structures.

$$\delta^- \overset{\overset{\delta^- Cl}{|}}{Cl - Al} \quad + \quad :NH_3 \quad \longrightarrow \quad \overset{\overset{Cl}{|}}{Cl - Al} \overset{+}{-} NH_3$$

Lewis acid
(electron pair acceptor)

Lewis base
(electron pair donor)

In the reaction with hydrogen chloride above, notice that the electron pair acceptor (the proton) must also lose an electron pair as the new bond is formed with nitrogen. This is necessary because the hydrogen atom had a full valence shell of electrons at the start. On the other hand, because the valence shell of the aluminum atom in aluminum chloride was not full at the beginning (it had only a sextet of valence electrons), it can accept an electron pair without breaking any bonds. The aluminum atom actually achieves an octet by accepting the pair from nitrogen, although it gains a formal negative charge. When it accepts the electron pair, aluminum chloride is, in the Lewis definition, *acting as an acid*.

Bases are much the same in the Lewis theory and in the Brønsted–Lowry theory, because in the Brønsted–Lowry theory a base must donate a pair of electrons in order to accept a proton.

- The Lewis theory, by virtue of its broader definition of acids, allows acid–base theory to include all of the Brønsted–Lowry reactions and, as we shall see, a great many others. Most of the reactions we shall study in organic chemistry involve Lewis acid–base interactions, and a sound understanding of Lewis acid–base chemistry will help greatly.

Carbonic anhydrase

A zinc ion acts as a Lewis acid in the mechanism of the enzyme carbonic anhydrase (Chapter 24).

Any *electron-deficient atom* can act as a Lewis acid. Many compounds containing group IIIA elements such as boron and aluminum are Lewis acids because group IIIA atoms have only a sextet of electrons in their outer shell. Many other compounds that have atoms with vacant orbitals also act as Lewis acids. Zinc and iron(III) halides (ferric halides) are frequently used as Lewis acids in organic reactions.

●●● SOLVED PROBLEM 3.2

Write an equation that shows the Lewis acid and Lewis base in the reaction of bromine (Br₂) with ferric bromide (FeBr₃).

ANSWER:

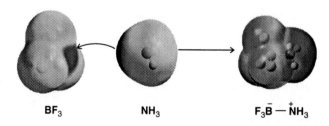

3.3A Opposite Charges Attract

* In Lewis acid–base theory, as in many organic reactions, the attraction of oppositely charged species is fundamental to reactivity.

As one further example, we consider boron trifluoride, an even more powerful Lewis acid than aluminum chloride, and its reaction with ammonia. The calculated structure for boron trifluoride in Fig. 3.1 shows electrostatic potential at its van der Waals surface (like that in Section 2.2A for HCl). It is obvious from this figure (and you should be able to predict this) that BF₃ has substantial positive charge centered on the boron atom and negative charge located on the three fluorines. (The convention in these structures is that blue represents relatively positive areas and red represents relatively negative areas.) On the other hand, the surface electrostatic potential for ammonia shows (as you would expect) that substantial negative charge is localized in the region of ammonia's nonbonding electron pair. Thus, the electrostatic properties of these two molecules are perfectly suited for a Lewis acid–base reaction. When the expected reaction occurs between them, the nonbonding electron pair of ammonia attacks the boron atom of boron trifluoride, filling boron's valence shell. The boron now carries a formal negative charge and the nitrogen carries a formal positive charge. This separation of charge is borne out in the electrostatic potential map for the product shown in Fig. 3.1. Notice that substantial negative charge resides in the BF₃ part of the molecule, and substantial positive charge is localized near the nitrogen.

Although calculated electrostatic potential maps like these illustrate charge distribution and molecular shape well, it is important that you are able to draw the same conclusions based on what you would have predicted about the structures of BF₃ and NH₃ and their reaction product using orbital hybridization (Sections 1.13–1.15), VSEPR models (Section 1.17), consideration of formal charges (Section 1.5), and electronegativity (Sections 1.3A and 2.2).

Helpful Hint

The need for a firm understanding of structure, formal charges, and electronegativity can hardly be emphasized enough as you build a foundation of knowledge for learning organic chemistry.

FIGURE 3.1 Electrostatic potential maps for BF₃ and NH₃ and the product that results from reaction between them. Attraction between the strongly positive region of BF₃ and the negative region of NH₃ causes them to react. The electrostatic potential map for the product shows that the fluorine atoms draw in the electron density of the formal negative charge, and the nitrogen atom, with its hydrogens, carries the formal positive charge.

Write equations showing the Lewis acid–base reaction that takes place when:

PRACTICE PROBLEM 3.2

(a) Methanol (CH_3OH) reacts with BF_3.

(b) Chloromethane (CH_3Cl) reacts with $AlCl_3$.

(c) Dimethyl ether (CH_3OCH_3) reacts with BF_3.

Which of the following are potential Lewis acids and which are potential Lewis bases?

PRACTICE PROBLEM 3.3

(a) $CH_3CH_2-\overset{\displaystyle CH_3}{\underset{\displaystyle |}{\ddot{N}}}-CH_3$

(c) $(C_6H_5)_3P\!:$

(e) $(CH_3)_3B$

(b) $H_3C-\overset{\displaystyle CH_3}{\underset{\displaystyle CH_3}{\overset{|}{\underset{|}{C^+}}}}$

(d) $:\!\ddot{Br}\!:^-$

(f) $H\!:^-$

3.4 HETEROLYSIS OF BONDS TO CARBON: CARBOCATIONS AND CARBANIONS

Heterolysis of a bond to a carbon atom can lead to either of two ions: either to an ion with a positive charge on the carbon atom, called a **carbocation**, or to an ion with a negatively charged carbon atom, called a **carbanion**:

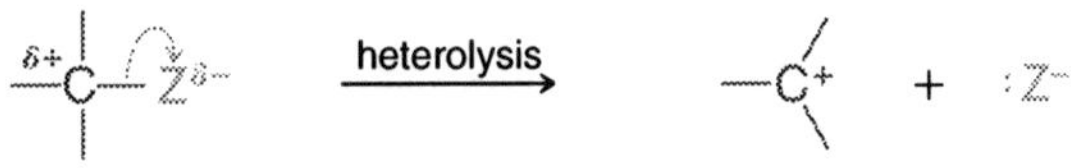

Carbocation

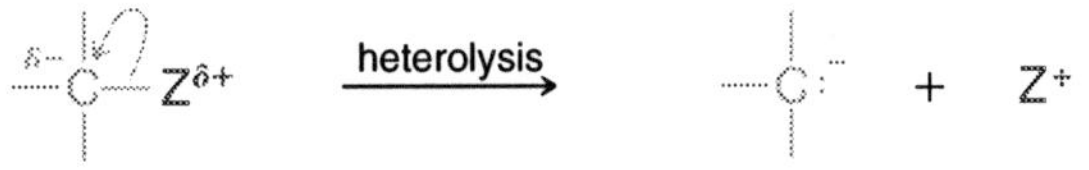

Carbanion

- Carbocations are electron deficient. They have only six electrons in their valence shell, and because of this, carbocations are Lewis acids.

In this way they are like BF_3 and $AlCl_3$. Most carbocations are also short-lived and highly reactive. They occur as intermediates in some organic reactions. Carbocations react rapidly with Lewis bases—with molecules or ions that can donate the electron pair that they need to achieve a stable octet of electrons (i.e., the electronic configuration of a noble gas):

Carbocation   **Anion**
(a Lewis acid)   **(a Lewis base)**

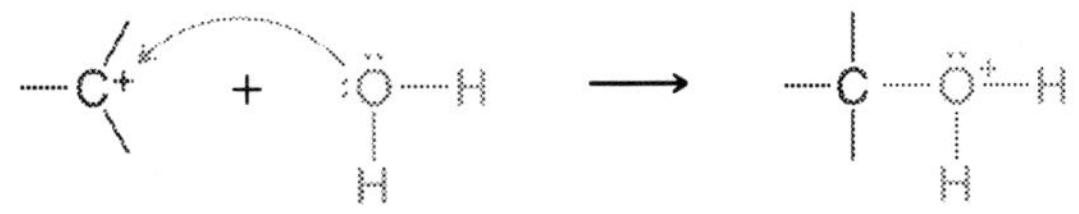

Carbocation   **Water**
(a Lewis acid)   **(a Lewis base)**

- **Carbanions** are electron rich. They are anions and have an unshared electron pair. Carbanions, therefore, are **Lewis bases and react accordingly** (Section 3.3).

3.4A Electrophiles and Nucleophiles

Because carbocations are electron-seeking reagents chemists call them **electrophiles** (meaning electron-loving).

- **Electrophiles are reagents that seek electrons so as to achieve a stable shell of electrons like that of a noble gas.**

- **All Lewis acids are electrophiles.** By accepting an electron pair from a Lewis base, a carbocation fills its valence shell.

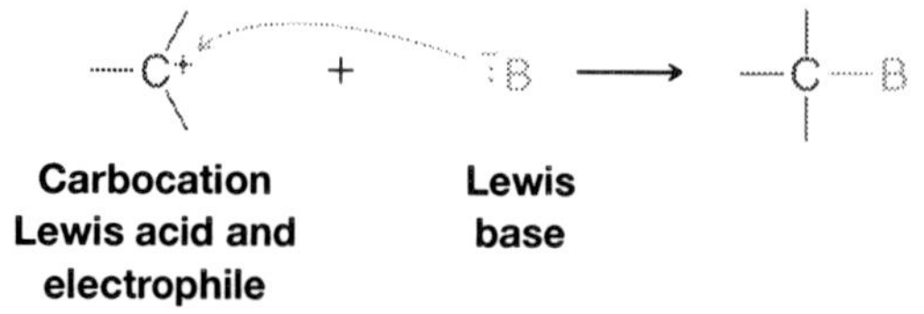

Carbocation
Lewis acid and
electrophile   Lewis
                        base

- **Carbon atoms that are electron poor because of bond polarity, but are not carbocations, can also be electrophiles.** They can react with the electron-rich centers of Lewis bases in reactions such as the following:

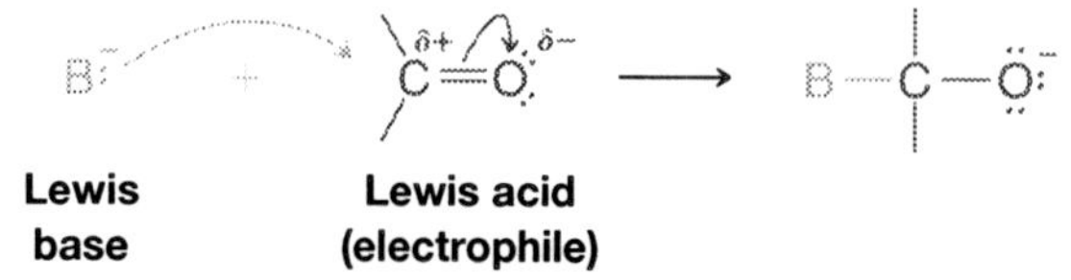

Lewis
base   Lewis acid
               (electrophile)

Carbanions are Lewis bases. Carbanions seek a proton or some other positive center to which they can donate their electron pair and thereby neutralize their negative charge.

When a Lewis base *seeks a positive center other than a proton, especially that of a carbon atom,* chemists call it a **nucleophile** (meaning nucleus loving; the *nucleo-* part of the name comes from *nucleus*, the positive center of an atom).

- **A nucleophile is a Lewis base that seeks a positive center such as a positively charged carbon atom.**

Since electrophiles are also Lewis acids (electron pair acceptors) and nucleophiles are Lewis bases (electron pair donors), why do chemists have two terms for them? The answer is that *Lewis acid* and *Lewis base* are terms that are used generally, but when one or the other reacts to form a bond to a carbon atom, we usually call it an *electrophile* or a *nucleophile*.

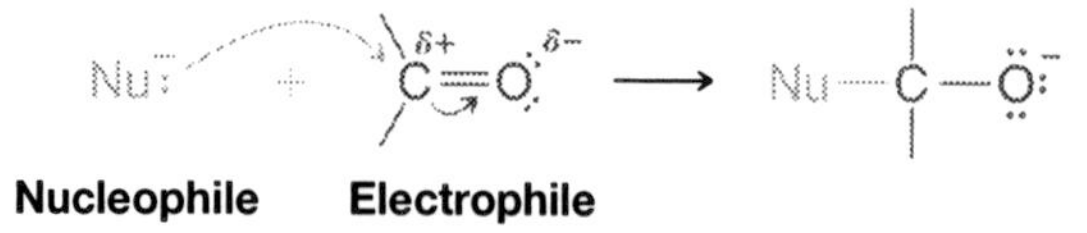

Nucleophile   Electrophile

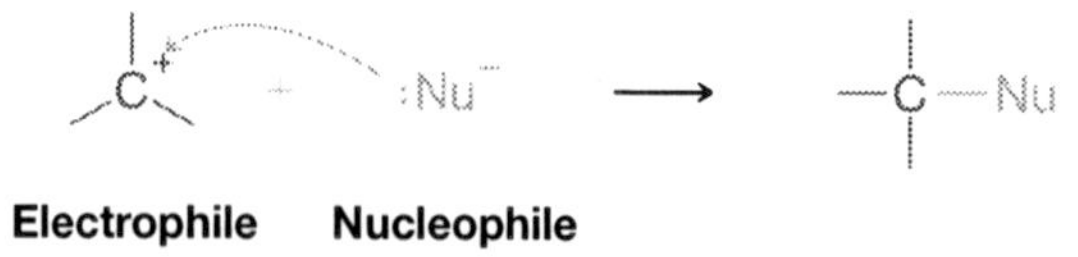

Electrophile   Nucleophile

●●● SOLVED PROBLEM 3.3

Identify the electrophile and the nucleophile in the following reaction, and add curved arrows to indicate the flow of electrons for the bond-forming and bond-breaking steps.

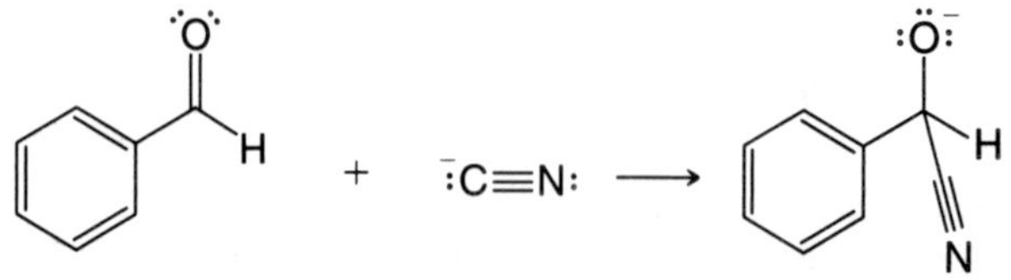

STRATEGY AND ANSWER: The aldehyde carbon is electrophilic due to the electronegativity of the carbonyl oxygen. The cyanide anion acts as a Lewis base and is the nucleophile, donating an electron pair to the carbonyl carbon, and causing an electron pair to shift to the oxygen so that no atom has more than an octet of electrons.

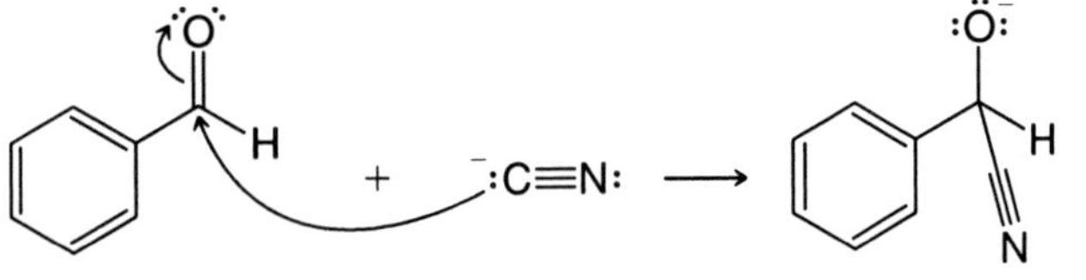

Use the curved-arrow notation to write the reaction that would take place between dimethylamine $(CH_3)_2NH$ and boron trifluoride. Identify the Lewis acid, Lewis base, nucleophile, and electrophile and assign appropriate formal charges.

PRACTICE PROBLEM 3.4

3.5 THE STRENGTH OF BRØNSTED–LOWRY ACIDS AND BASES: K_a AND pK_a

Many organic reactions involve the transfer of a proton by an acid–base reaction. An important consideration, therefore, is the relative strengths of compounds that could potentially act as Brønsted–Lowry acids or bases in a reaction.

In contrast to the strong acids, such as HCl and H_2SO_4, acetic acid is a much weaker acid. When acetic acid dissolves in water, the following reaction does not proceed to completion:

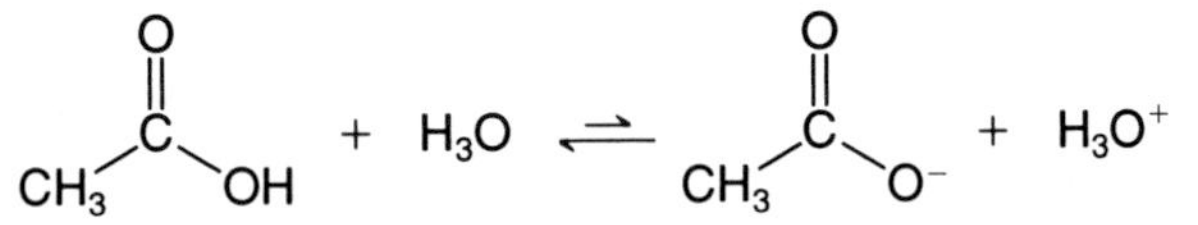

Experiments show that in a 0.1 M solution of acetic acid at 25 °C only about 1% of the acetic acid molecules ionize by transferring their protons to water. Therefore, acetic acid is a weak acid. As we shall see next, acid strength is characterized in terms of acidity constant (K_a) or pK_a values.

3.5A The Acidity Constant, K_a

Because the reaction that occurs in an aqueous solution of acetic acid is an equilibrium, we can describe it with an expression for the equilibrium constant (K_{eq}):

$$K_{eq} = \frac{[H_3O^+][CH_3CO_2^-]}{[CH_3CO_2H][H_2O]}$$

For dilute aqueous solutions, the concentration of water is essentially constant (~55.5 M), so we can rewrite the expression for the equilibrium constant in terms of a new constant (K_a) called the **acidity constant**:

$$K_a = K_{eq}[H_2O] = \frac{[H_3O^+][CH_3CO_2^-]}{[CH_3CO_2H]}$$

At 25 °C, the acidity constant for acetic acid is 1.76×10^{-5}.

We can write similar expressions for any weak acid dissolved in water. Using a generalized hypothetical acid (HA), the reaction in water is

$$HA + H_2O \rightleftharpoons H_3O^+ + A^-$$

and the expression for the acidity constant is

$$K_a = \frac{[H_3O^+][A^-]}{[HA]}$$

Because the concentrations of the products of the reaction are written in the numerator and the concentration of the undissociated acid in the denominator, **a large value of K_a means the acid is a strong acid and a small value of K_a means the acid is a weak acid.** If the K_a is greater than 10, the acid will be, for all practical purposes, completely dissociated in water at concentrations less than 0.01 M.

●●● SOLVED PROBLEM 3.4

Phenol (C_6H_5)OH has $K_a = 1.26 \times 10^{-10}$. **(a)** What is the molar concentration of hydronium ion in a 1.0 M solution of phenol? **(b)** What is the pH of the solution?

STRATEGY AND ANSWER: Use the equation for K_a for the equilibrium:

$$C_6H_5OH \quad + \quad H_2O \quad \rightleftharpoons \quad C_6H_5O^- \quad + \quad H_3O^+$$

Phenol   **Phenoxide**   **Hydronium**
                                  ion   **ion**

$$K_a = \frac{[H_3O]^+[C_6H_5O^-]}{[C_6H_5OH]} = 1.26 \times 10^{-10}$$

At equilibrium the concentration of hydronium ion will be the same as that of phenoxide ion, thus we can let them both equal x. Therefore

$$\frac{(x)(x)}{1.0} = \frac{x^2}{1.0} = 1.26 \times 10^{-10}$$

and

$$x = 1.1 \times 10^{-5}.$$

●●●

PRACTICE PROBLEM 3.5   Formic acid (HCO_2H) has $K_a = 1.77 \times 10^{-4}$. **(a)** What are the molar concentrations of the hydronium ion and formate ion (HCO_2^-) in a 0.1 M aqueous solution of formic acid? **(b)** What percentage of the formic acid is ionized?

3.5B Acidity and pK_a

Chemists usually express the acidity constant, K_a, as its negative logarithm, pK_a:

$$pK_a = -\log K_a$$

This is analogous to expressing the hydronium ion concentration as pH:

$$pH = -\log[H_3O^+]$$

For acetic acid the pK_a is 4.75:

$$pK_a = -\log(1.76 \times 10^{-5}) = -(-4.75) = 4.75$$

Notice that there is an inverse relationship between the magnitude of the pK_a and the strength of the acid.

● **The larger the value of the pK_a, the weaker is the acid.**

Helpful Hint

K_a and pK_a are indicators of acid strengths.

For example, acetic acid with p$K_a = 4.75$ is a weaker acid than trifluoroacetic acid with p$K_a = 0$ ($K_a = 1$). Hydrochloric acid with p$K_a = -7$ ($K_a = 10^7$) is a far stronger acid than trifluoroacetic acid. (It is understood that a positive pK_a is larger than a negative pK_a.)

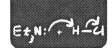

$$CH_3CO_2H < CF_3CO_2H < HCl$$

pK_a= 4.75	pK_a= 0	pK_a= −7
Weak acid		**Very strong acid**

→ Increasing acid strength →

Table 3.1 lists pK_a values for a selection of acids relative to water as the base.

TABLE 3.1 RELATIVE STRENGTH OF SELECTED ACIDS AND THEIR CONJUGATE BASES

	Acid	Approximate pK_a	Conjugate Base	
Strongest acid	$HSbF_6$	<−12	SbF_6^-	Weakest base
	HI	−10	I$^-$	
	H_2SO_4	−9	HSO_4^-	
	HBr	−9	Br$^-$	
	HCl	−7	Cl$^-$	
	$C_6H_5SO_3H$	−6.5	$C_6H_5SO_3^-$	
	$(CH_3)_2\overset{+}{O}H$	−3.8	$(CH_3)_2O$	
	$(CH_3)_2C=\overset{+}{O}H$	−2.9	$(CH_3)_2C=O$	
	$CH_3\overset{+}{O}H_2$	−2.5	CH_3OH	
	H_3O^+	−1.74	H_2O	
	HNO_3	−1.4	NO_3^-	
	CF_3CO_2H	0.18	$CF_3CO_2^-$	
	HF	3.2	F$^-$	
	$C_6H_5CO_2H$	4.21	$C_6H_5CO_2^-$	
	$C_6H_5NH_3^+$	4.63	$C_6H_5NH_2$	
	CH_3CO_2H	4.75	$CH_3CO_2^-$	
	H_2CO_3	6.35	HCO_3^-	
	$CH_3COCH_2COCH_3$	9.0	$CH_3CO\overset{-}{C}HCOCH_3$	
	NH_4^+	9.2	NH_3	
	C_6H_5OH	9.9	$C_6H_5O^-$	
	HCO_3^-	10.2	CO_3^{2-}	
	$CH_3NH_3^+$	10.6	CH_3NH_2	
	H_2O	15.7	HO$^-$	
	CH_3CH_2OH	16	$CH_3CH_2O^-$	
	$(CH_3)_3COH$	18	$(CH_3)_3CO^-$	
	CH_3COCH_3	19.2	$^-CH_2COCH_3$	
	$HC\equiv CH$	25	$HC\equiv C^-$	
	$C_6H_5NH_2$	31	$C_6H_5NH^-$	
	H_2	35	H$^-$	
	$(i\text{-}Pr)_2NH$	36	$(i\text{-}Pr)_2N^-$	
	NH_3	38	$^-NH_2$	
	$CH_2=CH_2$	44	$CH_2=CH^-$	
Weakest acid	CH_3CH_3	50	$CH_3CH_2^-$	Strongest base

↑ Increasing acid strength (left side)   ↓ Increasing base strength (right side)

The values in the middle pK_a range of Table 3.1 are the most accurate because they can be measured in aqueous solution. Special methods must be used to estimate the pK_a values for the very strong acids at the top of the table and for the very weak acids at the bottom.* The pK_a values for these very strong and weak acids are therefore approximate. All of the acids that we shall consider in this book will have strengths in between that of ethane (an extremely weak acid) and that of $HSbF_6$ (an acid that is so strong that it is called a "superacid"). As you examine Table 3.1, take care not to lose sight of the vast range of acidities that it represents (a factor of 10^{62}).

---

*Acids that are stronger than a hydronium ion and bases that are stronger than a hydroxide ion react completely with water (a phenomenon called the **leveling effect**; see Sections 3.1B and 3.14). Therefore, it is not possible to measure acidity constants for these acids in water. Other solvents and special techniques are used, but we do not have the space to describe those methods here.

PRACTICE PROBLEM 3.6 **(a)** An acid (HA) has $K_a = 10^{-7}$. What is its pK_a? **(b)** Another acid (HB) has $K_a = 5$. What is its pK_a? **(c)** Which is the stronger acid?

Water, itself, is a very weak acid and undergoes self-ionization even in the absence of acids and bases:

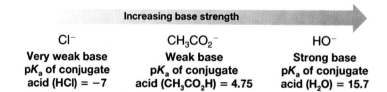

In pure water at 25 °C, the concentrations of hydronium and hydroxide ions are equal to 10^{-7} M. Since the concentration of water in pure water is 55.5 M, we can calculate the K_a for water.

$$K_a = \frac{[H_3O^+][OH^-]}{[H_2O]} \qquad K_a = \frac{(10^{-7})(10^{-7})}{55.5} = 1.8 \times 10^{-16} \qquad pK_a = 15.7$$

●●● SOLVED PROBLEM 3.5

Show calculations proving that the pK_a of the hydronium ion (H_3O^+) is -1.74 as given in Table 3.1.

STRATEGY AND ANSWER: When H_3O^+ acts as an acid in aqueous solution, the equilibrium is

$$H_3O^+ + H_2O \rightleftharpoons H_2O + H_3O^+$$

and K_a is equal to the molar concentration of water;

$$K_a = \frac{[H_2O][H_3O^+]}{[H_3O^+]} = [H_2O]$$

The molar concentration of H_2O in pure H_2O is equal to the number of moles of H_2O (MW = 18 g/mol) in 1000 g (one liter) of water. That is, $[H_2O] = 1000$ g L^{-1}/18 g/mole$^{-1} = 55.5$. Therefore, $K_a = 55.5$. The $pK = -\log 55.5 = -1.74$.

3.5C Predicting the Strength of Bases

In our discussion so far we have dealt only with the strengths of acids. Arising as a natural corollary to this is a principle that allows us to estimate the base strength. Simply stated, the principle is this:

• **The stronger the acid, the weaker will be its conjugate base.**

We can, therefore, **relate the strength of a base to the pK_a of its conjugate acid.**

• **The larger the pK_a of the conjugate acid, the stronger is the base.**

Consider the following as examples:

Increasing base strength →

Cl$^-$	CH$_3$CO$_2^-$	HO$^-$
Very weak base	**Weak base**	**Strong base**
pK_a of conjugate	**pK_a of conjugate**	**pK_a of conjugate**
acid (HCl) = −7	**acid (CH$_3$CO$_2$H) = 4.75**	**acid (H$_2$O) = 15.7**

We see that the hydroxide ion is the strongest in this series of three bases because its conjugate acid, water, is the weakest acid. We know that water is the weakest acid because it has the largest pK_a.

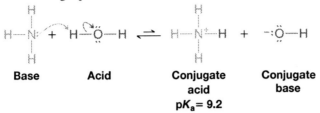

Amines are like ammonia in that they are weak bases. Dissolving ammonia in water brings about the following equilibrium:

Base	**Acid**	**Conjugate acid** $pK_a = 9.2$	**Conjugate base**

Dissolving methylamine in water causes the establishment of a similar equilibrium.

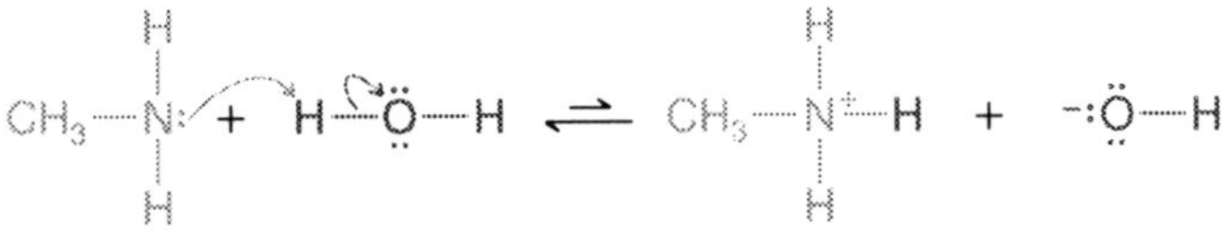

Base	**Acid**	**Conjugate acid** $pK_a = 10.6$	**Conjugate base**

Again we can relate the basicity of these substances to the strength of their conjugate acids. The conjugate acid of ammonia is the ammonium ion, NH_4^+. The pK_a of the ammonium ion is 9.2. The conjugate acid of methylamine is the $CH_3NH_3^+$ ion. This ion, called the methylaminium ion, has $pK_a = 10.6$. Since the conjugate acid of methylamine is a weaker acid than the conjugate acid of ammonia, we can conclude that methylamine is a stronger base than ammonia.

●●● SOLVED PROBLEM 3.6

Using the pK_a values in Table 3.1 decide which is the stronger base, CH_3OH or H_2O.

STRATEGY AND ANSWER: From Table 3.1, we find the pK_a values of the conjugate acids of water and methanol.

Weaker acid	$H-\overset{+}{O}-H$	$H_3C-\overset{+}{O}-H$	**Stronger acid**
	$pK_a = -1.74$	$pK_a = -2.5$	

Because water is the conjugate base of the weaker acid, it is the stronger base.

Stronger base	$H-\ddot{O}:$	$H_3C-\ddot{O}:$	**Weaker base**

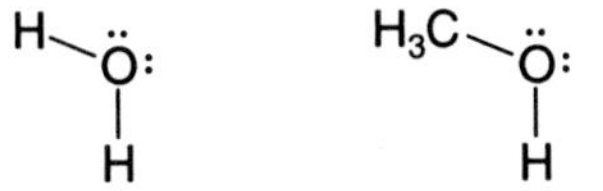

●●●

Using the pK_a values of analogous compounds in Table 3.1, predict which would be the stronger base.

PRACTICE PROBLEM 3.7

(a) 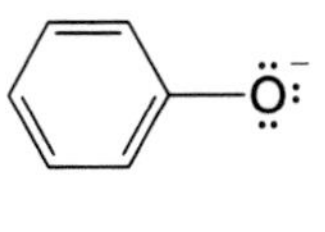 [phenoxide structure] $\ddot{O}:^-$ or [isopropoxide structure] $\ddot{O}:^-$

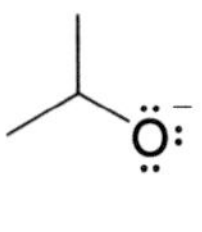

(b) $(CH_3)_3C\ddot{O}:^-$ or [acetylide structure] $\equiv:^-$

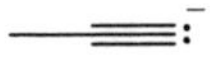

(c) 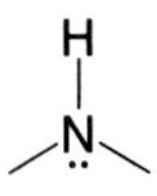 [dimethylamide structure with H on N] or [dimethyl ether oxygen structure]

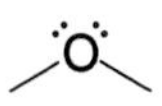

(d) 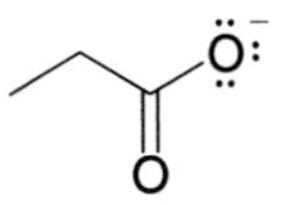 [propanoate structure] $\ddot{O}:^-$ or HO $\ddot{O}:^-$ [carbonate structure]

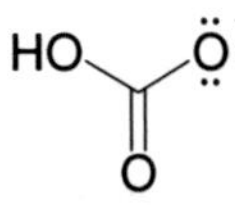

●●● **SOLVED PROBLEM 3.7**

Which would be the stronger base, HO^- or NH_3?

STRATEGY AND ANSWER: The conjugate acid of the hydroxide ion (HO^-) is H_2O, and water has $pK_a = 15.7$ (Table 3.1). The conjugate acid of ammonia is the ammonium ion $^+NH_4$, which has $pK_a = 9.2$ (meaning it is a stronger acid than water). Since ammonium ion is the stronger acid, its conjugate base NH_3 is the weaker base, and HO^-, the conjugate base of water (the weaker acid), is the stronger base.

●●●

PRACTICE PROBLEM 3.8   The pK_a of the anilinium ion ($C_6H_5\overset{+}{N}H_3$) is 4.63. On the basis of this fact, decide whether aniline ($C_6H_5NH_2$) is a stronger or weaker base than methylamine.

3.6 HOW TO PREDICT THE OUTCOME OF ACID–BASE REACTIONS

Table 3.1 gives the approximate pK_a values for a range of representative compounds. While you probably will not be expected to memorize all of the pK_a values in Table 3.1, it is a good idea to begin to learn the general order of acidity and basicity for some of the common acids and bases. The examples given in Table 3.1 are representative of their class or functional group. For example, acetic acid has a $pK_a = 4.75$, and carboxylic acids generally have pK_a values near this value (in the range $pK_a = 3$–5). Ethyl alcohol is given as an example of an alcohol, and alcohols generally have pK_a values near that of ethyl alcohol (in the pK_a range 15–18), and so on. There are exceptions, of course, and we shall learn what these exceptions are as we go on.

By learning the relative scale of acidity of common acids now, you will be able to predict whether or not an acid–base reaction will occur as written.

> **Helpful Hint**
>
> Formation of the weaker acid and base is an important general principle for predicting the outcome of acid–base reactions.

● The general principle to apply is this: **acid–base reactions always favor the formation of the weaker acid and the weaker base**.

The reason for this is that the outcome of an acid–base reaction is determined by the position of an equilibrium. Acid–base reactions are said, therefore, to be **under equilibrium control**, and reactions under equilibrium control always favor the formation of the most stable (lowest potential energy) species. The weaker acid and weaker base are more stable (lower in potential energy) than the stronger acid and stronger base.

Using this principle, we can predict that a carboxylic acid (RCO_2H) will react with aqueous NaOH in the following way because the reaction will lead to the formation of the weaker acid (H_2O) and weaker base (RCO_2^-):

| **Stronger acid** | **Stronger base** | **Weaker base** | **Weaker acid** |
| $pK_a = 3$–5 | | | $pK_a = 15.7$ |

Because there is a large difference in the value of the pK_a of the two acids, the position of equilibrium will greatly favor the formation of the products. In instances like these we commonly show the reaction with a one-way arrow even though the reaction is an equilibrium.

Consider the mixing of an aqueous solution of phenol, C_6H_5OH (see Table 3.1), and NaOH. What acid–base reaction, if any, would take place?

STRATEGY: Consider the relative acidities of the reactant (phenol) and of the acid that might be formed (water) by a proton transfer to the base (the hydroxide ion).

ANSWER: The following reaction would take place because it would lead to the formation of a weaker acid (water) from the stronger acid (phenol). It would also lead to the formation of a weaker base, C_6H_5ONa, from the stronger base, NaOH.

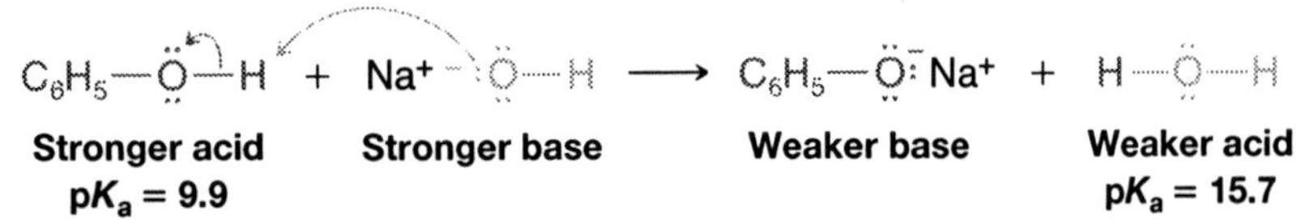

$$C_6H_5{-}\ddot{O}{-}H \ + \ Na^+ \ {:}\ddot{O}{-}H \longrightarrow C_6H_5{-}\ddot{O}{:}^- \ Na^+ \ + \ H{-}\ddot{O}{-}H$$

Stronger acid	Stronger base	Weaker base	Weaker acid
$pK_a = 9.9$			$pK_a = 15.7$

Using Table 3.1, explain why the acid–base reaction that takes place between NaH (as source of $:H^-$ ions) and CH_3OH is

$$CH_3\ddot{O}H \ + \ :H^- \longrightarrow CH_3\ddot{O}:^- \ + \ H_2$$

rather than

$$CH_3\ddot{O}H \ + \ :H^- \not\longrightarrow \ ^-:CH_2\ddot{O}H \ + \ H_2$$

ANSWER: A hydride ion is a very strong base, being the conjugate base of H_2 (a very weak acid, $pK_a = 35$). Hydride will remove the most acidic proton from CH_3OH. Although CH_3OH is not given in Table 3.1, we can compare it to CH_3CH_2OH, a similar alcohol whose hydroxyl group pK_a is 16, far more acidic than any proton attached to a carbon without a functional group (e.g., a proton of CH_3CH_3, which has $pK_a = 50$). Because the proton attached to the oxygen is much more acidic, it is removed preferentially.

●●●

Predict the outcome of the following reaction.

PRACTICE PROBLEM 3.9

$$\diagup\!\!\!\equiv \ + \ ^-NH_2 \longrightarrow$$

3.6A Water Solubility as the Result of Salt Formation

Although acetic acid and other carboxylic acids containing fewer than five carbon atoms are soluble in water, many other carboxylic acids of higher molecular weight are not appreciably soluble in water. Because of their acidity, however, *water-insoluble carboxylic acids dissolve in aqueous sodium hydroxide*; they do so by reacting to form water-soluble sodium salts:

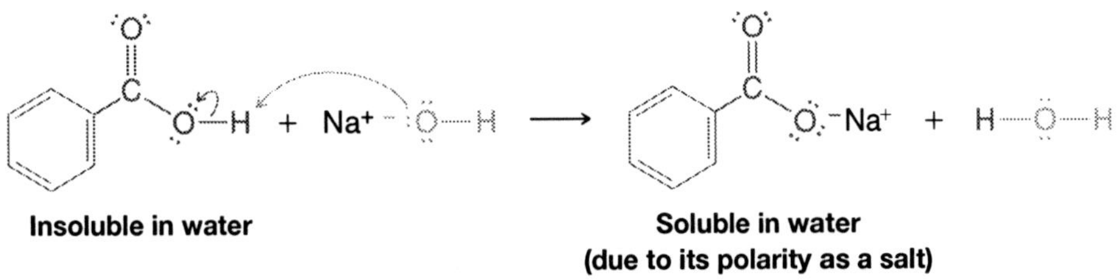

Insoluble in water	Soluble in water (due to its polarity as a salt)

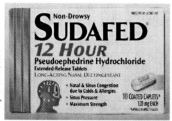

Pseudoephedrine is an amine that
is sold as its hydrochloride salt.

We can also predict that an amine will react with aqueous hydrochloric acid in the
following way:

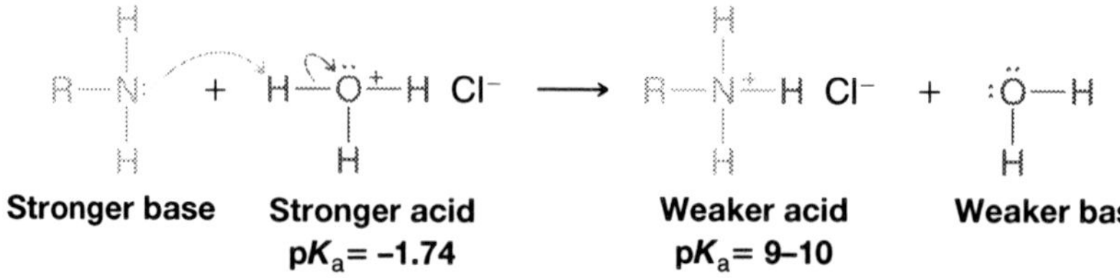

Stronger base   **Stronger acid**   **Weaker acid**   **Weaker base**
$pK_a = -1.74$ $pK_a = 9-10$

While methylamine and most amines of low molecular weight are very soluble in
water, amines with higher molecular weights, such as aniline ($C_6H_5NH_2$), have limited
water solubility. However, these *water-insoluble amines dissolve readily in hydrochloric acid*
because the acid–base reactions convert them into soluble salts:

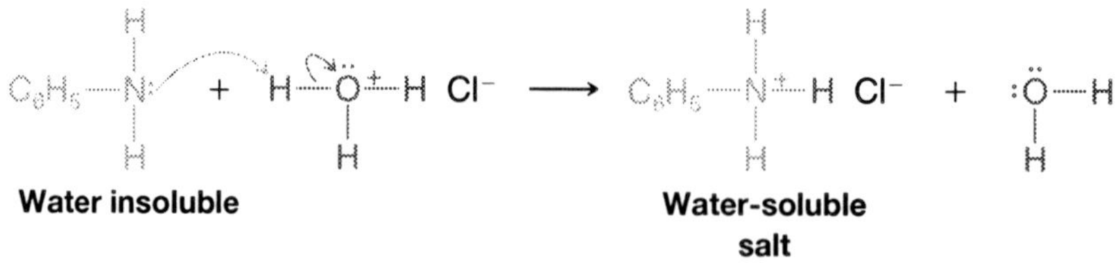

Water insoluble   **Water-soluble
salt**

● ● ◈

PRACTICE PROBLEM 3.10 Most carboxylic acids dissolve in aqueous solutions of sodium bicarbonate ($NaHCO_3$)
because, as carboxylate salts, they are more polar. Write curved arrows showing the reaction between a generic carboxylic acid and sodium bicarbonate to form a carboxylate salt
and H_2CO_3. (Note that H_2CO_3 is unstable and decomposes to carbon dioxide and water.
You do not need to show that process.)

3.7 RELATIONSHIPS BETWEEN STRUCTURE AND ACIDITY

The strength of a Brønsted–Lowry acid depends on the extent to which a proton can
be separated from it and transferred to a base. Removing the proton involves breaking a
bond to the proton, and it involves making the conjugate base more electrically negative.

When we compare compounds in a single column of the periodic table, the strength
of the bond to the proton is the dominating effect.

● Bond strength to the proton decreases as we move down the column, increasing
its acidity.

This phenomenon is mainly due to decreasing effectiveness of orbital overlap between the
hydrogen 1*s* orbital and the orbitals of successively larger elements in the column. The
less effective the orbital overlap, the weaker is the bond, and the stronger is the acid. The
acidities of the hydrogen halides furnish an example:

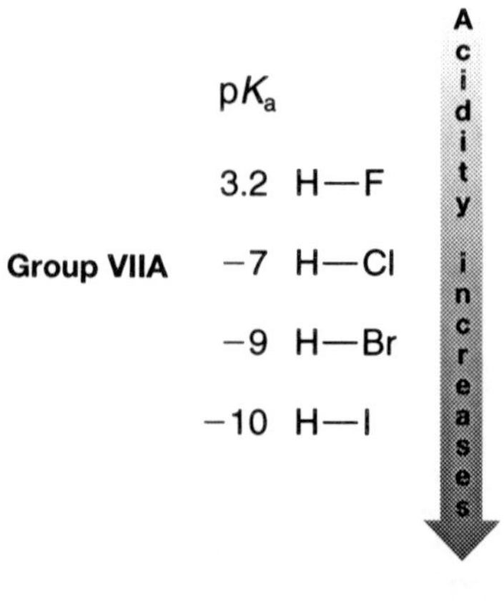

Helpful Hint

Proton acidity increases as we
descend a column in the periodic
table due to decreasing bond
strength to the proton.

pK_a

		Acidity increases →
3.2	H—F	
Group VIIA −7	H—Cl	
−9	H—Br	
−10	H—I	

Comparing the hydrogen halides with each other, H—F is the weakest acid and H—I is the strongest. This follows from the fact that the H—F bond is by far the strongest and the H—I bond is the weakest.

Because HI, HBr, and HCl are strong acids, their conjugate bases (I⁻, Br⁻, Cl⁻) are all weak bases. HF, however, is less acidic than the other hydrogen halides and fluoride ion is a stronger base. The fluoride anion is still not nearly as basic as other species we commonly think of as bases, such as the hydroxide anion, however.

- Acidity increases from left to right when we compare compounds in a given row of the periodic table.

Helpful Hint

Proton acidity increases from left to right in a given row of the periodic table due to increasing stability of the conjugate base.

Bond strengths vary somewhat, but the predominant factor becomes the electronegativity of the atom bonded to the hydrogen. The electronegativity of the atom in question affects acidity in two related ways: (1) it affects the polarity of the bond to the proton and (2) it affects the relative stability of the anion (conjugate base) that forms when the proton is lost.

We can see an example of this effect when we compare the acidities of the compounds CH_4, NH_3, H_2O, and HF. These compounds are all hydrides of first-row elements, and electronegativity increases across a row of the periodic table from left to right (see Table 1.2):

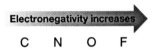

C   N   O   F

Because fluorine is the most electronegative, the bond in H—F is most polarized, and the proton in H—F is the most positive. Therefore, H—F loses a proton most readily and is the most acidic in this series:

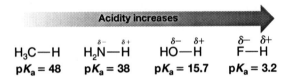

$H_3C—H$	$H_2N—H$	$HO—H$	$F—H$
$pK_a = 48$	$pK_a = 38$	$pK_a = 15.7$	$pK_a = 3.2$

Electrostatic potential maps for these compounds directly illustrate this trend based on electronegativity and increasing polarization of the bonds to hydrogen (Fig. 3.2). Almost no positive charge (indicated by the extent of color trending toward blue) is evident at the hydrogens of methane. Very little positive charge is present at the hydrogens of ammonia. This is consistent with the weak electronegativity of both carbon and nitrogen and hence with the behavior of methane and ammonia as exceedingly weak acids (pK_a values of 48 and 38, respectively). Water shows significant positive charge at its hydrogens (pK_a more than 20 units lower than ammonia), and hydrogen fluoride clearly has the highest amount of positive charge at its hydrogen (pK_a of 3.2), resulting in strong acidity.

Because H—F is the strongest acid in this series, its conjugate base, the fluoride ion (F^-), will be the weakest base. Fluorine is the most electronegative atom and it accommodates the negative charge most readily:

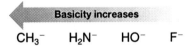

CH_3^- H_2N^- HO^- F^-

The methanide ion (CH_3^-) is the least stable anion of the four, because carbon being the least electronegative element is least able to accept the negative charge. The methanide ion, therefore, is the strongest base in this series. [The methanide ion, a **carbanion**, and the amide ion ($^-NH_2$) are exceedingly strong bases because they are the conjugate bases of extremely weak acids. We shall discuss some uses of these powerful bases in Section 3.14.]

| Methane | Ammonia | Water | Hydrogen fluoride |

FIGURE 3.2 The effect of increasing electronegativity among elements from left to right in the first row of the periodic table is evident in these maps of electrostatic potential for methane, ammonia, water, and hydrogen fluoride.

FIGURE 3.3 A summary of periodic trends in relative acidity. Acidity increases from left to right across a given row (electronegativity effect) and from top to bottom in a given column (bond strength effect) of the periodic table.

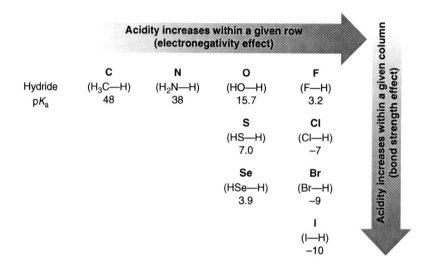

Trends in acidity within the periodic table are summarized in Fig. 3.3.

3.7A The Effect of Hybridization

● An alkyne hydrogen is weakly acid. Alkene and alkane hydrogens are essentially not acidic.

The pK_a values for ethyne, ethene, and ethane illustrate this trend.

Ethyne
pK_a = 25

Ethene
pK_a = 44

Ethane
pK_a = 50

We can explain this order of acidities on the basis of the hybridization state of carbon in each compound. Electrons of 2s orbitals have lower energy than those of 2p orbitals because *electrons in 2s orbitals tend, on the average, to be much closer to the nucleus than electrons in 2p orbitals.* (Consider the shapes of the orbitals: 2s orbitals are spherical and centered on the nucleus; 2p orbitals have lobes on either side of the nucleus and are extended into space.)

● With hybrid orbitals, **having more s character means that the electrons of the anion will, on the average, be lower in energy, and the anion will be more stable.**

The *sp* orbitals of the C—H bonds of ethyne have 50% s character (because they arise from the combination of one s orbital and one p orbital), those of the *sp²* orbitals of ethene have 33.3% s character, while those of the *sp³* orbitals of ethane have only 25% s character. This means, in effect, that the *sp* carbon atoms of ethyne act as if they were more electronegative than the *sp²* carbon atoms of ethene and the *sp³* carbon atoms of ethane. (Remember: electronegativity measures an atom's ability to hold bonding electrons close to its nucleus, and having electrons closer to the nucleus makes it more stable.)

● An *sp* carbon atom is effectively more electronegative than an *sp²* carbon, which in turn is more electronegative than an *sp³* carbon.

The effect of hybridization and effective electronegativity on acidity is borne out in the calculated electrostatic potential maps for ethyne, ethene, and ethane shown in Fig. 3.4. Some positive charge (indicated by blue color) is clearly evident on the hydrogens of ethyne (pK_a = 25), but almost no positive charge is present on the hydrogens of ethene and ethane (both having pK_a values more than 20 units greater than ethyne).

| Ethyne | Ethene | Ethane |

FIGURE 3.4 Electrostatic potential maps for ethyne, ethene, and ethane.

In summary, the order of relative acidities of ethyne, ethene, and ethane parallels the effective electronegativity of the carbon atom in each compound:

Relative Acidity of the Hydrocarbons

$$HC \equiv CH > H_2C = CH_2 > H_3C - CH_3$$

As expected based on the properties of acid–base conjugate pairs, an sp^3 carbanion is the strongest base in a series based on carbon hybridization, and an sp carbanion (an alkynide) is the weakest base. This trend is illustrated here with the conjugate bases of ethane, ethene, and ethyne.

Relative Basicity of the Carbanions

$$H_3C - CH_2{:}^- > H_2C = CH{:}^- > HC \equiv C{:}^-$$

3.7B Inductive Effects

The carbon–carbon bond of ethane is completely nonpolar because at each end of the bond there are two identical methyl groups:

$$CH_3 - CH_3$$

Ethane

The C — C bond is nonpolar.

This is not the case with the carbon–carbon bond of ethyl fluoride, however:

$$\overset{\delta+}{CH_3} \rightarrow \overset{\delta+}{CH_2} \rightarrow \overset{\delta-}{F}$$
$$2 1$$

One end of the bond, the one nearer the fluorine atom, is more negative than the other. This polarization of the carbon–carbon bond results from an intrinsic electron-attracting ability of the fluorine (because of its electronegativity) that is transmitted *through space* and *through the bonds of the molecule*. Chemists call this kind of effect an inductive effect.

- **Inductive effects** are electronic effects transmitted through bonds. The inductive effect of a group can be **electron donating** or **electron withdrawing**. Inductive effects weaken as the distance from the group increases.

In the case of ethyl fluoride, the positive charge that the fluorine imparts to C1 is greater than that imparted to C2 because the fluorine is closer to C1.

Figure 3.5 shows the dipole moment for ethyl fluoride (fluoroethane). The distribution of negative charge around the electronegative fluorine is plainly evident in the calculated electrostatic potential map.

FIGURE 3.5 Ethyl fluoride, showing its dipole moment inside a cutaway view of the electrostatic potential at its van der Waals surface.

3.8 ENERGY CHANGES

Energy is defined as the capacity to do work. The two fundamental types of energy are **kinetic energy** and **potential energy**.

Kinetic energy is the energy an object has because of its motion; it equals one-half the object's mass multiplied by the square of its velocity (i.e., $\frac{1}{2}mv^2$).

Potential energy is stored energy. It exists only when an attractive or repulsive force exists between objects. Two balls attached to each other by a spring (an analogy

FIGURE 3.6 Potential energy exists between objects that either attract or repel each other. In the case of atoms joined by a covalent bond, or objects connected by a spring, the lowest potential energy state occurs when atoms are at their ideal internuclear distance (bond length), or when a spring between objects is relaxed. Lengthening or shortening the bond distance, or compressing or stretching a spring, raises the potential energy.

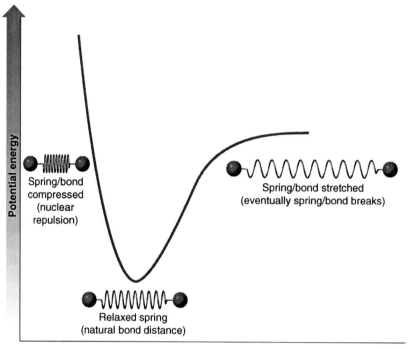

we used for covalent bonds when we discussed infrared spectroscopy in Section 2.15) can have their potential energy increased when the spring is stretched or compressed (Fig. 3.6). If the spring is stretched, an attractive force will exist between the balls. If it is compressed, a repulsive force will exist. In either instance releasing the balls will cause the potential energy (stored energy) of the balls to be converted into kinetic energy (energy of motion).

Chemical energy is a form of potential energy. It exists because attractive and repulsive electrical forces exist between different pieces of the molecules. Nuclei attract electrons, nuclei repel each other, and electrons repel each other.

It is usually impractical (and often impossible) to describe the *absolute* amount of potential energy contained by a substance. Thus we usually think in terms of its *relative potential energy*. We say that one system has *more* or *less* potential energy than another.

Another term that chemists frequently use in this context is the term **stability** or **relative stability**. *The relative stability of a system is inversely related to its relative potential energy.*

- The *more* potential energy an object has, the *less stable* it is.

Consider, as an example, the relative potential energy and the relative stability of snow when it lies high on a mountainside and when it lies serenely in the valley below. Because of the attractive force of gravity, the snow high on the mountain *has greater potential energy and is much less stable* than the snow in the valley. This greater potential energy of the snow on the mountainside can become converted into the enormous kinetic energy of an avalanche. By contrast, the snow in the valley, with its lower potential energy and with its greater stability, is incapable of releasing such energy.

3.8A Potential Energy and Covalent Bonds

Atoms and molecules possess potential energy—often called chemical energy—that can be released as heat when they react. Because heat is associated with molecular motion, this release of heat results from a change from potential energy to kinetic energy.

From the standpoint of covalent bonds, the state of greatest potential energy is the state of free atoms, the state in which the atoms are not bonded to each other at all. This is true because the formation of a chemical bond is always accompanied by the lowering

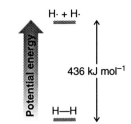

of the potential energy of the atoms (cf. Fig. 1.8). Consider as an example the formation of hydrogen molecules from hydrogen atoms:

$$H\cdot \; + \; H\cdot \longrightarrow H{-}H \qquad \Delta H^\circ = -436 \text{ kJ mol}^{-1}*$$

The potential energy of the atoms decreases by 436 kJ mol^{-1} as the covalent bond forms. This potential energy change is illustrated graphically in Fig. 3.7.

A convenient way to represent the relative potential energies of molecules is in terms of their relative **enthalpies**, or **heat contents**, H. (*Enthalpy* comes from *en + thalpein*, Greek: to heat.) The difference in relative enthalpies of reactants and products in a chemical change is called the enthalpy change and is symbolized by ΔH°. [The Δ (delta) in front of a quantity usually means the difference, or change, in the quantity. The superscript $^\circ$ indicates that the measurement is made under standard conditions.]

By convention, the sign of ΔH° for exothermic reactions (those evolving heat) is negative. Endothermic reactions (those that absorb heat) have a positive ΔH°. The heat of reaction, ΔH°, measures the change in enthalpy of the atoms of the reactants as they are converted to products. For an exothermic reaction, the atoms have a smaller enthalpy as products than they do as reactants. For endothermic reactions, the reverse is true.

FIGURE 3.7 The relative potential energies of hydrogen atoms and a hydrogen molecule.

3.9 THE RELATIONSHIP BETWEEN THE EQUILIBRIUM CONSTANT AND THE STANDARD FREE-ENERGY CHANGE, ΔG°

An important **relationship exists between the equilibrium constant (K_{eq}) and the standard free-energy change (ΔG°). for a reaction.**[†]

$$\Delta G^\circ = -RT \ln K_{eq}$$

where R is the gas constant and equals 8.314 J K^{-1} mol^{-1} and T is the absolute temperature in kelvins (K).

This equation tells us the following:

- **For a reaction to favor the formation of products when equilibrium is reached it must have a negative value for ΔG°.** Free energy must be *lost* as the reactants become products; that is, the reaction must go down an energy hill. For such a reaction the equilibrium constant will be greater than one. If ΔG° is more negative than 13 kJ mol^{-1} the equilibrium constant will be large enough for the reaction to *go to completion*, meaning that more than 99% of the reactants will be converted to products when equilibrium is reached.

- **For reactions with a positive ΔG°, the formation of products at equilibrium is unfavorable.** The equilibrium constant for these reactions will be less than one.

The free-energy change (ΔG°) has two components, the **enthalpy change** (ΔH°) and the **entropy change** (ΔS°). The relationship between these three thermodynamic quantities is

$$\Delta G^\circ = \Delta H^\circ - T \Delta S^\circ$$

We have seen (Section 3.8) that ΔH° is associated with changes in bonding that occur in a reaction. If, collectively, stronger bonds are formed in the products than existed in the starting materials, then ΔH° will be negative (i.e., the reaction is *exothermic*). If the reverse is true, then ΔH° will be positive (the reaction is *endothermic*). **A negative value for ΔH°, therefore, will contribute to making ΔG° negative and will consequently**

---

*The unit of energy in SI units is the joule, J, and 1 cal = 4.184 J. (Thus 1 kcal = 4.184 kJ.) A kilocalorie of energy (1000 cal) is the amount of energy in the form of heat required to raise by 1 °C the temperature of 1 kg (1000 g) of water at 15 °C.

[†]By standard free-energy change (ΔG°), we mean that the products and reactants are taken as being in their standard states (1 atm of pressure for a gas and 1 M for a solution). The free-energy change is often called the **Gibbs free-energy change**, to honor the contributions to thermodynamics of J. Willard Gibbs, a professor of mathematical physics at Yale University in the latter part of the nineteenth century.

favor the formation of products. For the ionization of an acid, the less positive or more negative the value of $\Delta H°$, the stronger the acid will be.

Entropy changes have to do with *changes in the relative order of a system*. **The more random a system is, the greater is its entropy**. Therefore, a positive entropy change $(+\Delta S°)$ is always associated with a change from a more ordered system to a less ordered one. A negative entropy change $(-\Delta S°)$ accompanies the reverse process. In the equation $\Delta G° = \Delta H° - T \Delta S°$, the entropy change (multiplied by T) is preceded by a negative sign; this means that **a positive entropy change (from order to disorder) makes a negative contribution to $\Delta G°$ and is energetically favorable for the formation of products**.

For many reactions in which the number of molecules of products equals the number of molecules of reactants (e.g., when two molecules react to produce two molecules), the entropy change will be small. This means that except at high temperatures (where the term $T \Delta S°$ becomes large even if $\Delta S°$ is small) the value of $\Delta H°$ will largely determine whether or not the formation of products will be favored. If $\Delta H°$ is large and negative (if the reaction is exothermic), then the reaction will favor the formation of products at equilibrium. If $\Delta H°$ is positive (if the reaction is endothermic), then the formation of products will be unfavorable.

• • •

PRACTICE PROBLEM 3.11 State whether you would expect the entropy change, $\Delta S°$, to be positive, negative, or approximately zero for each of the following reactions. (Assume the reactions take place in the gas phase.)

(a) $A + B \longrightarrow C$ **(b)** $A + B \longrightarrow C + D$ **(c)** $A \longrightarrow B + C$

• • •

PRACTICE PROBLEM 3.12 **(a)** What is the value of $\Delta G°$ for a reaction where $K_{eq} = 1$?   **(b)** Where $K_{eq} = 10$? (The change in $\Delta G°$ required to produce a 10-fold increase in the equilibrium constant is a useful term to remember.)   **(c)** Assuming that the entropy change for this reaction is negligible (or zero), what change in $\Delta H°$ is required to produce a 10-fold increase in the equilibrium constant?

3.10 ACIDITY: CARBOXYLIC ACIDS VERSUS ALCOHOLS

Carboxylic acids are weak acids, typically having pK_a values in the range of 3–5. Alcohols, by comparison, have pK_a values in the range of 15–18, and essentially do not give up a proton unless exposed to a very strong base.

To understand the reasons for this difference, let's consider acetic acid and ethanol as representative examples of simple carboxylic acids and alcohols.

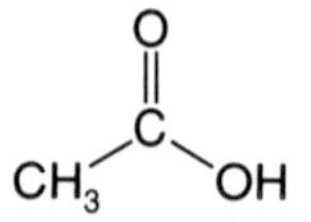

Acetic acid
$pK_a = 4.75$
$\Delta G° = 27$ kJ mol^{-1}

Ethanol
$pK_a = 16$
$\Delta G° = 90.8$ kJ mol^{-1}

($\Delta G°$ values are for OH proton ionization.)

Using the pK_a for acetic acid (4.75), one can calculate (Section 3.9) that the free-energy change ($\Delta G°$) for ionization of the carboxyl proton of acetic acid is $+27$ kJ mol^{-1}, a moderately endergonic (unfavorable) process, since the $\Delta G°$ value is positive. Using the pK_a of ethanol (16), one can calculate that the corresponding free-energy change for ionization of the hydroxyl proton of ethanol is $+90.8$ kJ mol^{-1}, a much more endergonic (and hence even less favorable) process. These calculations reflect the fact that ethanol

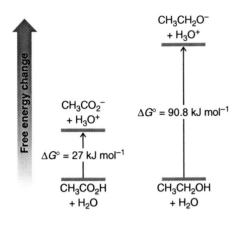

FIGURE 3.8 A diagram comparing the free-energy changes that accompany ionization of acetic acid and ethanol. Ethanol has a larger positive free-energy change and is a weaker acid because its ionization is more unfavorable.

is much less acidic than acetic acid. Figure 3.8 depicts the magnitude of these energy changes in a relative sense.

How do we explain the much greater acidity of carboxylic acids than alcohols? Consider first the structural changes that occur if both acetic acid and ethanol act as acids by donating a proton to water.

Acetic Acid Acting as an Acid

Acetic acid   Water   Acetate ion   Hydronium ion

Ethanol Acting as an Acid

$CH_3CH_2—\overset{..}{\underset{..}{O}}—H$ + $\overset{..}{\underset{..}{O}}$ ⇌ $CH_3CH_2—\overset{..}{\underset{..}{O}}:^-$ + $H—\overset{+}{\underset{H}{O}:}$

Ethanol   Water   Ethoxide ion   Hydronium ion

What we need to focus on is the relative stability of the conjugate bases derived from a carboxylic acid and an alcohol. This is because the smaller free-energy change for ionization of a carboxylic acid (e.g., acetic acid) as compared to an alcohol (e.g., ethanol) has been attributed to greater stabilization of the negative charge in the carboxylate ion as compared to an alkoxide ion. Greater stabilization of the carboxylate ion appears to arise from two factors: (a) delocalization of charge (as depicted by resonance structures for the carboxylate ion, Section 3.10A), and (b) an inductive electron-withdrawing effect (Section 3.7B).

3.10A The Effect of Delocalization

Delocalization of the negative charge is possible in a carboxylate anion, but it is not possible in an alkoxide ion. We can show how delocalization is possible in carboxylate ions by writing resonance structures for the acetate ion.

Two Resonance Structures That Can Be Written for Acetate Anion

Resonance stabilization in acetate ion
(The structures are equivalent and there is no requirement for charge separation.)

The two resonance structures we drew above distributed the negative charge to both oxygen atoms of the carboxylate group, thereby stabilizing the charge. This is a **delocalization effect** (by resonance). In contrast, no resonance structures are possible for an alkoxide ion, such as ethoxide. (You may wish to review the rules we have given in Section 1.8 for writing proper resonance structures.)

$$CH_3-CH_2-\overset{..}{\underset{..}{O}}-H \; + \; H_2O \; \rightleftharpoons \; CH_3-CH_2-\overset{..}{\underset{..}{O}}{:}^- \; + \; H_3O^+$$

**No resonance   No resonance
stabilization   stabilization**

No resonance structures can be drawn for either ethanol or ethoxide anion.

A rule to keep in mind is that **charge delocalization is always a stabilizing factor**, and because of charge stabilization, the energy difference for formation of a carboxylate ion from a carboxylic acid is less than the energy difference for formation of an alkoxide ion from an alcohol. Since the energy difference for ionization of a carboxylic acid is less than for an alcohol, the carboxylic acid is a stronger acid.

3.10B The Inductive Effect

We have already shown how the negative charge in a carboxylate ion can be delocalized over two oxygen atoms by resonance. However, the electronegativity of these oxygen atoms further helps to stabilize the charge, by what is called an **inductive electron-withdrawing effect**. A carboxylate ion has two oxygen atoms whose combined electronegativity stabilizes the charge more than in an alkoxide ion, which has only a single electronegative oxygen atom. In turn, this lowers the energy barrier to forming the carboxylate ion, making a carboxylic acid a stronger acid than an alcohol. This effect is evident in electrostatic potential maps depicting approximately the bonding electron density for the two anions (Fig. 3.9). Negative charge in the acetate anion is evenly distributed over the two oxygen atoms, whereas in ethoxide the negative charge is localized on its sole oxygen atom (as indicated by red in the electrostatic potential map).

It is also reasonable to expect that a carboxylic acid would be a stronger acid than an alcohol when considering each as a neutral molecule (i.e., prior to loss of a proton), because both functional groups have a highly polarized O—H bond, which in turn weakens the bond to the hydrogen atom. However, the significant electron-withdrawing effect of the carbonyl group in acetic acid and the absence of an adjacent electron-withdrawing group in ethanol make the carboxylic acid hydrogen much more acidic than the alcohol hydrogen.

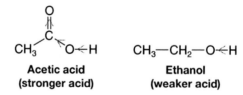

**Acetic acid   Ethanol
(stronger acid)   (weaker acid)**

Electrostatic potential maps at approximately the bond density surface for acetic acid and ethanol (Fig. 3.10) clearly show the positive charge at the carbonyl carbon of acetic acid, as compared to the CH_2 carbon of ethanol.

Acetate anion

Ethoxide anion

FIGURE 3.9 Calculated electrostatic potential maps at a surface approximating the bonding electron density for acetate anion and ethoxide anion. Although both molecules carry the same −1 net charge, acetate stabilizes the charge better by dispersing it over both oxygen atoms.

FIGURE 3.10 Maps of electrostatic potential at approximately the bond density surface for acetic acid and ethanol. The positive charge at the carbonyl carbon of acetic acid is evident in the blue color of the electrostatic potential map at that position, as compared to the hydroxyl carbon of ethanol. The inductive electron-withdrawing effect of the carbonyl group in carboxylic acids contributes to the acidity of this functional group.

Acetic acid

Ethanol

3.10C Summary and a Comparison of Conjugate Acid–Base Strengths

In summary, the greater acidity of a carboxylic acid is predominantly due to the ability of its conjugate base (a carboxylate ion) to stabilize a negative charge better than an alkoxide ion, the conjugate base of an alcohol. In other words, the conjugate base of a carboxylic acid is a weaker base than the conjugate base of an alcohol. Therefore, since there is an inverse strength relationship between an acid and its conjugate base, a carboxylic acid is a stronger acid than an alcohol.

> **Helpful Hint**
>
> The more stable a conjugate base is, the stronger the corresponding acid.

●●●
PRACTICE PROBLEM 3.13

Draw contributing resonance structures and a hybrid resonance structure that explain two related facts: the carbon–oxygen bond distances in the acetate ion are the same, and the oxygens of the acetate ion bear equal negative charges.

3.10D Inductive Effects of Other Groups

The acid-strengthening effect of other electron-attracting groups (other than the carbonyl group) can be shown by comparing the acidities of acetic acid and chloroacetic acid:

$$pK_a = 4.75 \qquad pK_a = 2.86$$

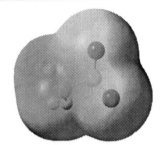
Acetate anion

This is an example of a **substituent effect**. The greater acidity of chloroacetic acid can be attributed, in part, to the extra electron-attracting inductive effect of the electronegative chlorine atom. By adding its inductive effect to that of the carbonyl group and the oxygen, it makes the hydroxyl proton of chloroacetic acid even more positive than that of acetic acid. It also stabilizes the chloroacetate ion that is formed when the proton is lost *by dispersing its negative charge* (Fig. 3.11):

$$+ \; H_2O \; \rightleftharpoons \; \cdots \; + \; H_3O^+$$

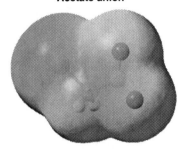
Chloroacetate anion

FIGURE 3.11 The electrostatic potential maps for acetate and chloroacetate ions show the relatively greater ability of chloroacetate to disperse the negative charge.

Dispersal of charge always makes a species more stable, and, as we have seen now in several instances, **any factor that stabilizes the conjugate base of an acid increases the strength of the acid.** (In Section 3.11, we shall see that entropy changes in the solvent are also important in explaining the increased acidity of chloroacetic acid.)

●●● **SOLVED PROBLEM 3.10**

Which compound in each pair would be most acidic?

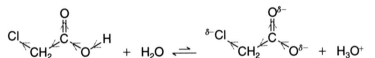

STRATEGY AND ANSWER: Decide what is similar in each pair and what is different. In pair (a), the difference is the halogen substituent on the carbon adjacent to the carboxyl group. In the first example it is fluorine; in the second it is bromine. Fluorine is much more electronegative (electron-attracting) than bromine (Table 1.2); therefore it will be able to disperse the negative charge of the anion formed when the proton is lost. Thus the first compound will be the stronger acid. In pair (b), the difference is the position of the fluorine substituents. In the second compound the fluorine is closer to the carboxyl group where it will be better able to disperse the negative charge in the anion formed when the proton is lost. The second compound will be the stronger acid.

• • ◦

PRACTICE PROBLEM 3.14 Which would you expect to be the stronger acid? Explain your reasoning in each instance.

(a) CH_2ClCO_2H or $CHCl_2CO_2H$

(b) CCl_3CO_2H or $CHCl_2CO_2H$

(c) CH_2FCO_2H or CH_2BrCO_2H

(d) CH_2FCO_2H or $CH_2FCH_2CO_2H$

3.11 THE EFFECT OF THE SOLVENT ON ACIDITY

In the absence of a solvent (i.e., in the gas phase), most acids are far weaker than they are in solution. In the gas phase, for example, acetic acid is estimated to have a pK_a of about 130 (a K_a of $\sim 10^{-130}$)! The reason is this: when an acetic acid molecule donates a proton to a water molecule in the gas phase, the ions that are formed are oppositely charged particles and the particles must become separated:

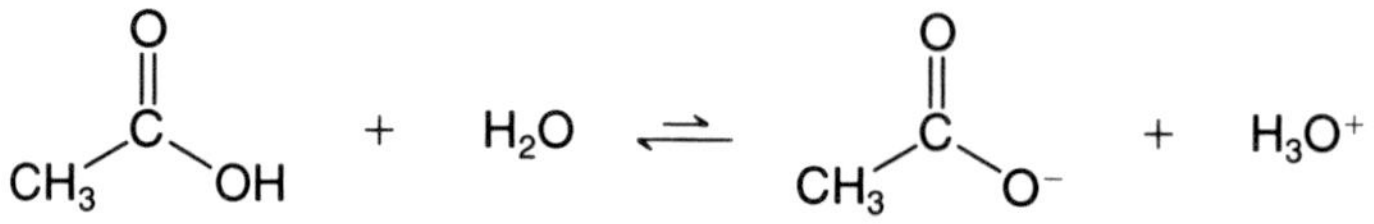

In the absence of a solvent, separation is difficult. In solution, solvent molecules surround the ions, insulating them from one another, stabilizing them, and making it far easier to separate them than in the gas phase.

In a solvent such as water, called a protic solvent, solvation by hydrogen bonding is important (Section 2.13D).

• A **protic solvent** is one that has a hydrogen atom attached to a strongly electronegative element such as oxygen or nitrogen.

A protic solvent, therefore, can form hydrogen bonds to the unshared electron pairs of an acid and its conjugate base, but they may not stabilize both equally.

• The stability of a conjugate base is enhanced if it is solvated to a greater extent than the corresponding acid.

Relative acidity cannot be predicted solely on the basis of solvation, however. Steric factors affecting solvation, and the relative order or disorder of the solvent molecules (entropic parameters), can enhance or decrease acidity.

3.12 ORGANIC COMPOUNDS AS BASES

If an organic compound contains an atom with an unshared electron pair, it is a potential base. We saw in Section 3.5C that compounds with an unshared electron pair on a nitrogen atom (i.e., amines) act as bases. Let us now consider several examples in which organic compounds having an unshared electron pair on an oxygen atom act in the same way.

Dissolving gaseous HCl in methanol brings about an acid–base reaction much like the one that occurs with water (Section 3.1A):

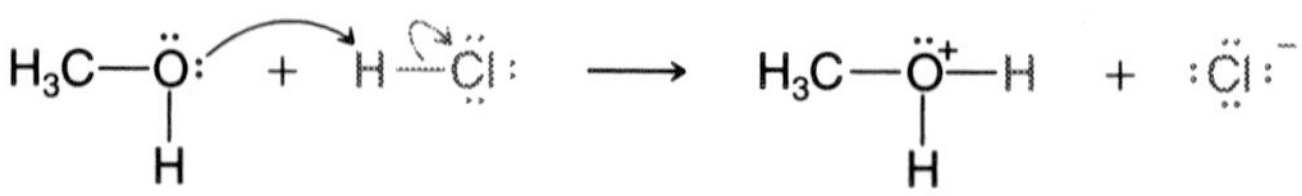

The conjugate acid of the alcohol is often called a **protonated alcohol**, although more formally it is called an **alkyloxonium ion** or simply an **oxonium ion**.

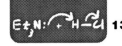

Alcohols, in general, undergo this same reaction when they are treated with solutions of strong acids such as HCl, HBr, HI, and H_2SO_4:

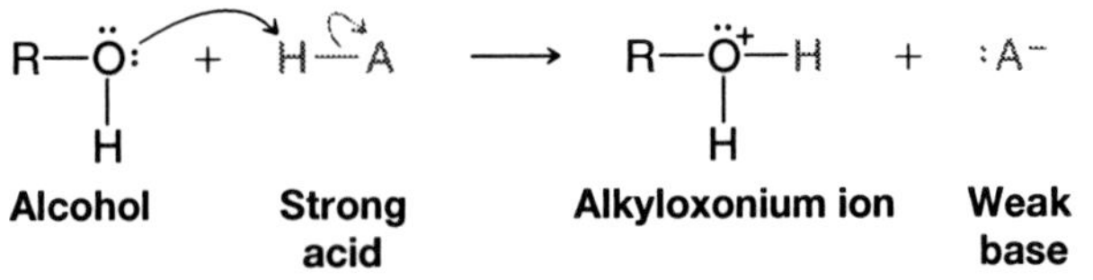

R—Ö: + H—A ⟶ R—Ö⁺—H + :A⁻
| | | |
H H

Alcohol **Strong acid** **Alkyloxonium ion** **Weak base**

So, too, do ethers:

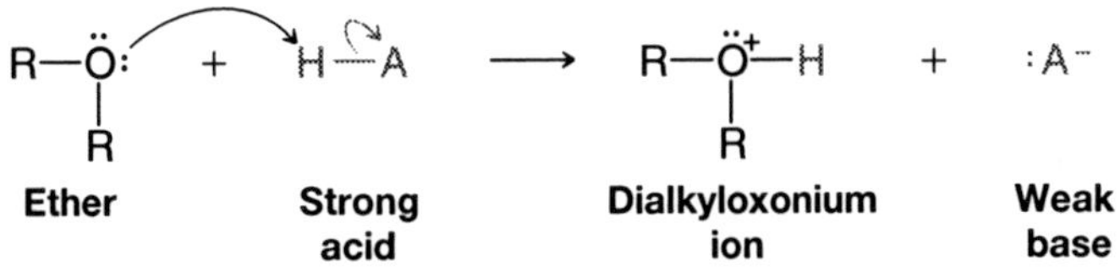

R—Ö: + H—A ⟶ R—Ö⁺—H + :A⁻
| | | |
R R

Ether **Strong acid** **Dialkyloxonium ion** **Weak base**

Compounds containing a carbonyl group also act as bases in the presence of a strong acid:

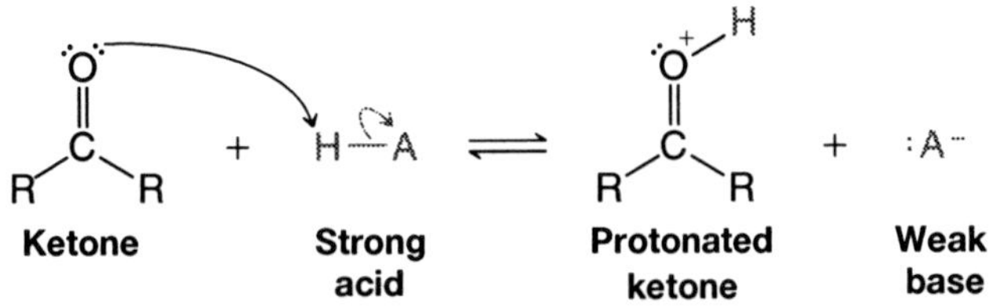

Ketone **Strong acid** ⇌ **Protonated ketone** **Weak base**

Proton transfer reactions like these are often the first step in many reactions that alcohols, ethers, aldehydes, ketones, esters, amides, and carboxylic acids undergo. The pK_a values for some of these protonated intermediates are given in Table 3.1.

An atom with an unshared electron pair is not the only locus that confers basicity on an organic compound. The π bond of an alkene can have the same effect. Later we shall study many reactions in which, as a first step, alkenes react with a strong acid by accepting a proton in the following way:

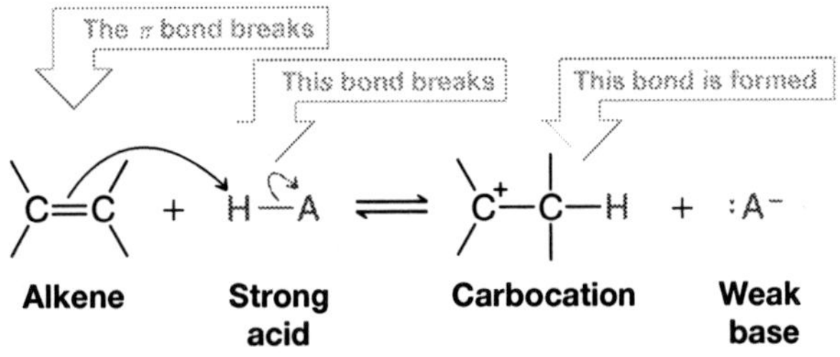

> The π bond breaks
> This bond breaks
> This bond is formed

C=C + H—A ⇌ C⁺—C—H + :A⁻
| |
H

Alkene **Strong acid** **Carbocation** **Weak base**

In this reaction the electron pair of the π bond of the alkene is used to form a bond between one carbon of the alkene and the proton donated by the strong acid. Notice that two bonds are broken in this process: the π bond of the double bond and the bond between the proton of the acid and its conjugate base. One new bond is formed: a bond between a carbon of the alkene and the proton. This process leaves the other carbon of the alkene trivalent, electron deficient, and with a formal positive charge. A compound containing a carbon of this type is called a **carbocation** (Section 3.4). As we shall see in later chapters, carbocations are unstable intermediates that react further to produce stable molecules.

Helpful Hint

Proton transfers are a common first step in many reactions we shall study.

● ● ●
PRACTICE PROBLEM 3.15

It is a general rule that any organic compound containing oxygen, nitrogen, or a multiple bond will dissolve in concentrated sulfuric acid. Explain the basis of this rule in terms of acid–base reactions and intermolecular forces.

3.13 A MECHANISM FOR AN ORGANIC REACTION

In Chapter 6 we shall begin our study of organic reaction mechanisms in earnest. Let us consider now one mechanism as an example, one that allows us to apply some of the chemistry we have learned in this chapter and one that, at the same time, will reinforce what we have learned about how curved arrows are used to illustrate mechanisms.

Dissolving *tert*-butyl alcohol in concentrated (concd) aqueous hydrochloric acid soon results in the formation of *tert*-butyl chloride. The reaction is a **substitution reaction**:

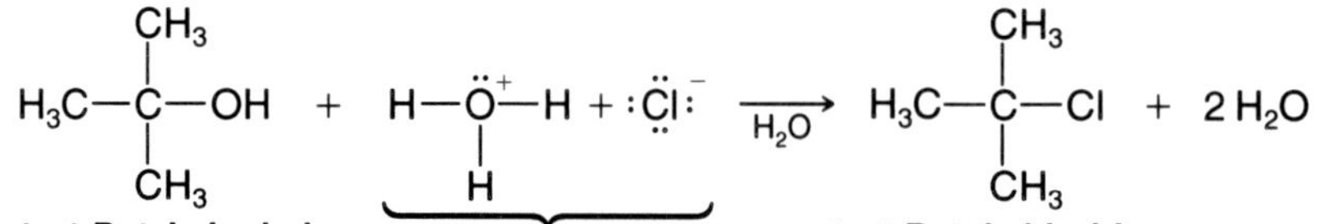

tert-Butyl alcohol (soluble in H_2O)   Concd HCl   *tert*-Butyl chloride (insoluble in H_2O)

That a reaction has taken place is obvious when one actually does the experiment. *tert*-Butyl alcohol is soluble in the aqueous medium; however, *tert*-butyl chloride is not, and consequently it separates from the aqueous phase as another layer in the flask. It is easy to remove this nonaqueous layer, purify it by distillation, and thus obtain the *tert*-butyl chloride.

Considerable evidence, described later, indicates that the reaction occurs in the following way.

[A MECHANISM FOR THE REACTION — **Reaction of *tert*-Butyl Alcohol with Concentrated Aqueous HCl**]

Step 1

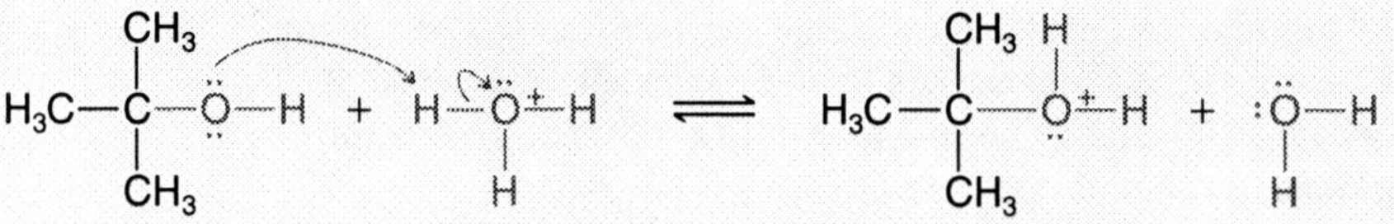

tert-Butyloxonium ion

tert-Butyl alcohol acts as a base and accepts a proton from the hydronium ion. (Chloride anions are spectators in this step of the reaction.)

The products are a protonated alcohol and water (the conjugate acid and base).

Step 2

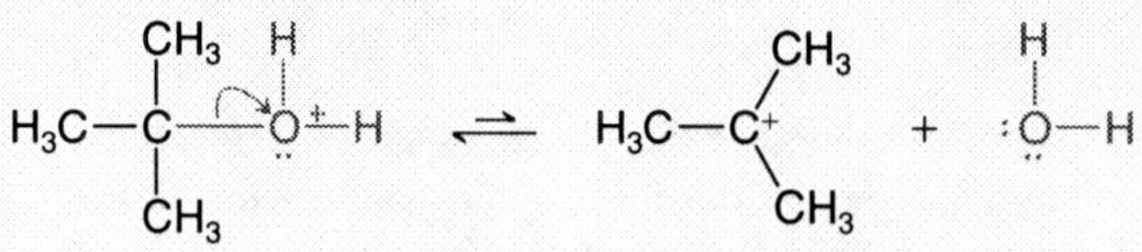

Carbocation

The bond between the carbon and oxygen of the tert-butyloxonium ion breaks heterolytically, leading to the formation of a carbocation and a molecule of water.

Step 3

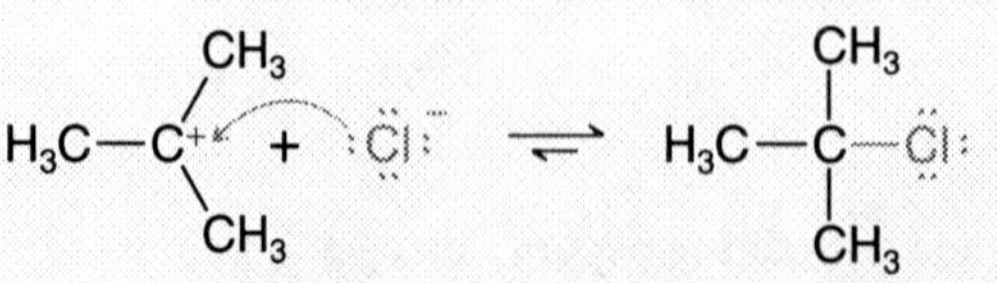

tert-Butyl chloride

The carbocation, acting as a Lewis acid, accepts an electron pair from a chloride ion to become the product.

Notice that **all of these steps involve acid–base reactions**. Step 1 is a straightforward Brønsted acid–base reaction in which the alcohol oxygen removes a proton from the hydronium ion. Step 2 is the reverse of a Lewis acid–base reaction. In it, the carbon–oxygen bond of the protonated alcohol breaks heterolytically as a water molecule departs with the electrons of the bond. This happens, in part, because the alcohol is protonated. The presence of a formal positive charge on the oxygen of the protonated alcohol weakens the carbon–oxygen bond by drawing the electrons in the direction of the positive oxygen. Step 3 is a Lewis acid–base reaction, in which a chloride anion (a Lewis base) reacts with the carbocation (a Lewis acid) to form the product.

A question might arise: why doesn't a molecule of water (also a Lewis base) instead of a chloride ion react with the carbocation? After all, there are many water molecules around, since water is the solvent. The answer is that this step does occur sometimes, but it is simply the reverse of step 2. That is to say, not all of the carbocations that form go on directly to become product. Some react with water to become protonated alcohols again. However, these will dissociate again to become carbocations (even if, before they do, they lose a proton to become the alcohol again). Eventually, however, most of them are converted to the product because, under the conditions of the reaction, the equilibrium of the last step lies far to the right, and the product separates from the reaction mixture as a second phase.

3.14 ACIDS AND BASES IN NONAQUEOUS SOLUTIONS

If you were to add sodium amide ($NaNH_2$) to water in an attempt to carry out a reaction using the amide ion ($^-NH_2$) as a very powerful base, the following reaction would take place immediately:

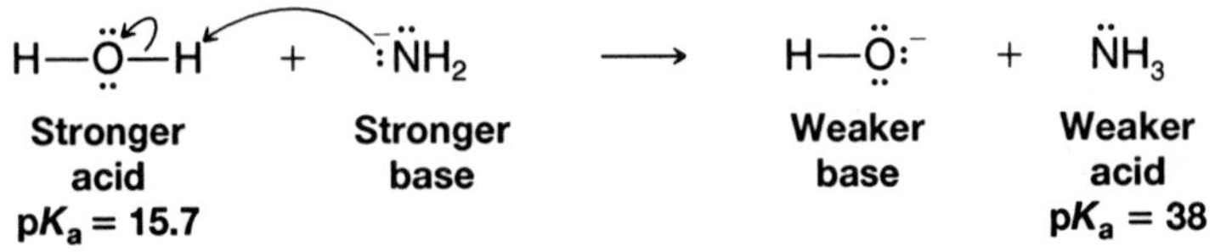

$$H\!-\!\ddot{O}\!-\!H \;+\; {}^-\!:\!\ddot{N}H_2 \longrightarrow H\!-\!\ddot{O}\!:^- \;+\; \ddot{N}H_3$$

Stronger acid	Stronger base	Weaker base	Weaker acid
$pK_a = 15.7$			$pK_a = 38$

The amide ion would react with water to produce a solution containing hydroxide ion (a much weaker base) and ammonia. This example illustrates what is called the *leveling effect of the solvent*. *Water, the solvent here, donates a proton to any base stronger than a hydroxide ion*. Therefore, *it is not possible to use a base stronger than hydroxide ion in aqueous solution*.

We can use bases stronger than hydroxide ion, however, if we choose solvents that are weaker acids than water. We can use amide ion (e.g., from $NaNH_2$) in a solvent such as hexane, diethyl ether, or liquid NH_3 (the liquified gas, bp $-33\,°C$, not the aqueous solution that you may have used in your general chemistry laboratory). All of these solvents are very weak acids (we generally don't think of them as acids), and therefore they will not donate a proton even to the strong base $^-NH_2$.

We can, for example, convert ethyne to its conjugate base, a carbanion, by treating it with sodium amide in liquid ammonia:

$$H\!-\!C\!\equiv\!C\!-\!H \;+\; {}^-\!:\!\ddot{N}H_2 \xrightarrow[\;NH_3\;]{liquid,} H\!-\!C\!\equiv\!C\!:^- \;+\; :NH_3$$

Stronger acid $pK_a = 25$	Stronger base (from $NaNH_2$)	Weaker base	Weaker acid $pK_a = 38$

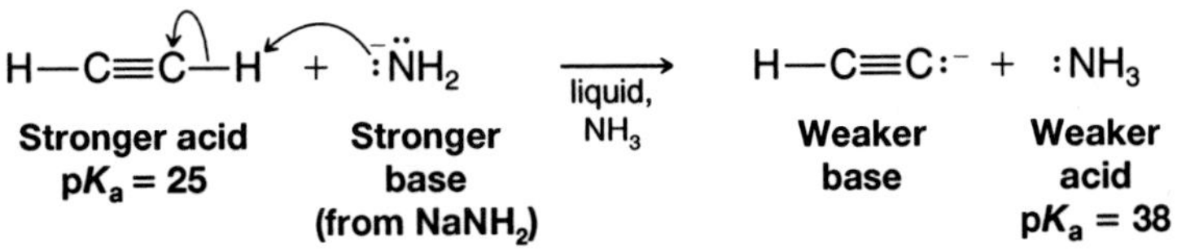

Helpful Hint

We shall use this reaction as part of our introduction to organic synthesis in Chapter 7.

Most **terminal alkynes** (alkynes with a proton attached to a triply bonded carbon) have pK_a values of about 25; therefore, all react with sodium amide in liquid ammonia in the same way that ethyne does. The general reaction is

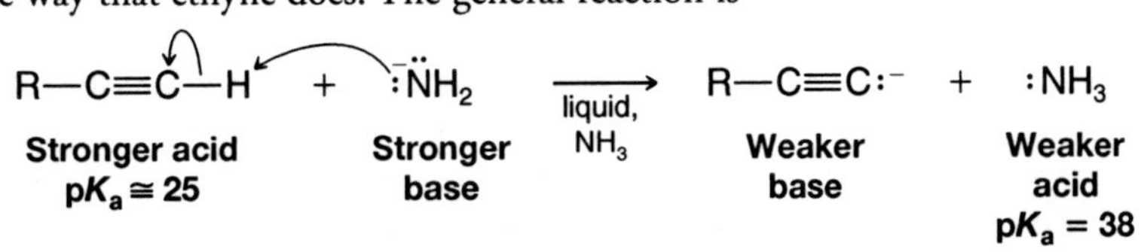

$$R\!-\!C\!\equiv\!C\!-\!H \;+\; {}^-\!:\!\ddot{N}H_2 \xrightarrow[\;NH_3\;]{liquid,} R\!-\!C\!\equiv\!C\!:^- \;+\; :NH_3$$

Stronger acid $pK_a \cong 25$	Stronger base	Weaker base	Weaker acid $pK_a = 38$

Alcohols are often used as solvents for organic reactions because, being somewhat less polar than water, they dissolve less polar organic compounds. Using alcohols as solvents also offers the advantage of using RO^- ions (called **alkoxide ions**) as bases. Alkoxide ions are somewhat stronger bases than hydroxide ions because alcohols are weaker acids than water. For example, we can create a solution of sodium ethoxide (CH_3CH_2ONa) in ethyl alcohol by adding sodium hydride (NaH) to ethyl alcohol. We use a large excess of ethyl alcohol because we want it to be the solvent. Being a very strong base, the hydride ion reacts readily with ethyl alcohol:

$$CH_3CH_2\overset{..}{\underset{..}{O}}\!-\!H \ + \ :H^- \ \xrightarrow{\text{ethyl alcohol}} \ CH_3CH_2\overset{..}{\underset{..}{O}}\!:^- \ + \ H_2$$

Stronger acid $pK_a = 16$	**Stronger base** (from NaH)		**Weaker base**	**Weaker acid** $pK_a = 35$

The *tert*-butoxide ion, $(CH_3)_3CO^-$, in *tert*-butyl alcohol, $(CH_3)_3COH$, is a stronger base than the ethoxide ion in ethyl alcohol, and it can be prepared in a similar way:

$$(CH_3)_3C\overset{..}{\underset{..}{O}}\!-\!H \ + \ :H^- \ \xrightarrow{\text{tert-butyl alcohol}} \ (CH_3)_3C\overset{..}{\underset{..}{O}}\!:^- \ + \ H_2$$

Stronger acid $pK_a = 18$	**Stronger base** (from NaH)		**Weaker base**	**Weaker acid** $pK_a = 35$

Although the carbon–lithium bond of an alkyllithium (RLi) has covalent character, it is polarized so as to make the carbon negative:

$$\overset{\delta^-}{R}\!-\!\!\leftarrow\!\overset{\delta^+}{Li}$$

Alkyllithium reagents react as though they contain alkanide ($R:^-$) ions and, being the conjugate bases of alkanes, alkanide ions are the strongest bases that we shall encounter. Ethyllithium (CH_3CH_2Li), for example, acts as though it contains an ethanide ($CH_3CH_2:^-$) carbanion. It reacts with ethyne in the following way:

$$H\!-\!C\!\equiv\!C\!-\!H \ + \ ^-\!:CH_2CH_3 \ \xrightarrow{\text{hexane}} \ H\!-\!C\!\equiv\!C:^- \ + \ CH_3CH_3$$

Stronger acid $pK_a = 25$	**Stronger base** (from CH_3CH_2Li)		**Weaker base**	**Weaker acid** $pK_a = 50$

Alkyllithiums can be easily prepared by allowing an alkyl bromide to react with lithium metal in an ether solvent (such as diethyl ether). See Section 12.6.

PRACTICE PROBLEM 3.16 Write equations for the acid–base reaction that would occur when each of the following compounds or solutions are mixed. In each case label the stronger acid and stronger base, and the weaker acid and weaker base, by using the appropriate pK_a values (Table 3.1). If no appreciable acid–base reaction would occur, you should indicate this.

(a) NaH is added to CH_3OH.
(b) $NaNH_3$ is added to CH_3CH_2OH.
(c) Gaseous NH_2 is added to ethyllithium in hexane.

(d) NH_4Cl is added to sodium amide in liquid ammonia.
(e) $(CH_3)_3CONa$ is added to H_2O.
(f) NaOH is added to $(CH_3)_3COH$.

3.15 ACID–BASE REACTIONS AND THE SYNTHESIS OF DEUTERIUM- AND TRITIUM-LABELED COMPOUNDS

Chemists often use compounds in which deuterium or tritium atoms have replaced one or more hydrogen atoms of the compound as a method of "labeling" or identifying particular hydrogen atoms. Deuterium (^2H) and tritium (^3H) are isotopes of hydrogen with masses of 2 and 3 atomic mass units (amu), respectively.

One way to introduce a deuterium or tritium atom into a specific location in a molecule is through the acid–base reaction that takes place when a very strong base is treated with D_2O or T_2O (water that has deuterium or tritium in place of its hydrogens). For example, treating a solution containing $(CH_3)_2CHLi$ (isopropyllithium) with D_2O results in the formation of propane labeled with deuterium at the central atom:

$$
\begin{array}{c}
CH_3 \\
| \\
CH_3CH:^-Li^+
\end{array}
\quad + \quad D_2O \quad \xrightarrow{\text{hexane}} \quad
\begin{array}{c}
CH_3 \\
| \\
CH_3CH\text{—}D
\end{array}
\quad + \quad DO^-
$$

Isopropyl-
lithium
*(stronger
base)*

*(stronger
acid)*

2-Deuterio-
propane
*(weaker
acid)*

*(weaker
base)*

●●● **SOLVED PROBLEM 3.11**

Assuming you have available propyne, a solution of sodium amide in liquid ammonia, and T_2O, show how you would prepare the tritium-labeled compound $CH_3C \equiv CT$.

ANSWER: First add propyne to sodium amide in liquid ammonia. The following acid–base reaction will take place:

$$CH_3C \equiv CH \;+\; {}^-NH_2 \;\xrightarrow{\text{liq. ammonia}}\; CH_3C \equiv C:^- \;+\; NH_3$$

Stronger
acid

Stronger
base

Weaker
base

Weaker
acid

Then adding T_2O (a much stronger acid than NH_3) to the solution will produce $CH_3C \equiv CT$:

$$CH_3C \equiv C:^- \;+\; T_2O \;\xrightarrow{\text{liq. ammonia}}\; CH_3C \equiv CT \;+\; TO^-$$

Stronger
base

Stronger
acid

Weaker
acid

Weaker
base

●●●

Complete the following acid–base reactions:

PRACTICE PROBLEM 3.17

(a) $HC \equiv CH + NaH \xrightarrow{\text{hexane}}$

(b) The solution obtained in **(a)** $+ D_2O \longrightarrow$

(c) $CH_3CH_2Li + D_2O \xrightarrow{\text{hexane}}$

(d) $CH_3CH_2OH + NaH \xrightarrow{\text{hexane}}$

(e) The solution obtained in **(d)** $+ T_2O \longrightarrow$

(f) $CH_3CH_2CH_2Li + D_2O \xrightarrow{\text{hexane}}$

3.16 APPLICATIONS OF BASIC PRINCIPLES

Again we review how certain basic principles apply to topics we have studied in this chapter.

Electronegativity Differences Polarize Bonds We saw how this principle applies to the heterolysis of bonds to carbon in Section 3.4 and in explaining the strength of acids in Sections 3.7 and 3.10B.

Polarized Bonds Underlie Inductive Effects In Section 3.10B we saw how polarized bonds explain effects that we call *inductive effects* and how these effects are part of the explanation for why carboxylic acids are more acidic than corresponding alcohols.

Opposite Charges Attract This principle is fundamental to understanding *Lewis acid–base theory* as we saw in Section 3.3A. Positively charged centers in molecules that are electron pair acceptors are attracted to negatively charged centers in electron pair donors. In Section 3.4 we saw this principle again in the reaction of carbocations (positively charged Lewis acids) with anions (which are negatively charged by definition) and other Lewis bases.

Nature Prefers States of Lower Potential Energy In Section 3.8A we saw how this principle explains the energy changes—called *enthalpy changes*—that take place when covalent bonds form, and in Section 3.9 we saw the role enthalpy changes play in explaining how large or how small the equilibrium constant for a reaction is. The lower the potential energy of the products, the larger is the equilibrium constant, and the more favored is the formation of the products when equilibrium is reached. This section also introduced a related principle: **Nature prefers disorder to order**—or, to put it another way, *a positive entropy change* for a reaction favors the formation of the products at equilibrium.

Resonance Effects Can Stabilize Molecules and Ions When a molecule or ion can be represented by two or more equivalent resonance structures, then the molecule or ion will be stabilized (will have its potential energy lowered) by delocalization of charge. In Section 3.10A we saw how this effect helps explain the greater acidity of carboxylic acids when compared to corresponding alcohols.

WHY Do These Topics Matter?]

THE RARITY OF CHEMICAL DISCOVERIES WITHOUT KNOWLEDGE OF THE MECHANISMS

From the time of its initial discovery in the 1630s until the middle of the twentieth century, the natural product quinine was the world's only real treatment for malaria. Yet, because it could only be obtained in small quantities from relatively remote places of the globe, it was a medicine that effectively was available to only a small number of very wealthy or well-connected individuals. In light of this issue, scientists began to wonder whether quinine could be synthesized in the laboratory, an idea that was first put to the test in 1856 by a graduate student in England named William Henry Perkin. Perkin's plan for synthesis was based on an idea posited in 1849 by his mentor, August Wilhelm von Hofmann, that quinine could be prepared from the constituents of coal tar. This notion was based on the balanced chemical equation shown below. The formulas were all that was known at the time, not the actual structures. We realize today that there was no chance for success in this endeavor simply because there is no mechanism by which these chemicals could react in the right way. Fortune, however, sometimes arrives in unexpected ways.

$$C_{10}H_{13}N \quad + \quad C_{10}H_{13}N \quad + \quad 3/2\ O_2 \quad \longrightarrow \quad C_{20}H_{24}N_2O_2 \quad + \quad H_2O$$

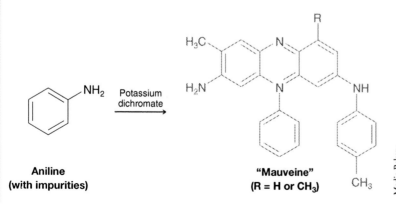

N-Allyltoluidine   **N-Allyltoluidine**   **Quinine**

Perkin did his most important experiment on this problem in a laboratory at his family home, an experiment in which he altered his supervisor's idea ever so slightly by using a different starting material (aniline, containing several different contaminants) and heating it in the presence of a strong oxidant (potassium dichromate). What resulted was a dark tar that looked a bit like asphalt. Although such products are often the result of reactions gone wrong, Perkin attempted to see if he could get anything in the tarry residue to dissolve by adding different solvents. Some did nothing, but when he added ethanol, a beautiful purple-colored solution was formed. This solution proved capable of turning any light-colored fabric the exact same purple shade. Although not quinine, what Perkin had discovered was the first synthetic dye, a way to color fabric a shade previously reserved for royalty. Indeed, before Perkin's discovery, the only way to obtain a purple-colored dye was by the tedious isolation of mucous secretions of select Mediterranean snails.

Aniline
(with impurities)

"Mauveine"
(R = H or CH₃)

W. H. Perkin

Perkin ended up making a fortune from his discovery, a material he called mauveine, which is actually composed of two compounds. The more important outcome, however, was that it showed for the first time that organic chemistry could really change the world, launching an entire industry of other chemists looking to make ever more fanciful and wonderful colors not readily found in nature.

The key message, though, is that no matter how wonderful this story is, it is only one of a handful of cases in which there was such a significant outcome in the absence of any real chemical knowledge of mechanism. Major discoveries are much more likely when it is known what the given compounds might actually do when they react together! Otherwise, organic chemistry would be just alchemy. That might explain why it took nearly another century of work before quinine actually succumbed to laboratory synthesis.

To learn more about these topics, see:

1. Garfield, S. *Mauve: How One Man Invented a Color that Changed the world*. Faber and Faber, **2001**, p. 240.
2. Nicolaou, K. C.; Montagnon, T. *Molecules that Changed the World*. Wiley-VCH: Weinheim, **2008**, p. 366.
3. Meth-Cohn, O; Smith, M. "What did W. D. Perkin actually make when he oxidised aniline to obtain mauveine?", *J. Chem. Soc. Perkin Trans 1*, **1994**, 5–7.

SUMMARY AND REVIEW TOOLS

In Chapter 3 you studied acid–base chemistry, one of the most important topics needed to learn organic chemistry. If you master acid–base chemistry you will be able to understand most of the reactions that you study in organic chemistry, and by understanding how reactions work, you will be able to learn and remember them more easily.

You have reviewed the Brønsted–Lowry definition of acids and bases and the meanings of pH and pK_a. You have learned to identify the most acidic hydrogen atoms in a molecule based on a comparison of pK_a values. You will see in many cases that Brønsted–Lowry acid–base reactions either initiate or complete an organic reaction, or prepare an organic molecule for further reaction. The Lewis definition of acids and bases may have been new to you. However, you will see over and over again that Lewis acid–base reactions which involve either the donation of an electron pair to form a new covalent bond or the departure of an electron pair to break a covalent bond are central steps in many organic reactions. The vast majority of organic reactions you will study are either Brønsted–Lowry or Lewis acid–base reactions.

Your knowledge of organic structure and polarity from Chapters 1 and 2 has been crucial to your understanding of acid–base reactions. You have seen that stabilization of charge by delocalization is key to determining how readily an acid will give up a proton, or how readily a base will accept a proton. In addition, you have learned the essential skill of drawing curved arrows to accurately show the movement of electrons in these processes. With these concepts and skills you will be prepared to understand how organic reactions occur on a step-by-step basis—something organic chemists call "a mechanism for the reaction."

So, continue to work hard to master acid–base chemistry and other fundamentals. Your toolbox is quickly filling with the tools you need for overall success in organic chemistry!

The study aids for this chapter include key terms and concepts (which are hyperlinked to the glossary from the bold, blue terms in the *WileyPLUS* version of the book at wileyplus.com) and a Concept Map after the end-of-chapter problems.

PROBLEMS PLUS

Note to Instructors: Many of the homework problems are available for assignment via *WileyPLUS*, an online teaching and learning solution.

BRØNSTED–LOWRY ACIDS AND BASES

3.18 What is the conjugate base of each of the following acids?

(a) NH_3 (b) H_2O (c) H_2 (d) $HC \equiv CH$ (e) CH_3OH (f) H_3O^+

3.19 List the bases you gave as answers to Exercise 3.18 in order of decreasing basicity.

3.20 What is the conjugate acid of each of the following bases?

(a) HSO_4^- (b) H_2O (c) CH_3NH_2 (d) $^-NH_2$ (e) $CH_3\bar{C}H_2$ (f) $CH_3CO_2^-$

3.21 List the acids you gave as answers to Exercise 3.20 in order of decreasing acidity.

LEWIS ACIDS AND BASES

3.22 Designate the Lewis acid and Lewis base in each of the following reactions:

(a) 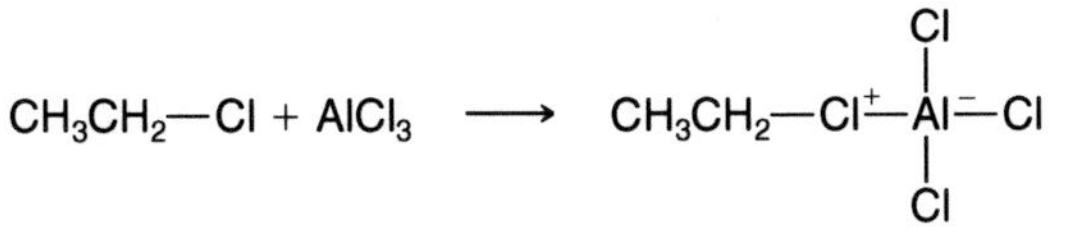 $CH_3CH_2{-}Cl + AlCl_3 \longrightarrow CH_3CH_2{-}\overset{+}{Cl}{-}\overset{Cl}{\underset{Cl}{\overset{|}{\overset{=}{Al}}}}{-}Cl$

(c) 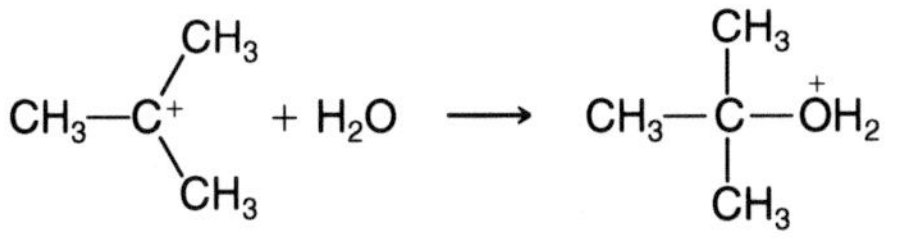 $CH_3{-}\overset{CH_3}{\underset{CH_3}{\overset{|}{\overset{+}{C}}}} + H_2O \longrightarrow CH_3{-}\overset{CH_3}{\underset{CH_3}{\overset{|}{\underset{|}{C}}}}{-}\overset{+}{O}H_2$

(b) 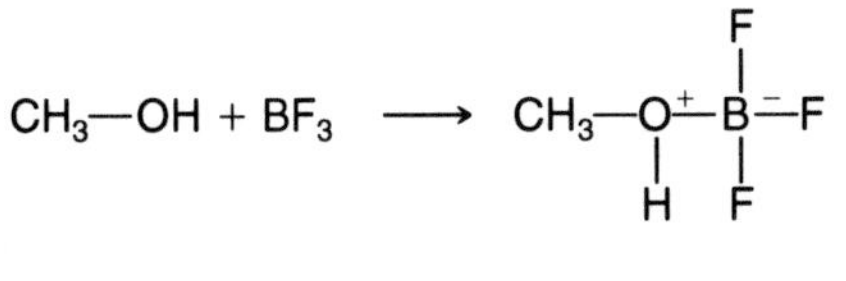 $CH_3{-}OH + BF_3 \longrightarrow CH_3{-}\overset{+}{\underset{H}{\overset{|}{O}}}{-}\overset{F}{\underset{F}{\overset{|}{\overset{-}{B}}}}{-}F$

CURVED-ARROW NOTATION

3.23 Rewrite each of the following reactions using curved arrows and show all nonbonding electron pairs:

(a) CH_3OH + HI $\longrightarrow$ $CH_3\overset{+}{O}H_2$ + I$^-$

(b) CH_3NH_2 + HCl $\longrightarrow$ $CH_3\overset{+}{N}H_3$ + Cl$^-$

(c) 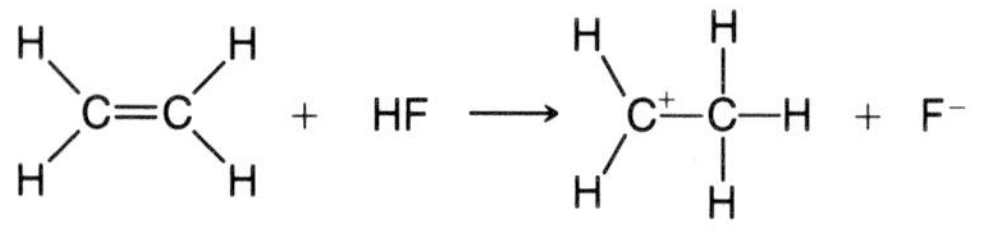 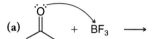 + HF $\longrightarrow$ 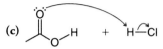 + F$^-$

3.24 Follow the curved arrows and write the products.

(a)    + BF$_3$ $\longrightarrow$

(b) 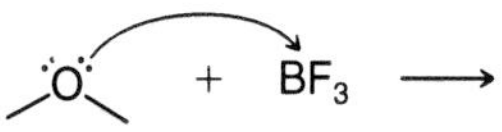 :Ö.   + BF$_3$ $\longrightarrow$

(c) + H⌒Cl

(d) + $CH_3CH_2CH_2CH_2$—Li

3.25 Write an equation, using the curved-arrow notation, for the acid–base reaction that will take place when each of the following are mixed. If no appreciable acid–base reaction takes place, because the equilibrium is unfavorable, you should so indicate.

(a) Aqueous NaOH and $CH_3CH_2CO_2H$

(b) Aqueous NaOH and $C_6H_5SO_3H$

(c) CH_3CH_2ONa in ethyl alcohol and ethyne

(d) CH_3CH_2Li in hexane and ethyne

(e) CH_3CH_2Li in hexane and ethyl alcohol

ACID–BASE STRENGTH AND EQUILIBRIA

3.26 When methyl alcohol is treated with NaH, the product is $CH_3O^-Na^+$ (and H_2) and not Na^+ $^-CH_2OH$ (and H_2). Explain why this is so.

3.27 What reaction will take place if ethyl alcohol is added to a solution of $HC\equiv C{:}^-$ Na^+ in liquid ammonia?

3.28 **(a)** The K_a of formic acid (HCO_2H) is 1.77×10^{-4}. What is the pK_a? **(b)** What is the K_a of an acid whose $pK_a = 13$?

3.29 Acid HA has $pK_a = 20$; acid HB has $pK_a = 10$.

(a) Which is the stronger acid?

(b) Will an acid–base reaction with an equilibrium lying to the right take place if Na^+A^- is added to HB? Explain your answer.

3.30 Starting with appropriate unlabeled organic compounds, show syntheses of each of the following:

(a) C_6H_5—C≡C—T

(b) 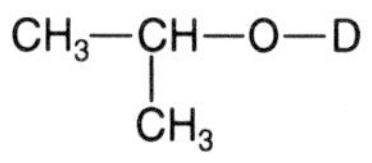 CH_3—CH—O—D
           |
          CH_3

(c) $CH_3CH_2CH_2OD$

3.31 **(a)** Arrange the following compounds in order of decreasing acidity and explain your answer: $CH_3CH_2NH_2$, CH_3CH_2OH, and $CH_3CH_2CH_3$. **(b)** Arrange the conjugate bases of the acids given in part (a) in order of increasing basicity and explain your answer.

3.32 Arrange the following compounds in order of decreasing acidity:

(a) $CH_3CH=CH_2$, $CH_3CH_2CH_3$, $CH_3C\equiv CH$

(b) $CH_3CH_2CH_2OH$, $CH_3CH_2CO_2H$, $CH_3CHClCO_2H$

(c) CH_3CH_2OH, $CH_3CH_2\overset{+}{O}H_2$, CH_3OCH_3

3.33 Arrange the following in order of increasing basicity:

(a) CH_3NH_2, $CH_3\overset{+}{N}H_3$, $CH_3\bar{N}H$

(b) CH_3O^-, $CH_3\bar{N}H$, $CH_3\bar{C}H_2$

(c) $CH_3CH=\bar{C}H$, $CH_3CH_2\bar{C}H_2$, $CH_3C\equiv C^-$

GENERAL PROBLEMS

3.34 Whereas H_3PO_4 is a triprotic acid, H_3PO_3 is a diprotic acid. Draw structures for these two acids that account for this difference in behavior.

3.35 Supply the curved arrows necessary for the following reactions:

(a)

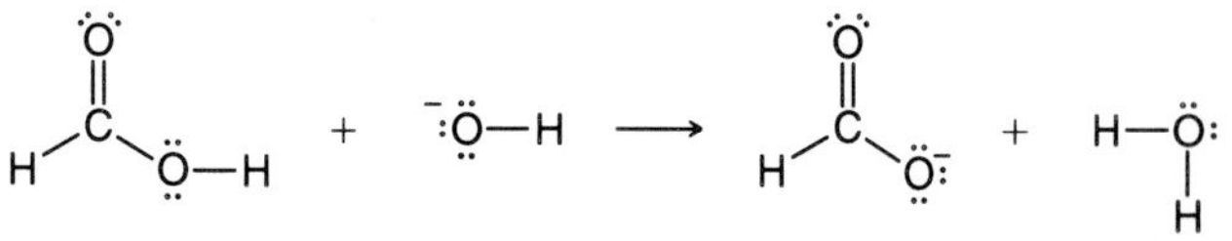

(b)

$$\underset{\underset{H}{\overset{O}{\|}}}{C}\overset{}{\underset{}{}}\text{O}-CH_3 \quad + \quad \overset{-}{:}\ddot{O}-H \quad \longrightarrow \quad H-\underset{\underset{\ddot{O}-CH_3}{|}}{\overset{\overset{:\ddot{O}:^-}{|}}{C}}-\ddot{O}-H$$

(c)

$$H-\underset{\underset{:\ddot{O}-CH_3}{|}}{\overset{\overset{:\ddot{O}:^-}{|}}{C}}-\ddot{O}-H \quad \longrightarrow \quad \underset{\underset{H}{}}{\overset{O}{\|}}C\overset{}{\underset{}{}}\ddot{O}-H \quad + \quad \overset{-}{:}\ddot{O}-CH_3$$

(d) $\quad H-\ddot{O}:^- \ + \ CH_3-\ddot{I}: \quad \longrightarrow \quad H-\ddot{O}-CH_3 \ + \ :\ddot{I}:^-$

(e) $\quad H-\ddot{O}:^- \ + \ H-CH_2-\underset{\underset{CH_3}{|}}{\overset{\overset{CH_3}{|}}{C}}-\ddot{C}l: \quad \longrightarrow \quad \underset{H_2C}{}\overset{\overset{CH_3}{|}}{C}\overset{}{\underset{CH_3}{}} \ + \ :\ddot{C}l:^- \ + \ H-\ddot{O}-H$

3.36 Glycine is an amino acid that can be obtained from most proteins. In solution, glycine exists in equilibrium between two forms:

$$H_2NCH_2CO_2H \rightleftharpoons H_3\overset{+}{N}CH_2CO_2^-$$

(a) Consult Table 3.1 and state which form is favored at equilibrium.

(b) A handbook gives the melting point of glycine as 262 °C (with decomposition). Which of the structures given above best represents glycine?

3.37 Malonic acid, $HO_2CCH_2CO_2H$, is a diprotic acid. The pK_a for the loss of the first proton is 2.83; the pK_a for the loss of the second proton is 5.69. **(a)** Explain why malonic acid is a stronger acid than acetic acid ($pK_a = 4.75$). **(b)** Explain why the anion, $^-O_2CCH_2CO_2H$, is so much less acidic than malonic acid itself.

3.38 The free-energy change, $\Delta G°$, for the ionization of acid HA is 21 kJ mol^{-1}; for acid HB it is −21 kJ mol^{-1}. Which is the stronger acid?

3.39 At 25 °C the enthalpy change, $\Delta H°$, for the ionization of trichloroacetic acid is +6.3 kJ mol^{-1} and the entropy change, $\Delta S°$, is +0.0084 kJ mol^{-1} K^{-1}. What is the pK_a of trichloroacetic acid?

3.40 The compound at right has (for obvious reasons) been given the trivial name **squaric acid**. Squaric acid is a diprotic acid, with both protons being more acidic than acetic acid. In the dianion obtained after the loss of both protons, all of the carbon–carbon bonds are the same length as well as all of the carbon–oxygen bonds. Provide a resonance explanation for these observations.

Squaric acid

CHALLENGE PROBLEMS

3.41 $CH_3CH_2SH + CH_3O^- \longrightarrow$ **A** (contains sulfur) + **B**

$\quad$ **A** $+ \ \underset{\overset{\diagdown O \diagup}{}}{CH_2-CH_2} \ \longrightarrow$ **C** (which has the partial structure **A**—CH_2CH_2O)

$\quad$ **C** $+ \ H_2O \ \longrightarrow$ **D** $+$ **E** (which is inorganic)

(a) Given the above sequence of reactions, draw structures for **A** through **E**.

(b) Rewrite the reaction sequence, showing all nonbonding electron pairs and using curved arrows to show electron pair movements.

3.42 First, complete and balance each of the equations below. Then, choosing among ethanol, hexane, and liquid ammonia, state which (there may be more than one) might be suitable solvents for each of these reactions. Disregard the practical limitations that come from consideration of "like dissolves like" and base your answers only on relative acidities.

(a) $CH_3(CH_2)_8OD \ + \ CH_3(CH_2)_8Li \ \longrightarrow$ $\qquad$ **(c)** $HCl \ + \ \langle\!\!\bigcirc\!\!\rangle-NH_2 \ \longrightarrow$

(b) $NaNH_2 \ + \ CH_3C{\equiv}CH \ \longrightarrow$

$\quad$ (The conjugate acid of this amine, aniline, has a pK_a of 4.63.)

3.43 Dimethylformamide (DMF), $HCON(CH_3)_2$, is an example of a polar aprotic solvent, aprotic meaning it has no hydrogen atoms attached to highly electronegative atoms.

(a) Draw its dash structural formula, showing unshared electron pairs.

(b) Draw what you predict to be its most important resonance forms [one is your answer to part (a)].

(c) DMF, when used as the reaction solvent, greatly enhances the reactivity of nucleophiles (e.g., ^-CN from sodium cyanide) in reactions like this:

$$NaCN + CH_3CH_2Br \longrightarrow CH_3CH_2C{\equiv}N + NaBr$$

$\quad$ Suggest an explanation for this effect of DMF on the basis of Lewis acid–base considerations. (*Hint:* Although water or an alcohol solvates both cations and anions, DMF is only effective in solvating cations.)

3.44 As noted in Table 3.1, the pK_a of acetone, CH_3COCH_3, is 19.2.

(a) Draw the bond-line formula of acetone and of any other contributing resonance form.

(b) Predict and draw the structure of the conjugate base of acetone and of any other contributing resonance form.

(c) Write an equation for a reaction that could be used to synthesize CH_3COCH_2D.

3.45 Formamide ($HCONH_2$) has a pK_a of approximately 25. Predict, based on the map of electrostatic potential for formamide shown here, which hydrogen atom(s) has this pK_a value. Support your conclusion with arguments having to do with the electronic structure of formamide.

LEARNING GROUP PROBLEMS

Suppose you carried out the following synthesis of 3-methylbutyl ethanoate (isoamyl acetate):

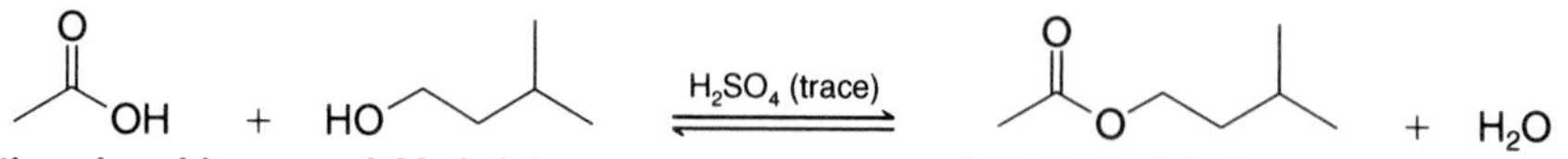

As the chemical equation shows, 3-methyl-1-butanol (also called isoamyl alcohol or isopentyl alcohol) was mixed with an excess of acetic acid (ethanoic acid by its systematic name) and a trace of sulfuric acid (which serves as a catalyst). This reaction is an equilibrium reaction, so it is expected that not all of the starting materials will be consumed. The equilibrium should lie quite far to the right due to the excess of acetic acid used, but not completely.

After an appropriate length of time, isolation of the desired product from the reaction mixture was begun by adding a volume of 5% aqueous sodium bicarbonate ($NaHCO_3$ has an effective pK_a of 7) roughly equal to the volume of the reaction mixture. Bubbling occurred and a mixture consisting of two layers resulted—a basic aqueous layer and an organic layer. The layers were separated and the aqueous layer was removed. The addition of aqueous sodium bicarbonate to the layer of organic materials and separation of the layers were repeated twice. Each time the predominantly aqueous layers were removed, they were combined in the same collection flask. The organic layer that remained after the three bicarbonate extractions was dried and then subjected to distillation in order to obtain a pure sample of 3-methylbutyl ethanoate (isoamyl acetate).

1. List all the chemical species likely to be present at the end of the reaction but before adding aqueous $NaHCO_3$. Note that the H_2SO_4 was not consumed (since it is a catalyst), and is thus still available to donate a proton to atoms that can be protonated.

2. Use a table of pK_a values, such as Table 3.1, to estimate pK_a values for any potentially acidic hydrogens in each of the species you listed in part 1 (or for the conjugate acid).

3. Write chemical equations for all the acid–base reactions you would predict to occur (based on the pK_a values you used) when the species you listed above encounter the aqueous sodium bicarbonate solution. (*Hint*: Consider whether each species might be an acid that could react with $NaHCO_3$.)

4. (a) Explain, on the basis of polarities and solubility, why separate layers formed when aqueous sodium bicarbonate was added to the reaction mixture. (*Hint*: Most sodium salts of organic acids are soluble in water, as are neutral oxygen-containing organic compounds of four carbons or less.)

(b) List the chemical species likely to be present after the reaction with $NaHCO_3$ in (i) the organic layer and (ii) the aqueous layer.

(c) Why was the aqueous sodium bicarbonate extraction step repeated three times?

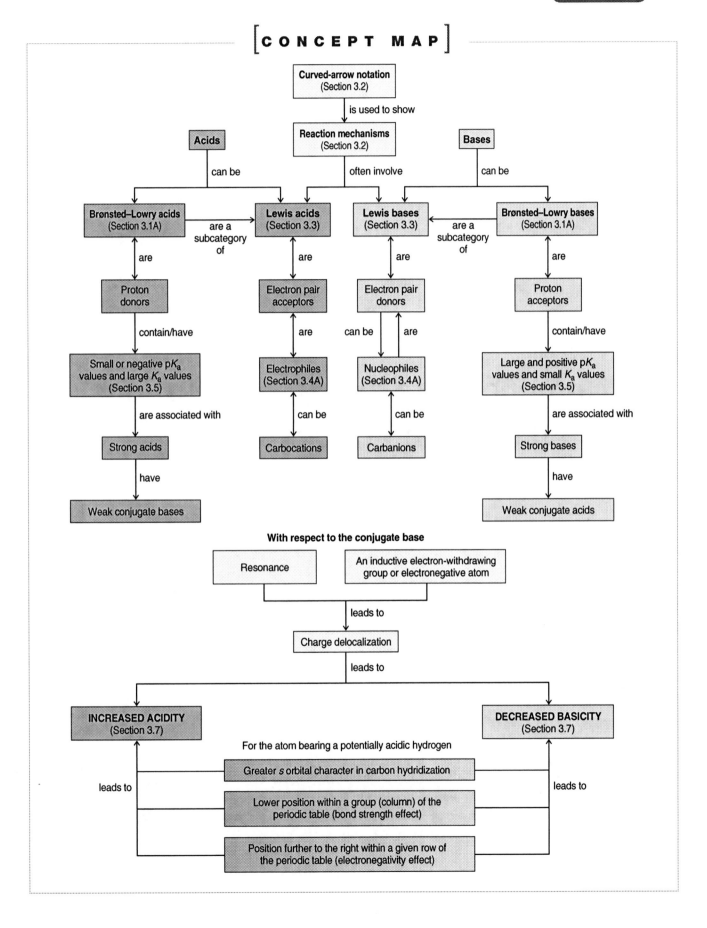

[CONCEPT MAP]

Nomenclature and Conformations of Alkanes and Cycloalkanes

Diamond is an exceptionally hard material. One reason diamond is so strong is that it contains a rigid network of carbon-carbon bonds. Muscle, on the other hand, which also contains many carbon-carbon bonds, is strong yet has great flexibility. This remarkable contrast in properties, from the rigidity of diamond to the flexibility of muscles, depends on whether rotation is possible about individual carbon-carbon bonds. In this chapter we shall consider changes in molecular structure and energy that result from rotation about carbon-carbon bonds, using a process called conformational analysis.

We learned in Chapter 2 that our study of organic chemistry can be organized around functional groups. Now we consider the hydrocarbon framework to which functional groups are attached—the framework that consists of only carbon and hydrogen atoms. From the standpoint of an architect, hydrocarbon frameworks present a dream of limitless possibilities, which is part of what makes organic chemistry such a fascinating discipline. Buckminsterfullerene, named after the visionary architect Buckminster Fuller, is just one example of a carbon-based molecule with an intriguing molecular architecture.

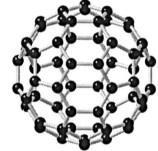

Buckminsterfullerene

PHOTO CREDIT: © Evgeny Terentev/iStockphoto

142

IN THIS CHAPTER WE WILL CONSIDER:

- how to name many simple organic molecules

- the flexible, three-dimensional nature of organic molecules

- an organic reaction that can convert alkenes and alkynes to alkanes

[WHY DO THESE TOPICS MATTER?] At the end of the chapter, we will show how, using the same set of rules, both chemists and nature have created some unique arrangements of carbon and hydrogen atoms. Some of these structural arrangements were not expected to exist, one structural arrangement lets you write, and others are fueling advances in the area of materials research and nanotechnology.

4.1 INTRODUCTION TO ALKANES AND CYCLOALKANES

We noted earlier that the family of organic compounds called hydrocarbons can be divided into several groups on the basis of the type of bond that exists between the individual carbon atoms. Those hydrocarbons in which all of the carbon–carbon bonds are single bonds are called alkanes, those hydrocarbons that contain a carbon–carbon double bond are called alkenes, and those with a carbon–carbon triple bond are called alkynes.

Cycloalkanes are alkanes in which all or some of the carbon atoms are arranged in a ring. Alkanes have the general formula C_nH_{2n+2}; cycloalkanes containing a single ring have two fewer hydrogen atoms and thus have the general formula C_nH_{2n}.

Cyclohexane

4.1A Sources of Alkanes: Petroleum

The primary source of alkanes is petroleum. Petroleum is a complex mixture of organic compounds, most of which are alkanes and aromatic compounds (cf. Chapter 14). It also contains small amounts of oxygen-, nitrogen-, and sulfur-containing compounds.

Some of the molecules in petroleum are clearly of biological origin. Most scientists believe that petroleum originated with accumulation of dead microorganisms that settled to the bottom of the sea and that were entombed in sedimentary rock. These microbial remains eventually were transformed into oil by the heat radiating from Earth's core.

Hydrocarbons are also found in outer space. Asteroids and comets contain a variety of organic compounds. Methane and other hydrocarbons are found in the atmospheres of Jupiter, Saturn, and Uranus. Saturn's moon Titan has a solid form of methane–water ice at its surface and an atmosphere rich in methane. Whether of terrestrial or celestial origin, we need to understand the properties of alkanes. We begin with a consideration of their shapes and how we name them.

Tom McHugh/Photo Researchers, Inc.

Petroleum is a finite resource that likely originated with decay of primordial microbes. At the La Brea Tar Pits in Los Angeles, many prehistoric animals perished in a natural vat containing hydrocarbons.

THE CHEMISTRY OF... Petroleum Refining

The first step in refining petroleum is distillation; the object here is to separate the petroleum into fractions based on the volatility of its components. Complete separation into fractions containing individual compounds is economically impractical and virtually impossible technically. More than 500 different compounds are contained in the petroleum distillates boiling below 200 °C, and many have almost the same boiling points. Thus the fractions taken contain mixtures of alkanes of similar boiling points (see the table below). Mixtures of alkanes, fortunately, are perfectly suitable for uses as fuels, solvents, and lubricants, the primary uses of petroleum.

The demand for gasoline is much greater than that supplied by the gasoline fraction of petroleum. Important processes in the petroleum industry, therefore, are concerned with converting hydrocarbons from other fractions into gasoline. When a mixture of alkanes from the gas oil fraction (C_{12} and higher) is heated at very high temperatures (~500 °C) in the presence of a variety of catalysts, the molecules break apart and rearrange to smaller, more highly branched hydrocarbons containing 5–10 carbon atoms. This process is called *catalytic cracking*. **Cracking** can also be done in the absence of a catalyst—called ***thermal***

(continues on next page)

cracking—but in this process the products tend to have unbranched chains, and alkanes with unbranched chains have a very low "octane rating."

The highly branched compound 2,2,4-trimethylpentane (called isooctane in the petroleum industry) burns very smoothly (without knocking) in internal combustion engines and is used as one of the standards by which the octane rating of gasolines is established. According to this scale, 2,2,4-trimethylpentane has an octane rating of 100. Heptane, $CH_3(CH_2)_5CH_3$, a compound that produces much knocking when it is burned in an internal combustion engine, is given an octane rating of 0. Mixtures of 2,2,4-trimethylpentane and heptane are used as standards for octane ratings between 0 and 100. A gasoline, for example, that has the same characteristics in an engine as a mixture of 87% 2,2,4-trimethylpentane and 13% heptane would be rated as 87-octane gasoline.

2,2,4-Trimethylpentane
("isooctane")

TYPICAL FRACTIONS OBTAINED BY DISTILLATION OF PETROLEUM		
Boiling Range of Fraction (°C)	**Number of Carbon Atoms per Molecule**	**Use**
Below 20	C_1–C_4	Natural gas, bottled gas, petrochemicals
20–60	C_5–C_6	Petroleum ether, solvents
60–100	C_6–C_7	Ligroin, solvents
40–200	C_5–C_{10}	Gasoline (straight-run gasoline)
175–325	C_{12}–C_{18}	Kerosene and jet fuel
250–400	C_{12} and higher	Gas oil, fuel oil, and diesel oil
Nonvolatile liquids	C_{20} and higher	Refined mineral oil, lubricating oil, and grease
Nonvolatile solids	C_{20} and higher	Paraffin wax, asphalt, and tar

Adapted with permission of John Wiley & Sons, Inc., from Holum, J. R., *General, Organic, and Biological Chemistry*, Ninth Edition, p. 213. Copyright 1995.

4.2 SHAPES OF ALKANES

A general tetrahedral orientation of groups—and thus sp^3 hybridization—is the rule for the carbon atoms of all alkanes and cycloalkanes. We can represent the shapes of alkanes as shown in Fig. 4.1.

Butane and pentane are examples of alkanes that are sometimes called "straight-chain" alkanes. One glance at three-dimensional models, however, shows that because of their tetrahedral carbon atoms the chains are zigzagged and not at all straight. Indeed,

FIGURE 4.1 Ball-and-stick models for three simple alkanes.

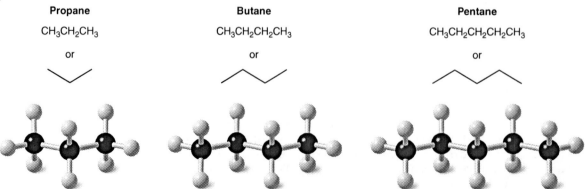

Propane	Butane	Pentane
$CH_3CH_2CH_3$	$CH_3CH_2CH_2CH_3$	$CH_3CH_2CH_2CH_2CH_3$
or	or	or

the structures that we have depicted in Fig. 4.1 are the straightest possible arrangements of the chains because rotations about the carbon–carbon single bonds produce arrangements that are even less straight. A better description is **unbranched**. This means that each carbon atom within the chain is bonded to no more than two other carbon atoms and that unbranched alkanes contain only primary and secondary carbon atoms. Primary, secondary, and tertiary carbon atoms were defined in Section 2.5.

Isobutane, isopentane, and neopentane (Fig. 4.2) are examples of branched-chain alkanes. In neopentane the central carbon atom is bonded to four carbon atoms.

Helpful Hint

You should build your own molecular models of the compounds in Figs. 4.1 and 4.2. View them from different perspectives and experiment with how their shapes change when you twist various bonds. Make drawings of your structures.

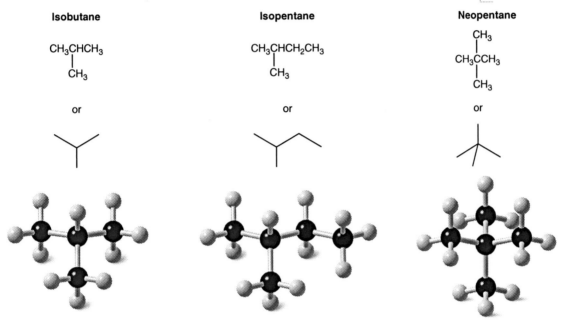

FIGURE 4.2 Ball-and-stick models for three branched-chain alkanes. In each of the compounds one carbon atom is attached to more than two other carbon atoms.

Butane and isobutane have the same molecular formula: C_4H_{10}. The two compounds have their atoms connected in a different order and are, therefore, constitutional isomers (Section 1.3). Pentane, isopentane, and neopentane are also constitutional isomers. They, too, have the same molecular formula (C_5H_{12}) but have different structures.

● ● ●

PRACTICE PROBLEM 4.1

Write condensed and bond-line structural formulas for all of the constitutional isomers with the molecular formula C_7H_{16}. (There are a total of nine constitutional isomers.)

Constitutional isomers, as stated earlier, have different physical properties. The differences may not always be large, but constitutional isomers are always found to have different melting points, boiling points, densities, indexes of refraction, and so forth. Table 4.1 gives some of the physical properties of the C_6H_{14} isomers, of which there are only five. Note that the number of constitutional isomers that is possible increases dramatically as the number of carbon atoms in the alkane increases.

Prior to the development near the end of the nineteenth century of a formal system for naming organic compounds, many organic compounds had already been discovered or synthesized. Early chemists named these compounds, often on the basis of the source of the compound. Acetic acid (systematically called ethanoic acid) is an example; it was obtained by distilling vinegar, and it got its name from the Latin word for vinegar, *acetum*. Formic acid (systematically called methanoic acid) had been obtained by the distillation of the bodies of ants, so it got the name from the Latin word for ants, *formicae*. Many of these older names for compounds, called common or trivial names, are still in wide use today.

Today, chemists use a systematic nomenclature developed and updated by the International Union of Pure and Applied Chemistry (IUPAC). Underlying the IUPAC

TABLE 4.1 PHYSICAL CONSTANTS OF THE HEXANE ISOMERS

Molecular Formula	Condensed Structural Formula	Bond-Line Formula	mp (°C)	bp (°C)[a] (1 atm)	Density (g mL^{-1}) at 20 °C	Index of Refraction[b] (n_D 20 °C)
C_6H_{14}	$CH_3CH_2CH_2CH_2CH_2CH_3$	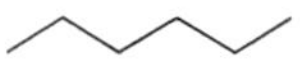	−95	68.7	0.6594	1.3748
C_6H_{14}	$CH_3CHCH_2CH_2CH_3$ $\;\;\;\;CH_3$		−153.7	60.3	0.6532	1.3714
C_6H_{14}	$CH_3CH_2CHCH_2CH_3$ $\;\;\;\;\;\;\;CH_3$		−118	63.3	0.6643	1.3765
C_6H_{14}	$CH_3CH-CHCH$ $\;\;\;CH_3\;\;CH_3$		−128.8	58	0.6616	1.3750
C_6H_{14}	CH_3 CH_3-C-CH_2CH CH_3		−98	49.7	0.6492	1.3688

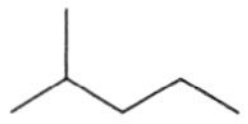

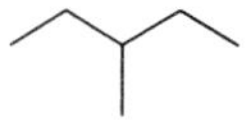

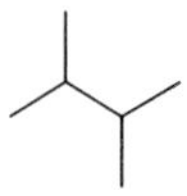

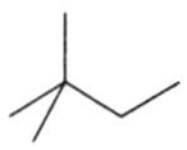

[a]Unless otherwise indicated, all boiling points given in this book are at 1 atm or 760 torr.
[b]The index of refraction is a measure of the ability of the alkane to bend (refract) light rays. The values reported are for light of the D line of the sodium spectrum (n_D).

system is a fundamental principle: **each different compound should have a different and unambiguous name.***

4.3 HOW TO NAME ALKANES, ALKYL HALIDES, AND ALCOHOLS: THE IUPAC SYSTEM

The **IUPAC system** for naming alkanes is not difficult to learn, and the principles involved are used in naming compounds in other families as well. For these reasons we begin our study of the IUPAC system with the rules for naming alkanes and then study the rules for alkyl halides and alcohols.

The names for several of the unbranched alkanes are listed in Table 4.2. The ending for all of the names of alkanes is -*ane*. The stems of the names of most of the alkanes (above C_4) are of Greek and Latin origin. Learning the stems is like learning to count in organic chemistry. Thus, one, two, three, four, and five become meth-, eth-, prop-, but-, and pent-.

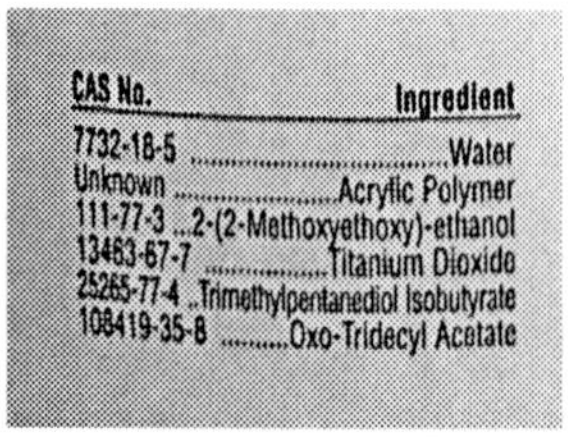

TABLE 4.2 THE UNBRANCHED ALKANES

Name	Number of Carbon Atoms	Structure	Name	Number of Carbon Atoms	Structure
Methane	1	CH_4	Undecane	11	$CH_3(CH_2)_9CH_3$
Ethane	2	CH_3CH_3	Dodecane	12	$CH_3(CH_2)_{10}CH_3$
Propane	3	$CH_3CH_2CH_3$	Tridecane	13	$CH_3(CH_2)_{11}CH_3$
Butane	4	$CH_3(CH_2)_2CH_3$	Tetradecane	14	$CH_3(CH_2)_{12}CH_3$
Pentane	5	$CH_3(CH_2)_3CH_3$	Pentadecane	15	$CH_3(CH_2)_{13}CH_3$
Hexane	6	$CH_3(CH_2)_4CH_3$	Hexadecane	16	$CH_3(CH_2)_{14}CH_3$
Heptane	7	$CH_3(CH_2)_5CH_3$	Heptadecane	17	$CH_3(CH_2)_{15}CH_3$
Octane	8	$CH_3(CH_2)_6CH_3$	Octadecane	18	$CH_3(CH_2)_{16}CH_3$
Nonane	9	$CH_3(CH_2)_7CH_3$	Nonadecane	19	$CH_3(CH_2)_{17}CH_3$
Decane	10	$CH_3(CH_2)_8CH_3$	Eicosane	20	$CH_3(CH_2)_{18}CH_3$

Photo by Lisa Gee

CAS No. **Ingredient**
7732-18-5 .... Water
Unknown .... Acrylic Polymer
111-77-3 ...2-(2-Methoxyethoxy)-ethanol
13463-67-7 ....Titanium Dioxide
25265-77-4 .Trimethylpentanediol Isobutyrate
108419-35-8 ....Oxo-Tridecyl Acetate

The Chemical Abstracts Service assigns a CAS Registry Number to every compound. CAS numbers make it easy to find information about a compound in the chemical literature. The CAS numbers for ingredients in a can of latex paint are shown here.

*The complete IUPAC rules for nomenclature can be found through links at the IUPAC website.

4.3A HOW TO Name Unbranched Alkyl Groups

If we remove one hydrogen atom from an alkane, we obtain what is called an **alkyl group**. These alkyl groups have names that end in **-yl**. When the alkane is **unbranched**, and the hydrogen atom that is removed is a **terminal** hydrogen atom, the names are straightforward:

CH_3-H	CH_3CH_2-H	$CH_3CH_2CH_2-H$	$CH_3CH_2CH_2CH_2-H$
Methane	**Ethane**	**Propane**	**Butane**
CH_3-	CH_3CH_2-	$CH_3CH_2CH_2-$	$CH_3CH_2CH_2CH_2-$
Methyl	**Ethyl**	**Propyl**	**Butyl**
Me-	**Et-**	**Pr-**	**Bu-**

4.3B HOW TO Name Branched-Chain Alkanes

Branched-chain alkanes are named according to the following rules:

1. **Locate the longest continuous chain of carbon atoms; this chain determines the parent name for the alkane.** We designate the following compound, for example, as a *hexane* because the longest continuous chain contains six carbon atoms:

   $$\text{Longest chain} \rightarrow CH_3CH_2CH_2CH_2CHCH_3 \quad \text{or}$$
   $$\underset{CH_3}{|}$$

   The longest continuous chain may not always be obvious from the way the formula is written. Notice, for example, that the following alkane is designated as a *heptane* because the longest chain contains seven carbon atoms:

2. **Number the longest chain beginning with the end of the chain nearer the substituent.** Applying this rule, we number the two alkanes that we illustrated previously in the following way:

   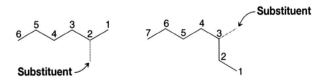

3. **Use the numbers obtained by application of rule 2 to designate the location of the substituent group.** The parent name is placed last, and the substituent group, preceded by the number designating its location on the chain, is placed first. Numbers

are separated from words by a hyphen. Our two examples are 2-methylhexane and 3-methylheptane, respectively:

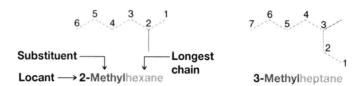

Substituent ⟶ ↓ ←⟶ Longest chain
Locant ⟶ **2-Methylhexane**   **3-Methylheptane**

4. **When two or more substituents are present, give each substituent a number corresponding to its location on the longest chain.** For example, we designate the following compound as 4-ethyl-2-methylhexane:

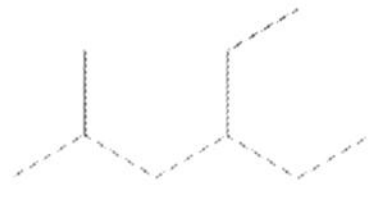

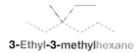

4-Ethyl-2-methylhexane

The substituent groups should be listed *alphabetically* (i.e., ethyl before methyl).* In deciding on alphabetical order, disregard multiplying prefixes such as "di" and "tri."

5. **When two substituents are present on the same carbon atom, use that number twice:**

3-Ethyl-3-methylhexane

6. **When two or more substituents are identical, indicate this by the use of the prefixes di-, tri-, tetra-,** and so on. Then make certain that each and every substituent has a number. Commas are used to separate numbers from each other:

2,3-Dimethylbutane   **2,3,4-Trimethylpentane**   **2,2,4,4-Tetramethylpentane**

Application of these six rules allows us to name most of the alkanes that we shall encounter. Two other rules, however, may be required occasionally:

7. **When two chains of equal length compete for selection as the parent chain, choose the chain with the greater number of substituents:**

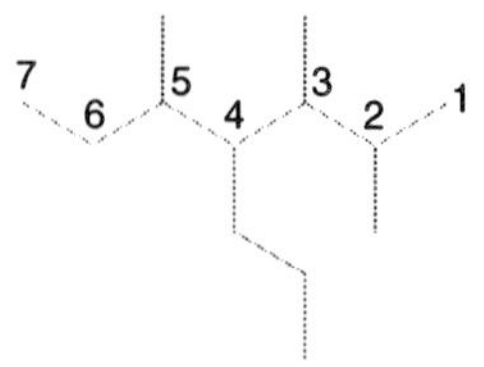

2,3,5-Trimethyl-4-propylheptane
(four substituents)

8. **When branching first occurs at an equal distance from either end of the longest chain, choose the name that gives the lower number at the first point of difference:**

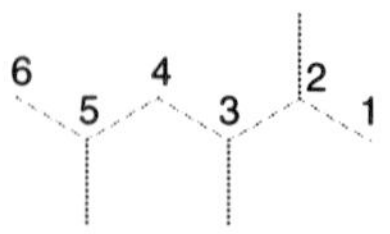

2,3,5-Trimethylhexane
(*not* 2,4,5-trimethylhexane)

---

*Some handbooks also list the groups in order of increasing size or complexity (i.e., methyl before ethyl). An alphabetical listing, however, is now by far the most widely used system.

●●● SOLVED PROBLEM 4.1

Provide an IUPAC name for the following alkane.

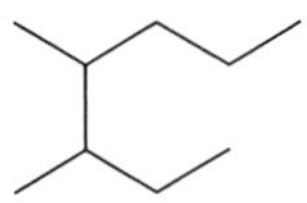

STRATEGY AND SOLUTION: We find the longest chain (shown in blue) to be seven carbons; therefore the parent name is heptane. There are two methyl substituents (shown in red). We number the chain so as to give the first methyl group the lower number. The correct name, therefore, is 3,4-dimethylheptane. Numbering the chain from the other end to give 4,5-dimethylheptane would have been incorrect.

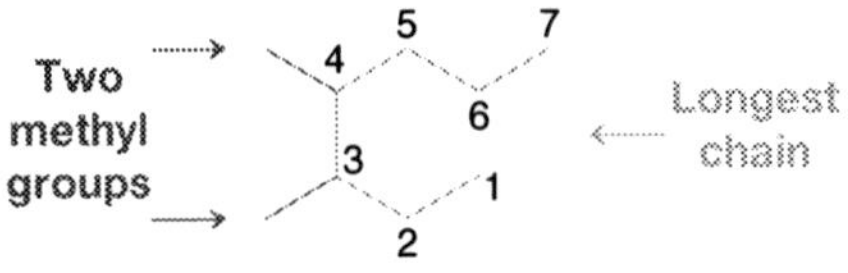

Two methyl groups → Longest chain ←

5 7
4 6
3 1
2

●●●

Which structure does not represent 2-methylpentane?

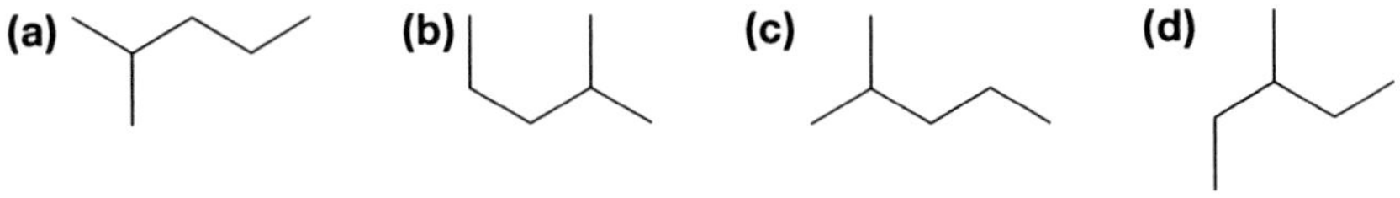

PRACTICE PROBLEM 4.2

(a)   **(b)**   **(c)**   **(d)**

●●◆

Write the structure and give the IUPAC name for an alkane with formula C_6H_{14} that has only primary and secondary carbon atoms.

PRACTICE PROBLEM 4.3

●●◆

Draw bond-line formulas for all of the isomers of C_8H_{18} that have **(a)** methyl substituents, and **(b)** ethyl substituents.

PRACTICE PROBLEM 4.4

4.3C HOW TO Name Branched Alkyl Groups

In Section 4.3A you learned the names for the unbranched alkyl groups such as methyl, ethyl, propyl, and butyl, groups derived by removing a terminal hydrogen from an alkane. For alkanes with more than two carbon atoms, more than one derived group is possible. Two groups can be derived from propane, for example; the **propyl group** is derived by removal of a terminal hydrogen, and the **1-methylethyl** or **isopropyl group** is derived by removal of a hydrogen from the central carbon:

Three-Carbon Groups

$CH_3CH_2CH_2$

Propane

$CH_3CH_2CH_2$— CH_3CHCH_3
                              |

Propyl   **Isopropyl**

Pr-   i-Pr-

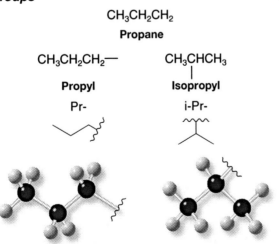

1-Methylethyl is the systematic name for this group; isopropyl is a common name. Systematic nomenclature for alkyl groups is similar to that for branched-chain alkanes, with the provision that *numbering always begins at the point where the group is attached to the main chain*. There are four C_4 groups.

Four-Carbon Groups

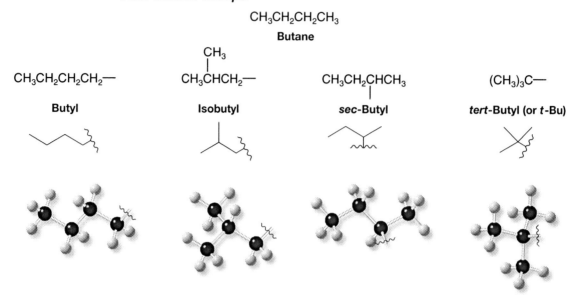

$CH_3CH_2CH_2CH_3$
Butane

$CH_3CH_2CH_2CH_2$—

Butyl

CH_3CHCH_2— (with CH_3 above)

Isobutyl

$CH_3CH_2CHCH_3$ (with bond below)

sec-Butyl

$(CH_3)_3C$—

tert-Butyl (or t-Bu)

The following examples show how the names of these groups are employed:

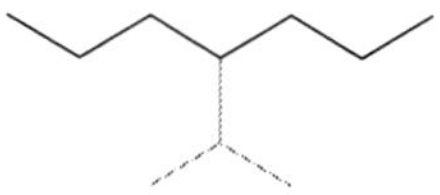

4-(1-Methylethyl)heptane or **4-isopropylheptane**

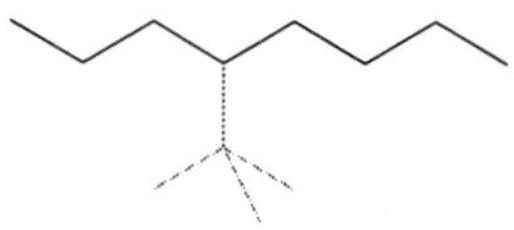

4-(1,1-Dimethylethyl)octane or **4-tert-butyloctane**

The common names **isopropyl, isobutyl, sec-butyl,** and **tert-butyl** are approved by the IUPAC for the unsubstituted groups, and they are still very frequently used. You should learn these groups so well that you can recognize them any way they are written. In deciding on alphabetical order for these groups you should disregard structure-defining prefixes that are written in italics and separated from the name by a hyphen. Thus *tert*-butyl precedes ethyl, but ethyl precedes isobutyl.*

There is one five-carbon group with an IUPAC approved common name that you should also know: the 2,2-dimethylpropyl group, commonly called the **neopentyl group**.

$$CH_3-\overset{\overset{\displaystyle CH_3}{|}}{\underset{\underset{\displaystyle CH_3}{|}}{C}}-CH_2-$$

2,2-Dimethylpropyl or neopentyl group

• • •

PRACTICE PROBLEM 4.5 **(a)** In addition to the 2,2-dimethylpropyl (or neopentyl) group just given, there are seven other five-carbon groups. Draw bond-line formulas for their structures and give each structure its systematic name. **(b)** Draw bond-line formulas and provide IUPAC names for all of the isomers of C_7H_{16}.

*The abbreviations *i-*, *s-*, and *t-* are sometimes used for iso-, sec-, and *tert*-, respectively.

4.3D HOW TO Classify Hydrogen Atoms

The hydrogen atoms of an alkane are classified on the basis of the carbon atom to which they are attached. A hydrogen atom attached to a primary carbon atom is a primary (1°) hydrogen atom, and so forth. The following compound, 2-methylbutane, has primary, secondary (2°), and tertiary (3°) hydrogen atoms:

1° Hydrogen atoms

$$CH_3$$
$$CH_3-CH-CH_2-CH_3$$

3° Hydrogen atom   2° Hydrogen atoms

On the other hand, 2,2-dimethylpropane, a compound that is often called **neopentane**, has only primary hydrogen atoms:

$$H_3C-\underset{\underset{CH_3}{|}}{\overset{\overset{CH_3}{|}}{C}}-CH_3$$

2,2-Dimethylpropane
(neopentane)

4.3E HOW TO Name Alkyl Halides

Alkanes bearing halogen substituents are named in the IUPAC substitutive system as haloalkanes:

$$CH_3CH_2Cl \qquad CH_3CH_2CH_2F \qquad CH_3CHBrCH_3$$

Chloroethane   **1-Fluoropropane**   **2-Bromopropane**

• When the parent chain has both a halo and an alkyl substituent attached to it, number the chain from the end nearer the first substituent, regardless of whether it is halo or alkyl. If two substituents are at equal distance from the end of the chain, then number the chain from the end nearer the substituent that has alphabetical precedence:

2-Chloro-3-methylpentane   2-Chloro-4-methylpentane

Common names for many simple haloalkanes are still widely used, however. In this common nomenclature system, called **functional class nomenclature**, haloalkanes are named as alkyl halides. (The following names are also accepted by the IUPAC.)

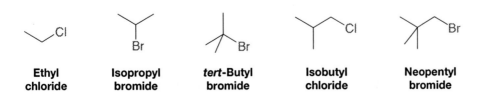

| **Ethyl chloride** | **Isopropyl bromide** | ***tert*-Butyl bromide** | **Isobutyl chloride** | **Neopentyl bromide** |

● ● ●

PRACTICE PROBLEM 4.6 Draw bond-line formulas and give IUPAC substitutive names for all of the isomers of
(a) C_4H_9Cl and (b) $C_5H_{11}Br$.

4.3F HOW TO Name Alcohols

In what is called IUPAC **substitutive nomenclature**, a name may have as many as four
features: **locants, prefixes, parent compound**, and **suffixes**. Consider the following compound as an illustration without, for the moment, being concerned as to how the name arises:

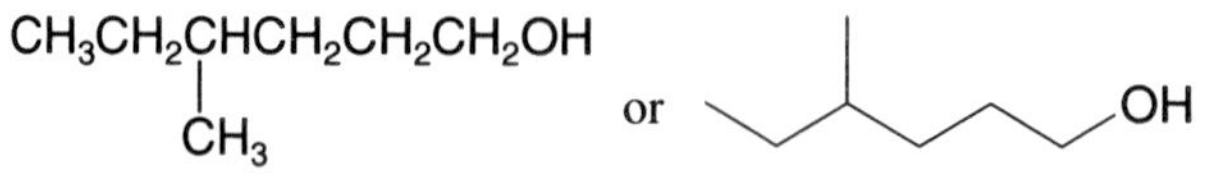

$$CH_3CH_2CHCH_2CH_2CH_2OH$$
$$|$$
$$CH_3$$

or

4-Methyl-1-hexanol

Locant Prefix Locant Parent Suffix

The *locant* **4-** tells that the substituent **methyl** group, named as a *prefix*, is
attached to the *parent compound* at **C4**. The parent compound contains six carbon
atoms and no multiple bonds, hence the parent name **hexane**, and it is an alcohol;
therefore it has the *suffix* **-ol**. The locant **1-** tells that C1 bears the hydroxyl group.
**In general, numbering of the chain always begins at the end nearer the group
named as a suffix.**

The locant for a suffix (whether it is for an alcohol or another functional group) may be
placed before the parent name as in the above example or, according to a 1993 IUPAC revi-
sion of the rules, immediately before the suffix. Both methods are IUPAC approved. Therefore,
the above compound could also be named **4-methylhexan-1-ol**.

The following procedure should be followed in giving alcohols IUPAC substitutive
names:

1. Select the longest continuous carbon chain *to which the hydroxyl is directly attached*.
   Change the name of the alkane corresponding to this chain by dropping the final *-e* and
   adding the suffix *-ol*.

2. Number the longest continuous carbon chain so as to give the carbon atom bearing
   the hydroxyl group the lower number. Indicate the position of the hydroxyl group by
   using this number as a locant; indicate the positions of other substituents (as prefixes)
   by using the numbers corresponding to their positions along the carbon chain as
   locants.

The following examples show how these rules are applied:

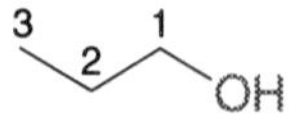

1-Propanol 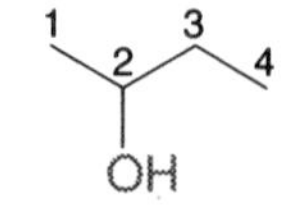   **2-Butanol** 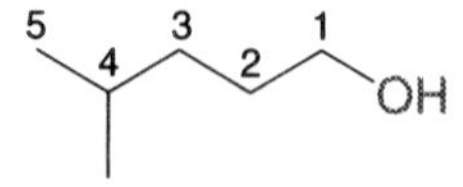   **4-Methyl-1-pentanol**
or 4-methylpentan-1-ol
(*not* 2-methyl-5-pentanol)

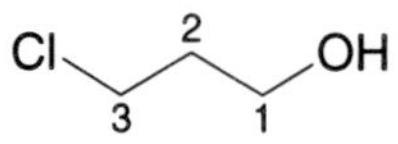

3-Chloro-1-propanol   **4,4-Dimethyl-2-pentanol**
or 3-chloropropan-1-ol   or 4,4-dimethylpentan-2-ol

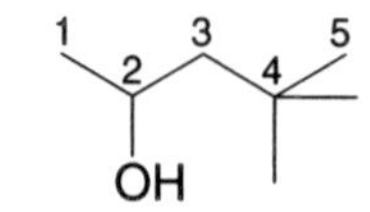

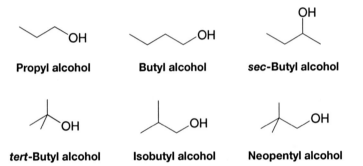

Give an IUPAC name for the compound shown.

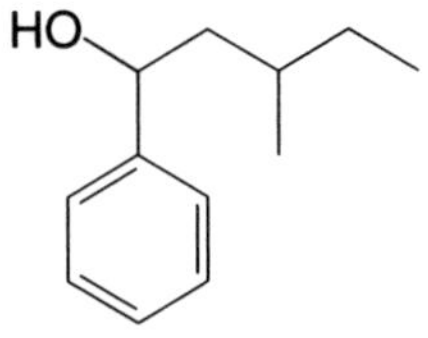

STRATEGY AND ANSWER: We find that the longest carbon chain (in red at right) has five carbons and it bears a hydroxyl group on the first carbon. So we name this part of the molecule as a 1-pentanol. There is a phenyl group on carbon-1 and a methyl group on carbon-3, so the full name is 3-methyl-1-phenyl-1-pentanol.

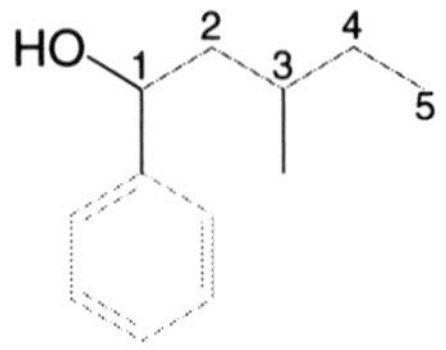

●●●

Draw bond-line formulas and give IUPAC substitutive names for all of the isomeric alcohols with the formulas **(a)** $C_4H_{10}O$ and **(b)** $C_5H_{12}O$.

PRACTICE PROBLEM 4.7

Simple alcohols are often called by *common* functional class names that are also approved by the IUPAC. We have seen several examples already (Section 2.6). In addition to *methyl alcohol, ethyl alcohol,* and *isopropyl alcohol,* there are several others, including the following:

Propyl alcohol 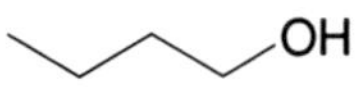   **Butyl alcohol**   *sec*-**Butyl alcohol**

tert-**Butyl alcohol**   **Isobutyl alcohol**   **Neopentyl alcohol**

Alcohols containing two hydroxyl groups are commonly called glycols. In the IUPAC substitutive system they are named as **diols**:

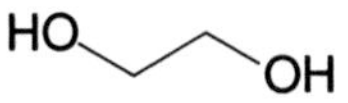

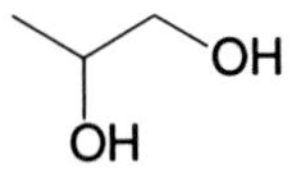

Substitutive	1,2-Ethanediol or ethane-1,2-diol	1,2-Propanediol or propane-1,2-diol	1,3-Propanediol or propane-1,3-diol
Common	Ethylene glycol	Propylene glycol	Trimethylene glycol

4.4 HOW TO NAME CYCLOALKANES

4.4A HOW TO Name Monocyclic Cycloalkanes

Cycloalkanes are named by adding "cyclo" before the parent name.

1. *Cycloalkanes with one ring and no substituents:* Count the number of carbon atoms in the ring, then add "cyclo" to the beginning of the name of the alkane with that number of carbons. For example, cyclopropane has three carbons and cyclopentane has five carbons.

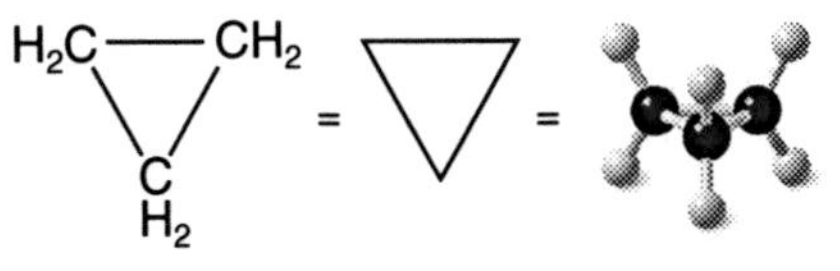

H_2C——CH_2 = $\triangledown$ =

Cyclopropane

H_2C——CH_2

H_2C CH_2 =   =

C
H_2

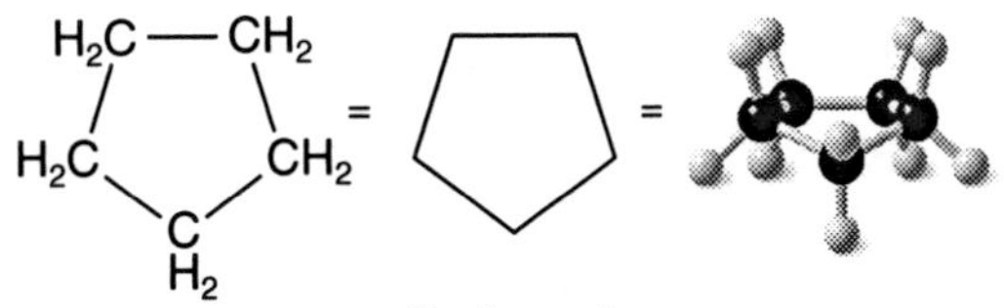

Cyclopentane

2. *Cycloalkanes with one ring and one substituent:* Add the name of the substituent to the beginning of the parent name. For example, cyclohexane with an attached isopropyl group is isopropylcyclohexane. For compounds with only one substituent, it is not necessary to specify a number (locant) for the carbon bearing the substituent.

Isopropylcyclohexane   **Chlorocyclopentane**

3. *Cycloalkanes with one ring and two or more substituents:* For a ring with two substituents, begin by numbering the carbons in the ring, starting at the carbon with the substituent that is first in the alphabet and number in the direction that gives the next substituent the lower number possible. When there are three or more substituents, begin at the substituent that leads to the lowest set of numbers (locants). The substituents are listed in alphabetical order, not according to the number of their carbon atom.

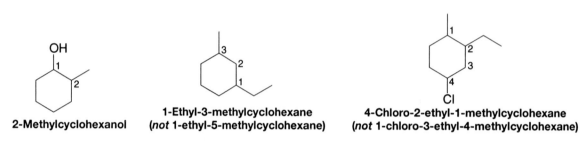

2-Methylcyclohexanol   **1-Ethyl-3-methylcyclohexane**   **4-Chloro-2-ethyl-1-methylcyclohexane**
                            (*not* 1-ethyl-5-methylcyclohexane) (*not* 1-chloro-3-ethyl-4-methylcyclohexane)

4. When a single ring system is attached to a single chain with a greater number of carbon atoms, or when more than one ring system is attached to a single chain, then it is appropriate to name the compounds as *cycloalkylalkanes.* For example.

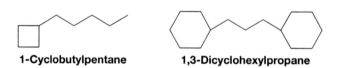

1-Cyclobutylpentane   **1,3-Dicyclohexylpropane**

• • •

PRACTICE PROBLEM 4.8   Give names for the following substituted alkanes:

(a) 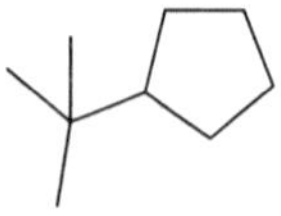   (c) 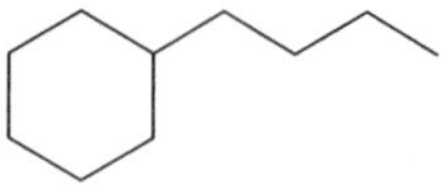   (e)

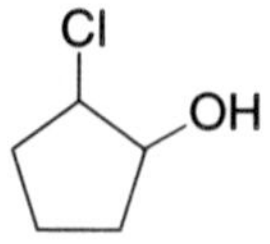

(b) 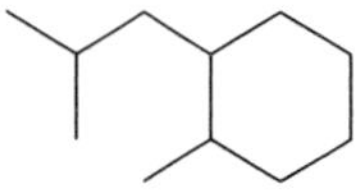   (d) 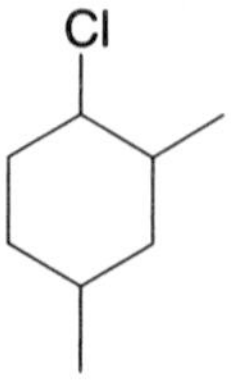   (f)

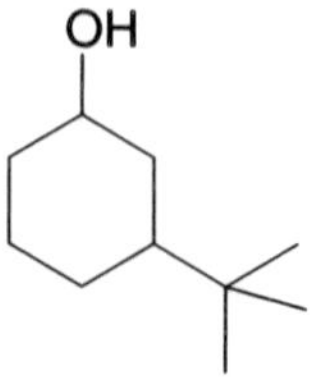

4.4B HOW TO Name Bicyclic Cycloalkanes

1. We name compounds containing two fused or bridged rings as bicycloalkanes and we use the name of the alkane corresponding to the total number of carbon atoms in the rings as the parent name. The following compound, for example, contains seven carbon atoms and is, therefore, a bicycloheptane. The carbon atoms common to both rings are called bridgeheads, and each bond, or each chain of atoms connecting the bridgehead atoms, is called a bridge.

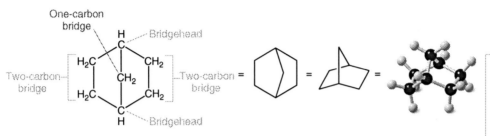

A bicycloheptane

> **Helpful Hint**
>
> Explore the structures of these **bicyclic compounds** by building handheld molecular models.

2. We then interpose an expression in brackets within the name that denotes the number of carbon atoms in each bridge (in order of decreasing length). Fused rings have zero carbons in their bridge. For example,

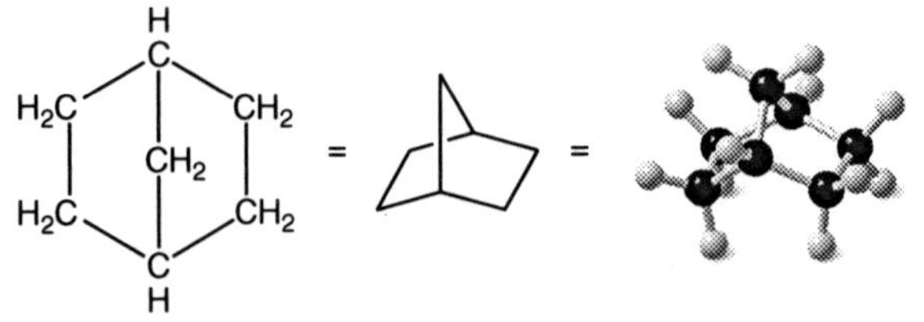

Bicyclo[2.2.1]heptane
(also called *norbornane*)

Bicyclo[1.1.0]butane

3. In bicycloalkanes with substituents, we number the bridged ring system beginning at one bridgehead, proceeding first along the longest bridge to the other bridgehead, then along the next longest bridge back to the first bridgehead; the shortest bridge is numbered last.

Bridged

8-Methylbicyclo[3.2.1]octane

Fused

8-Methylbicyclo[4.3.0]nonane

●●● **SOLVED PROBLEM 4.3**

Write a structural formula for 7,7-dichlorobicyclo[2.2.1]heptane.

STRATEGY AND ANSWER: First we write a bicyclo[2.2.1]heptane ring and number it. Then we add the substituents (two chlorine atoms) to the proper carbon.

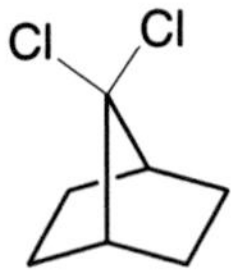

PRACTICE PROBLEM 4.9 Give names for each of the following bicyclic alkanes:

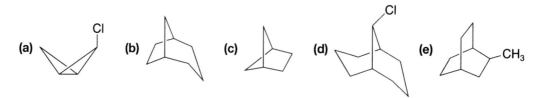

(a)　　　(b)　　　(c)　　　(d)　　　(e)

(f) Write the structure of a bicyclic compound that is a constitutional isomer of bicyclo[2.2.0]hexane and give its name.

4.5 HOW TO NAME ALKENES AND CYCLOALKENES

Many older names for alkenes are still in common use. Propene is often called propylene, and 2-methylpropene frequently bears the name isobutylene:

$$CH_2=CH_2 \qquad CH_3CH=CH_2 \qquad \begin{matrix} CH_3 \\ | \\ CH_3-C=CH_2 \end{matrix}$$

IUPAC: Ethene	Propene	2-Methylpropene
Common: *Ethylene*	*Propylene*	*Isobutylene*

The IUPAC rules for naming alkenes are similar in many respects to those for naming alkanes:

1. **Determine the parent name by selecting the longest chain that contains the double bond and change the ending of the name of the alkane of identical length from -ane to -ene.** Thus, if the longest chain contains five carbon atoms, the parent name for the alkene is *pentene*; if it contains six carbon atoms, the parent name is *hexene*, and so on.

2. **Number the chain so as to include both carbon atoms of the double bond, and begin numbering at the end of the chain nearer the double bond. Designate the location of the double bond by using the number of the first atom of the double bond as a prefix. The locant for the alkene suffix may precede the parent name or be placed immediately before the suffix.** We will show examples of both styles:

$$\overset{1}{C}H_2=\overset{2}{C}H\overset{3}{C}H_2\overset{4}{C}H_3 \qquad CH_3CH=CHCH_2CH_2CH_3$$

1-Butene   **2-Hexene**
(*not* 3-butene)   (*not* 4-hexene)

3. **Indicate the locations of the substituent groups by the numbers of the carbon atoms to which they are attached:**

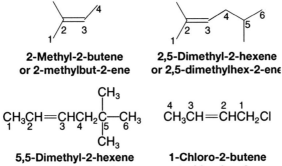

2-Methyl-2-butene or 2-methylbut-2-ene

2,5-Dimethyl-2-hexene or 2,5-dimethylhex-2-ene

$\overset{1}{C}H_3\overset{2}{C}H{=}\overset{3}{C}H\overset{4}{C}H_2\overset{5}{C}(CH_3)_2{-}\overset{6}{C}H_3$

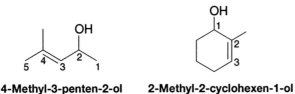

5,5-Dimethyl-2-hexene or 5,5-dimethylhex-2-ene

$\overset{4}{C}H_3\overset{3}{C}H{=}\overset{2}{C}H\overset{1}{C}H_2Cl$

1-Chloro-2-butene or 1-chlorobut-2-ene

4. **Number substituted cycloalkenes in the way that gives the carbon atoms of the double bond the 1 and 2 positions and that also gives the substituent groups the lower numbers at the first point of difference.** With substituted cycloalkenes it is not necessary to specify the position of the double bond since it will always begin with C1 and C2. The two examples shown here illustrate the application of these rules:

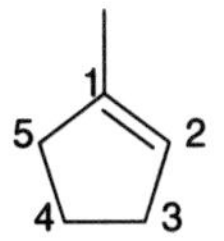

1-Methylcyclopentene (*not* 2-methylcyclopentene)

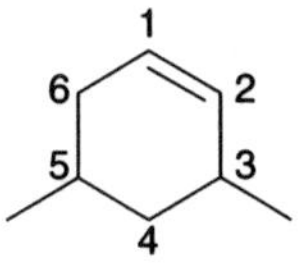

3,5-Dimethylcyclohexene (*not* 4,6-dimethylcyclohexene)

5. Name compounds containing a double bond and an alcohol group as alkenols (or cycloalkenols) and give the alcohol carbon the lower number:

4-Methyl-3-penten-2-ol or 4-methylpent-3-en-2-ol

2-Methyl-2-cyclohexen-1-ol or 2-methylcyclohex-2-en-1-ol

6. Two frequently encountered alkenyl groups are the **vinyl group** and the **allyl group**:

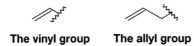

The vinyl group

The allyl group

Using substitutive nomenclature, the vinyl and allyl groups are called *ethenyl* and *prop-2-en-1-yl*, respectively. The following examples illustrate how these names are employed:

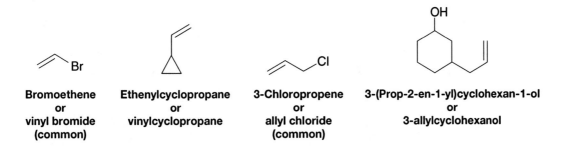

Bromoethene or vinyl bromide (common)

Ethenylcyclopropane or vinylcyclopropane

3-Chloropropene or allyl chloride (common)

3-(Prop-2-en-1-yl)cyclohexan-1-ol or 3-allylcyclohexanol

7. If two identical or substantial groups are on the same side of the double bond, the compound can be designated *cis*; if they are on opposite sides it can be designated *trans*:

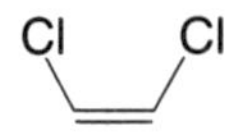

cis-1,2-Dichloroethene 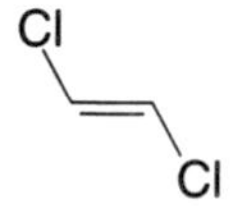   **trans-1,2-Dichloroethene**

(In Section 7.2 we shall see another method for designating the geometry of the double bond.)

••• SOLVED PROBLEM 4.4

Give an IUPAC name for the molecule shown.

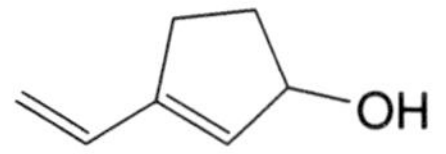

STRATEGY AND ANSWER: We number the ring as shown below starting with the hydroxyl group so as to give the double bond the lower possible number. We include in the name the substituent (an ethenyl group) and the double bond (*-ene-*), and the hydroxyl group (*-ol*) with numbers for their respective positions. Hence the IUPAC name is 3-ethenyl-2-cyclopenten-1-ol.

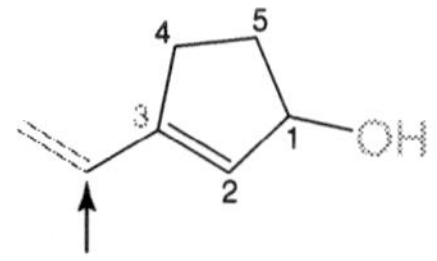

Ethenyl group

PRACTICE PROBLEM 4.10 Give IUPAC names for the following alkenes:

(a) 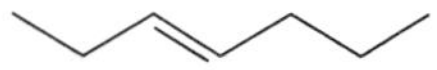   **(c)** 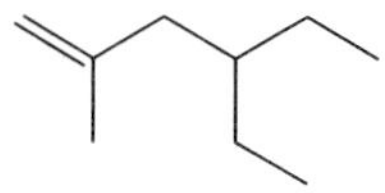   **(e)**

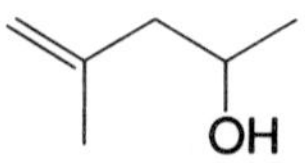

(b) 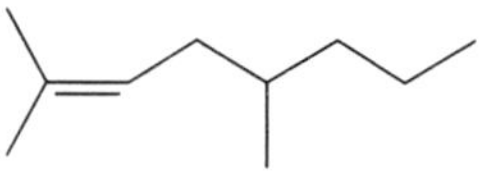   **(d)** 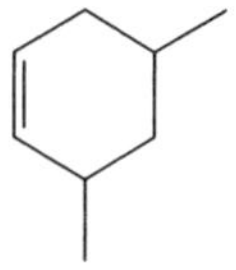   **(f)**

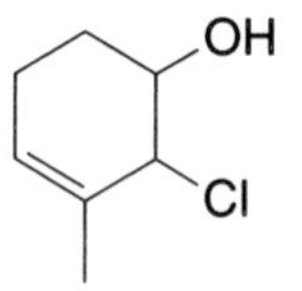

PRACTICE PROBLEM 4.11 Write bond-line formulas for the following:

(a) *cis*-3-Octene
(b) *trans*-2-Hexene
(c) 2,4-Dimethyl-2-pentene
(d) *trans*-1-Chlorobut-2-ene
(e) 4,5-Dibromo-1-pentene

(f) 1-Bromo-2-methyl-1-(prop-2-en-1-yl)cyclopentane
(g) 3,4-Dimethylcyclopentene
(h) Vinylcyclopentane
(i) 1,2-Dichlorocyclohexene
(j) *trans*-1,4-Dichloro-2-pentene

4.6 HOW TO NAME ALKYNES

Alkynes are named in much the same way as alkenes. Unbranched alkynes, for example, are named by replacing the **-ane** of the name of the corresponding alkane with the ending **-yne.** The chain is numbered to give the carbon atoms of the triple bond the lower possible numbers. The lower number of the two carbon atoms of the triple bond is used to designate the location of the triple bond. The IUPAC names of three unbranched alkynes are shown here:

$$H-C\equiv C-H$$

Ethyne or acetylene*   **2-Pentyne**    **1-Penten-4-yne[†] or pent-1-en-4-yne**

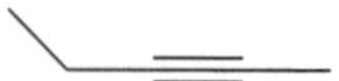

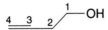

The locations of substituent groups of branched alkynes and substituted alkynes are also indicated with numbers. An —OH group has priority over the triple bond when numbering the chain of an alkynol:

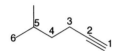

3-Chloropropyne

1-Chloro-2-butyne or 1-chlorobut-2-yne

3-Butyn-1-ol or but-3-yn-1-ol

5-Methyl-1-hexyne or 5-methylhex-1-yne

4,4-Dimethyl-1-pentyne or 4,4-dimethylpent-1-yne

2-Methyl-4-pentyn-2-ol or 2-methylpent-4-yn-2-ol

●●◆·········
Give the structures and IUPAC names for all the alkynes with the formula C_6H_{10}.   **PRACTICE PROBLEM 4.12**

Monosubstituted acetylenes or 1-alkynes are called **terminal alkynes**, and the hydrogen attached to the carbon of the triple bond is called the acetylenic hydrogen atom:

Acetylenic hydrogen
$$R—C\equiv C—H$$
A terminal alkyne

When named as a substituent, the HC≡C— group is called the ethynyl group.

The anion obtained when the acetylenic hydrogen is removed is known as an *alkynide ion* or an acetylide ion. As we shall see in Section 7.11, these ions are useful in synthesis:

$$R—C\equiv C:^-\qquad CH_3C\equiv C:^-$$
or   or
$$R—\equiv:^-\qquad —\equiv:^-$$
An alkynide ion (an acetylide ion)   **The propynide ion**

4.7 PHYSICAL PROPERTIES OF ALKANES AND CYCLOALKANES

If we examine the unbranched alkanes in Table 4.2, we notice that each alkane differs from the preceding alkane by one —CH_2— group. Butane, for example, is $CH_3(CH_2)_2CH_3$ and pentane is $CH_3(CH_2)_3CH_3$. A series of compounds like this, where each member differs from the next member by a constant unit, is called a homologous series. Members of a homologous series are called **homologues.**

At room temperature (25 °C) and 1 atm pressure the first four members of the homologous series of unbranched alkanes are gases (Fig. 4.3), the C_5—C_{17} unbranched alkanes (pentane to heptadecane) are liquids, and the unbranched alkanes with 18 and more carbon atoms are solids.

---

*The name acetylene is retained by the IUPAC system for the compound HC≡CH and is used frequently.

†When double and triple bonds are present, the direction of numbering is chosen so as to give the lowest overall set of locants. In the face of equivalent options, then preference is given to assigning lowest numbers to the double bonds.

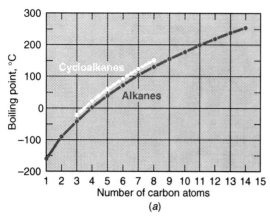

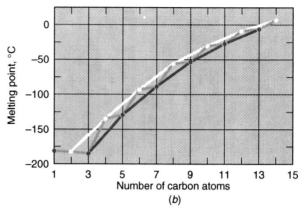

FIGURE 4.3 (a) Boiling points of unbranched alkanes (in red) and cycloalkanes (in white). (b) Melting points of unbranched alkanes.

Boiling Points The boiling points of the unbranched alkanes show a regular increase with increasing molecular weight (Fig. 4.3a) in the homologous series of straight-chain alkanes. Branching of the alkane chain, however, lowers the boiling point. The hexane isomers in Table 4.1 examplify this trend.

Part of the explanation for these effects lies in the dispersion forces that we studied in Section 2.13B. With unbranched alkanes, as molecular weight increases, so too do molecular size and, even more importantly, molecular surface area. With increasing surface area, the dispersion forces between molecules increase; therefore, more energy (a higher temperature) is required to separate molecules from one another and produce boiling. Chain branching, on the other hand, makes a molecule more compact, reducing its surface area and with it the strength of the dispersion forces operating between it and adjacent molecules; this has the effect of lowering the boiling point. Figure 4.4 illustrates this for two **C₈** isomers.

FIGURE 4.4 Chain-branching decreases the contact surface area between molecules, as for the branched **C8** isomer in (b), lessening the dispersion forces between them and leading to a lower boiling point than for the unbranched **C8** isomer (a).

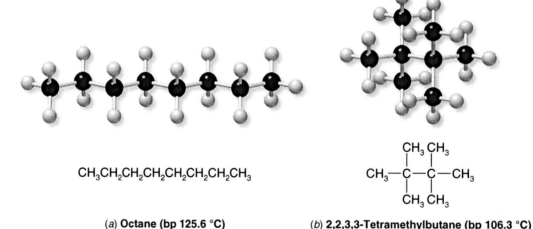

$$CH_3CH_2CH_2CH_2CH_2CH_2CH_2CH_3$$

(a) Octane (bp 125.6 °C)

(b) 2,2,3,3-Tetramethylbutane (bp 106.3 °C)

Melting Points The unbranched alkanes do not show the same smooth increase in melting points with increasing molecular weight (blue line in Fig. 4.3b) that they show in their boiling points. There is an alternation as one progresses from an unbranched alkane with an even number of carbon atoms to the next one with an odd number of carbon atoms. If, however, the even- and odd-numbered alkanes are plotted on *separate* curves (white and red lines in Fig. 4.3b), there *is* a smooth increase in melting point with increasing molecular weight.

X-ray diffraction studies, which provide information about molecular structure, have revealed the reason for this apparent anomaly. Alkane chains with an even number of carbon atoms pack more closely in the crystalline state. As a result, attractive forces between individual chains are greater and melting points are higher.

Cycloalkanes also have much higher melting points than their open-chain counterparts (Table 4.3).

TABLE 4.3 PHYSICAL CONSTANTS OF CYCLOALKANES

Number of Carbon Atoms	Name	bp (°C) (1 atm)	mp (°C)	Density at 20 °C (g mL^{-1})	Refractive Index (n_D^{20})
3	Cyclopropane	−33	−126.6	—	—
4	Cyclobutane	13	−90	—	1.4260
5	Cyclopentane	49	−94	0.751	1.4064
6	Cyclohexane	81	6.5	0.779	1.4266
7	Cycloheptane	118.5	−12	0.811	1.4449
8	Cyclooctane	149	13.5	0.834	—

Density As a class, the alkanes and cycloalkanes are the least dense of all groups of organic compounds. All alkanes and cycloalkanes have densities considerably less than 1.00 g mL^{-1} (the density of water at 4 °C). As a result, petroleum (a mixture of hydrocarbons rich in alkanes) floats on water.

Solubility Alkanes and cycloalkanes are almost totally insoluble in water because of their very low polarity and their inability to form hydrogen bonds. Liquid alkanes and cycloalkanes are soluble in one another, and they generally dissolve in solvents of low polarity. Good solvents for them are benzene, carbon tetrachloride, chloroform, and other hydrocarbons.

THE CHEMISTRY OF ... Pheromones: Communication by Means of Chemicals

Many animals communicate with other members of their species using a language based not on sounds or even visual signals but on the odors of chemicals called **pheromones** that these animals release. For insects, this appears to be the chief method of communication. Although pheromones are secreted by insects in extremely small amounts, they can cause profound and varied biological effects. Some insects use pheromones in courtship as sex attractants. Others use pheromones as warning substances, and still others secrete chemicals called "aggregation compounds" to cause members of their species to congregate. Often these pheromones are relatively simple compounds, and some are hydrocarbons. For example, a species of cockroach uses undecane as an aggregation pheromone:

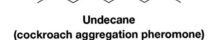

Undecane
(cockroach aggregation pheromone)

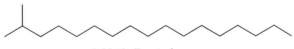

2-Methylheptadecane
(sex attractant of female tiger moth)

Danilo Donadoni/Photoshot Holdings Ltd.

When a female tiger moth wants to mate, she secretes 2-methylheptadecane, a perfume that the male tiger moth apparently finds irresistible.

The sex attractant of the common housefly (*Musca domestica*) is a 23-carbon alkene with a cis double bond between atoms 9 and 10 called muscalure:

Muscalure
(sex attractant of common housefly)

(continues on next page)

Many insect sex attractants have been synthesized and are used to lure insects into traps as a means of insect control, a much more environmentally sensitive method than the use of insecticides.

Research suggests there are roles for pheromones in the lives of humans as well. For example, studies have shown that the phenomenon of menstrual synchronization among women who live or work with each other is likely caused by pheromones. Olfactory sensitivity to musk, which includes steroids such as androsterone, large cyclic ketones, and lactones (cyclic esters), also varies cyclically in women, differs between the sexes, and may influence our behavior. Some of these compounds are used in perfumes, including civetone, a natural product isolated from glands of the civet cat, and pentalide, a synthetic musk.

Androsterone   **Civetone**   **Pentalide**

4.8 SIGMA BONDS AND BOND ROTATION

Two groups bonded by only a single bond can undergo rotation about that bond with respect to each other.

- The temporary molecular shapes that result from such a rotation are called **conformations** of the molecule.
- Each possible structure is called a **conformer**.
- An analysis of the energy changes that occur as a molecule undergoes rotations about single bonds is called a **conformational analysis**.

4.8A Newman Projections and HOW TO Draw Them

Helpful Hint

Learn to draw Newman projections and sawhorse formulas. Build handheld molecular models and compare them with your drawings.

When we do conformational analysis, we will find that certain types of structural formulas are especially convenient to use. One of these types is called a **Newman projection formula** and another type is a **sawhorse formula**. Sawhorse formulas are much like dash–wedge three-dimensional formulas we have used so far. In conformational analyses, we will make substantial use of Newman projections.

Newman projection formula   **Sawhorse formula**

To write a Newman projection formula:

- We imagine ourselves taking a view from one atom (usually a carbon) directly along a selected bond axis to the next atom (also usually a carbon atom).
- The front carbon and its other bonds are represented as ⅄.
- The back carbon and its bonds are represented as ⊥.

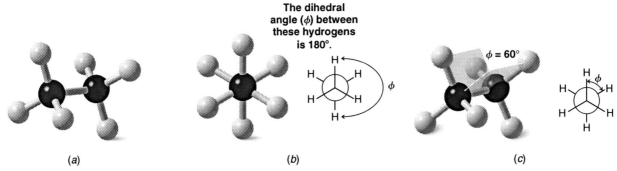

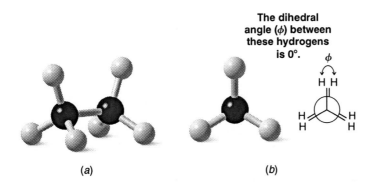

FIGURE 4.5 (a) The staggered conformation of ethane. (b) The Newman projection formula for the staggered conformation. (c) The dihedral angle between these hydrogen atoms is 60°.

In Figs. 4.5a,b we show ball-and-stick models and a Newman projection formula for the staggered conformation of ethane. The staggered conformation of a molecule is that conformation where the dihedral angle between the bonds at each of the carbon–carbon bonds is 180° and where atoms or groups bonded to carbons at each end of a carbon–carbon bond are as far apart as possible. The 180° dihedral angle in the staggered conformation of ethane is indicated in Fig. 4.5b.

The eclipsed conformation of ethane is shown in Fig. 4.6 using ball-and-stick models and a Newman projection. In an eclipsed conformation the atoms bonded to carbons at each end of a carbon–carbon bond are directly opposed to one another. The dihedral angle between them is 0°.

FIGURE 4.6 (a) The eclipsed conformation of ethane. (b) The Newman projection formula for the eclipsed conformation.

4.8B HOW TO Do a Conformational Analysis

Now let us consider a conformational analysis of ethane. Clearly, infinitesimally small changes in the dihedral angle between C—H bonds at each end of ethane could lead to an infinite number of conformations, including, of course, the staggered and eclipsed conformations. These different conformations are not all of equal stability, however, and it is known that the staggered conformation of ethane is the most stable conformation (i.e., it is the conformation of lowest potential energy). The explanation for greater stability of the staggered conformation relates mainly to steric replusion between bonding pairs of electrons. In the eclipsed conformation electron clouds from the C—H bonds are closer and repel one another. The staggered conformation allows the maximum possible separation of the electron pairs in the C—H bonds. In addition, there is a phenomenon called **hyperconjugation** that involves favorable overlap between filled and unfilled sigma orbitals in the staggered conformation. Hyperconjugation helps to stabilize the staggered conformation. The more important factor, however, is the minimization of steric repulsions in the staggered form. In later chapters we shall explain hyperconjugation further and the role it plays in relative stability of reactive species called carbocations.

● The energy difference between the conformations of ethane can be represented graphically in a **potential energy diagram**, as shown in Figure 4.7.

In ethane the energy difference between the staggered and eclipsed conformations is about 12 kJ mol^{-1}. This small barrier to rotation is called the **torsional barrier** of the single bond. Because of this barrier, some molecules will wag back and forth with their atoms in staggered or nearly staggered conformations, while others with slightly more energy will rotate through an eclipsed conformation to another staggered conformation. At any given moment, unless the temperature is extremely low (−250 °C), most ethane molecules will have enough energy to undergo bond rotation from one conformation to another.

FIGURE 4.7 Potential energy changes that accompany rotation of groups about the carbon–carbon bond of ethane.

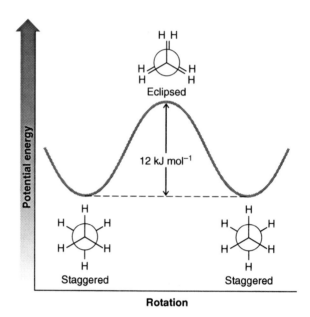

What does all this mean about ethane? We can answer this question in two different ways. If we consider a single molecule of ethane, we can say, for example, that it will spend most of its time in the lowest energy, staggered conformation, or in a conformation very close to being staggered. Many times every second, however, it will acquire enough energy through collisions with other molecules to surmount the torsional barrier and it will rotate through an eclipsed conformation. If we speak in terms of a large number of ethane molecules (a more realistic situation), we can say that at any given moment most of the molecules will be in staggered or nearly staggered conformations.

The idea that certain conformations of molecules are favored originates from the work of J.H. van't Hoff. He was also winner of the first Nobel Prize in Chemistry (1901) for his work in chemical kinetics.

4.9 CONFORMATIONAL ANALYSIS OF BUTANE

Now let us consider rotation about the C2—C3 bond of butane. The barriers to rotation about the C2—C3 bond in butane are larger than for rotation about the C—C bond in ethane, but still not large enough to prevent the rotations that lead to all possible butane conformers.

● The factors involved in barriers to bond rotation are together called **torsional strain** and include the repulsive interactions called **steric hindrance** between electron clouds of the bonded groups.

In butane, torsional strain results from steric hindrance between the terminal methyl groups and hydrogen atoms at C-2 and C-3 and from steric hindrance directly between

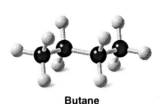

the two methyl groups. These interactions result in six important conformers of butane, shown as **I–VI** below.

I
An anti conformation

II
An eclipsed conformation

III
A gauche conformation

IV
An eclipsed conformation

V
A gauche conformation

VI
An eclipsed conformation

Butane

Helpful Hint

You should build a molecular model of butane and examine its various conformations as we discuss their relative potential energies.

The **anti conformation** (**I**) does not have torsional strain from steric hindrance because the groups are staggered and the methyl groups are far apart. The anti conformation is the most stable. The methyl groups in the **gauche conformations III** and **V** are close enough to each other that the dispersion forces between them are *repulsive*; the electron clouds of the two groups are so close that they repel each other. This repulsion causes the gauche conformations to have approximately 3.8 kJ mol^{-1} more energy than the anti conformation.

The eclipsed conformations (**II, IV,** and **VI**) represent energy maxima in the potential energy diagram (Fig. 4.8). Eclipsed conformations **II** and **VI** have repulsive dispersion forces arising from the eclipsed methyl groups and hydrogen atoms. Eclipsed conformation **IV** has the greatest energy of all because of the added large repulsive dispersion forces between the eclipsed methyl groups as compared to **II** and **VI**.

Although the barriers to rotation in a butane molecule are larger than those of an ethane molecule (Section 4.8), they are still far too small to permit isolation of the gauche and anti conformations at normal temperatures. Only at extremely low temperatures would the molecules have insufficient energies to surmount these barriers.

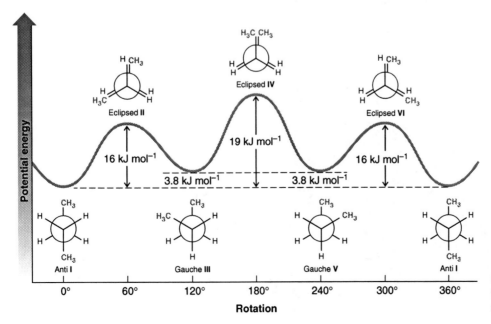

FIGURE 4.8 Energy changes that arise from rotation about the C2—C3 bond of butane.

171

We saw earlier (Section 2.16C) that dispersion forces can be *attractive*. Here, however, we find that they can also be *repulsive*, leading to steric hindrance. Whether dispersion interactions lead to attraction or to repulsion depends on the distance that separates the two groups. As two nonpolar groups are brought closer and closer together, the first effect is one in which a momentarily unsymmetrical distribution of electrons in one group induces an opposite polarity in the other. The opposite charges induced in those portions of the two groups that are in closest proximity lead to attraction between them. This attraction increases to a maximum as the internuclear distance of the two groups decreases. The internuclear distance at which the attractive force is at a maximum is equal to the sum of what are called the *van der Waals radii* of the two groups. The van der Waals radius of a group is, in effect, a measure of its size. If the two groups are brought still closer—closer than the sum of their van der Waals radii—their electron clouds begin to penetrate each other, and strong electron–electron repulsion occurs.

4.9A Stereoisomers and Conformational Stereoisomers

Gauche conformers **III** and **V** of butane are examples of stereoisomers.

- Stereoisomers have the same molecular formula and connectivity but different arrangements of atoms in three-dimensional space.
- Conformational stereoisomers are related to one another by bond rotations.

Conformational analysis is but one of the ways in which we will consider the three-dimensional shapes and stereochemistry of molecules. We shall see that there are other types of stereoisomers that cannot be interconverted simply by rotations about single bonds. Among these are cis–trans cycloalkane isomers (Section 4.13) and others that we shall consider in Chapter 5.

PRACTICE PROBLEM 4.13 Sketch a curve similar to that in Fig. 4.8 showing in general terms the energy changes that arise from rotation about the **C2—C3** bond of 2-methylbutane. You need not concern yourself with the actual numerical values of the energy changes, but you should label all maxima and minima with the appropriate conformations.

THE CHEMISTRY OF ... Muscle Action

Muscle proteins are essentially very long linear molecules (folded into a compact shape) whose atoms are connected by single bonds in a chainlike fashion. Relatively free rotation is possible about atoms joined by single bonds, as we have seen. When your muscles contract to do work, like they are for the person shown exercising here, the cumulative effect of rotations about many single bonds is to move the tail of each myosin molecule 60 Å along the adjacent protein (called actin) in a step called the "power stroke." This process occurs over and over again as part of a ratcheting mechanism between many myosin and actin molecules for each muscle movement.

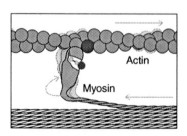

Power stroke in muscle

4.10 THE RELATIVE STABILITIES OF CYCLOALKANES: RING STRAIN

Cycloalkanes do not all have the same relative stability. Experiments have shown that cyclohexane is the most stable cycloalkane and that, in comparison, cyclopropane and cyclobutane are much less stable. This difference in relative stability is due to **ring strain**, which comprises **angle strain** and **torsional strain.**

* **Angle strain** is the result of deviation from ideal bond angles caused by inherent structural constraints (such as ring size).

* **Torsional strain** is the result of repulsive dispersion forces that cannot be relieved due to restricted conformational mobility.

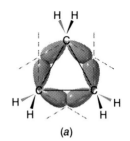

(a)

4.10A Cyclopropane

The carbon atoms of alkanes are sp^3 hybridized. The normal tetrahedral bond angle of an sp^3-hybridized atom is 109.5°. In cyclopropane (a molecule with the shape of a regular triangle), the internal angles must be 60° and therefore they must depart from this ideal value by a very large amount—by 49.5°:

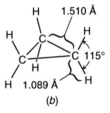

(b)

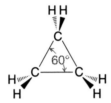

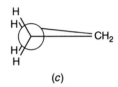

(c)

Angle strain exists in a cyclopropane ring because the sp^3 orbitals comprising the carbon–carbon σ bonds cannot overlap as effectively (Fig. 4.9a) as they do in alkanes (where perfect end-on overlap is possible). The carbon–carbon bonds of cyclopropane are often described as being "bent." Orbital overlap is less effective. (The orbitals used for these bonds are not purely sp^3; they contain more p character.) The carbon–carbon bonds of cyclopropane are weaker, and as a result the molecule has greater potential energy.

While angle strain accounts for most of the ring strain in cyclopropane, it does not account for it all. Because the ring is (of necessity) planar, the C—H bonds of the ring are all *eclipsed* (Figs. 4.9b,c), and the molecule has torsional strain from repulsive dispersion forces as well.

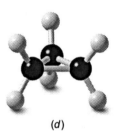

(d)

FIGURE 4.9 (a) Orbital overlap in the carbon–carbon bonds of cyclopropane cannot occur perfectly end-on. This leads to weaker "bent" bonds and to angle strain. (b) Bond distances and angles in cyclopropane. (c) A Newman projection formula as viewed along one carbon–carbon bond shows the eclipsed hydrogens. (Viewing along either of the other two bonds would show the same picture.) (d) Ball-and-stick model of cyclopropane.

4.10B Cyclobutane

Cyclobutane also has considerable angle strain. The internal angles are 88°—a departure of more than 21° from the normal tetrahedral bond angle. The cyclobutane ring is not planar but is slightly "folded" (Fig. 4.10a). If the cyclobutane ring were planar, the angle strain would be somewhat less (the internal angles would be 90° instead of 88°), but torsional strain would be considerably larger because all eight C—H bonds would be eclipsed. By folding or bending slightly the cyclobutane ring relieves more of its torsional strain than it gains in the slight increase in its angle strain.

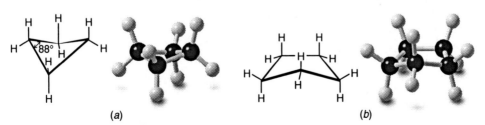

(a)   (b)

FIGURE 4.10 (a) The "folded" or "bent" conformation of cyclobutane. (b) The "bent" or "envelope" form of cyclopentane. In this structure the front carbon atom is bent upward. In actuality, the molecule is flexible and shifts conformations constantly.

4.10C Cyclopentane

The internal angles of a regular pentagon are 108°, a value very close to the normal tetrahedral bond angles of 109.5°. Therefore, if cyclopentane molecules were planar, they would have very little angle strain. Planarity, however, would introduce considerable torsional strain because all ten C—H bonds would be eclipsed. Consequently, like cyclobutane, cyclopentane assumes a slightly bent conformation in which one or two of the atoms of the ring are out of the plane of the others (Fig. 4.10b). This relieves some of the torsional strain. Slight twisting of carbon–carbon bonds can occur with little change in energy and causes the out-of-plane atoms to move into plane and causes others to move out. Therefore, the molecule is flexible and shifts rapidly from one conformation to another. With little torsional strain and angle strain, cyclopentane is almost as stable as cyclohexane.

4.11 CONFORMATIONS OF CYCLOHEXANE: THE CHAIR AND THE BOAT

FIGURE 4.11 Representations of the chair conformation of cyclohexane: (a) tube format; (b) ball-and-stick format; (c) line drawing; (d) space-filling model of cyclohexane. Notice that there are two orientations for the hydrogen substituents—those that project obviously up or down (shown in red) and those that lie around the perimeter of the ring in more subtle up or down orientations (shown in black or gray). We shall discuss this further in Section 4.12.

Cyclohexane is more stable than the other cycloalkanes we have discussed, and it has several conformations that are important for us to consider.

- The most stable conformation of cyclohexane is the chair conformation.
- There is no angle or torsional strain in the chair form of cyclohexane.

In a chair conformation (Fig. 4.11), all of the carbon–carbon bond angles are 109.5°, and are thereby free of angle strain. The chair conformation is free of torsional strain, as well. When viewed along any carbon–carbon bond (viewing the structure from an end, Fig. 4.12), the bonds are seen to be perfectly staggered. Moreover, the hydrogen atoms at opposite corners of the cyclohexane ring are maximally separated.

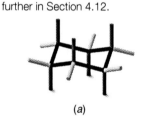

(a)

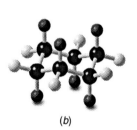

(b)

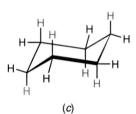

(c)

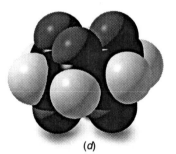

(d)

- By partial rotations about the carbon–carbon single bonds of the ring, the chair conformation can assume another shape called the boat conformation (Fig. 4.13).
- The boat conformation has no angle strain, but it does have torsional strain.

When a model of the boat conformation is viewed down carbon–carbon bond axes along either side (Fig. 4.14a), the C—H bonds at those carbon atoms are found to be eclipsed, causing torsional strain. Additionally, two of the hydrogen atoms on C1 and C4 are close enough to each other to cause van der Waals repulsion (Fig. 4.14b). This latter effect has been called the "flagpole" interaction of the boat conformation. Torsional strain and flagpole interactions cause the boat conformation to have considerably higher energy than the chair conformation.

FIGURE 4.12 (a) A Newman projection of the chair conformation of cyclohexane. (Comparisons with an actual molecular model will make this formulation clearer and will show that similar staggered arrangements are seen when other carbon–carbon bonds are chosen for sighting.) (b) Illustration of large separation between hydrogen atoms at opposite corners of the ring (designated C1 and C4) when the ring is in the chair conformation.

174

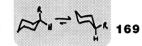

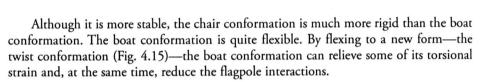

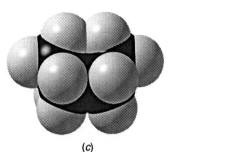

(a)   (b)

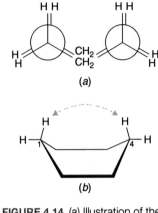

(a)

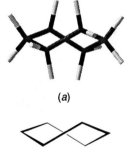

(b)

FIGURE 4.13 (a) The boat conformation of cyclohexane is formed by "flipping" one end of the chair form up (or down). This flip requires only rotations about carbon–carbon single bonds. (b) Ball-and-stick model of the boat conformation. (c) A space-filling model of the boat conformation.

(c)

Although it is more stable, the chair conformation is much more rigid than the boat conformation. The boat conformation is quite flexible. By flexing to a new form—the twist conformation (Fig. 4.15)—the boat conformation can relieve some of its torsional strain and, at the same time, reduce the flagpole interactions.

- The twist boat conformation of cyclohexane has a lower energy than the pure boat conformation, but is not as stable as the chair conformation.

The stability gained by flexing is insufficient, however, to cause the twist conformation to be more stable than the chair conformation. The chair conformation is estimated to be lower in energy than the twist conformation by approximately 23 kJ mol⁻¹.

The energy barriers between the chair, boat, and twist conformations of cyclohexane are low enough (Fig. 4.16) to make separation of the conformers impossible at room temperature. At room temperature the thermal energies of the molecules are great enough to cause approximately 1 million interconversions to occur each second.

- *Because of the greater stability of the chair, more than 99% of the molecules are estimated to be in a chair conformation at any given moment.*

FIGURE 4.14 (a) Illustration of the eclipsed conformation of the boat conformation of cyclohexane. (b) Flagpole interaction of the C1 and C4 hydrogen atoms of the boat conformation. The C1–C4 flagpole interaction is also readily apparent in Fig. 4.13c.

FIGURE 4.15 (a) Tube model and (b) line drawing of the twist conformation of cyclohexane.

FIGURE 4.16 The relative energies of the various conformations of cyclohexane. The positions of maximum energy are conformations called half-chair conformations, in which the carbon atoms of one end of the ring have become coplanar.

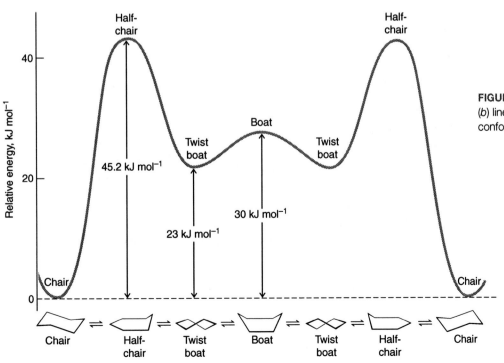

●●THE CHEMISTRY OF ... Nanoscale Motors and Molecular Switches

Molecular rings that interlock with one another and compounds that are linear molecules threaded through rings are proving to have fascinating potential for the creation of molecular switches and motors. Molecules consisting of interlocking rings, like a chain, are called **catenanes**. The first catenanes were synthesized in the 1960s and have come to include examples such as olympiadane, as mentioned in Section 4.11A. Further research by J. F. Stoddart (UCLA) and collaborators on interlocking molecules has led to examples such as the catenane molecular switch shown here in (*i*). In an application that could be useful in design of binary logic circuits, one ring of this molecule can be made to circumrotate in controlled fashion about the other, such that it switches between two defined states. As a demonstration of its potential for application in electronics fabrication, a monolayer of these molecules has been "tiled" on a surface (*ii*) and shown to have characteristics like a conventional magnetic memory bit.

   Molecules where a linear molecule is threaded through a ring are called **rotaxanes**. One captivating example of a rotaxane system is the one shown here in (*iii*), under development by V. Balzani (University of Bologna) and collaborators. By conversion of light energy to mechanical energy at the molecular level, this rotaxane behaves like a "four-stroke" shuttle engine. In step (*a*) light excitation of an electron in the **P** group leads to transfer of the electron to the initially +2 **A$_1$** group, at which point **A$_1$** is reduced to the +1 state. Ring **R**, which was attracted to **A$_1$** when it was in the +2 state, now slides over to **A$_2$** in step (*b*), which remains +2. Back transfer of the electron from **A$_1$** to **P$^+$** in step (*c*) restores the +2 state of **A1**, causing ring **R** to return to its original location in step (*d*). Modifications envisioned for this system include attaching binding sites to **R** such that some other molecular species could be transported from one location to another as **R** slides along the linear molecule, or linking **R** by a springlike tether to one end of the "piston rod" such that additional potential and mechanical energy can be incorporated in the system.

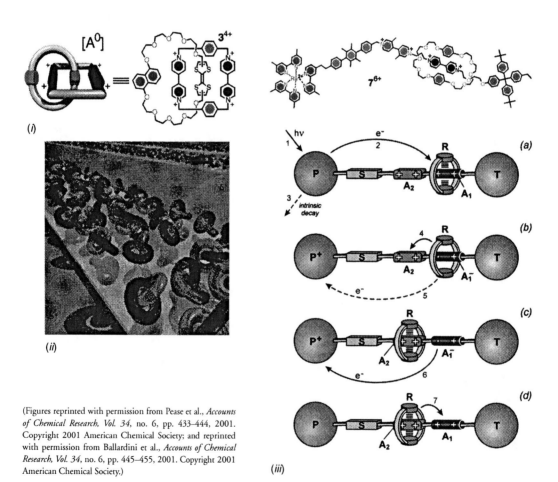

(*i*)

(*ii*)

(*iii*)

(Figures reprinted with permission from Pease et al., *Accounts of Chemical Research, Vol. 34*, no. 6, pp. 433–444, 2001. Copyright 2001 American Chemical Society; and reprinted with permission from Ballardini et al., *Accounts of Chemical Research, Vol. 34*, no. 6, pp. 445–455, 2001. Copyright 2001 American Chemical Society.)

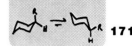

4.11A Conformations of Higher Cycloalkanes

Cycloheptane, cyclooctane, and cyclononane and other higher cycloalkanes also exist in nonplanar conformations. The small instabilities of these higher cycloalkanes appear to be caused primarily by torsional strain and repulsive dispersion forces between hydrogen atoms across rings, called *transannular strain*. The nonplanar conformations of these rings, however, are essentially free of angle strain.

X-ray crystallographic studies of cyclodecane reveal that the most stable conformation has carbon–carbon–carbon bond angles of 117°. This indicates some angle strain. The wide bond angles apparently allow the molecules to expand and thereby minimize unfavorable repulsions between hydrogen atoms across the ring.

There is very little free space in the center of a cycloalkane unless the ring is quite large. Calculations indicate that cyclooctadecane, for example, is the smallest ring through which a —$CH_2CH_2CH_2$— chain can be threaded. Molecules have been synthesized, however, that have large rings threaded on chains and that have large rings that are interlocked like links in a chain. These latter molecules are called **catenanes**:

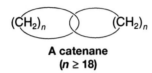

A catenane
($n \geq 18$)

In 1994 J. F. Stoddart and co-workers, then at the University of Birmingham (England), achieved a remarkable synthesis of a catenane containing a linear array of five interlocked rings. Because the rings are interlocked in the same way as those of the olympic symbol, they named the compound **olympiadane**.

DEREK H. R. BARTON (1918–1998) and ODD HASSEL (1897–1981) shared the Nobel Prize in 1969 "for developing and applying the principles of conformation in chemistry." Their work led to fundamental understanding of not only the conformations of cyclohexane rings but also the structures of steroids (Section 23.4) and other compounds containing cyclohexane rings.

4.12 SUBSTITUTED CYCLOHEXANES: AXIAL AND EQUATORIAL HYDROGEN GROUPS

The six-membered ring is the most common ring found among nature's organic molecules. For this reason, we shall give it special attention. We have already seen that the chair conformation of cyclohexane is the most stable one and that it is the predominant conformation of the molecules in a sample of cyclohexane.

The chair conformation of a cyclohexane ring has two distinct orientations for the bonds that project from the ring. These positions are called axial and equatorial, as shown for cyclohexane in Fig. 4.17.

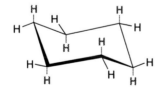

FIGURE 4.17 The chair conformation of cyclohexane. Axial hydrogen atoms are shown in red, equatorial hydrogens are shown in black.

- The **axial bonds** of cyclohexane are those that are perpendicular to the average plane of the ring. There are three axial bonds on each face of the cyclohexane ring, and their orientation (up or down) alternates from one carbon to the next.

- The **equatorial bonds** of cyclohexane are those that extend from the perimeter of the ring. The equatorial bonds alternate from slightly up to slightly down in their orientation from one carbon to the next.

* When a cyclohexane ring undergoes a chair–chair conformational change (a **ring flip**), all of the bonds that were axial become equatorial, and all bonds that were equatorial become axial.

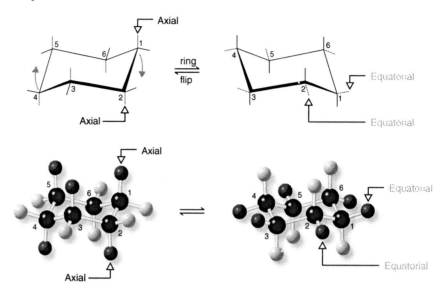

4.12A HOW TO Draw Chair Conformational Structures

A set of guidelines will help you draw chair conformational structures that are clear and that have unambiguous axial and equatorial bonds.

* Notice in Fig. 4.18a that sets of parallel lines define opposite sides of the chair. Notice, too, that equatorial bonds are parallel to ring bonds that are one bond away from them in either direction. When you draw chair conformational structures, try to make the corresponding bonds parallel in your drawings.

* When a chair formula is drawn as shown in Fig. 4.18, the axial bonds are all either up or down, in a vertical orientation (Fig. 4.18b). When a vertex of bonds in the ring points up, the axial bond at that position is also up, and the equatorial bond at the same carbon is angled slightly down. When a vertex of ring bonds is down, the axial bond at that position is also down, and the equatorial bond is angled slightly upward.

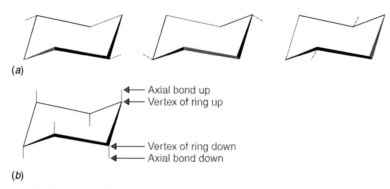

FIGURE 4.18 (a) Sets of parallel lines that constitute the ring and equatorial C—H bonds of the chair conformation. (b) The axial bonds are all vertical. When the vertex of the ring points up, the axial bond is up and vice versa.

Now, try to draw some chair conformational structures for yourself that include the axial and equatorial bonds. Then, compare your drawings with those here and with actual models. You will see that with a little practice your chair conformational structures can be perfect.

4.12B A Conformational Analysis of Methylcyclohexane

Now let us consider methylcyclohexane. Methylcyclohexane has two possible chair conformations (Fig. 4.19, **I** and **II**), and these are interconvertible through the bond rotations that constitute a ring flip. In conformation (Fig. 4.19a) the methyl group (with yellow hydrogens in the space-filling model) occupies an *axial* position, and in conformation **II** the methyl group occupies an *equatorial* position.

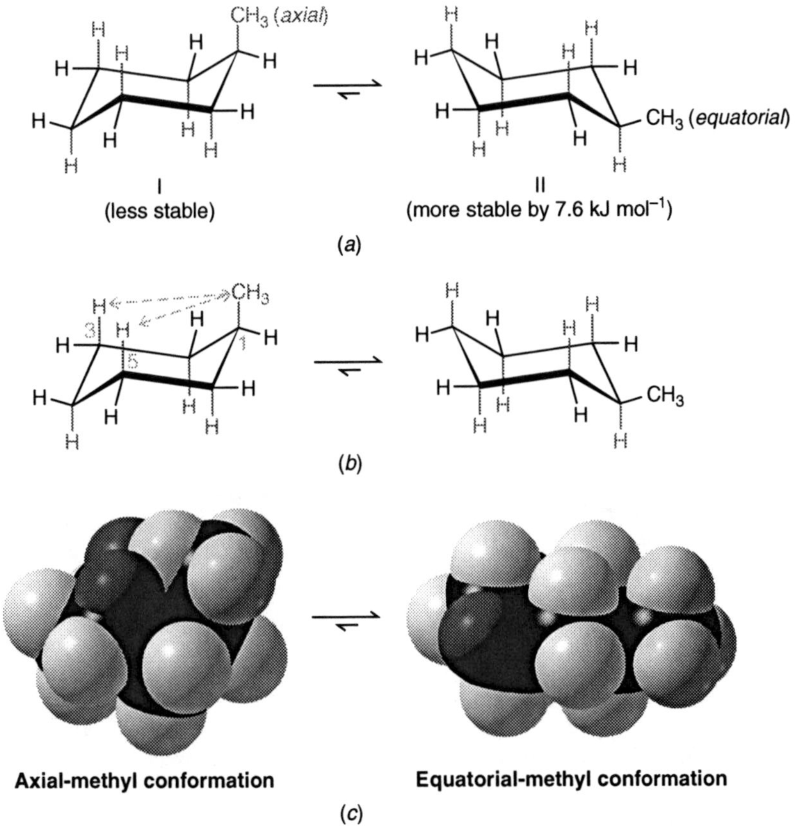

FIGURE 4.19 (a) The conformations of methylcyclohexane with the methyl group axial (**I**) and equatorial (**II**). (b) 1,3-Diaxial interactions between the two axial hydrogen atoms and the axial methyl group in the axial conformation of methylcyclohexane are shown with dashed arrows. Less crowding occurs in the equatorial conformation. (c) Space-filling molecular models for the axial–methyl and equatorial–methyl conformers of methylcyclohexane. In the axial–methyl conformer the methyl group (shown with yellow hydrogen atoms) is crowded by the 1,3-diaxial hydrogen atoms (red), as compared to the equatorial–methyl conformer, which has no 1,3-diaxial interactions with the methyl group.

- The most stable conformation for a monosubstituted cyclohexane ring (a cyclohexane ring where one carbon atom bears a group other than hydrogen) is the conformation where the substituent is equatorial.

Studies indicate that conformation **II** with the equatorial methyl group is more stable than conformation **I** with the axial methyl group by about 7.6 kJ mol^{-1}. Thus, in the equilibrium mixture, the conformation with the methyl group in the equatorial position is the predominant one, constituting about 95% of the equilibrium mixture.

The greater stability of methylcyclohexane with an equatorial methyl group can be understood through an inspection of the two forms as they are shown in Figs. 4.19a–c.

- Studies done with models of the two conformations show that when the methyl group is axial, it is so close to the two axial hydrogens on the same side of the ring (attached to the **C3** and **C5** atoms) that **the dispersion forces between them are repulsive**.

- This type of steric strain, because it arises from an interaction between an axial group on carbon atom 1 and an axial hydrogen on carbon atom 3 (or 5), is called a **1,3-diaxial interaction**.

- Studies with other substituents show that **there is generally less repulsion when any group larger than hydrogen is equatorial rather than axial**.

The strain caused by a 1,3-diaxial interaction in methylcyclohexane is the same as the strain caused by the close proximity of the hydrogen atoms of methyl groups in the gauche form of butane (Section 4.9). Recall that the interaction in *gauche*-butane (called, for convenience, a *gauche interaction*) causes *gauche*-butane to be less stable than *anti*-butane by 3.8 kJ mol^{-1}. The following Newman projections will help you to see that the two steric interactions are the same. In the second projection we view axial methyl-cyclohexane along the C1—C2 bond and see that what we call a 1,3-diaxial interaction is simply a gauche interaction between the hydrogen atoms of the methyl group and the hydrogen atom at C3:

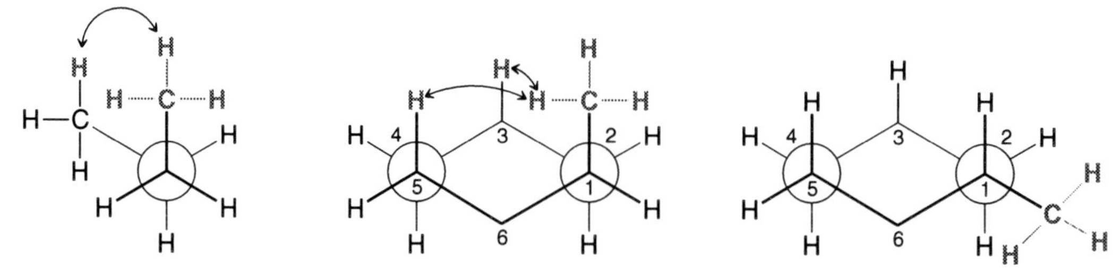

gauche-Butane
(3.8 kJ mol^{-1} steric strain)

Axial methylcyclohexane
(two gauche interactions =
7.6 kJ mol^{-1} steric strain)

Equatorial methylcyclohexane
(more stable by 7.6 kJ mol^{-1})

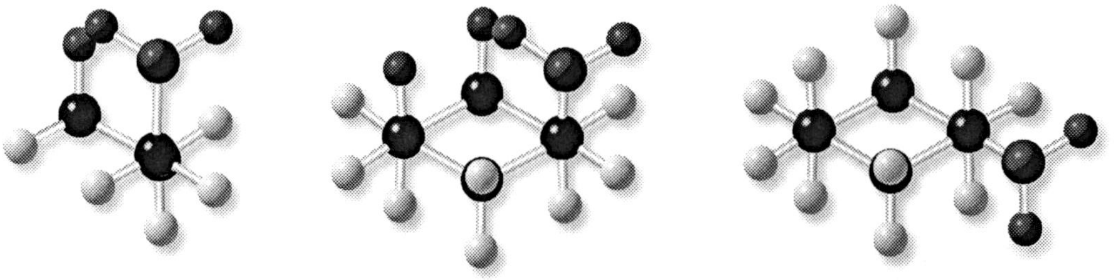

Viewing methylcyclohexane along the C1—C6 bond (do this with a model) shows that it has a second identical gauche interaction between the hydrogen atoms of the methyl group and the hydrogen atom at C5. The methyl group of axial methylcyclohexane, therefore, has two gauche interactions and, consequently, it has 7.6 kJ mol^{-1} of strain. The methyl group of equatorial methylcyclohexane does not have a gauche interaction because it is anti to C3 and C5.

•••

PRACTICE PROBLEM 4.14 Show by a calculation (using the formula $\Delta G° = -RT \ln K_{eq}$) that a free-energy difference of 7.6 kJ mol^{-1} between the axial and equatorial forms of methylcyclo-hexane at 25 °C (with the equatorial form being more stable) does correlate with an equilibrium mixture in which the concentration of the equatorial form is approximately 95%.

4.12C 1,3-Diaxial Interactions of a *tert*-Butyl Group

In cyclohexane derivatives with larger alkyl substituents, the strain caused by 1,3-diaxial interactions is even more pronounced. The conformation of *tert*-butylcyclohexane with the *tert*-butyl group equatorial is estimated to be approximately 21 kJ mol^{-1} more stable than the axial form (Fig. 4.20). This large energy difference between the two conformations means that, at room temperature, 99.99% of the molecules of *tert*-butylcyclohexane have the *tert*-butyl group in the equatorial position. (The molecule is not conformationally "locked," however; it still flips from one chair conformation to the other.)

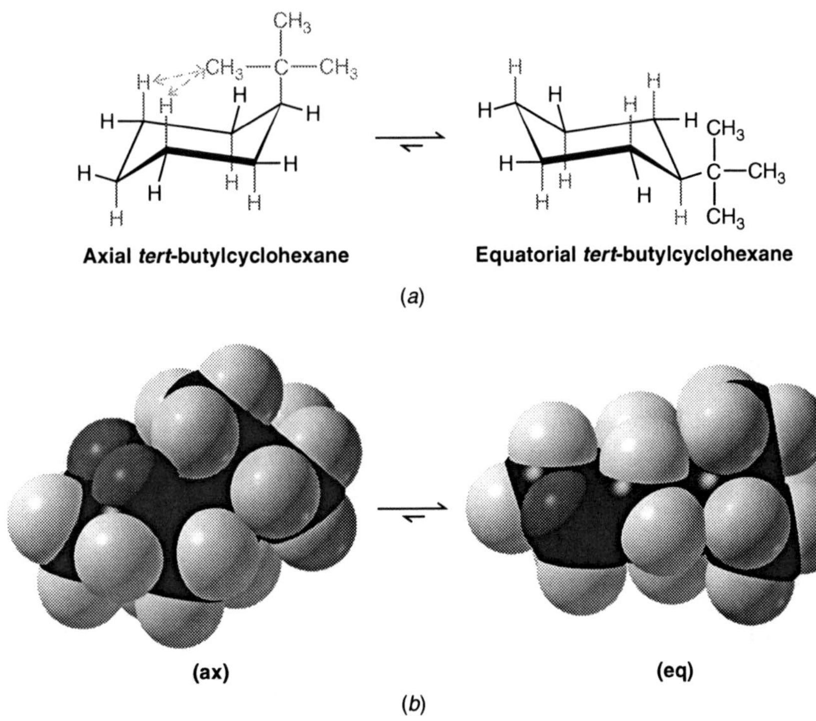

CH₃

Axial *tert*-butylcyclohexane   Equatorial *tert*-butylcyclohexane

(*a*)

FIGURE 4.20 (*a*) Diaxial interactions with the large *tert*-butyl group axial cause the conformation with the *tert*-butyl group equatorial to be the predominant one to the extent of 99.99%. (*b*) Space-filling molecular models of *tert*-butylcyclohexane in the axial (ax) and equatorial (eq) conformations, highlighting the position of the 1,3-hydrogens (red) and the *tert*-butyl group (shown with yellow hydrogen atoms).

(ax)   (eq)

(*b*)

4.13 DISUBSTITUTED CYCLOALKANES: CIS–TRANS ISOMERISM

The presence of two substituents on different carbons of a cycloalkane allows for the possibility of **cis–trans isomerism** similar to the kind we saw for alkenes in Section 1.14B. These cis–trans isomers are also **stereoisomers** because they differ from each other only in the arrangement of their atoms in space. Consider 1,2-dimethylcyclopropane (Fig. 4.21) as an example.

cis-1,2-Dimethylcyclopropane   *trans*-1,2-Dimethylcyclopropane

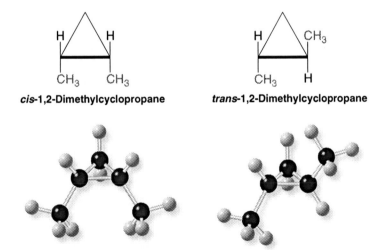

FIGURE 4.21 The *cis*- and *trans*-1,2-dimethylcyclopropane isomers.

The planarity of the cyclopropane ring makes the cis–trans isomerism obvious. In the first structure the methyl groups are on the same side of the ring; therefore, they are cis. In the second structure, they are on opposite sides of the ring; they are trans.

Cis and trans isomers such as these cannot be interconverted without breaking carbon–carbon bonds. They will have different physical properties (boiling points, melting points, and so on). As a result, they can be separated, placed in separate bottles, and kept indefinitely.

·⊕⊕

PRACTICE PROBLEM 4.15   Write structures for the cis and trans isomers of **(a)** 1,2-dichlorocyclopentane and **(b)** 1,3-dibromocyclobutane. **(c)** Are cis–trans isomers possible for 1,1-dibromocyclobutane?

4.13A Cis–Trans Isomerism and Conformational Structures of Cyclohexanes

Trans 1,4-Disubstituted Cyclohexanes If we consider dimethylcyclohexanes, the structures are somewhat more complex because the cyclohexane ring is not planar. Beginning with *trans*-1,4-dimethylcyclohexane, because it is easiest to visualize, we find there are two possible chair conformations (Fig. 4.22). In one conformation both methyl groups are axial; in the other both are equatorial. The diequatorial conformation is, as we would expect it to be, the more stable conformation, and it represents the structure of at least 99% of the molecules at equilibrium.

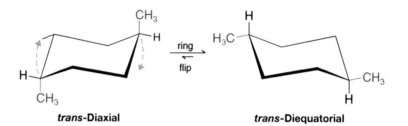

FIGURE 4.22 The two chair conformations of trans-1,4-dimethylcyclohexane: trans–diequatorial and trans–diaxial. The trans–diequatorial form is more stable by 15.2 kJ mol^{-1}.

That the diaxial form of *trans*-1,4-dimethylcyclohexane is a trans isomer is easy to see; the two methyl groups are clearly on opposite sides of the ring. The trans relationship of the methyl groups in the diequatorial form is not as obvious, however.

How do we know two groups are cis or trans? A general way to recognize a trans-disubstituted cyclohexane is to notice that one group is attached by the *upper* bond (of the two to its carbon) and one by the *lower* bond:

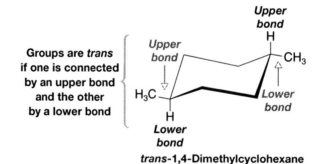

In a cis 1,4-disubstituted cyclohexane both groups are attached by an upper bond or both by a lower bond. For example,

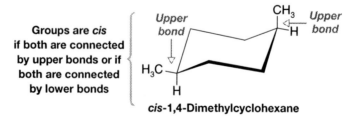

Cis 1,4-Disubstituted Cyclohexanes *cis*-1,4-Dimethylcyclohexane exists in two *equivalent* chair conformations (Fig. 4.23). In a cis 1,4-disubstituted cyclohexane, one group is axial and the other is equatorial in both of the possible chair conformations.

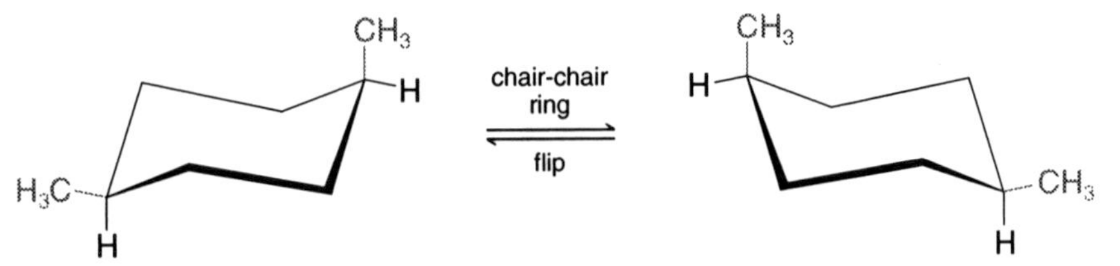

Equatorial–axial   **Axial–equatorial**

FIGURE 4.23 Equivalent conformations of *cis*-1,4-dimethylcyclohexane.

●●● SOLVED PROBLEM 4.5

Consider each of the following conformational structures and tell whether each is cis or trans:

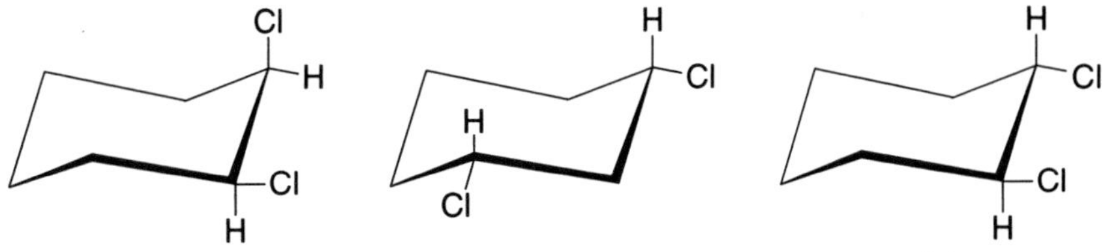

(a)   **(b)**   **(c)**

ANSWER: (a) Each chlorine is attached by the upper bond at its carbon; therefore, both chlorine atoms are on the same side of the molecule and this is a cis isomer. This is a *cis*-1,2-dichlorocyclohexane. **(b)** Here both chlorine atoms are attached by a lower bond; therefore, in this example, too, both chlorine atoms are on the same side of the molecule and this, too, is a cis isomer. It is *cis*-1,3-dichlorocyclohexane. **(c)** Here one chlorine atom is attached by a lower bond and one by an upper bond. The two chlorine atoms, therefore, are on opposite sides of the molecule, and this is a trans isomer. It is *trans*-1,2-dichlorocyclohexane. Verify these facts by building models.

The two conformations of cis 1,4-disubstituted cyclohexanes *are not equivalent* if one group is larger than the other. Consider *cis*-1-*tert*-butyl-4-methylcyclohexane:

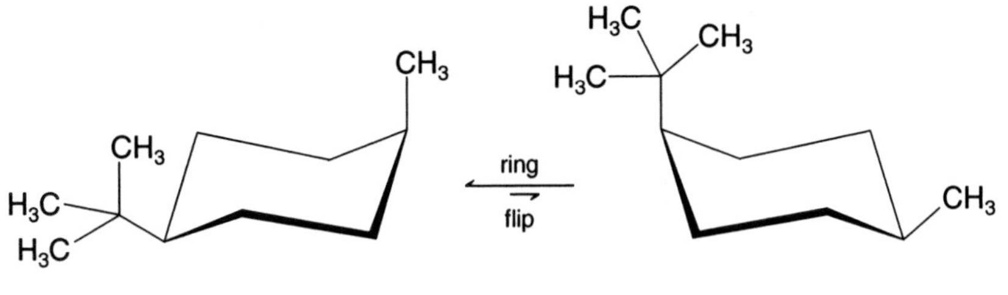

(More stable because large group is equatorial)   **(Less stable because large group is axial)**

cis-1-*tert*-**Butyl-4-methylcyclohexane**

Here the more stable conformation is the one with the larger group equatorial. This is a general principle:

● When one ring substituent group is larger than the other and they cannot both be equatorial, the conformation with the larger group equatorial will be more stable.

●●●

(a) Write structural formulas for the two chair conformations of *cis*-1-isopropyl-4-methylcyclohexane. **(b)** Are these two conformations equivalent? **(c)** If not, which would be more stable? **(d)** Which would be the preferred conformation at equilibrium?

PRACTICE PROBLEM 4.16

Trans 1,3-Disubstituted Cyclohexanes *trans*-1,3-Dimethylcyclohexane is like the cis 1,4 compound in that each conformation has one methyl group in an axial position and one methyl group in an equatorial position. The following two conformations are of equal energy and are equally populated at equilibrium:

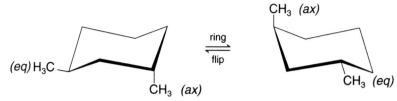

trans-1,3-Dimethylcyclohexane
Equal energy and equally populated conformations

The situation is different for *trans*-1-*tert*-butyl-3-methylcyclohexane (shown below) because the two ring substituents are not the same. Again, we find that the lower energy conformation is that with the largest group equatorial.

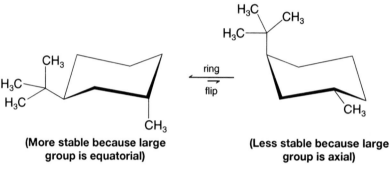

(More stable because large   (Less stable because large
group is equatorial)   group is axial)

trans-1-tert-Butyl-3-methylcyclohexane

Cis 1,3-Disubstituted Cyclohexanes *cis*-1,3-Dimethylcyclohexane has a conformation in which both methyl groups are equatorial and one in which both methyl groups are axial. **As we would expect, the conformation with both methyl groups equatorial is the more stable one.**

Trans 1,2-Disubstituted Cyclohexanes *trans*-1,2-Dimethylcyclohexane has a conformation in which both methyl groups are equatorial and one in which both methyl groups are axial. **As we would expect, the conformation with both methyl groups equatorial is the more stable one.**

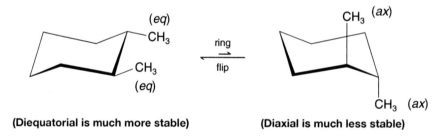

(Diequatorial is much more stable)   (Diaxial is much less stable)

trans-1,2-Dimethylcyclohexane

Cis 1,2-Disubstituted Cyclohexanes *cis*-1,2-Dimethylcyclohexane has one methyl group that is axial and one methyl group that is equatorial in each of its chair conformations, thus its two conformations are of equal stability.

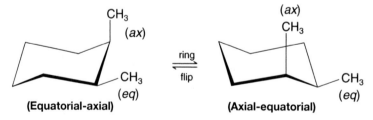

(Equatorial-axial)   (Axial-equatorial)

cis-1,2-Dimethylcyclohexane
Equal energy and equally populated conformations

Write a conformational structure for 1,2,3-trimethylcyclohexane in which all the methyl groups are axial and then show its more stable conformation.

ANSWER: A ring flip gives a conformation in which all the groups are equatorial and, therefore, much more stable.

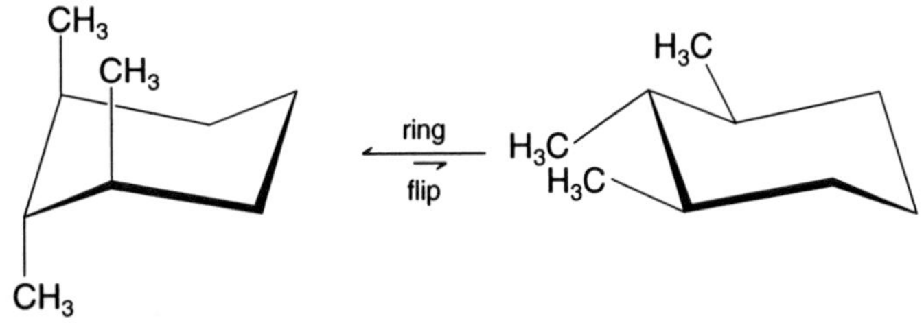

All groups axial. Much less stable conformation.

All groups are equatorial. Much more stable conformation.

●●●

Write a conformational structure for 1-bromo-3-chloro-5-fluorocyclohexane in which all the substituents are equatorial. Then write its structure after a ring flip.

PRACTICE PROBLEM 4.17

●●●

(a) Write the two conformations of *cis*-1-*tert*-butyl-2-methylcyclohexane. **(b)** Which conformer has the lowest potential energy?

PRACTICE PROBLEM 4.18

4.14 BICYCLIC AND POLYCYCLIC ALKANES

Many of the molecules that we encounter in our study of organic chemistry contain more than one ring (Section 4.4B). One of the most important bicyclic systems is bicyclo [4.4.0]decane, a compound that is usually called by its common name, *decalin*:

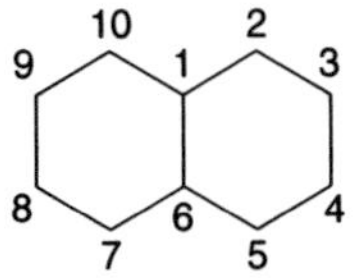

Decalin (bicyclo[4.4.0]decane)
(carbon atoms 1 and 6 are bridgehead carbon atoms)

Decalin shows cis–trans isomerism:

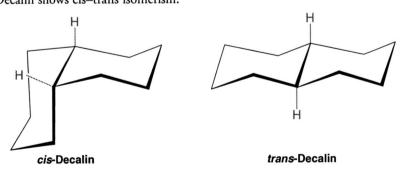

cis-Decalin

trans-Decalin

Helpful Hint

Chemical Abstracts Service (CAS) determines the number of rings by the formula $S - A + 1 = N$, where S is the number of single bonds in the ring system, A is the number of atoms in the ring system, and N is the calculated number of rings (see Problem 4.30).

185

In *cis*-decalin the two hydrogen atoms attached to the bridgehead atoms lie on the same side of the ring; in *trans*-decalin they are on opposite sides. We often indicate this by writing their structures in the following way:

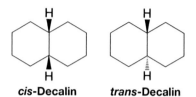

cis-**Decalin**   *trans*-**Decalin**

Simple rotations of groups about carbon–carbon bonds do not interconvert *cis*- and *trans*-decalins. They are stereoisomers and they have different physical properties.

Adamantane is a tricyclic system that contains a three-dimensional array of cyclohexane rings, all of which are in the chair form.

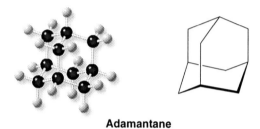

Adamantane

In the chapter closer we shall see several examples of other unusual and highly strained, cyclic hydrocarbons.

4.15 CHEMICAL REACTIONS OF ALKANES

Alkanes, as a class, are characterized by a general inertness to many chemical reagents. Carbon–carbon and carbon–hydrogen bonds are quite strong; they do not break unless alkanes are heated to very high temperatures. Because carbon and hydrogen atoms have nearly the same electronegativity, the carbon–hydrogen bonds of alkanes are only slightly polarized. As a consequence, they are generally unaffected by most bases. Molecules of alkanes have no unshared electrons to offer as sites for attack by acids. This low reactivity of alkanes toward many reagents accounts for the fact that alkanes were originally called paraffins (*parum affinis*, Latin: little affinity).

The term paraffin, however, was probably not an appropriate one. We all know that alkanes react vigorously with oxygen when an appropriate mixture is ignited. This combustion occurs, for example, in the cylinders of automobiles, in furnaces, and, more gently, with paraffin candles. When heated, alkanes also react with chlorine and bromine, and they react explosively with fluorine. We shall study these reactions in Chapter 10.

4.16 SYNTHESIS OF ALKANES AND CYCLOALKANES

A chemical synthesis may require, at some point, the conversion of a carbon–carbon double or triple bond to a single bond. Synthesis of the following compound, used as an ingredient in some perfumes, is an example.

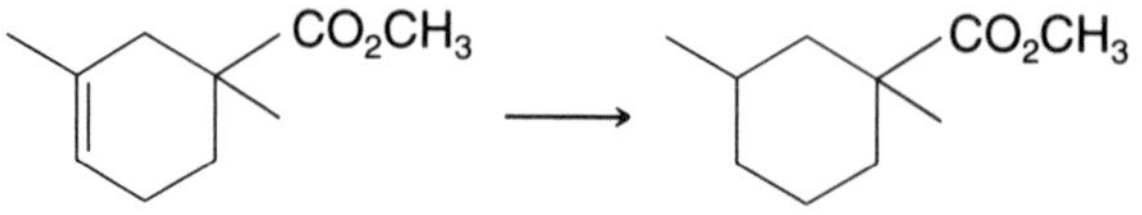

CO_2CH_3 CO_2CH_3

(used in some perfumes)

This conversion is easily accomplished by a reaction called hydrogenation. There are several reaction conditions that can be used to carry out hydrogenation, but among the common ways is use of hydrogen gas and a solid metal catalyst such as platinum, palladium, or nickel. Equations in the following section represent general examples for the hydrogenation of alkenes and alkynes.

4.16A Hydrogenation of Alkenes and Alkynes

- Alkenes and alkynes react with hydrogen in the presence of metal catalysts such as nickel, palladium, and platinum to produce alkanes.

The general reaction is one in which the atoms of the hydrogen molecule add to each atom of the carbon–carbon double or triple bond of the alkene or alkyne. This converts the alkene or alkyne to an alkane:

General Reaction

Alkene + H₂ $\xrightarrow[\substack{\text{solvent,}\\\text{pressure}}]{\text{Pt, Pd, or Ni}}$ Alkane   Alkyne + 2 H₂ $\xrightarrow[\substack{\text{solvent,}\\\text{pressure}}]{\text{Pt}}$ Alkane

The reaction is usually carried out by dissolving the alkene or alkyne in a solvent such as ethyl alcohol (C_2H_5OH), adding the metal catalyst, and then exposing the mixture to hydrogen gas under pressure in a special apparatus. One molar equivalent of hydrogen is required to reduce an alkene to an alkane. Two molar equivalents are required to reduce an alkyne. (We shall discuss the mechanism of this reaction in Chapter 7.)

Specific Examples

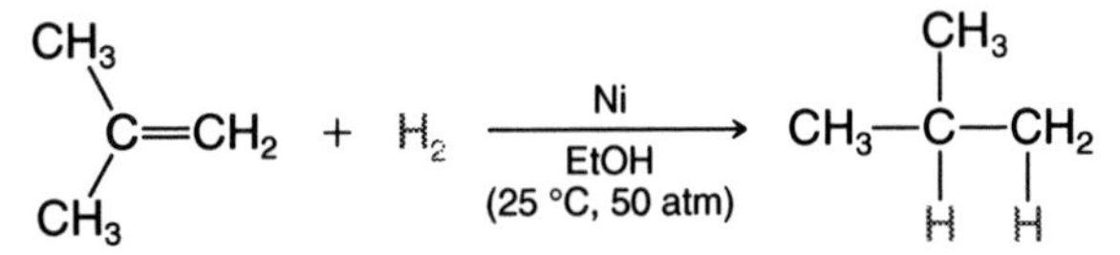

2-Methylpropene + H_2 $\xrightarrow[\substack{\text{EtOH}\\\text{(25 °C, 50 atm)}}]{\text{Ni}}$ Isobutane

Cyclohexene + H_2 $\xrightarrow[\substack{\text{EtOH}\\\text{(25 °C, 1 atm)}}]{\text{Pd}}$ Cyclohexane

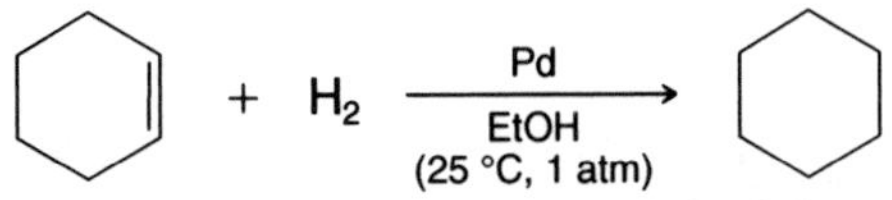

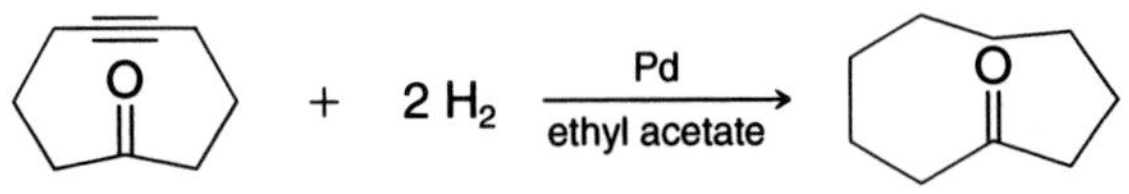

Cyclononyn-6-one + 2 H_2 $\xrightarrow[\text{ethyl acetate}]{\text{Pd}}$ Cyclononanone

●●● **SOLVED PROBLEM 4.7**

Write the structures of three pentenes that would all yield pentane on hydrogenation.

ANSWER:

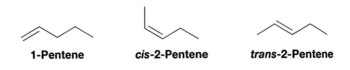

1-Pentene   *cis*-**2-Pentene**   *trans*-**2-Pentene**

• • •

PRACTICE PROBLEM 4.19 Show the reactions involved for hydrogenation of all the alkenes and alkynes that would yield 2-methylbutane.

4.17 HOW TO GAIN STRUCTURAL INFORMATION FROM MOLECULAR FORMULAS AND THE INDEX OF HYDROGEN DEFICIENCY

A chemist working with an unknown compound can obtain considerable information about its structure from the compound's molecular formula and its **index of hydrogen deficiency (IHD)**.

* The **index of hydrogen deficiency** (IHD)* is defined as the difference in the *number of pairs* of hydrogen atoms between the compound under study and an acyclic alkane having the same number of carbons.

Saturated acyclic hydrocarbons have the general molecular formula C_nH_{2n+2}. Each double bond or ring reduces the number of hydrogen atoms by two as compared with the formula for a saturated compound. Thus each ring or double bond provides one unit of hydrogen deficiency. For example, 1-hexene and cyclohexane have the same molecular formula (C_6H_{12}) and they are constitutional isomers.

1-Hexene
(C_6H_{12})

Cyclohexane
(C_6H_{12})

Both 1-hexene and cyclohexane (C_6H_{12}) have an index of hydrogen deficiency equal to 1 (meaning one pair of hydrogen atoms), because the corresponding acyclic alkane is hexane (C_6H_{14}).

C_6H_{14} = formula of corresponding alkane (hexane)

$\underline{C_6H_{12}}$ = formula of compound (1-hexene or cyclohexane)

H_2 = difference = 1 pair of hydrogen atoms

Index of hydrogen deficiency = 1

Alkynes and alkadienes (alkenes with two double bonds) have the general formula C_nH_{2n-2}. Alkenynes (hydrocarbons with one double bond and one triple bond) and alkatrienes (alkenes with three double bonds) have the general formula C_nH_{2n-4}, and so forth.

1,3-Butadiene
IHD = 2

But-1-en-3-yne
IHD = 3

1,3,5-Hexatriene
IHD = 3

The index of hydrogen deficiency is easily determined by comparing the molecular formula of a given compound with the formula for its hydrogenation product.

* Each double bond consumes one molar equivalent of hydrogen and counts for one unit of hydrogen deficiency.

* Each triple bond consumes two molar equivalents of hydrogen and counts for two units of hydrogen deficiency.

* Rings are not affected by hydrogenation, but each ring still counts for one unit of hydrogen deficiency.

*Some organic chemists refer to the index of hydrogen deficiency as the "degree of unsaturation" or "the number of double-bond equivalencies."

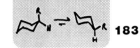

Hydrogenation, therefore, allows us to distinguish between rings and double or triple bonds. Consider again two compounds with the molecular formula C_6H_{12}: 1-hexene and cyclohexane. 1-Hexene reacts with one molar equivalent of hydrogen to yield hexane; under the same conditions cyclohexane does not react:

$$\text{(1-hexene)} \; + \; H_2 \; \xrightarrow[25\,°C]{Pt} \; \text{(hexane)}$$

$$\text{(cyclohexane)} \; + \; H_2 \; \xrightarrow[25\,°C]{Pt} \; \text{no reaction}$$

Or consider another example. Cyclohexene and 1,3-hexadiene have the same molecular formula (C_6H_{10}). Both compounds react with hydrogen in the presence of a catalyst, but cyclohexene, because it has a ring and only one double bond, reacts with only one molar equivalent. 1,3-Hexadiene adds two molar equivalents:

$$\text{(cyclohexene)} \; + \; H_2 \; \xrightarrow[25\,°C]{Pt} \; \text{(cyclohexane)}$$

Cyclohexene

$$\text{(1,3-hexadiene)} \; + \; 2\,H_2 \; \xrightarrow[25\,°C]{Pt} \; \text{(hexane)}$$

1,3-Hexadiene

●●◉········

PRACTICE PROBLEM 4.20

(a) What is the index of hydrogen deficiency of 2-hexene? **(b)** Of methylcyclopentane? **(c)** Does the index of hydrogen deficiency reveal anything about the location of the double bond in the chain? **(d)** About the size of the ring? **(e)** What is the index of hydrogen deficiency of 2-hexyne? **(f)** In general terms, what structural possibilities exist for a compound with the molecular formula $C_{10}H_{16}$?

●●◉········

PRACTICE PROBLEM 4.21

Zingiberene, a fragrant compound isolated from ginger, has the molecular formula $C_{15}H_{24}$ and is known not to contain any triple bonds. **(a)** What is the index of hydrogen deficiency of zingiberene? **(b)** When zingiberene is subjected to catalytic hydrogenation using an excess of hydrogen, 1 mol of zingiberene absorbs 3 mol of hydrogen and produces a compound with the formula $C_{15}H_{30}$. How many double bonds does a molecule of zingiberene have? **(c)** How many rings?

4.17A Compounds Containing Halogens, Oxygen, or Nitrogen

Calculating the index of hydrogen deficiency (IHD) for compounds other than hydrocarbons is relatively easy.

For compounds containing halogen atoms, we simply count the halogen atoms as though they were hydrogen atoms. Consider a compound with the formula $C_4H_6Cl_2$. To calculate the IHD, we change the two chlorine atoms to hydrogen atoms, considering the formula as though it were C_4H_8. This formula has two hydrogen atoms fewer than the formula for a saturated alkane (C_4H_{10}), and this tells us that the compound has IHD = 1. It could, therefore, have either one ring or one double bond. [We can tell which it has from a hydrogenation experiment: If the compound adds one molar equivalent of hydrogen (H_2) on catalytic hydrogenation at room temperature, then it must have a double bond; if it does not add hydrogen, then it must have a ring.]

For compounds containing oxygen, we simply ignore the oxygen atoms and calculate the IHD from the remainder of the formula. Consider as an example a compound with the formula C_4H_8O. For the purposes of our calculation we consider the compound to be simply C_4H_8 and we calculate IHD = 1. Again, this means that the compound contains either a ring or a double bond. Some structural possibilities for this compound are shown next. Notice that the double bond may be present as a carbon–oxygen double bond:

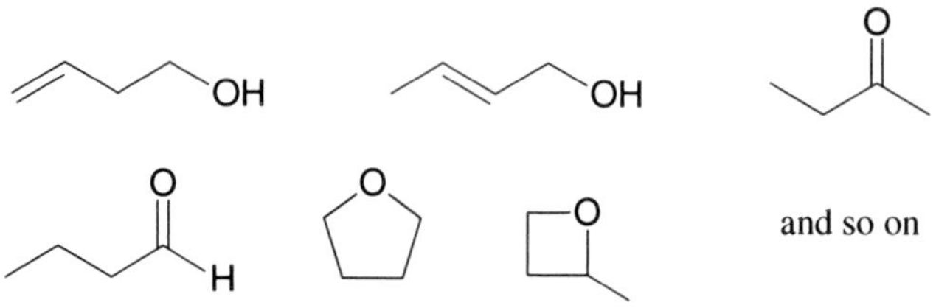

and so on

For compounds containing nitrogen atoms we subtract one hydrogen for each nitrogen atom, and then we ignore the nitrogen atoms. For example, we treat a compound with the formula C_4H_9N as though it were C_4H_8, and again we get IHD = 1. Some structural possibilities are the following:

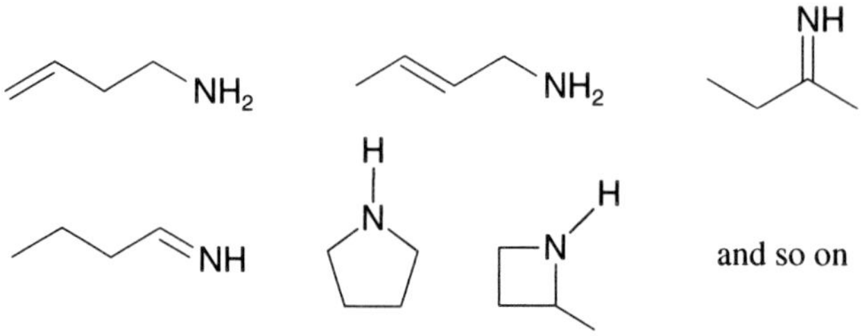

and so on

PRACTICE PROBLEM 4.22 Carbonyl groups also count for a unit of hydrogen deficiency. What are the indices of hydrogen deficiency for the reactant and for the product in the equation shown at the beginning of Section 4.16 for synthesis of a perfume ingredient?

4.18 APPLICATIONS OF BASIC PRINCIPLES

In this chapter we have seen repeated applications of one basic principle in particular:

Nature Prefers States of Lower Potential Energy This principle underlies our explanations of conformational analysis in Sections 4.8–4.13. The staggered conformation of ethane (Section 4.8) is preferred (more populated) in a sample of ethane because its potential energy is lowest. In the same way, the anti conformation of butane (Section 4.9) and the chair conformation of cyclohexane (Section 4.11) are the preferred conformations of these molecules because these conformations are of lowest potential energy. Methylcyclohexane (Section 4.12) exists mainly in the chair conformation with its methyl group equatorial for the same reason. Disubstituted cycloalkanes (Section 4.13) prefer a conformation with both substituents equatorial if this is possible, and, if not, they prefer a conformation with the larger group equatorial. The preferred conformation in each instance is the one of lowest potential energy.

Another effect that we encounter in this chapter, and one we shall see again and again, is how **steric factors** (spatial factors) can affect the stability and reactivity of molecules. Unfavorable spatial interactions between groups are central to explaining why certain conformations are higher in energy than others. But fundamentally this effect is derived itself from another familiar principle: **like charges repel.** Repulsive interactions between the electrons of groups that are in close proximity cause certain conformations to have higher potential energy than others. We call this kind of effect *steric hindrance*.

[WHY Do These Topics Matter?

PUSHING THE BOUNDARIES OF BONDING, ALL WITHIN THE RULES

In this chapter we have learned many of the rules of bond formation and of conformation. Although there are only a few kinds of bonds in organic molecules, they can be combined in an infinite number of ways, sometimes leading to molecules whose existence defies our expectations. For example, using just C—C and C—H bonds, chemists have been able to synthesize structures such as cubane, prismane, and bicyclo[1.1.0]butane, materials that have incredible strain built into their structures. Strained compounds are also found in nature, with one recent discovery being pentacycloanammoxic acid, a material isolated from a particular bacterial strain. This compound is also known as a ladderane because it has a connected set of five 4-membered rings that exist in three-dimensional space like a ladder, or staircase.

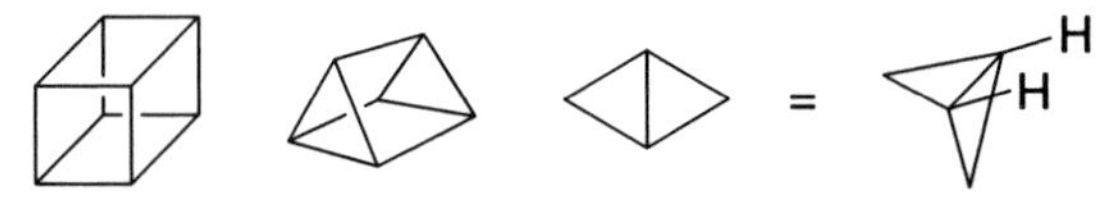

Cubane **Prismane** **Bicyclo[1.1.0]butane**

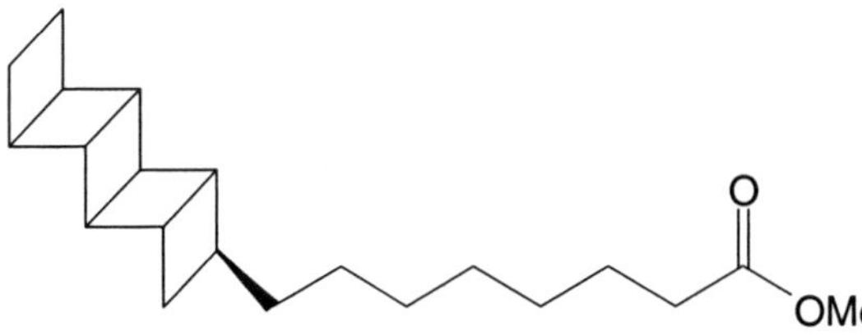

Pentacycloanammoxic acid methyl ester
(a ladderane)

An important thing to note is that these different bond combinations and resultant three-dimensional shapes lead to completely distinct physical properties that can be harnessed for unique practical applications. Perhaps one of the best illustrations of this concept is found in materials comprised only of carbon, materials also known as allotropes since they are formed solely from a single, pure element. For example, when carbon is bonded with itself through single bonds with sp^3 hybridization, the result is diamond, the hardest of all materials found in nature and a popular component of jewelry. When carbon is bonded with itself with sp^2 hybridization through a series of interconnecting C—C and C=C bonds, it forms flat, interconnected sheets of benzene-like rings. These sheets can stack with one another, forming graphite. This material is much softer than diamond and is the material that constitutes the "lead" of pencils. Graphene, which is just one of these sheets, can be wrapped through new bonds into tubes (also called nanotubes) that have impressive properties as thermal and electrical conductors.

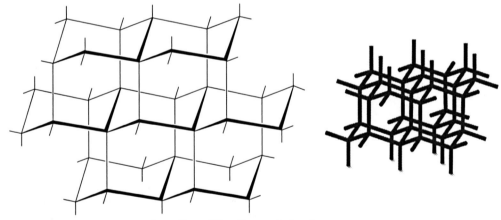

A portion of the diamond structure

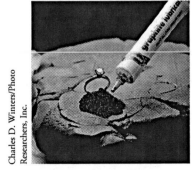

Carbon is shown here in its
diamond and graphite forms

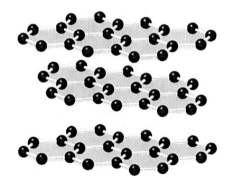

A portion of the structure of graphite

(continues on next page)

If the rings of graphite and graphene are combined together into discrete balls possessing a finite number of carbon atoms, then materials such as buckminsterfullerene (also known as buckyballs) result. The name of this material derives from its resemblance to the geodesic dome first designed by architect Buckminster Fuller. This particular compound, which is comprised of 60 carbon atoms, has bonds that look exactly like the seams of a soccer ball through its possession of 32 interlocking rings of which 20 are hexagons and 12 are pentagons. The center is large enough, in fact, to hold an atom of argon (such a compound has been made). Another variant of this type of structure is dodecahedrane, a compound composed of 20 carbon atoms and first synthesized in 1982 by scientists at the Ohio State University. Materials of this type collectively are believed to have potential in applications as diverse as armor, drug delivery, and superconductivity.

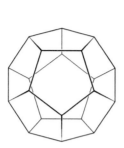

Dodecahedrane   **Buckminsterfullerene**

The key point is that the molecular variations are nearly endless, increasing exponentially as more and more atoms are added. This fact is one of the most beautiful elements of organic chemistry, because it means that we are largely limited in terms of possible structures by just two factors: our ability to imagine a molecule and having the tools necessary to forge it in the form of appropriate chemical reactions. This outcome is because the rules, the language, of organic chemistry are consistent.

To learn more about these topics, see:

Hopf, H. *Classics in Hydrocarbon Chemistry*. Wiley-VCH: Weinheim, **2000**, p. 560.

SUMMARY AND REVIEW TOOLS

One of the reasons we organic chemists love our discipline is that, besides knowing each molecule has a family, we also know that each one has its own architecture, "personality," and unique name. You have already learned in Chapters 1–3 about molecular personalities with regard to charge distribution, polarity, and relative acidity or basicity. In this chapter you have now learned how to give unique names to simple molecules using the IUPAC system. You also learned more about the overall shapes of organic molecules, how their shapes can change through bond rotations, and how we can compare the relative energies of those changes using conformational analysis. You now know that the extent of flexibility or rigidity in a molecule has to do with the types of bonds present (single, double, triple), and whether there are rings or bulky groups that inhibit bond rotation. Some organic molecules are very flexible members of the family, such as the molecules in our muscle fibers, while others are very rigid, like the carbon lattice of diamond. Most molecules, however, have both flexible and rigid aspects to their structures. With the knowledge from this chapter, added to other fundamentals you have already learned, you are on your way to developing an understanding of organic chemistry that we hope will be as strong as diamonds, and that you can flex like a muscle when you approach a problem. When you are finished with this chapter's homework, maybe you can even take a break by resting your mind on the chair conformation of cyclohexane.

PROBLEMS WILEY PLUS

Note to Instructors: Many of the homework problems are available for assignment via *WileyPLUS*, an online teaching and learning solution program.

NOMENCLATURE AND ISOMERISM

4.23 Write a bond-line formula for each of the following compounds:

(a) 1,4-Dichloropentane

(b) *sec*-Butyl bromide

(c) 4-Isopropylheptane

(d) 2,2,3-Trimethylpentane

(e) 3-Ethyl-2-methylhexane

(f) 1,1-Dichlorocyclopentane

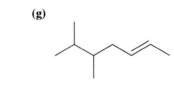

(g) *cis*-1,2-Dimethylcyclopropane

(h) *trans*-1,2-Dimethylcyclopropane

(i) 4-Methyl-2-pentanol

(j) *trans*-4-Isobutylcyclohexanol

(k) 1,4-Dicyclopropylhexane

(l) Neopentyl alcohol

(m) Bicyclo[2.2.2]octane

(n) Bicyclo[3.1.1]heptane

(o) Cyclopentylcyclopentane

4.24 Give systematic IUPAC names for each of the following:

(a)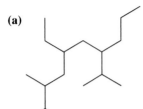

(c)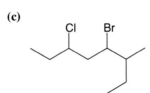

(e)

(g)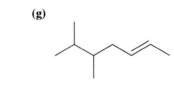

(b)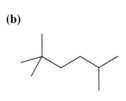

(d)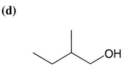

(f)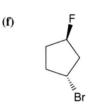

(h)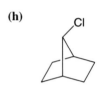

4.25 The name *sec*-butyl alcohol defines a specific structure but the name *sec*-pentyl alcohol is ambiguous. Explain.

4.26 Write the structure and give the IUPAC systematic name of an alkane or cycloalkane with the formulas **(a)** C_8H_{18} that has only primary hydrogen atoms, **(b)** C_6H_{12} that has only secondary hydrogen atoms, **(c)** C_6H_{12} that has only primary and secondary hydrogen atoms, and **(d)** C_8H_{14} that has 12 secondary and 2 tertiary hydrogen atoms.

4.27 Write the structure(s) of the simplest alkane(s), i.e., one(s) with the fewest number of carbon atoms, wherein each possesses primary, secondary, tertiary, and quaternary carbon atoms. (A quaternary carbon is one that is bonded to four other carbon atoms.) Assign an IUPAC name to each structure.

4.28 Ignoring compounds with double bonds, write structural formulas and give names for all of the isomers with the formula C_5H_{10}.

4.29 Write structures for the following bicyclic alkanes:

(a) Bicyclo[1.1.0]butane

(b) Bicyclo[2.1.0]pentane

(c) 2-Chlorobicyclo[3.2.0]heptane

(d) 7-Methylbicyclo[2.2.1]heptane

4.30 Use the $S - A + 1 = N$ method (Helpful Hint, Section 4.14) to determine the number of rings in cubane (Section 4.14).

4.31 A spiro ring junction is one where two rings that share no bonds originate from a single carbon atom. Alkanes containing such a ring junction are called spiranes.

(a) For the case of bicyclic spiranes of formula C_7H_{12}, write structures for all possibilities where all carbons are incorporated into rings.

(b) Write structures for other bicyclic molecules that fit this formula.

4.32 Tell what is meant by a homologous series and illustrate your answer by writing structures for a homologous series of alkyl halides.

HYDROGENATION

4.33 Four different cycloalkenes will all yield methylcyclopentane when subjected to catalytic hydrogenation. What are their structures? Show the reactions.

4.34 **(a)** Three different alkenes yield 2-methylbutane when they are hydrogenated in the presence of a metal catalyst. Give their structural formulas and write equations for the reactions involved. **(b)** One of these alkene isomers has characteristic absorptions at approximately 998 and 914 cm^{-1} in its IR spectrum. Which one is it?

4.35 An alkane with the formula C_6H_{14} can be prepared by hydrogenation of either of only two precursor alkenes having the formula C_6H_{12}. Write the structure of this alkane, give its IUPAC name, and show the reactions.

CONFORMATIONS AND STABILITY

4.36 Rank the following compounds in order of increasing stability based on 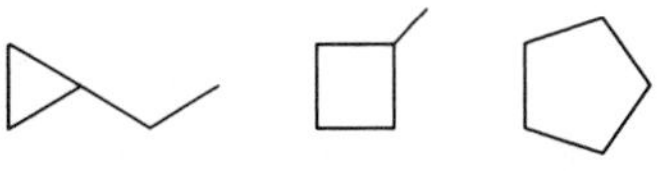   relative ring strain.

4.37 Write the structures of two chair conformations of 1-*tert*-butyl-1-methylcyclohexane. Which conformation is more stable? Explain your answer.

4.38 Sketch curves similar to the one given in Fig. 4.8 showing the energy changes that arise from rotation about the C2—C3 bond of **(a)** 2,3-dimethylbutane and **(b)** 2,2,3,3-tetramethylbutane. You need not concern yourself with actual numerical values of the energy changes, but you should label all maxima and minima with the appropriate conformations.

4.39 Without referring to tables, decide which member of each of the following pairs would have the higher boiling point. Explain your answers.

(a) Pentane or 2-methylbutane

(b) Heptane or pentane

(c) Propane or 2-chloropropane

(d) Butane or 1-propanol

(e) Butane or CH_3COCH_3

4.40 One compound whose molecular formula is C_4H_6 is a bicyclic compound. Another compound with the same formula has an infrared absorption at roughly 2250 cm^{-1} (the bicyclic compound does not). Draw structures for each of these two compounds and explain how the IR absorption allows them to be differentiated.

4.41 Which compound would you expect to be the more stable: *cis*-1,2-dimethylcyclopropane or *trans*-1,2-dimethylcyclopropane? Explain your answer.

4.42 Consider that cyclobutane exhibits a puckered geometry. Judge the relative stabilities of the 1,2-disubstituted cyclobutanes and of the 1,3-disubstituted cyclobutanes. (You may find it helpful to build handheld molecular models of representative compounds.)

4.43 Write the two chair conformations of each of the following and in each part designate which conformation would be the more stable: **(a)** *cis*-1-*tert*-butyl-3-methylcyclohexane, **(b)** *trans*-1-*tert*-butyl-3-methylcyclohexane, **(c)** *trans*-1-*tert*-butyl-4-methylcyclohexane, **(d)** *cis*-1-*tert*-butyl-4-methylcyclohexane.

4.44 Provide an explanation for the surprising fact that all-*trans*-1,2,3,4,5,6-hexaisopropylcyclohexane is a stable molecule in which all isopropyl groups are axial. (You may find it helpful to build a handheld molecular model.)

4.45 *trans*-1,3-Dibromocyclobutane has a measurable dipole moment. Explain how this proves that the cyclobutane ring is not planar.

SYNTHESIS

4.46 Specify the missing compounds and/or reagents in each of the following syntheses:

(a) *trans*-5-Methyl-2-hexene $\xrightarrow{?}$ 2-methylhexane

(b)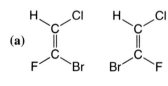

(c) Chemical reactions rarely yield products in such initially pure form that no trace can be found of the starting materials used to make them. What evidence in an IR spectrum of each of the crude (unpurified) products from the above reactions would indicate the presence of one of the organic reactants used to synthesize each target molecule? That is, predict one or two key IR absorptions for the reactants that would distinguish it/them from IR absorptions predicted for the product.

CHALLENGE PROBLEMS

4.47 Consider the cis and trans isomers of 1,3-di-*tert*-butylcyclohexane (build molecular models). What unusual feature accounts for the fact that one of these isomers apparently exists in a twist boat conformation rather than a chair conformation?

4.48 Using the rules found in this chapter, give systematic names for the following or indicate that more rules need to be provided:

(a)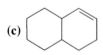

(b)

(c)

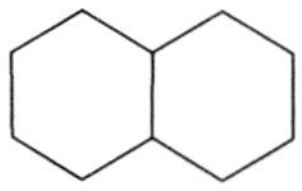

(d)

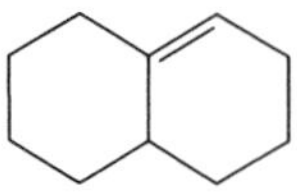

4.49 Open the energy-minimized 3D Molecular Models on the book's website for *trans*-1-*tert*-butyl-3-methylcyclohexane and *trans*-1,3-di-*tert*-butylcyclohexane. What conformations of cyclohexane do the rings in these two compounds resemble most closely? How can you account for the difference in ring conformations between them?

4.50 Open the 3D Molecular Models on the book's website for cyclopentane and vitamin B_{12}. Compare cyclopentane with the nitrogen-containing five-membered rings in vitamin B_{12}. Is the conformation of cyclopentane represented in the specified rings of vitamin B_{12}? What factor(s) account for any differences you observe?

4.51 Open the 3D Molecular Model on the book's website for buckminsterfullerene. What molecule has its type of ring represented 16 times in the surface of buckminsterfullerene?

LEARNING GROUP PROBLEMS

1. This is the predominant conformation for D-glucose:

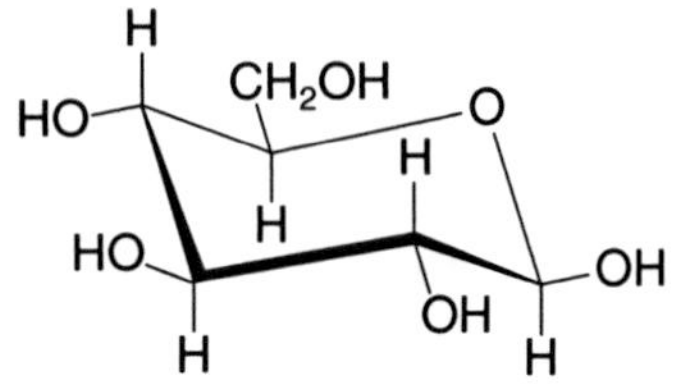

Why is it not surprising that D-glucose is the most commonly found sugar in nature? (*Hint*: Look up structures for sugars such as D-galactose and D-mannose, and compare these with D-glucose.)

2. Using Newman projections, depict the relative positions of the substituents on the bridgehead atoms of *cis*- and *trans*-decalin. Which of these isomers would be expected to be more stable, and why?

3. When 1,2-dimethylcyclohexene (below) is allowed to react with hydrogen in the presence of a platinum catalyst, the product of the reaction is a cycloalkane that has a melting point of −50 °C and a boiling point of 130 °C (at 760 torr). **(a)** What is the structure of the product of this reaction? **(b)** Consult an appropriate resource (such as the web or a CRC handbook) and tell which stereoisomer it is. **(c)** What does this experiment suggest about the mode of addition of hydrogen to the double bond?

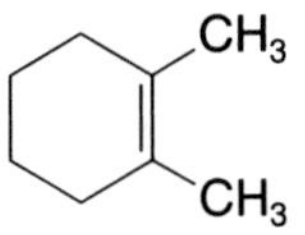

1,2-Dimethylcyclohexene

4. When cyclohexene is dissolved in an appropriate solvent and allowed to react with chlorine, the product of the reaction, $C_6H_{10}Cl_2$, has a melting point of −7 °C and a boiling point (at 16 torr) of 74 °C. **(a)** Which stereoisomer is this? **(b)** What does this experiment suggest about the mode of addition of chlorine to the double bond?

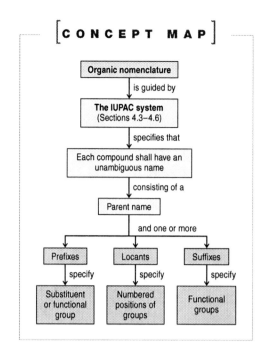

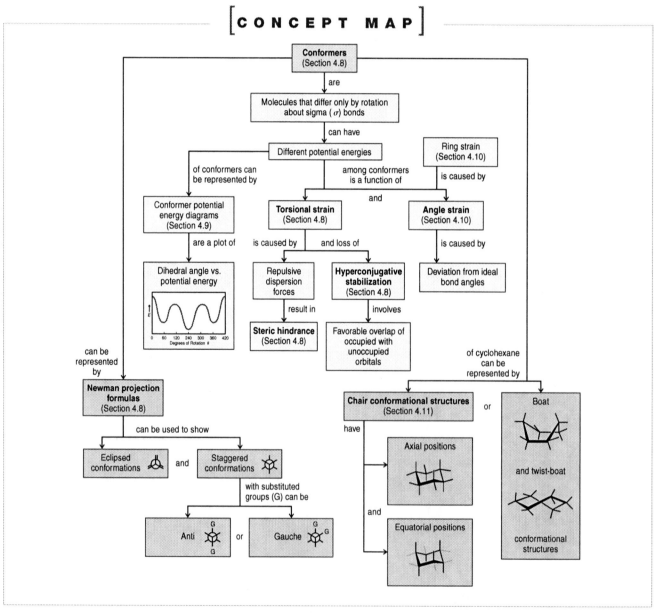

190

CHAPTER

Stereochemistry

CHIRAL MOLECULES

We are all aware of the fact that certain everyday objects such as gloves and shoes possess the quality of "handedness". A right-handed glove only fits a right hand; a left-handed shoe only fits a left foot. Many other objects have the potential to exist in right- and left-handed forms, and those that do are said to be "chiral". For example, the screws shown above are chiral. One screw has a right-handed thread. A right-handed person would find using it to be quite comfortable. The other screw has a left-handed thread and would better suit a left-handed person. (Unfortunately, for left-handed persons, most screws are right-handed.) We shall now find that chirality also has important consequences for chemistry.

IN THIS CHAPTER WE WILL CONSIDER:

- how to identify, categorize, and name chiral molecules
- how chirality can affect the chemical and biochemical behavior of organic compounds

[**WHY** DO THESE TOPICS MATTER?]   At the end of this chapter, we will explain what may have been the origin of chirality in the universe, and why many of the important molecules found in living organisms, such as peptides, DNA, and carbohydrates exist in only one chiral form when the other form seems equally likely.

PHOTO CREDITS: Nicholas Eveleigh/Stockbyte/Getty Images, Inc.

191

5.1 CHIRALITY AND STEREOCHEMISTRY

The glass and its mirror image are superposable.

Chirality is a phenomenon that pervades the universe. How can we know whether a particular object is **chiral** or **achiral** (not chiral)?

- We can tell if an object has chirality by examining the object and its mirror image.

Every object has a mirror image. Many objects are achiral. By this we mean that *the object and its mirror image are identical*—that is, the object and its mirror image are superposable one on the other.* Superposable means that one can, in one's mind's eye, place one object on the other so that all parts of each coincide. Simple geometrical objects such as a sphere or a cube are achiral. So is an object like a water glass.

- **A chiral object is one that cannot be superposed on its mirror image.**

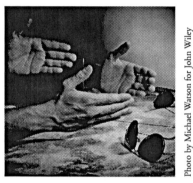

FIGURE 5.1 The mirror image of a right hand is a left hand.

FIGURE 5.2 Left and right hands are not superposable.

Each of our hands is chiral. When you view your right hand in a mirror, the image that you see in the mirror *is a left hand* (Fig. 5.1). However, as we see in Fig. 5.2, your left hand and your right hand are not identical because *they are not superposable*. Your hands are chiral. In fact, the word chiral comes from the Greek word cheir meaning hand. An object such as a mug may or may not be chiral. If it has no markings on it, it is achiral. If the mug has a logo or image on one side, it is chiral.

This mug is chiral because it is not superposable on its mirror image.

*To be superposable is different than to be super*im*posable. Any two objects can be superimposed simply by putting one object on top of the other, whether or not the objects are the same. To *superpose* two objects (as in the property of superposition) means, on the other hand, that **all parts of each object must coincide.** The condition of superposability must be met for two things to be **identical.**

5.1A The Biological Significance of Chirality

The human body is structurally chiral, with the heart lying to the left of center and the liver to the right. Helical seashells are chiral and most are spiral, such as a right-handed screw. Many plants show chirality in the way they wind around supporting structures. Honeysuckle winds as a left-handed helix; bindweed winds in a right-handed way. DNA is a chiral molecule. The double helical form of DNA turns in a right-handed way.

Chirality in molecules, however, involves more than the fact that some molecules adopt left- or right-handed conformations. As we shall see in this chapter, it is the nature of groups bonded at specific atoms that can bestow chirality on a molecule. Indeed, all but one of the 20 amino acids that make up naturally occurring proteins are chiral, and all of these are classified as being left-handed. The molecules of natural sugars are almost all classified as being right-handed. In fact, most of the molecules of life are chiral, and most are found in only one mirror image form.*

Chirality has tremendous importance in our daily lives. Most pharmaceuticals are chiral. Usually only one mirror-image form of a drug provides the desired effect. The other mirror-image form is often inactive or, at best, less active. In some cases the other mirror-image form of a drug actually has severe side effects or toxicity (see Section 5.5 regarding thalidomide). Our senses of taste and smell also depend on chirality. As we shall see, one mirror-image form of a chiral molecule may have a certain odor or taste while its mirror image smells and tastes completely different. The food we eat is largely made of molecules of one mirror-image form. If we were to eat food that was somehow made of molecules with the unnatural mirror-image form, we would likely starve because the enzymes in our bodies are chiral and preferentially react with the natural mirror-image form of their substrates.

Let us now consider what causes some molecules to be chiral. To begin, we will return to aspects of isomerism.

Bindweed (top photo) (*Convolvulus sepium*) winds in a right-handed fashion, like the right-handed helix of DNA. (DNA spiral: Reprinted with permission of the McGraw-Hill Companies. From Neal, L.; *Chemistry and Biochemistry: A Comprehensive Introduction.* © 1971.)

5.2 ISOMERISM: CONSTITUTIONAL ISOMERS AND STEREOISOMERS

5.2A Constitutional Isomers

Isomers are different compounds that have the same molecular formula. In our study thus far, much of our attention has been directed toward isomers we have called constitutional isomers.

- **Constitutional isomers** have the same molecular formula but different connectivity, meaning that their atoms are connected in a different order. Examples of constitutional isomers are the following:

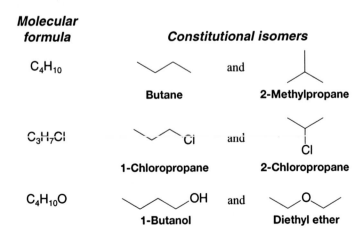

*For interesting reading, see Hegstrum, R. A. and Kondepudi, D. K. The Handedness of the Universe. *Sci. Am.* **1990**, *262*, 98–105, and Horgan, J. The Sinister Cosmos. *Sci. Am.* **1997**, *276*, 18–19.

5.2B Stereoisomers

Stereoisomers are not constitutional isomers.

- Stereoisomers have their atoms connected in the same sequence (the same constitution), but they differ in the arrangement of their atoms in space. The consideration of such spatial aspects of molecular structure is called stereochemistry.

We have already seen examples of some types of stereoisomers. The cis and trans forms of alkenes are stereoisomers (Section 1.13B), as are the cis and trans forms of substituted cyclic molecules (Section 4.13).

5.2C Enantiomers and Diastereomers

Stereoisomers can be subdivided into two general categories: those that are enantiomers of each other, and those that are **diastereomers** of each other.

- **Enantiomers are stereoisomers whose molecules are nonsuperposable mirror images of each other.**

All other stereoisomers are diastereomers.

- **Diastereomers are stereoisomers whose molecules are not mirror images of each other.**

The alkene isomers *cis-* and *trans-*1,2-dichloroethene shown here are stereoisomers that are **diastereomers**.

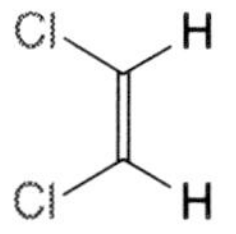

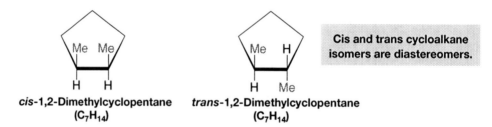

cis-1,2-Dichloroethene
($C_2H_2Cl_2$)

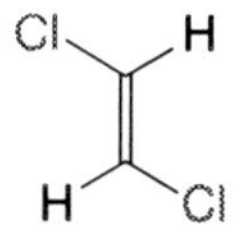

trans-1,2-Dichloroethene
($C_2H_2Cl_2$)

Cis and trans alkene isomers are diastereomers.

By examining the structural formulas for *cis-* and *trans-*1,2-dichloroethene, we see that they have the same molecular formula ($C_2H_2Cl_2$) and the same connectivity (both compounds have two central carbon atoms joined by a double bond, and both compounds have one chlorine and one hydrogen atom attached to each carbon atom). But, their atoms have a different arrangement in space that is not interconvertible from one to another (due to the large barrier to rotation of the carbon–carbon double bond), making them stereoisomers. Furthermore, they are stereoisomers that are not mirror images of each other; therefore they are diastereomers and not enantiomers.

Cis and trans isomers of cycloalkanes furnish us with another example of stereoisomers that are diastereomers. Consider the following two compounds:

cis-1,2-Dimethylcyclopentane
(C_7H_{14})

trans-1,2-Dimethylcyclopentane
(C_7H_{14})

Cis and trans cycloalkane isomers are diastereomers.

These two compounds have the same molecular formula (C_7H_{14}), the same sequence of connections for their atoms, but different arrangements of their atoms in space. In one compound both methyl groups are bonded to the same face of the ring, while in the other compound the two methyl groups are bonded to opposite faces of the ring. Furthermore, the positions of the methyl groups cannot be interconverted by conformational changes. Therefore, these compounds are stereoisomers, and because they are stereoisomers that are not mirror images of each other, they can be further classified as diastereomers.

In Section 5.12 we shall study other molecules that can exist as diastereomers but are not cis and trans isomers of each other. First, however, we need to consider enantiomers further.

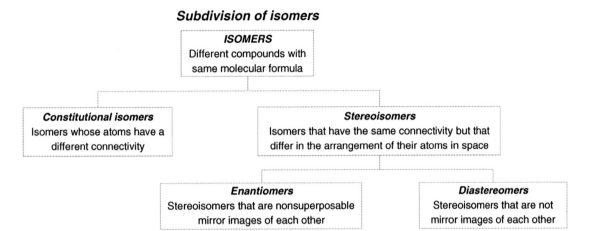

Subdivision of isomers

ISOMERS
Different compounds with same molecular formula

Constitutional isomers
Isomers whose atoms have a different connectivity

Stereoisomers
Isomers that have the same connectivity but that differ in the arrangement of their atoms in space

Enantiomers
Stereoisomers that are nonsuperposable mirror images of each other

Diastereomers
Stereoisomers that are not mirror images of each other

5.3 ENANTIOMERS AND CHIRAL MOLECULES

Enantiomers occur only with compounds whose molecules are chiral.

- A chiral molecule is one that is not superposable on its mirror image.

The trans isomer of 1,2-dimethylcyclopentane is **chiral** because it is **not superposable** on its mirror image, as the following formulas illustrate.

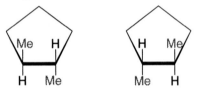

Mirror images of *trans*-1,2-dimethylcyclopentane
They are not superposable and therefore are enantiomers.

Enantiomers do not exist for achiral molecules.

- An achiral molecule is superposable on its mirror image.

The cis and trans isomers of 1,2-dichloroethene are both **achiral** because each isomer is **superposable** on its mirror image, as the following formulas illustrate.

cis-1,2-Dichloroethene mirror images   *trans*-1,2-Dichloroethene mirror images

The mirror images of the cis isomer are superposable on each other (try rotating one by 180° to see that it is identical to the other), and therefore the cis formulas both represent the same, achiral molecule. The same analysis is true for the trans isomer.

- Enantiomers only occur with compounds whose molecules are chiral.
- A chiral molecule and its mirror image are called a **pair of enantiomers**. The relationship between them is **enantiomeric**.

The universal test for chirality of a molecule, or any object, is the nonsuperposability of the molecule or object on its mirror image. We encounter chiral and achiral objects throughout our daily life. Shoes are chiral, for example, whereas most socks are achiral.

PRACTICE PROBLEM 5.1   Classify each of the following objects as to whether it is chiral or achiral:

(a) A screwdriver   (d) A tennis shoe   (g) A car
(b) A baseball bat   (e) An ear   (h) A hammer
(c) A golf club   (f) A woodscrew

The chirality of molecules can be demonstrated with relatively simple compounds. Consider, for example, 2-butanol:

2-Butanol

Until now, we have presented the formula for 2-butanol as though it represented only one compound and we have not mentioned that molecules of 2-butanol are chiral. Because they are, there are actually two different 2-butanols and these two 2-butanols are enantiomers. We can understand this if we examine the drawings and models in Fig. 5.3.

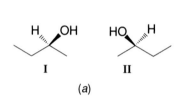

(a)

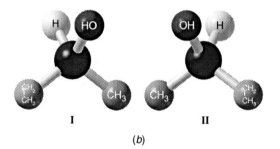

(b)   (c)

FIGURE 5.3 (a) Three-dimensional drawings of the 2-butanol enantiomers **I** and **II**. (b) Models of the 2-butanol enantiomers. (c) An unsuccessful attempt to superpose models of **I** and **II**.

Helpful Hint

Working with models is a helpful study technique whenever three-dimensional aspects of chemistry are involved.

If model **I** is held before a mirror, model **II** is seen in the mirror and vice versa. Models **I** and **II** are not superposable on each other; therefore, they represent different, but isomeric, molecules. *Because models I and II are nonsuperposable mirror images of each other, the molecules that they represent are enantiomers.*

PRACTICE PROBLEM 5.2   Construct handheld models of the 2-butanols represented in Fig. 5.3 and demonstrate for yourself that they are not mutually superposable. **(a)** Make similar models of 2-bromopropane. Are they superposable? **(b)** Is a molecule of 2-bromopropane chiral? **(c)** Would you expect to find enantiomeric forms of 2-bromopropane?

5.4 MOLECULES HAVING ONE CHIRALITY CENTER ARE CHIRAL

- A **chirality center** is a tetrahedral carbon atom that is bonded to four different groups.
- A molecule that contains **one chirality** center is chiral and can exist as a pair of enantiomers.

Molecules with more than one chirality center can also exist as enantiomers, but only if the molecule is not superposable on its mirror image. (We shall discuss that situation later in Section 5.12.) For now we will focus on molecules having a single chirality center.

Chirality centers are often designated with an asterisk (*). The chirality center in 2-butanol is **C2** (Figure 5.4). The four different groups attached to **C2** are a hydroxyl group, a hydrogen atom, a methyl group, and an ethyl group. (It is important to note that

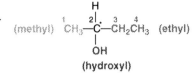

chirality is a property of a molecule as a whole, and that a chirality center is a structural feature that can cause a molecule to be chiral.)

An ability to find chirality centers in structural formulas will help us recognize molecules that are chiral, and that can exist as enantiomers.

- The presence of a single chirality center in a molecule guarantees that the molecule is chiral and that enantiomeric forms are possible.

Figure 5.5 demonstrates that enantiomeric compounds can exist whenever a molecule contains a single chirality center.

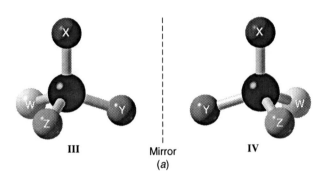

(hydrogen)

FIGURE 5.4 The tetrahedral carbon atom of 2-butanol that bears four different groups. [By convention, chirality centers are often designated with an asterisk (*).]

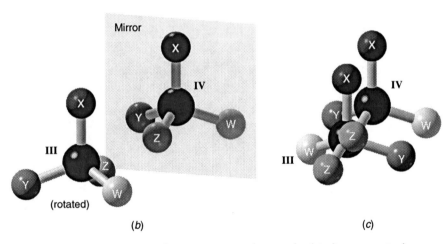

FIGURE 5.5 A demonstration of chirality of a generalized molecule containing one chirality center. (a) The four different groups around the carbon atom in **III** and **IV** are arbitrary. (b) **III** is rotated and placed in front of a mirror. **III** and **IV** are found to be related as an object and its mirror image. (c) **III** and **IV** are not superposable; therefore, the molecules that they represent are chiral and are enantiomers.

- An important property of enantiomers with a single chirality center is that *interchanging any two groups at the chirality center converts one enantiomer into the other.*

In Fig. 5.3b it is easy to see that interchanging the methyl and ethyl groups converts one enantiomer into the other. You should now convince yourself that interchanging any other two groups has the same result.

- Any atom at which an interchange of groups produces a stereoisomer is called a **stereogenic center**. (If the atom is a carbon atom it is usually called a **stereogenic carbon**.)

When we discuss interchanging groups like this, we must take care to notice that what we are describing is *something we do to a molecular model or something we do on paper*. An interchange of groups in a real molecule, if it can be done, requires breaking covalent bonds, and this is something that requires a large input of energy. This means that enantiomers such as the 2-butanol enantiomers **do not interconvert** spontaneously.

The *chirality center* of 2-butanol is one example of a *stereogenic center*, but there are stereogenic centers that are not chirality centers. The carbon atoms of *cis*-1,2-dichloroethene and of *trans*-1,2-dichloroethene (Section 5.2C) are stereogenic centers because an interchange of groups at either carbon atom produces the other stereoisomer. The carbon atoms of *cis*-1,2-dichloroethene and *trans*-1,2-dichloroethene are not chirality centers, however, because they do not have four different groups attached to them.

Helpful Hint

Interchanging two groups of a model or three-dimensional formula is a useful test for determining whether structures of two chiral molecules are the same or different.

● ● ●

PRACTICE PROBLEM 5.3 Demonstrate the validity of what we have represented in Fig. 5.5 by constructing models. Demonstrate for yourself that **III** and **IV** are related as an object and its mirror image and *that they are not superposable* (i.e., that **III** and **IV** are chiral molecules and are enantiomers). **(a)** Take **IV** and exchange the positions of any two groups. What is the new relationship between the molecules? **(b)** Now take either model and exchange the positions of any two groups. What is the relationship between the molecules now?

● If all of the tetrahedral atoms in a molecule have two or more groups attached that *are the same*, the molecule does not have a chirality center. The molecule is superposable on its mirror image and is an achiral molecule.

An example of a molecule of this type is 2-propanol; carbon atoms 1 and 3 bear three identical hydrogen atoms and the central atom bears two identical methyl groups. If we write three-dimensional formulas for 2-propanol, we find (Fig. 5.6) that one structure can be superposed on its mirror image.

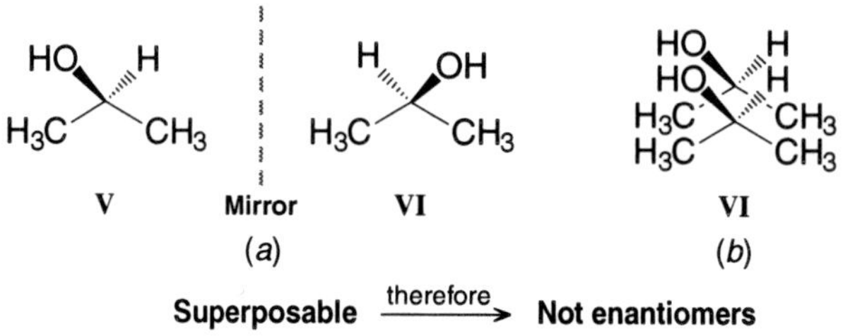

FIGURE 5.6 (a) 2-Propanol (**V**) and its mirror image (**VI**). (b) When either one is rotated, the two structures are superposable and so do not represent enantiomers. They represent two molecules of the same compound. 2-Propanol does not have a chirality center.

V   **Mirror**   **VI**   **VI**
          (a)   (b)

Superposable $\xrightarrow{\text{therefore}}$ Not enantiomers

Thus, we would not predict the existence of enantiomeric forms of 2-propanol, and experimentally only one form of 2-propanol has ever been found.

● ● ● **SOLVED PROBLEM 5.1**

Does 2-bromopentane have a chirality center? If so, write three-dimensional structures for each enantiomer.

STRATEGY AND ANSWER: First we write a structural formula for the molecule and look for a carbon atom that has four different groups attached to it. In this case, carbon 2 has four different groups: a hydrogen, a methyl group, a bromine, and a propyl group. Thus, carbon 2 is a **chirality center**.

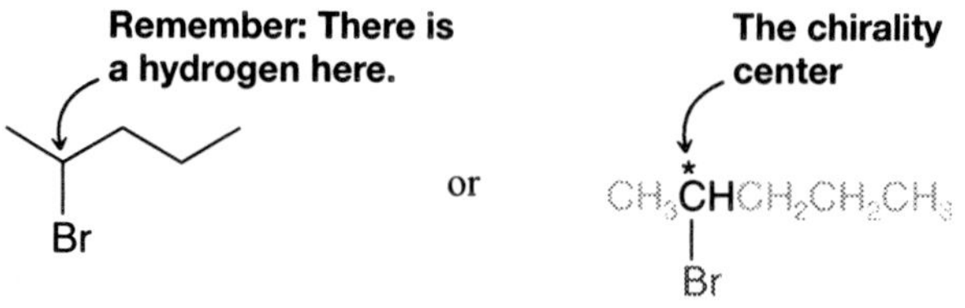

Remember: There is a hydrogen here.   **The chirality center**

or

2-Bromopentane

The enantiomers are

These formulas are nonsuperposable mirror images

● ● ●

PRACTICE PROBLEM 5.4 Some of the molecules listed here have a chirality center; some do not. Write three-dimensional formulas for both enantiomers of those molecules that do have a chirality center.

(a) 2-Fluoropropane	**(e)** *trans*-2-Butene	**(i)** 2-Methyl-2-pentene
(b) 2-Methylbutane	**(f)** 2-Bromopentane	**(j)** 1-Chloro-2-methylbutane
(c) 2-Chlorobutane	**(g)** 3-Methylpentane	
(d) 2-Methyl-1-butanol	**(h)** 3-Methylhexane	

5.4A Tetrahedral versus Trigonal Stereogenic Centers

It is important to clarify the difference between stereogenic centers, in general, and a chirality center, which is one type of stereogenic center. The chirality center in 2-butanol is a tetrahedral stereogenic center. The carbon atoms of *cis*- and *trans*-1,2-dichloroethene are also stereogenic centers, but they are trigonal stereogenic centers. They are *not* chirality centers. An interchange of groups at the alkene carbons of either 1,2-dichloroethene isomer produces a stereoisomer (a molecule with the same connectivity but a different arrangement of atoms in space), but it does not produce a nonsuperposable mirror image. A chirality center, on the other hand, is one that must have the possibility of nonsuperposable mirror images.

- Chirality centers are tetrahedral stereogenic centers.
- Cis and trans alkene isomers contain trigonal stereogenic centers.

5.5 MORE ABOUT THE BIOLOGICAL IMPORTANCE OF CHIRALITY

The origin of biological properties relating to chirality is often likened to the specificity of our hands for their respective gloves; the binding specificity for a chiral molecule (like a hand) at a chiral receptor site (a glove) is only favorable in one way. If either the molecule or the biological receptor site had the wrong handedness, the natural physiological response (e.g., neural impulse, reaction catalysis) would not occur. A diagram showing how only one amino acid in a pair of enantiomers can interact in an optimal way with a hypothetical binding site (e.g., in an enzyme) is shown in Fig. 5.7. Because of the chirality center of the amino acid, three-point binding can occur with proper alignment for only one of the two enantiomers.

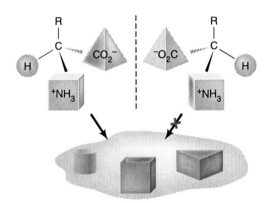

FIGURE 5.7 Only one of the two amino acid enantiomers shown (the left-hand one) can achieve three-point binding with the hypothetical binding site (e.g., in an enzyme).

Chiral molecules can show their handedness in many ways, including the way they affect human beings. One enantiomeric form of a compound called limonene (Section 23.3) is primarily responsible for the odor of oranges and the other enantiomer for the odor of lemons.

 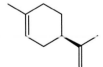 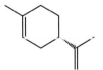 

(+)-Limonene (the enantiomer of limonene found in oranges)

(−)-Limonene (the enantiomer of limonene found in lemons)

One enantiomer of a compound called carvone (Practice Problem 5.14) is the essence of caraway, and the other is the essence of spearmint.

The activity of drugs containing chirality centers can similarly vary between enantiomers, sometimes with serious or even tragic consequences. For several years before 1963 the drug thalidomide was used to alleviate the symptoms of morning sickness in pregnant women. In 1963 it was discovered that thalidomide was the cause of horrible birth defects in many children born subsequent to the use of the drug.

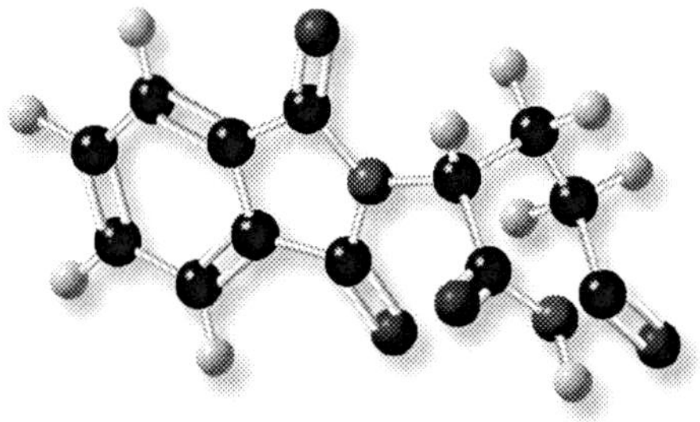

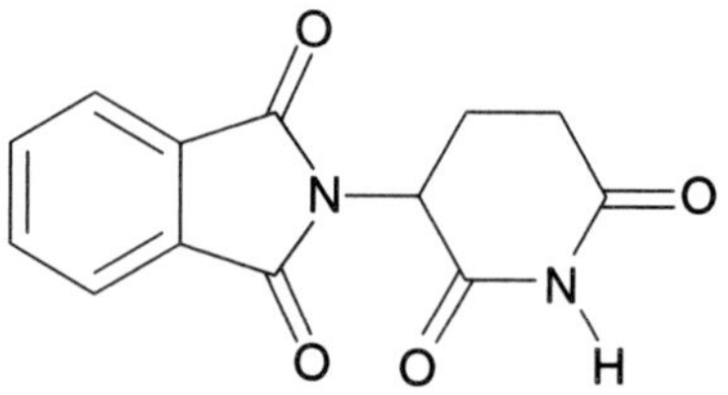

Thalidomide (Thalomid®)

Even later, evidence began to appear indicating that whereas one of the thalidomide enantiomers (the right-handed molecule) has the intended effect of curing morning sickness, the other enantiomer, which was also present in the drug (in an equal amount), may be the cause of the birth defects. The evidence regarding the effects of the two enantiomers is complicated by the fact that, under physiological conditions, the two enantiomers are interconverted. Now, however, thalidomide is approved under highly strict regulations for treatment of some forms of cancer and a serious complication associated with leprosy. Its potential for use against other conditions including AIDS and rheumatoid arthritis is also under investigation. We shall consider other aspects of chiral drugs in Section 5.11.

PRACTICE PROBLEM 5.5   Which atom is the chirality center of **(a)** limonene and **(b)** of thalidomide?

PRACTICE PROBLEM 5.6   Which atoms in each of the following molecules are chirality centers?

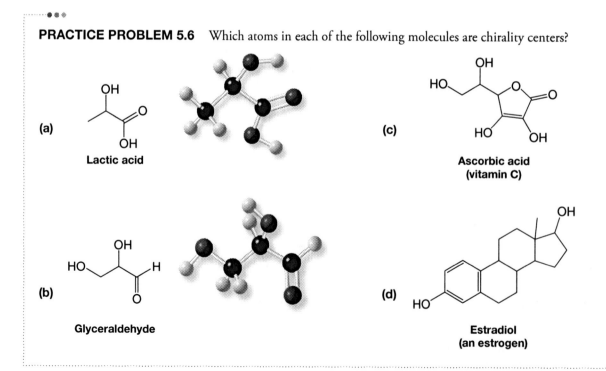

(a) Lactic acid

(b) Glyceraldehyde

(c) Ascorbic acid (vitamin C)

(d) Estradiol (an estrogen)

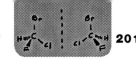

5.6 HOW TO TEST FOR CHIRALITY: PLANES OF SYMMETRY

The ultimate way to test for molecular **chirality** is to construct models of the molecule and its mirror image and then determine whether they are superposable. If the two models are superposable, the molecule that they represent is achiral. If the models are not superposable, then the molecules that they represent are chiral. We can apply this test with actual models, as we have just described, or we can apply it by drawing three-dimensional structures and attempting to superpose them in our minds.

There are other aids, however, that will assist us in recognizing chiral molecules. We have mentioned one already: **the presence of a *single* chirality center**. Other aids are based on the absence of certain symmetry elements in the molecule.

* A molecule will not be chiral if it possesses a plane of symmetry.

* A **plane of symmetry** (also called a mirror plane) is defined as an imaginary plane that bisects a molecule in such a way that the two halves of the molecule are mirror images of each other.

The plane may pass through atoms, between atoms, or both. For example, 2-chloropropane has a plane of symmetry (Fig. 5.8*a*), whereas 2-chlorobutane does not (Fig. 5.8*b*).

* All molecules with a plane of symmetry in their most symmetric conformation are achiral.

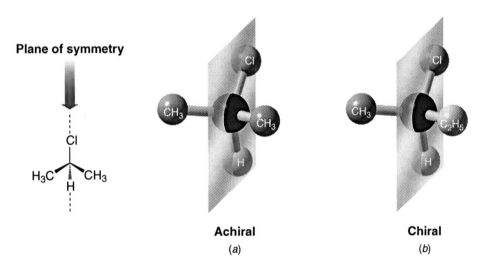

FIGURE 5.8 (*a*) 2-Chloropropane has a plane of symmetry and is achiral. (*b*) 2-Chlorobutane does not possess a plane of symmetry and is chiral.

Plane of symmetry

Achiral
(*a*)

Chiral
(*b*)

●●● SOLVED PROBLEM 5.2

Glycerol, CH$_2$OHCHOHCH$_2$OH, is an important constituent in the biological synthesis of fats, as we shall see in Chapter 23. **(a)** Does glycerol have a plane of symmetry? If so, write a three-dimensional structure for glycerol and indicate where it is. **(b)** Is glycerol chiral?

STRATEGY AND ANSWER: (a) Yes, glycerol has a plane symmetry. Notice that we have to choose the proper conformation and orientation of the molecule to see the plane of symmetry. **(b)** No, glycerol is achiral because it has a conformation containing a plane of symmetry.

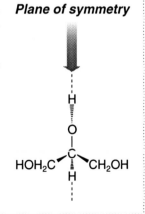

Plane of symmetry

●●●

Which of the objects listed in Practice Problem 5.1 possess a plane of symmetry and are, therefore, achiral?

PRACTICE PROBLEM 5.7

•••

PRACTICE PROBLEM 5.8   Write three-dimensional formulas and designate a plane of symmetry for all of the achiral molecules in Practice Problem 5.4. (In order to be able to designate a plane of symmetry you may need to write the molecule in an appropriate conformation.)

5.7 NAMING ENANTIOMERS: THE *R,S*-SYSTEM

The two enantiomers of 2-butanol are the following:

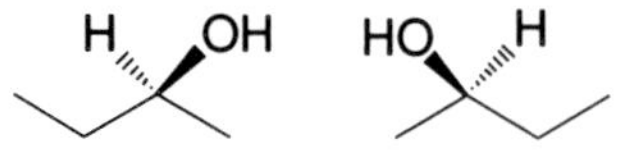

If we name these two enantiomers using only the IUPAC system of nomenclature that we have learned so far, both enantiomers will have the same name: 2-butanol (or *sec*-butyl alcohol) (Section 4.3F). This is undesirable because *each compound must have its own distinct name.* Moreover, the name that is given a compound should allow a chemist who is familiar with the rules of nomenclature to write the structure of the compound from its name alone. Given the name 2-butanol, a chemist could write either structure **I** or structure **II**.

Three chemists, R. S. Cahn (England), C. K. Ingold (England), and V. Prelog (Switzerland), devised a system of nomenclature that, when added to the IUPAC system, solves both of these problems. This system, called the *R,S*-system or the Cahn–Ingold–Prelog system, is part of the IUPAC rules.

According to this system, one enantiomer of 2-butanol should be designated (*R*)-2-butanol and the other enantiomer should be designated (*S*)-2-butanol. [(*R*) and (*S*) are from the Latin words *rectus* and *sinister*, meaning right and left, respectively.] These molecules are said to have opposite configurations at C2.

5.7A HOW TO Assign (*R*) and (*S*) Configurations

We assign (*R*) and (*S*) configurations on the basis of the following procedure.

1. Each of the four groups attached to the chirality center is assigned a **priority** or **preference** *a*, *b*, *c*, or *d*. Priority is first assigned on the basis of the **atomic number** of the atom that is directly attached to the chirality center. The group with the lowest atomic number is given the lowest priority, *d*; the group with next higher atomic number is given the next higher priority, *c*; and so on. (In the case of isotopes, the isotope of greatest atomic mass has highest priority.)

We can illustrate the application of the rule with the following 2-butanol enantiomer:

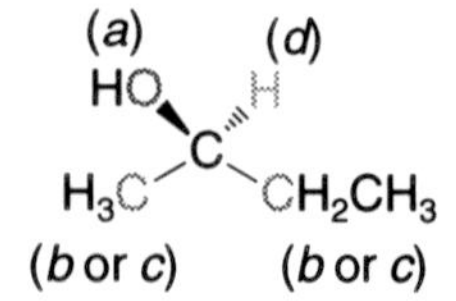

One of the 2-butanol enantiomers

Oxygen has the highest atomic number of the four atoms attached to the chirality center and is assigned the highest priority, *a*. Hydrogen has the lowest atomic number and is assigned the lowest priority, *d*. A priority cannot be assigned for the methyl group and the ethyl group by this approach because the atom that is directly attached to the chirality center is a carbon atom in both groups.

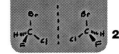

2. When a priority cannot be assigned on the basis of the atomic number of the atoms that are directly attached to the chirality center, then the next set of atoms in the unassigned groups is examined. This process is continued until a decision can be made. *We assign a priority at the first point of difference.**

When we examine the methyl group of the 2-butanol enantiomer above, we find that the next set of atoms bonded to the carbon consists of three hydrogen atoms (H, H, H). In the ethyl group the next set of atoms bonded to the carbon consists of one carbon atom and two hydrogen atoms (C, H, H). Carbon has a higher atomic number than hydrogen, so we assign the ethyl group the higher priority, *b*, and the methyl group the lower priority, *c*, since (C, H, H) > (H, H, H):

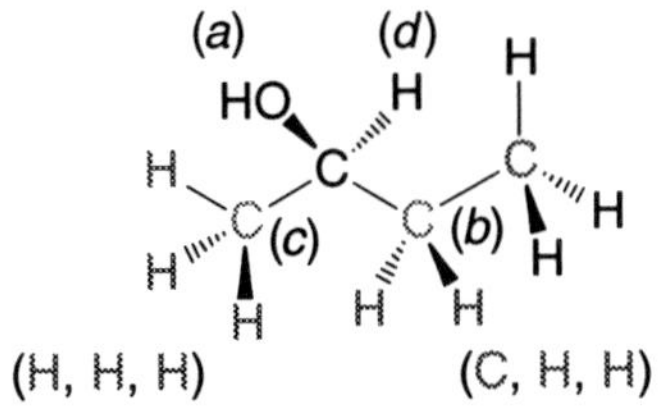

3. We now rotate the formula (or model) so that the group with lowest priority (*d*) is directed away from us:

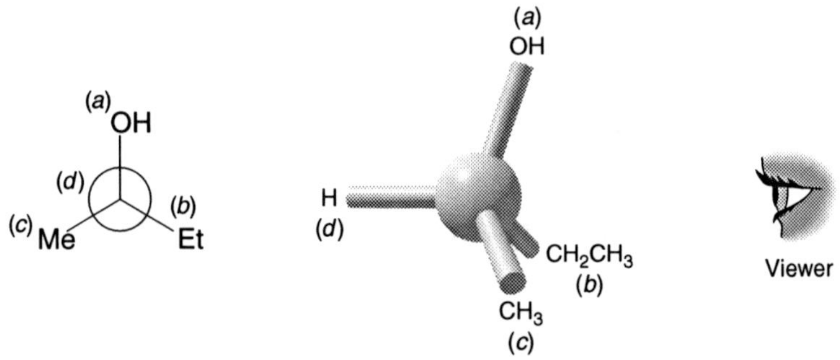

Newman projection

One of the 2-butanol enantiomers

Viewer

Then we trace a path from *a* to *b* to *c*. If, as we do this, the direction of our finger (or pencil) is *clockwise*, the enantiomer is designated (*R*). If the direction is *counterclockwise*, the enantiomer is designated (*S*).

On this basis the 2-butanol enantiomer **II** is (*R*)-2-butanol:

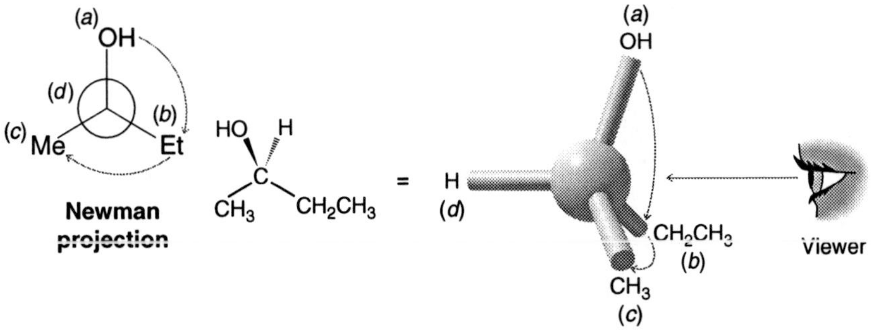

Newman projection

Viewer

Arrows are clockwise.

(*R*)-2-Butanol

---

*The rules for a branched chain require that we follow the chain with the highest priority atoms.

••• SOLVED PROBLEM 5.3

Shown here is an enantiomer of bromochlorofluoroiodomethane. Is it (R) or (S)?

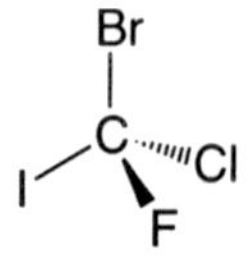

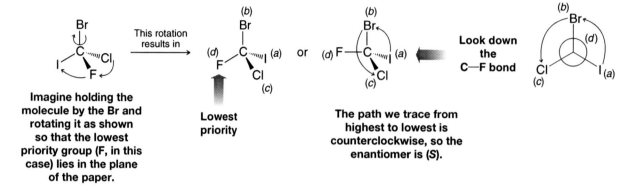

STRATEGY AND ANSWER:

Imagine holding the molecule by the Br and rotating it as shown so that the lowest priority group (F, in this case) lies in the plane of the paper.

This rotation results in

Lowest priority

or

Look down the C—F bond

The path we trace from highest to lowest is counterclockwise, so the enantiomer is **(S)**.

•••

PRACTICE PROBLEM 5.9 Write the enantiomeric forms of bromochlorofluoromethane and assign each enantiomer its correct (R) or (S) designation.

•••

PRACTICE PROBLEM 5.10 Give (R) and (S) designations for each pair of enantiomers given as answers to Practice Problem 5.4.

The first three rules of the Cahn–Ingold–Prelog system allow us to make an (R) or (S) designation for most compounds containing single bonds. For compounds containing multiple bonds one other rule is necessary:

4. Groups containing double or triple bonds are assigned priorities as if both atoms were duplicated or triplicated—that is,

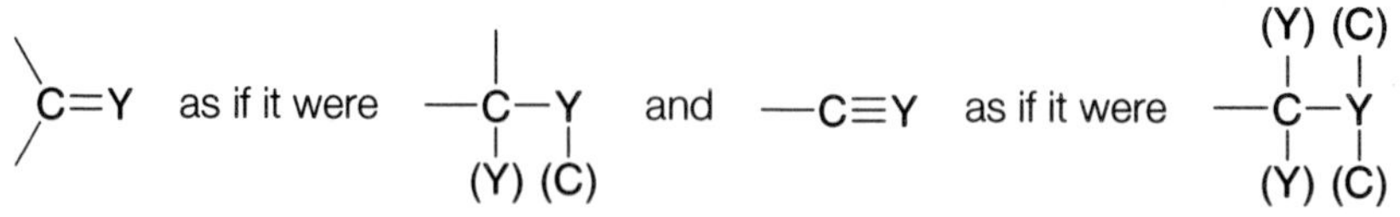

$$\text{C=Y}\quad\text{as if it were}\quad -\overset{|}{\underset{(Y)\ (C)}{C}}-Y\quad\text{and}\quad -C\equiv Y\quad\text{as if it were}\quad -\overset{(Y)\ (C)}{\underset{(Y)\ (C)}{C}}-Y$$

where the symbols in parentheses are duplicate or triplicate representations of the atoms at the other end of the multiple bond.

Thus, the vinyl group, $-CH=CH_2$, is of higher priority than the isopropyl group, $-CH(CH_3)_2$. That is,

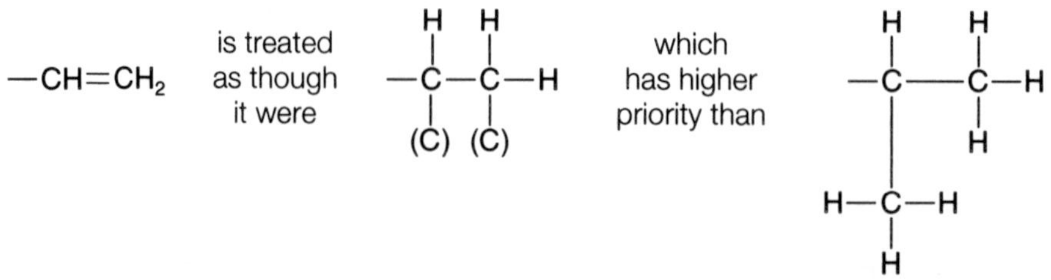

$-CH=CH_2$ is treated as though it were

$$-\overset{H}{\underset{(C)}{C}}-\overset{H}{\underset{(C)}{C}}-H$$

which has higher priority than

$$-\overset{H}{\underset{H-\overset{H}{\underset{H}{C}}-H}{C}}-\overset{H}{\underset{H}{C}}-H$$

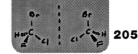

because at the second set of atoms out, the vinyl group (see the following structure) is C, H, H, whereas the isopropyl group along either branch is H, H, H. (At the first set of atoms both groups are the same: C, C, H.)

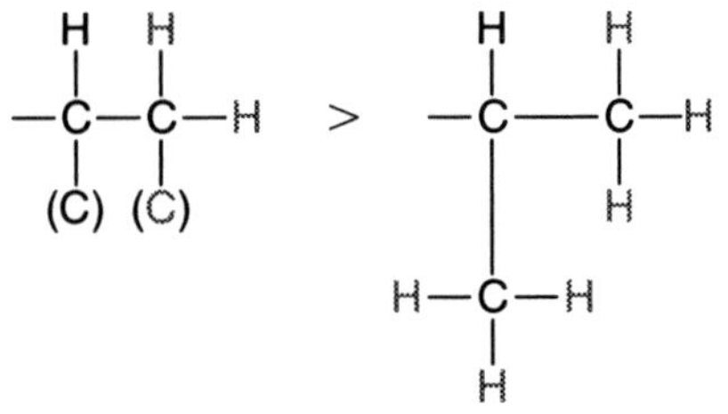

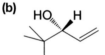

C, H, H > **H, H, H**
Vinyl group **Isopropyl group**

Other rules exist for more complicated structures, but we shall not study them here.*

PRACTICE PROBLEM 5.11

List the substituents in each of the following sets in order of priority, from highest to lowest:

(a) —Cl, —OH, —SH, —H

(b) —CH₃, —CH₂Br, —CH₂Cl, —CH₂OH

(c) —H, —OH, —CHO, —CH₃

(d) —CH(CH₃)₂, —C(CH₃)₃, —H,
  —CH=CH₂

(e) —H, —N(CH₃)₂, —OCH₃, —CH₃

(f) —OH, —OPO₃H₂, —H, —CHO

PRACTICE PROBLEM 5.12

Assign (*R*) or (*S*) designations to each of the following compounds:

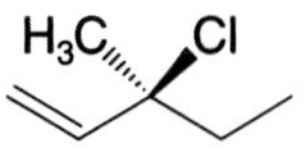

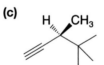

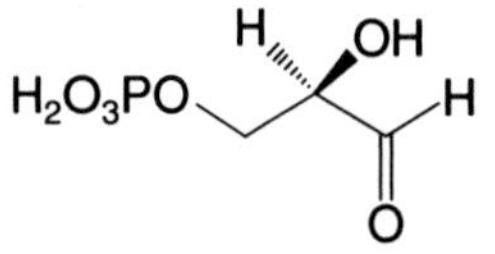

**D-Glyceraldehyde-3-phosphate
(a glycolysis intermediate)**

●●● SOLVED PROBLEM 5.4

Consider the following pair of structures and tell whether they represent enantiomers or two molecules of the same compound in different orientations:

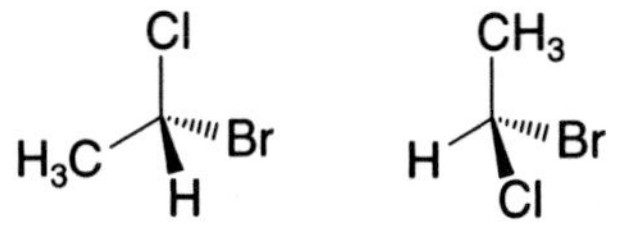

STRATEGY: One way to approach this kind of problem is to take one structure and, in your mind, hold it by one group. Then rotate the other groups until at least one group is in the same place as it is in the other structure. (Until you can do this easily in your mind, practice with models.) By a series of rotations like this you will be able to convert the structure you are manipulating into one that is either identical with or the mirror image of the other. For example, take **A**, hold it

(continues on next page)

---

*Further information can be found in the Chemical Abstracts Service *Index Guide*.

by the Cl atom and then rotate the other groups about the C*—Cl bond until the hydrogen occupies the same position as in **B**. Then hold it by the H and rotate the other groups about the C*—H bond. This will make **B** identical with **A**:

Another approach is to recognize that exchanging two groups at the chirality center *inverts the configuration of* that carbon atom and converts a structure *with only one chirality center* into its enantiomer; a second exchange recreates the original molecule. So we proceed this way, keeping track of how many exchanges are required to convert **A** into **B**. In this instance we find that two exchanges are required, and, again, we conclude that **A** and **B** are the same:

A useful check is to name each compound including its (*R,S*) designation. If the names are the same, then the structures are the same. In this instance both structures are (*R*)-1-bromo-1-chloroethane.

Another method for assigning (*R*) and (*S*) configurations using one's hands as chiral templates has been described (Huheey, J. E., *J. Chem. Educ.* **1986**, *63*, 598–600). Groups at a chirality center are correlated from lowest to highest priority with one's wrist, thumb, index finger, and second finger, respectively. With the ring and little finger closed against the palm and viewing one's hand with the wrist away, if the correlation between the chirality center is with the left hand, the configuration is (*S*), and if with the right hand, (*R*).

ANSWER: **A** and **B** are two molecules of the same compound oriented differently.

••◆

PRACTICE PROBLEM 5.13 Tell whether the two structures in each pair represent enantiomers or two molecules of the same compound in different orientations.

5.8 PROPERTIES OF ENANTIOMERS: OPTICAL ACTIVITY

The molecules of enantiomers are not superposable and, on this basis alone, we have concluded that enantiomers are different compounds. How are they different? Do enantiomers resemble constitutional isomers and diastereomers in having different melting and boiling points? The answer is *no*.

● Pure enantiomers have *identical* melting and boiling points.

Do pure enantiomers have different indexes of refraction, different solubilities in common solvents, different infrared spectra, and different rates of reaction with achiral reagents? The answer to each of these questions is also *no*.

Many of these properties (e.g., boiling points, melting points, and solubilities) are dependent on the magnitude of the intermolecular forces operating between the molecules (Section 2.13), and for molecules that are mirror images of each other these forces will be identical. We can see an example of this if we examine Table 5.1, where boiling points of the 2-butanol enantiomers are listed.

Mixtures of the enantiomers of a compound have different properties than pure samples of each, however. The data in Table 5.1 illustrate this for tartaric acid. The natural isomer, (+)-tartaric acid, has a melting point of 168–170°C, as does its unnatural

TABLE 5.1 PHYSICAL PROPERTIES OF 2-BUTANOL AND TARTARIC ACID ENANTIOMERS

Compound	Boiling Point (bp) or Melting Point (mp)
(*R*)-2-Butanol	99.5 °C (bp)
(*S*)-2-Butanol	99.5 °C (bp)
(+)-(*R*,*R*)-Tartaric acid	168–170 °C (mp)
(−)-(*S*,*S*)-Tartaric acid	168–170 °C (mp)
(+/−)-Tartaric acid	210–212 °C (mp)

enantiomer, (−)-tartaric acid. An equal mixture tartaric acid enantiomers, (+/−)-tartaric acid, has a melting point of 210–212 °C, however.

● Enantiomers show different behavior only when they interact with other chiral substances, including their own enantiomer.

This is evident in the melting point data above. Enantiomers also show different rates of reaction toward other chiral molecules—that is, toward reagents that consist of a single enantiomer or an excess of a single enantiomer. And, enantiomers show different solubilities in solvents that consist of a single enantiomer or an excess of a single enantiomer.

One easily observable way in which enantiomers differ is in *their behavior toward plane-polarized light.*

● When a beam of plane-polarized light passes through an enantiomer, the plane of polarization **rotates.**

● Separate enantiomers rotate the plane of plane-polarized light equal amounts *but in opposite directions.*

● Separate enantiomers are said to be **optically active compounds.** Because of their effect on plane-polarized light.

In order to understand this behavior of enantiomers, we need to understand the nature of plane-polarized light. We also need to understand how an instrument called a polarimeter operates.

Tartaric acid is found naturally in grapes and many other plants. Crystals of tartaric acid can sometimes be found in wine.

5.8A Plane-Polarized Light

Light is an electromagnetic phenomenon. A beam of light consists of two mutually perpendicular oscillating fields: an oscillating electric field and an oscillating magnetic field (Fig. 5.9).

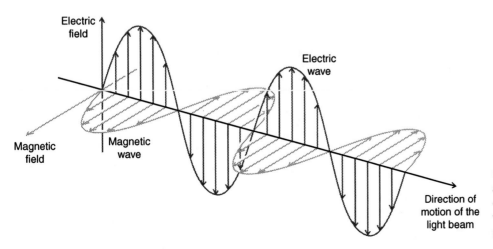

FIGURE 5.9 The oscillating electric and magnetic fields of a beam of ordinary light in one plane. The waves depicted here occur in all possible planes in ordinary light.

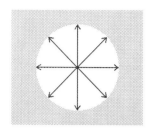

FIGURE 5.10 Oscillation of the electric field of ordinary light occurs in all possible planes perpendicular to the direction of propagation.

If we were to view a beam of ordinary light from one end, and if we could actually see the planes in which the electrical oscillations were occurring, we would find that oscillations of the electric field were occurring in all possible planes perpendicular to the direction of propagation (Fig. 5.10). (The same would be true of the magnetic field.)

When ordinary light is passed through a polarizer, the polarizer interacts with the electric field so that the electric field of the light that emerges from the polarizer (and the magnetic field perpendicular to it) is oscillating only in one plane. Such light is called plane-polarized light (Fig. 5.11*a*). If the plane-polarized beam encounters a filter with perpendicular polarization, the light is blocked (Fig. 5.11*b*). This phenomenon can readily be demonstrated with lenses from a pair of polarizing sunglasses or a sheet of polarizing film (Fig. 5.11*c*).

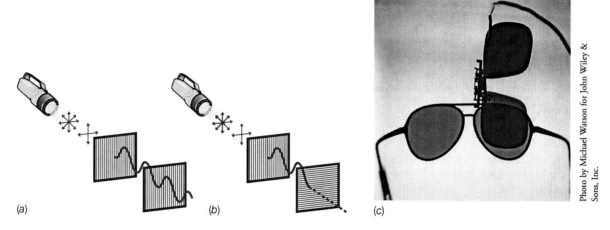

(a)   (b)   (c)

Photo by Michael Watson for John Wiley & Sons, Inc.

FIGURE 5.11 (a) Ordinary light passing through the first polarizing filter emerges with an electric wave oscillating in only one plane (and a perpendicular magnetic wave plane not shown). When the second filter is aligned with its polarizing direction the same as the first filter, as shown, the plane-polarized light can pass through. (b) If the second filter is turned 90°, the plane-polarized light is blocked. (c) Two polarizing sunglass lenses oriented perpendicular to each other block the light beam.

5.8B The Polarimeter

- The device that is used for measuring the effect of optically active compounds on plane-polarized light is a polarimeter.

A sketch of a polarimeter is shown in Fig. 5.12. The principal working parts of a polarimeter are (1) a light source (usually a sodium lamp), (2) a polarizer, (3) a cell for holding the optically active substance (or solution) in the light beam, (4) an analyzer, and (5) a scale for measuring the angle (in degrees) that the plane of polarized light has been rotated.

The analyzer of a polarimeter (Fig. 5.12) is nothing more than another polarizer. If the cell of the polarimeter is empty or if an optically *inactive* substance is present, the axes of the plane-polarized light and the analyzer will be exactly parallel when the instrument reads 0°, and the observer will detect the maximum amount of light passing through. If, by contrast, the cell contains an optically active substance, a solution of one enantiomer, for example, the plane of polarization of the light will be rotated as it passes through the cell. In order to detect the maximum brightness of light, the observer will have to rotate the axis of the analyzer in either a clockwise or counterclockwise direction. If the analyzer is rotated in a clockwise direction, the rotation, α (measured in degrees), is said to be positive (+). If the rotation is counterclockwise, the rotation is said to be negative (−). A substance that rotates plane-polarized light in the clockwise direction is also said to be dextrorotatory, and one that rotates plane-polarized light in a counterclockwise direction is said to be levorotatory (Latin: *dexter*, right, and *laevus*, left).

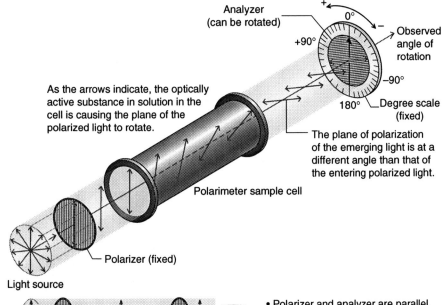

As the arrows indicate, the optically active substance in solution in the cell is causing the plane of the polarized light to rotate.

The plane of polarization of the emerging light is at a different angle than that of the entering polarized light.

Polarimeter sample cell

Polarizer (fixed)

Light source

Analyzer (can be rotated)

Observed angle of rotation

Degree scale (fixed)

(a)
- Polarizer and analyzer are parallel.
- No optically active substance is present.
- Polarized light can get through analyzer.

(b)
- Polarizer and analyzer are perpendicular.
- No optically active substance is present.
- No polarized light can emerge from analyzer.

(c)
- Substance in cell between polarizer and analyzer is optically active.
- Analyzer has been rotated to the left (from observer's point of view) to permit rotated polarized light through (substance is levorotatory in this example).

Polarizer   Analyzer   Observer

FIGURE 5.12 The principal working parts of a polarimeter and the measurement of optical rotation. (Reprinted with permission of John Wiley & Sons, Inc. from Holum, J. R., *Organic Chemistry: A Brief Course*, p. 316. Copyright 1975.)

5.8C Specific Rotation

- The number of degrees that the plane of polarization is rotated as the light passes through a solution of an enantiomer depends on the number of chiral molecules that it encounters.

To normalize optical rotation data relative to experimental variables such as tube length and the concentration of the enantiomer, chemists calculate a quantity called the specific rotation, $[\alpha]$, by the following equation:

$$[\alpha] = \frac{\alpha}{c \cdot l}$$

where $[\alpha]$ = the specific rotation

α = the observed rotation

c = the concentration of the solution in grams per milliliter of solution (or density in g mL^{-1} for neat liquids)

l = the length of the cell in decimeters (1 dm = 10 cm)

The specific rotation also depends on the temperature and the wavelength of light that is employed. Specific rotations are reported so as to incorporate these quantities as well. A specific rotation might be given as follows:

$$[\alpha]_D^{25} = +3.12$$

This means that the D line of a sodium lamp ($\lambda = 589.6$ nm) was used for the light, that a temperature of 25 °C was maintained, and that a sample containing 1.00 g mL^{-1} of the optically active substance, in a 1 dm tube, produced a rotation of 3.12° in a clockwise direction.*

The specific rotations of (R)-2-butanol and (S)-2-butanol are given here:

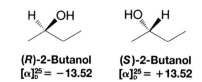

(R)-2-Butanol	(S)-2-Butanol
$[\alpha]_D^{25} = -13.52$	$[\alpha]_D^{25} = +13.52$

* The direction of rotation of plane-polarized light is often incorporated into the names of optically active compounds.

The following two sets of enantiomers show how this is done:

(R)-(+)-2-Methyl-1-butanol
$[\alpha]_D^{25} = +5.756$

(S)-(−)-2-Methyl-1-butanol
$[\alpha]_D^{25} = -5.756$

(R)-(−)-1-Chloro-2-methylbutane
$[\alpha]_D^{25} = -1.64$

(S)-(+)-1-Chloro-2-methylbutane
$[\alpha]_D^{25} = +1.64$

The previous compounds also illustrate an important principle:

* No obvious correlation exists between the (R) and (S) configurations of enantiomers and the direction [(+) or (−)] in which they rotate plane-polarized light.

(R)-(+)-2-Methyl-1-butanol and (R)-(−)-1-chloro-2-methylbutane have the same *configuration*; that is, they have the same general arrangement of their atoms in space. They have, however, an opposite effect on the direction of rotation of the plane of plane-polarized light:

Same configuration

(R)-(+)-2-Methyl-1-butanol   (R)-(−)-1-Chloro-2-methylbutane

These same compounds also illustrate a second important principle:

* No necessary correlation exists between the (R) and (S) designation and the direction of rotation of plane-polarized light.

(R)-2-Methyl-1-butanol is dextrorotatory (+), and (R)-1-chloro-2-methylbutane is levorotatory (−).

A method based on the measurement of optical rotation at many different wavelengths, called optical rotatory dispersion, has been used to correlate configurations of chiral molecules. A discussion of the technique of optical rotatory dispersion, however, is beyond the scope of this text.

---

*The magnitude of rotation is dependent on the solvent used when solutions are measured. This is the reason the solvent is specified when a rotation is reported in the chemical literature.

● ● ●
PRACTICE PROBLEM 5.14

(+)-Carvone

Shown is the configuration of (+)-carvone. (+)-Carvone is the principal component of caraway seed oil and is responsible for its characteristic odor. (−)-Carvone, its enantiomer, is the main component of spearmint oil and gives it its characteristic odor. The fact that the carvone enantiomers do not smell the same suggests that the receptor sites in the nose for these compounds are chiral, and that only the correct enantiomer binds well to its particular site (just as a hand requires a glove of the correct chirality for a proper fit). Give the correct (*R*) and (*S*) designations for (+)- and (−)-carvone.

5.9 THE ORIGIN OF OPTICAL ACTIVITY

Optical activity is measured by the degree of rotation of plane-polarized light passing through a chiral medium. The theoretical explanation for the origin of optical activity requires consideration of *circularly*-polarized light, however, and its interaction with chiral molecules. While it is not possible to provide a full theoretical explanation for the origin of optical activity here, the following explanation will suffice. A beam of plane-polarized light (Fig. 5.13*a*) can be described in terms of circularly-polarized light. A beam of

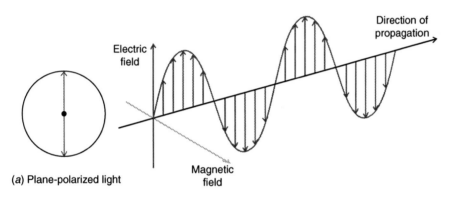

(*a*) Plane-polarized light

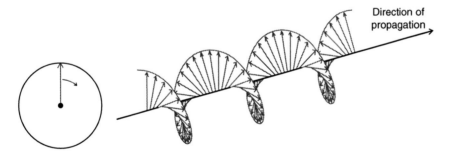

(*b*) Circularly-polarized light

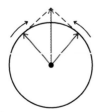

(*c*) Two circularly-polarized beams counter-rotating at the same velocity (in phase), and their vector sum. The net result is like (*a*).

(*d*) Two circularly-polarized beams counter-rotating at different velocities, such as after interaction with a chiral molecule, and their vector sum. The net result is like (*b*).

FIGURE 5.13 (*a*) Plane-polarized light. (*b*) Circularly-polarized light. (*c*) Two circularly-polarized beams counterrotating at the same velocity (in phase) and their vector sum. The net result is like (*a*). (*d*) Two circularly-polarized beams counter-rotating at different velocities, such as after interaction with a chiral molecule, and their vector sum. The net result is like (*b*).

circularly-polarized light rotating in one direction is shown in Fig. 5.13*b*. The vector sum of *two* counterrotating in-phase circularly-polarized beams is a beam of plane-polarized light (Fig. 5.13*c*). The optical activity of chiral molecules results from the fact that the two *counterrotating circularly-polarized beams travel with different velocities through the chiral medium.* As the difference between the two circularly-polarized beams propagates through the sample, their vector sum describes a plane that is progressively rotated (Fig. 5.13*d*). What we measure when light emerges from the sample is the net rotation of the plane-polarized light caused by differences in velocity of the circularly-polarized beam components. The origin of the differing velocities has ultimately to do with interactions between electrons in the chiral molecule and light.

Achiral molecules in solution cause no difference in velocity of the two circularly-polarized beams; hence there is no rotation of the plane of polarized light described by their vector sum. Randomly-oriented achiral molecules, therefore, are not optically active. (However, oriented achiral molecules and crystals having specific symmetric characteristics can rotate plane-polarized light.)

5.9A Racemic Forms

A sample that consists exclusively or predominantly of one enantiomer causes a net rotation of plane-polarized light. Figure 5.14*a* depicts a plane of polarized light as it encounters a molecule of (*R*)-2-butanol, causing the plane of polarization to rotate slightly in one direction. (For the remaining purposes of our discussion we shall limit our description of polarized light to the resultant plane, neglecting consideration of the circularly-polarized components from which plane-polarized light arises.) Each additional molecule of (*R*)-2-butanol that the beam encounters would cause further rotation in the same direction. If, on the other hand, the mixture contained molecules of (*S*)-2-butanol, each molecule of that enantiomer would cause the plane of polarization to rotate in the opposite direction (Fig. 5.14*b*). If the (*R*) and (*S*) enantiomers were present in equal amounts, there would be no net rotation of the plane of polarized light.

- An equimolar mixture of two enantiomers is called a **racemic mixture** (or **racemate** or **racemic form**). **A racemic mixture causes no net rotation of plane-polarized light.**

FIGURE 5.14 (*a*) A beam of plane-polarized light encounters a molecule of (*R*)-2-butanol, a chiral molecule. This encounter produces a slight rotation of the plane of polarization. (*b*) Exact cancellation of this rotation occurs if a molecule of (*S*)-2-butanol is encountered. (*c*) Net rotation of the plane of polarization occurs if (*R*)-2-butanol is present predominantly or exclusively.

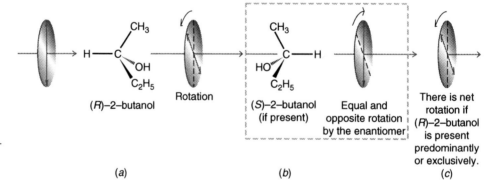

In a racemic mixture the effect of each molecule of one enantiomer on the circularly-polarized beam cancels the effect of molecules of the other enantiomer, resulting in no net optical activity.

The racemic form of a sample is often designated as being ($\pm$). A racemic mixture of (*R*)-($-$)-2-butanol and (*S*)-($+$)-2-butanol might be indicated as

$$(\pm)\text{-2-butanol} \quad \text{or} \quad (\pm)\text{-CH}_3\text{CH}_2\text{CHOHCH}_3$$

5.9B Racemic Forms and Enantiomeric Excess

A sample of an optically active substance that consists of a single enantiomer is said to be **enantiomerically pure** or to have an **enantiomeric excess** of 100%. An enantiomerically

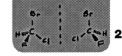

pure sample of (S)-(+)-2-butanol shows a specific rotation of +13.52 ($[\alpha]_D^{25} = +13.52$). On the other hand, a sample of (S)-(+)-2-butanol that contains less than an equimolar amount of (R)-(−)-2-butanol will show a specific rotation that is less than +13.52 but greater than zero. Such a sample is said to have an *enantiomeric excess* less than 100%. The **enantiomeric excess (ee)**, also known as the *optical purity*, is defined as follows:

$$\% \text{ Enantiomeric excess} = \frac{\text{moles of one enantiomer } - \text{ moles of other enantiomer}}{\text{total moles of both enantiomers}} \times 100$$

The enantiomeric excess can be calculated from optical rotations:

$$\% \text{ Enantiomeric excess*} = \frac{\text{observed specific rotation}}{\text{specific rotation of the pure enantiomer}} \times 100$$

Let us suppose, for example, that a mixture of the 2-butanol enantiomers showed a specific rotation of +6.76. We would then say that the enantiomeric excess of the (S)-(+)-2-butanol is 50%:

$$\text{Enantiomeric excess} = \frac{+6.76}{+13.52} \times 100 = 50\%$$

When we say that the enantiomeric excess of this mixture is 50%, we mean that 50% of the mixture consists of the (+) enantiomer (the excess) and the other 50% consists of the racemic form. Since for the 50% that is racemic the optical rotations cancel one another out, only the 50% of the mixture that consists of the (+) enantiomer contributes to the observed optical rotation. The observed rotation is, therefore, 50% (or one-half) of what it would have been if the mixture had consisted only of the (+) enantiomer.

●●● **SOLVED PROBLEM 5.5**

What is the actual stereoisomeric composition of the mixture referred to above?

ANSWER: Of the total mixture, 50% consists of the racemic form, which contains equal numbers of the two enantiomers. Therefore, half of this 50%, or 25%, is the (−) enantiomer and 25% is the (+) enantiomer. The other 50% of the mixture (the excess) is also the (+) enantiomer. Consequently, the mixture is 75% (+) enantiomer and 25% (−) enantiomer.

●●●

PRACTICE PROBLEM 5.15

A sample of 2-methyl-1-butanol (see Section 5.8C) has a specific rotation, $[\alpha]_D^{25}$, equal to +1.151. **(a)** What is the percent enantiomeric excess of the sample? **(b)** Which enantiomer is in excess, the (R) or the (S)?

5.10 THE SYNTHESIS OF CHIRAL MOLECULES

5.10A Racemic Forms

Reactions carried out with achiral reactants can often lead to *chiral* products. In the absence of any chiral influence from a catalyst, reagent, or solvent, the outcome of such a reaction is a racemic mixture. In other words, the chiral product is obtained as a 50:50 mixture of enantiomers.

---

*This calculation should be applied to a single enantiomer or to mixtures of enantiomers only. It should not be applied to mixtures in which some other compound is present.

An example is the synthesis of 2-butanol by the nickel-catalyzed hydrogenation of butanone. In this reaction the hydrogen molecule adds across the carbon–oxygen double bond in much the same way that it adds to a carbon–carbon double bond.

$$CH_3CH_2CCH_3 + H\!-\!H \xrightarrow{\text{Ni}} (\pm)\text{-}CH_3CH_2\overset{*}{C}HCH_3$$

Butanone	Hydrogen	(±)-2-Butanol
(achiral molecules)	(achiral molecules)	[chiral molecules but 50:50 mixture (R) and (S)]

Figure 5.15 illustrates the stereochemical aspects of this reaction. Because butanone is achiral, there is no difference in presentation of either face of the molecule to the surface of the metal catalyst. The two faces of the trigonal planar carbonyl group interact with the metal surface with equal probability. Transfer of the hydrogen atoms from the metal to the carbonyl group produces a chirality center at carbon 2. Since there has been no chiral influence in the reaction pathway, the product is obtained as a racemic mixture of the two enantiomers, (R)-(–)-2-butanol and (S)-(+)-2-butanol.

We shall see that when reactions like this are carried out in the presence of a chiral influence, such as an enzyme or chiral catalyst, the result is usually not a racemic mixture.

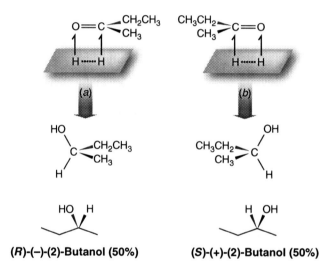

FIGURE 5.15 The reaction of butanone with hydrogen in the presence of a nickel catalyst. The reaction rate by path (a) is equal to that by path (b). (R-15)-(–)-2-Butanol and (S)-(+)-2-butanol are produced in equal amounts, as a racemate.

(R)-(–)-(2)-Butanol (50%)   **(S)-(+)-(2)-Butanol (50%)**

5.10B Stereoselective Syntheses

Stereoselective reactions are reactions that lead to a preferential formation of one stereoisomer over other stereoisomers that could possibly be formed.

- If a reaction produces preferentially one enantiomer over its mirror image, the reaction is said to be an **enantioselective reaction.**
- If a reaction leads preferentially to one diastereomer over others that are possible, the reaction is said to be an **diastereoselective reaction.**

For a reaction to be either enantioselective or diastereoselective, a chiral reagent, catalyst, or solvent must assert an influence on the course of the reaction.

In nature, where most reactions are stereoselective, the chiral influences come from protein molecules called **enzymes.** Enzymes are biological catalysts of extraordinary efficiency. Not only do they have the ability to cause reactions to take place much more rapidly than they would otherwise, they also have the ability to assert a *dramatic chiral influence* on a reaction. Enzymes do this because they, too, are chiral, and they possess an active site where the reactant molecules are momentarily bound while the reaction takes place. The active site is chiral (see Fig. 5.7), and only one enantiomer of a chiral reactant fits it properly and is able to undergo the reaction.

Many enzymes have found use in the organic chemistry laboratory, where organic chemists take advantage of their properties to bring about stereoselective reactions. One

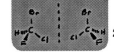

of these is an enzyme called **lipase**. Lipase catalyzes a reaction called **hydrolysis**, whereby an ester (Section 2.10B) reacts with a molecule of water to produce a carboxylic acid and an alcohol.

$$\underset{\textbf{Ester}}{R-C(=O)-OR'} \;+\; \underset{\textbf{Water}}{HOH} \;\xrightarrow{\text{hydrolysis}}\; \underset{\substack{\textbf{Carboxylic}\\\textbf{acid}}}{R-C(=O)-OH} \;+\; \underset{\textbf{Alcohol}}{HO-R'}$$

If the starting ester is chiral and present as a mixture of its enantiomers, the lipase enzyme reacts selectively with one enantiomer to release the corresponding chiral carboxylic acid and an alcohol, while the other ester enantiomer remains unchanged or reacts much more slowly. The result is a mixture that consists predominantly of one stereoisomer of the reactant and one stereoisomer of the product, which can usually be separated easily on the basis of their different physical properties. Such a process is called a kinetic resolution, where the rate of a reaction with one enantiomer is different than with the other, leading to a preponderance of one product stereoisomer. We shall say more about the resolution of enantiomers in Section 5.16. The following hydrolysis is an example of a kinetic resolution using lipase:

Ethyl (±)-2-fluorohexanoate
[an ester that is a racemate of (R) and (S) forms]

$\xrightarrow[\text{H-OH}]{\text{lipase}}$

Ethyl (R)-(+)-2-fluorohexanoate
(>99% enantiomeric excess)

+

(S)-(−)-2-Fluorohexanoic acid
(>69% enantiomeric excess)

+ H—OEt

Other enzymes called hydrogenases have been used to effect enantioselective versions of carbonyl reductions like that in Section 5.10A. We shall have more to say about the stereoselectivity of enzymes in Chapter 12.

5.11 CHIRAL DRUGS

The U.S. Food and Drug Administration and the pharmaceutical industry are very interested in the production of chiral drugs—that is, drugs that contain a single enantiomer rather than a racemate. The antihypertensive drug **methyldopa** (Aldomet), for example, owes its effect exclusively to the (S) isomer. In the case of **penicillamine**, the (S) isomer is a highly potent therapeutic agent for primary chronic arthritis, while the (R) isomer has no therapeutic action and is highly toxic. The anti-inflammatory agent **ibuprofen** (Advil, Motrin, Nuprin) is marketed as a racemate even though only the (S) enantiomer is the active agent. The (R) isomer of ibuprofen has no anti-inflammatory action and is slowly converted to the (S) isomer in the body. A formulation of ibuprofen based on solely the (S) isomer, however, would be more effective than the racemate.

Ibuprofen

Methyldopa

Penicillamine

PRACTICE PROBLEM 5.16 Write three-dimensional formulas for the (*S*) isomers of **(a)** methyldopa, **(b)** penicillamine, and **(c)** ibuprofen.

PRACTICE PROBLEM 5.17 The antihistamine Allegra (fexofenadine) has the following structural formula. For any chirality centers in fexofenadine, draw a substructure that would have an (*R*) configuration.

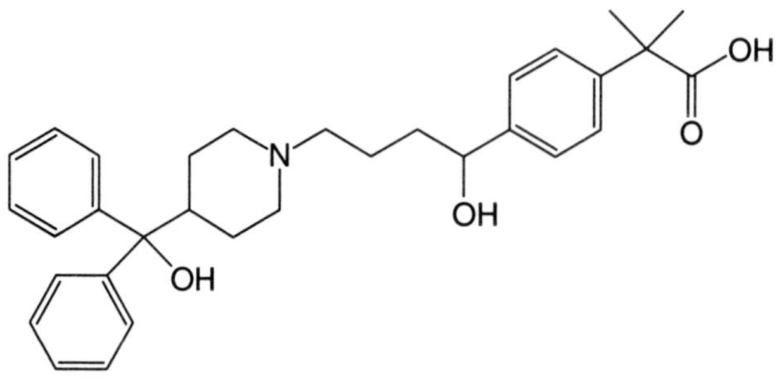

Fexofenadine (Allegra)

PRACTICE PROBLEM 5.18 Assign the (*R,S*) configuration at each chirality center in Darvon (dextropropoxyphene).

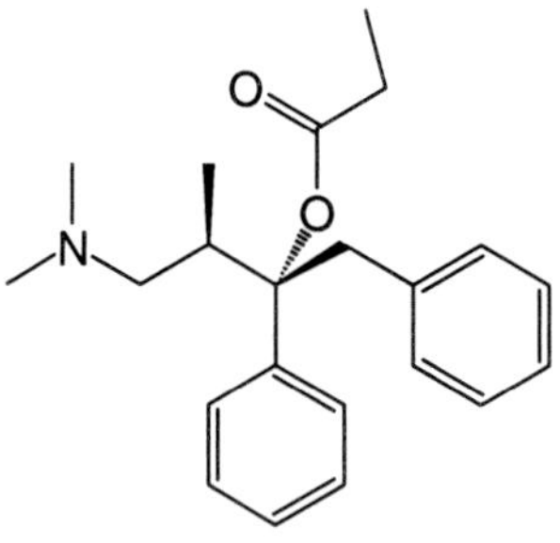

Darvon

WILLIAM KNOWLES, RYOJI NOYORI, AND BARRY SHARPLESS were awarded the 2001 Nobel Prize in Chemistry for catalytic stereoselective reactions.

There are many other examples of drugs like these, including drugs where the enantiomers have distinctly different effects. The preparation of enantiomerically pure drugs, therefore, is one factor that makes stereoselective synthesis (Section 5.10B) and the resolution of racemic drugs (separation into pure enantiomers, Section 5.16) major areas of research today.

Underscoring the importance of stereoselective synthesis is the fact that the 2001 Nobel Prize in Chemistry was given to researchers who developed reaction catalysts that are now widely used in industry and academia. William Knowles (Monsanto Company, deceased 2012) and Ryoji Noyori (Nagoya University) were awarded half of the prize for their development of reagents used for catalytic stereoselective hydrogenation reactions. The other half of the prize was awarded to Barry Sharpless (Scripps Research Institute) for development of catalytic stereoselective oxidation reactions (see Chapter 11). An important example resulting from the work of Noyori and based on earlier work by Knowles is a synthesis of the anti-inflammatory agent **naproxen,** involving a stereoselective catalytic hydrogenation reaction:

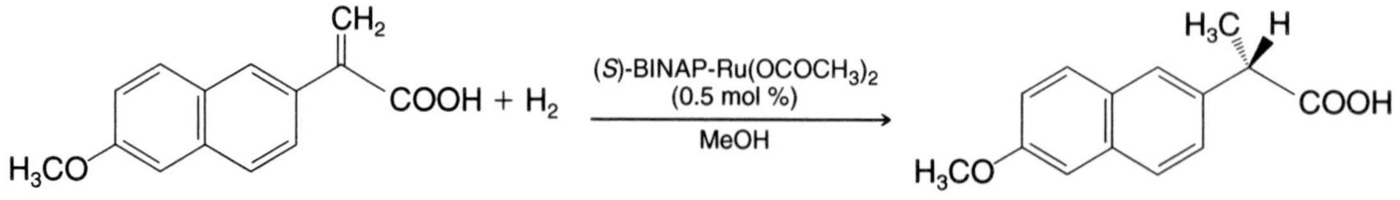

(*S*)-Naproxen
(an anti-inflammatory agent)
(92% yield, 97% ee)

The hydrogenation catalyst in this reaction is an organometallic complex formed from ruthenium and a chiral organic ligand called (*S*)-BINAP. The reaction itself is truly remarkable because it proceeds with excellent enantiomeric excess (97%) and in very high yield (92%). We will have more to say about BINAP ligands and the origin of their chirality in Section 5.18.

THE CHEMISTRY OF... Selective Binding of Drug Enantiomers to Left- and Right-Handed Coiled DNA

Would you like left- or right-handed DNA with your drug? That's a question that can now be answered due to the recent discovery that each enantiomer of the drug daunorubicin selectively binds DNA coiled with opposite handedness. (+)-Daunorubicin binds selectively to DNA coiled in the typical right-handed conformation (B-DNA). (−)-Daunorubicin binds selectively to DNA coiled in the left-handed conformation (Z-DNA). Furthermore, daunorubicin is capable of inducing conformational changes in DNA from one coiling direction to the other, depending on which coiling form is favored when a given daunorubicin enantiomer binds to the DNA. It has long been known that DNA adopts a number of secondary and tertiary structures, and it is presumed that some of these conformations are involved in turning on or off transcription of a given section of DNA. The discovery of specific interactions between each daunorubicin enantiomer and the left- and right-handed coil forms of DNA will likely assist in design and discovery of new drugs with anticancer or other activities.

Enantiomeric forms of daunorubicin bind with DNA and cause it to coil with opposite handedness.
(Graphic courtesy John O. Trent, Brown Cancer Center, Department of Medicine, University of Louisville, KY. Based on work from Qu, X., Trent, J.O., Fokt, I., Priebe, W., and Chaires, J.B., *Allosteric, Chiral-Selective Drug Binding to DNA, Proc. Natl. Acad. Sci. U.S.A.*, 2000 (Oct 24): 97(22), 12032–12037.)

5.12 MOLECULES WITH MORE THAN ONE CHIRALITY CENTER

So far we have mainly considered chiral molecules that contain only one chirality center. Many organic molecules, especially those important in biology, contain more than one chirality center. Cholesterol (Section 23.4B), for example, contains eight chirality centers. (Can you locate them?) We can begin, however, with simpler molecules. Let us consider 2,3-dibromopentane, shown here in a two-dimensional bond-line formula. 2,3-Dibromopentane has two chirality centers:

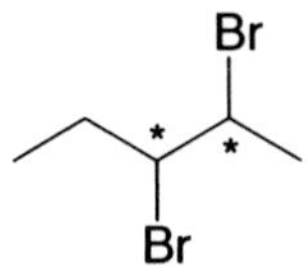

2,3-Dibromopentane

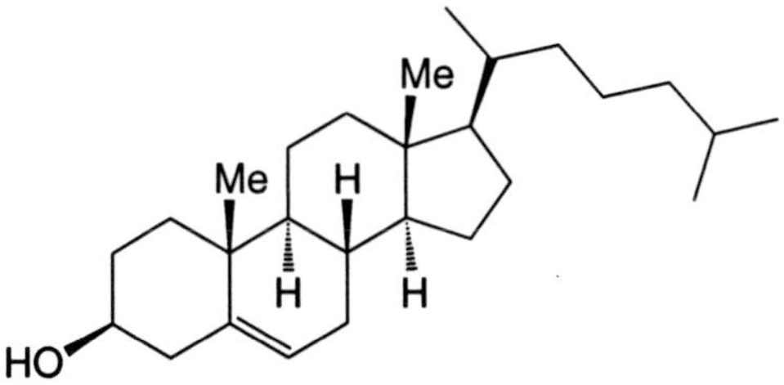

Cholesterol

A useful rule gives the maximum number of stereoisomers:

* In compounds whose stereoisomerism is due to chirality centers, *the total number of stereoisomers will not exceed 2^n, where n is equal to the number of chirality centers.*

For 2,3-dibromopentane we should not expect more than four stereoisomers ($2^2 = 4$). Our next task is to write three-dimensional bond-line formulas for the possible stereoisomers.

Helpful Hint

Cholesterol, having eight chirality centers, hypothetically could exist in 2^8 (256) stereoisomeric forms, yet biosynthesis via enzymes produces only *one* stereoisomer.

5.12A HOW TO Draw Stereoisomers for Molecules Having More Than One Chirality Center

Using 2,3-dibromopentane as an example, the following sequence explains how we can draw all of the possible isomers for a molecule that contains more than one chirality center. Remember that in the case of 2,3-dibromopentane we expect a maximum of four possible isomers because there are two chirality centers (2^n, where n is the number of chirality centers).

1. Start by drawing the portion of the carbon skeleton that contains the chirality centers in such a way that as many of the chirality centers are placed in the plane of the paper as possible, and as symmetrically as possible. In the case of 2,3-dibromopentane, we simply begin by drawing the bond between C2 and C3, since these are the only chirality centers.

2. Next we add the remaining groups that are bonded at the chirality centers in such a way as to maximize the symmetry between the chirality centers. In this case we start by drawing the two bromine atoms so that they project either both outward or both inward relative to the plane of the paper, and we add the hydrogen atoms at each chirality center. Drawing the bromine atoms outward results in formula **1**, shown below. Even though there are eclipsing interactions in this conformation, and it is almost certainly not the most stable conformation for the molecule, we draw it this way so as to maximize the possibility of finding symmetry in the molecule.

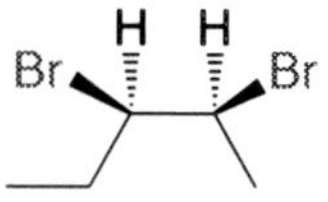

1

3. To draw the enantiomer of the first stereoisomer, we simply draw its mirror image, either side-by-side or top and bottom, by imagining a mirror between them. The result is formula **2**.

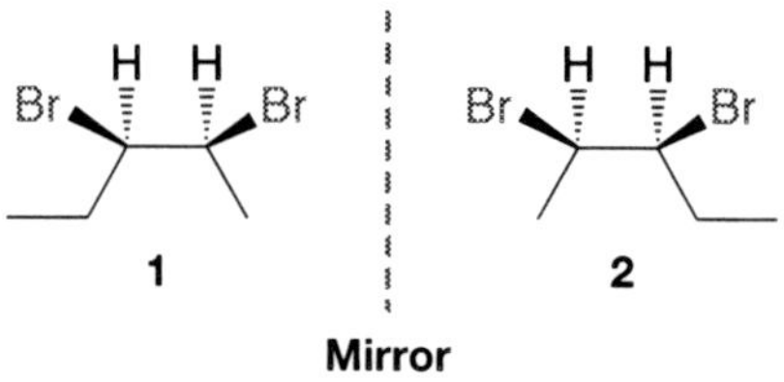

1 | **2**

Mirror

4. To draw another stereoisomer, we interchange two groups at any one of the chirality centers. By doing so we invert the R,S configuration at that chirality center.

   ⁕ All of the possible stereoisomers for a compound can be drawn by successively interchanging two groups at each chirality center.

   If we interchange the bromine and hydrogen atoms at C2 in formula **1** for 2,3-dibromopentane, the result is formula **3**. Then to generate the enantiomer of **3**, we simply draw its mirror image, and the result is **4**.

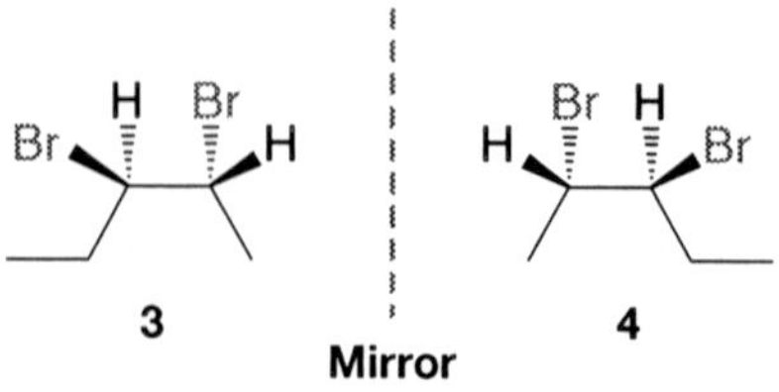

3 | **4**

Mirror

5. Next we examine the relationship between all of the possible pairings of formulas to determine which are pairs of enantiomers, which are diastereomers, and, for special cases like we shall see in Section 5.12B, which formulas are actually identical due to an internal plane of symmetry.

Since structures **1** and **2** are not superposable, they represent different compounds. Since structures **1** and **2** differ only in the arrangement of their atoms in space, they represent stereoisomers. Structures **1** and **2** are also mirror images of each other; thus **1** and **2** represent a pair of enantiomers. Structures **3** and **4** correspond to another pair of enantiomers. Structures **1–4** are all different, so there are, in total, four stereoisomers of 2,3-dibromopentane.

At this point you should convince yourself that there are no other stereoisomers by writing other structural formulas. You will find that rotation about the single bonds, or of the entire structure, or of any other arrangement of the atoms will cause the structure to become superposable with one of the structures that we have written here. Better yet, using different colored balls, make molecular models as you work this out.

The compounds represented by structures **1–4** are all optically active compounds. Any one of them, if placed separately in a polarimeter, would show optical activity.

The compounds represented by structures **1** and **2** are enantiomers. The compounds represented by structures **3** and **4** are also enantiomers. But what is the isomeric relation between the compounds represented by **1** and **3**?

We can answer this question by observing that **1** and **3** *are stereoisomers* and that they *are not mirror images of each other*. They are, therefore, *diastereomers*.

- Diastereomers have different physical properties—different melting points and boiling points, different solubilities, and so forth.

PRACTICE PROBLEM 5.19

1   **2**   **3**   **4**

(a) If **3** and **4** are enantiomers, what are **1** and **4**? **(b)** What are **2** and **3**, and **2** and **4**? **(c)** Would you expect **1** and **3** to have the same melting point? **(d)** The same boiling point? **(e)** The same vapor pressure?

••• SOLVED PROBLEM 5.6

Draw all possible stereoisomers for 2-bromo-4-chloropentane.

STRATEGY AND ANSWER: C2 and C4 are chirality centers in 2-bromo-4-chloropentane. We begin by drawing the carbon chain with as many carbons depicted in the plane of the paper as possible, and in a way that maximizes the symmetry between C2 and C4. In this case, an ordinary zig-zag bond-line formula provides symmetry between C2 and C4. Then we add the bromine and chlorine atoms at C2 and C4, respectively, as well as the hydrogen atoms at these carbons, resulting in formula I. To draw its enantiomer (II), we imagine a mirror and draw a reflection of the molecule.

I   **II**

Mirror

To draw another stereoisomer we invert the configuration at one chirality center by interchanging two groups at one chirality center, as shown for C2 in III. Then we draw the enantiomer of III by imagining its mirror reflection.

III   **IV**

Mirror

(continues on next page)

Last, we check that none of these formulas is identical to another by testing the superposability of each one with the others. We should not expect any to be identical because none of the formulas has an internal plane of symmetry. The case would have been different for 2,4-dibromopentane, however, in which case there would have been one meso stereoisomer (a type of stereoisomer that we shall study in the next section).

5.12B Meso Compounds

A structure with two chirality centers does not always have four possible stereoisomers. Sometimes there are only *three*. As we shall see:

- Some molecules are achiral even though they contain chirality centers.

To understand this, let us write stereochemical formulas for 2,3-dibromobutane. We begin in the same way as we did before. We write formulas for one stereoisomer and for its mirror image:

Structures **A** and **B** are nonsuperposable and represent a pair of enantiomers.

When we write the new structure **C** (see below) and its mirror image **D**, however, the situation is different. *The two structures are superposable.* This means that **C** and **D** do not represent a pair of enantiomers. Formulas **C** and **D** represent identical orientations of the same compound:

The molecule represented by structure **C** (or **D**) is not chiral even though it contains two chirality centers.

- If a molecule has an internal plane of symmetry it is achiral.
- A meso compound is an achiral molecule that contains chirality centers and has an internal plane of symmetry. Meso compounds are not optically active.

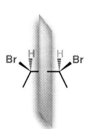

FIGURE 5.16 The plane of symmetry of meso-2,3-dibromobutane. This plane divides the molecule into halves that are mirror images of each other.

Another test for molecular chirality is to construct a model (or write the structure) of the molecule and then test whether or not the model (or structure) is superposable on its mirror image. If it is, the molecule is achiral. If it *is not*, the molecule is chiral.

We have already carried out this test with structure **C** and found that it is achiral. We can also demonstrate that **C** is achiral in another way. Figure 5.16 shows that structure **C** *has an internal plane of symmetry* (Section 5.6).

The following two problems relate to compounds **A–D** in the preceding paragraphs.

PRACTICE PROBLEM 5.20 Which of the following would be optically active?

   (a) A pure sample of **A**
   (b) A pure sample of **B**
   (c) A pure sample of **C**
   (d) An equimolar mixture of **A** and **B**

The following are formulas for three compounds, written in noneclipsed conformations. In each instance tell which compound (**A**, **B**, or **C** above) each formula represents.

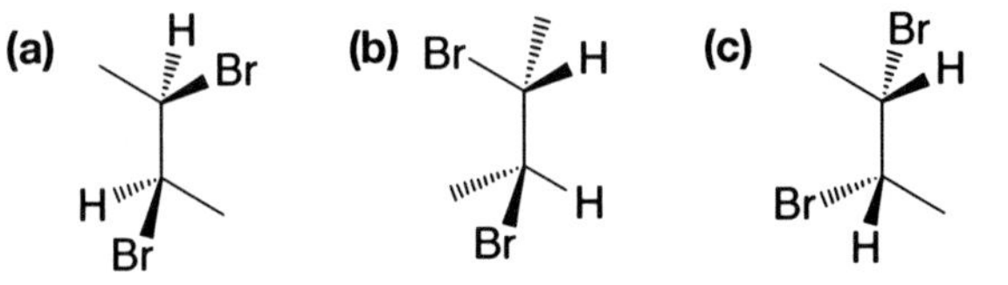

(a) **(b)** **(c)**

Which of the following (**X**, **Y**, or **Z**) is a meso compound?

STRATEGY AND ANSWER: In each molecule, rotating the groups joined by the C_2—C_3 bond by 180° brings the two methyl groups into comparable position. In the case of compound Z, a plane of symmetry results, and therefore, Z is a meso compound. No plane of symmetry is possible in X and Y.

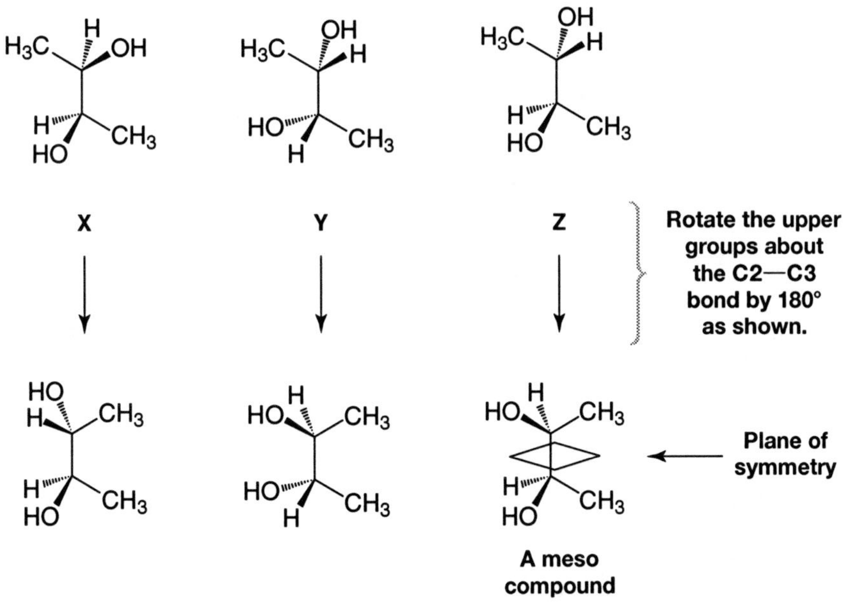

X   Y   Z

Rotate the upper
groups about
the C2—C3
bond by 180°
as shown.

Plane of
symmetry

**A meso
compound**

Write three-dimensional formulas for all of the stereoisomers of each of the following compounds. Label pairs of enantiomers and label meso compounds.

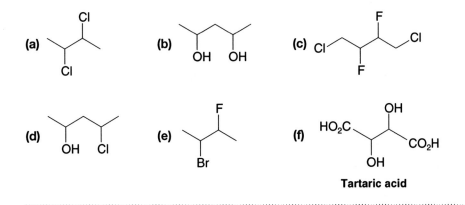

(a)   **(b)**   **(c)**

(d)   **(e)**   **(f)**

Tartaric acid

5.12C HOW TO Name Compounds with More Than One Chirality Center

1. If a compound has more than one chirality center, we analyze each center separately and decide whether it is (R) or (S).

2. Then, using numbers, we tell which designation refers to which carbon atom.

Consider stereoisomer **A** of 2,3-dibromobutane:

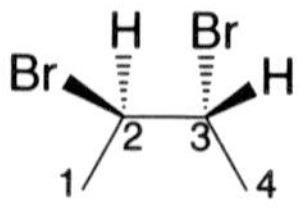

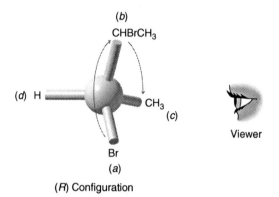

A

2,3-Dibromobutane

When this formula is rotated so that the group of lowest priority attached to C2 is directed away from the viewer, it resembles the following:

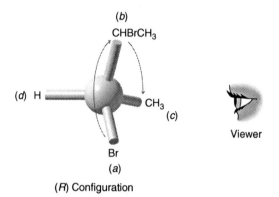

(R) Configuration

The order of progression from the group of highest priority to that of next highest priority (from —Br, to —CHBrCH$_3$, to —CH$_3$) is clockwise. Therefore, C2 has the (R) configuration.

When we repeat this procedure with C3, we find that C3 also has the (R) configuration:

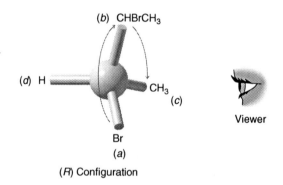

(R) Configuration

Compound **A**, therefore, is (2R,3R)-2,3-dibromobutane.

PRACTICE PROBLEM 5.23 Give names that include (R) and (S) designations for compounds **B** and **C** in Section 5.12B.

PRACTICE PROBLEM 5.24 Give names that include (R) and (S) designations for your answers to Practice Problem 5.22.

Chloramphenicol (at right) is a potent antibiotic, isolated from *Streptomyces venezuelae*, that is particularly effective against typhoid fever. It was the first naturally occurring substance shown to contain a nitro (—NO₂) group attached to an aromatic ring. Both chirality centers in chloramphenicol are known to have the (*R*) configuration. Identify the two chirality centers and write a three-dimensional formula for chloramphenicol.

NO_2

$HO—C—H$

$H—C—NHCOCHCl_2$

CH_2OH

Chloramphenicol

5.13 FISCHER PROJECTION FORMULAS

So far in writing structures for chiral molecules we have only used formulas that show three dimensions with solid and dashed wedges, and we shall largely continue to do so until we study carbohydrates in Chapter 22. The reason is that formulas with solid and dashed wedges unambiguously show three dimensions, and they can be manipulated on paper in any way that we wish so long as we do not break bonds. Their use, moreover, teaches us to see molecules (in our mind's eye) in three dimensions, and this ability will serve us well.

Chemists, however, sometimes use formulas called **Fischer projections** to show three dimensions in chiral molecules such as acyclic carbohydrates. Fischer projection formulas are useful in cases where there are chirality centers at several adjacent carbon atoms, as is often the case in carbohydrates. Use of Fischer projection formulas requires rigid adherence to certain conventions, however. **Used carelessly, these projection formulas can easily lead to incorrect conclusions.**

5.13A HOW TO Draw and Use Fischer Projections

Let us consider how we would relate a three-dimensional formula for 2,3-dibromobutane using solid and dashed wedges to the corresponding Fischer projection formula.

1. The carbon chain in a Fischer projection is always drawn from top to bottom, rather than side to side as is often the case with bond-line formulas. We consider the molecule in a conformation that has eclipsing interactions between the groups at each carbon.

   For 2,3-dibromobutane we turn the bond-line formula so that the carbon chain runs up and down and we orient it so that groups attached to the main carbon chain project out of the plane like a bow tie. The carbon–carbon bonds of the chain, therefore, either lie in the plane of the paper or project behind it.

   A   **A**

2. From the vertical formula with the groups at each carbon eclipsed we "project" all of the bonds onto the paper, replacing all solid and dashed wedges with ordinary lines. The vertical line of the formula now represents the carbon chain, each point of intersection between the vertical line and a horizontal line represents a carbon atom in the chain, and we interpret the horizontal lines as bonds that project out toward us.

Doing this with the vertical, eclipsed form of 2,3-dibromobutane leads to the Fischer projection shown here.

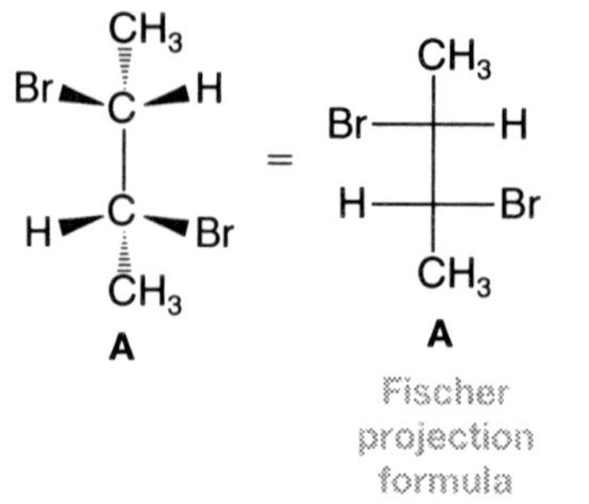

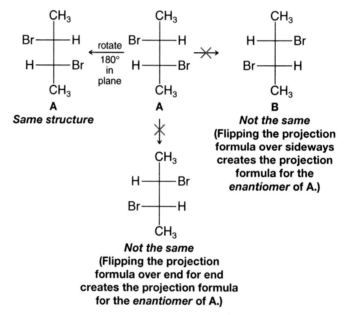

3. To test the superposability of two structures represented by Fischer projections we are allowed to rotate them in the plane of the paper by 180°, *but by no other angle*. We must always keep the Fischer projection formulas in the plane of the paper, and **we are not allowed to flip them over**. If we flip a Fischer projection over, the horizontal bonds project behind the plane instead of in front, and every configuration would be *misrepresented* as the opposite of what was intended.

Helpful Hint

Build handheld models of **A** and **B** and relate them to the Fischer projections shown here.

Because Fischer projections must be used with such care, we introduce them now only so that you can understand Fischer projections when you see them in the context of other courses. Our emphasis for most of this book will be on the use of solid and dashed wedges to represent three-dimensional formulas (or chair conformational structures in the case of cyclohexane derivatives), except in Chapter 22 when we will use Fischer projections again in our discussion of carbohydrates. If your instructor wishes to utilize Fischer projections further, you will be so advised.

PRACTICE PROBLEM 5.26 **(a)** Give the (*R,S*) designations for each chirality center in compound **A** and for compound **B**. **(b)** Write the Fischer projection formula for a compound **C** that is the diastereomer of **A** and **B**. **(c)** Would **C** be optically active?

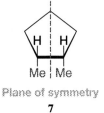

5.14 STEREOISOMERISM OF CYCLIC COMPOUNDS

Cyclopentane derivatives offer a convenient starting point for a discussion of the stereo-isomerism of cyclic compounds. For example, 1,2-dimethylcyclopentane has two chirality centers and exists in three stereoisomeric forms **5**, **6**, and **7**:

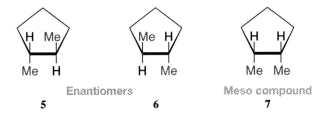

The trans compound exists as a pair of enantiomers **5** and **6**. *cis*-1,2-Dimethylcyclopentane (**7**) is a meso compound. It has a plane of symmetry that is perpendicular to the plane of the ring:

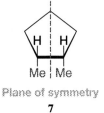

Plane of symmetry

7

●●●

PRACTICE PROBLEM 5.27

(a) Is *trans*-1,2-dimethylcyclopentane (**5**) superposable on its mirror image (i.e., on compound **6**)? **(b)** Is *cis*-1,2-dimethylcyclopentane (**7**) superposable on its mirror image? **(c)** Is *cis*-1,2-dimethylcyclopentane a chiral molecule? **(d)** Would *cis*-1,2-dimethylcyclo-pentane show optical activity? **(e)** What is the stereoisomeric relationship between **5** and **7**? **(f)** Between **6** and **7**?

●●●

PRACTICE PROBLEM 5.28

Write structural formulas for all of the stereoisomers of 1,3-dimethylcyclopentane. Label pairs of enantiomers and meso compounds if they exist.

5.14A Cyclohexane Derivatives

1,4-Dimethylcyclohexanes If we examine a formula of 1,4-dimethylcyclohexane, we find that it does not contain any chirality centers. However, it does have two **stereogenic centers**. As we learned in Section 4.13, 1,4-dimethylcyclohexane can exist as cis–trans isomers. The cis and trans forms (Fig. 5.17) are *diastereomers*. Neither compound is chi-ral and, therefore, neither is optically active. Notice that both the cis and trans forms of 1,4-dimethylcyclohexane have a plane of symmetry.

Helpful Hint

Build handheld molecular models of the 1,4-, 1,3-, and 1,2-dimethylcyclohexane isomers discussed here and examine their stereochemical properties. Experiment with flipping the chairs and also switching between cis and trans isomers.

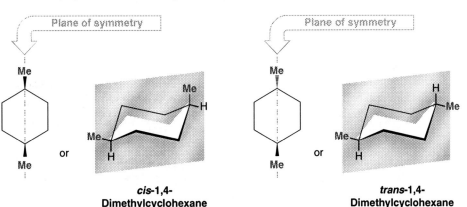

cis-1,4-Dimethylcyclohexane

trans-1,4-Dimethylcyclohexane

FIGURE 5.17 The cis and trans forms of 1,4-dimethylcyclohexane are diastereomers of each other. Both compounds are achiral, as the internal plane of symmetry (blue) shows for each.

1,3-Dimethylcyclohexanes 1,3-Dimethylcyclohexane has two chirality centers; we can, therefore, expect as many as four stereoisomers ($2^2 = 4$). In reality there are only three. *cis*-1,3-Dimethylcyclohexane has a plane of symmetry (Fig. 5.18) and is achiral.

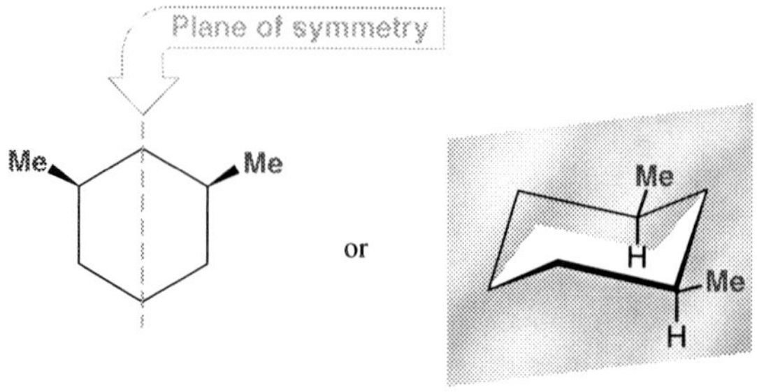

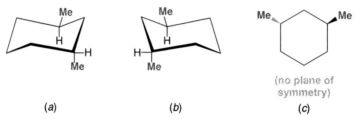

FIGURE 5.18 *cis*-1,3-Dimethylcyclohexane has a plane of symmetry, shown in blue, and is therefore achiral.

trans-1,3-Dimethylcyclohexane does not have a plane of symmetry and exists as a pair of enantiomers (Fig. 5.19). You may want to make models of the *trans*-1,3-dimethylcyclohexane enantiomers. Having done so, convince yourself that they cannot be superposed as they stand and that they cannot be superposed after one enantiomer has undergone a ring flip.

(a)   (b)   (c)

FIGURE 5.19 *trans*-1,3-Dimethylcyclohexane does not have a plane of symmetry and exists as a pair of enantiomers. The two structures (*a* and *b*) shown here are not superposable as they stand, and flipping the ring of either structure does not make it superposable on the other. (*c*) A simplified representation of (*b*).

1,2-Dimethylcyclohexanes 1,2-Dimethylcyclohexane also has two chirality centers, and again we might expect as many as four stereoisomers. Indeed there are four, but we find that we can *isolate* only *three* stereoisomers. *trans*-1,2-Dimethylcyclohexane (Fig. 5.20) exists as a pair of enantiomers. Its molecules do not have a plane of symmetry.

FIGURE 5.20 *trans*-1,2-Dimethylcyclohexane has no plane of symmetry and exists as a pair of enantiomers (*a* and *b*). [Notice that we have written the most stable conformations for (*a*) and (*b*). A ring flip of either (*a*) or (*b*) would cause both methyl groups to become axial.]

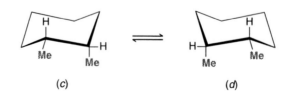

(a)   (b)

cis-1,2-Dimethylcyclohexane, shown in Fig. 5.21, presents a somewhat more complex situation. If we consider the two conformational structures (*c*) and (*d*), we find that these two mirror-image structures are not identical. Neither has a plane of symmetry and each is a chiral molecule, *but they are interconvertible by a ring flip.*

FIGURE 5.21 *cis*-1,2-Dimethylcyclohexane exists as two rapidly interconverting chair conformations (*c*) and (*d*).

(c)   (d)

Therefore, although the two structures represent enantiomers, *they cannot be separated* because they rapidly interconvert even at low temperature. They simply represent *different conformations of the same compound*. Therefore, structures (*c*) and (*d*) are not configurational stereoisomers; they are **conformational stereoisomers** (see Section 4.9A). This means that at normal temperatures there are only three *isolable stereoisomers* of 1,2-dimethylcyclohexane.

As we shall see later, there are some compounds whose conformational stereoisomers *can* be isolated in enantiomeric forms. Isomers of this type are called **atropisomers** (Section 5.18).

Write formulas for all of the isomers of each of the following. Designate pairs of enantiomers and achiral compounds where they exist.

(a) 1-Bromo-2-chlorocyclohexane   **(c)** 1-Bromo-4-chlorocyclohexane

(b) 1-Bromo-3-chlorocyclohexane

PRACTICE PROBLEM 5.29

Give the (*R,S*) designation for each compound given as an answer to Practice Problem 5.29.

PRACTICE PROBLEM 5.30

5.15 RELATING CONFIGURATIONS THROUGH REACTIONS IN WHICH NO BONDS TO THE CHIRALITY CENTER ARE BROKEN

● A reaction is said to proceed with retention of **configuration** at a chirality center if no bonds to the chirality center are broken. This is true even if the *R,S* designation for the chirality center changes because the relative priorities of groups around it changes as a result of the reaction.

First consider an example that occurs with retention of configuration and that also retains the same *R,S* designation in the product as in the reactant. Such is the case when (*S*)-(−)-2-methyl-1-butanol reacts with hydrochloric acid to form (*S*)-(+)-1-chloro-2-methylbutanol. Note that none of the bonds at the chirality center are broken (we shall study how this reaction takes place in Section 11.8A).

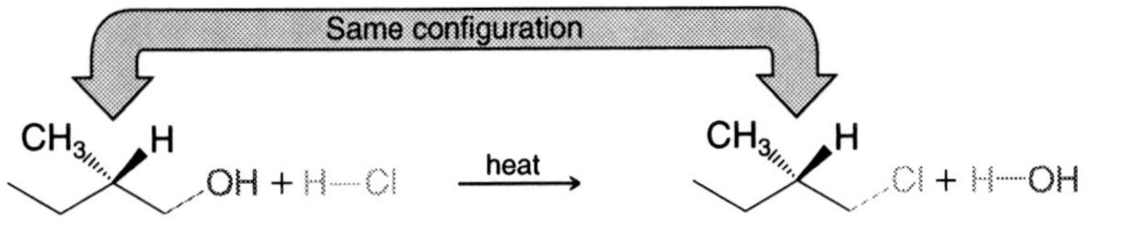

Same configuration

CH_3 H
$\diagdown$ $\diagup$
OH + H—Cl $\xrightarrow{\text{heat}}$ Cl + H—OH

(*S*)-(−)-2-Methyl-1-butanol   (*S*)-(+)-1-Chloro-2-methylbutane
$[\alpha]_D^{25} = -5.756$ $[\alpha]_D^{25} = +1.64$

This example also reminds us that the sign of optical rotation is not directly correlated with the *R,S* configuration of a chirality center, since the sign of rotation changes but the *R,S* configuration does not.

Next consider the reaction of (R)-1-bromo-2-butanol with zinc and acid to form (S)-2-butanol. At this point we do not need to know how this reaction takes place, except to observe that none of the bonds to the chirality center are broken.

H OH
⟍⟋
⟍⟍Br   →Zn, H+ (−ZnBr₂)→   H OH
retention of configuration   ⟍H

(R)-1-Bromo-2-butanol   **(S)-2-Butanol**

This reaction takes place with retention of configuration because no bonds to the chirality center are broken, but the R,S configuration changes because the relative priorities of groups bonded at the chirality center changes due to substitution of hydrogen for bromine.

••• SOLVED PROBLEM 5.8

When (R)-1-bromo-2-butanol reacts with KI in acetone the product is 1-iodo-2-butanol. Would the product be (R) or (S)?

STRATEGY AND ANSWER: No bonds to the chirality center would be broken, so we can reason that the product would be the following.

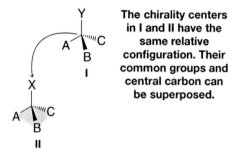

(R)-1-Bromo-2-butanol   **(R)-1-Iodo-2-butanol**

The configuration of the product would still be (R) because replacing the bromine at **C1** with an iodine atom does not change the relative priority of **C1**.

5.15A Relative and Absolute Configurations

Reactions in which no bonds to the chirality center are broken are useful in relating configurations of chiral molecules. That is, they allow us to demonstrate that certain compounds have the same relative configuration. In each of the examples that we have just cited, the products of the reactions have the same *relative configurations* as the reactants.

- Chirality centers in different molecules have the same **relative configuration** if they share three groups in common and if these groups **with** the central carbon can be superposed in a pyramidal arrangement.

Y
|
A⟍⟋C
B
I

X
|
A⟍⟋C
B
II

The chirality centers in I and II have the same relative configuration. Their common groups and central carbon can be superposed.

Before 1951 only relative configurations of chiral molecules were known. No one prior to that time had been able to demonstrate with certainty what the actual spatial arrangement of groups was in any chiral molecule. To say this another way, no one had been able to determine the absolute configuration of an optically active compound.

- The **absolute configuration** of a chirality center is its (R) or (S) designation, which can only be specified by knowledge of the actual arrangement of groups in space at the chirality center.

Prior to any known absolute configurations, the configurations of chiral molecules were related to each other *through reactions of known stereochemistry*. Attempts were also

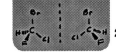

made to relate all configurations to a single compound that had been chosen arbitrarily to be the standard. This standard compound was glyceraldehyde:

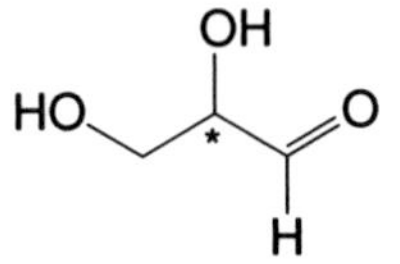

OH

HO $\overset{\ast}{}$ O

H

Glyceraldehyde

Glyceraldehyde has one chirality center; therefore, glyceraldehyde exists as a pair of enantiomers:

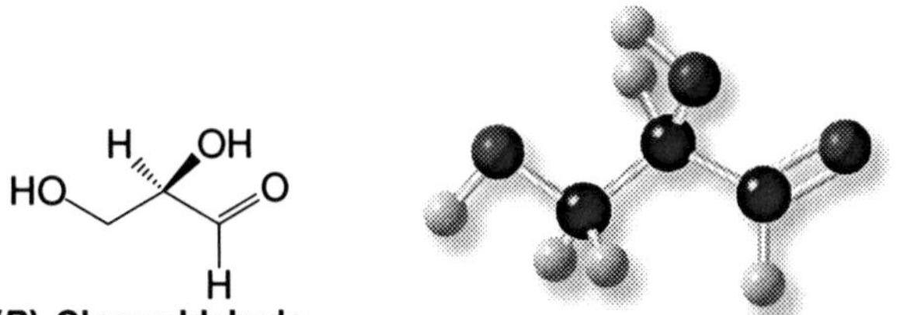

H OH

HO O

H

(R)-Glyceraldehyde

(also known as D-glyceraldehyde)

and

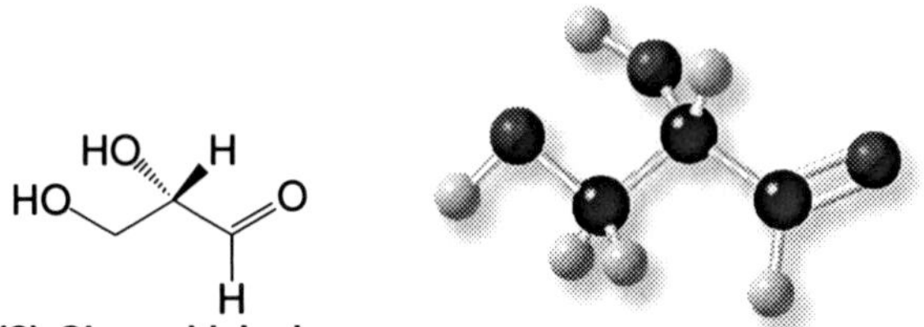

HO H

HO O

H

(S)-Glyceraldehyde

(also known as L-glyceraldehyde)

In one system for designating configurations, (R)-glyceraldehyde is called D-glyceraldehyde and (S)-glyceraldehyde is called L-glyceraldehyde. This system of nomenclature is used with a specialized meaning in the nomenclature of carbohydrates. (See Section 22.2B.)

One glyceraldehyde enantiomer is dextrorotatory (+) and the other, of course, is levorotatory (−). Before 1951 no one was sure, however, which configuration belonged to which enantiomer. Chemists decided arbitrarily to assign the (R) configuration to the (+)-enantiomer. Then, configurations of other molecules were related to one glyceraldehyde enantiomer or the other through reactions of known stereochemistry.

For example, the configuration of (−)-lactic acid can be related to (+)-glyceraldehyde through the following sequence of reactions in which no bond to the chirality center is broken:

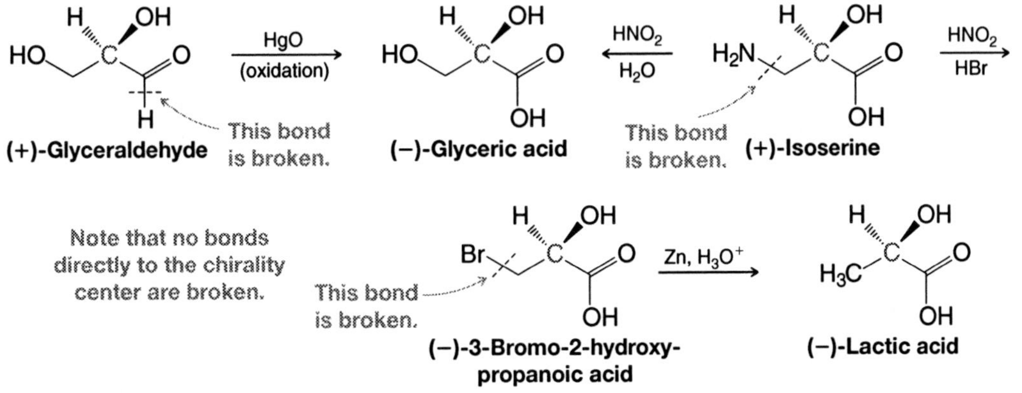

H OH

HO C O

H

This bond is broken.

(+)-Glyceraldehyde

→ HgO (oxidation) →

H OH

HO C O

OH

(−)-Glyceric acid

← HNO₂ / H₂O ←

This bond is broken.

H OH

H₂N C O

OH

(+)-Isoserine

→ HNO₂ / HBr →

Note that no bonds directly to the chirality center are broken.

This bond is broken.

Br C O

H OH

OH

(−)-3-Bromo-2-hydroxy-propanoic acid

→ Zn, H₃O⁺ →

H OH

H₃C C O

OH

(−)-Lactic acid

The stereochemistry of all of these reactions is known. Because none of the bonds to the chirality center (shown in red) has been broken during the sequence, its original configuration is retained. If the assumption is made that (+)-glyceraldehyde is the (R) stereoisomer, and therefore has the following configuration,

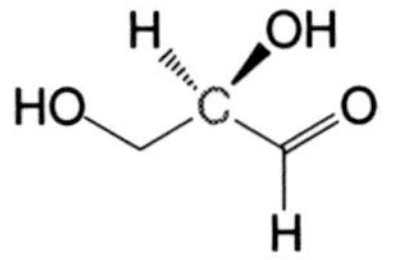

H OH

HO C O

H

(R)-(+)-Glyceraldehyde

then (−)-lactic acid is also an (R) stereoisomer and its configuration is

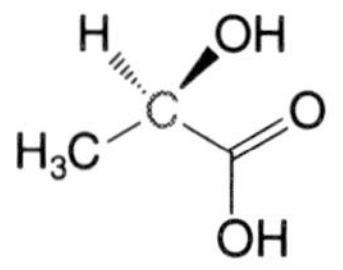

(R)-(−)-Lactic acid

● ● ●

PRACTICE PROBLEM 5.31 Write bond-line three-dimensional formulas for the starting compound, the product, and all of the intermediates in a synthesis similar to the one just given that relates the configuration of (−)-glyceraldehyde with (+)-lactic acid. Label each compound with its proper (R) or (S) and (+) or (−) designation.

The configuration of (−)-glyceraldehyde was also related through reactions of known stereochemistry to (+)-tartaric acid:

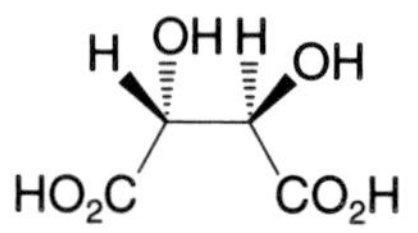

(+)-Tartaric acid

In 1951 J. M. Bijvoet, the director of the van't Hoff Laboratory of the University of Utrecht in the Netherlands, using a special technique of X-ray diffraction, was able to show conclusively that (+)-tartaric acid had the absolute configuration shown above. This meant that the original arbitrary assignment of the configurations of (+)- and (−)-glyceraldehyde was also correct. It also meant that the configurations of all of the compounds that had been related to one glyceraldehyde enantiomer or the other were now known with certainty and were now **absolute configurations**.

● ● ●

PRACTICE PROBLEM 5.32 Fischer projection formulas are often used to depict compounds such as glyceraldehyde, lactic acid, and tartaric acid. Draw Fischer projections for both enantiomers of **(a)** glyceraldehyde, **(b)** tartaric acid, and **(c)** lactic acid, and specify the (R) or (S) configuration at each chirality center. [Note that in Fischer projection formulas the terminal carbon that is most highly oxidized is placed at the top of the formula (an aldehyde or carboxylic acid group in the specific examples here).]

● ● ● **SOLVED PROBLEM 5.9**

Write a Fischer projection formula for a tartaric acid isomer that is not chiral.

STRATEGY AND ANSWER: We reason that because tartaric acid has two chirality centers, the achiral isomer must have a plane of symmetry and be a meso compound.

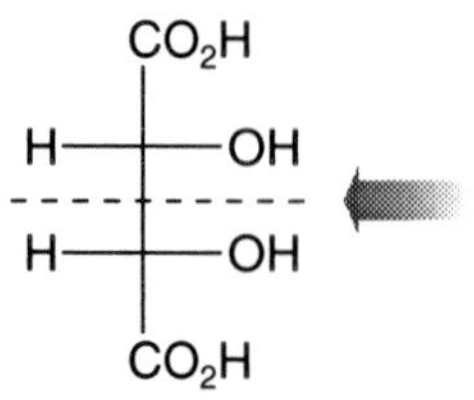

meso-Tartaric acid
(achiral)

5.16 SEPARATION OF ENANTIOMERS: RESOLUTION

So far we have left unanswered an important question about optically active compounds and racemic forms: How are enantiomers separated? Enantiomers have identical solubilities in ordinary solvents, and they have identical boiling points. Consequently, the conventional methods for separating organic compounds, such as crystallization and distillation, fail when applied to a racemic form.

5.16A Pasteur's Method for Separating Enantiomers

It was, in fact, Louis Pasteur's separation of a racemic form of a salt of tartaric acid in 1848 that led to the discovery of the phenomenon called enantiomerism. Pasteur, consequently, is often considered to be the founder of the field of stereochemistry.

(+)-Tartaric acid is one of the by-products of wine making (nature usually only synthesizes one enantiomer of a chiral molecule). Pasteur had obtained a sample of racemic tartaric acid from the owner of a chemical plant. In the course of his investigation Pasteur began examining the crystal structure of the sodium ammonium salt of racemic tartaric acid. He noticed that two types of crystals were present. One was identical with crystals of the sodium ammonium salt of (+)-tartaric acid that had been discovered earlier and had been shown to be dextrorotatory. Crystals of the other type were *non*superposable mirror images of the first kind. The two types of crystals were actually chiral. Using tweezers and a magnifying glass, Pasteur separated the two kinds of crystals, dissolved them in water, and placed the solutions in a polarimeter. The solution of crystals of the first type was dextrorotatory, and the crystals themselves proved to be identical with the sodium ammonium salt of (+)-tartaric acid that was already known. The solution of crystals of the second type was levorotatory; it rotated plane-polarized light in the opposite direction and by an equal amount. The crystals of the second type were of the sodium ammonium salt of (−)-tartaric acid. The chirality of the crystals themselves disappeared, of course, as the crystals dissolved into their solutions, *but the optical activity* remained. Pasteur reasoned, therefore, that the molecules themselves must be chiral.

Pasteur's discovery of enantiomerism and his demonstration that the optical activity of the two forms of tartaric acid was a property of the molecules themselves led, in 1874, to the proposal of the tetrahedral structure of carbon by van't Hoff and Le Bel.

Unfortunately, few organic compounds give chiral crystals as do the (+)- and (−)-tartaric acid salts. Few organic compounds crystallize into separate crystals (containing separate enantiomers) that are visibly chiral like the crystals of the sodium ammonium salt of tartaric acid. Pasteur's method, therefore, is not generally applicable to the separation of enantiomers.

Tartaric acid crystals.

Sinclair Stammers/Photo Researchers, Inc.

5.16B Modern Methods for Resolution of Enantiomers

One of the most useful procedures for separating enantiomers is based on the following:

- When a racemic mixture reacts with a single enantiomer of another compound, a mixture of diastereomers results, and diastereomers, because they have different melting points, boiling points, and solubilities, can be separated by conventional means.

Diastereomeric recrystallization is one such process. We shall see how this is done in Section 20.3F. Another method is **resolution** by enzymes, whereby an enzyme selectively converts one enantiomer in a racemic mixture to another compound, after which the unreacted enantiomer and the new compound are separated. The reaction by lipase in Section 5.10B is an example of this type of resolution. Chromatography using chiral media is also widely used to resolve enantiomers. This approach is applied in high-performance liquid chromatography (HPLC) as well as in other forms of chromatography. Diastereomeric interactions between molecules of the racemic mixture and the chiral chromatography medium cause enantiomers of the racemate to move through the chromatography apparatus at different rates. The enantiomers are then collected separately as they elute from the chromatography device. (See "*The Chemistry of . . .* HPLC Resolution of Enantiomers," Section 20.3.)

5.17 COMPOUNDS WITH CHIRALITY CENTERS OTHER THAN CARBON

Any tetrahedral atom with four different groups attached to it is a **chirality center**. Shown here are general formulas of compounds whose molecules contain chirality centers other than carbon. Silicon and germanium are in the same group of the periodic table as carbon. They form tetrahedral compounds as carbon does. When four different groups are situated around the central atom in silicon, germanium, and nitrogen compounds, the molecules are chiral and the enantiomers can, in principle, be separated. Sulfoxides, like certain examples of other functional groups where one of the four groups is a nonbonding electron pair, are also chiral. This is not the case for amines, however (Section 20.2B):

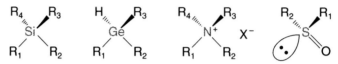

5.18 CHIRAL MOLECULES THAT DO NOT POSSESS A CHIRALITY CENTER

A molecule is chiral if it is not superposable on its mirror image. The presence of a tetrahedral atom with four different groups is only one type of chirality center, however. While most of the chiral molecules we shall encounter have chirality centers, there are other structural attributes that can confer chirality on a molecule. For example, there are compounds that have such large rotational barriers between conformers that individual conformational isomers can be separated and purified, and some of these conformational isomers are stereoisomers.

Conformational isomers that are stable, isolable compounds are called **atropisomers**. The existence of chiral atropisomers has been exploited to great effect in the development of chiral catalysts for stereoselective reactions. An example is BINAP, shown below in its enantiomeric forms:

(S)-BINAP   **(R)-BINAP**

The origin of chirality in BINAP is the restricted rotation about the bond between the two nearly perpendicular naphthalene rings. This torsional barrier leads to two resolvable enantiomeric conformers, (S)- and (R)-BINAP. When each enantiomer is used as a ligand for metals such as ruthenium and rhodium (bound by unshared electron pairs on the phosphorus atoms), chiral organometallic complexes result that are capable of catalyzing stereoselective hydrogenation and other important industrial reactions. The significance of chiral ligands is highlighted by the industrial synthesis each year of approximately 3500 *tons* of (−)-menthol using an isomerization reaction involving a rhodium (S)-BINAP catalyst.

Allenes are compounds that also exhibit stereoisomerism. Allenes are molecules that contain the following double-bond sequence:

The planes of the π bonds of allenes are perpendicular to each other:

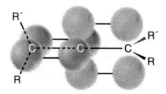

This geometry of the π bonds causes the groups attached to the end carbon atoms to lie in perpendicular planes, and, because of this, allenes with different substituents on the end carbon atoms are chiral (Fig. 5.22). (Allenes do not show cis–trans isomerism.)

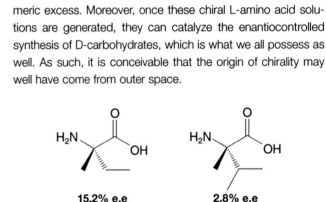

Mirror

FIGURE 5.22 Enantiomeric forms of 1,3-dichloroallene. These two molecules are nonsuperposable mirror images of each other and are therefore chiral. They do not possess a tetrahedral atom with four different groups, however.

[WHY Do These Topics Matter?

THE POTENTIAL ORIGIN OF CHIRALITY

In the opening chapter of the book, we described the ground-breaking 1952 experiment by two chemists at the University of Chicago, Harold Urey and Stanley Miller, who showed how many of the amino acids found in living things were made spontaneously under simple, primordial-like conditions with simple chemicals. What we did not mention, however, was the proof that these amino acids had actually been synthesized during the experiment and were not the product of some contaminant within the apparatus itself. Urey and Miler's proof was that all of the amino acids were produced as racemates. As this chapter has shown, any amino acid produced by a life form on Earth exists as a single enantiomer. The question we are left with, then, is why do the molecules of life (such as amino acids) exist as single enantiomers? In other words, what is the origin of chirality on our planet? Potential answers to this question are more recent in origin, though it is a question that has interested scientists for well over a century.

In 1969, a large meteorite landed near the town of Murchison, Australia. Chemical analysis of its organic molecules showed it possessed over 100 amino acids, including dozens not found on Earth. Some of the amino acids possessed enantiomeric excess (e.e.) to the extent of 2–15%, all in favor of the L-amino acids, the same enantiomers found in all of

Earth's life forms. Careful analytical work proved that this optical activity was not the result of some Earth-based contaminant. In the past decade experiments have shown that with only the small amount of enantiomeric excess that these amino acids possess, some of them, such as the two shown below which have a fully substituted chirality center and cannot racemize, can effect a resolution of racemic amino acids through relatively simple processes such as crystallization. These events leave behind aqueous solutions of L-amino acids in high enantiomeric excess. Moreover, once these chiral L-amino acid solutions are generated, they can catalyze the enantiocontrolled synthesis of D-carbohydrates, which is what we all possess as well. As such, it is conceivable that the origin of chirality may well have come from outer space.

15.2% e.e   **2.8% e.e**

But what generated that initial enantiomeric excess? No one is quite sure, but some scientists speculate that electromagnetic radiation emitted in a corkscrew fashion from the poles of spinning neutron stars could lead to the bias of one mirror-image isomer over another when those molecules were formed in interstellar space. If that is true, then it is possible that on the other side of the galaxy there is a world that is the chiral opposite of Earth, where there are life forms with D-amino acids and L-sugars. Ronald Breslow of Columbia University, a leading researcher in this area, has said of such a possibility: "Since such life forms could well be advanced versions of dinosaurs, assuming that mammals did not have the good fortune to have the dinosaurs wiped out by an asteroidal collision as on earth, we may be better off not finding out."

Argonne National Laboratory/Photo Researchers, Inc.

To learn more about these topics, see:
Breslow, R. "The origin of homochirality in amino acids and sugars on prebiotic earth" *Tetrahedron Lett.* **2011**, *52*, 2028–2032 and references therein.

SUMMARY AND REVIEW TOOLS

In this chapter you learned that the handedness of life begins at the molecular level. Molecular recognition, signaling, and chemical reactions in living systems often hinge on the handedness of chiral molecules. Molecules that bear four different groups at a tetrahedral carbon atom are chiral if they are nonsuperposable with their mirror image. The atoms bearing four different groups are called chirality centers.

Mirror planes of symmetry have been very important to our discussion. If we want to draw the enantiomer of a molecule, one way to do so is to draw the molecule as if it were reflected in a mirror. If a mirror plane of symmetry exists *within* a molecule, then it is achiral (not chiral), even if it contains chirality centers. Using mirror planes to test for symmetry is an important technique.

In this chapter you learned how to give unique names to chiral molecules using the Cahn–Ingold–Prelog *R,S* system. You have also exercised your mind's eye in visualizing molecular structures in three dimensions, and you have refined your skill at drawing three-dimensional molecular formulas. You learned that pairs of enantiomers have identical physical properties except for the equal and opposite rotation of plane-polarized light, whereas diastereomers have different physical properties from one another. Interactions between each enantiomer of a chiral molecule and any other chiral material lead to diastereomeric interactions, which lead to different physical properties that can allow the separation of enantiomers.

Chemistry happens in three dimensions. Now, with the information from this chapter building on fundamentals you have learned about molecular shape and polarity in earlier chapters, you are ready to embark on your study of the reactions of organic molecules. Use the Key Terms and Concepts (which are hyperlinked to the Glossary from the bold, blue terms in the *WileyPLUS* version of the book at wileyplus.com) and the Concept Map that follows to help you reveiw and see the relationships between topics. Practice drawing molecules that show three dimensions at chirality centers, practice naming molecules, and label their regions of partial positive and negative charge. Paying attention to these things will help you learn about the reactivity of molecules in succeeding chapters. Most important of all, do your homework!

PROBLEMS PLUS

Note to Instructors: Many of the homework problems are available for assignment via *WileyPLUS*, an online teaching and learning solution.

CHIRALITY AND STEREOISOMERISM

5.33 Which of the following are chiral and, therefore, capable of existing as enantiomers?

(a) 1,3-Dichlorobutane

(b) 1,2-Dibromopropane

(c) 1,5-Dichloropentane

(d) 3-Ethylpentane

(e) 2-Bromobicyclo[1.1.0]butane

(f) 2-Fluorobicyclo[2.2.2]octane

(g) 2-Chlorobicyclo[2.1.1]hexane

(h) 5-Chlorobicyclo[2.1.1]hexane

5.34 **(a)** How many carbon atoms does an alkane (not a cycloalkane) need before it is capable of existing in enantiomeric forms? **(b)** Give correct names for two sets of enantiomers with this minimum number of carbon atoms.

5.35 Designate the (*R*) or (*S*) configuration at each chirality center in the following molecules.

5.36 Albuterol, shown here, is a commonly prescribed asthma medication. For either enantiomer of albuterol, draw a three-dimensional formula using dashes and wedges for bonds that are not in the plane of the paper. Choose a perspective that allows as many carbon atoms as possible to be in the plane of the paper, and show all unshared electron pairs and hydrogen atoms (except those on the methyl groups labeled Me). Specify the (*R,S*) configuration of the enantiomer you drew.

Albuterol

5.37 **(a)** Write the structure of 2,2-dichlorobicyclo[2.2.1]heptane. **(b)** How many chirality centers does it contain? **(c)** How many stereoisomers are predicted by the 2^n rule? **(d)** Only one pair of enantiomers is possible for 2,2-dichlorobicyclo[2.2.1]heptane. Explain.

5.38 Shown below are Newman projection formulas for (R,R)-, (S,S)-, and (R,S)-2,3-dichlorobutane. **(a)** Which is which? **(b)** Which formula is a meso compound?

5.39 Write appropriate structural formulas for **(a)** a cyclic molecule that is a constitutional isomer of cyclohexane, **(b)** molecules with the formula C_6H_{12} that contain one ring and that are enantiomers of each other, **(c)** molecules with the formula C_6H_{12} that contain one ring and that are diastereomers of each other, **(d)** molecules with the formula C_6H_{12} that contain no ring and that are enantiomers of each other, and **(e)** molecules with the formula C_6H_{12} that contain no ring and that are diastereomers of each other.

5.40 Consider the following pairs of structures. Designate each chirality center as (R) or (S) and identify the relationship between them by describing them as representing enantiomers, diastereomers, constitutional isomers, or two molecules of the same compound. Use handheld molecular models to check your answers.

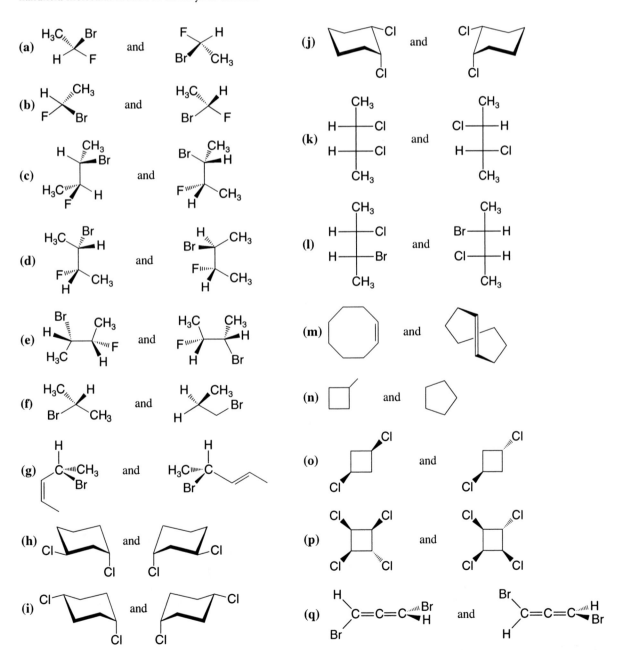

5.41 Discuss the anticipated stereochemistry of each of the following compounds.
(a) $ClCH{=}C{=}C{=}CHCl$ (b) $CH_2{=}C{=}C{=}CHCl$ (c) $ClCH{=}C{=}C{=}CCl_2$

5.42 Tell whether the compounds of each pair are enantiomers, diastereomers, constitutional isomers, or not isomeric.

(a)

(b)

(c)

(d)

5.43 A compound **D** with the molecular formula C_6H_{12} is optically inactive but can be resolved into enantiomers. On catalytic hydrogenation, **D** is converted to **E** (C_6H_{14}) and **E** is optically inactive. Propose structures for **D** and **E**.

5.44 Compound **F** has the molecular formula C_5H_8 and is optically active. On catalytic hydrogenation **F** yields **G** (C_5H_{12}) and **G** is optically inactive. Propose structures for **F** and **G**.

5.45 Compound **H** is optically active and has the molecular formula C_6H_{10}. On catalytic hydrogenation **H** is converted to **I** (C_6H_{12}) and **I** is optically inactive. Propose structures for **H** and **I**.

5.46 Aspartame is an artificial sweetener. Give the (R,S) designation for each chirality center of aspartame.

Aspartame

5.47 There are four dimethylcyclopropane isomers. (a) Write three-dimensional formulas for these isomers. (b) Which of the isomers are chiral? (c) If a mixture consisting of 1 mol of each of these isomers were subjected to simple gas chromatography (an analytical method that can separate compounds according to boiling point), how many fractions would be obtained and which compounds would each fraction contain? (d) How many of these fractions would be optically active?

5.48 For the following molecule, draw its enantiomer as well as one of its diastereomers. Designate the (R) or (S) configuration at each chirality center.

5.49 (Use models to solve this problem.) (a) Write a conformational structure for the most stable conformation of *trans*-1,2-diethyl-cyclohexane and write its mirror image. (b) Are these two molecules superposable? (c) Are they interconvertible through a ring "flip"? (d) Repeat the process in part (a) with *cis*-1,2-diethylcyclohexane. (e) Are these structures superposable? (f) Are they interconvertible?

5.50 (Use models to solve this problem.) (a) Write a conformational structure for the most stable conformation of *trans*-1,4-diethylcyclohexane and for its mirror image. (b) Are these structures superposable? (c) Do they represent enantiomers? (d) Does *trans*-1,4-diethylcyclohexane have a stereoisomer, and if so, what is it? (e) Is this stereoisomer chiral?

5.51 (Use models to solve this problem.) Write conformational structures for all of the stereoisomers of 1,3-diethylcyclohexane. Label pairs of enantiomers and meso compounds if they exist.

CHALLENGE PROBLEMS

5.52 Tartaric acid [$HO_2CCH(OH)CH(OH)CO_2H$] was an important compound in the history of stereochemistry. Two naturally occurring forms of tartaric acid are optically inactive. One optically inactive form has a melting point of 210–212 °C, the other a melting point of 140 °C. The inactive tartaric acid with a melting point of 210–212 °C can be separated into two optically active forms of tartaric acid with the same melting point (168–170 °C). One optically active tartaric acid has $[\alpha]_D^{25} = +12$, and the other, $[\alpha]_D^{25} = -12$. All attempts to separate the other inactive tartaric acid (melting point 140 °C) into optically active compounds fail. **(a)** Write the three-dimensional structure of the tartaric acid with melting point 140 °C. **(b)** Write structures for the optically active tartaric acids with melting points of 168–170 °C. **(c)** Can you determine from the formulas which tartaric acid in (b) has a positive rotation and which has a negative rotation? **(d)** What is the nature of the form of tartaric acid with a melting point of 210–212 °C?

5.53 (a) An aqueous solution of pure stereoisomer X of concentration 0.10 g mL^{-1} had an observed rotation of $-30°$ in a 1.0-dm tube at 589.6 nm (the sodium D line) and 25 °C. What do you calculate its $[\alpha]_D$ to be at this temperature?

(b) Under identical conditions but with concentration 0.050 g mL^{-1}, a solution of X had an observed rotation of $+165°$. Rationalize how this could be and recalculate $[\alpha]_D$ for stereoisomer X.

(c) If the optical rotation of a substance studied at only one concentration is zero, can it definitely be concluded to be achiral? Racemic?

5.54 If a sample of a pure substance that has two or more chirality centers has an observed rotation of zero, it could be a racemate. Could it possibly be a pure stereoisomer? Could it possibly be a pure enantiomer?

5.55 Unknown Y has a molecular formula of $C_3H_6O_2$. It contains one functional group that absorbs infrared radiation in the 3200–3550-cm^{-1} region (when studied as a pure liquid; i.e., "neat"), and it has no absorption in the 1620–1780-cm^{-1} region. No carbon atom in the structure of Y has more than one oxygen atom bonded to it, and Y can exist in two (and only two) stereoisomeric forms. What are the structures of these forms of Y?

LEARNING GROUP PROBLEMS

1. Streptomycin is an antibiotic that is especially useful against penicillin-resistant bacteria. The structure of streptomycin is shown in Section 22.17. **(a)** Identify all of the chirality centers in the structure of streptomycin. **(b)** Assign the appropriate (R) or (S) designation for the configuration of each chirality center in streptomycin.

2. D-Galactitol is one of the toxic compounds produced by the disease galactosemia. Accumulation of high levels of D-galactitol causes the formation of cataracts. A Fischer projection for D-galactitol is shown at right:

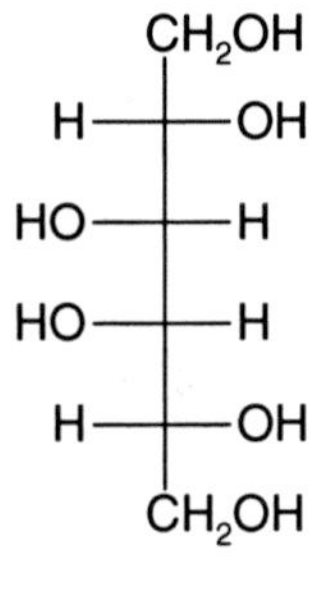

(a) Draw a three-dimensional structure for D-galactitol.

(b) Draw the mirror image of D-galactitol and write its Fischer projection formula.

(c) What is the stereochemical relationship between D-galactitol and its mirror image?

3. Cortisone is a natural steroid that can be isolated from the adrenal cortex. It has anti-inflammatory properties and is used to treat a variety of disorders (e.g., as a topical application for common skin diseases). The structure of cortisone is shown in Section 23.4D. **(a)** Identify all of the chirality centers in cortisone. **(b)** Assign the appropriate (R) or (S) designation for the configuration of each chirality center in cortisone.

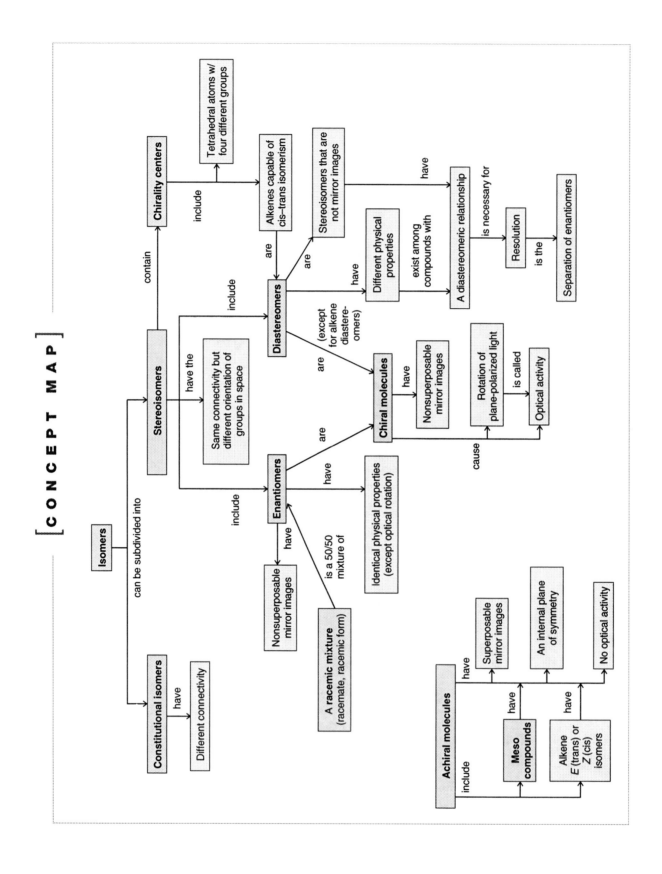

CHAPTER

6

Ionic Reactions

NUCLEOPHILIC SUBSTITUTION AND
ELIMINATION REACTIONS OF ALKYL HALIDES

Not all substitutions are a good thing; for instance, we wouldn't want to accidentally use salt in place of the needed amount of sugar in a batch of chocolate chip cookies. But with some substitutions, we get something even better. In organic chemistry that is often the case, since nucleophilic substitution reactions (which we will learn about in this chapter) allow the conversion of functional groups within a given molecule into entirely different functional groups, leading to new compounds with distinct properties. Moreover, nature utilizes a number of specific substitution reactions that are required for life.

IN THIS CHAPTER WE WILL CONSIDER:

- what groups can be replaced (i.e., substituted) or eliminated
- the various mechanisms by which such processes occur
- the conditions that can promote such reactions

[WHY DO THESE TOPICS MATTER?] At the end of the chapter, we will show an example where just a few substitution reactions can convert table sugar into a sweetener that has no calories—a sugar substitute that is not salty, but is in fact 600 times sweeter than sugar itself!

PHOTO CREDIT: (sugar bowl) Sylvie Shirazi Photography/Getty Images (salt pouring) Tom Grill/Getty Images (sugar pouring) Tom Grill/Getty Images

239

6.1 ALKYL HALIDES

- An **alkyl halide** has a halogen atom bonded to an sp^3-hybridized (tetrahedral) carbon atom.

- The carbon–halogen bond in an alkyl halide is polarized because the halogen is more electronegative than carbon. Therefore, the carbon atom has a partial positive charge ($\delta+$) and the halogen has a partial negative charge ($\delta-$).

$$\overset{\delta+}{\text{C}}\longrightarrow\overset{\delta-}{\text{X}}$$

- Alkyl halides are classified as primary (1°), secondary (2°), or tertiary (3°) according to the number of carbon groups (R) directly bonded to the carbon bearing the halogen atom (Section 2.5).

H	R	R
|	|	|
R—C—X	R′—C—X	R′—C—X
|	|	|
H	H	R″
Primary (1°)	**Secondary (2°)**	**Tertiary (3°)**

Halogen atom size increases as we go down the periodic table: fluorine atoms are the smallest and iodine atoms the largest. Consequently, the carbon–halogen *bond length increases* and carbon–halogen *bond strength decreases* as we go down the periodic table (Table 6.1). Maps of electrostatic potential (see Table 6.1) at the van der Waals surface for the four methyl halides, with ball-and-stick models inside, illustrate the trend in polarity, C—X bond length, and halogen atom size as one progresses from fluorine to iodine substitution. Fluoromethane is highly polar and has the shortest C—X bond length and the strongest C—X bond. Iodomethane is much less polar and has the longest C—X bond length and the weakest C—X bond.

In the laboratory and in industry, alkyl halides are used as solvents for relatively nonpolar compounds, and they are used as the starting materials for the synthesis of many compounds. As we shall learn in this chapter, the halogen atom of an alkyl halide can be easily replaced by other groups, and the presence of a halogen atom on a carbon chain also affords us the possibility of introducing a multiple bond.

Compounds in which a halogen atom is bonded to an alkene carbon are called **alkenyl halides**. In older nomenclature these were called vinylic halides. Compounds having a halogen bonded to an aromatic ring are called **aryl halides**. When the aromatic

---

TABLE 6.1 CARBON–HALOGEN BOND LENGTHS AND BOND STRENGTHS

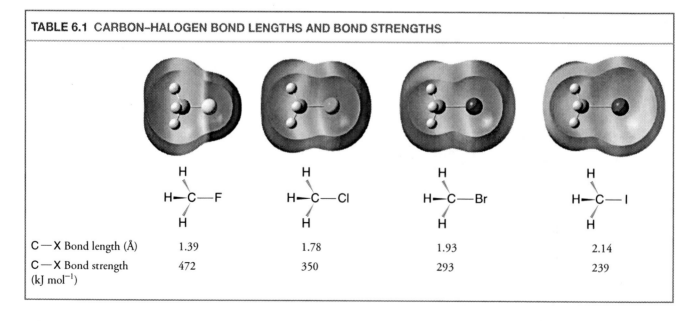

	H | H—C—F | H	H | H—C—Cl | H	H | H—C—Br | H	H | H—C—I | H
C—X Bond length (Å)	1.39	1.78	1.93	2.14
C—X Bond strength (kJ mol⁻¹)	472	350	293	239

ring is specifically a benzene ring these compounds are called phenyl halides. The reactivity of compounds in which a halogen is bonded to an sp^2 carbon, as in alkenyl, aryl, and phenyl halides, is markedly different than when a halogen is bonded to an sp^3 carbon, as in an alkyl halide. The reactions that we discuss in this chapter will pertain to alkyl halides, not alkenyl, aryl, or phenyl halides.

An alkenyl halide   A phenyl halide or aryl halide

6.1A Physical Properties of Alkyl Halides

Most alkyl halides have very low solubilities in water, but as we might expect, they are miscible with each other and with other relatively nonpolar solvents. Dichloromethane (CH_2Cl_2, also called *methylene chloride*), trichloromethane ($CHCl_3$, also called *chloroform*), and tetrachloromethane (CCl_4, also called *carbon tetrachloride*) are sometimes used as solvents for nonpolar and moderately polar compounds. Many chloroalkanes, including CH_2Cl_2, $CHCl_3$, and CCl_4, have cumulative toxicity and are carcinogenic, however, and should therefore be used only in fume hoods and with great care.

Dichloromethane (CH_2Cl_2), a common laboratory solvent

PRACTICE PROBLEM 6.1

Give IUPAC names for each of the following.

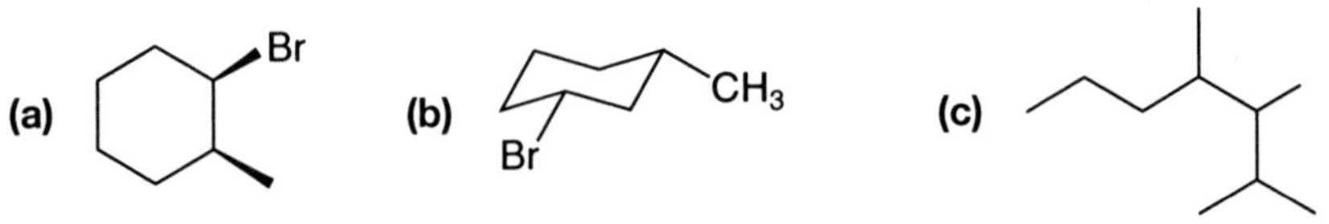

(a)   (b)   (c)

PRACTICE PROBLEM 6.2

Classify each of the following organic halides as primary, secondary, tertiary, alkenyl, or aryl.

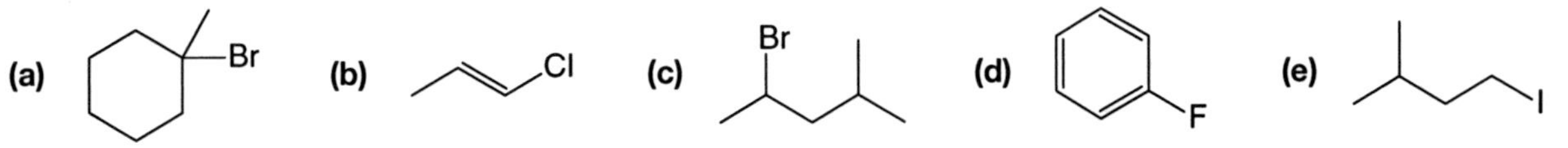

(a)   (b)   (c)   (d)   (e)

6.2 NUCLEOPHILIC SUBSTITUTION REACTIONS

Nucleophilic substitution reactions are among the most fundamental types of organic reactions. In a **nucleophilic substitution reaction** a nucleophile (Nu:) displaces a leaving group (LG) in the molecule that undergoes the substitution (the substrate).

- The **nucleophile** is always a Lewis base, and it may be negatively charged or neutral.
- The **leaving group** is always a species that takes a pair of electrons with it when it departs.

Often the **substrate** is an alkyl halide (R—$\ddot{X}$:) and the leaving group is a halide anion (:$\ddot{X}$:$^-$). The following equations include a generic nucleophilic substitution reaction and some specific examples.

$$Nu:^- \quad + \quad R\text{---}LG \quad \longrightarrow \quad R\text{---}Nu \quad + \quad {}^-LG$$

| The nucleophile is a Lewis base that donates an electron pair to the substrate. | The bond between the carbon and the leaving group breaks, giving both electrons from the bond to the leaving group. | The nucleophile uses its electron pair to form a new covalent bond with the substrate carbon. | The leaving group gains the pair of electrons that originally bonded it in the substrate. |

Helpful Hint

In color-coded reactions of this chapter, we will use red to indicate a nucleophile and blue to indicate a leaving group.

$$HÖ^- \quad + \quad CH_3\text{---}\ddot{I} \quad \longrightarrow \quad CH_3\text{---}\ddot{O}H \quad + \quad \ddot{I}^-$$

$$CH_3\ddot{O}:^- \quad + \quad CH_3CH_2\text{---}\ddot{B}r: \quad \longrightarrow \quad CH_3CH_2\text{---}\ddot{O}CH_3 \quad + \quad :\ddot{B}r:^-$$

Helpful Hint

In Section 6.14 we shall see examples of biological nucleophilic substitution.

$$:\ddot{I}:^- \quad + \quad \diagdown\diagup{}^{\ddot{C}l:} \quad \longrightarrow \quad \diagdown\diagup{}^{\ddot{I}:} \quad + \quad :\ddot{C}l:^-$$

$$\begin{array}{c} R \\ | \\ R\text{---}\ddot{N}: \\ | \\ R \end{array} \quad + \quad H_3C\text{---}\ddot{I}: \quad \longrightarrow \quad \begin{array}{c} R \\ | \\ R\text{---}\overset{+}{N}\text{---}CH_3 \\ | \\ R \end{array} \quad + \quad \ddot{I}:^-$$

In nucleophilic substitution reactions the bond between the substrate carbon and the leaving group undergoes *heterolytic* bond cleavage. The unshared electron pair of the nucleophile forms the new bond to the carbon atom.

A key question we shall want to address later in this chapter is this: when does the bond between the leaving group and the carbon break? Does it break at the same time that the new bond between the nucleophile and carbon forms, as shown below?

$$Nu:^- \quad + \quad R\text{---}\ddot{X}: \quad \longrightarrow \quad Nu\text{---}\,\text{-}\,\text{-}R\text{---}\,\text{-}\,\ddot{X}: \quad \longrightarrow \quad Nu\text{---}R \quad + \quad :\ddot{X}:$$

Or, does the bond to the leaving group break first?

$$R\text{---}\ddot{X}: \quad \longrightarrow \quad R^+ \quad + \quad :\ddot{X}:$$

Followed by

$$Nu:^- \quad + \quad R^+ \quad \longrightarrow \quad Nu\text{---}R$$

We shall find in Sections 6.9 and 6.14A that the answer depends greatly on the structure of the substrate.

●●● SOLVED PROBLEM 6.1

(a) A solution containing methoxide ions, CH_3O^- ions (as $NaOCH_3$), in methanol can be prepared by adding sodium hydride (NaH) to methanol (CH_3OH). A flammable gas is the other product. Write the acid–base reaction that takes place.
(b) Write the nucleophilic substitution that takes place when CH_3I is added and the resulting solution is heated.

STRATEGY AND ANSWER:

(a) We recall from Section 3.15 that sodium hydride consists of Na^+ ions and hydride ions ($H:^-$ ions), and that the hydride ion is a very strong base. [It is the conjugate base of H_2, a very weak acid ($pK_a = 35$, see Table 3.1).] The acid–base reaction that takes place is

$$CH_3\ddot{O}\text{---}H \quad + \quad Na^+:H^- \quad \longrightarrow \quad H_3C\text{---}\ddot{O}:^- \; Na^+ \quad + \quad H:H$$

| Methanol (stronger acid) | Sodium hydride (stronger base) | Sodium methoxide (weaker base) | Hydrogen (weaker acid) |

(b) The methoxide ion reacts with the alkyl halide (CH_3I) in a nucleophilic substitution:

$$CH_3\text{---}\ddot{O}:^- \; Na^+ \quad + \quad CH_3\text{---}\ddot{I}: \quad \xrightarrow{CH_3OH} \quad H_3C\text{---}\ddot{O}\text{---}CH_3 \quad + \quad Na^+ \quad + \quad :\ddot{I}:^-$$

6.3 NUCLEOPHILES

A nucleophile is a reagent that seeks a positive center.

- Any negative ion or uncharged molecule with an unshared electron pair is a potential nucleophile.

When a nucleophile reacts with an alkyl halide, the carbon atom bearing the halogen atom is the positive center that attracts the nucleophile. This carbon carries a partial positive charge because the electronegative halogen pulls the electrons of the carbon–halogen bond in its direction.

Helpful Hint

You may wish to review Section 3.3A, "Opposite Charges Attract."

This is the positive center that the nucleophile seeks.

The electronegative halogen polarizes the C—X bond.

Let us look at two examples, one in which the nucleophile is a negatively charged Lewis base, and one in which the nucleophile is a neutral Lewis base.

1. Use of a **negatively charged nucleophile** (hydroxide in this case) **results in a neutral product** (an alcohol in this case). Formation of the covalent bond between the negative nucleophile and the substrate neutralizes the formal charge of the nucleophile.

Nucleophilic Substitution by a Negatively Charged Nucleophile Results Directly in a Neutral Product

$$ H\!-\!\ddot{O}\!:^{-} \quad + \quad R\!-\!\ddot{X}\!: \quad \longrightarrow \quad H\!-\!\ddot{O}\!-\!R \quad + \quad :\!\ddot{X}\!:^{-} $$

Negative nucleophile   **Alkyl halide**   **Neutral product**   **Leaving group**

2. Use of a **neutral nucleophile** (water in this case) **results initially in a positively charged product**. The neutral nucleophile gains a positive formal charge through formation of the covalent bond with the substrate. A neutral product results only after a proton is removed from the atom with the formal positive charge in the initial product.

Nucleophilic Substitution by a Neutral Nucleophile Results Initially in a Positively Charged Product

$$ H\!-\!\ddot{O}\!: \quad + \quad R\!-\!\ddot{X}\!: \quad \longrightarrow \quad H\!-\!\overset{+}{\underset{|}{\ddot{O}}}\!-\!R \quad + \quad :\!\ddot{X}\!:^{-} $$

H		H

Neutral nucleophile   **Alkyl halide**   **Initial positively charged product**

$H_2\ddot{O}$ ↑ **Proton transfer**

$$ H\!-\!\ddot{O}\!-\!R \quad + \quad H_3\ddot{O}^{+} \quad + \quad :\!\ddot{X}\!:^{-} $$

Neutral product

Helpful Hint

A deprotonation step is always required to complete the reaction when the nucleophile was a neutral atom that bore a proton.

In a reaction like this the nucleophile is a solvent molecule (as is often the case when neutral nucleophiles are involved). Since solvent molecules are present in great excess, the equilibrium favors transfer of a proton from the alkyloxonium ion to a water molecule. This type of reaction is an example of solvolysis, which we shall discuss further in Section 6.12B.

The reaction of ammonia (NH_3) with an alkyl halide, as shown below, provides another example where the nucleophile is uncharged. An excess of ammonia favors equilibrium removal of a proton from the alkylaminium ion to form the neutral amine.

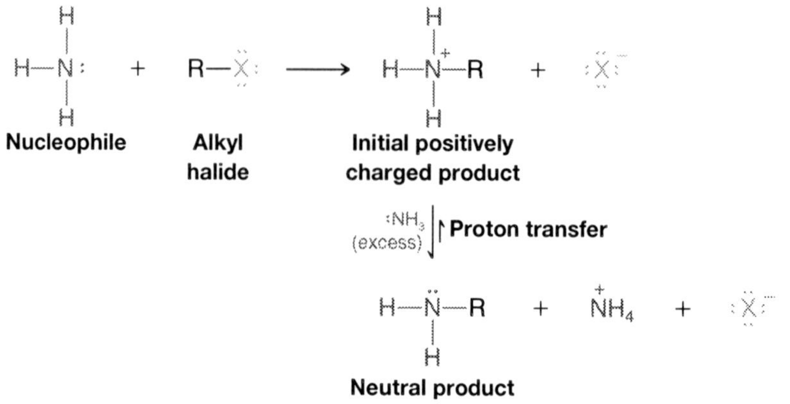

Nucleophile   Alkyl halide   Initial positively charged product

:NH₃ (excess) ↑ **Proton transfer**

Neutral product

●●● SOLVED PROBLEM 6.2

Write the following as net ionic equations and designate the nucleophile, substrate, and leaving group in each case.

(a)

(b)

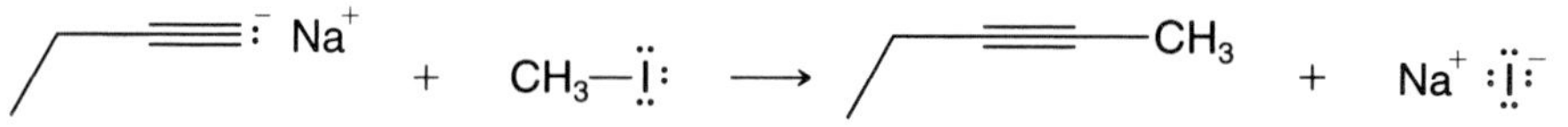

(c) (excess)

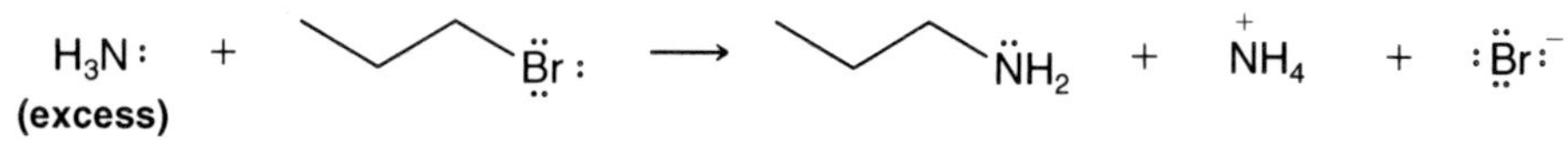

STRATEGY: A net ionic equation does not include spectator ions but is still balanced in terms of charges and the remaining species. Spectator ions are those ions that have not been involved in covalent bonding changes during a reaction, and that appear on both sides of a chemical equation. In reactions **(a)** and **(b)** the sodium ion is a spectator ion, thus the net ionic equation would not include them, and their net ionic equations would have a net negative charge on each side of the arrow. Equation **(c)** has no ions present among the reactants, and thus the ions found with the products are not spectator ions—they have resulted from covalent bonding changes. Equation **(c)** cannot be simplified to a net ionic equation.

   Nucleophiles use a pair of electrons to form a covalent bond that is present in a product molecule. In all of the above reactions we can identify a species that used a pair of electrons in this way. These are the nucleophiles. **Leaving groups** depart from one of the reactant molecules and take a pair of electrons with them. In each reaction above we can identify such a species. Finally, the reactants to which the nucleophiles became bonded and from which the leaving groups departed are the **substrates**.

ANSWER: The net ionic equations are as follows for **(a)** and **(b)**, and there is no abbreviated equation possible for **(c)**. Nucleophiles, substrates, and leaving groups are labeled accordingly.

(a)

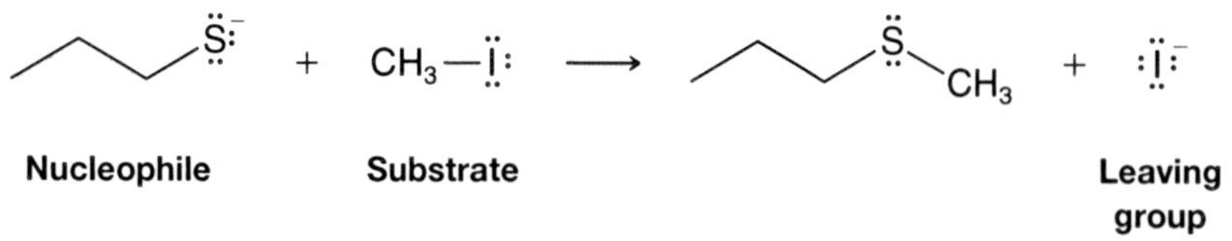

Nucleophile   Substrate   Leaving group

(b)

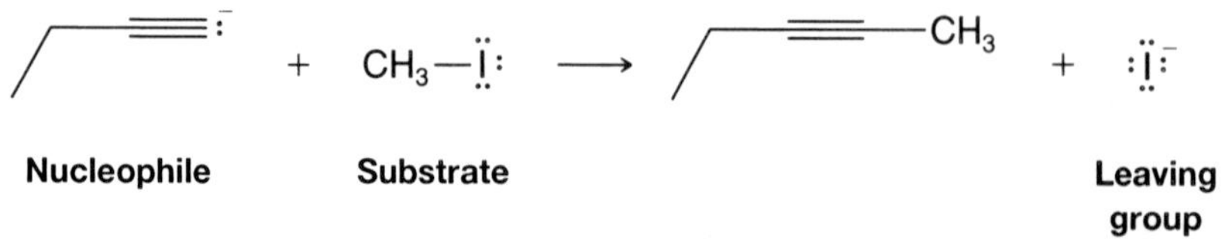

Nucleophile   Substrate   Leaving group

(c)

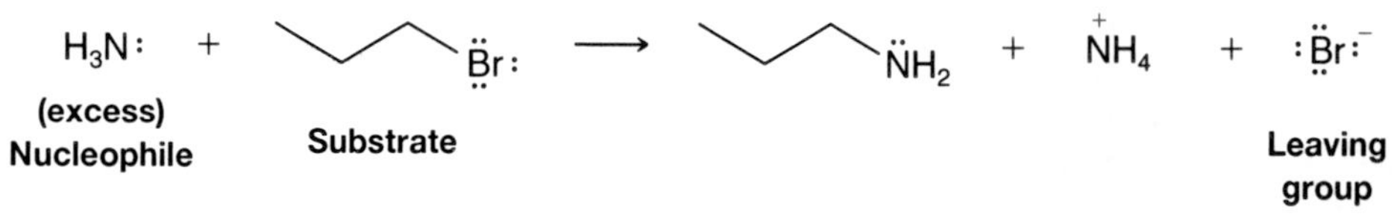

(excess) Nucleophile   Substrate   Leaving group

Write the following as net ionic equations and designate the nucleophile, substrate, and leaving group in each reaction:

(a) CH_3I + CH_3CH_2ONa $\longrightarrow$ $CH_3OCH_2CH_3$ + NaI

(b) NaI + CH_3CH_2Br $\longrightarrow$ CH_3CH_2I + $NaBr$

(c) $2 CH_3OH$ + $(CH_3)_3CCl$ $\longrightarrow$ $(CH_3)_3COCH_3$ + $CH_3\overset{+}{O}H_2$ + Cl^-

(d) 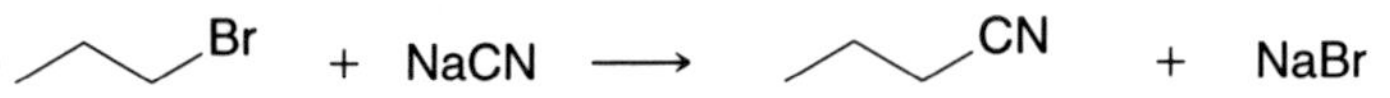 ⌇⌇Br + $NaCN$ $\longrightarrow$ ⌇⌇CN + $NaBr$

(e) 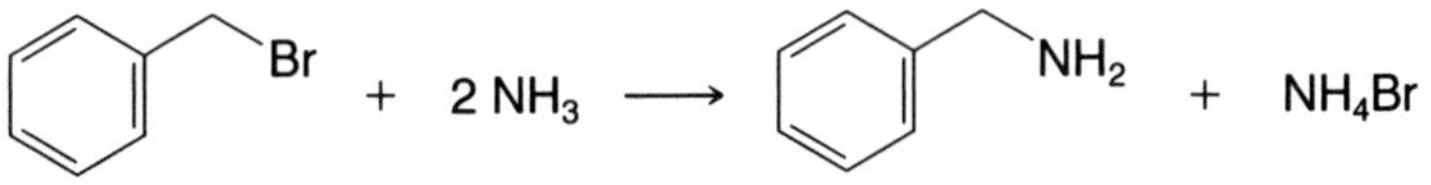 [benzyl bromide structure]Br + $2 NH_3$ $\longrightarrow$ [benzylamine structure]NH_2 + NH_4Br

6.4 LEAVING GROUPS

To act as the substrate in a nucleophilic substitution reaction, a molecule must have a good leaving group.

- A good **leaving group** is a substituent that can leave as a relatively stable, weakly basic molecule or ion.

In the examples shown above (Sections 6.2 and 6.3) the leaving group has been a halogen. Halide anions are weak bases (they are the conjugate bases of strong acids, **HX**), and therefore halogens are good leaving groups.

Some leaving groups depart as neutral molecules, such as a molecule of water or an alcohol. For this to be possible, the leaving group must have a formal positive charge while it is bonded to the substrate. When this group departs with a pair of electrons the leaving group's formal charge goes to zero. The following is an example where the leaving group departs as a water molecule.

$$CH_3-\overset{..}{\underset{H}{O}}: + CH_3-\overset{..}{\underset{H}{\overset{+}{O}}}-H \longrightarrow CH_3-\overset{..}{\underset{H}{\overset{+}{O}}}-CH_3 + :\overset{..}{\underset{H}{O}}-H$$

Helpful Hint

Note that the net charge is the same on each side of a properly written chemical equation.

As we shall see later, the positive charge on a leaving group (like that above) usually results from protonation of the substrate by an acid. However, use of an acid to protonate the substrate and make a positively charged leaving group is feasible only when the nucleophile itself is not strongly basic, and when the nucleophile is present in abundance (such as in solvolysis).

Let us now begin to consider the mechanisms of nucleophilic substitution reactions. How does the nucleophile replace the leaving group? Does the reaction take place in one step or is more than one step involved? If more than one step is involved, what kinds of intermediates are formed? Which steps are fast and which are slow? In order to answer these questions, we need to know something about the rates of chemical reactions.

6.5 KINETICS OF A NUCLEOPHILIC SUBSTITUTION REACTION: AN S$_N$2 REACTION

To understand how the rate of a reaction (kinetics) might be measured, let us consider an actual example: the reaction that takes place between chloromethane and hydroxide ion in aqueous solution:

$$CH_3-Cl + {}^-OH \xrightarrow[H_2O]{60°C} CH_3-OH + Cl^-$$

Although chloromethane is not highly soluble in water, it is soluble enough to carry out our kinetic study in an aqueous solution of sodium hydroxide. Because reaction rates are known to be temperature dependent (Section 6.7), we carry out the reaction at a constant temperature.

6.5A How Do We Measure the Rate of This Reaction?

The rate of the reaction can be determined experimentally by measuring the rate at which chloromethane or hydroxide ion *disappears* from the solution or the rate at which methanol or chloride ion *appears* in the solution. We can make any of these measurements by withdrawing a small sample from the reaction mixture soon after the reaction begins and analyzing it for the concentrations of CH_3Cl or HO^- and CH_3OH or Cl^-. We are interested in what are called *initial rates*, because as time passes the concentrations of the reactants change. Since we also know the initial concentrations of reactants (because we measured them when we made up the solution), it will be easy to calculate the rate at which the reactants are disappearing from the solution or the products are appearing in the solution.

We perform several such experiments keeping the temperature the same but varying the initial concentrations of the reactants. The results that we might get are shown in Table 6.2.

TABLE 6.2 RATE STUDY OF REACTION OF CH_3Cl WITH HO^- AT 60 °C			
Experiment Number	Initial [CH₃Cl]	Initial [HO⁻]	Initial Rate (mol L⁻¹ s⁻¹)
1	0.0010	1.0	4.9×10^{-7}
2	0.0020	1.0	9.8×10^{-7}
3	0.0010	2.0	9.8×10^{-7}
4	0.0020	2.0	19.6×10^{-7}

Notice that the experiments show that the rate depends on the concentration of chloromethane *and* on the concentration of hydroxide ion. When we doubled the concentration of chloromethane in experiment 2, the rate *doubled*. When we doubled the concentration of hydroxide ion in experiment 3, the rate *doubled*. When we doubled both concentrations in experiment 4, the rate increased by a factor of *four*.

We can express these results as a proportionality,

$$\text{Rate} \propto [CH_3Cl][HO^-]$$

and this proportionality can be expressed as an equation through the introduction of a proportionality constant (k) called the rate constant:

$$\text{Rate} = k[CH_3Cl][HO^-]$$

For this reaction at this temperature we find that $k = 4.9 \times 10^{-4}$ L mol⁻¹ s⁻¹. (Verify this for yourself by doing the calculation.)

6.5B What Is the Order of This Reaction?

This reaction is said to be **second order overall**.* It is reasonable to conclude, therefore, that *for the reaction to take place a hydroxide ion and a chloromethane molecule must collide.* We also say that the reaction is **bimolecular**. (By *bimolecular* we mean that two species are involved in the step whose rate is being measured. In general the number of species involved in a reaction step is called the **molecularity** of the reaction.) We call this kind of reaction an S_N2 reaction, meaning **substitution, nucleophilic, bimolecular**.

6.6 A MECHANISM FOR THE S_N2 REACTION

A schematic representation of orbitals involved in an S_N2 reaction—based on ideas proposed by Edward D. Hughes and Sir Christopher Ingold in 1937—is outlined below.

---

*In general, the overall order of a reaction is equal to the sum of the exponents a and b in the rate equation Rate $= k[A]^a[B]^b$. If in some other reaction, for example, we found that Rate $= k[A]^2[B]$, then we would say that the reaction is second order with respect to [A], first order with respect to [B], and third order overall.

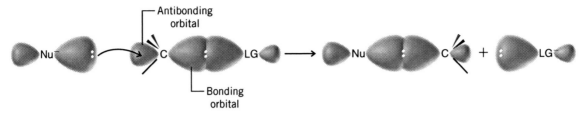

- Antibonding orbital
- Bonding orbital

According to this mechanism:

- The nucleophile approaches the carbon bearing the leaving group from the **back side**, that is, from the side directly opposite the leaving group.

The orbital that contains the electron pair of the nucleophile (its highest occupied molecular orbital, or HOMO) begins to overlap with an empty orbital (the lowest unoccupied molecular orbital, or LUMO) of the carbon atom bearing the leaving group. As the reaction progresses, the bond between the nucleophile and the carbon atom strengthens, and the bond between the carbon atom and the leaving group weakens.

- As the nucleophile forms a bond and the leaving group departs, the substrate carbon atom undergoes *inversion*—its tetrahedral bonding configuration is turned inside out.

The formation of the bond between the nucleophile and the carbon atom provides most of the energy necessary to break the bond between the carbon atom and the leaving group. We can represent this mechanism with chloromethane and hydroxide ion as shown in the "Mechanism for the S$_N$2 Reaction" box below.

- The S$_N$2 reaction proceeds in a single step (without any intermediates) through an unstable arrangement of atoms called the **transition state**.

A MECHANISM FOR THE REACTION — Mechanism for the S$_N$2 Reaction

Reaction

$$HO^- + CH_3Cl \longrightarrow CH_3OH + Cl^-$$

Mechanism

Transition state

The negative hydroxide ion brings a pair of electrons to the partially positive carbon from the back side with respect to the leaving group. The chlorine begins to move away with the pair of electrons that bonded it to the carbon.

In the transition state, a bond between oxygen and carbon is partially formed and the bond between carbon and chlorine is partially broken. The configuration of the carbon atom begins to invert.

Now the bond between the oxygen and carbon has formed and the chloride ion has departed. The configuration of the carbon has inverted.

*Considerable evidence had appeared in the years prior to Hughes and Ingold's 1937 publication indicating that in reactions like this an inversion of configuration of the carbon bearing the leaving group takes place. The first observation of such an inversion was made by the Latvian chemist Paul Walden in 1896, and such inversions are called **Walden inversions** in his honor. We shall study this aspect of the S$_N$2 reaction further in Section 6.8.

The transition state is a fleeting arrangement of the atoms in which the nucleophile and the leaving group are both partially bonded to the carbon atom undergoing substitution. Because the transition state involves both the nucleophile (e.g., a hydroxide ion) and the substrate (e.g., a molecule of chloromethane), this mechanism accounts for the second-order reaction kinetics that we observe.

- The S_N2 reaction is said to be a **concerted reaction**, because bond forming and bond breaking occur in concert (*simultaneously*) through a single transition state.

The transition state has an extremely brief existence. It lasts only as long as the time required for one molecular vibration, about 10^{-12} s. The structure and energy of the transition state are highly important aspects of any chemical reaction. We shall, therefore, examine this subject further in Section 6.7.

6.7 TRANSITION STATE THEORY: FREE-ENERGY DIAGRAMS

- A reaction that proceeds with a negative free-energy change (releases energy to its surroundings) is said to be **exergonic**; one that proceeds with a positive free-energy change (absorbs energy from its surroundings) is said to be **endergonic**.

The reaction between chloromethane and hydroxide ion in aqueous solution is highly exergonic; at 60 °C (333 K), $\Delta G° = -100$ kJ mol^{-1}. (The reaction is also exothermic, $\Delta H° = -75$ kJ mol^{-1}.)

$$CH_3\!-\!Cl + {}^-OH \longrightarrow CH_3\!-\!OH + Cl^- \qquad \Delta G° = -100 \text{ kJ mol}^{-1}$$

The equilibrium constant for the reaction is extremely large, as we show by the following calculation:

$$\Delta G° = -RT \ln K_{eq}$$

$$\ln K_{eq} = \frac{-\Delta G°}{RT}$$

$$\ln K_{eq} = \frac{-(-100 \text{ kJ mol}^{-1})}{0.00831 \text{ kJ K}^{-1}\text{mol}^{-1} \times 333 \text{ K}}$$

$$\ln K_{eq} = 36.1$$

$$K_{eq} = 5.0 \times 10^{15}$$

An equilibrium constant as large as this means that the reaction goes to completion.

Because the free-energy change is negative, we can say that in energy terms the reaction goes **downhill**. The products of the reaction are at a lower level of free energy than the reactants. However, if covalent bonds are broken in a reaction, the reactants must go up an energy hill first, before they can go downhill. This will be true even if the reaction is exergonic.

We can represent the energy changes in a reaction using a graph called a **free-energy diagram**, where we plot the free energy of the reacting particles (*y*-axis) against the reaction coordinate (*x*-axis). Figure 6.1 is an example for a generalized S_N2 reaction.

- The **reaction coordinate** indicates the progress of the reaction, in terms of the conversion of reactants to products.
- The top of the energy curve corresponds to the **transition state** for the reaction.
- The **free energy of activation** ($\Delta G^\ddagger$) for the reaction is the difference in energy between the reactants and the transition state.
- The **free energy change for the reaction** ($\Delta G°$) is the difference in energy between the reactants and the products.

The top of the energy hill corresponds to the transition state. *The difference in free energy between the reactants and the transition state is the free energy of activation, $\Delta G^\ddagger$. The difference in free energy between the reactants and products is the free-energy change for the reaction, $\Delta G°$. For our example in Fig. 6.1, the free-energy level of the products is lower*

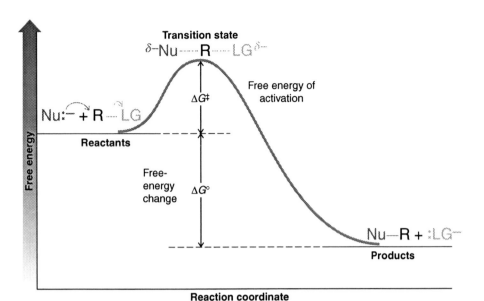

FIGURE 6.1 A free-energy diagram for a hypothetical exergonic S_N2 reaction (i.e., that takes place with a negative $\Delta G°$, releasing energy to the surroundings).

than that of the reactants. In terms of our analogy, we can say that the reactants in one energy valley must surmount an energy hill (the transition state) in order to reach the lower energy valley of the products.

If a reaction in which covalent bonds are broken proceeds with a positive free-energy change (Fig. 6.2), there will still be a free energy of activation. That is, if the products have greater free energy than reactants, the free energy of activation will be even higher. ($\Delta G^{\ddagger}$ will be larger than $\Delta G°$.) In other words, in the **uphill** (endergonic) reaction an even larger energy hill lies between the reactants in one valley and the products in a higher one.

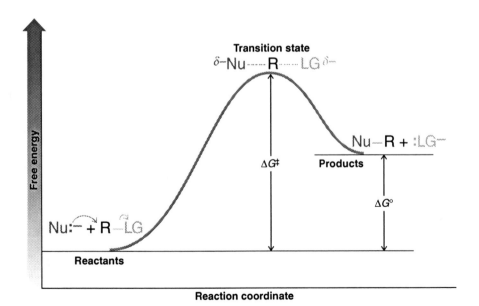

FIGURE 6.2 A free-energy diagram for a hypothetical endergonic S_N2 reaction (i.e., that takes place with a positive $\Delta G°$, absorbing energy from the surroundings).

6.7A Temperature and Reaction Rate

Most chemical reactions occur much more rapidly at higher temperatures. The increase in reaction rate for S_N2 reactions relates to the fact that at higher temperatures the number of collisions between reactants with sufficient energy to surmount the activation energy ($\Delta G^{\ddagger}$) increases significantly (see Fig. 6.3).

- A 10 °C increase in temperature will cause the reaction rate to double for many reactions taking place near room temperature.

This dramatic increase in reaction rate results from a large increase in the number of collisions between reactants that together have sufficient energy to surmount the barrier at the higher temperature. The kinetic energies of molecules at a given temperature are not all the same. Figure 6.3 shows the distribution of energies brought to collisions at two temperatures (that do not differ greatly), labeled T_{Low} and T_{High}. Because of the way energies are distributed at different temperatures (as indicated by the shapes of the curves), increasing the temperature by only a small amount causes a large increase in the number of collisions with larger energies. In Fig. 6.3 we have designated an arbitrary minimum free energy of activation as being required to bring about a reaction between colliding molecules.

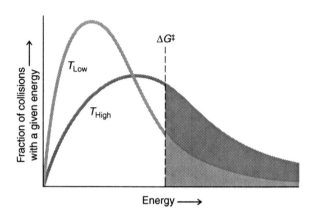

FIGURE 6.3 The distribution of energies at two different temperatures, T_{Low} and T_{High}. The number of collisions with energies greater than the free energy of activation is indicated by the corresponding shaded area under each curve.

A free-energy diagram for the reaction of chloromethane with hydroxide ion is shown in Fig. 6.4. At 60 °C, $\Delta G^{\ddagger} = 103$ kJ mol^{-1}, which means that at this temperature the reaction reaches completion in a matter of a few hours.

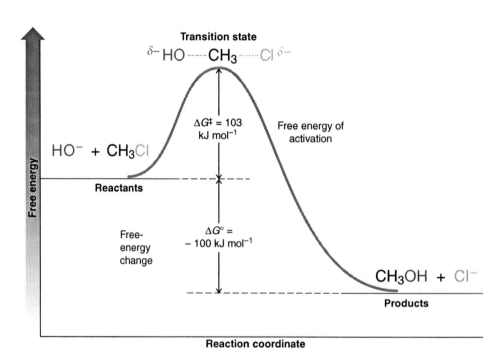

FIGURE 6.4 A free-energy diagram for the reaction of chloromethane with hydroxide ion at 60 °C.

● ● ◆

PRACTICE PROBLEM 6.4   Draw a hypothetical free-energy diagram for the S_N2 reaction of iodide anion with 1-chlorobutane. Label the diagram as in Fig. 6.4, and assume it is exergonic but without specific values for $\Delta G^{\ddagger}$ and ΔG°.

6.8 THE STEREOCHEMISTRY OF S$_N$2 REACTIONS

The stereochemistry of S$_N$2 reactions is directly related to key features of the mechanism that we learned earlier:

- **The nucleophile approaches the substrate carbon from the back side with respect to the leaving group.** In other words, the bond to the nucleophile that is forming is opposite (at 180°) to the bond to the leaving group that is breaking.
- Nucleophilic displacement of the leaving group in an S$_N$2 reaction causes **inversion of configuration** at the substrate carbon.

We depict the inversion process as follows. It is much like the way an umbrella is inverted in a strong wind.

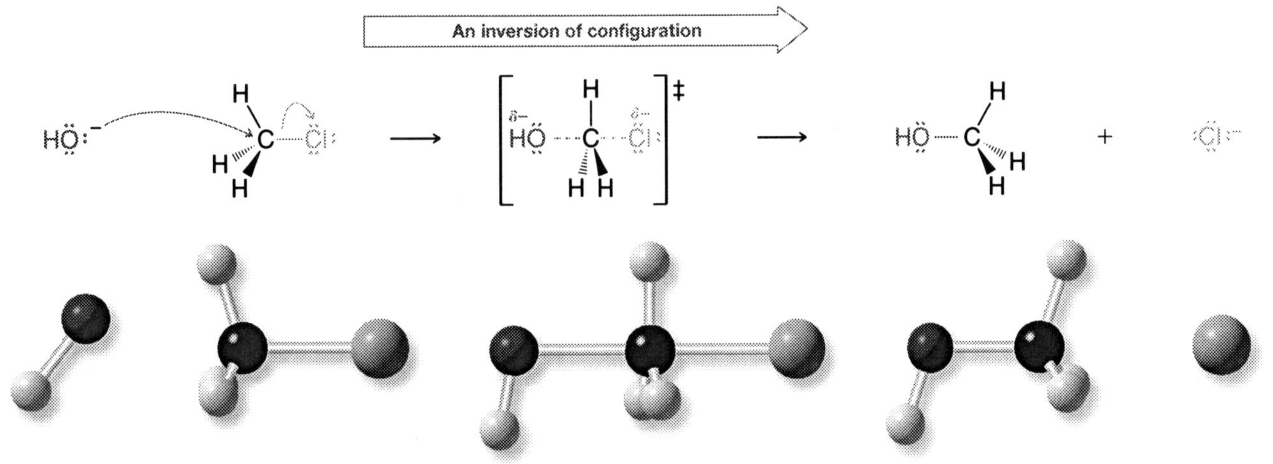

Transition state for an S$_N$2 reaction

With a molecule such as chloromethane, however, there is no way to prove that attack by the nucleophile has involved inversion of configuration of the carbon atom because one form of methyl chloride is identical to its inverted form. With a molecule containing chirality centers such as *cis*-1-chloro-3-methylcyclopentane, however, we can observe the results of an inversion of configuration by the change in stereochemistry that occurs. When *cis*-1-chloro-3-methylcyclopentane reacts with hydroxide ion in an S$_N$2 reaction, the product is *trans*-3-methylcyclopentanol. *The hydroxyl group ends up bonded on the opposite side of the ring from the chlorine it replaces*:

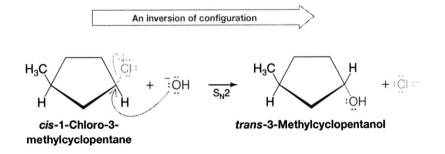

cis-1-Chloro-3-methylcyclopentane   **trans-3-Methylcyclopentanol**

Presumably, the transition state for this reaction is like that shown here.

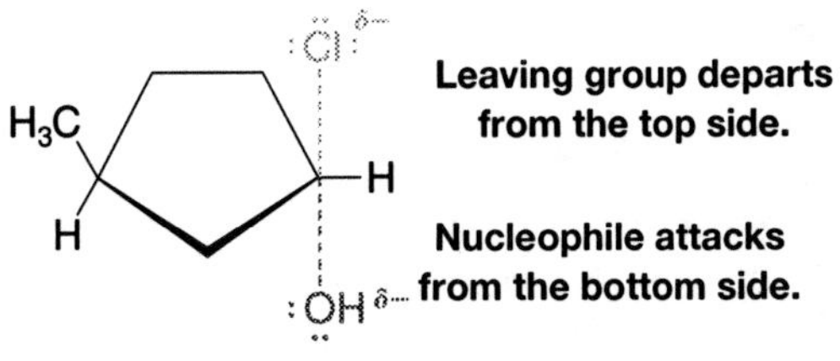

Leaving group departs from the top side.

Nucleophile attacks from the bottom side.

●●● SOLVED PROBLEM 6.3

Give the structure of the product that would be formed when *trans*-1-bromo-3-methylcyclobutane undergoes an S_N2 reaction with NaI.

STRATEGY AND ANSWER: First, write the formulas for the reactants and identify the nucleophile, the substrate, and the leaving group. Then, recognizing that the nucleophile will attack the back side of the substrate carbon atom that bears the leaving group, causing an inversion of configuration at that carbon, write the structure of the product.

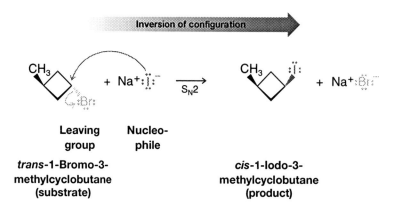

Leaving group	Nucleophile

trans-1-Bromo-3-methylcyclobutane (substrate)   *cis*-1-Iodo-3-methylcyclobutane (product)

●●●

PRACTICE PROBLEM 6.5   Using chair conformational structures (Section 4.11), show the nucleophilic substitution reaction that would take place when *trans*-1-bromo-4-*tert*-butylcyclohexane reacts with iodide ion. (Show the most stable conformation of the reactant and the product.)

● S_N2 **reactions always occur with inversion of configuration**.

We can also observe inversion of configuration when an S_N2 reaction occurs at a chirality center in an acyclic molecule. The reaction of (*R*)-(−)-2-bromooctane with sodium hydroxide provides an example. We can determine whether or not inversion of configuration occurs in this reaction because the configurations and optical rotations for both enantiomers of 2-bromooctane and the expected product, 2-octanol, are known.

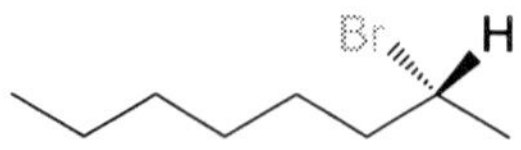

(*R*)-(−)-2-Bromooctane   **(*S*)-(+)-2-Bromooctane**
$[\alpha]_D^{25} = -34.25$ $[\alpha]_D^{25} = +34.25$

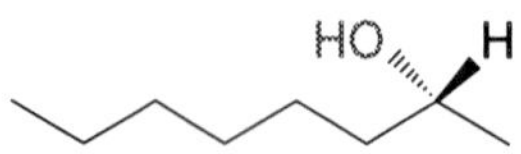

(*R*)-(−)-2-Octanol   **(*S*)-(+)-2-Octanol**
$[\alpha]_D^{25} = -9.90$ $[\alpha]_D^{25} = +9.90$

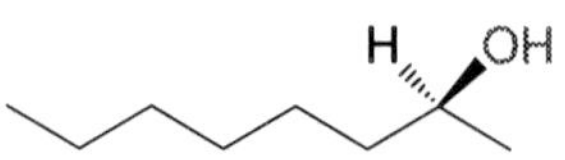

When the reaction is carried out, we find that enantiomerically pure (*R*)-(−)-2-bromooctane ($[\alpha]_D^{25} = -34.25$) has been converted to enantiomerically pure (*S*)-(+)-2-octanol ($[\alpha]_D^{25} = +9.90$).

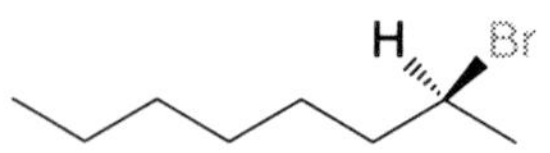

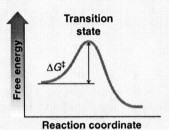

[**A MECHANISM FOR THE REACTION** ⋯ **The Stereochemistry of an S$_N$2 Reaction**]

The reaction of (*R*)-(−)-2-bromooctane with hydroxide is an S$_N$2 reaction and takes place with *inversion of configuration*:

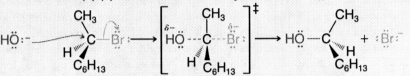

An inversion of configuration

(*R*)-(−)-2-Bromooctane	(*S*)-(1)-2-Octanol	
$[\alpha]_D^{25} = -34.25°$	$[\alpha]_D^{25} = +9.90°$	
Enantiomeric purity = 100%	Enantiomeric purity = 100%	

An S$_N$2 reaction has one transition state.

Transition state

$\Delta G^{\ddagger}$

Reaction coordinate

S$_N$2 reactions that involve breaking a bond to a chirality center can be used to relate configurations of molecules because the *stereochemistry* of the reaction is known.

PRACTICE PROBLEM 6.6

(a) Illustrate how this is true by assigning *R,S* configurations to the 2-chlorobutane enantiomers based on the following data. [The configuration of (−)-2-butanol is given in Section 5.8C.]

$$\text{(+)-2-Chlorobutane} \xrightarrow[\text{S}_N2]{\text{HO}^-} \text{(−)-2-Butanol}$$

$[\alpha]_D^{25} = +36.00$	$[\alpha]_D^{25} = -13.52$
Enantiomerically pure	**Enantiomerically pure**

(b) When optically pure (+)-2-chlorobutane is allowed to react with potassium iodide in acetone in an S$_N$2 reaction, the 2-iodobutane that is produced has a minus rotation. What is the configuration of (−)-2-iodobutane? Of (+)-2-iodobutane?

6.9 THE REACTION OF *TERT*-BUTYL CHLORIDE WITH WATER: AN S$_N$1 REACTION

Let us now consider another mechanism for nucleophilic substitution: the S$_N$1 reaction. When Hughes (Section 6.6) and co-workers studied the reaction of *tert*-butyl chloride with water they found the kinetics leading to formation of *tert*-butyl alcohol to be quite different than for other substitution reactions that they had studied.

$$\underset{\substack{\text{CH}_3 \\ | \\ \text{CH}_3-\text{C}-\text{Cl} \\ | \\ \text{CH}_3}}{} + \text{H}_2\text{O} \longrightarrow \underset{\substack{\text{CH}_3 \\ | \\ \text{CH}_3-\text{C}-\text{OH} \\ | \\ \text{CH}_3}}{} + \text{HCl}$$

tert-Butyl chloride   **_tert_-Butyl alcohol**

Hughes found that the rate of *tert*-butyl chloride substitution was the same whether the reaction was run at pH 7, where the hydroxide ion concentration is 10^{-7} M and the predominant nucleophile is water, or in 0.05 M hydroxide, where the more powerful hydroxide nucleophile is present in roughly 500,000 times higher concentration. These results suggest that neither water nor hydroxide ions are involved in the rate-determining step of the reaction. Instead, the rate of substitution is dependent only on the concentration of *tert*-butyl chloride. The reaction is thus first order in *tert*-butyl chloride, and first order overall.

$$\text{Rate} = k[(\text{CH}_3)_3\text{CCl}]$$

The reaction rate is first order in _tert_-butyl chloride and first order overall.

Furthermore, these results indicate that the transition state governing the rate of reaction involves only molecules of *tert*-butyl chloride, and not water or hydroxide ions. The reaction is said to be **unimolecular** (first-order) in the rate-determining step, and we call it an S_N1 reaction (**substitution, nucleophilic, unimolecular**). In Section 6.15 we shall see that elimination reactions can compete with S_N1 reactions, leading to the formation of alkenes, but in the case of the conditions used above for the experiments with *tert*-butyl chloride (moderate temperature and dilute base), S_N1 is the dominant process.

How can we explain an S_N1 reaction in terms of a mechanism? To do so, we shall need to consider the possibility that the mechanism involves more than one step. But what kind of kinetic results should we expect from a multistep reaction? Let us consider this point further.

6.9A Multistep Reactions and the Rate-Determining Step

- If a reaction takes place in a series of steps, and if one step is intrinsically slower than all the others, then the rate of the overall reaction will be essentially the same as the rate of this slow step. This slow step, consequently, is called the **rate-limiting step** or the rate-determining step.

Consider a multistep reaction such as the following:

$$\text{Reactant} \xrightarrow[\text{(slow)}]{k_1} \text{intermediate 1} \xrightarrow[\text{(fast)}]{k_2} \text{intermediate 2} \xrightarrow[\text{(fast)}]{k_3} \text{product}$$

$$\textbf{\textit{Step 1}} \qquad\qquad \textbf{\textit{Step 2}} \qquad\qquad \textbf{\textit{Step 3}}$$

When we say that the first step in this example is intrinsically slow, we mean that the rate constant for step 1 is very much smaller than the rate constant for step 2 or for step 3. That is, $k_1 << k_2$ or k_3. When we say that steps 2 and 3 are *fast*, we mean that because their rate constants are larger, they could (in theory) take place rapidly if the concentrations of the two intermediates ever became high. In actuality, the concentrations of the intermediates are always very small because of the slowness of step 1.

As an analogy, imagine an hourglass modified in the way shown in Fig. 6.5. The opening between the top chamber and the one just below is considerably smaller than the other two. The overall rate at which sand falls from the top to the bottom of the hourglass is limited by the rate at which sand passes through the small orifice. This step, in the passage of sand, is analogous to the rate-determining step of the multistep reaction.

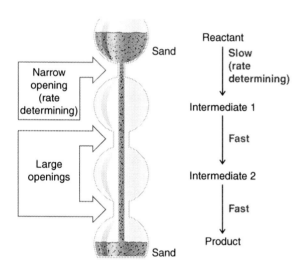

FIGURE 6.5 A modified hourglass that serves as an analogy for a multistep reaction. The overall rate is limited by the rate of the slow step.

6.10 A MECHANISM FOR THE S_N1 REACTION

The mechanism for the reaction of *tert*-butyl chloride with water (Section 6.9) can be described in three steps. See the box "Mechanism for the S_N1 Reaction" below, with a schematic free-energy diagram highlighted for each step. Two distinct intermediates are formed. The first step is the slow step—it is the rate-determining step. In it a molecule of *tert*-butyl chloride ionizes and becomes a *tert*-butyl cation and a chloride ion. In the transition state for this step the carbon–chlorine bond of *tert*-butyl chloride is largely broken and ions are beginning to develop:

$$CH_3{-}\underset{\underset{CH_3}{|}}{\overset{\overset{CH_3}{|}}{C}}{}^{\delta+}\text{-----}Cl^{\delta-}$$

The solvent (water) stabilizes these developing ions by solvation. Carbocation formation, in general, takes place slowly because it is usually a highly endothermic process and is uphill in terms of free energy.

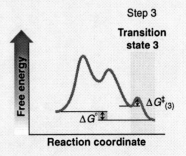

The first step requires heterolytic cleavage of the carbon–chlorine bond. Because no other bonds are formed in this step, it should be highly endothermic and it should have a high free energy of activation, as we see in the free-energy diagram. **That departure of the halide takes place at all is largely because of the ionizing ability of the solvent, water.** Experiments indicate that in the gas phase (i.e., in the absence of a solvent), the free energy of activation is about 630 kJ mol^{-1}! In aqueous solution, however, the free energy of activation is much lower—about 84 kJ mol^{-1}. **Water molecules surround and stabilize the cation and anion that are produced** (cf. Section 2.13D).

In the second step the intermediate *tert*-butyl cation reacts rapidly with water to produce a *tert*-butyloxonium ion, $(CH_3)_3COH_2^+$, which in the third step, rapidly transfers a proton to a molecule of water producing *tert*-butyl alcohol.

[A MECHANISM FOR THE REACTION ···· Mechanism for the S_N1 Reaction]

Reaction

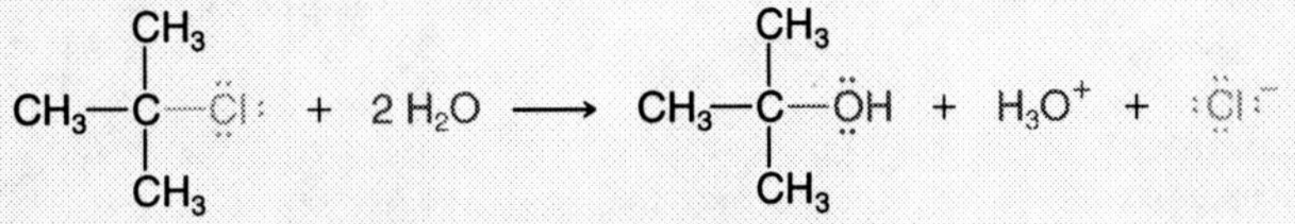

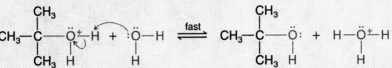

Mechanism

Step 1

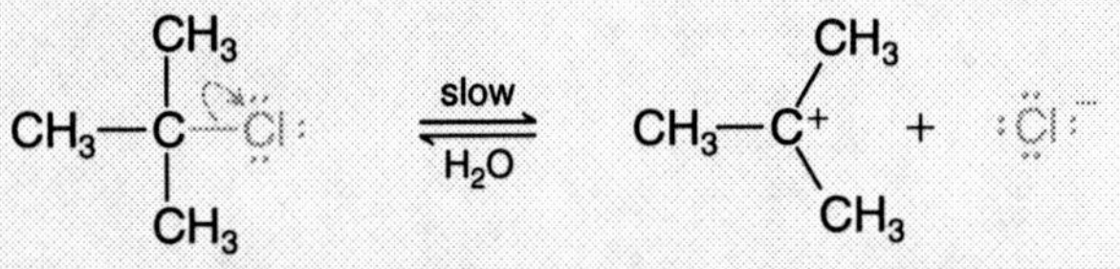

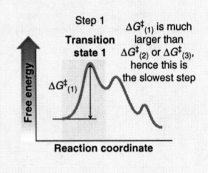

Aided by the polar solvent, a chlorine departs with the electron pair that bonded it to the carbon.

This slow step produces the 3° carbocation intermediate and a chloride ion. Although not shown here, the ions are solvated (and stabilized) by water molecules.

Step 1
Transition state 1
$\Delta G^{\ddagger}_{(1)}$ is much larger than $\Delta G^{\ddagger}_{(2)}$ or $\Delta G^{\ddagger}_{(3)}$, hence this is the slowest step

Step 2

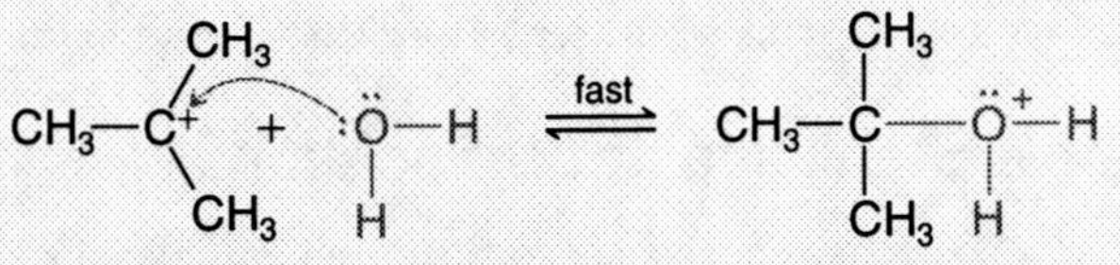

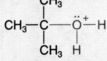

A water molecule acting as a Lewis base donates an electron pair to the carbocation (a Lewis acid). This gives the cationic carbon eight electrons.

The product is a *tert*-butyloxonium ion (or protonated *tert*-butyl alcohol).

Step 2
Transition state 2
$\Delta G^{\ddagger}_{(2)}$

Step 3

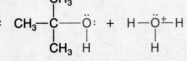

A water molecule acting as a Brønsted base accepts a proton from the *tert*-butyloxonium ion.

The products are *tert*-butyl alcohol and a hydronium ion.

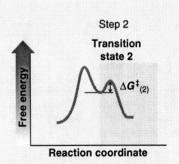

Step 3
Transition state 3
$\Delta G^{\ddagger}$
$\Delta G^{\ddagger}_{(3)}$

6.11 CARBOCATIONS

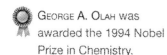 GEORGE A. OLAH was awarded the 1994 Nobel Prize in Chemistry.

Beginning in the 1920s much evidence began to accumulate implicating simple alkyl cations as intermediates in a variety of ionic reactions. However, because alkyl cations are highly unstable and highly reactive, they were, in all instances studied before 1962, very short-lived, transient species that could not be observed directly.* However, in 1962 George A. Olah (University of Southern California) and co-workers published the first of a series of papers describing experiments in which alkyl cations were prepared in an environment in which they were reasonably stable and in which they could be observed by a number of spectroscopic techniques.

6.11A The Structure of Carbocations

- Carbocations are trigonal planar.

Just as the trigonal planar structure of BF_3 (Section 1.16D) can be accounted for on the basis of sp^2 hybridization, so, too (Fig. 6.6), can the trigonal planar structure of carbocations.

FIGURE 6.6 *(a)* A stylized orbital structure of the methyl cation. The bonds are sigma (σ) bonds formed by overlap of the carbon atom's three sp^2 orbitals with the 1s orbitals of the hydrogen atoms. The p orbital is vacant. *(b)* A dashed line–wedge representation of the *tert*-butyl cation. The bonds between carbon atoms are formed by overlap of sp^3 orbitals of the methyl groups with sp^2 orbitals of the central carbon atom.

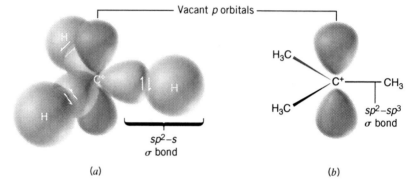

Vacant p orbitals

sp^2–s σ bond

sp^2–sp^3 σ bond

(a)   *(b)*

- The central carbon atom in a carbocation is electron deficient; it has only six electrons in its valence shell.

In our model (Fig. 6.6) these six electrons are used to form three sigma (σ) covalent bonds to hydrogen atoms or alkyl groups.

- The p orbital of a carbocation contains no electrons, but it can accept an electron pair when the carbocation undergoes further reaction.

Not all types of carbocations have the same relative stability, as we shall learn in the next section.

Helpful Hint

An understanding of carbocation structure and relative stability is important for learning a variety of reaction processes.

6.11B The Relative Stabilities of Carbocations

The relative stabilities of carbocations are related to the number of alkyl groups attached to the positively charged trivalent carbon.

- Tertiary carbocations are the most stable, and the methyl carbocation is the least stable.
- The overall order of stability is as follows:

3° (most stable) > 2° > 1° > Methyl (least stable)

This order of carbocation stability can be explained on the basis of hyperconjugation.

- **Hyperconjugation** involves electron delocalization (via partial orbital overlap) from a filled bonding orbital to an adjacent unfilled orbital (Section 4.8).

*As we shall learn later, carbocations bearing aromatic groups can be much more stable; one of these had been studied as early as 1901.

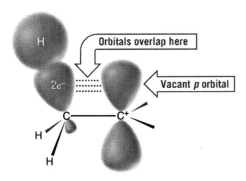

FIGURE 6.7 How an adjacent sigma bond helps stabilize the positive charge of a carbocation. Electron density from one of the carbon–hydrogen sigma bonds of the methyl group flows into the vacant p orbital of the carbocation because the orbitals can partly overlap. Shifting electron density in this way makes the sp^2-hybridized carbon of the carbocation somewhat less positive, and the hydrogens of the methyl group assume some of the positive charge. Delocalization (dispersal) of the charge in this way leads to greater stability. This interaction of a bond orbital with a p orbital is called hyperconjugation.

In the case of a carbocation, the unfilled orbital is the vacant p orbital of the carbocation, and the filled orbitals are C—H or C—C sigma bonds at the carbons *adjacent* to the p orbital of the carbocation. Sharing of electron density from adjacent C—H or C—C sigma bonds with the carbocation p orbital delocalizes the positive charge.

● Any time a charge can be dispersed or delocalized by hyperconjugation, inductive effects, or resonance, a system will be stabilized.

Figure 6.7 shows a stylized representation of hyperconjugation between a sigma bonding orbital and an adjacent carbocation p orbital.

Tertiary carbocations have three carbons with C—H bonds (or, depending on the specific example, C—C bonds instead of C—H) adjacent to the carbocation that can overlap partially with the vacant p orbital. Secondary carbocations have only two adjacent carbons with C—H or C—C bonds to overlap with the carbocation; hence, the possibility for hyperconjugation is less and the secondary carbocation is less stable. Primary carbocations have only one adjacent carbon from which to derive hyperconjugative stabilization, and so they are even less stable. A methyl carbocation has no possibility for hyperconjugation, and it is the least stable of all in this series. The following are specific examples:

tert-Butyl cation (3°) (most stable) is more stable than **Isopropyl cation (2°)** is more stable than **Ethyl cation (1°)** is more stable than **Methyl cation (least stable)**

In summary:

● **The relative stability of carbocations is 3° > 2° > 1° > methyl.**

This trend is also readily seen in electrostatic potential maps for these carbocations (Fig. 6.8).

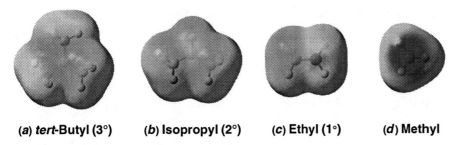

(a) tert-Butyl (3°) **(b) Isopropyl (2°)** **(c) Ethyl (1°)** **(d) Methyl**

FIGURE 6.8 Maps of electrostatic potential for (a) tert-butyl (3°), (b) isopropyl (2°), (c) ethyl (1°), and (d) methyl carbocations show the trend from greater to lesser delocalization (stabilization) of the positive charge in these structures. Less blue color indicates greater delocalization of the positive charge. (The structures are mapped on the same scale of electrostatic potential to allow direct comparison.)

●●● SOLVED PROBLEM 6.4

Rank the following carbocations in order of increasing stability:

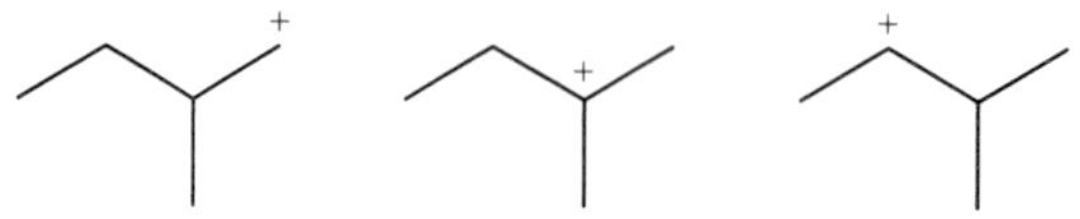

A   B   C

STRATEGY AND ANSWER: Structure **A** is a primary carbocation, **B** is tertiary, and **C** is secondary. Therefore, in order of increasing stability, **A < C < B**.

PRACTICE PROBLEM 6.7 Rank the following carbocations in order of increasing stability:

(a) 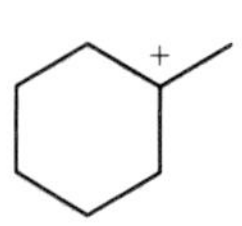   (b) 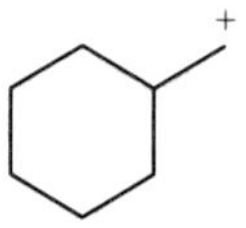   (c)

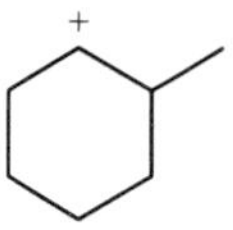

6.12 THE STEREOCHEMISTRY OF S_N1 REACTIONS

Because the carbocation formed in the first step of an S_N1 reaction has a trigonal planar structure (Section 6.11A), when it reacts with a nucleophile, it may do so from either the front side or the back side (see below). With the *tert*-butyl cation this makes no difference; since the *tert*-butyl group is not a chirality center, the same product is formed by either mode of attack. (Convince yourself of this result by examining models.)

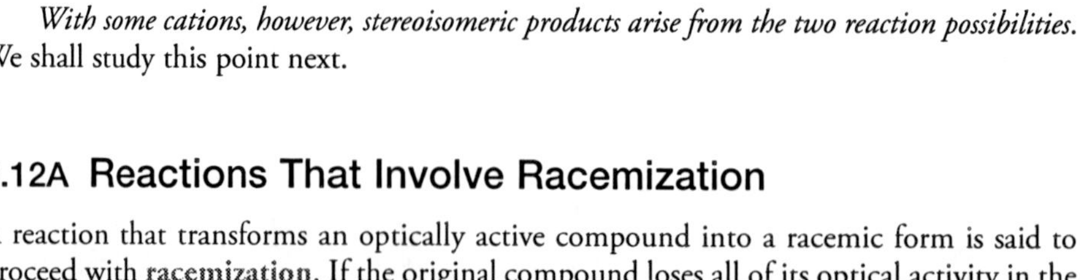

Same product

With some cations, however, stereoisomeric products arise from the two reaction possibilities. We shall study this point next.

6.12A Reactions That Involve Racemization

A reaction that transforms an optically active compound into a racemic form is said to proceed with **racemization**. If the original compound loses all of its optical activity in the course of the reaction, chemists describe the reaction as having taken place with *complete* racemization. If the original compound loses only part of its optical activity, as would be the case if an enantiomer were only partially converted to a racemic form, then chemists describe this as proceeding with *partial* racemization.

- Racemization takes place whenever the reaction causes chiral molecules to be converted to an achiral intermediate.

Examples of this type of reaction are S_N1 reactions in which the leaving group departs from a chirality center. These reactions almost always result in extensive and sometimes complete racemization. For example, heating optically active (*S*)-3-bromo-3-methylhexane with aqueous acetone results in the formation of 3-methyl-3-hexanol as a mixture of 50% (*R*) and 50% (*S*).

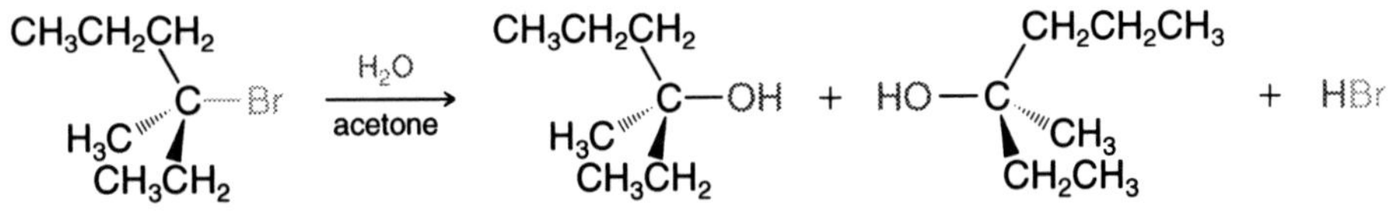

(S)-3-Bromo-3-methylhexane	**50%**	**50%**	
(optically active)	**(S)-3-Methyl-3-hexanol**	**(R)-3-Methyl-3-hexanol**	
	(optically inactive, a racemic form)		

The reason: the S$_N$1 reaction proceeds through the formation of an intermediate carbocation and the carbocation, because of its trigonal planar configuration, *is achiral*. It reacts with water at equal rates from either side to form the enantiomers of 3-methyl-3-hexanol in equal amounts.

[A MECHANISM FOR THE REACTION — The Stereochemistry of an S$_N$1 Reaction]

Reaction

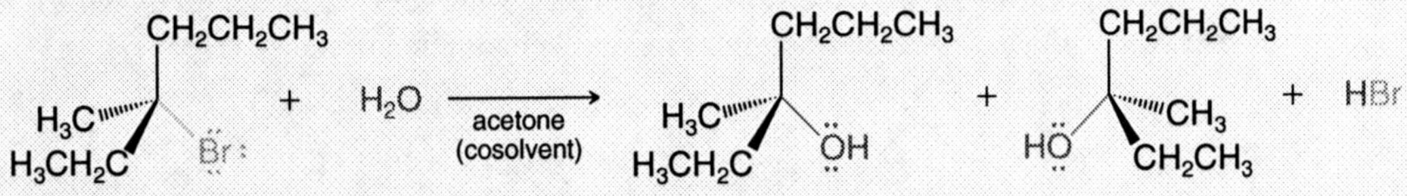

Mechanism

Step 1

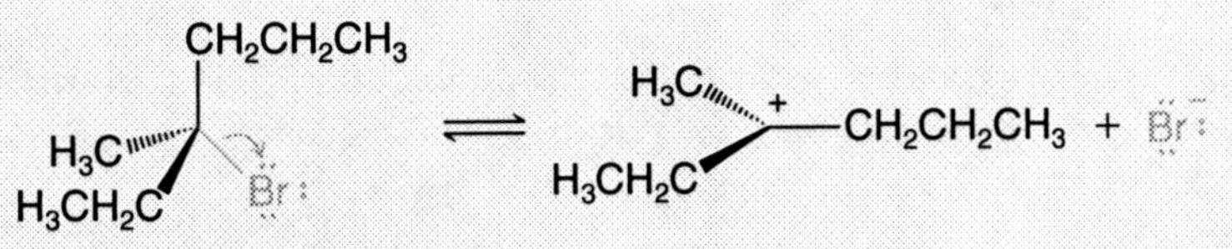

Departure of the leaving group (assisted by hydrogen bonding with water) leads to the carbocation.

Step 2

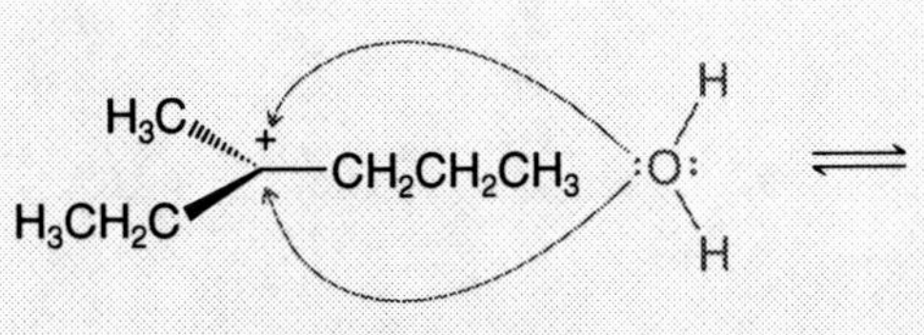

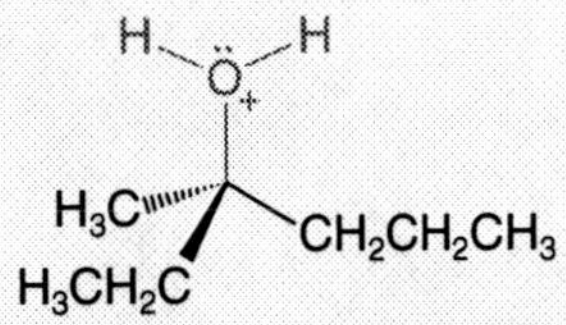

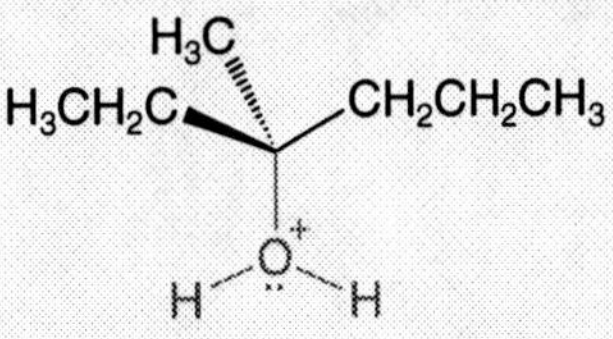

Attack at either face:
The carbocation is an achiral intermediate. Because both faces of the carbocation are the same, the nucleophile can bond with either face to form a mixture of stereoisomers.

A racemic mixture of protonated alcohols results.

(mechanism continues on the next page)

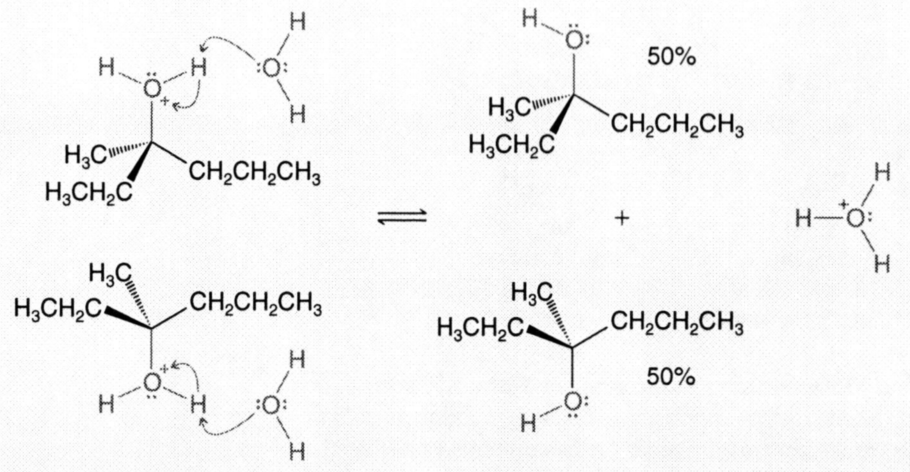

Additional solvent molecules (water) deprotonate the alkyloxonium ion.

The product is a racemic mixture.

The S_N1 reaction of (S)-3-bromo-3-methylhexane proceeds with racemization because the intermediate carbocation is achiral and attack by the nucleophile can occur from either side.

PRACTICE PROBLEM 6.8 Keeping in mind that carbocations have a trigonal planar structure, (a) write a structure for the carbocation intermediate and (b) write structures for the alcohol (or alcohols) that you would expect from reaction of iodocyclohexane in water:

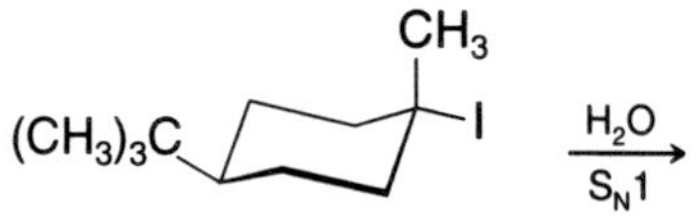

6.12B Solvolysis

- A solvolysis reaction is a nucleophilic substitution in which *the nucleophile is a molecule of the solvent* (*solvent* + *lysis*: cleavage by the solvent). The S_N1 reaction of an alkyl halide with water is an example of **solvolysis**.

When the solvent is water, we could also call the reaction a **hydrolysis**. If the reaction had taken place in methanol, we would call it a **methanolysis**.

Examples of Solvolysis

$$(CH_3)_3C-Br + H_2O \longrightarrow (CH_3)_3C-OH + HBr$$

$$(CH_3)_3C-Cl + CH_3OH \longrightarrow (CH_3)_3C-OCH_3 + HCl$$

••• SOLVED PROBLEM 6.5

What product(s) would you expect from the following solvolysis?

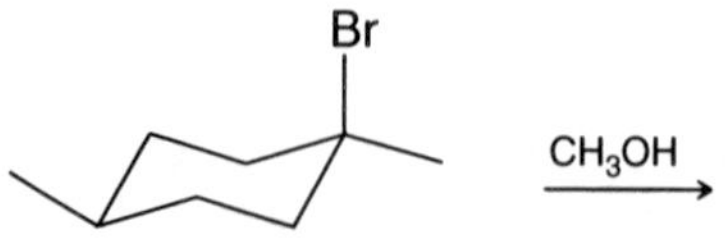

STRATEGY AND ANSWER: We observe that this cyclohexyl bromide is tertiary, and therefore in methanol it should lose a bromide ion to form a tertiary carbocation. Because the carbocation is trigonal planar at the positive carbon, it can react with a solvent molecule (methanol) to form two products.

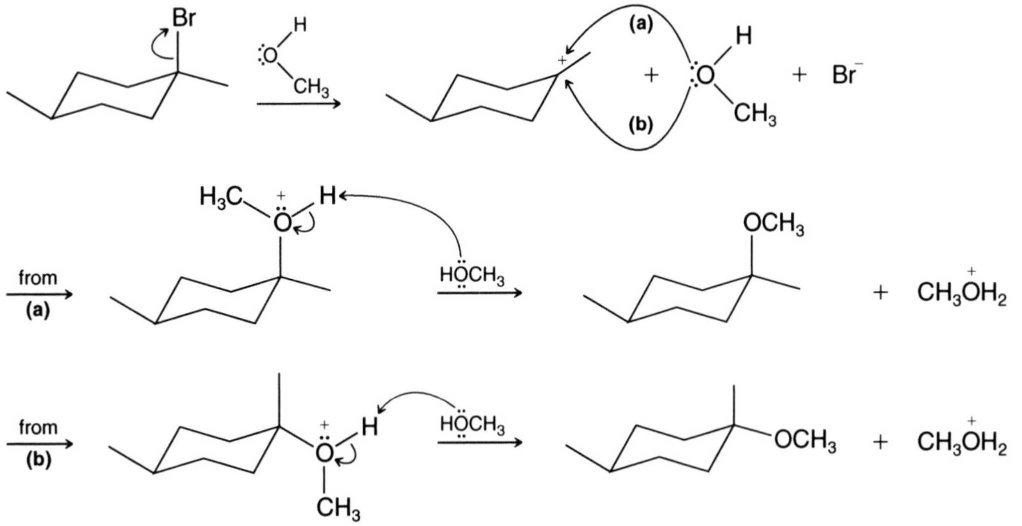

What product(s) would you expect from the methanolysis of the iodocyclohexane derivative given as the reactant in Practice Problem 6.8?

PRACTICE PROBLEM 6.9

6.13 FACTORS AFFECTING THE RATES OF S$_N$1 AND S$_N$2 REACTIONS

Now that we have an understanding of the mechanisms of S$_N$2 and S$_N$1 reactions, our next task is to explain why chloromethane reacts by an S$_N$2 mechanism and *tert*-butyl chloride by an S$_N$1 mechanism. We would also like to be able to predict which pathway—S$_N$1 or S$_N$2—would be followed by the reaction of any alkyl halide with any nucleophile under varying conditions.

The answer to this kind of question is to be found in the *relative rates of the reactions that occur.* If a given alkyl halide and nucleophile react *rapidly* by an S$_N$2 mechanism but *slowly* by an S$_N$1 mechanism under a given set of conditions, then an S$_N$2 pathway will be followed by most of the molecules. On the other hand, another alkyl halide and another nucleophile may react very slowly (or not at all) by an S$_N$2 pathway. If they react rapidly by an S$_N$1 mechanism, then the reactants will follow an S$_N$1 pathway.

- A number of factors affect the relative rates of S$_N$1 and S$_N$2 reactions. The most important factors are:

    1. the structure of the substrate,

    2. the concentration and reactivity of the nucleophile (for S$_N$2 reactions only),

    3. the effect of the solvent, and

    4. the nature of the leaving group.

6.13A The Effect of the Structure of the Substrate

S$_N$2 Reactions Simple alkyl halides show the following general order of reactivity in S$_N$2 reactions:

Methyl > primary > secondary >> (tertiary—unreactive)

Methyl halides react most rapidly, and tertiary halides react so slowly as to be unreactive by the S$_N$2 mechanism. Table 6.3 gives the relative rates of typical S$_N$2 reactions.

TABLE 6.3 RELATIVE RATES OF REACTIONS OF ALKYL HALIDES IN S_N2 REACTIONS		
Substituent	Compound	Approximate Relative Rate
Methyl	CH_3X	30
1°	CH_3CH_2X	1
2°	$(CH_3)_2CHX$	0.03
Neopentyl	$(CH_3)_3CCH_2X$	0.00001
3°	$(CH_3)_3CX$	~0

Neopentyl halides, even though they are primary halides, are very unreactive:

A neopentyl halide

The important factor behind this order of reactivity is a steric effect, and in this case, steric hindrance.

- A **steric effect** is an effect on the relative rates caused by the space-filling properties of those parts of a molecule attached at or near the reacting site.
- **Steric hindrance** is when the spatial arrangement of atoms or groups at or near a reacting site of a molecule hinders or retards a reaction.

For particles (molecules and ions) to react, their reactive centers must be able to come within bonding distance of each other. Although most molecules are reasonably flexible, very large and bulky groups can often hinder the formation of the required transition state. In some cases they can prevent its formation altogether.

An S_N2 reaction requires an approach by the nucleophile to a distance within the bonding range of the carbon atom bearing the leaving group. Because of this, bulky substituents on *or near* that carbon atom have a dramatic inhibiting effect (Fig. 6.9). Nearby bulky groups cause the free energy of an S_N2 transition state to be higher and, consequently, the free energy of activation for the reaction is larger, and the rate of reaction is slower. Of the simple alkyl halides, methyl halides react most rapidly in S_N2 reactions because only three small hydrogen atoms interfere with the approaching nucleophile. Neopentyl and tertiary halides are the least reactive because bulky groups present a strong hindrance to the approaching nucleophile. (Tertiary substrates, for all practical purposes, do not react by an S_N2 mechanism.)

Helpful Hint

You can best appreciate the steric effects in these structures by building models.

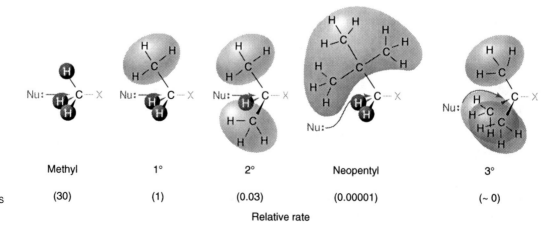

FIGURE 6.9 Steric effects and relative rates in the S_N2 reaction.

Methyl	1°	2°	Neopentyl	3°
(30)	(1)	(0.03)	(0.00001)	(~ 0)

Relative rate

Rank the following alkyl bromides in order of decreasing reactivity (from fastest to slowest) as a substrate in an S_N2 reaction.

A   **B**   **C**   **D**

STRATEGY AND ANSWER: We examine the carbon bearing the leaving group in each instance to assess the steric hindrance to an S_N2 reaction at that carbon. In **C** it is 3°; therefore, three groups would hinder the approach of a nucleophile, so this alkyl bromide would react most slowly. In **D** the carbon bearing the leaving group is 2° (two groups hinder the approach of the nucleophile), while in both **A** and **B** it is 1° (one group hinders the nucleophile's approach). Therefore, **D** would react faster than **C**, but slower than either **A** or **B**. But, what about **A** and **B**? They are both 1° alkyl bromides, but **B** has a methyl group on the carbon adjacent to the one bearing the bromine, which would provide steric hindrance to the approaching nucleophile that would not be present in **A**. The order of reactivity, therefore, is **A** > **B** > **D** ≫ **C**.

S_N1 Reactions

- The primary factor that determines the reactivity of organic substrates in an S_N1 reaction is the relative stability of the carbocation that is formed.

Of the simple alkyl halides that we have studied so far, this means (for all practical purposes) that only tertiary halides react by an S_N1 mechanism. (Later we shall see that certain organic halides, called *allylic halides* and *benzylic halides*, can also react by an S_N1 mechanism because they can form relatively stable carbocations; see Sections 13.4 and 15.15.)

Tertiary carbocations are stabilized because sigma bonds at three adjacent carbons contribute electron density to the carbocation p orbital by hyperconjugation (Section 6.11B). Secondary and primary carbocations have less stabilization by hyperconjugation. A methyl carbocation has no stabilization. Formation of a relatively stable carbocation is important in an S_N1 reaction because it means that the free energy of activation for the slow step of the reaction (e.g., $R-L \longrightarrow R^+ + L^-$) will be low enough for the reaction to take place at a reasonable rate.

●●●

PRACTICE PROBLEM 6.10

Which of the following alkyl halides is most likely to undergo substitution by an S_N1 mechanism?

(a)   (b)   (c)

The Hammond–Leffler Postulate If you review the free-energy diagrams that accompany the mechanism for the S_N1 reaction of *tert*-butyl chloride and water (Section 6.10), you will see that step 1, the ionization of the leaving group to form the carbocation, is *uphill in terms of free energy* ($\Delta G°$ for this step is positive). It is also uphill in terms of enthalpy ($\Delta H°$ is also positive), and, therefore, this step is *endothermic*.

- According to the Hammond–Leffler postulate, **the transition-state structure for a step that is uphill in energy should show a strong resemblance to the structure of the product of that step.**

Since the product of this step (actually an intermediate in the overall reaction) is a carbocation, any factor that stabilizes the carbocation—such as dispersal of the positive charge by electron-releasing groups—should also stabilize the transition state in which the positive charge is developing.

Ionization of the Leaving Group

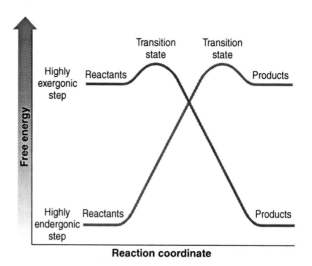

Reactant   **Transition state**   **Product of step**

Resembles product of step because ΔG° is positive   *Stabilized by three electron-releasing groups*

A methyl, primary, or secondary alkyl halide would have to ionize to form a methyl, primary, or secondary carbocation to react by an S_N1 mechanism. These carbocations, however, are much higher in energy than a tertiary carbocation, and the transition states leading to these carbocations are even higher in energy.

- The activation energy for an S_N1 reaction of a simple methyl, primary, or secondary halide is so large (therefore the reaction is so slow) that, for all practical purposes, an S_N1 reaction with a methyl, primary, or secondary halide does not compete with the corresponding S_N2 reaction.

The Hammond–Leffler postulate is quite general and can be better understood through consideration of Fig. 6.10. One way that the postulate can be stated is to say that *the structure of a transition state resembles the stable species that is nearest it in free energy.* For example, in a highly **endergonic** step (blue curve) the transition state lies close to the products in free energy, and we assume, therefore, that **it resembles the products of that step in structure.** Conversely, in a highly exergonic step (red curve) the transition state lies close to the reactants in free energy, and we assume **it resembles the reactants in structure** as well. The great value of the Hammond–Leffler postulate is that it gives us an intuitive way of visualizing those important, but fleeting, species that we call transition states. We shall make use of it in many future discussions.

FIGURE 6.10 The transition state for a highly exergonic step (red curve) lies close to and resembles the reactants. The transition state for an endergonic step (blue curve) lies close to and resembles the products of a reaction. (Reprinted with permission of the McGraw-Hill Companies from Pryor, W., *Free Radicals*, p. 156, copyright 1966.)

PRACTICE PROBLEM 6.11   The relative rates of ethanolysis of four primary alkyl halides are as follows: CH_3CH_2Br, 1.0; $CH_3CH_2CH_2Br$, 0.28; $(CH_3)_2CHCH_2Br$, 0.030; $(CH_3)_3CCH_2Br$, 0.00000042.

(a) Is each of these reactions likely to be S_N1 or S_N2?

(b) Provide an explanation for the relative reactivities that are observed.

6.13B The Effect of the Concentration and Strength of the Nucleophile

- The rate of an S$_N$1 reaction is unaffected by either the concentration or the identity of the nucleophile, because the nucleophile does not participate in the rate-determining step of an S$_N$1 reaction.

- The rate of an S$_N$2 reaction depends on *both* the concentration *and* the identity of the attacking nucleophile.

We saw in Section 6.5 how increasing the concentration of the nucleophile increases the rate of an S$_N$2 reaction. We can now examine how the rate of an S$_N$2 reaction depends on the identity of the nucleophile.

- The relative strength of a nucleophile (its nucleophilicity) is measured in terms of the relative rate of its S$_N$2 reaction with a given substrate.

A good nucleophile is one that reacts rapidly in an S$_N$2 reaction with a given substrate. A poor nucleophile is one that reacts slowly in an S$_N$2 reaction with the same substrate under comparable reaction conditions. (As mentioned above, we cannot compare nucleophilicities with regard to S$_N$1 reactions because the nucleophile does not participate in the rate-determining step of an S$_N$1 reaction.)

Methoxide anion, for example, is a good nucleophile for a substitution reaction with iodomethane. It reacts rapidly by an S$_N$2 mechanism to form dimethyl ether:

$$CH_3O^- + CH_3I \xrightarrow{\text{rapid}} CH_3OCH_3 + I^-$$

Methanol, on the other hand, is a poor nucleophile for reaction with iodomethane. Under comparable conditions it reacts very slowly. It is not a sufficiently powerful Lewis base (i.e., nucleophile) to cause displacement of the iodide leaving group at a significant rate:

$$CH_3OH + CH_3I \xrightarrow{\text{very slow}} CH_3\overset{+}{\underset{|}{O}}CH_3 + I^-$$
$$\qquad\qquad\qquad\qquad\quad H$$

- The relative strengths of nucleophiles can be correlated with three structural features:

   1. **A negatively charged nucleophile is always a more reactive nucleophile than its conjugate acid.** Thus HO$^-$ is a better nucleophile than H$_2$O and RO$^-$ is better than ROH.

   2. **In a group of nucleophiles in which the nucleophilic atom is the same, nucleophilicities parallel basicities.** Oxygen compounds, for example, show the following order of reactivity:

      $$RO^- > HO^- \gg RCO_2^- > ROH > H_2O$$

      This is also their order of basicity. An alkoxide ion (RO$^-$) is a slightly stronger base than a hydroxide ion (HO$^-$), a hydroxide ion is a much stronger base than a carboxylate ion (RCO$_2^-$), and so on.

   3. **When the nucleophilic atoms are different, nucleophilicities may not parallel basicities.** For example, in protic solvents HS$^-$, N≡C$^-$, and I$^-$ are all weaker bases than HO$^-$, yet they are **stronger nucleophiles** than HO$^-$.

      $$HS^- > N{\equiv}C^- > I^- > HO^-$$

Nucleophilicity versus Basicity While nucleophilicity and basicity are related, they are not measured in the same way.

- Basicity, as expressed by pK_a, is measured *by the position of an equilibrium* in an acid–base reaction.

- Nucleophilicity is measured *by the relative rates of substitution reactions.*

For example, the hydroxide ion (HO⁻) is a stronger base than a cyanide ion (N≡C⁻); at equilibrium it has the greater affinity for a proton (the pK_a of H_2O is ~16, while the pK_a of HCN is ~10). Nevertheless, cyanide ion is a stronger nucleophile; it reacts more rapidly with a carbon bearing a leaving group than does hydroxide ion.

PRACTICE PROBLEM 6.12   Rank the following in terms of *decreasing* nucleophilicity:

$$CH_3CO_2^- \quad CH_3OH \quad CH_3O^- \quad CH_3CO_2H \quad N\equiv C^-$$

6.13C Solvent Effects in S$_N$2 and S$_N$1 Reactions

- S$_N$2 reactions are favored by **polar aprotic solvents** (e.g., acetone, DMF, DMSO).
- S$_N$1 reactions are favored by **polar protic solvents** (e.g., EtOH, MeOH, H$_2$O).

Important reasons for these solvent effects have to do with (a) minimizing the solvent's interaction with the nucleophile in S$_N$2 reactions, and (b) facilitating ionization of the leaving group and stabilizing ionic intermediates by solvents in S$_N$1 reactions. In the following subsections we will explain these factors in further detail.

Polar Aprotic Solvents Favor S$_N$2 Reactions

- An aprotic solvent does not have hydrogen atoms that are capable of hydrogen bonding.
- Polar, aprotic solvents such as acetone, DMF, DMSO, and HMPA are often used alone or as co-solvents for S$_N$2 reactions.

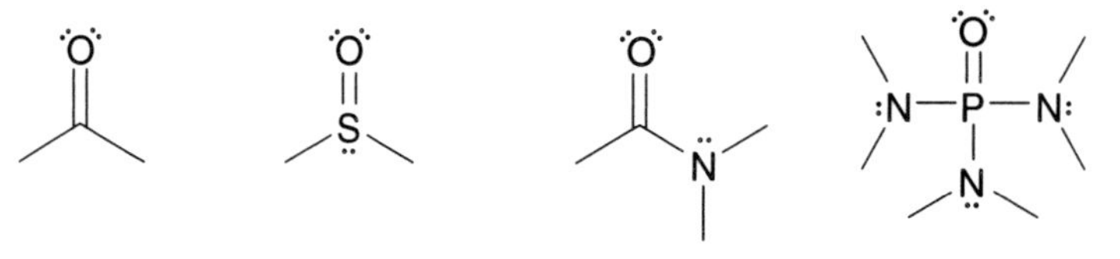

| **Acetone** | **DMSO** (Dimethylsulfoxide) | **DMF** (*N,N*-Dimethyl-formamide) | **HMPA** (Hexamethyl phosphoramide) |

- The rates of S$_N$2 reactions generally are vastly increased when they are carried out in polar aprotic solvents. The increase in rate can be as large as a millionfold.

Polar aprotic solvents solubilize cations well using their unshared electron pairs, but do not interact as strongly with anions because they cannot hydrogen bond with them and because the positive regions of the solvent are shielded by steric effects from the anion. This differential solvation leaves anions more free to act as nucleophiles because they are less encumbered by the cation and solvent, thus enhancing the rate of S$_N$2 reaction. Sodium ions of sodium iodide, for example, can be solvated by DMSO as shown here, leaving the iodide anion more free to act as a nucleophile.

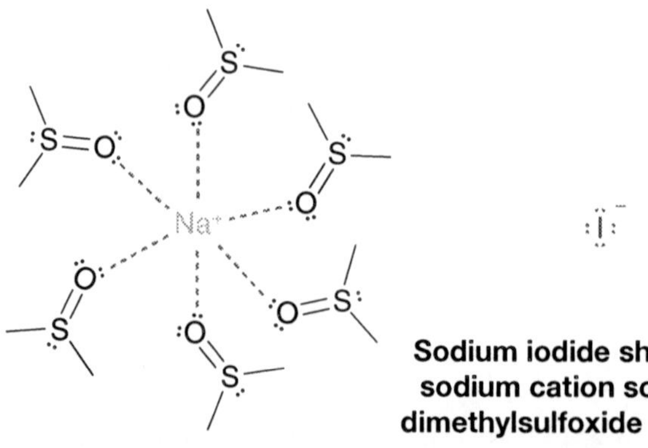

Sodium iodide showing the sodium cation solvated by dimethylsulfoxide molecules.

"Naked" anions in polar aprotic solvents are also more reactive as bases, as well as in their capacity as nucleophiles. In DMSO, for example, the relative order of halide ion basicity is the same as their relative order of nucleophilicity. Halide basicity is opposite to nucleophilicity in protic solvents, however, as we shall explain shortly.

$$F^- \; > \; Cl^- \; > \; Br^- \; > \; I^-$$

Halide nucleophilicity in aprotic solvents

> ## Helpful Hint
>
> Polar aprotic solvents increase S$_N$2 rates.

Polar Protic Solvents Favor S$_N$1 Reactions

- A protic solvent has at least one hydrogen atom capable of participating in a hydrogen bond.
- Protic solvents, such as water, EtOH, and MeOH, facilitate formation of a carbocation by forming hydrogen bonds with the leaving group as it departs, thereby lowering the energy of the transition state leading to a carbocation.

| Hydrogen bonding with the substrate | Departure of the leaving group is assisted by hydrogen bonding in the transition state | Carbocation intermediate | Solvated leaving group |

A rough indication of a solvent's polarity is a quantity called the **dielectric constant.** The dielectric constant is a measure of the solvent's ability to insulate opposite charges (or separate ions) from each other. Electrostatic attractions and repulsions between ions are smaller in solvents with higher dielectric constants. Table 6.4 gives the dielectric constants of some common solvents.

TABLE 6.4 DIELECTRIC CONSTANTS OF COMMON SOLVENTS

	Solvent	Formula	Dielectric Constant
	Water	H_2O	80
	Formic acid	HCO_2H	59
	Dimethyl sulfoxide (DMSO)	CH_3SOCH_3	49
Increasing solvent polarity	N,N-Dimethylformamide (DMF)	$HCON(CH_3)_2$	37
	Acetonitrile	$CH_3C\equiv N$	36
	Methanol	CH_3OH	33
	Hexamethylphosphoramide (HMPA)	$[(CH_3)_2N]_3P{=}O$	30
	Ethanol	CH_3CH_2OH	24
	Acetone	CH_3COCH_3	21
	Acetic acid	CH_3CO_2H	6

Water is the most effective solvent for promoting ionization, but most organic compounds do not dissolve appreciably in water. They usually dissolve, however, in alcohols, and quite often mixed solvents are used. Methanol—water and ethanol—water are common mixed solvents for nucleophilic substitution reactions.

Protic Solvents Hinder the Nucleophile in S$_N$2 Reactions

A solvated nucleophile must shed some of its solvent molecules to react with the substrate. In a polar aprotic solvent, the nucleophile is less unencumbered by solvent molecules because hydrogen bonding between the solvent and the nucleophile is not possible.

• Hydrogen bonding with a protic solvent such as water, EtOH, or MeOH, encumbers a nucleophile and hinders its reactivity in a nucleophilic substitution reaction.

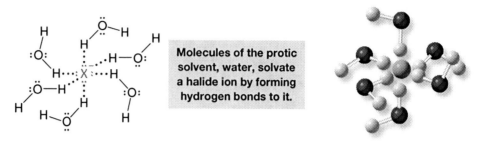

Molecules of the protic solvent, water, solvate a halide ion by forming hydrogen bonds to it.

• The extent of hydrogen bonding with the nucleophile varies with the identity of the nucleophile. Hydrogen bonding with a small nucleophilic atom is stronger than to a larger nucleophilic atom among elements in the same group (column) of the periodic table.

For example, fluoride anion is more strongly solvated than the other halides because it is the smallest halide anion and its charge is the most concentrated. Hence, in a protic solvent fluoride is not as effective a nucleophile as the other halide anions. Iodide is the largest halide anion and it is the most weakly solvated in a protic solvent; hence, it is the strongest nucleophile among the halide anions.

• In a protic solvent, the general trend in *nucleophilicity* among the halide anions is as follows:

$$I^- > Br^- > Cl^- > F^-$$

Halide nucleophilicity in protic solvents

The same effect holds true when we compare sulfur nucleophiles with oxygen nucleophiles. Sulfur atoms are larger than oxygen atoms and hence they are not solvated as strongly in a protic solvent. Thus, thiols (R—SH) are stronger nucleophiles than alcohols, and RS$^-$ anions are better nucleophiles than RO$^-$ anions.

The greater reactivity of nucleophiles with large nucleophilic atoms is not entirely related to solvation. Larger atoms have greater **polarizability** (their electron clouds are more easily distorted); therefore, a larger nucleophilic atom can donate a greater degree of electron density to the substrate than a smaller nucleophile whose electrons are more tightly held.

The relative nucleophilicities of some common nucleophiles in protic solvents are as follows:

$$HS^- > N \equiv C^- > I^- > HO^- > N_3^- > Br^- > CH_3CO_2^- > Cl^- > F^- > H_2O$$

Relative nucleophilicity in protic solvents

PRACTICE PROBLEM 6.13 Rank the following in terms of decreasing nucleophilicity in a protic solvent.

$$CH_3CO_2^- \qquad CH_3O^- \qquad CH_3S^- \qquad CH_3SH \qquad CH_3OH$$

PRACTICE PROBLEM 6.14 Classify the following solvents as being protic or aprotic: formic acid, HCO_2H; acetone, CH_3COCH_3; acetonitrile, $CH_3C \equiv N$; formamide, $HCONH_2$; sulfur dioxide, SO_2; ammonia, NH_3; trimethylamine, $N(CH_3)_3$; ethylene glycol, $HOCH_2CH_2OH$.

PRACTICE PROBLEM 6.15 Would you expect the reaction of propyl bromide with sodium cyanide (NaCN), that is,

$$CH_3CH_2CH_2Br + NaCN \longrightarrow CH_3CH_2CH_2CN + NaBr$$

to occur faster in DMF or in ethanol? Explain your answer.

PRACTICE PROBLEM 6.16

Which would you expect to be the stronger nucleophile in a polar aprotic solvent?
(a) CH$_3$CO$_2^-$ or CH$_3$O$^-$ **(b)** H$_2$O or H$_2$S   **(c)** (CH$_3$)$_3$P or (CH$_3$)$_3$N

PRACTICE PROBLEM 6.17

When *tert*-butyl bromide undergoes solvolysis in a mixture of methanol and water, the rate of solvolysis (measured by the rate at which bromide ions form in the mixture) *increases* when the percentage of water in the mixture is increased. **(a)** Explain this occurrence. **(b)** Provide an explanation for the observation that the rate of the S$_N$2 reaction of ethyl chloride with potassium iodide in methanol and water *decreases* when the percentage of water in the mixture is increased.

6.13D The Nature of the Leaving Group

- Leaving groups depart with the electron pair that was used to bond them to the substrate.
- The best leaving groups are those that become either a relatively stable anion or a neutral molecule when they depart.

Helpful Hint

Good leaving groups are weak bases.

First, let us consider leaving groups that become anions when they separate from the substrate. Because weak bases stabilize a negative charge effectively, leaving groups that become weak bases are good leaving groups.

The reason that stabilization of the negative charge is important can be understood by considering the structure of the transition states. In either an S$_N$1 or S$_N$2 reaction the leaving group begins to acquire a negative charge as the transition state is reached:

S$_N$1 Reaction (Rate-Limiting Step)

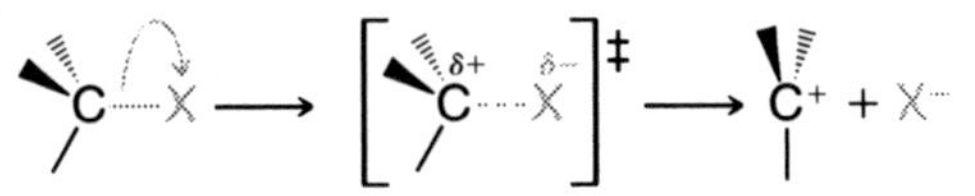

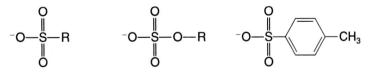

Transition state

S$_N$2 Reaction

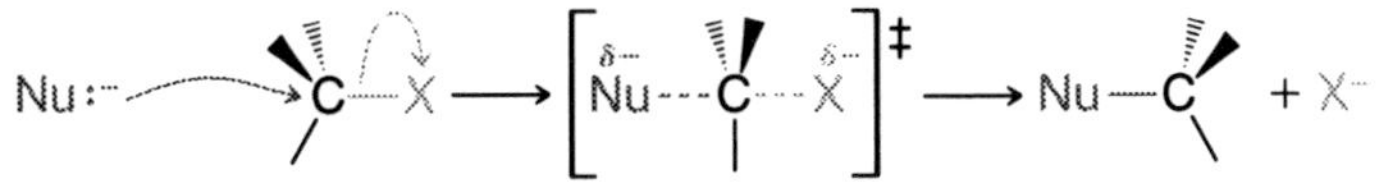

Transition state

Stabilization of this developing negative charge at the leaving group stabilizes the transition state (lowers its free energy); this lowers the free energy of activation and thereby increases the rate of the reaction.

- Among the halogens, an iodide ion is the best leaving group and a fluoride ion is the poorest:

$$I^- > Br^- > Cl^- \gg F^-$$

The order is the opposite of the basicity in an aprotic solvent:

$$F^- \gg Cl^- > Br^- > I^-$$

Other weak bases that are good leaving groups, which we shall study later, are alkanesulfonate ions, alkyl sulfate ions, and the *p*-toluenesulfonate ion:

An alkanesulfonate ion	**An alkyl sulfate ion**	**p-Toluenesulfonate ion**

These anions are all the conjugate bases of very strong acids.

The trifluoromethanesulfonate ion ($CF_3SO_3^-$, commonly called the **triflate ion**) is one of the best leaving groups known to chemists. It is the conjugate base of CF_3SO_3H, an exceedingly strong acid ($pK_a \sim -5$ to -6):

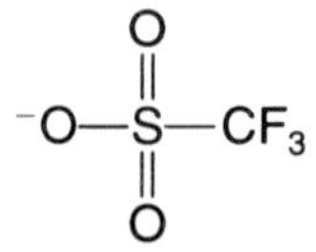

$$^-O-\overset{\displaystyle O}{\underset{\displaystyle O}{\overset{\|}{\underset{\|}{S}}}}-CF_3$$

**Triflate ion
(a "super" leaving group)**

• Strongly basic ions rarely act as leaving groups.

The hydroxide ion, for example, is a strong base and thus reactions like the following do not take place:

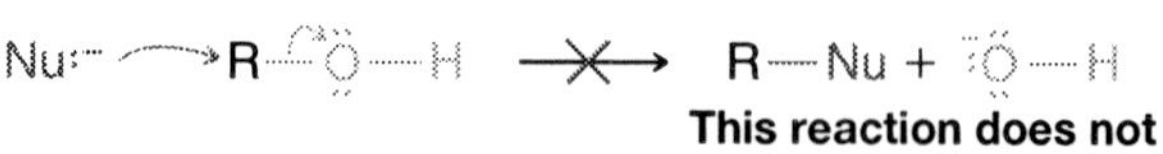

$$Nu:^- \longrightarrow R \overset{\frown}{\ddot{O}} - H \quad \xrightarrow{\quad\times\quad} \quad R-Nu + \ \ddot{:O} - H$$

**This reaction does not
take place because the
leaving group is a strongly
basic hydroxide ion.**

However, when an alcohol is dissolved in a strong acid, it can undergo substitution by a nucleophile. Because the acid protonates the —OH group of the alcohol, the leaving group no longer needs to be a hydroxide ion; it is now a molecule of water—a much weaker base than a hydroxide ion and a good leaving group:

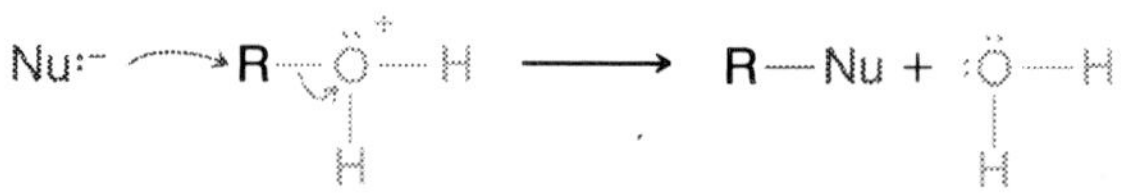

$$Nu:^- \longrightarrow R \overset{+}{\underset{\underset{\displaystyle H}{|}}{\ddot{O}}} - H \quad \longrightarrow \quad R-Nu + \overset{}{\underset{\underset{\displaystyle H}{|}}{\ddot{:O}}} - H$$

**This reaction takes place
because the leaving
group is a weak base.**

PRACTICE PROBLEM 6.18 List the following compounds in order of decreasing reactivity toward CH_3O^- in an S_N2 reaction carried out in CH_3OH: CH_3F, CH_3Cl, CH_3Br, CH_3I, $CH_3OSO_2CF_3$, $^{14}CH_3OH$.

• Very powerful bases such as hydride ions ($H:^-$) and alkanide ions ($R:^-$) virtually never act as leaving groups.

Therefore, **reactions such as the following are not feasible**:

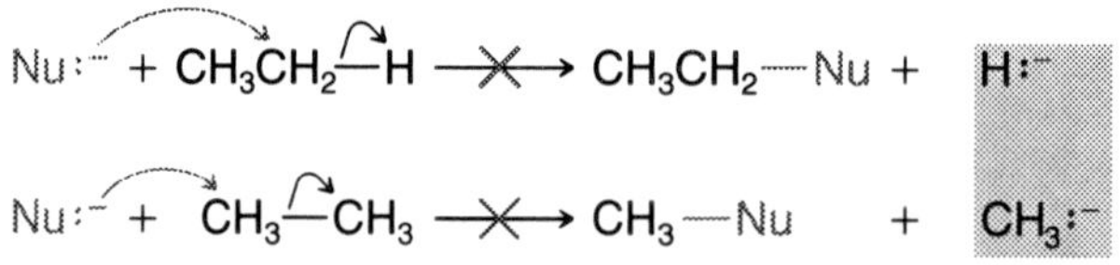

$$Nu:^- + CH_3CH_2 \overset{\frown}{-} H \xrightarrow{\quad\times\quad} CH_3CH_2 - Nu + \boxed{H:^-}$$

$$Nu:^- + CH_3 \overset{\frown}{-} CH_3 \xrightarrow{\quad\times\quad} CH_3 - Nu \quad + \boxed{CH_3:^-}$$

These are not leaving groups.

Remember: The best leaving groups are weak bases after they depart.

●●● SOLVED PROBLEM 6.7

Explain why the following reaction is not feasible as a synthesis of butyl iodide.

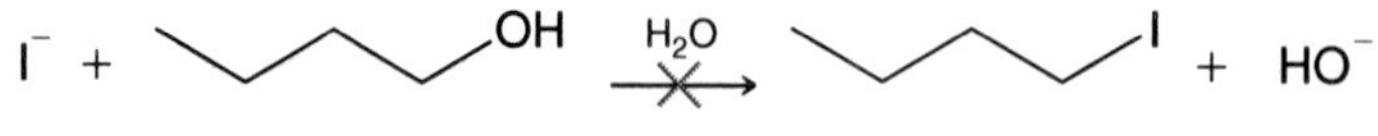

$$I^- + \text{\Large \diagdown\diagup\diagdown\diagup}OH \xrightarrow[\quad\times\quad]{H_2O} \text{\Large \diagdown\diagup\diagdown\diagup}I + HO^-$$

STRATEGY AND ANSWER: The strongly basic HO^- ion (hydroxide ion) virtually never acts as a leaving group, something this reaction would require. This reaction would be feasible under acidic conditions, in which case the leaving group would be a water molecule.

SUMMARY OF S_N1 VERSUS S_N2 REACTIONS

S_N1: The Following Conditions Favor an S_N1 Reaction

1. A substrate that can form a relatively stable carbocation (such as a substrate with a leaving group at a tertiary position)

2. A relatively weak nucleophile

3. A polar, protic solvent such as EtOH, MeOH, or H_2O

The S_N1 mechanism is, therefore, important in solvolysis reactions of tertiary alkyl halides, especially when the solvent is highly polar. In a solvolysis reaction the nucleophile is weak because it is a neutral molecule (of the polar protic solvent) rather than an anion.

S_N2: The Following Conditions Favor an S_N2 Reaction

1. A substrate with a relatively unhindered leaving group (such as a methyl, primary, or secondary alkyl halide). The order of reactivity is

$$CH_3-X \; > \; R-CH_2-X \; > \; \overset{\overset{\displaystyle R}{\displaystyle |}}{R-CH-X}$$
$$\textbf{Methyl} \; > \quad\quad \textbf{1°} \quad\quad > \quad\quad \textbf{2°}$$

Tertiary halides do not react by an S_N2 mechanism.

2. A strong nucleophile (usually negatively charged)

3. High concentration of the nucleophile

4. A polar, aprotic solvent

The trend in reaction rate for a halogen as the leaving group is the same in S_N1 and S_N2 reactions:

$$R-I > R-Br > R-Cl \quad\quad S_N1 \text{ or } S_N2$$

Because alkyl fluorides react so slowly, they are seldom used in nucleophilic substitution reactions.

These factors are summarized in Table 6.5.

TABLE 6.5 FACTORS FAVORING S_N1 VERSUS S_N2 REACTIONS

Factor	S_N1	S_N2
Substrate	3° (requires formation of a relatively stable carbocation)	Methyl > 1° > 2° (requires unhindered substrate)
Nucleophile	Weak Lewis base, neutral molecule, nucleophile may be the solvent (solvolysis)	Strong Lewis base, rate increased by high concentration of nucleophile
Solvent	Polar protic (e.g., alcohols, water)	Polar aprotic (e.g., DMF, DMSO)
Leaving group	I > Br > Cl > F for both S_N1 and S_N2 (the weaker the base after the group departs, the better the leaving group)	

6.14 ORGANIC SYNTHESIS: FUNCTIONAL GROUP TRANSFORMATIONS USING S_N2 REACTIONS

S_N2 reactions are highly useful in organic synthesis because they enable us to convert one functional group into another—a process that is called a **functional group transformation** or a **functional group interconversion**. With the S_N2 reactions shown in Fig. 6.11, methyl, primary, or secondary alkyl halides can be transformed into alcohols, ethers, thiols, thioethers, nitriles, esters, and so on. (*Note*: The use of the prefix *thio-* in a name means that a sulfur atom has replaced an oxygen atom in the compound.)

FIGURE 6.11 Functional group interconversions of methyl, primary, and secondary alkyl halides using S_N2 reactions.

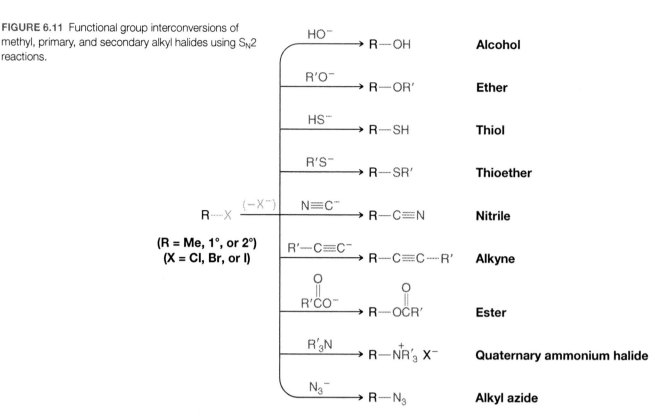

HO⁻	R—OH	**Alcohol**
R′O⁻	R—OR′	**Ether**
HS⁻	R—SH	**Thiol**
R′S⁻	R—SR′	**Thioether**
N≡C⁻	R—C≡N	**Nitrile**
R′—C≡C⁻	R—C≡C—R′	**Alkyne**
R′CO⁻ (O)	R—OCR′ (O)	**Ester**
R′₃N	R—N⁺R′₃ X⁻	**Quaternary ammonium halide**
N₃⁻	R—N₃	**Alkyl azide**

R—X (—X⁻)

(R = Me, 1°, or 2°)
(X = Cl, Br, or I)

Alkyl chlorides and bromides are also easily converted to alkyl iodides by nucleophilic substitution reactions.

$$R—Cl \text{ or } R—Br \xrightarrow{\;I^-\;} R—I \; (+ Cl^- \text{ or } Br^-)$$

One other aspect of the S_N2 reaction that is of great importance is **stereochemistry** (Section 6.8). S_N2 reactions always occur with **inversion of configuration** at the atom that bears the leaving group. This means that when we use S_N2 reactions in syntheses we can be sure of the configuration of our product if we know the configuration of our reactant. For example, suppose we need a sample of the following nitrile with the (S) configuration:

$$:N≡C—C\overset{CH_3}{\underset{CH_2CH_3}{|}}H$$

(S)-2-Methylbutanenitrile

If we have available (R)-2-bromobutane, we can carry out the following synthesis:

$$:N≡C:^- + H\overset{CH_3}{\underset{CH_2CH_3}{—C—}}Br \xrightarrow[\text{(inversion)}]{S_N2} :N≡C—C\overset{CH_3}{\underset{CH_2CH_3}{|}}H + Br^-$$

(R)-2-Bromobutane   **(S)-2-Methylbutanenitrile**

PRACTICE PROBLEM 6.19   Starting with (S)-2-bromobutane, outline syntheses of each of the following compounds:

(a) (R)-CH₃CHCH₂CH₃
　　　　　|
　　　　　OCH₂CH₃

(b) (R)-CH₃CHCH₂CH₃
　　　　　|
　　　　　OCCH₃
　　　　　‖
　　　　　O

(c) (R)-CH₃CHCH₂CH₃
　　　　　|
　　　　　SH

(d) (R)-CH₃CHCH₂CH₃
　　　　　|
　　　　　SCH₃

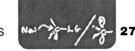

THE CHEMISTRY OF... Biological Methylation: A Biological Nucleophilic Substitution Reaction

The cells of living organisms synthesize many of the compounds they need from smaller molecules. Often these biosyntheses resemble the syntheses organic chemists carry out in their laboratories. Let us examine one example now.

Many reactions taking place in the cells of plants and animals involve the transfer of a methyl group from an amino acid called methionine to some other compound. That this transfer takes place can be demonstrated experimentally by feeding a plant or animal methionine containing an isotopically labeled carbon atom (e.g., ^{13}C or ^{14}C) in its methyl group. Later, other compounds containing the "labeled" methyl group can be isolated from the organism. Some of the compounds that get their methyl groups from methionine are the following. The isotopically labeled carbon atom is shown in green.

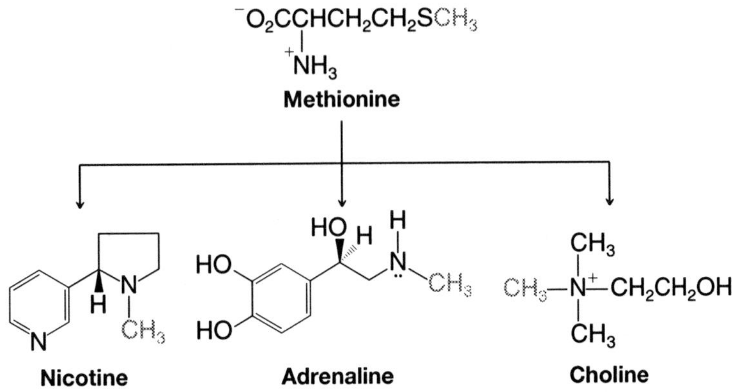

$$^-O_2CCHCH_2CH_2SCH_3$$
$$\overset{|}{\underset{+NH_3}{}}$$

Methionine

Nicotine   Adrenaline   Choline

Choline is important in the transmission of nerve impulses, adrenaline causes blood pressure to increase, and nicotine is the compound contained in tobacco that makes smoking tobacco addictive. (In large doses nicotine is poisonous.)

The transfer of the methyl group from methionine to these other compounds does not take place directly. The actual methylating agent is not methionine; it is *S*-adenosylmethionine,* a compound that results when methionine reacts with adenosine triphosphate (ATP):

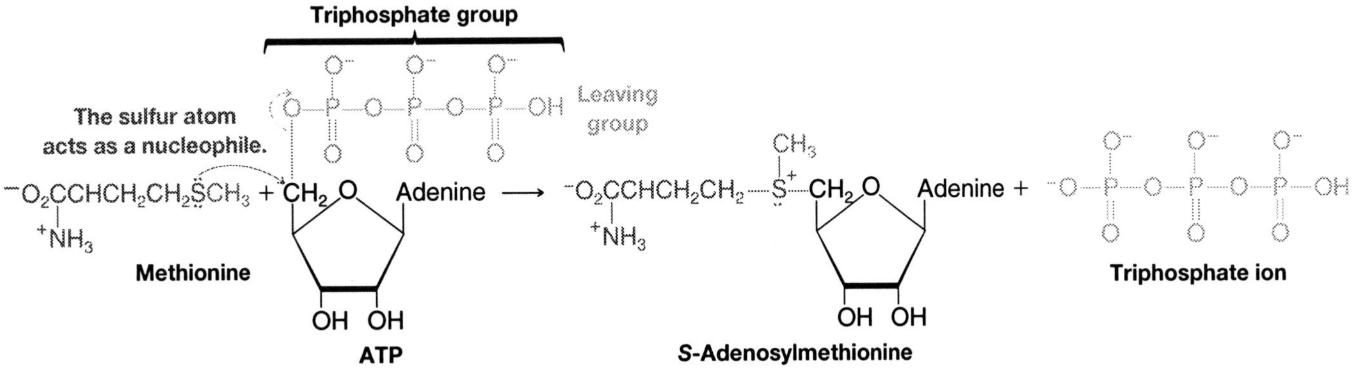

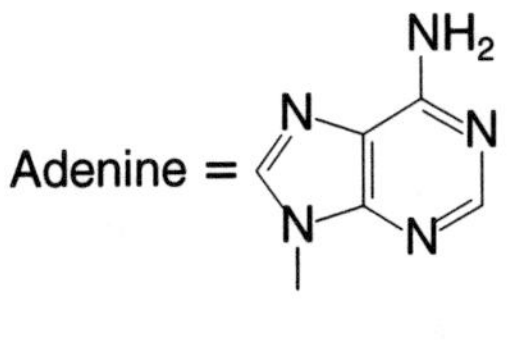

Triphosphate group

The sulfur atom acts as a nucleophile.

Leaving group

$$^-O_2CCHCH_2CH_2\overset{..}{\underset{+NH_3}{S}}CH_3 + CH_2O \quad \text{Adenine} \longrightarrow ^-O_2CCHCH_2CH_2\overset{CH_3}{\overset{+}{\underset{+NH_3}{S}}}CH_2O \quad \text{Adenine} + \quad \text{Triphosphate ion}$$

Methionine   **ATP**   ***S*-Adenosylmethionine**

Adenine =

*The prefix *S* is a locant meaning "on the sulfur atom" and should not be confused with the (*S*) used to define absolute configuration. Another example of this kind of locant is *N*, meaning "on the nitrogen atom."

(continues on next page)

This reaction is a nucleophilic substitution reaction. The nucleophilic atom is the sulfur atom of methionine. The leaving group is the weakly basic triphosphate group of ATP. The product, *S*-adenosylmethionine, contains a methyl-sulfonium group,

$CH_3-\overset{|}{\underset{|}{S}}{}^+-$.

S-Adenosylmethionine then acts as the substrate for other nucleophilic substitution reactions. In the biosynthesis of choline, for example, it transfers its methyl group to a nucleophilic nitrogen atom of 2-(*N,N*-dimethylamino)ethanol:

2-(*N,N*-Dimethylamino)ethanol

Choline

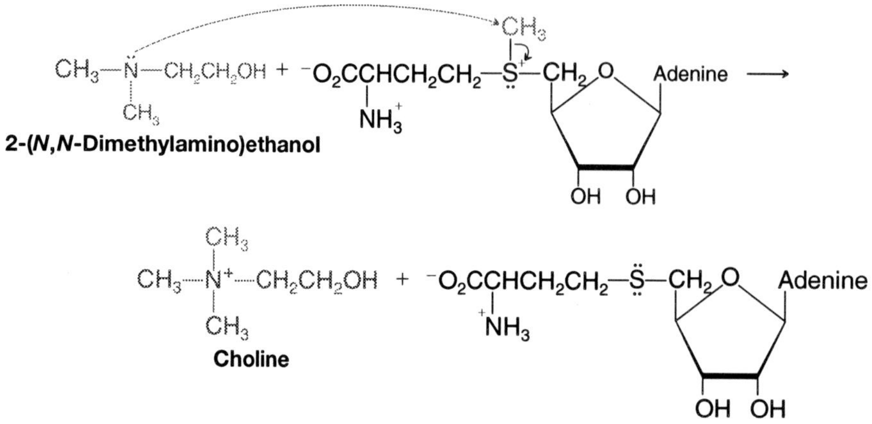

These reactions appear complicated only because the structures of the nucleophiles and substrates are complex. Yet conceptually they are simple, and they illustrate many of the principles we have encountered thus far in Chapter 6. In them we see how nature makes use of the high nucleophilicity of sulfur atoms. We also see how a weakly basic group (e.g., the triphosphate group of ATP) functions as a leaving group. In the reaction of 2-(*N,N*-dimethylamino) ethanol we see that the more basic $(CH_3)_2N-$ group acts as the nucleophile rather than the less basic $-OH$ group. And when a nucleophile attacks *S*-adenosylmethionine, we see that the attack takes place at the less hindered CH_3- group rather than at one of the more hindered $-CH_2-$ groups.

Study Problem

(a) What is the leaving group when 2-(*N,N*-dimethylamino)ethanol reacts with *S*-adenosylmethionine?

(b) What would the leaving group have to be if methionine itself were to react with 2-(*N,N*-dimethylamino)ethanol?

(c) Of what special significance is this difference?

6.14A The Unreactivity of Vinylic and Phenyl Halides

As we learned in Section 6.1, compounds that have a halogen atom attached to one carbon atom of a double bond are called **alkenyl** or **vinylic halides**; those that have a halogen atom attached to a benzene ring are called **aryl** or **phenyl halides**:

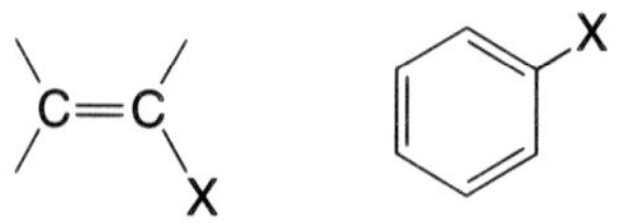

An alkenyl halide   A phenyl halide

● Alkenyl and phenyl halides are generally unreactive in S_N1 or S_N2 reactions.

They are unreactive in S_N1 reactions because alkenyl and phenyl cations are relatively unstable and do not form readily. They are unreactive in S_N2 reactions because the carbon–halogen bond of an alkenyl or phenyl halide is stronger than that of an alkyl halide (we shall see why later), and the electrons of the double bond or benzene ring repel the approach of a nucleophile from the back side.

6.15 ELIMINATION REACTIONS OF ALKYL HALIDES

Elimination reactions of alkyl halides are important reactions that compete with substitution reactions. In an **elimination reaction** the fragments of some molecule (**YZ**) are removed (eliminated) from adjacent atoms of the reactant. This elimination leads to the creation of a multiple bond:

$$-\overset{\overset{\displaystyle Y}{|}}{\underset{}{C}}-\overset{\overset{}{|}}{\underset{\underset{\displaystyle Z}{|}}{C}}- \quad \xrightarrow[(-YZ)]{\text{elimination}} \quad \overset{\diagdown}{\underset{\diagup}{C}}=\overset{\diagup}{\underset{\diagdown}{C}}$$

6.15A Dehydrohalogenation

A widely used method for synthesizing alkenes is the elimination of **HX** from adjacent atoms of an alkyl halide. Heating the alkyl halide with a strong base causes the reaction to take place. The following are two examples:

$$\underset{\underset{\displaystyle Br}{|}}{CH_3CHCH_3} \quad \xrightarrow[C_2H_5OH,\ 55°C]{C_2H_5ONa} \quad \underset{\textbf{(79\%)}}{CH_2=CH-CH_3} \ + \ NaBr \ + \ C_2H_5OH$$

$$\underset{\underset{\displaystyle CH_3}{|}}{\overset{\overset{\displaystyle CH_3}{|}}{CH_3-C-Br}} \quad \xrightarrow[C_2H_5OH,\ 55°C]{C_2H_5ONa} \quad \underset{\textbf{(91\%)}}{\overset{\overset{\displaystyle CH_3}{|}}{\underset{CH_3}{C}}\diagdown_{CH_2}} \ + \ NaBr \ + \ C_2H_5OH$$

Reactions like these are not limited to the elimination of hydrogen bromide. Chloroalkanes also undergo the elimination of hydrogen chloride, iodoalkanes undergo the elimination of hydrogen iodide, and, in all cases, alkenes are produced. When the elements of a hydrogen halide are eliminated from a haloalkane in this way, the reaction is often called **dehydrohalogenation**:

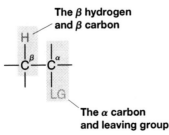

In these eliminations, as in S_N1 and S_N2 reactions, there is a leaving group and an attacking Lewis base that possesses an electron pair.

Chemists often call the carbon atom that bears the leaving group (e.g., the halogen atom in the previous reaction) the **alpha (α) carbon atom** and any carbon atom adjacent to it a **beta (β) carbon atom**. A hydrogen atom attached to the β carbon atom is called a **β hydrogen atom**. Since the hydrogen atom that is eliminated in dehydrohalogenation is from the β carbon atom, these reactions are often called **β eliminations**. They are also often referred to as **1,2 eliminations**.

We shall have more to say about dehydrohalogenation in Chapter 7, but we can examine several important aspects here.

6.15B Bases Used in Dehydrohalogenation

Various strong bases have been used for dehydrohalogenations. Potassium hydroxide dissolved in ethanol (KOH/EtOH) is a reagent sometimes used, but the conjugate bases of alcohols, such as sodium ethoxide (EtONa), often offer distinct advantages.

The conjugate base of an alcohol (an alkoxide) can be prepared by treating an alcohol with an alkali metal. For example:

$$2\,R\!-\!\ddot{O}H \;+\; 2\,Na \;\longrightarrow\; 2\,R\!-\!\ddot{O}\!:^- Na^+ \;+\; H_2$$

Alcohol   **Sodium**
                                alkoxide

This reaction is an **oxidation–reduction reaction**. Metallic sodium reacts with hydrogen atoms that are bonded to oxygen atoms to generate hydrogen gas, sodium cations, and the alkoxide anion. The reaction with water is vigorous and at times explosive.

$$2\,H\ddot{O}H \;+\; 2\,Na \;\longrightarrow\; 2\,H\ddot{O}\!:^- Na^+ \;+\; H_2$$

Sodium
hydroxide

Sodium alkoxides can also be prepared by allowing an alcohol to react with sodium hydride (NaH). The hydride ion ($H\!:^-$) is a very strong base. (The pK_a of H_2 is 35.)

$$R\!-\!\ddot{O}\!-\!H \;+\; Na^+\!:\!H^- \;\longrightarrow\; R\!-\!\ddot{O}\!:^- Na^+ \;+\; H\!-\!H$$

Sodium (and potassium) alkoxides are usually prepared by using an excess of the alcohol, and the excess alcohol becomes the solvent for the reaction. Sodium ethoxide is frequently prepared in this way using excess ethanol.

$$2\,CH_3CH_2\ddot{O}H \;+\; 2\,Na \;\longrightarrow\; 2\,CH_3CH_2\ddot{O}\!:^- Na^+ \;+\; H_2$$

Ethanol   **Sodium ethoxide**
(excess)   **dissolved in**
                            excess ethanol

Potassium *tert*-butoxide (*t*-BuOK) is another highly effective dehydrohalogenating reagent. It can be made by the reaction below, or purchased as a solid.

$$2\,CH_3\underset{\underset{\textstyle CH_3}{|}}{\overset{\overset{\textstyle CH_3}{|}}{C}}\!-\!\ddot{O}H \;+\; 2\,K \;\longrightarrow\; 2\,CH_3\underset{\underset{\textstyle CH_3}{|}}{\overset{\overset{\textstyle CH_3}{|}}{C}}\!-\!\ddot{O}\!:^- K^+ \;+\; H_2$$

tert-Butanol   **Potassium tert-butoxide**
(excess)

6.15C Mechanisms of Dehydrohalogenations

Elimination reactions occur by a variety of mechanisms. With alkyl halides, two mechanisms are especially important because they are closely related to the S_N2 and S_N1 reactions that we have just studied. One mechanism, called the **E2 reaction**, is bimolecular in the rate-determining step; the other mechanism is the **E1 reaction**, which is unimolecular in the rate-determining step.

6.16 THE E2 REACTION

When isopropyl bromide is heated with sodium ethoxide in ethanol to form propene, the reaction rate depends on the concentration of isopropyl bromide and the concentration of ethoxide ion. The rate equation is first order in each reactant and second order overall:

$$\text{Rate} = k[CH_3CHBrCH_3][C_2H_5O^-]$$

- From the reaction order we infer that the transition state for the rate-determining step must involve both the alkyl halide and the alkoxide ion: The reaction must be bimolecular. We call this type of elimination an E2 reaction.

Considerable experimental evidence indicates that an E2 reaction takes place in the following way:

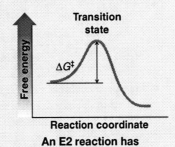

[A MECHANISM FOR THE REACTION — Mechanism for the E2 Reaction]

Reaction

$$C_2H_5O^- + CH_3CHBrCH_3 \longrightarrow CH_2{=}CHCH_3 + C_2H_5OH + Br^-$$

Mechanism

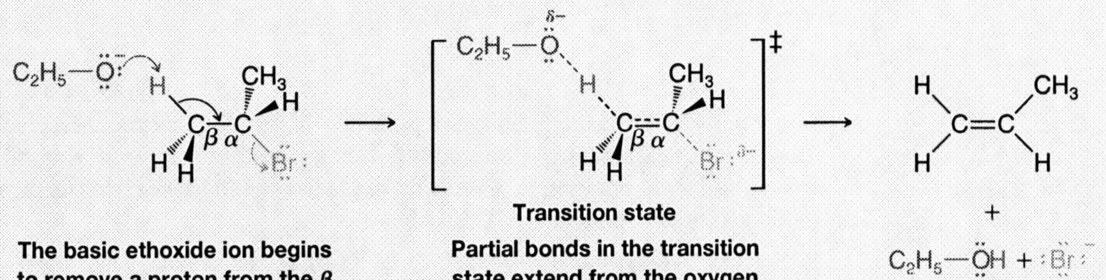

Transition state

The basic ethoxide ion begins to remove a proton from the β carbon using its electron pair to form a bond to it. At the same time, the electron pair of the β C—H bond begins to move in to become the π bond of a double bond, and the bromine begins to depart with the electrons that bonded it to the α carbon.

Partial bonds in the transition state extend from the oxygen atom that is removing the β hydrogen, through the carbon skeleton of the developing double bond, to the departing leaving group. The flow of electron density is from the base toward the leaving group as an electron pair fills the π bonding orbital of the alkene.

At completion of the reaction, the double bond is fully formed and the alkene has a trigonal planar geometry at each carbon atom. The other products are a molecule of ethanol and a bromide ion.

Transition state

$\Delta G^{\ddagger}$

Free energy

Reaction coordinate

An E2 reaction has one transition state

When we study the E2 reaction further in Section 7.6D, we shall find that the orientations of the hydrogen atom being removed and the leaving group are not arbitrary and that an orientation where they are all in the same plane, like that shown above and in the example that follows, is required.

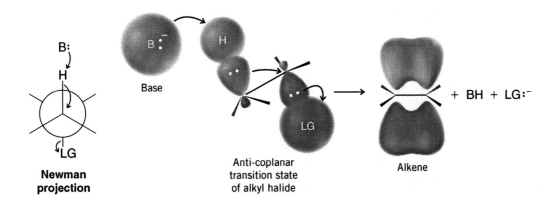

Newman projection

Base

Anti-coplanar transition state of alkyl halide

Alkene

$+ \; BH + LG{:}^-$

Notice that the geometry required here is similar to that of the S_N2 reaction. In the S_N2 reaction (Section 6.6) the nucleophile must push out the leaving group from the **opposite side**. In the E2 reaction the **electron pair of the C—H** bond pushes the leaving group away from the **opposite side** as the base removes the hydrogen. (We shall also find in Section 7.7C that a syn-coplanar E2 transition state is possible, though not as favorable.)

6.17 THE E1 REACTION

Some elimination reactions follow a pathway that exhibits first-order kinetics. We call these types of eliminations E1 reactions. Treating *tert*-butyl chloride with 80% aqueous ethanol at 25°C, for example, gives *substitution products* in 83% yield and an elimination product (2-methylpropene) in 17% yield:

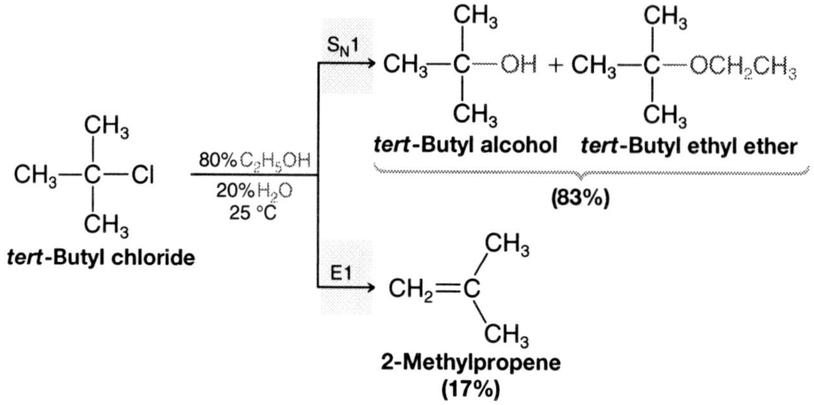

* The initial step for both the substitution and the elimination pathways is the formation of a *tert*-butyl cation as a common intermediate. This is also the slowest step for both reactions; thus both reactions exhibit first-order kinetics and are unimolecular in the rate-determining step.

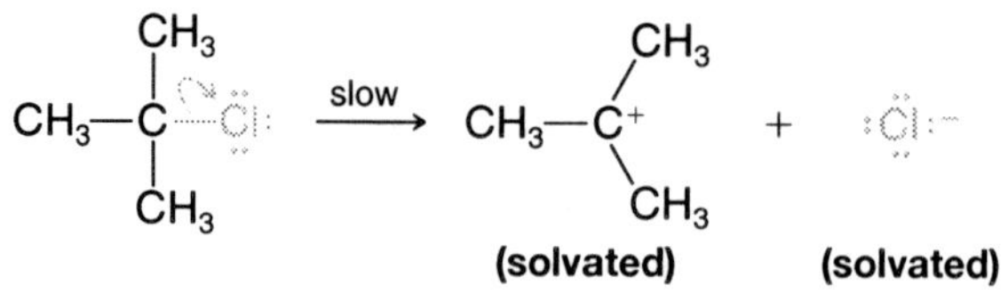

Whether substitution or elimination takes place depends on the next step (the fast step).

* If a solvent molecule reacts as a nucleophile at the positive carbon atom of the *tert*-butyl cation, the product is *tert*-butyl alcohol or *tert*-butyl ethyl ether and the reaction is S_N1:

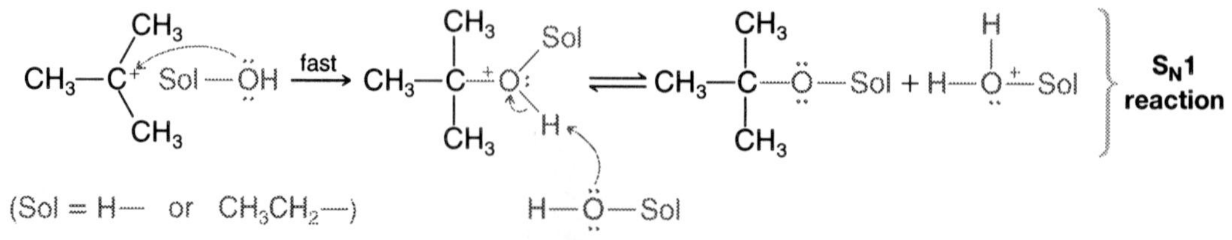

* If, however, a solvent molecule acts as a base and removes one of the β hydrogen atoms, the product is 2-methylpropene and the reaction is E1.

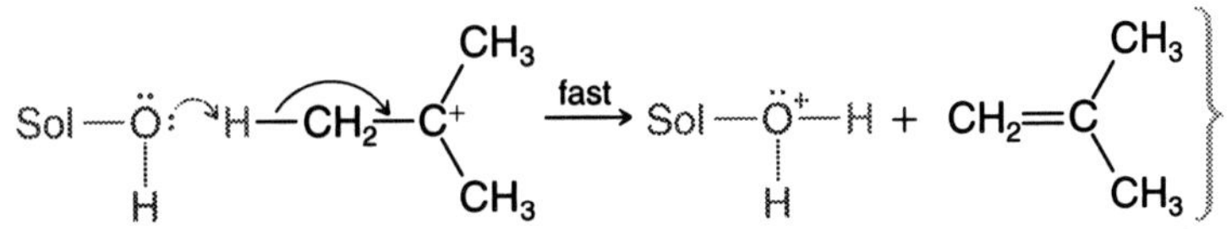

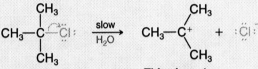

2-Methylpropene

E1 reactions almost always accompany S_N1 reactions.

[A MECHANISM FOR THE REACTION ⋯ **Mechanism for the E1 Reaction**]

Reaction

$$(CH_3)_3CCl + H_2O \longrightarrow CH_2=C(CH_3)_2 + H_3O^+ + Cl^-$$

Mechanism

Step 1

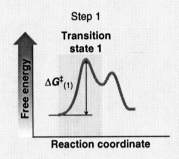

Step 1
Transition state 1
$\Delta G^{\ddagger}_{(1)}$
Reaction coordinate

$$CH_3-\underset{\underset{CH_3}{|}}{\overset{\overset{CH_3}{|}}{C}}-\ddot{Cl} \quad \xrightarrow[H_2O]{slow} \quad CH_3-\underset{\underset{CH_3}{|}}{\overset{\overset{CH_3}{|}}{C^+}} \quad + \quad :\ddot{Cl}:^-$$

Aided by the polar solvent, a chlorine departs with the electron pair that bonded it to the carbon.

This slow step produces the relatively stable 3° carbocation and a chloride ion. The ions are solvated (and stabilized) by surrounding water molecules.

Step 2

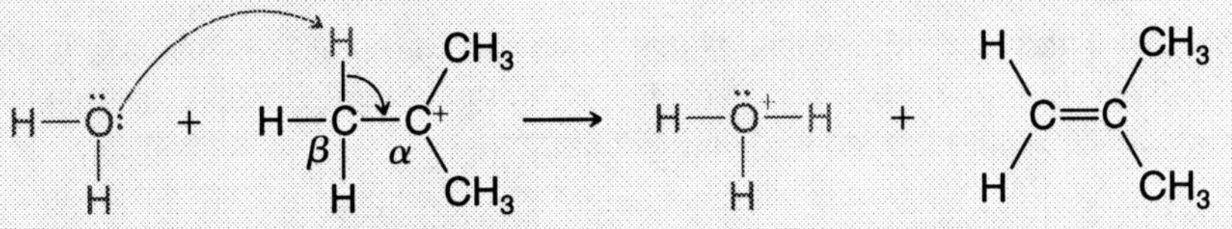

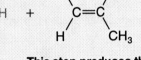

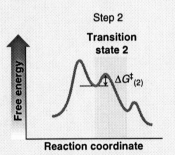

Step 2
Transition state 2
$\Delta G^{\ddagger}_{(2)}$
Reaction coordinate

A molecule of water removes one of the hydrogens from the β carbon of the carbocation. These hydrogens are acidic due to the adjacent positive charge. At the same time an electron pair moves in to form a double bond between the α and β carbon atoms.

This step produces the alkene and a hydronium ion.

6.18 HOW TO DETERMINE WHETHER SUBSTITUTION OR ELIMINATION IS FAVORED

All nucleophiles are potential bases and all bases are potential nucleophiles. This is because the reactive part of both nucleophiles and bases is an unshared electron pair. It should not be surprising, then, that nucleophilic substitution reactions and elimination reactions often compete with each other. We shall now summarize factors that influence which type of reaction is favored, and provide some examples.

Helpful Hint

This section draws together the various factors that influence the competition between substitution and elimination.

6.18A S_N2 versus E2

S_N2 and E2 reactions are both favored by a high concentration of a strong nucleophile or base. When the nucleophile (base) attacks a β hydrogen atom, elimination occurs. When the nucleophile attacks the carbon atom bearing the leaving group, substitution results:

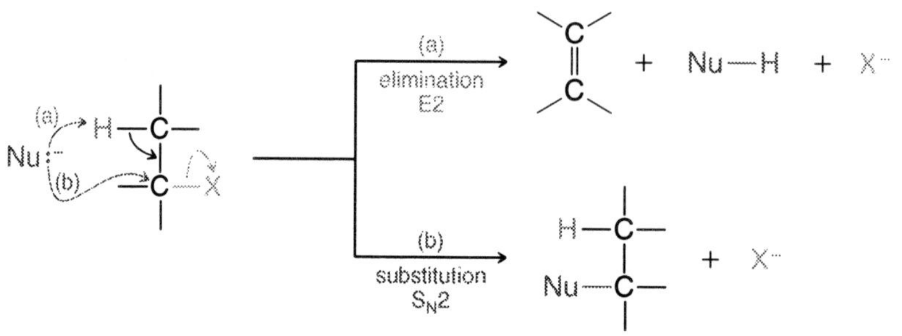

The following examples illustrate the effects of several parameters on substitution and elimination: relative steric hindrance in the substrate (class of alkyl halide), temperature, size of the base/nucleophile (**EtONa** versus ***t*-BuOK**), and the effects of basicity and polarizability. In these examples we also illustrate a very common way of writing organic reactions, where reagents are written over the reaction arrow, solvents and temperatures are written under the arrow, and only the substrate and major organic products are written to the left and right of the reaction arrow. We also employ typical shorthand notations of organic chemists, such as exclusive use of bond-line formulas and use of commonly accepted abbreviations for some reagents and solvents.

Primary Substrate When the substrate is a *primary* halide and the base is strong and unhindered, like ethoxide ion, substitution is highly favored because the base can easily approach the carbon bearing the leaving group:

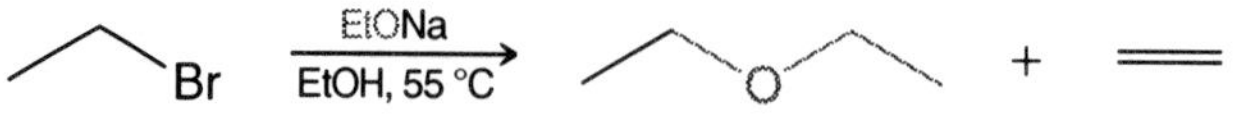

Primary **S_N2 Major (90%)** **E2 Minor (10%)**

Secondary Substrate With *secondary* halides, however, a strong base favors elimination because steric hindrance in the substrate makes substitution more difficult:

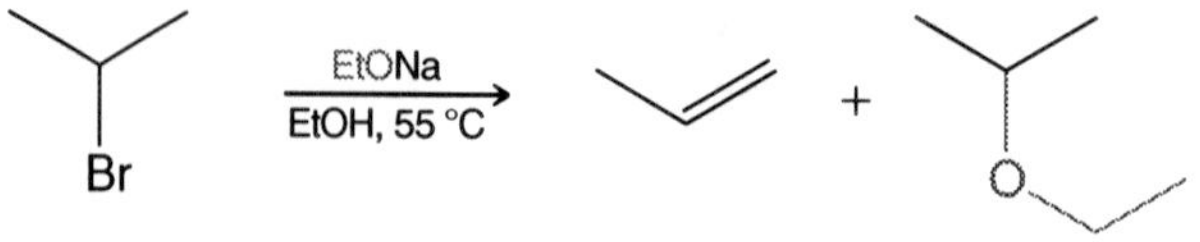

Secondary **E2 Major (79%)** **S_N2 Minor (21%)**

Tertiary Substrate With *tertiary* halides, steric hindrance in the substrate is severe and an S_N2 reaction cannot take place. Elimination is highly favored, especially when the reaction is carried out at higher temperatures. Any substitution that occurs must take place through an S_N1 mechanism:

Without Heating

| Tertiary | EtONa
EtOH, 25 °C
(room temp.) | E2 Major
(91%) | + | S$_N$1 Minor
(9%) |

With Heating

| Tertiary | EtONa
EtOH, 55 °C | E2 + E1 Only
(100%) |

Temperature Increasing the reaction temperature favors elimination (E1 and E2) over substitution. Elimination reactions have greater free energies of activation than substitution reactions because more bonding changes occur during elimination. When higher temperature is used, the proportion of molecules able to surmount the energy of activation barrier for elimination increases more than the proportion of molecules able to undergo substitution, although the rate of both substitution and elimination will be increased. Furthermore, elimination reactions are entropically favored over substitution because the products of an elimination reaction are greater in number than the reactants. Additionally, because temperature is the coefficient of the entropy term in the Gibbs free-energy equation $\Delta G° = \Delta H° - T\Delta S°$, an increase in temperature further enhances the entropy effect.

Size of the Base/Nucleophile Increasing the reaction temperature is one way of favorably influencing an elimination reaction of an alkyl halide. Another way is to use a *strong sterically hindered base* such as the *tert*-butoxide ion. The bulky methyl groups of the *tert*-butoxide ion inhibit its reaction by substitution, allowing elimination reactions to take precedence. We can see an example of this effect in the following two reactions. The relatively unhindered methoxide ion reacts with octadecyl bromide primarily by *substitution*, whereas the bulky *tert*-butoxide ion gives mainly *elimination*.

Unhindered (Small) Base/Nucleophile

| | CH$_3$ONa
CH$_3$OH, 65 °C | E2
(1%) | + | S$_N$2
(99%) |

Hindered Base/Nucleophile

| | *t*-BuOK
t-BuOK, 40 °C | E2
(85%) | + | S$_N$2
(15%) |

Basicity and Polarizability Another factor that affects the relative rates of E2 and S$_N$2 reactions is the relative basicity and polarizability of the base/nucleophile. Use of a strong, slightly polarizable base such as hydroxide ion, amide ion (NH$_2^-$), or alkoxide ion (especially a hindered one) tends to increase the likelihood of elimination (E2). Use of a weakly basic ion such as a chloride ion (Cl$^-$) or an acetate ion (CH$_3$CO$_2^-$) or a weakly basic and highly polarizable one such as Br$^-$, I$^-$, or RS$^-$ increases the likelihood of substitution (S$_N$2). Acetate ion, for example, reacts with isopropyl bromide almost exclusively by the S$_N$2 path:

The more strongly basic ethoxide ion (Section 6.15B) reacts with the same compound mainly by an E2 mechanism.

6.18B Tertiary Halides: S$_N$1 versus E1

Because E1 and S$_N$1 reactions proceed through the formation of a common intermediate, the two types respond in similar ways to factors affecting reactivities. E1 reactions are favored with substrates that can form stable carbocations (i.e., tertiary halides); they are also favored by the use of poor nucleophiles (weak bases) and they are generally favored by the use of polar solvents.

It is usually difficult to influence the relative partition between S$_N$1 and E1 products because the free energy of activation for either reaction proceeding from the carbocation (loss of a proton or combination with a molecule of the solvent) is very small.

In most unimolecular reactions the S$_N$1 reaction is favored over the E1 reaction, especially at lower temperatures. *In general, however, substitution reactions of tertiary halides do not find wide use as synthetic methods. Such halides undergo eliminations much too easily.*

Increasing the temperature of the reaction favors reaction by the E1 mechanism at the expense of the S$_N$1 mechanism.

* **If an elimination product is desired from a tertiary substrate, it is advisable to use a strong base so as to encourage an E2 mechanism over the competing E1 and S$_N$1 mechanisms.**

6.19 OVERALL SUMMARY

The most important reaction pathways for the substitution and elimination reactions of simple alkyl halides are summarized in Table 6.6.

Helpful Hint

Use this table as an overall summary.

TABLE 6.6 OVERALL SUMMARY OF S$_N$1, S$_N$2, E1, AND E2 REACTIONS

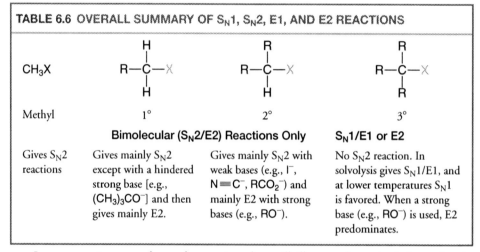

	Methyl	1°	2°	3°
		Bimolecular (S$_N$2/E2) Reactions Only		**S$_N$1/E1 or E2**
	Gives S$_N$2 reactions	Gives mainly S$_N$2 except with a hindered strong base [e.g., $(CH_3)_3CO^-$] and then gives mainly E2.	Gives mainly S$_N$2 with weak bases (e.g., I$^-$, N≡C$^-$, RCO$_2^-$) and mainly E2 with strong bases (e.g., RO$^-$).	No S$_N$2 reaction. In solvolysis gives S$_N$1/E1, and at lower temperatures S$_N$1 is favored. When a strong base (e.g., RO$^-$) is used, E2 predominates.

Let us examine several sample exercises that will illustrate how the information in Table 6.6 can be used.

●●● SOLVED PROBLEM 6.8

Give the product (or products) that you would expect to be formed in each of the following reactions. In each case give the mechanism (S$_N$1, S$_N$2, E1, or E2) by which the product is formed and predict the relative amount of each (i.e., would the product be the only product, the major product, or a minor product?).

(a) 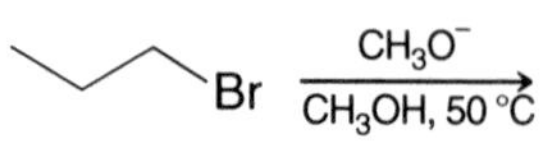 ⟍⟋⟍Br $\xrightarrow[\text{CH}_3\text{OH, 50 °C}]{\text{CH}_3\text{O}^-}$

(b) ⟍⟋⟍Br $\xrightarrow[\text{\textit{t}-BuOH, 50 °C}]{\text{\textit{t}-BuO}^-}$

(c) H⟍⟋Br $\xrightarrow[\text{CH}_3\text{OH, 50 °C}]{\text{HS}^-}$

(d) ⟍⟋⟍Br $\xrightarrow[\text{CH}_3\text{OH, 50 °C}]{\text{HO}^-}$

(e) ⟍⟋⟍Br $\xrightarrow[\text{CH}_3\text{OH, 25 °C}]{}$

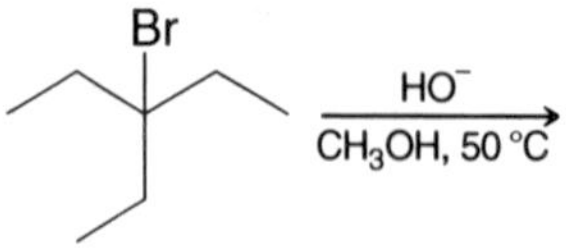

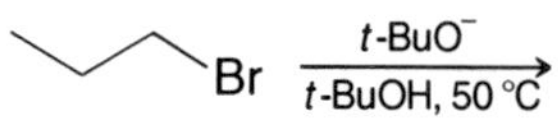

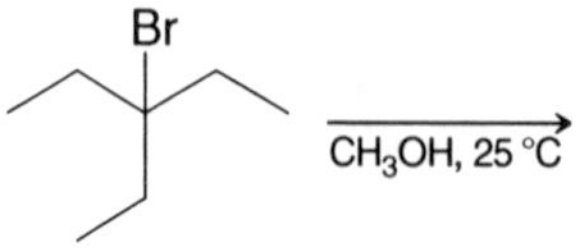

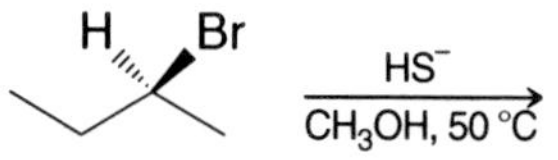

STRATEGY AND ANSWER:

(a) The substrate is a 1° halide. The base/nucleophile is CH_3O^-, a strong base (but not a hindered one) and a good nucleophile. According to Table 6.6, we should expect an S_N2 reaction mainly, and the major product should be

OCH₃. A minor product might be 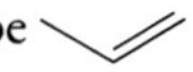 by an E2 pathway.

(b) Again the substrate is a 1° halide, but the base/nucleophile, t-BuO^-, is a strong hindered base. We should expect, therefore, the major product to be 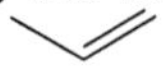 by an E2 pathway and a minor product to be 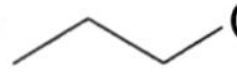 O-t-Bu by an S_N2 pathway.

(c) The reactant is (S)-2-bromobutane, a 2° halide and one in which the leaving group is attached to a chirality center. The base/nucleophile is HS^-, a strong nucleophile but a weak base. We should expect mainly an S_N2 reaction, causing an inversion of configuration at the chirality center and producing the (R) stereoisomer:

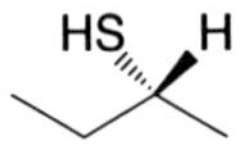

(d) The base/nucleophile is HO^-, a strong base and a strong nucleophile. The substrate is a 3° halide; therefore, we should not expect an S_N2 reaction. The major product should be 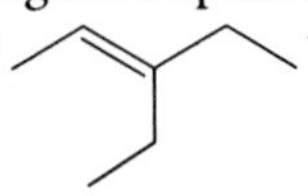 via an E2 reaction. At this higher temperature and in

the presence of a strong base, we should not expect an appreciable amount of the S_N1 solvolysis, product, .

(e) This is solvolysis; the only base/nucleophile is the solvent, CH_3OH, which is a weak base (therefore, no E2 reaction) and a poor nucleophile. The substrate is tertiary (therefore, no S_N2 reaction). At this lower temperature we should expect mainly an S_N1 pathway leading to OCH₃ . A minor product, by an E1 pathway, would be .

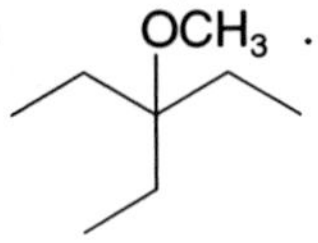

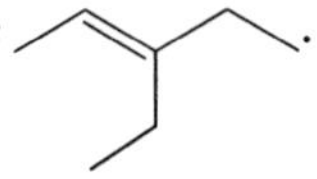

[WHY Do These Topics Matter?

SUBSTITUTING THE CALORIES OF TABLE SUGAR

As we shall see in more detail in Chapter 24, simple carbohydrates, or monosaccharides, can exist in the form of a six-membered ring system with a chair conformation. The name carbohydrate derives from "hydrated carbon" since most carbon atoms have an H and OH attached. In the examples below, the structural differences of the monosaccharides glucose, mannose, and galactose are based on the change of one or more chirality centers through what we could formally consider to be an inversion reaction. As such, all of these carbohydrates are diastereomers of each other. Based on what you already know about torsional strain from Chapter 4, it should come as no surprise that D-glucose is the most common monosaccharide: D-glucose has the least strain because all of its substituents are in equatorial positions. All other six-carbon sugars have at least one axial group, and thus possess some 1,3-diaxial strain. Standard table sugar, or sucrose, is a disaccharide, since it combines a molecule of D-glucose with the slightly less common carbohydrate called D-fructose.

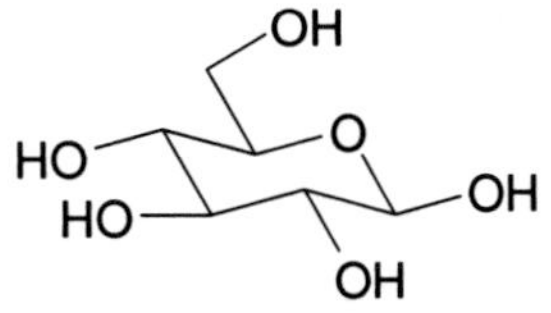

D-glucose 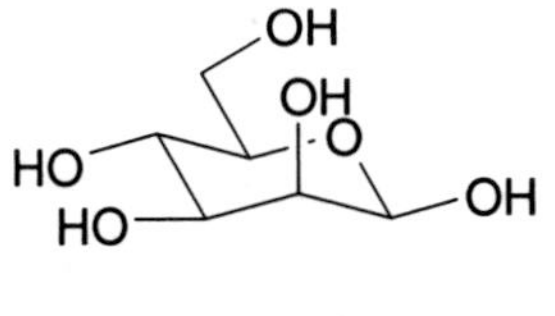   **D-mannose** 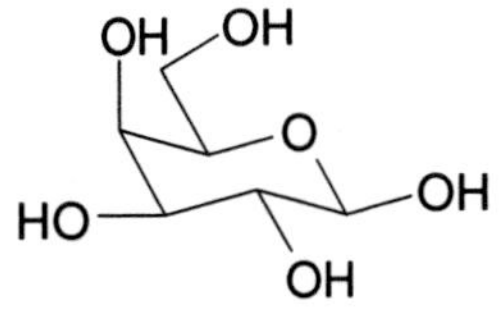   **D-galactose** 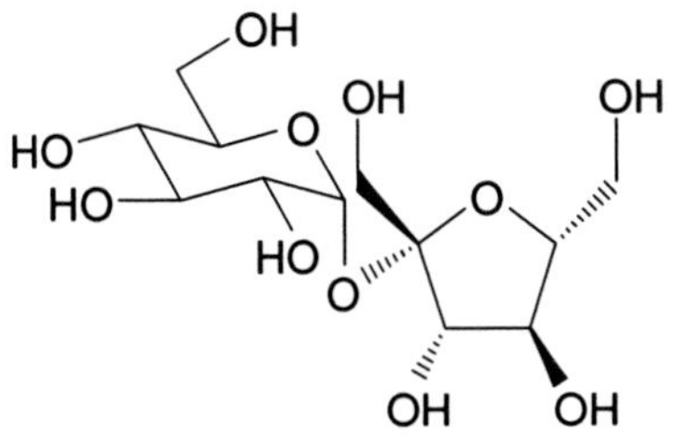   **Sucrose**

All carbohydrates taste sweet, though not equally so. D-Fructose, for example, tastes approximately 1.5 times sweeter than the same amount of simple table sugar, while D-glucose is only about 0.75 times as sweet. Irrespective of their individual degrees of sweetness, however, it is the fact that they are all sweet that lets us perceive their presence in foods whether they are found naturally or have been added (often from corn syrup or cane sugar) to create a more unique flavor profile. Either way, their

(continues on next page)

sweet taste always comes at a cost: calories that can be converted into fat in our bodies. At present, it is estimated by some that Americans consume well over 100 pounds of sugar per person per year from sources both natural and unnatural. That amounts to a lot of calories! What is amazing is that organic chemistry can come to the rescue and knock those calories out. Shown below is the structure of a popular artificial (or synthetic) sweetener known as sucralose, or Splenda. It is the product of some of the chemistry that you have learned in this chapter. Can you guess what that chemistry is?

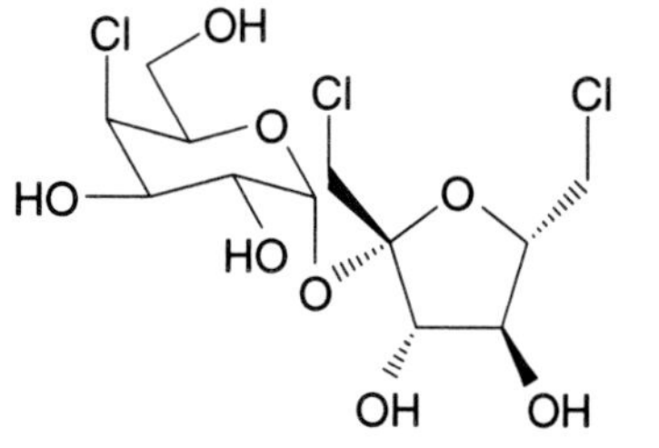

Sucralose

Absolutely right—it is the replacement of three alcohol groups within sucrose, two of them primary and one of them secondary, with chloride through an inversion reaction. Achieving these events in a laboratory setting is quite difficult, since it means selective reaction of only certain hydroxyls in the presence of many others, but it is possible over several steps under the right conditions, including solvent, temperature, and time. What results is a compound that, when ingested, is sensed by our taste receptors as being sweet like table sugar—in fact, 600 times as sweet! What is perhaps even more amazing, however, is that sucralose has, in effect, no calories. We have metabolic pathways that can, in principle, carry out the reverse reactions and replace those chlorines with alcohols through inversion chemistry, thereby re-creating table sugar and leading to calories. But those replacements do not happen fast enough physiologically. As a result, sucralose leaves our bodies before it can be converted into energy and/or stored as fat. Pretty amazing what just a few substitutions can do!

Media Bakery

SUMMARY AND REVIEW TOOLS

The study aids for this chapter include Key Terms and Concepts (which are highlighted in bold, blue text within the chapter and defined in the glossary (at the back of the book) and have hyperlinked definitions in the accompanying *WileyPLUS* course (www.wileyplus.com), and a Mechanism Review regarding substitution and elimination reactions.

PROBLEMS PLUS

Note to Instructors: Many of the homework problems are available for assignment via *WileyPlus*, an online teaching and learning solution.

RELATIVE RATES OF NUCLEOPHILIC SUBSTITUTION

6.20 Which alkyl halide would you expect to react more rapidly by an S_N2 mechanism? Explain your answer.

(a)  [structure: CH₃CH₂CH₂Br] Br   or   [structure: (CH₃)₃CBr] Br

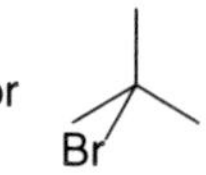

(b)  [structure] Cl   or   [structure] I

(c) 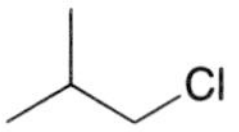 [structure] Cl   or   [structure] Cl

(d) 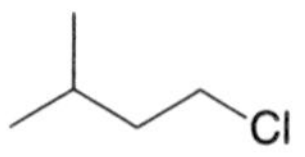 [structure] Cl   or   [structure] Cl

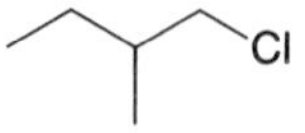

(e) 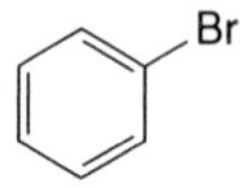 [structure with benzene ring] Br   or   [structure] Cl

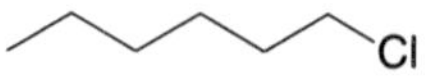

6.21 Which S_N2 reaction of each pair would you expect to take place more rapidly in a protic solvent?

(a) 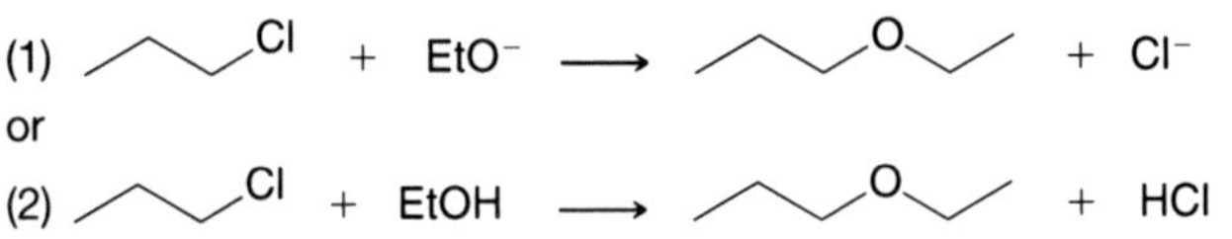 (1) $\diagup\!\!\diagup^{Cl}$ + EtO⁻ ⟶ $\diagup\!\!\diagup^{O}\diagdown$ + Cl⁻

or

(2) $\diagup\!\!\diagup^{Cl}$ + EtOH ⟶ $\diagup\!\!\diagup^{O}\diagdown$ + HCl

(b) 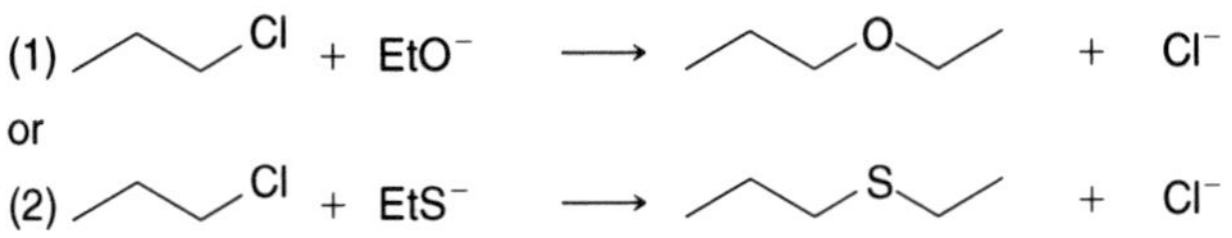 (1) $\diagup\!\!\diagup^{Cl}$ + EtO⁻ ⟶ $\diagup\!\!\diagup^{O}\diagdown$ + Cl⁻

or

(2) $\diagup\!\!\diagup^{Cl}$ + EtS⁻ ⟶ $\diagup\!\!\diagup^{S}\diagdown$ + Cl⁻

(c) 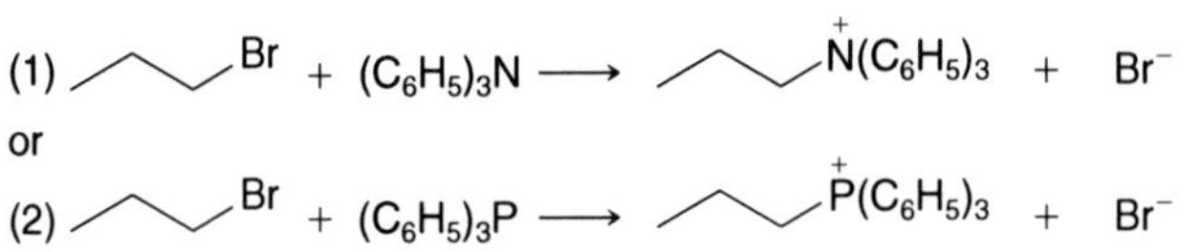 (1) $\diagup\!\!\diagup^{Br}$ + $(C_6H_5)_3N$ ⟶ $\diagup\!\!\diagup^{\overset{+}{N}(C_6H_5)_3}$ + Br⁻

or

(2) $\diagup\!\!\diagup^{Br}$ + $(C_6H_5)_3P$ ⟶ $\diagup\!\!\diagup^{\overset{+}{P}(C_6H_5)_3}$ + Br⁻

(d) 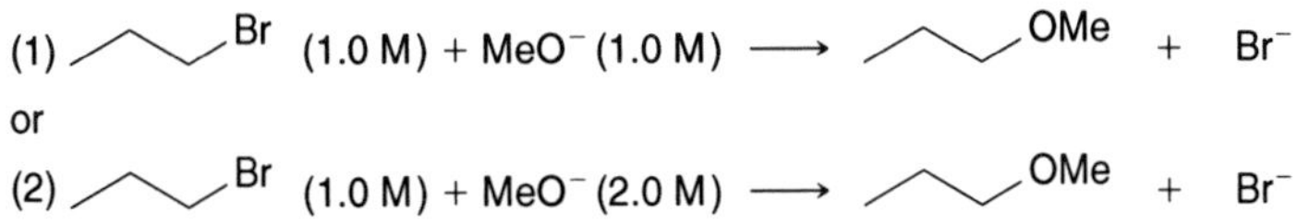 (1) $\diagup\!\!\diagup^{Br}$ (1.0 M) + MeO⁻ (1.0 M) ⟶ $\diagup\!\!\diagup^{OMe}$ + Br⁻

or

(2) $\diagup\!\!\diagup^{Br}$ (1.0 M) + MeO⁻ (2.0 M) ⟶ $\diagup\!\!\diagup^{OMe}$ + Br⁻

6.22 Which S_N1 reaction of each pair would you expect to take place more rapidly? Explain your answer.

(a) 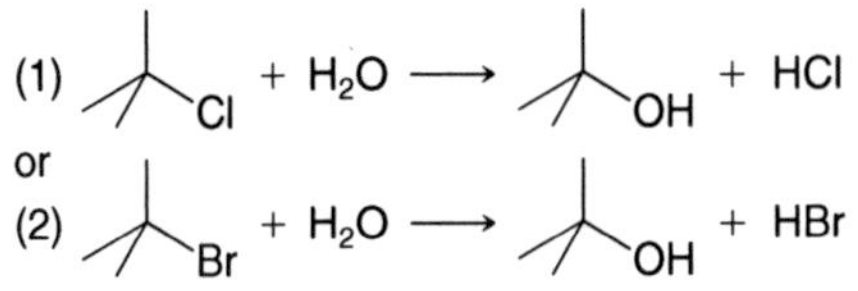 (1) $\diagup\!\!\!\underset{Cl}{\diagdown}$ + H_2O ⟶ $\diagup\!\!\!\underset{OH}{\diagdown}$ + HCl

or

(2) $\diagup\!\!\!\underset{Br}{\diagdown}$ + H_2O ⟶ $\diagup\!\!\!\underset{OH}{\diagdown}$ + HBr

(b) 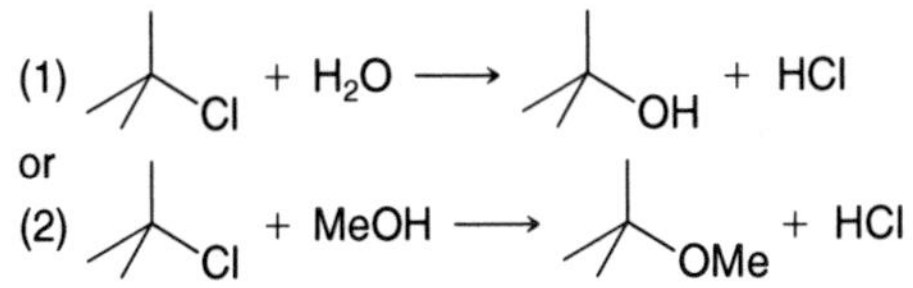 (1) $\diagup\!\!\!\underset{Cl}{\diagdown}$ + H_2O ⟶ $\diagup\!\!\!\underset{OH}{\diagdown}$ + HCl

or

(2) $\diagup\!\!\!\underset{Cl}{\diagdown}$ + MeOH ⟶ $\diagup\!\!\!\underset{OMe}{\diagdown}$ + HCl

(c) 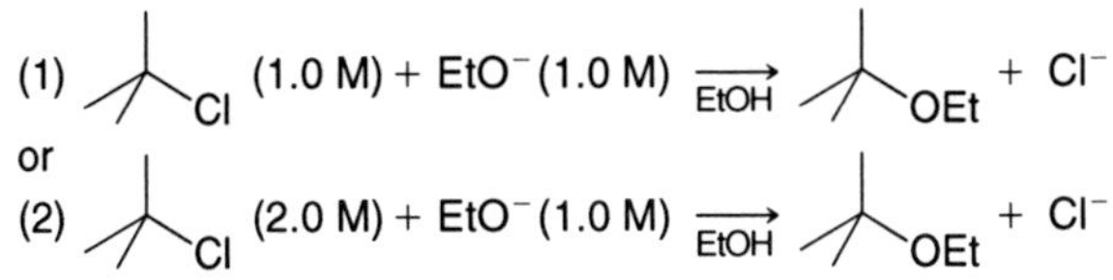 (1) $\diagup\!\!\!\underset{Cl}{\diagdown}$ (1.0 M) + EtO⁻ (1.0 M) $\xrightarrow{EtOH}$ $\diagup\!\!\!\underset{OEt}{\diagdown}$ + Cl⁻

or

(2) $\diagup\!\!\!\underset{Cl}{\diagdown}$ (2.0 M) + EtO⁻ (1.0 M) $\xrightarrow{EtOH}$ $\diagup\!\!\!\underset{OEt}{\diagdown}$ + Cl⁻

(d) 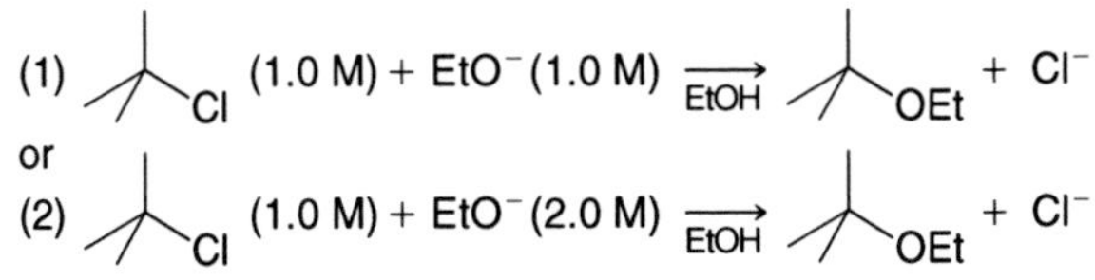 (1) $\diagup\!\!\!\underset{Cl}{\diagdown}$ (1.0 M) + EtO⁻ (1.0 M) $\xrightarrow{EtOH}$ $\diagup\!\!\!\underset{OEt}{\diagdown}$ + Cl⁻

or

(2) $\diagup\!\!\!\underset{Cl}{\diagdown}$ (1.0 M) + EtO⁻ (2.0 M) $\xrightarrow{EtOH}$ $\diagup\!\!\!\underset{OEt}{\diagdown}$ + Cl⁻

(e) 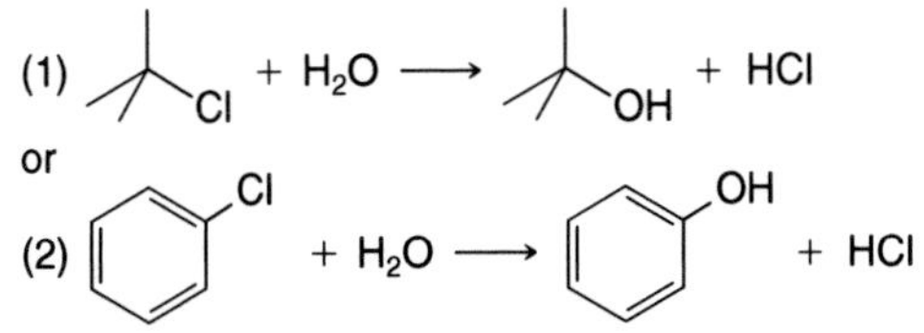 (1) $\diagup\!\!\!\underset{Cl}{\diagdown}$ + H_2O ⟶ $\diagup\!\!\!\underset{OH}{\diagdown}$ + HCl

or

(2) Ph—Cl + H_2O ⟶ Ph—OH + HCl

SYNTHESIS

6.23 Show how you might use a nucleophilic substitution reaction of 1-bromopropane to synthesize each of the following compounds. (You may use any other compounds that are necessary.)

(a)  $\diagup\!\!\diagup^{OH}$

(b) 1-Iodopropane

(c) 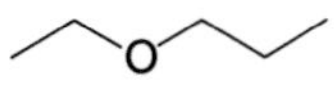 $\diagup\diagdown^{O}\diagup\diagdown$

(d) $CH_3CH_2CH_2—S—CH_3$

(e) 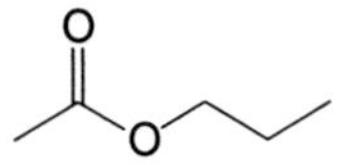 $CH_3\overset{O}{\underset{\|}{C}}—O\diagup\!\!\diagup$

(f) 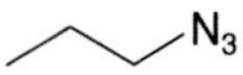 $\diagup\!\!\diagup^{N_3}$

(g) 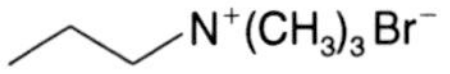 $\diagup\!\!\diagup^{N^+(CH_3)_3 \, Br^-}$

(h) 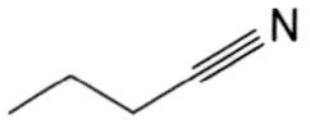 $\diagup\!\!\diagup^{C\equiv N}$

(i)  $\diagup\!\!\diagup^{SH}$

6.24 With methyl, ethyl, or cyclopentyl halides as your organic starting materials and using any needed solvents or inorganic reagents, outline syntheses of each of the following. More than one step may be necessary and you need not repeat steps carried out in earlier parts of this problem.

(a) CH_3I

(b) 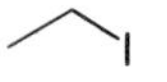 ⌃⌃I

(c) CH_3OH

(d) 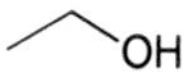 ⌃⌃OH

(e) CH_3SH

(f) 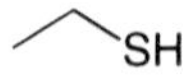 ⌃⌃SH

(g) CH_3CN

(h) 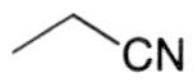 ⌃⌃CN

(i) CH_3OCH_3

(j) 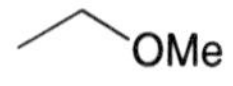 ⌃⌃OMe

(k)  ⬠

6.25 Listed below are several hypothetical nucleophilic substitution reactions. None is synthetically useful because the product indicated is not formed at an appreciable rate. In each case provide an explanation for the failure of the reaction to take place as indicated.

(a) 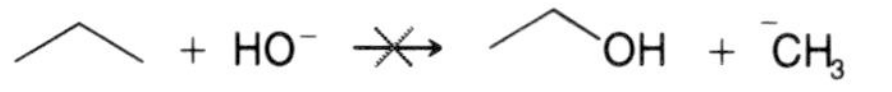 ⌃⌃ + HO⁻ ⇸ ⌃⌃OH + ⁻CH₃

(b) 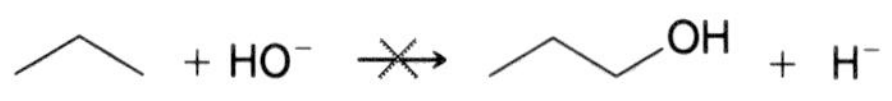 ⌃⌃ + HO⁻ ⇸ ⌃⌃OH + H⁻

(c) 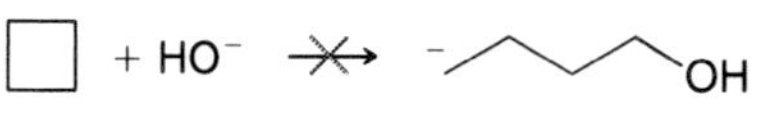 ⬜ + HO⁻ ⇸ ⁻⌃⌃⌃OH

(d) 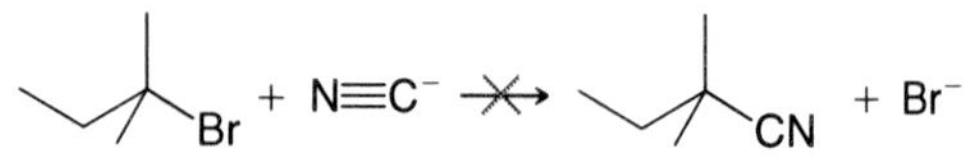 ⌉⌈Br + N≡C⁻ ⇸ ⌉⌈CN + Br⁻

(e) $NH_3 + CH_3OCH_3$ ⇸ $CH_3NH_2 + CH_3OH$

(f) $NH_3 + CH_3\overset{+}{O}H_2$ ⇸ $CH_3\overset{+}{N}H_3 + H_2O$

6.26 Your task is to prepare styrene by one of the following reactions. Which reaction would you choose to give the better yield of styrene? Explain your answer.

(1) 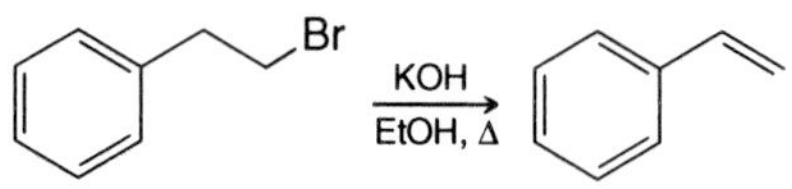 [structure: phenyl-CH₂CH₂Br] $\xrightarrow[\text{EtOH, }\Delta]{\text{KOH}}$ [styrene structure]   or   (2) 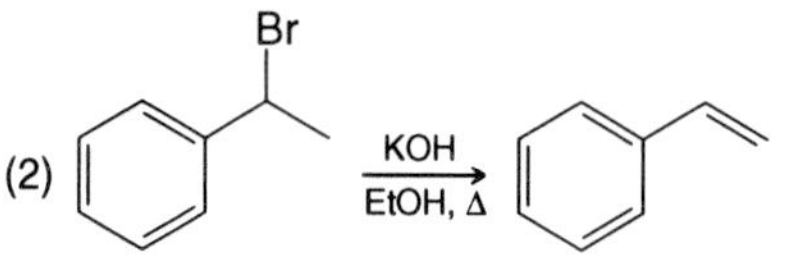 [structure: phenyl-CHBrCH₃] $\xrightarrow[\text{EtOH, }\Delta]{\text{KOH}}$ [styrene structure]

Styrene   **Styrene**

6.27 Your task is to prepare isopropyl methyl ether by one of the following reactions. Which reaction would give the better yield? Explain your answer.

(1) 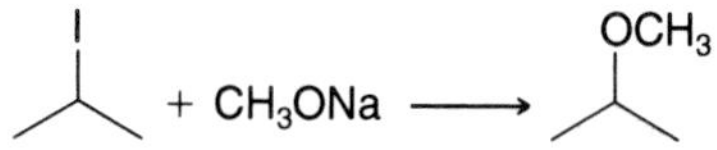 [isopropyl iodide] + CH_3ONa ⟶ [isopropyl methyl ether, OCH₃]   or   (2) 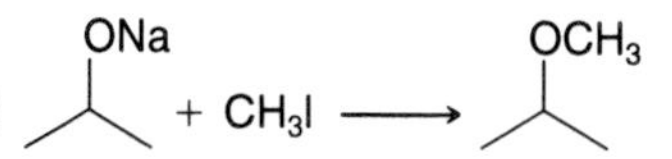 [isopropyl ONa] + CH_3I ⟶ [isopropyl methyl ether, OCH₃]

Isopropyl methyl ether   **Isopropyl methyl ether**

6.28 Starting with an appropriate alkyl halide and using any other needed reagents, outline syntheses of each of the following. When alternative possibilities exist for a synthesis, you should be careful to choose the one that gives the better yield.

(a) Butyl *sec*-butyl ether

(b) 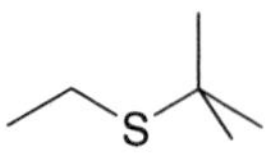 [structure: ethyl *tert*-butyl sulfide]

(c) Methyl neopentyl ether

(d) Methyl phenyl ether

(e) 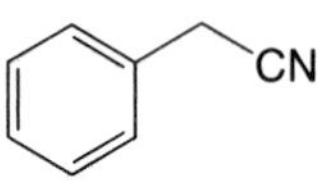 [structure: benzyl-CH₂CN]

(f) 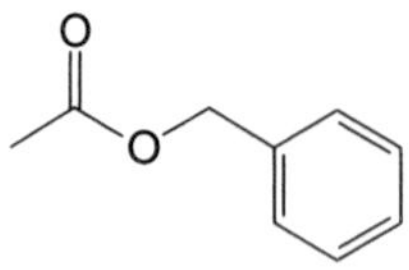 [structure: benzyl acetate ester]

(g) (*S*)-2-Pentanol

(h) (*R*)-2-Iodo-4-methylpentane

(i) 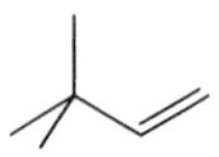 [structure: alkene]

(j) *cis*-4-Isopropylcyclohexanol

(k) 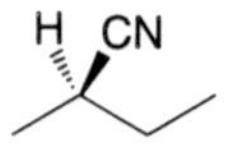 [structure: H, CN substituted]

(l) *trans*-1-Iodo-4-methylcyclohexane

GENERAL S_N1, S_N2, AND ELIMINATION

6.29 Which product (or products) would you expect to obtain from each of the following reactions? In each part give the mechanism (S_N1, S_N2, E1, or E2) by which each product is formed and predict the relative amount of each product (i.e., would the product be the only product, the major product, a minor product, etc.?).

(a) [structure: pentyl bromide] $\xrightarrow[\text{EtOH, 50 °C}]{\text{EtO}^-}$

(b) [structure: pentyl bromide] $\xrightarrow[\text{t-BuOH, 50 °C}]{\text{t-BuOK}}$

(c) [structure: tert-butyl bromide] $\xrightarrow[\text{MeOH, 50 °C}]{\text{MeO}^-}$

(d) [structure: tert-butyl bromide] $\xrightarrow[\text{t-BuOH, 50 °C}]{\text{t-BuOK}}$

(e) [structure: t-Bu cyclohexyl chloride] $\xrightarrow[\text{acetone, 50 °C}]{\text{I}^-}$

(f) [structure: t-Bu cyclohexyl chloride] $\xrightarrow{\text{MeOH, 25 °C}}$

(g) 3-Chloropentane $\xrightarrow[\text{MeOH, 50 °C}]{\text{MeO}^-}$

(h) 3-Chloropentane $\xrightarrow[\text{CH}_3\text{CO}_2\text{H, 50 °C}]{\text{CH}_3\text{CO}_2^-}$

(i) (R)-2-bromobutane $\xrightarrow[\text{25 °C}]{\text{HO}^-}$

(j) (S)-3-Bromo-3-methylhexane $\xrightarrow[\text{MeOH}]{\text{25 °C}}$

(k) (S)-2-Bromooctane $\xrightarrow[\text{MeOH, 50 °C}]{\text{I}^-}$

6.30 Write conformational structures for the substitution products of the following deuterium-labeled compounds:

(a) [cyclohexane structure with Cl, H, D, H] $\xrightarrow{\text{MeOH}}$

(c) [cyclohexane structure with Cl, H, D] $\xrightarrow{\text{MeOH}}$

(b) [cyclohexane structure with Cl, H, D] $\xrightarrow{\text{MeOH}}$

(d) [cyclohexane structure with Cl, CH$_3$, H, D] $\xrightarrow{\text{MeOH, H}_2\text{O}}$

6.31 Although ethyl bromide and isobutyl bromide are both primary halides, ethyl bromide undergoes S_N2 reactions more than 10 times faster than isobutyl bromide does. When each compound is treated with a strong base/nucleophile (EtO$^-$), isobutyl bromide gives a greater yield of elimination products than substitution products, whereas with ethyl bromide this behavior is reversed. What factor accounts for these results?

6.32 Consider the reaction of I$^-$ with CH$_3$CH$_2$Cl.

(a) Would you expect the reaction to be S_N1 or S_N2? The rate constant for the reaction at 60 °C is 5×10^{-5} L mol^{-1} s^{-1}.

(b) What is the reaction rate if [I$^-$] = 0.1 mol L^{-1} and [CH$_3$CH$_2$Cl] = 0.1 mol L^{-1}?

(c) If [I$^-$] = 0.1 mol L^{-1} and [CH$_3$CH$_2$Cl] = 0.2 mol L^{-1}?

(d) If [I$^-$] = 0.2 mol L^{-1} and [CH$_3$CH$_2$Cl] = 0.1 mol L^{-1}?

(e) If [I$^-$] = 0.2 mol L^{-1} and [CH$_3$CH$_2$Cl] = 0.2 mol L^{-1}?

6.33 Which reagent in each pair listed here would be the more reactive nucleophile in a polar aprotic solvent?

(a) CH$_3\overline{\text{N}}$H or CH$_3$NH$_2$

(b) CH$_3$O$^-$ or CH$_3$CO$_2^-$ ($^-$OAc)

(c) CH$_3$SH or CH$_3$OH

(d) (C$_6$H$_5$)$_3$N or (C$_6$H$_5$)$_3$P

(e) H$_2$O or H$_3$O$^+$

(f) NH$_3$ or $^+$NH$_4$

(g) H$_2$S or HS$^-$

(h) CH$_3$CO$_2^-$ ($^-$OAc) or HO$^-$

6.34 Write mechanisms that account for the products of the following reactions:

(a) HO—[structure]—Br $\xrightarrow[\text{H}_2\text{O}]{\text{HO}^-}$ [epoxide structure with O]

(b) H$_2$N—[structure]—Br $\xrightarrow[\text{H}_2\text{O}]{\text{HO}^-}$ [pyrrolidine structure N–H]

6.35 Draw a three-dimensional representation for the transition state structure in the S_N2 reaction of N≡C:$^-$ (cyanide anion) with bromoethane, showing all nonbonding electron pairs and full or partial charges.

6.36 Many S_N2 reactions of alkyl chlorides and alkyl bromides are catalyzed by the addition of sodium or potassium iodide. For example, the hydrolysis of methyl bromide takes place much faster in the presence of sodium iodide. Explain.

6.37 Explain the following observations: When tert-butyl bromide is treated with sodium methoxide in a mixture of methanol and water, the rate of formation of tert-butyl alcohol and tert-butyl methyl ether does not change appreciably as the concentration of sodium methoxide is increased. However, increasing the concentration of sodium methoxide causes a marked increase in the rate at which tert-butyl bromide disappears from the mixture.

6.38

(a) Consider the general problem of converting a tertiary alkyl halide to an alkene, for example, the conversion of *tert*-butyl chloride to 2-methylpropene. What experimental conditions would you choose to ensure that elimination is favored over substitution?

(b) Consider the opposite problem, that of carrying out a substitution reaction on a tertiary alkyl halide. Use as your example the conversion of *tert*-butyl chloride to *tert*-butyl ethyl ether. What experimental conditions would you employ to ensure the highest possible yield of the ether?

6.39 1-Bromobicyclo[2.2.1]heptane is extremely unreactive in either S_N2 or S_N1 reactions. Provide explanations for this behavior.

6.40 When ethyl bromide reacts with potassium cyanide in methanol, the major product is CH_3CH_2CN. Some CH_3CH_2NC is formed as well, however. Write Lewis structures for the cyanide ion and for both products and provide a mechanistic explanation of the course of the reaction.

6.41 Give structures for the products of each of the following reactions:

(a)
$$\xrightarrow[\text{acetone}]{\text{NaI (1 mol)}} \quad C_5H_8FI \quad + \quad NaBr$$

(b)
(1 mol) $\xrightarrow[\text{acetone}]{\text{NaI (1 mol)}} C_6H_{12}CII + NaCl$

(c)
Br (1 mol) $\xrightarrow{\text{NaS} \quad \text{SNa}} C_4H_8S_2 + 2\,NaBr$

(d)
$\xrightarrow[\text{Et}_2O]{\text{NaH }(-H_2)} C_4H_8ClONa \xrightarrow{\text{Et}_2O,\ \text{heat}} C_4H_8O + NaCl$

(e)
$\xrightarrow[\text{liq. NH}_3]{\text{NaNH}_2\ (-NH_3)} C_3H_3Na \xrightarrow{CH_3I} C_4H_6 + NaI$

6.42 When *tert*-butyl bromide undergoes S_N1 hydrolysis, adding a "common ion" (e.g., NaBr) to the aqueous solution has no effect on the rate. On the other hand, when $(C_6H_5)_2CHBr$ undergoes S_N1 hydrolysis, adding NaBr retards the reaction. Given that the $(C_6H_5)_2CH^+$ cation is known to be much more stable than the $(CH_3)_3C^+$ cation (and we shall see why in Section 15.12A), provide an explanation for the different behavior of the two compounds.

6.43 When the alkyl bromides (listed here) were subjected to hydrolysis in a mixture of ethanol and water (80% EtOH/20% H_2O) at 55 °C, the rates of the reaction showed the following order:

$$(CH_3)_3CBr > CH_3Br > CH_3CH_2Br > (CH_3)_2CHBr$$

Provide an explanation for this order of reactivity.

6.44 The reaction of 1° alkyl halides with nitrite salts produces both RNO_2 and $RONO$. Account for this behavior.

6.45 What would be the effect of increasing solvent polarity on the rate of each of the following nucleophilic substitution reactions?

(a) $Nu: \quad + \quad R-L \longrightarrow R-Nu^+ \quad + \quad :L^-$ **(b)** $R-L^+ \longrightarrow R^+ \quad + \quad :L$

6.46 Competition experiments are those in which two reactants at the same concentration (or one reactant with two reactive sites) compete for a reagent. Predict the major product resulting from each of the following competition experiments:

(a)
$\xrightarrow[\text{DMF}]{I^-}$

(b)
$\xrightarrow[\text{acetone}]{H_2O}$

6.47 In contrast to S_N2 reactions, S_N1 reactions show relatively little nucleophile selectivity. That is, when more than one nucleophile is present in the reaction medium, S_N1 reactions show only a slight tendency to discriminate between weak nucleophiles and strong nucleophiles, whereas S_N2 reactions show a marked tendency to discriminate.

(a) Provide an explanation for this behavior.

(b) Show how your answer accounts for the following:

$\xrightarrow[\text{EtOH}]{\text{NaCN (0.01 M)}}$

Major product

$\xrightarrow[\text{EtOH}]{\text{NaCN (0.01 M)}}$

Major product

CHALLENGE PROBLEMS

6.48 The reaction of chloroethane with water *in the gas phase* to produce ethanol and hydrogen chloride has $\triangle H° = +26.6$ kJ mol^{-1} and $\triangle S° = +4.81$ J K^{-1} mol^{-1} at 25 °C.

(a) Which of these terms, if either, favors the reaction going to completion?

(b) Calculate $\triangle G°$ for the reaction. What can you now say about whether the reaction will proceed to completion?

(c) Calculate the equilibrium constant for the reaction.

(d) In aqueous solution the equilibrium constant is very much larger than the one you just calculated. How can you account for this fact?

6.49 When (S)-2-bromopropanoic acid [(S)-CH$_3$CHBrCO$_2$H] reacts with concentrated sodium hydroxide, the product formed (after acidification) is (R)-2-hydroxypropanoic acid [(R)-CH$_3$CHOHCO$_2$H, commonly known as (R)-lactic acid]. This is, of course, the normal stereochemical result for an S$_N$2 reaction. However, when the same reaction is carried out with a low concentration of hydroxide ion in the presence of Ag$_2$O (where Ag$^+$ acts as a Lewis acid), it takes place with overall *retention of configuration* to produce (S)-2-hydroxypropanoic acid. The mechanism of this reaction involves a phenomenon called neighboring-group participation. Write a detailed mechanism for this reaction that accounts for the net retention of configuration when Ag$^+$ and a low concentration of hydroxide are used.

6.50 The phenomenon of configuration inversion in a chemical reaction was discovered in 1896 by Paul Walden (Section 6.6). Walden's proof of configuration inversion was based on the following cycle:

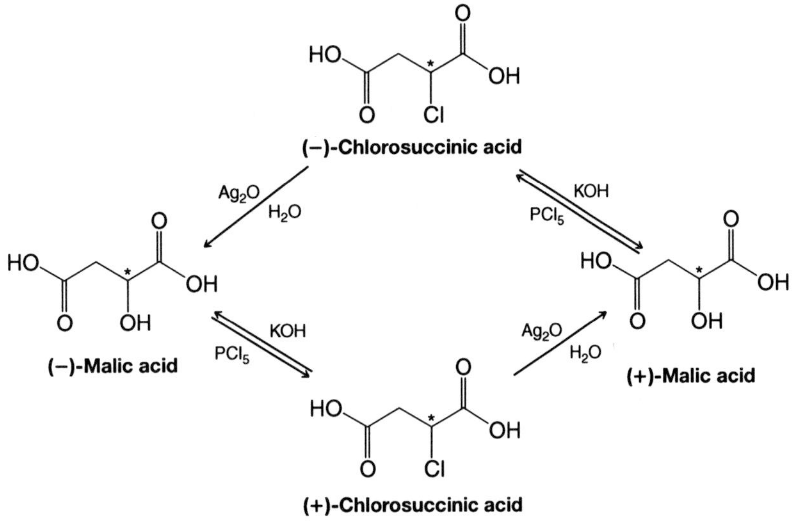

The Walden Cycle

(a) Basing your answer on the preceding problem, which reactions of the Walden cycle are likely to take place with overall inversion of configuration and which are likely to occur with overall retention of configuration?

(b) Malic acid with a negative optical rotation is now known to have the (S) configuration. What are the configurations of the other compounds in the Walden cycle?

(c) Walden also found that when (+)-malic acid is treated with thionyl chloride (rather than PCl$_5$), the product of the reaction is (+)-chlorosuccinic acid. How can you explain this result?

(d) Assuming that the reaction of (−)-malic acid and thionyl chloride has the same stereochemistry, outline a Walden cycle based on the use of thionyl chloride instead of PCl$_5$.

6.51 (R)-(3-Chloro-2-methylpropyl) methyl ether **(A)** on reaction with azide ion (N$_3^-$) in aqueous ethanol gives (S)-(3-azido-2-methylpropyl) methyl ether **(B)**. Compound **A** has the structure ClCH$_2$CH(CH$_3$)CH$_2$OCH$_3$.

(a) Draw wedge–dashed wedge–line formulas of both **A** and **B**.

(b) Is there a change of configuration during this reaction?

6.52 Predict the structure of the product of this reaction:

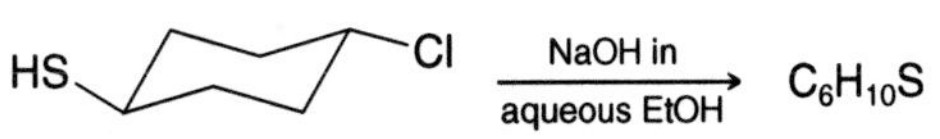

The product has no infrared absorption in the 1620–1680-cm^{-1} region.

6.53 *cis*-4-Bromocyclohexanol $\xrightarrow[t\text{-BuOH}]{t\text{-BuO}^-}$ racemic C$_6$H$_{10}$O (compound **C**)

Compound **C** has infrared absorption in the 1620–1680-cm^{-1} and in the 3590–3650-cm^{-1} regions. Draw and label the (R) and (S) enantiomers of product **C**.

6.54 1-Bromo[2.2.1]bicycloheptane is unreactive toward both S$_N$2 and S$_N$1 reactions. Open the computer molecular model at the book's website titled "1-Bromo[2.2.1]bicycloheptane" and examine the structure. What barriers are there to substitution of 1-bromo[2.2.1]bicycloheptane by both S$_N$2 and S$_N$1 reaction mechanisms?

6.55 Open the computer molecular model titled "1-Bromo[2.2.1]bicycloheptane LUMO" at the book's website for the lowest unoccupied molecular orbital (LUMO) of this compound. Where is the lobe of the LUMO with which the HOMO of a nucleophile would interact in an S$_N$2 reaction?

6.56 In the previous problem and the associated molecular model at the book's website, you considered the role of HOMOs and LUMOs in an S_N2 reaction.

(a) What is the LUMO in an S_N1 reaction and in what reactant and species is it found?

(b) Open the molecular model at the book's website titled "Isopropyl Methyl Ether Carbocation LUMO." Identify the lobe of the LUMO in this carbocation model with which a nucleophile would interact.

(c) Open the model titled "Isopropyl Methyl Ether Carbocation HOMO." Why is there a large orbital lobe between the oxygen and the carbon of the carbocation?

LEARNING GROUP PROBLEMS

1. Consider the solvolysis reaction of (1S,2R)-1-bromo-1,2-dimethylcyclohexane in 80% H_2O/20% CH_3CH_2OH at room temperature.

(a) Write the structure of all chemically reasonable products from this reaction and predict which would be the major one.

(b) Write a detailed mechanism for formation of the major product.

(c) Write the structure of all transition states involved in formation of the major product.

2. Consider the following sequence of reactions, taken from the early steps in a synthesis of ω-fluorooleic acid, a toxic natural compound from an African shrub. (ω-Fluorooleic acid, also called "ratsbane," has been used to kill rats and also as an arrow poison in tribal warfare. Two more steps beyond those below are required to complete its synthesis.)

(i)   1-Bromo-8-fluorooctane + sodium acetylide (the sodium salt of ethyne) $\longrightarrow$ compound **A** ($C_{10}H_{17}F$)

(ii)   Compound **A** + $NaNH_2$ $\longrightarrow$ compound **B** ($C_{10}H_{16}FNa$)

(iii)   Compound **B** + I—$(CH_2)_7$—Cl $\longrightarrow$ compound **C** ($C_{17}H_{30}ClF$)

(iv)   Compound **C** + NaCN $\longrightarrow$ compound **D** ($C_{18}H_{30}NF$)

(a) Elucidate the structures of compounds **A**, **B**, **C**, and **D** above.

(b) Write the mechanism for each of the reactions above.

(c) Write the structure of the transition state for each reaction.

[S U M M A R Y   A N D   R E V I E W   T O O L S]

Mechanism Review: Substitution versus Elimination

S_N2	S_N1 and E1
Primary substrate	Tertiary substrate
Back side attack of Nu: with respect to LG	Carbocation intermediate
Strong/polarizable unhindered nucleophile	Weak nucleophile/base (e.g., solvent)
Bimolecular in rate-determining step	Unimolecular in rate-determining step
Concerted bond forming/bond breaking	Racemization if S_N1
Inversion of stereochemistry	Removal of β-hydrogen if E1
Favored by polar aprotic solvent	Protic solvent assists ionization of LG
	Low temperature (S_N1) / high temperature (E1)

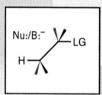

S_N2 and E2	E2
Secondary or primary substrate	Tertiary or secondary substrate
Strong unhindered base/nucleophile leads to S_N2	Concerted anti-coplanar transition state
Strong hindered base/nucleophile leads to E2	
Low temperature (S_N2) / high temperature (E2)	Bimolecular in rate-determining step
	Strong hindered base
	High temperature

CHAPTER 7

Alkenes and Alkynes I

PROPERTIES AND SYNTHESIS. ELIMINATION REACTIONS OF ALKYL HALIDES

Despite being a world of seven billion people spread over seven continents, a popular but unproven theory claims that there are only six degrees of separation between each of us and every other person. In other words, we are all a friend of a friend, and so on. As strange as it might sound, organic molecules are not much different, with alkenes and alkynes being the key connectors to numerous other functional groups as well as to C—C bond-formation processes that can rapidly create molecular complexity. In truth, it rarely takes six steps to find where an alkene or alkyne may have played a role in the synthesis of a molecule; more typically, it takes only one or two steps.

IN THIS CHAPTER WE WILL CONSIDER:

- the properties of alkenes and alkynes and how they are named
- how alkenes and alkynes can be transformed into alkanes
- how to plan the synthesis of any organic molecule

[**WHY** DO THESE TOPICS MATTER?]   At the end of the chapter, we will show how simple changes in the placement of alkene functional groups can lead to distinct properties, from the strength of the rubber in our tires to our ability to see.

PHOTO CREDIT: Media Bakery

7.1 INTRODUCTION

Alkenes are hydrocarbons whose molecules contain a carbon–carbon double bond. An old name for this family of compounds that is still often used is the name **olefins**. Ethene (ethylene), the simplest olefin (alkene), was called olefiant gas (Latin: *oleum,* oil + *facere,* to make) because gaseous ethene (C_2H_4) reacts with chlorine to form $C_2H_4Cl_2$, a liquid (oil).

Hydrocarbons whose molecules contain the carbon–carbon triple bond are called alkynes. The common name for this family is **acetylenes,** after the simplest member, $HC\equiv CH$:

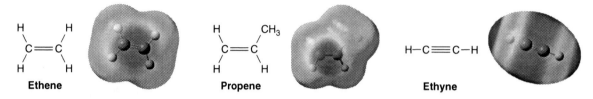

| Ethene | Propene | Ethyne |

7.1A Physical Properties of Alkenes and Alkynes

Alkenes and alkynes have physical properties similar to those of corresponding alkanes. Alkenes and alkynes up to four carbons (except 2-butyne) are gases at room temperature. Being relatively nonpolar themselves, alkenes and alkynes dissolve in nonpolar solvents or in solvents of low polarity. Alkenes and alkynes are only *very slightly soluble* in water (with alkynes being slightly more soluble than alkenes). The densities of alkenes and alkynes are lower than that of water.

7.2 THE (E)–(Z) SYSTEM FOR DESIGNATING ALKENE DIASTEREOMERS

In Section 4.5 we learned to use the terms cis and trans to designate the stereochemistry of alkene diastereomers (cis–trans isomers). These terms are unambiguous, however, only when applied to disubstituted alkenes. If the alkene is trisubstituted or tetrasubstituted, the terms cis and trans are either ambiguous or do not apply at all. Consider the following alkene as an example:

$$\underset{\textbf{A}}{\underset{H}{\overset{Br}{}}C=C\underset{F}{\overset{Cl}{}}}$$

It is impossible to decide whether **A** is cis or trans since no two groups are the same.

A system that works in all cases is based on the priorities of groups in the Cahn–Ingold–Prelog convention (Section 5.7). This system, called the *(E)–(Z) system,* applies to alkene diastereomers of all types.

7.2A HOW TO Use The (E)–(Z) System

1. Examine the two groups attached to one carbon atom of the double bond and decide which has higher priority.

2. Repeat that operation at the other carbon atom:

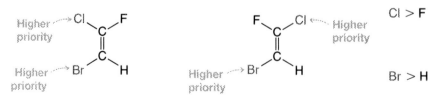

Cl > F

Br > H

| **(Z)-2-Bromo-1-chloro-1-fluoroethene** | **(E)-2-Bromo-1-chloro-1-fluoroethene** |

3. Compare the group of higher priority on one carbon atom with the group of higher priority on the other carbon atom. If the two groups of higher priority are on the same side of the double bond, the alkene is designated (Z) (from the German word *zusammen,* meaning together). If the two groups of higher priority are on opposite sides of the double bond, the alkene is designated (E) (from the German word *entgegen,* meaning opposite). The following isomers provide another example.

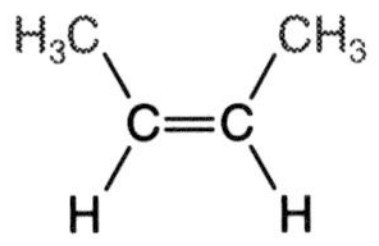

$$CH_3 > H$$

(Z)-2-Butene or (Z)-but-2-ene
(*cis*-2-butene)

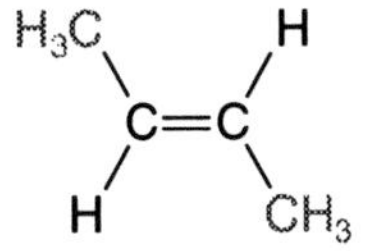

(E)-2-Butene or (E)-but-2-ene
(*trans*-2-butene)

●●● SOLVED PROBLEM 7.1

The two stereoisomers of 1-bromo-1,2-dichloroethene cannot be designated as cis and trans in the normal way because the double bond is trisubstituted. They can, however, be given (E) and (Z) designations. Write a structural formula for each isomer and give each the proper designation.

STRATEGY AND ANSWER: We write the structures (below), then note that chlorine has a higher priority than hydrogen, and bromine has a higher priority than chlorine. The group with higher priority on C1 is bromine and the group with higher priority at C2 is chlorine. In the first structure the higher priority chlorine and bromine atoms are on opposite sides of the double bond, and therefore this isomer is (E). In the second structure those chlorine and bromine atoms are on the same side, so the latter isomer is (Z).

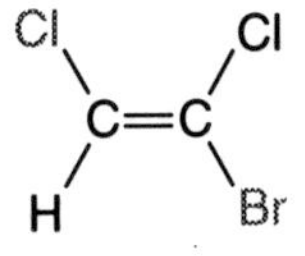

$$Cl > H$$
$$Br > Cl$$

(E)-1-Bromo-1,2-dichloroethene

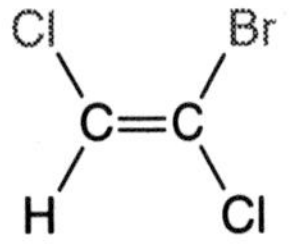

(Z)-1-Bromo-1,2-dichloroethene

●●◆

PRACTICE PROBLEM 7.1

Using the (E)–(Z) designation [and in parts **(e)** and **(f)** the (R)–(S) designation as well] give IUPAC names for each of the following:

(a)

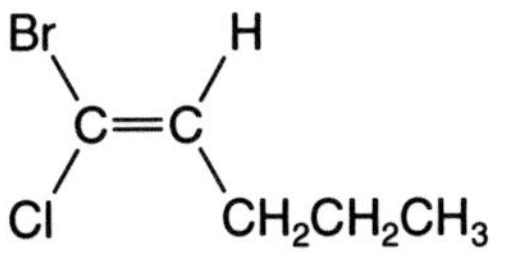

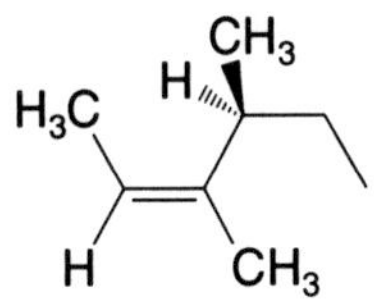

(b)

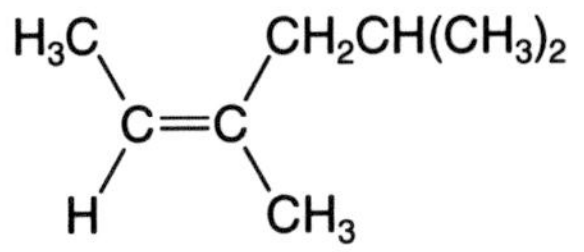

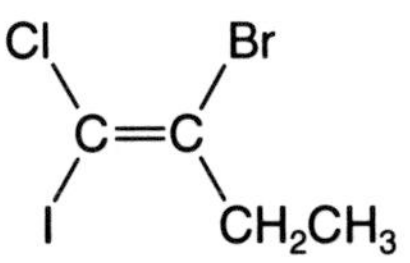

(c)

(d)

(e)

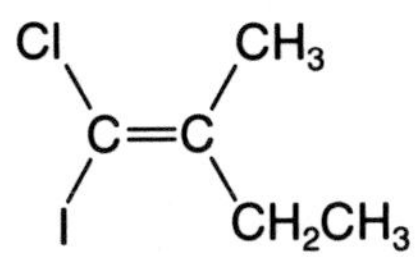

(f)

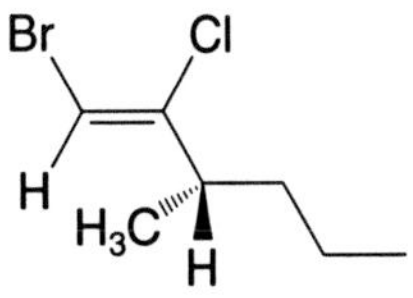

7.3 RELATIVE STABILITIES OF ALKENES

Cis and trans isomers of alkenes do not have the same stability.

● Strain caused by crowding of two alkyl groups on the same side of a double bond makes cis isomers generally less stable than trans isomers (Fig. 7.1).

This effect can be measured quantitatively by comparing thermodynamic data from experiments involving alkenes with related structures, as we shall see later.

FIGURE 7.1 Cis and trans alkene isomers. The cis isomer is less stable due to greater strain from crowding by the adjacent alkyl groups.

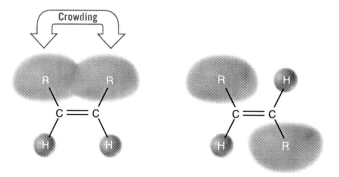

7.3A Heat of Reaction

The addition of hydrogen to an alkene (hydrogenation, Sections 4.16A and 7.13) is an exothermic reaction; the enthalpy change involved is called the **heat of reaction** or, in this specific case, the **heat of hydrogenation**.

$$\begin{array}{c} \diagdown \\ C=C \\ \diagup \end{array}\ \diagup + H\!-\!H \xrightarrow{\ Pt\ } \begin{array}{c} | \quad | \\ -C\!-\!C- \\ | \quad | \\ H \quad H \end{array} \qquad \Delta H^{\circ} \cong -120\ \text{kJ mol}^{-1}$$

We can gain a quantitative measure of relative alkene stabilities by comparing the heats of hydrogenation for a family of alkenes that all become the same alkane product on hydrogenation. The results of such an experiment involving platinum-catalyzed hydrogenation of three butene isomers are shown in Fig. 7.2. All three isomers yield the same product—butane—but the heat of reaction is different in each case. On conversion to butane, 1-butene liberates the most heat (127 kJ mol^{-1}), followed by *cis*-2-butene (120 kJ mol^{-1}), with *trans*-2-butene producing the least heat (115 kJ mol^{-1}). These data indicate that the trans isomer is more stable than the cis isomer, since less energy is released when the trans isomer is converted to butane. Furthermore, it shows that the terminal alkene, 1-butene, is less stable than either of the disubstituted alkenes, since its reaction is the most exothermic. Of course, alkenes that do not yield the same hydrogenation products cannot be compared on the basis of their respective heats of hydrogenation. In such cases it is necessary to compare other thermochemical data, such as heats of combustion, although we will not go into analyses of that type here.

FIGURE 7.2 An energy diagram for platinum-catalyzed hydrogenation of the three butene isomers. The order of stability based on the differences in their heats of hydrogenation is *trans*-2-butene > *cis*-2-butene > 1-butene.

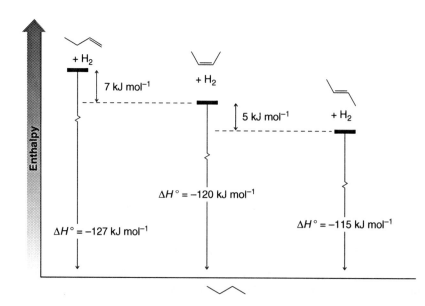

7.3B Overall Relative Stabilities of Alkenes

Studies of numerous alkenes reveal a pattern of stabilities that is related to the number of alkyl groups attached to the carbon atoms of the double bond.

- The greater the number of attached alkyl groups (i.e., the more highly substituted the carbon atoms of the double bond), the greater is the alkene's stability.

This order of stabilities can be given in general terms as follows:*

Relative Stabilities of Alkenes

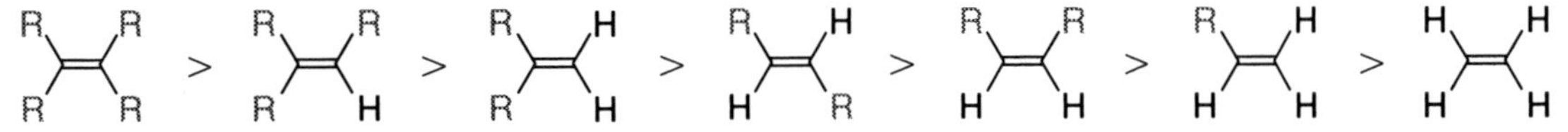

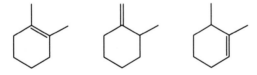

2-Methyl-2-pentene has three substituents on its double bond, whereas 2-methyl-1-pentene has two, and therefore 2-methyl-2-pentene is the more stable.

●●● SOLVED PROBLEM 7.2

Consider the two alkenes 2-methyl-1-pentene and 2-methyl-2-pentene and decide which would be most stable.

STRATEGY AND ANSWER: First write the structures of the two alkenes, then decide how many substituents the double bond of each has.

2-Methyl-1-pentene
(disubstituted, less stable)

2-Methyl-2-pentene
(trisubstituted, more stable)

2-Methyl-2-pentene has three substituents on its double bond, whereas 2-methyl-1-pentene has two, and therefore 2-methyl-2-pentene is the more stable.

●●●

PRACTICE PROBLEM 7.2

Rank the following cycloalkenes in order of increasing stability.

●●●

PRACTICE PROBLEM 7.3

Heats of hydrogenation of three alkenes are as follows:

$$2\text{-methyl-1-butene } (-119 \text{ kJ mol}^{-1})$$
$$3\text{-methyl-1-butene } (-127 \text{ kJ mol}^{-1})$$
$$2\text{-methyl-2-butene } (-113 \text{ kJ mol}^{-1})$$

(a) Write the structure of each alkene and classify it as to whether its doubly bonded atoms are monosubstituted, disubstituted, trisubstituted, or tetrasubstituted. **(b)** Write the structure of the product formed when each alkene is hydrogenated. **(c)** Can heats of hydrogenation be used to relate the relative stabilities of these three alkenes? **(d)** If so, what is the predicted order of stability? If not, why not? **(e)** What other alkene isomers are possible for these alkenes? Write their structures. **(f)** What are the relative stabilities among just these isomers?

---

*This order of stabilities may seem contradictory when compared with the explanation given for the relative stabilities of cis and trans isomers. Although a detailed explanation of the trend given here is beyond our scope, the relative stabilities of substituted alkenes can be rationalized. Part of the explanation can be given in terms of the electron-releasing effect of alkyl groups (Section 6.11B), an effect that satisfies the electron-withdrawing properties of the sp^2-hybridized carbon atoms of the double bond.

●●◦

PRACTICE PROBLEM 7.4　Predict the more stable alkene of each pair: **(a)** 2-methyl-2-pentene or 2,3-dimethyl-2-butene; **(b)** *cis*-3-hexene or *trans*-3-hexene; **(c)** 1-hexene or *cis*-3-hexene; **(d)** *trans*-2-hexene or 2-methyl-2-pentene.

●●◦

PRACTICE PROBLEM 7.5　How many stereoisomers are possible for 4-methyl-2-hexene, and how many fractions would you obtain if you distilled the mixture?

7.4 CYCLOALKENES

The rings of cycloalkenes containing five carbon atoms or fewer exist only in the cis form (Fig. 7.3). The introduction of a trans double bond into rings this small would, if it were possible, introduce greater strain than the bonds of the ring atoms could accommodate.

Cyclopropene　　**Cyclobutene**　　**Cyclopentene**　　**Cyclohexene**

FIGURE 7.3 *cis*-Cycloalkenes.

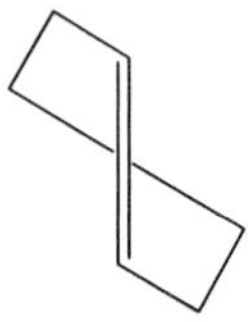

FIGURE 7.4 Hypothetical *trans*-cyclohexene. This molecule is apparently too strained to exist at room temperature.

(Verify this with handheld molecular models.) *trans*-Cyclohexene might resemble the structure shown in Fig. 7.4. There is evidence that it can be formed as a very reactive short-lived intermediate in some chemical reactions, but it is not isolable as a stable molecule.

trans-Cycloheptene has been observed spectroscopically, but it is a substance with a very short lifetime and has not been isolated.

trans-Cyclooctene (Fig. 7.5) has been isolated, however. Here the ring is large enough to accommodate the geometry required by a trans double bond and still be stable at room temperature. *trans*-Cyclooctene is chiral and exists as a pair of enantiomers. You may wish to verify this using handheld models.

Helpful Hint

Exploring all of these cycloalkenes with handheld molecular models, including both enantiomers of *trans*-cyclooctene, will help illustrate their structural differences.

***cis*-Cyclooctene**　　***trans*-Cyclooctene**

FIGURE 7.5 The cis and trans forms of cyclooctene.

7.5 SYNTHESIS OF ALKENES VIA ELIMINATION REACTIONS

Elimination reactions are the most important means for synthesizing alkenes. In this chapter we shall study two methods for alkene synthesis based on elimination reactions: dehydrohalogenation of alkyl halides and dehydration of alcohols.

Dehydrohalogenation of Alkyl Halides (Sections 6.15, 6.16, and 7.6)

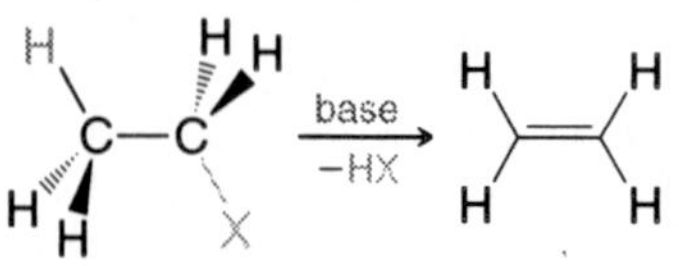

$$\underset{\substack{H \\ H}}{\overset{H}{C}} - \underset{\substack{H \\ X}}{\overset{H}{C}} \xrightarrow[\text{−HX}]{\text{base}} \underset{\substack{H \\ H}}{\overset{H}{C}} = \underset{\substack{H \\ H}}{\overset{H}{C}}$$

Dehydration of Alcohols (Sections 7.7 and 7.8)

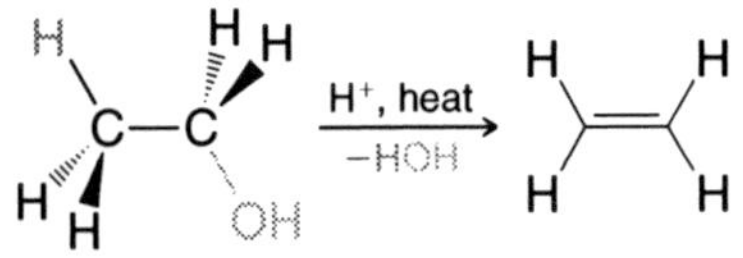

7.6 DEHYDROHALOGENATION OF ALKYL HALIDES

- The best reaction conditions to use when synthesizing an alkene by dehydrohalogenation are those that promote an E2 mechanism.

In an E2 mechanism, a base removes a β hydrogen from the β carbon, as the double bond forms and a leaving group departs from the α carbon.

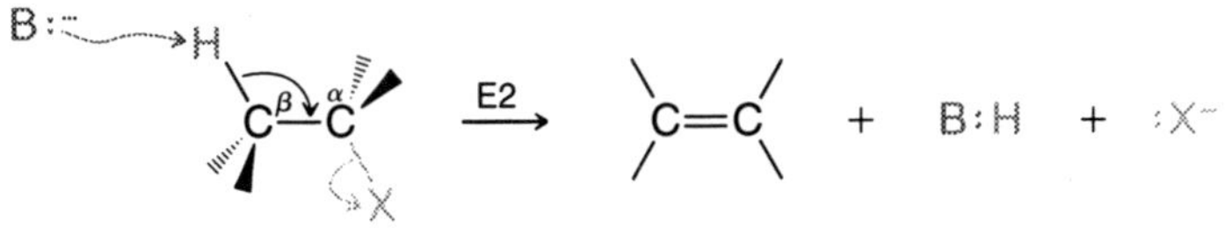

Reaction conditions that favor elimination by an E1 mechanism should be avoided because the results can be too variable. The carbocation intermediate that accompanies an E1 reaction can undergo rearrangement of the carbon skeleton, as we shall see in Section 7.8, and it can also undergo substitution by an S_N1 mechanism, which competes strongly with formation of products by an E1 path.

7.6A HOW TO Favor an E2 Mechanism

1. **Use a secondary or tertiary alkyl halide if possible.**
   Why? Because steric hindrance in the substrate will inhibit substitution.

2. **When a synthesis must begin with a primary alkyl halide, use a bulky base.**
   Why? Because the steric bulk of the base will inhibit substitution.

3. **Use a high concentration of a strong and nonpolarizable base such as an alkoxide.**
   Why? Because a weak and polarizable base would not drive the reaction toward a bimolecular reaction, thereby allowing unimolecular processes (such as S_N1 or E1 reactions) to compete.

4. **Sodium ethoxide in ethanol (EtONa/EtOH) and potassium *tert*-butoxide in *tert*-butyl alcohol (*t*-BuOK/*t*-BuOH) are bases typically used to promote E2 reactions.**
   Why? Because they meet criterion 3 above. Note that in each case the alkoxide base is dissolved in its corresponding alcohol. (Potassium hydroxide dissolved in ethanol or *tert*-butyl alcohol is also sometimes used, in which case the active base includes both the alkoxide and hydroxide species present at equilibrium.)

5. **Use elevated temperature because heat generally favors elimination over substitution.**
   Why? Because elimination reactions are entropically favored over substitution reactions (because the products are greater in number than the reactants). Hence $\Delta S°$ in the Gibbs free-energy equation, $\Delta G° = \Delta H° - T\Delta S°$ is significant, and $\Delta S°$ will be increased by higher temperature since T is a coefficient, leading to a more negative (favorable) $\Delta G°$.

7.6B Zaitsev's Rule: Formation of the More Substituted Alkene Is Favored with a Small Base

We showed examples in Sections 6.15–6.17 of dehydrohalogenations where only a single elimination product was possible. For example:

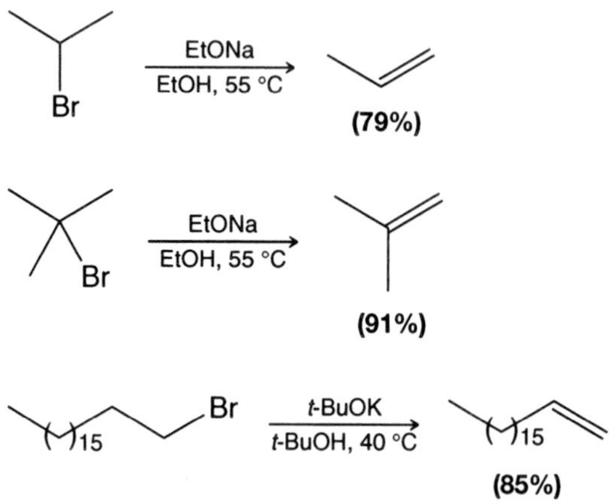

Dehydrohalogenation of many alkyl halides, however, yields more than one product. For example, dehydrohalogenation of 2-bromo-2-methylbutane can yield two products: 2-methyl-2-butene and 2-methyl-1-butene, as shown here by pathways (a) and (b), respectively:

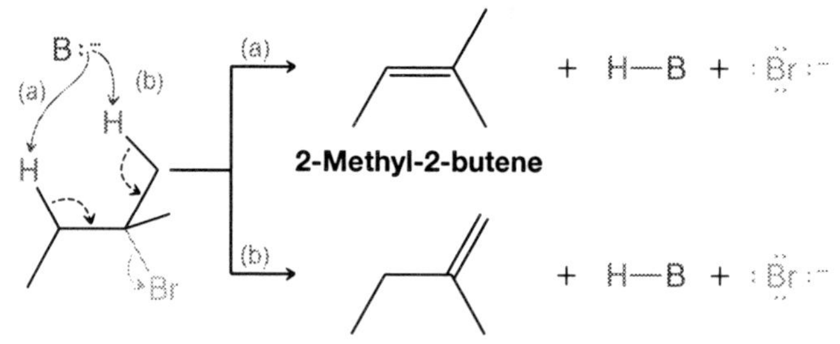

2-Bromo-2-methylbutane **2-Methyl-1-butene**

- If we use a small base such as ethoxide or hydroxide, the major product of the reaction will be the more highly substituted alkene (which is also the more stable alkene).

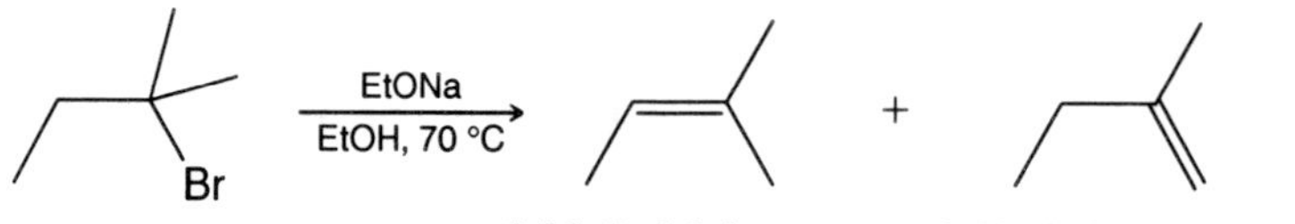

2-Methyl-2-butene (69%)	**2-Methyl-1-butene (31%)**
Trisubstituted: more stable	**Disubstituted: less stable**

2-Methyl-2-butene is a trisubstituted alkene (three methyl groups are attached to carbon atoms of the double bond), whereas 2-methyl-1-butene is only disubstituted. 2-Methyl-2-butene is the major product.

- Whenever an elimination occurs to give the more stable, more highly substituted alkene, chemists say that the elimination follows **Zaitsev's rule**, named for the nineteenth-century Russian chemist A. N. Zaitsev (1841–1910) who formulated it. (Zaitsev's name is also transliterated as Zaitzev, Saytzeff, Saytseff, or Saytzev.)

Helpful Hint

The Zaitsev product is that which is the more stable product.

The reason for this behavior is related to the double-bond character that develops in the transition state (cf. Section 6.16) for each reaction:

The β hydrogen and leaving group are anti coplanar.

Transition state for an E2 reaction

The carbon–carbon bond has the developing character of a double bond.

The transition state for the reaction leading to 2-methyl-2-butene (Fig. 7.6) has the developing character of the double bond in a trisubstituted alkene. The transition state for the reaction leading to 2-methyl-1-butene has the developing character of a double bond in a disubstituted alkene. Because the transition state leading to 2-methyl-2-butene resembles a more stable alkene, this transition state is more stable (recall the Hammond–Leffler postulate, Fig. 6.10). Because this transition state is more stable (occurs at lower free energy), the free energy of activation for this reaction is lower and 2-methyl-2-butene is formed faster. This explains why 2-methyl-2-butene is the major product.

- In general, the preferential formation of one product because the free energy of activation leading to its formation is lower than that for another product, and therefore the rate of its formation faster, is called **kinetic control** of product formation. (See also Section 13.10A.)

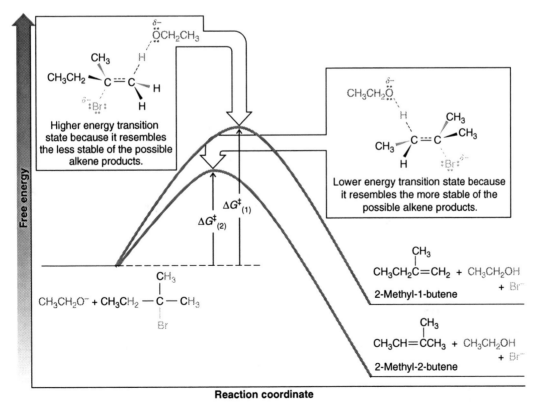

FIGURE 7.6 Reaction (2) leading to the more stable alkene occurs faster than reaction (1) leading to the less stable alkene; $\Delta G^{\ddagger}_{(2)}$ is less than $\Delta G^{\ddagger}_{(1)}$.

●●● SOLVED PROBLEM 7.3

Using Zaitsev's rule, predict which would be the major product of the following reaction:

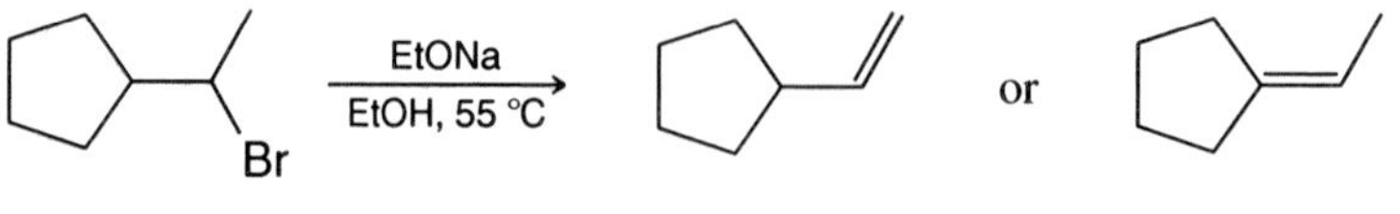

STRATEGY AND ANSWER: Alkene **B** has a trisubstituted double bond whereas the double bond of **A** is only mono-substituted. Therefore, **B** is more stable and, according to Zaitsev's rule, would be the major product.

●●●

PRACTICE PROBLEM 7.6 Predict the major product formed when 2-bromobutane is subjected to dehydrobromination using sodium ethoxide in ethanol at 55 °C.

●●●

PRACTICE PROBLEM 7.7 List the alkenes that would be formed when each of the following alkyl halides is subjected to dehydrohalogenation with potassium ethoxide in ethanol and use Zaitsev's rule to predict the major product of each reaction: **(a)** 2-bromo-3-methylbutane and **(b)** 2-bromo-2,3-dimethylbutane.

7.6C Formation of the Less Substituted Alkene Using a Bulky Base

● Carrying out dehydrohalogenations with a bulky base such as potassium *tert*-butoxide (*t*-BuOK) in *tert*-butyl alcohol (*t*-BuOH) favors the formation of the **less substituted alkene:**

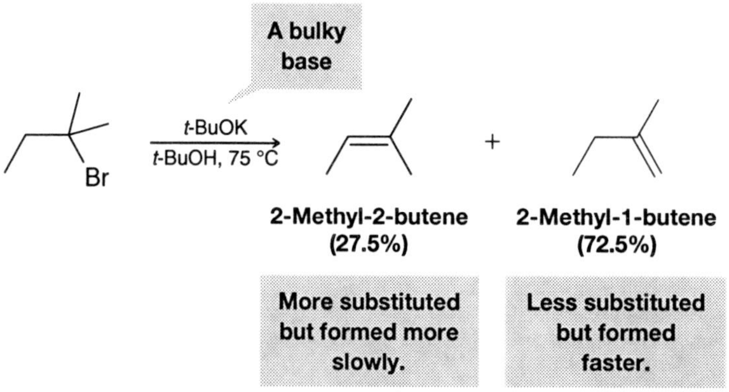

The reasons for this behavior are related in part to the steric bulk of the base and to the fact that in *tert*-butyl alcohol the base is associated with solvent molecules and thus made even larger. The large *tert*-butoxide ion appears to have difficulty removing one of the internal (2°) hydrogen atoms because of greater crowding at that site in the transition state. It removes one of the more exposed (1°) hydrogen atoms of the methyl group instead.

● When an elimination yields the less substituted alkene, we say that it follows the Hofmann rule (see also Section 20.12A).

●●● SOLVED PROBLEM 7.4

Your task is the following synthesis. Which base would you use to maximize the yield of this specific alkene?

STRATEGY AND ANSWER: Here you want the Hofmann rule to apply (you want the less substituted alkene to be formed). Therefore, use a bulky base such as potassium *tert*-butoxide in *tert*-butyl alcohol.

● ● ◆ ······

Examine Solved Problem 7.3. Your task is to prepare **A** in the highest possible yield by dehydrobromination. Which base would you use?

PRACTICE PROBLEM 7.8

7.6D The Stereochemistry of E2 Reactions: The Orientation of Groups in the Transition State

● The five atoms involved in the transition state of an E2 reaction (including the base) must be coplanar, i.e., lie in the same plane.

The requirement for coplanarity of the H—C—C—LG unit arises from a need for proper overlap of orbitals in the developing π bond of the alkene that is being formed (see Section 6.16). There are two ways that this can happen:

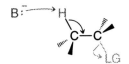 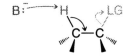

Anti coplanar   **Syn coplanar**
transition state   **transition state**
(preferred)   **(only with certain**
        rigid molecules)

● The anti coplanar conformation is the preferred transition state geometry.

The syn coplanar transition state occurs only with rigid molecules that are unable to assume the anti arrangement. The reason: the anti coplanar transition state is staggered (and therefore of lower energy), while the syn coplanar transition state is eclipsed. Practice Problem 7.9 will help to illustrate this difference.

Helpful Hint

Be able to draw a three-dimensional representation of an anti coplanar E2 transition state.

● ● ◆ ······

Consider a simple molecule such as ethyl bromide and show with Newman projection formulas how the anti coplanar transition state would be favored over the syn coplanar one.

PRACTICE PROBLEM 7.9

Part of the evidence for the preferred anti coplanar arrangement of groups comes from experiments done with cyclic molecules. Two groups axially oriented on adjacent carbons in a chair conformation of cyclohexane are anti coplanar. If one of these groups is a hydrogen and the other a leaving group, the geometric requirements for an anti coplanar E2 transition state are met. Neither an axial–equatorial nor an equatorial–equatorial orientation of the groups allows formation of an anti coplanar transition state. (Note that there are no syn coplanar groups in a chair conformation, either.)

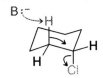

Here the β hydrogen and the   **A Newman projection formula**
chlorine are both axial. This   **shows that the β hydrogen and**
allows an anti coplanar   **the chlorine are anti coplanar**
transition state.   **when they are both axial.**

As examples, let us consider the different behavior in E2 reactions shown by two compounds containing cyclohexane rings, neomenthyl chloride and menthyl chloride:

H_3C—⬡—ᴵᴵᴵᴵ$CH(CH_3)_2$ H_3C—⬡—ᴵᴵᴵᴵ$CH(CH_3)_2$

     Cl Cl
 Neomenthyl chloride   **Menthyl chloride**

Helpful Hint

Examine the conformations of neomenthyl chloride using handheld models.

In the more stable conformation of neomenthyl chloride (see the following mechanism), the alkyl groups are both equatorial and the chlorine is axial. There are also axial hydrogen atoms on both C1 and C3. The base can attack either of these hydrogen atoms and achieve an anti coplanar transition state for an E2 reaction. Products corresponding to each of these transition states (2-menthene and 1-menthene) are formed rapidly. In accordance with Zaitsev's rule, 1-menthene (with the more highly substituted double bond) is the major product.

[**A MECHANISM FOR THE REACTION** — **E2 Elimination Where There Are Two Axial β Hydrogens**]

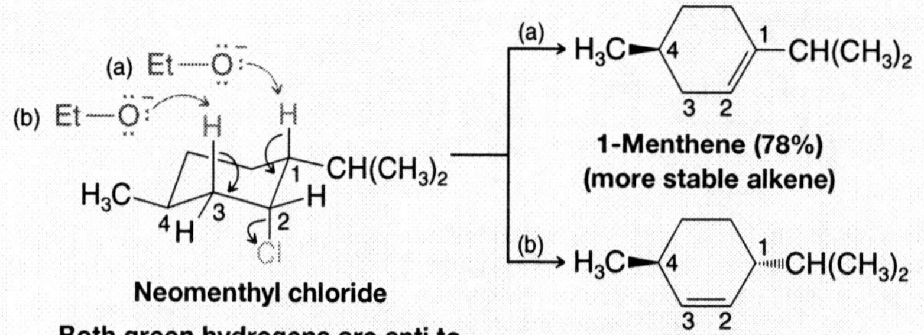

Neomenthyl chloride

Both green hydrogens are anti to the chlorine in this, the more stable conformation. Elimination by path (a) leads to 1-menthene; by path (b) to 2-menthene.

1-Menthene (78%)
(more stable alkene)

2-Menthene (22%)
(less stable alkene)

On the other hand, the more stable conformation of menthyl chloride has all three groups (including the chlorine) equatorial. For the chlorine to become axial, menthyl chloride has to assume a conformation in which the large isopropyl group and the methyl group are also axial. This conformation is of much higher energy, and the free energy of activation for the reaction is large because it includes the energy necessary for the conformational change. Consequently, menthyl chloride undergoes an E2 reaction very slowly, and the product is entirely 2-menthene because the hydrogen atom at C1 cannot be anti to the chlorine. This product (or any resulting from an elimination to yield the less substituted alkene) is sometimes called the *Hofmann product* (Sections 7.6C and 20.12A).

[**A MECHANISM FOR THE REACTION** — **E2 Elimination Where the Only Axial β Hydrogen Is from a Less Stable Conformer**]

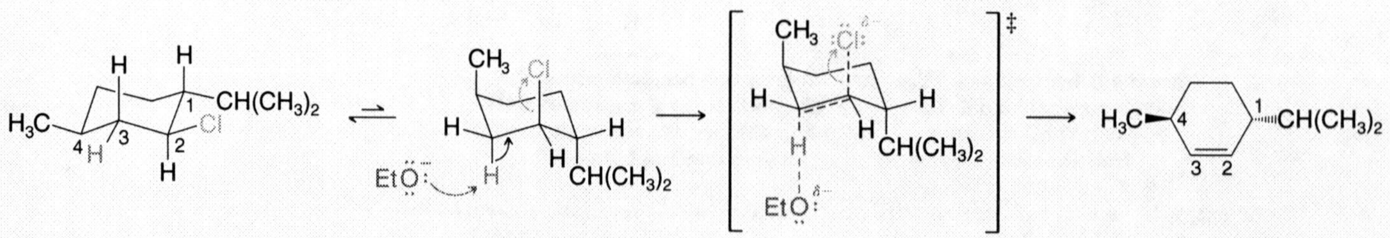

Menthyl chloride
(*more stable conformation*)
Elimination is not possible for this conformation because no hydrogen is anti to the leaving group.

Menthyl chloride
(*less stable conformation*)
Elimination is possible from this conformation because the green hydrogen is anti to the chlorine.

The transition state for the E2 elimination is anti coplanar.

2-Menthene (100%)

308

Predict the major product formed when the following compound is subjected to dehydrochlorination with sodium ethoxide in ethanol.

H_3C———⟨ ⟩——C_6H_5
Cl

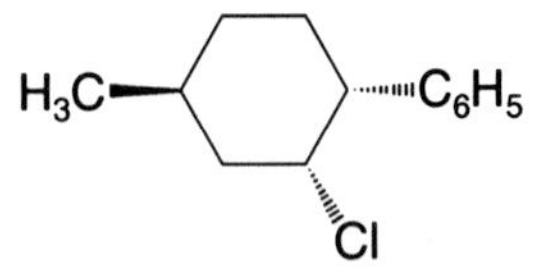

STRATEGY AND ANSWER: We know that for an E2 dehydrochlorination to take place the chlorine will have to be axial. The following conformation has the chlorine axial and has two hydrogen atoms that are anti coplanar to the chlorine. Two products will be formed but **(B)** being more stable should be the major product.

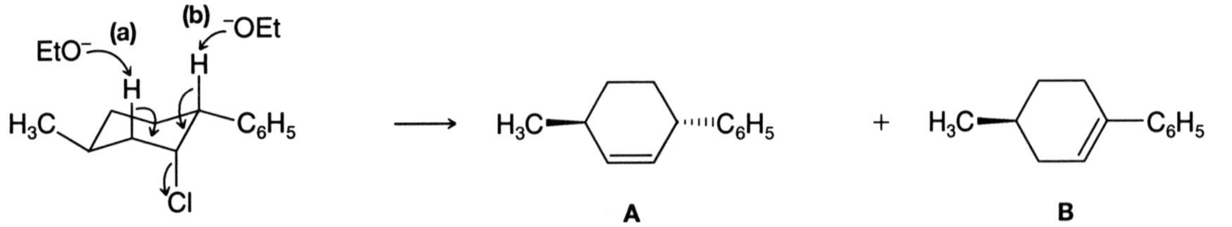

	A		B
	Disubstituted, less stable		Trisubstituted, more stable
	(minor product)		(major product)

●●●

PRACTICE PROBLEM 7.10

When *cis*-1-bromo-4-*tert*-butylcyclohexane is treated with sodium ethoxide in ethanol, it reacts rapidly; the product is 4-*tert*-butylcyclohexene. Under the same conditions, *trans*-1-bromo-4-*tert*-butylcyclohexane reacts very slowly. Write conformational structures and explain the difference in reactivity of these cis–trans isomers.

●●●

PRACTICE PROBLEM 7.11

(a) When *cis*-1-bromo-2-methylcyclohexane undergoes an E2 reaction, two products (cycloalkenes) are formed. What are these two cycloalkenes, and which would you expect to be the major product? Write conformational structures showing how each is formed.
(b) When *trans*-1-bromo-2-methylcyclohexane reacts in an E2 reaction, only one cycloalkene is formed. What is this product? Write conformational structures showing why it is the only product.

7.7 ACID-CATALYZED DEHYDRATION OF ALCOHOLS

- Most alcohols undergo dehydration (lose a molecule of water) to form an alkene when heated with a strong acid.

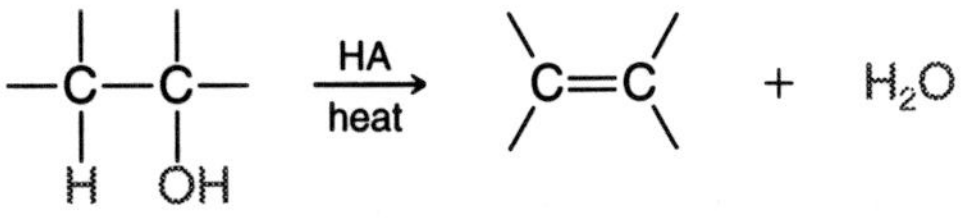

$$-\overset{|}{\underset{H}{C}}-\overset{|}{\underset{OH}{C}}- \xrightarrow[\text{heat}]{HA} \overset{\diagdown}{\diagup}C=C\overset{\diagup}{\diagdown} + H_2O$$

The reaction is an elimination and is favored at higher temperatures (Section 6.18A). The most commonly used acids in the laboratory are Brønsted acids—proton donors such as sulfuric acid and phosphoric acid. Lewis acids such as alumina (Al_2O_3) are often used in industrial, gas-phase dehydrations.

1. **The temperature and concentration of acid required to dehydrate an alcohol depend on the structure of the alcohol substrate.**

   (a) **Primary alcohols** are the most difficult to dehydrate. Dehydration of ethanol, for example, requires concentrated sulfuric acid and a temperature of 180 °C:

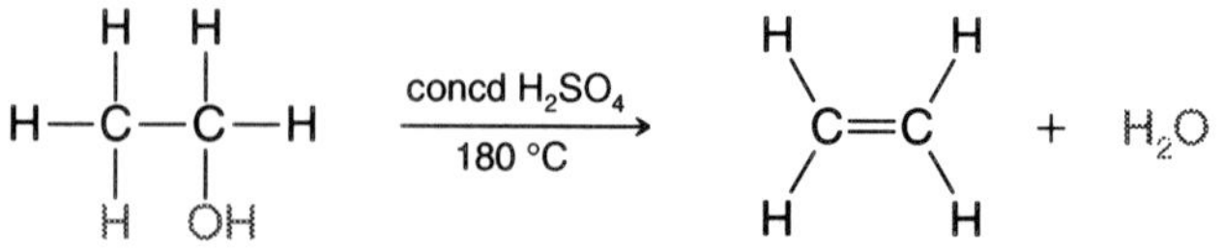

Ethanol (a 1° alcohol) **Ethene**

(b) Secondary alcohols usually dehydrate under milder conditions. Cyclohexanol, for example, dehydrates in 85% phosphoric acid at 165–170 °C:

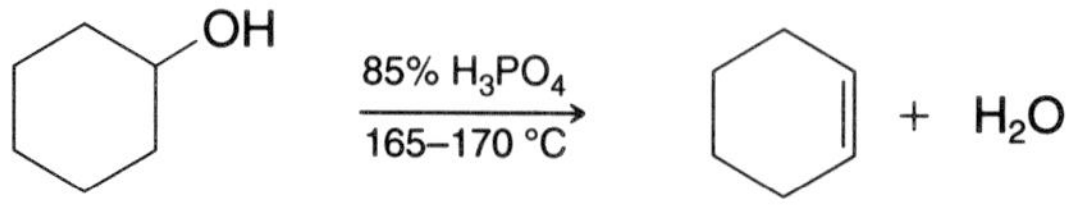

Cyclohexanol **Cyclohexene (80%)**

(c) Tertiary alcohols are usually so easily dehydrated that relatively mild conditions can be used. *tert*-Butyl alcohol, for example, dehydrates in 20% aqueous sulfuric acid at a temperature of 85 °C:

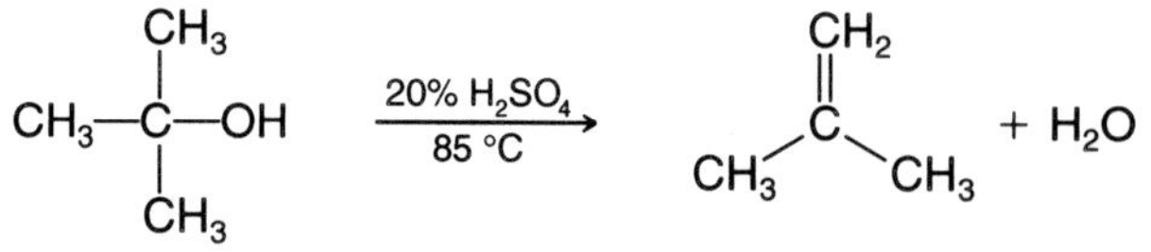

***tert*-Butyl alcohol** **2-Methylpropene (84%)**

- The relative ease with which alcohols undergo dehydration is 3° > 2° > 1°.

Helpful Hint

Be able to classify any alcohol as 1°, 2°, or 3°, and thereby assess its relative ease of dehydration.

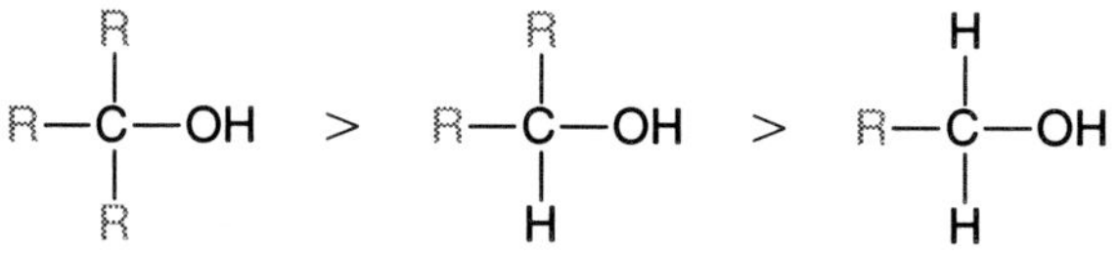

3° Alcohol **2° Alcohol** **1° Alcohol**

This behavior, as we shall see in Section 7.7B, is related to the relative stabilities of carbocations.

2. **Some primary and secondary alcohols also undergo rearrangements of their carbon skeletons during dehydration.** Such a rearrangement occurs in the dehydration of 3,3-dimethyl-2-butanol:

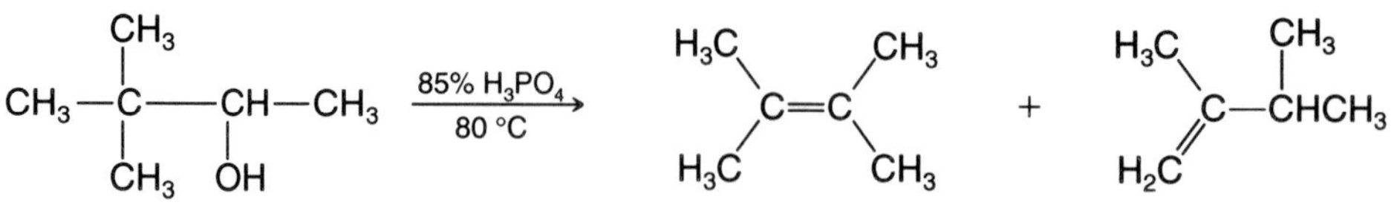

3,3-Dimethyl-2-butanol **2,3-Dimethyl-2-butene (80%)** **2,3-Dimethyl-1-butene (20%)**

Notice that the carbon skeleton of the reactant is

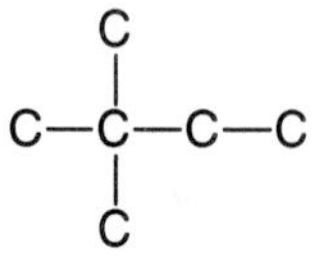 while that of the products is 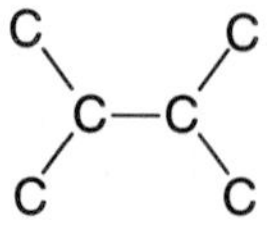

The carbon skeleton has rearranged

We shall see in Section 7.8 that this reaction involves the migration of a methyl group from one carbon to the next so as to form a more stable carbocation. (Rearrangements to carbocations of approximately equal energy may also be possible with some substrates.)

7.7A Mechanism for Dehydration of Secondary and Tertiary Alcohols: An E1 Reaction

Explanations for these observations can be based on a stepwise mechanism originally proposed by F. Whitmore (of Pennsylvania State University).

The mechanism is an E1 reaction in which the substrate is a protonated alcohol. Consider the dehydration of *tert*-butyl alcohol as an example:

Step 1

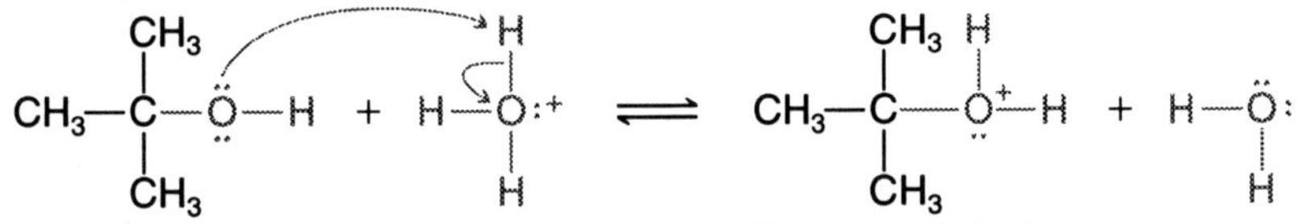

Protonation of the alcohol

Protonated alcohol

In this step, an acid–base reaction, a proton is rapidly transferred from the acid to one of the unshared electron pairs of the alcohol. In dilute sulfuric acid the acid is a hydronium ion; in concentrated sulfuric acid the initial proton donor is sulfuric acid itself. This step is characteristic of all reactions of an alcohol with a strong acid.

The presence of the positive charge on the oxygen of the protonated alcohol weakens all bonds to oxygen, including the carbon–oxygen bond, and in step 2 the carbon–oxygen bond breaks. The leaving group is a molecule of water:

Step 2

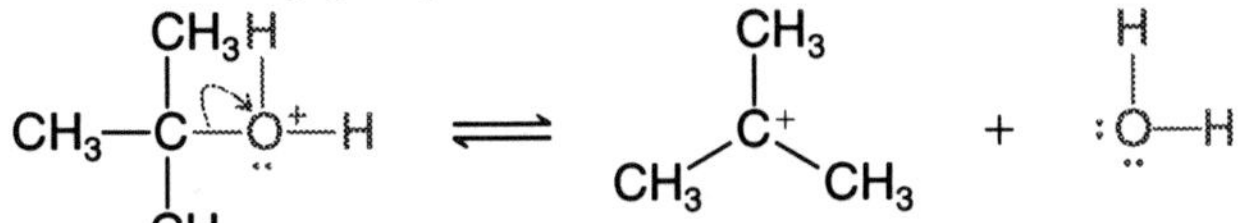

A carbocation

Departure of a water molecule

The carbon–oxygen bond breaks **heterolytically.** The bonding electrons depart with the water molecule and leave behind a carbocation. The carbocation is, of course, highly reactive because the central carbon atom has only six electrons in its valence level, not eight.

Finally, in step 3, a water molecule removes a proton from the β carbon of the carbocation by the process shown below. The result is the formation of a hydronium ion and an alkene:

Step 3

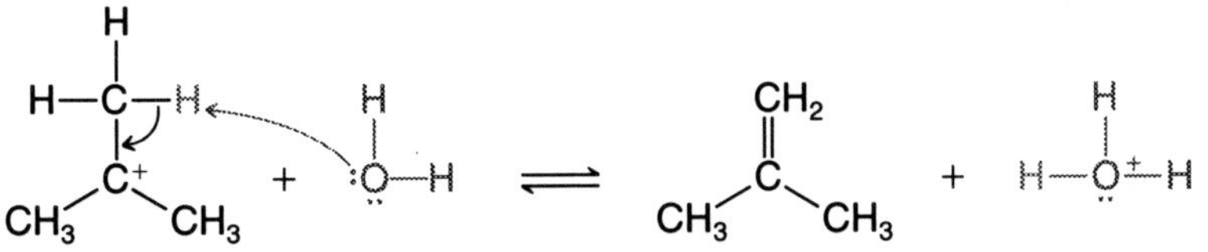

2-Methylpropene

Removal of a β hydrogen

In step 3, also an acid–base reaction, any one of the nine protons available at the three methyl groups can be transferred to a molecule of water. The electron pair left behind when a proton is removed becomes the second bond of the double bond of the alkene. Notice that this step restores an octet of electrons to the central carbon atom. An orbital representation of this process, with the transition state, is as follows.

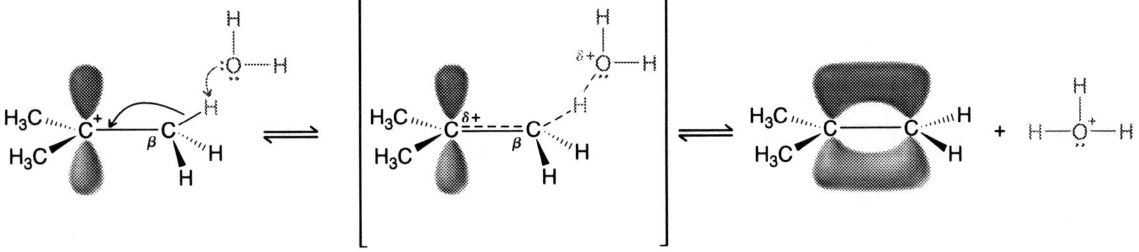

Transition state for removal of a proton from the β carbon of the carbocation

311

PRACTICE PROBLEM 7.12 Dehydration of 2-propanol occurs in 14 M H_2SO_4 at 100 °C. **(a)** Using curved arrows, write all steps in a mechanism for the dehydration. **(b)** Explain the essential role performed in alcohol dehydrations by the acid catalyst. [*Hint:* Consider what would have to happen if no acid were present.]

7.7B Carbocation Stability and the Transition State

We saw in Section 6.11B that the order of stability of carbocations is tertiary > secondary > primary > methyl:

$$
\underset{\substack{3° \\ \text{(most stable)}}}{R-\overset{R}{\underset{R}{C^+}}} \quad > \quad \underset{2°}{R-\overset{H}{\underset{R}{C^+}}} \quad > \quad \underset{1°}{R-\overset{H}{\underset{H}{C^+}}} \quad > \quad \underset{\substack{\text{Methyl} \\ \text{(least stable)}}}{H-\overset{H}{\underset{H}{C^+}}}
$$

In the dehydration of secondary and tertiary alcohols the slowest step is formation of the carbocation as shown in step 2 of the "A Mechanism for the Reaction" box in this section. The first and third steps involve simple acid–base proton transfers, which occur very rapidly. The second step involves loss of the protonated hydroxyl as a leaving group, a highly endergonic process (Section 6.7), and hence it is the rate-determining step.

Because step 2 is the rate-determining step, it is this step that determines the overall reactivity of alcohols toward dehydration. With that in mind, we can now understand why tertiary alcohols are the most easily dehydrated. The formation of a tertiary carbocation is easiest because the free energy of activation for step 2 of a reaction leading to a tertiary carbocation is lowest (see Fig. 7.7). Secondary alcohols are not so easily dehydrated because the free energy of activation for their dehydration is higher—a secondary carbocation is less stable. The free energy of activation for dehydration of primary alcohols via a carbocation is so high that they undergo dehydration by another mechanism (Section 7.7C).

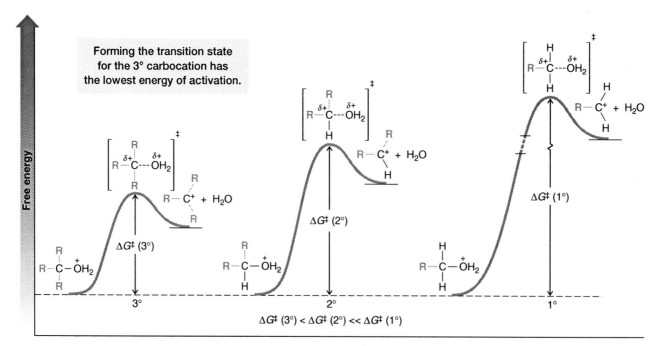

FIGURE 7.7 Free-energy diagrams for the formation of carbocations from protonated tertiary, secondary, and primary alcohols. The relative free energies of activation are tertiary < secondary ≪ primary.

| **A MECHANISM FOR THE REACTION** | **Acid-Catalyzed Dehydration of Secondary or Tertiary Alcohols: An E1 Reaction** |

Step 1

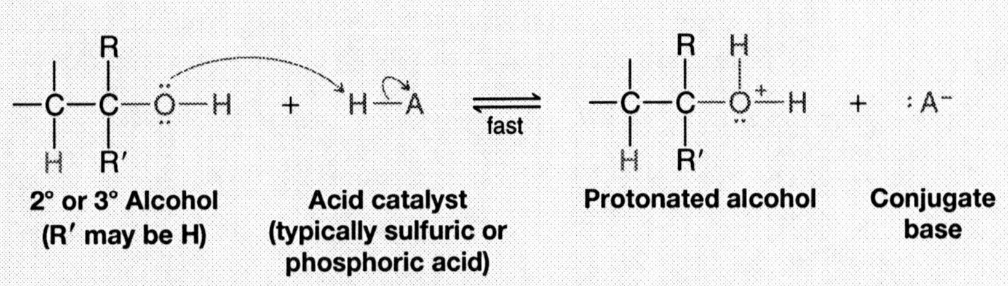

2° or 3° Alcohol (R′ may be H) + Acid catalyst (typically sulfuric or phosphoric acid) ⇌ (fast) Protonated alcohol + Conjugate base

The alcohol accepts a proton from the acid in a fast step.

Step 2

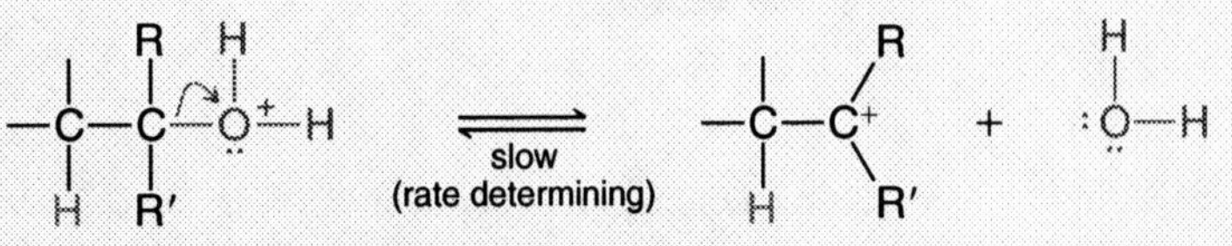

⇌ slow (rate determining)

The protonated alcohol loses a molecule of water to become a carbocation. This step is slow and rate determining.

Step 3

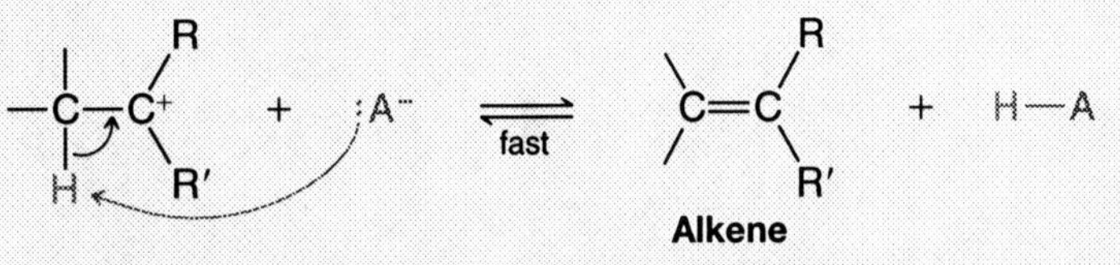

+ :A⁻ ⇌ (fast) Alkene + H—A

The carbocation loses a proton to a base. In this step, the base may be another molecule of the alcohol, water, or the conjugate base of the acid. The proton transfer results in the formation of the alkene. Note that the overall role of the acid is catalytic (it is used in the reaction and regenerated).

The reactions by which carbocations are formed from protonated alcohols are all highly *endergonic*. Based on the Hammond–Leffler postulate (Section 6.13A), there should be a strong resemblance between the transition state and the carbocation in each case.

- *The transition state that leads to the tertiary carbocation is lowest in free energy because it resembles the carbocation that is lowest in energy.*

By contrast, the transition state that leads to the primary carbocation occurs at highest free energy because it resembles the carbocation that is highest in energy. In each instance, moreover, the same factor stabilizes the transition state that stabilizes the carbocation itself: **delocalization of the charge**. We can understand this if we examine the process by which the transition state is formed:

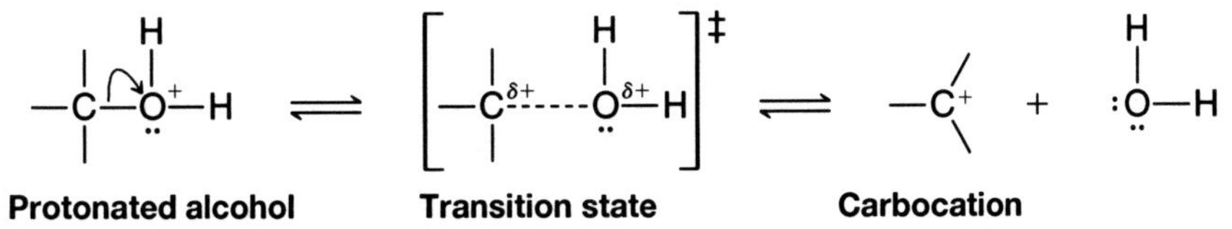

Protonated alcohol ⇌ Transition state ⇌ Carbocation + :O—H

The oxygen atom of the protonated alcohol bears a full positive charge. As the transition state develops, this oxygen atom begins to separate from the carbon atom to which it is attached. The carbon atom begins to develop a partial positive charge because it is losing the electrons that bonded it to the oxygen atom. This developing positive charge *is most effectively delocalized in the transition state leading to a tertiary carbocation because three alkyl groups are present to contribute electron density by hyperconjugation (Section 6.11B) to the developing carbocation.* The positive charge is less effectively delocalized in the transition state leading to a secondary carbocation (*two* electron-releasing groups) and is least effectively delocalized in the transition state leading to a primary carbocation (*one* electron-releasing group). For this reason the dehydration of a primary alcohol proceeds through a different mechanism—an E2 mechanism.

Hyperconjugative stabilization (see Figure 6.7) is greatest for a tertiary carbocation.

Transition state leading to 3° carbocation (most stable)

Transition state leading to 2° carbocation

Transition state leading to 1° carbocation (least stable)

PRACTICE PROBLEM 7.13 Rank the following alcohols in order of increasing ease of acid-catalyzed dehydration.

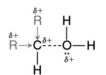

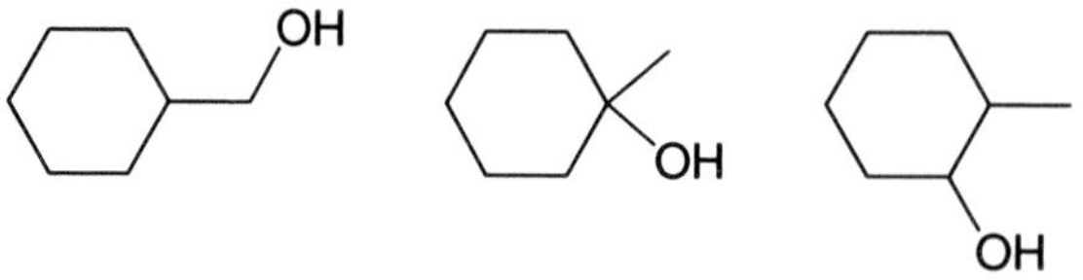

(a)   (b)   (c)

7.7C A Mechanism for Dehydration of Primary Alcohols: An E2 Reaction

Dehydration of primary alcohols apparently proceeds through an E2 mechanism because the primary carbocation required for dehydration by an E1 mechanism is relatively unstable. The first step in dehydration of a primary alcohol is protonation, just as in the E1 mechanism. Then, with the protonated hydroxyl as a good leaving group, a Lewis base in the reaction mixture removes a β hydrogen simultaneously with formation of the alkene double bond and departure of the protonated hydroxyl group (water).

[**A MECHANISM FOR THE REACTION** ⎯ **Dehydration of a Primary Alcohol: An E2 Reaction**]

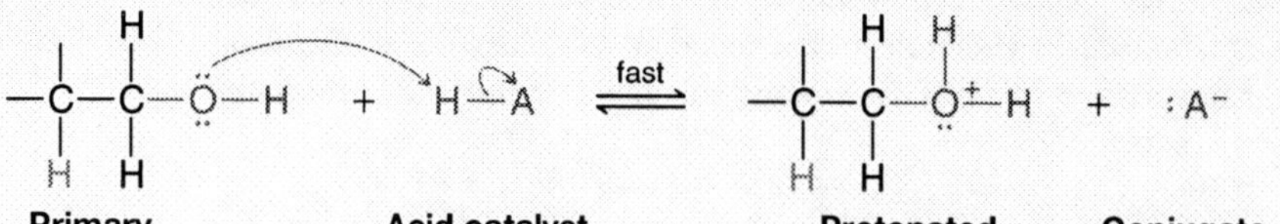

Primary alcohol   **Acid catalyst (typically sulfuric or phosphoric acid)**   **Protonated alcohol**   **Conjugate base**

The alcohol accepts a proton from the acid in a fast step.

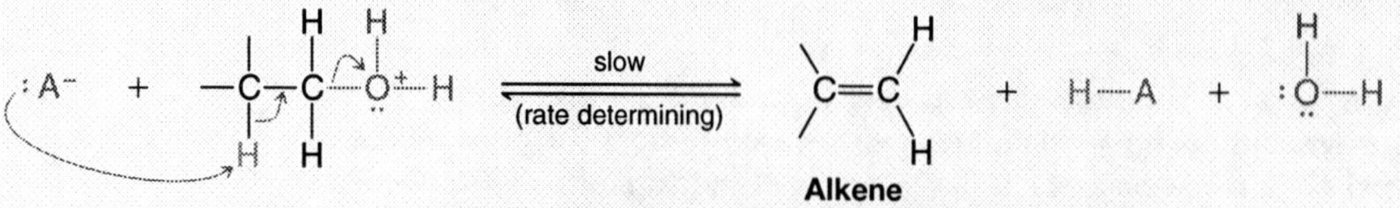

:A⁻ + ⎯⎯ $\xrightarrow[\text{(rate determining)}]{\text{slow}}$ **Alkene** + H⎯⎯A + :O⎯H

A base removes a hydrogen from the β carbon as the double bond forms and the protonated hydroxyl group departs. The base may be another molecule of the alcohol or the conjugate base of the acid.

7.8 CARBOCATION STABILITY AND THE OCCURRENCE OF MOLECULAR REARRANGEMENTS

With an understanding of carbocation stability and its effect on transition states, we can now proceed to explain the rearrangements of carbon skeletons that occur in some alcohol dehydrations.

7.8A Rearrangements During Dehydration of Secondary Alcohols

Consider again the rearrangement that occurs when 3,3-dimethyl-2-butanol is dehydrated:

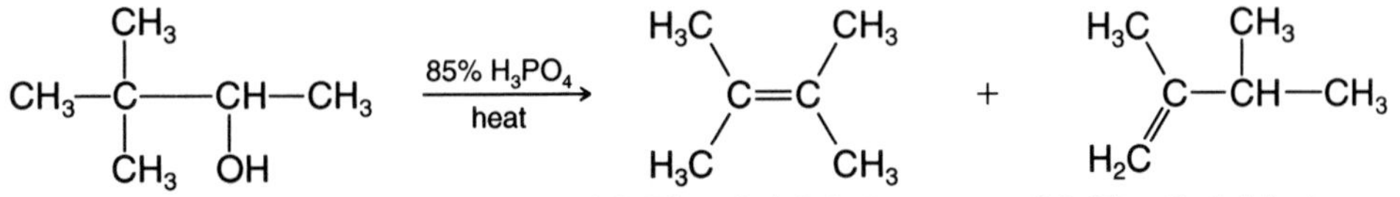

CH₃—C(CH₃)(CH₃)—CH(OH)—CH₃ →(85% H₃PO₄, heat)→ (CH₃)₂C=C(CH₃)₂ + (CH₃)₂C=CH—CH₃(CH₃)(H₂C)

3,3-Dimethyl-2-butanol   **2,3-Dimethyl-2-butene** (major product)   **2,3-Dimethyl-1-butene** (minor product)

The first step of this dehydration is the formation of the protonated alcohol in the usual way:

Step 1

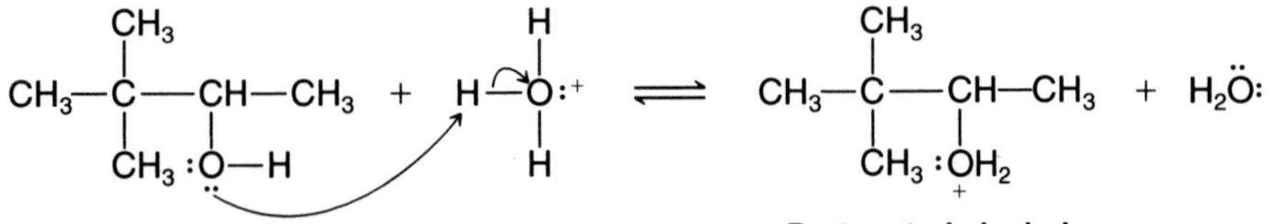

CH₃—C(CH₃)(CH₃)—CH(ÖH)—CH₃ + H—Ö:⁺(H)(H) ⇌ CH₃—C(CH₃)(CH₃)—CH(ÖH₂⁺)—CH₃ + H₂Ö:

Protonation of the alcohol   **Protonated alcohol**

In the second step the protonated alcohol loses water and a secondary carbocation forms:

Step 2

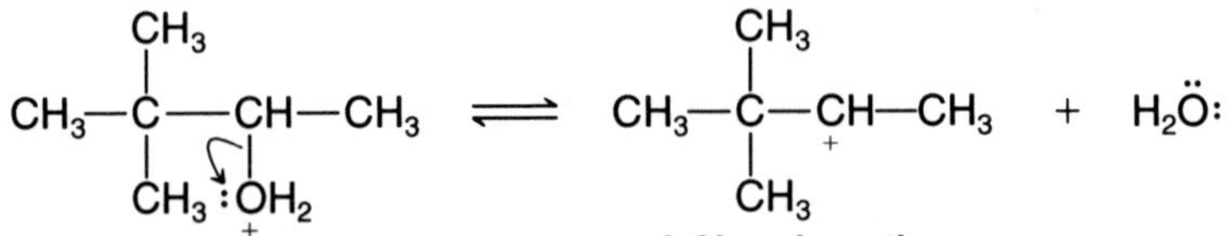

CH₃—C(CH₃)(CH₃)—CH(ÖH₂⁺)—CH₃ ⇌ CH₃—C(CH₃)(CH₃)—C⁺H—CH₃ + H₂Ö:

Departure of a water molecule   **A 2° carbocation**

Now the rearrangement occurs. *The less stable, secondary carbocation rearranges to a more stable tertiary carbocation:*

Step 3

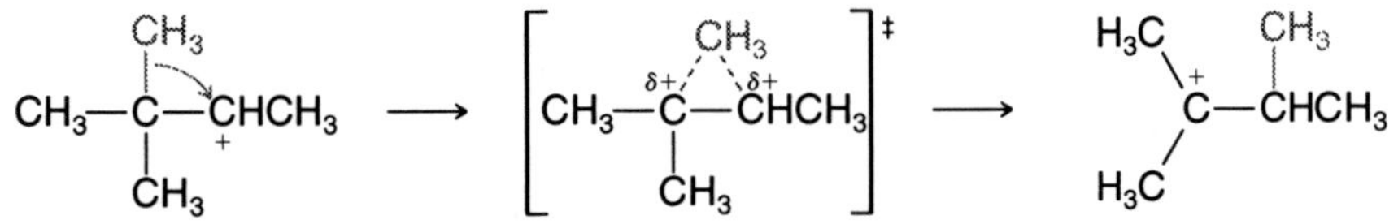

CH₃—C⁺(CH₃)(CH₃)—CHCH₃ → [CH₃—C(CH₃)(δ+)—CHCH₃(δ+)]‡ → (H₃C)(H₃C)C⁺—CHCH₃(CH₃)

2° Carbocation (less stable)   **Transition state**   **3° Carbocation** (more stable)

Rearrangement by migration of a methyl group

315

The rearrangement occurs through the migration of an alkyl group (methyl) from the carbon atom adjacent to the one with the positive charge. The methyl group migrates **with its pair of electrons** (called a methanide shift). In the transition state the shifting methyl is partially bonded to both carbon atoms by the pair of electrons with which it migrates. It never leaves the carbon skeleton. After the migration is complete, the carbon atom that the methyl anion left has become a carbocation, and the positive charge on the carbon atom to which it migrated has been neutralized. Because a group migrates from one carbon to an adjacent one, this kind of rearrangement is also called a **1,2 shift**.

The final step of the reaction is the removal of a proton from the new carbocation (by a Lewis base in the reaction mixture) and the formation of an alkene. This step, however, can occur in two ways:

Step 4

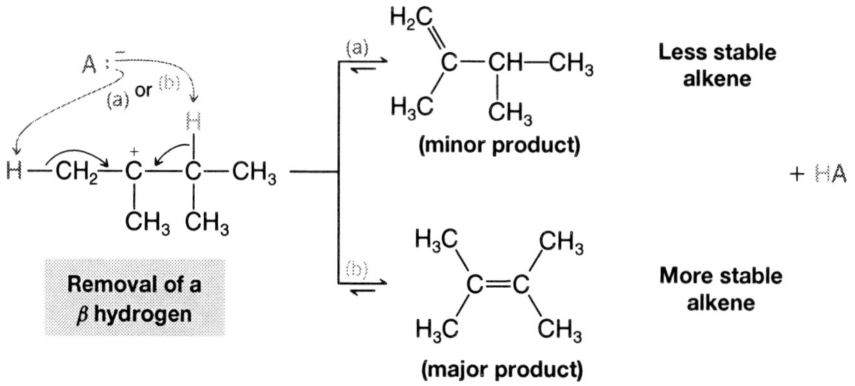

The more favored product is dictated by the stability of the alkene being formed. The conditions for the reaction (heat and acid) allow **equilibrium to be achieved** between the two forms of the alkene, and **the more stable alkene is the major product because it has lower potential energy.** Such a reaction is said to be **under equilibrium** or **thermodynamic control**. Path (b) leads to the highly stable tetrasubstituted alkene and this is the path followed by most of the carbocations. Path (a), on the other hand, leads to a less stable, disubstituted alkene, and because its potential energy is higher, it is the minor product of the reaction.

Helpful Hint

Alcohol dehydration follows Zaitsev's rule.

- **Formation of the more stable alkene is the general rule in acid-catalyzed dehydration of alcohols (Zaitsev's rule).**

Studies of many reactions involving carbocations show that rearrangements like those just described are general phenomena. *They occur almost invariably when an alkanide shift or hydride shift can lead to a more stable carbocation.* The following are examples:

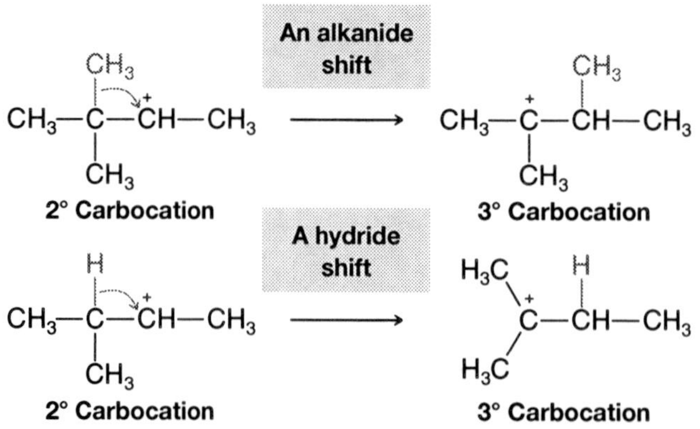

We shall see biological examples of alkanide (specifically methanide) and hydride migrations in "The Chemistry of … Cholesterol Biosynthesis" (online in *WileyPLUS* for Chapter 8).

Rearrangements of carbocations can also lead to a change in ring size, as the following example shows:

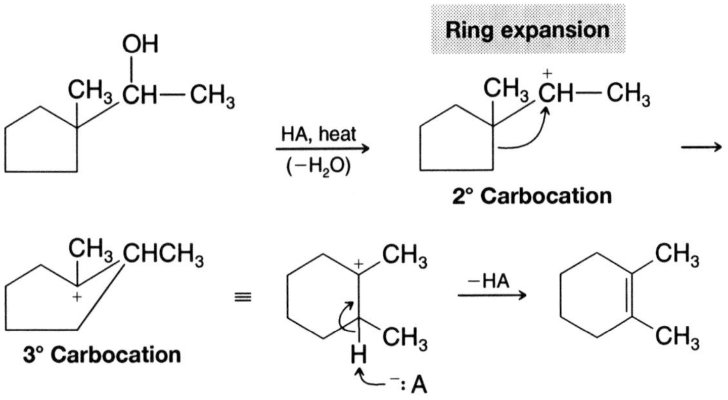

Ring expansion

$$\xrightarrow[\text{(−H}_2\text{O)}]{\text{HA, heat}}$$

2° Carbocation

3° Carbocation ≡ $\xrightarrow{-HA}$

Ring expansion by migration is especially favorable if relief in ring strain occurs.

It is important to note that rearrangements to carbocations having approximately equal energy are also possible (e.g., from one secondary carbocation to another), and this can complicate the mixture of products that might be obtained from a reaction.

●●● **SOLVED PROBLEM 7.6**

Explain why the major product of the dehydration above is 1,2-dimethylcyclohexene (as shown) and not 2,3-dimethyl-1-cyclohexene.

1,2-Dimethylcyclohexene
(major product)

2,3-Dimethyl-1-cyclohexene
(minor product)

STRATEGY AND ANSWER: We have just learned that dehydration leads mainly to the more stable alkene (when two are possible). We also know that the stability of an alkene is related to the number of alkyl groups that are attached to the carbons of the double bond. 1,2-Dimethylcyclohexene has a tetrasubstituted double bond (and is more stable), while in 2,3-dimethylcyclohexene the double bond is only trisubstituted.

●●● **PRACTICE PROBLEM 7.14**

Acid-catalyzed dehydration of neopentyl alcohol, $(CH_3)_3CCH_2OH$, yields 2-methyl-2-butene as the major product. Outline a mechanism showing all steps in its formation.

●●● **PRACTICE PROBLEM 7.15**

Acid-catalyzed dehydration of either 2-methyl-1-butanol or 3-methyl-1-butanol gives 2-methyl-2-butene as the major product. Write plausible mechanisms that explain these results.

●●● **PRACTICE PROBLEM 7.16**

When the compound called *isoborneol* is heated with 9 M sulfuric acid, the product of the reaction is the compound called camphene and not bornylene, as one might expect. Using models to assist you, write a step-by-step mechanism showing how camphene is formed.

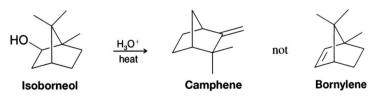

Isoborneol $\xrightarrow[\text{heat}]{H_3O^+}$ **Camphene** not **Bornylene**

7.8B Rearrangement After Dehydration of a Primary Alcohol

Rearrangements also accompany the dehydration of primary alcohols. Since a primary carbocation is unlikely to be formed during dehydration of a primary alcohol, the alkene that is produced initially from a primary alcohol arises by an E2 mechanism, as described in Section 7.7C. However, an alkene can accept a proton to *generate* a carbocation in a process that is essentially the reverse of the *deprotonation* step in the E1 mechanism for dehydration of an alcohol (Section 7.7A). When a terminal alkene does this by using its π electrons to bond a proton at the terminal carbon, a carbocation forms at the second carbon of the chain.* This carbocation, since it is internal to the chain, will be secondary or tertiary, depending on the specific substrate. Various processes that you have already learned can now occur from this carbocation: (1) a different β hydrogen may be removed, leading to a more stable alkene than the initially formed terminal alkene; (2) a hydride or alkanide rearrangement may occur leading to a yet more stable carbocation (e.g., moving from a 2° to a 3° carbocation) or to a carbocation of approximately equal stability, after which the elimination may be completed; or (3) a nucleophile may attack any of these carbocations to form a substitution product. Under the high-temperature conditions for alcohol dehydration the principal products will be alkenes rather than substitution products.

[A MECHANISM FOR THE REACTION — Formation of a Rearranged Alkene During Dehydration of a Primary Alcohol]

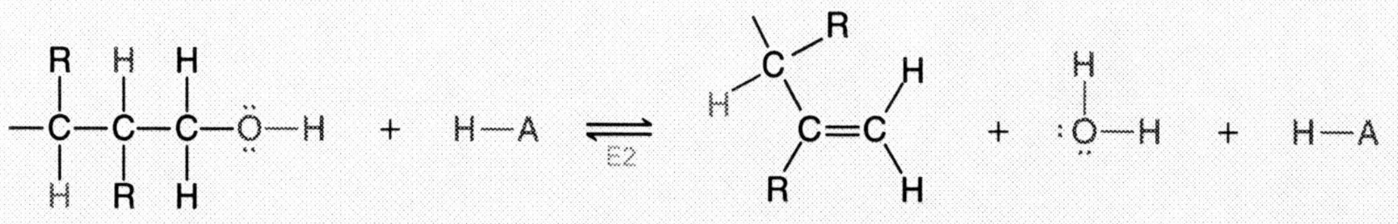

The primary alcohol initially undergoes acid-catalyzed dehydration by an E2 mechanism (Section 7.7C).

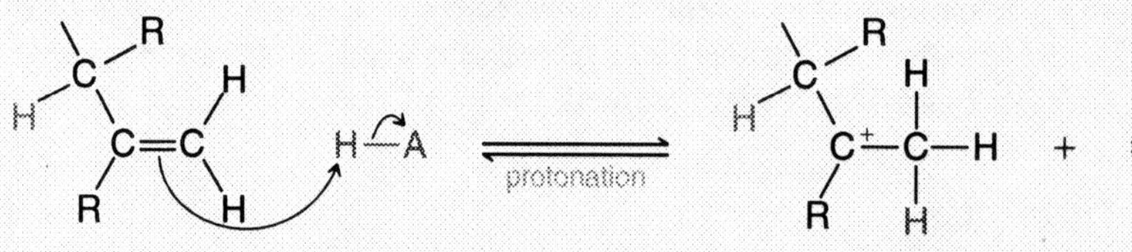

The π electrons of the initial alkene can then be used to form a bond with a proton at the terminal carbon, forming a secondary or tertiary carbocation.*

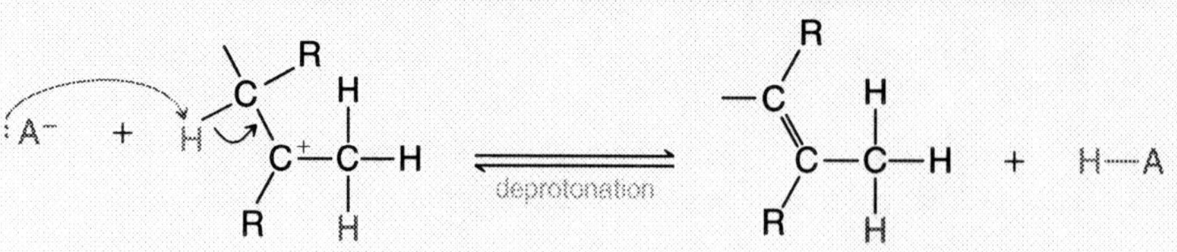

A different β hydrogen can be removed from the carbocation, so as to form a more highly substituted alkene than the initial alkene. This deprotonation step is the same as the usual completion of an E1 elimination. (This carbocation could experience other fates, such as further rearrangement before elimination or substitution by an S$_N$1 process.)

*The carbocation could also form directly from the primary alcohol by a hydride shift from its β carbon to the terminal carbon as the protonated hydroxyl group departs:

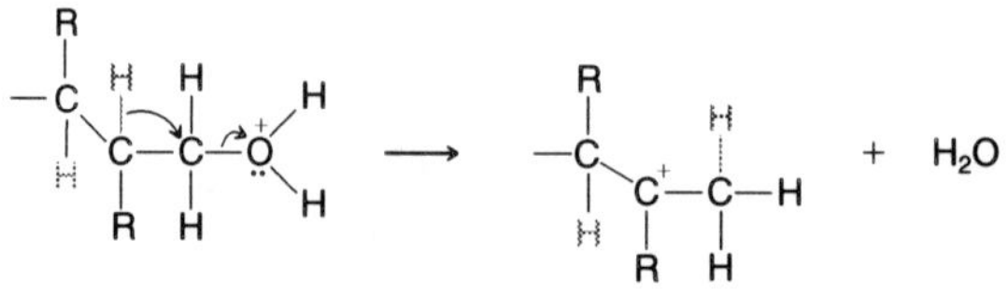

7.9 THE ACIDITY OF TERMINAL ALKYNES

The hydrogen bonded to the carbon of a terminal alkyne, called an acetylenic hydrogen atom, is considerably more acidic than those bonded to carbons of an alkene or alkane (see Section 3.8A). The pK_a values for ethyne, ethene, and ethane illustrate this point:

A terminal alkyne is ~10^{20} times more acidic than an alkene or alkane.		

$$H-C{\equiv}C-H \qquad \overset{H}{\underset{H}{>}}C{=}C\overset{H}{\underset{H}{<}} \qquad H-\overset{H}{\underset{H}{C}}-\overset{H}{\underset{H}{C}}-H$$

$$pK_a = 25 \qquad\qquad pK_a = 44 \qquad\qquad pK_a = 50$$

The order of basicity of their anions is opposite that of their relative acidity:

Relative Basicity

$$CH_3CH_2{:}^- > CH_2{=}CH{:}^- > HC{\equiv}C{:}^-$$

If we include in our comparison hydrogen compounds of other first-row elements of the periodic table, we can write the following orders of relative acidities and basicities. This comparison is useful as we consider what bases and solvents to use with terminal alkynes.

Relative Acidity

Most acidic					Least acidic

$$H-\ddot{O}H > H-\ddot{O}R > H-C{\equiv}CR > H-\ddot{N}H_2 > H-CH{=}CH_2 > H-CH_2CH_3$$

$$pK_a \quad 15.7 \qquad 16\text{–}17 \qquad\quad 25 \qquad\qquad 38 \qquad\qquad 44 \qquad\qquad 50$$

Relative Basicity

	Least basic			Most basic	

$$^-{:}\ddot{O}H < {}^-{:}\ddot{O}R < {}^-{:}C{\equiv}CR < {}^-{:}\ddot{N}H_2 < {}^-{:}CH{=}CH_2 < {}^-{:}CH_2CH_3$$

We see from the order just given that while terminal alkynes are more acidic than ammonia, they are less acidic than alcohols and are less acidic than water.

●●● SOLVED PROBLEM 7.7

As we shall soon see, sodium amide ($NaNH_2$) is useful, especially when a reaction requires a very strong base. Explain why a solvent such as methanol cannot be used to carry out a reaction in which you might want to use sodium amide as a base.

STRATEGY AND ANSWER: An alcohol has $pK_a = 16\text{–}17$, and ammonia has $pK_a = 38$. This means that methanol is a significantly stronger acid than ammonia, and the conjugate base of ammonia (the $^-NH_2$ ion) is a significantly stronger base than an alkoxide ion. Therefore, the following acid–base reaction would take place as soon as sodium amide is added to methanol.

$$\underset{\substack{\text{Stronger} \\ \text{acid}}}{CH_3OH} + \underset{\substack{\text{Stronger} \\ \text{base}}}{NaNH_2} \xrightarrow{CH_3OH} \underset{\substack{\text{Weaker} \\ \text{base}}}{CH_3ONa} + \underset{\substack{\text{Weaker} \\ \text{acid}}}{NH_3}$$

With a pK_a difference this large, the sodium amide would convert all of the methanol to sodium methoxide, a much weaker base than sodium amide. (This is an example of what is called the leveling effect of a solvent.)

PRACTICE PROBLEM 7.17 Predict the products of the following acid–base reactions. If the equilibrium would not result in the formation of appreciable amounts of products, you should so indicate. In each case label the stronger acid, the stronger base, the weaker acid, and the weaker base:

(a) $CH_3CH=CH_2 + NaNH_2 \longrightarrow$

(b) $CH_3C\equiv CH + NaNH_2 \longrightarrow$

(c) $CH_3CH_2CH_3 + NaNH_2 \longrightarrow$

(d) $CH_3C\equiv C:^- + CH_3CH_2OH \longrightarrow$

(e) $CH_3C\equiv C:^- + NH_4Cl \longrightarrow$

7.10 SYNTHESIS OF ALKYNES BY ELIMINATION REACTIONS

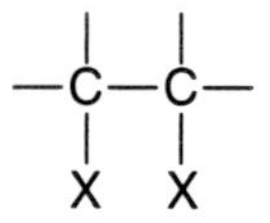

A vic–dihalide

• Alkynes can be synthesized from alkenes via compounds called vicinal dihalides.

A vicinal dihalide (abbreviated *vic-dihalide*) is a compound bearing the halogens on adjacent carbons (*vicinus,* Latin: adjacent). Vicinal dihalides are also called 1,2-dihalides. A vicinal dibromide, for example, can be synthesized by addition of bromine to an alkene (Section 8.1). The *vic*-dibromide can then be subjected to a double dehydrohalogenation reaction with a strong base to yield an alkyne.

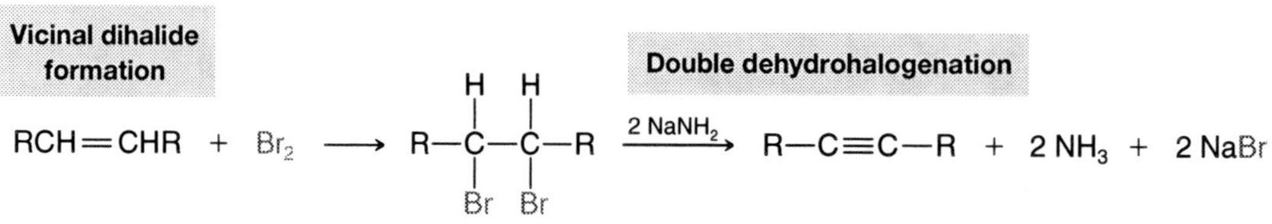

The dehydrohalogenations occur in two steps, the first yielding a bromoalkene, and the second, the alkyne.

7.10A Laboratory Application of This Alkyne Synthesis

The two dehydrohalogenations may be carried out as separate reactions, or they may be carried out consecutively in a single mixture. Sodium amide (NaNH$_2$), a very strong base, can be used to cause both reactions in a single mixture. At least two molar equivalents of sodium amide per mole of the dihalide must be used. For example, adding bromine to 1,2-diphenylethene provides the vicinal dihalide needed for a synthesis of 1,2-diphenylethyne:

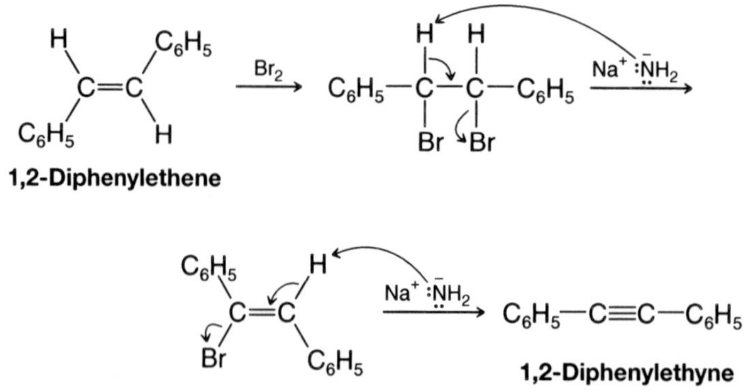

A MECHANISM FOR THE REACTION — Dehydrohalogenation of *vic*-Dibromides to Form Alkynes

Reaction

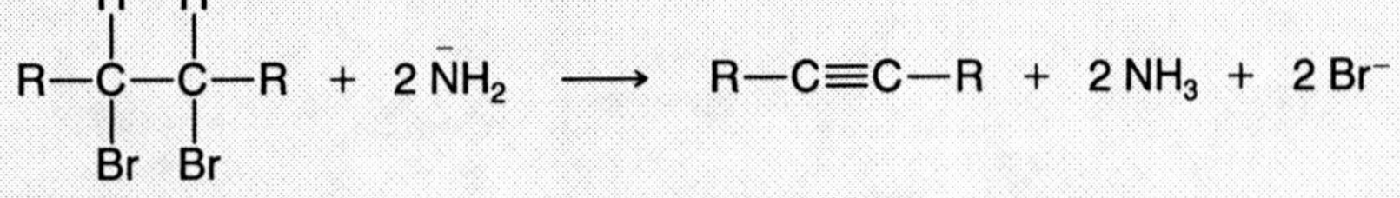

$$R-\overset{\overset{H}{|}}{\underset{\underset{Br}{|}}{C}}-\overset{\overset{H}{|}}{\underset{\underset{Br}{|}}{C}}-R \ + \ 2\ \overset{-}{N}H_2 \ \longrightarrow \ R-C\equiv C-R \ + \ 2\ NH_3 \ + \ 2\ Br^-$$

Mechanism

Step 1

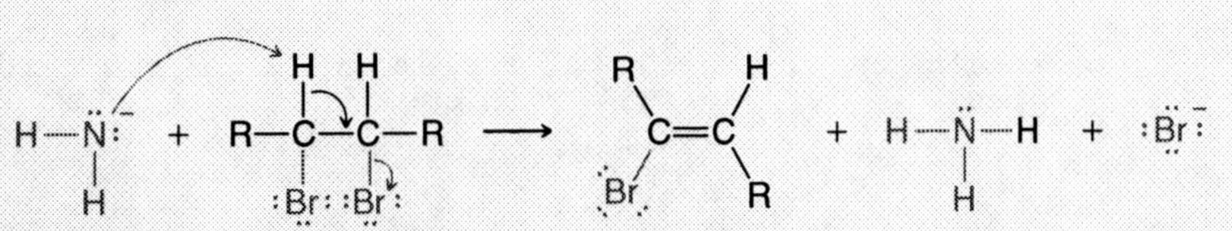

| Amide ion | *vic*-Dibromide | | Bromoalkene | Ammonia | Bromide ion |

The strongly basic amide ion brings about an E2 reaction.

Step 2

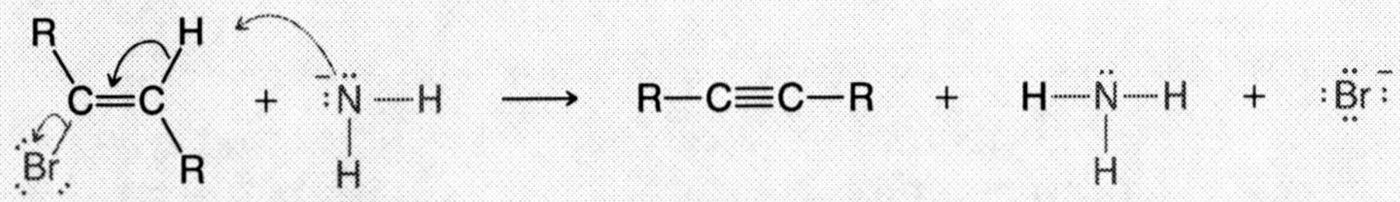

| Bromoalkene | Amide ion | Alkyne | Ammonia | Bromide ion |

A second E2 reaction produces the alkyne.

- If the product is to be an alkyne with a triple bond at the end of the chain (a terminal alkyne) as we show in the example below, then three molar equivalents of sodium amide are required.

Initial dehydrohalogenation of the *vic*-dihalide produces a mixture of two bromoalkenes that are not isolated but that undergo a second dehydrohalogenation. The terminal alkyne that results from this step is deprotonated (because of its acidity) by the third mole of sodium amide (see Section 7.9). To complete the process, addition of ammonium chloride converts the sodium alkynide to the desired product, 1-butyne.

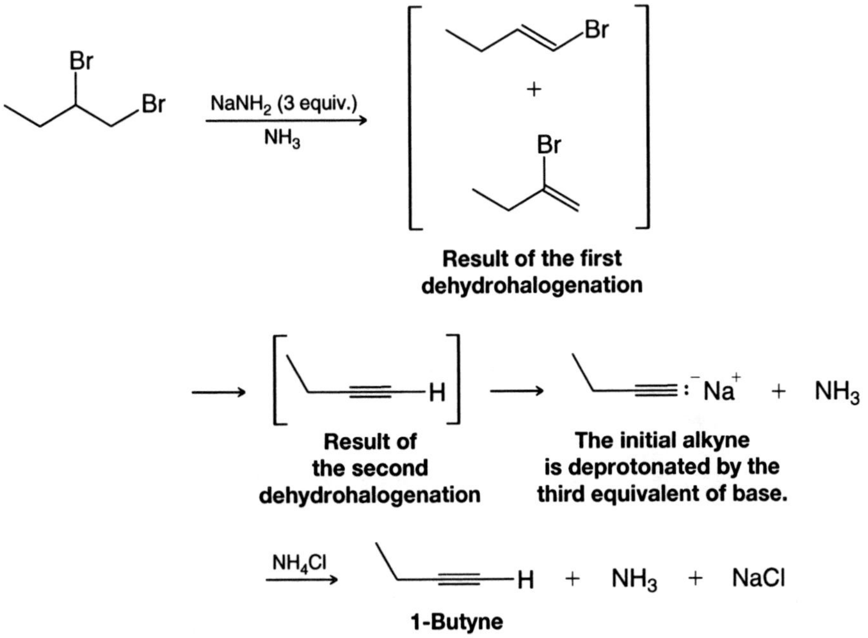

Result of the first dehydrohalogenation

Result of the second dehydrohalogenation

The initial alkyne is deprotonated by the third equivalent of base.

1-Butyne

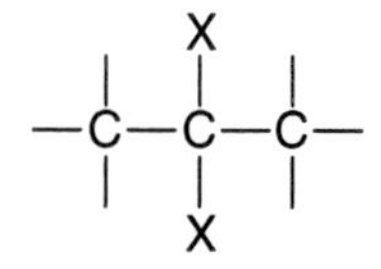

A gem–dihalide

• Geminal dihalides can also be converted to alkynes by dehydrohalogenation.

A geminal dihalide (abbreviated *gem-dihalide*) has two halogen atoms bonded to the same carbon (*geminus*, Latin: twins). Ketones can be converted to *gem*-dichlorides by reaction with phosphorus pentachloride, and the *gem*-dichlorides can be used to synthesize alkynes.

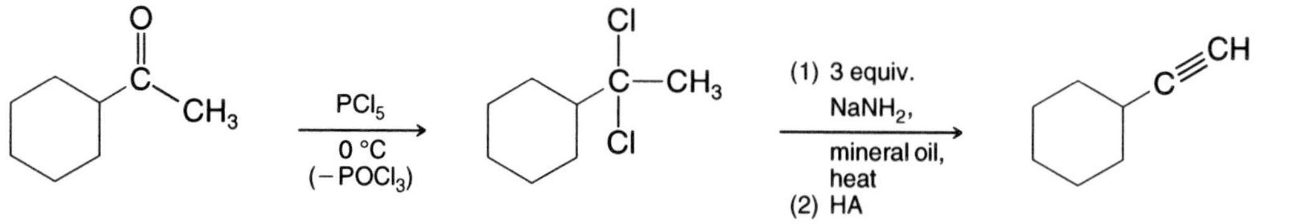

Cyclohexyl methyl ketone   **A gem-dichloride (70–80%)**   **Cyclohexylacetylene (46%)**

PRACTICE PROBLEM 7.18 Show how you might synthesize ethynylbenzene from methyl phenyl ketone.

PRACTICE PROBLEM 7.19 Outline all steps in a synthesis of propyne from each of the following:

(a) CH_3COCH_3 (c) $CH_3CHBrCH_2Br$

(b) $CH_3CH_2CHBr_2$ (d) $CH_3CH=CH_2$

7.11 TERMINAL ALKYNES CAN BE CONVERTED TO NUCLEOPHILES FOR CARBON–CARBON BOND FORMATION

• The acetylenic proton of ethyne or any terminal alkyne (pK_a 25) can be removed with a strong base such as sodium amide ($NaNH_2$). The result is an alkynide anion.

$$H-C\equiv C-H + NaNH_2 \xrightarrow{\text{liq. } NH_3} H-C\equiv C:^- Na^+ + NH_3$$

$$CH_3C\equiv C-H + NaNH_2 \xrightarrow{\text{liq. } NH_3} CH_3C\equiv C:^- Na^+ + NH_3$$

• Alkynide anions are useful nucleophiles for carbon–carbon bond forming reactions with primary alkyl halides or other primary substrates.

The following are general and specific examples of carbon–carbon bond formation by alkylation of an alkynide anion with a primary alkyl halide.

General Example

$$R-C\equiv C:^- Na^+ + R'CH_2-Br \longrightarrow R-C\equiv C-CH_2R' + NaBr$$

Sodium alkynide   **Primary alkyl halide**   **Mono- or disubstituted acetylene**

(R or R′ or both may be hydrogen.)

Specific Example

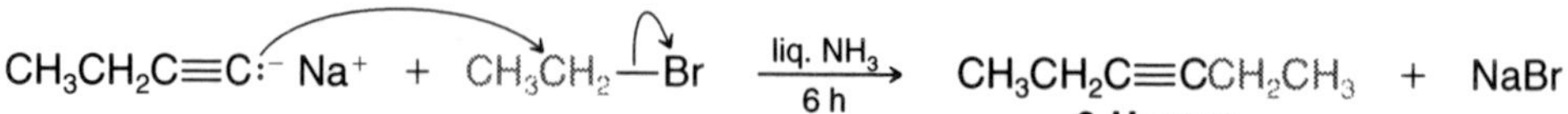

$$CH_3CH_2C\equiv C:^- Na^+ + CH_3CH_2-Br \xrightarrow[\text{6 h}]{\text{liq. } NH_3} CH_3CH_2C\equiv CCH_2CH_3 + NaBr$$

3-Hexyne (75%)

The alkynide anion acts as a nucleophile and displaces the halide ion from the primary alkyl halide. We now recognize this as an S_N2 reaction (Section 6.5).

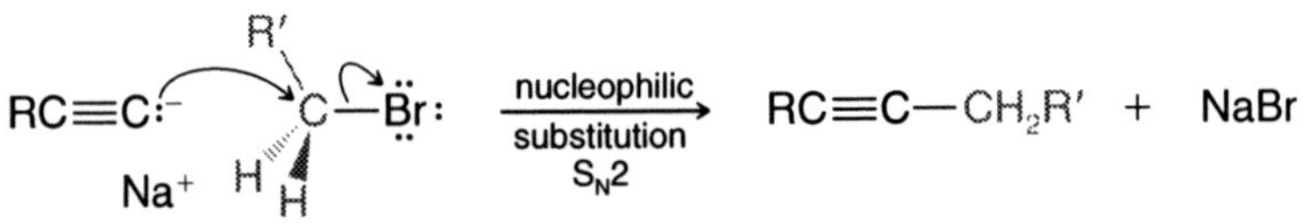

$$RC \equiv C:^- \quad \overset{R'}{\underset{H}{\overset{|}{C}}} - \ddot{B}r: \quad \xrightarrow[\substack{\text{substitution} \\ S_N2}]{\text{nucleophilic}} \quad RC \equiv C - CH_2R' \quad + \quad NaBr$$

$$Na^+ \quad H$$

Sodium alkynide	**1° Alkyl halide**

- Primary alkyl halides should be used in the alkylation of alkynide anions, so as to avoid competition by elimination.

Use of a secondary or tertiary substrate causes E2 elimination instead of substitution because the alkynide anion is a strong base as well as a good nucleophile.

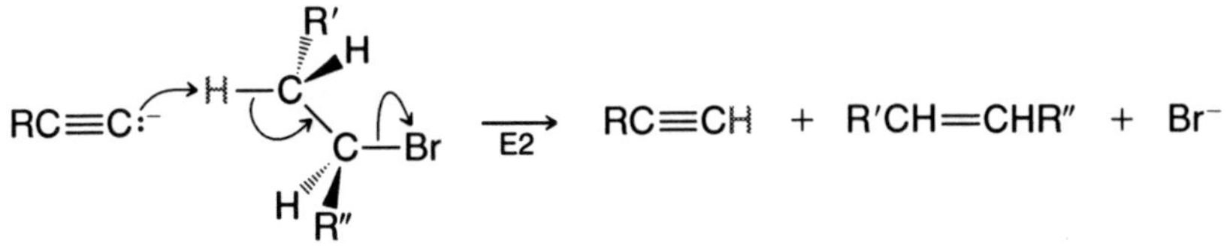

$$RC \equiv C:^- \quad H - \overset{R'}{\underset{\underset{R''}{H}}{\overset{H}{C}}} \overset{H}{\underset{Br}{C}} \quad \xrightarrow{E2} \quad RC \equiv CH \ + \ R'CH = CHR'' \ + \ Br^-$$

2° Alkyl halide

Outline a synthesis of 4-phenyl-2-butyne from 1-propyne.

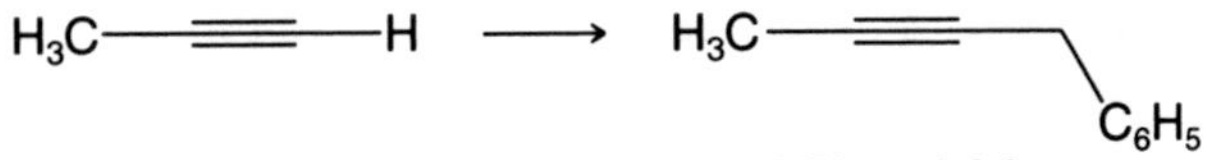

$$H_3C \longrightarrow\!\!\!\equiv\!\!\!\longrightarrow H \quad \longrightarrow \quad H_3C \longrightarrow\!\!\!\equiv\!\!\!\longrightarrow \overset{}{\underset{C_6H_5}{}}$$

1-Propyne	**4-Phenyl-2-butyne**

STRATEGY AND ANSWER: Take advantage of the acidity of the acetylenic hydrogen of propyne and convert it to an alkynide anion using sodium amide, a base that is strong enough to remove the acetylenic hydrogen. Then use the akynide ion as a nucleophile in an S_N2 reaction with benzyl bromide.

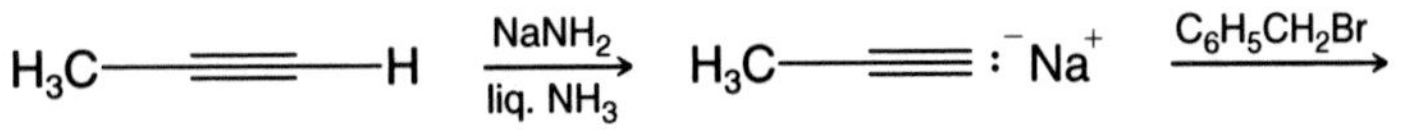

$$H_3C \longrightarrow\!\!\!\equiv\!\!\!\longrightarrow H \quad \xrightarrow[\text{liq. } NH_3]{NaNH_2} \quad H_3C \longrightarrow\!\!\!\equiv\!\!\!\longrightarrow :^-Na^+ \quad \xrightarrow{C_6H_5CH_2Br}$$

1-Propyne	**Alkynide ion**	**Benzyl bromide**

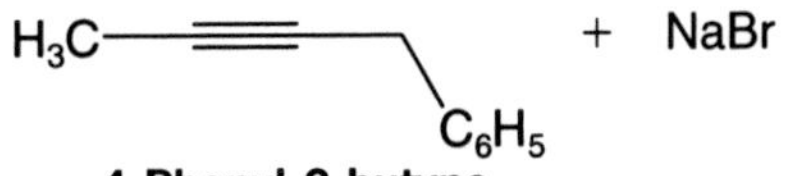

$$H_3C \longrightarrow\!\!\!\equiv\!\!\!\longrightarrow \overset{}{\underset{C_6H_5}{}} \quad + \quad NaBr$$

4-Phenyl-2-butyne

●●●

Your goal is to synthesize 4,4-dimethyl-2-pentyne. You have a choice of beginning with any of the following reagents:

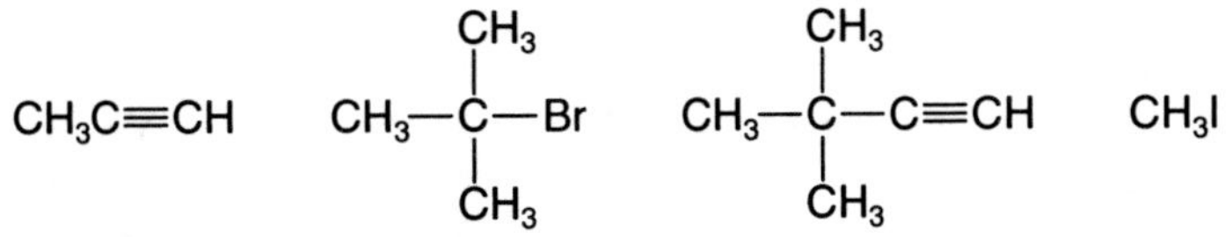

PRACTICE PROBLEM 7.20

$$CH_3C \equiv CH \qquad CH_3 - \overset{\overset{\displaystyle CH_3}{|}}{\underset{\underset{\displaystyle CH_3}{|}}{C}} - Br \qquad CH_3 - \overset{\overset{\displaystyle CH_3}{|}}{\underset{\underset{\displaystyle CH_3}{|}}{C}} - C \equiv CH \qquad CH_3I$$

Assume that you also have available sodium amide and liquid ammonia. Outline the best synthesis of the required compound.

7.11A General Principles of Structure and Reactivity Illustrated by the Alkylation of Alkynide Anions

The alkylation of alkynide anions illustrates several essential aspects of structure and reactivity that have been important to our study of organic chemistry thus far.

1. Preparation of the alkynide anion involves simple **Brønsted–Lowry acid–base chemistry.** As you have seen (Sections 7.9 and 7.11), the hydrogen of a terminal alkyne is weakly acidic ($pK_a \cong 25$), and with a strong base such as sodium amide it can be removed. The reason for this acidity was explained in Section 3.8A.

2. Once formed, the alkynide anion is a **Lewis base** (Section 3.3) with which the alkyl halide reacts as an electron pair acceptor (a **Lewis acid**). The alkynide anion can thus be called a *nucleophile* (Sections 3.4 and 6.3) because of the negative charge concentrated at its terminal carbon—it is a reagent that seeks positive charge.

3. The alkyl halide can be called an *electrophile* (Sections 3.4 and 8.1) because of the partial positive charge at the carbon bearing the halogen—it is a reagent that seeks negative charge. Polarity in the alkyl halide is the direct result of the difference in electronegativity between the halogen atom and carbon atom.

The electrostatic potential maps for ethynide (acetylide) anion and chloromethane in Fig. 7.8 illustrate the complementary nucleophilic and electrophilic character of a typical alkynide anion and alkyl halide. The ethynide anion has strong localization of negative charge at its terminal carbon, indicated by red in the electrostatic potential map. Conversely, chloromethane has partial positive charge at the carbon bonded to the electronegative chlorine atom. (The dipole moment for chloromethane is aligned directly along the carbon–chlorine bond.) Thus, acting as a Lewis base, the alkynide anion is attracted to the partially positive carbon of the alkyl halide. Assuming a collision between the two occurs with the proper orientation and sufficient kinetic energy, as the alkynide anion brings two electrons to the alkyl halide to form a new bond, it will displace the halogen from the alkyl halide. The halogen leaves as an anion with the pair of electrons that formerly bonded it to the carbon. This is an S_N2 reaction, of course, akin to others we discussed in Chapter 6.

> **Helpful Hint**
>
> You should pay attention to the bookkeeping of valence electrons and formal charges in the reaction shown in Fig. 7.8, just as with every other reaction you study in organic chemistry.

FIGURE 7.8 The reaction of ethynide (acetylide) anion and chloromethane. Electrostatic potential maps illustrate the complementary nucleophilic and electrophilic character of the alkynide anion and the alkyl halide. The dipole moment of chloromethane is shown by the red arrow.

$$H-C\equiv\bar{C}: \quad + \quad \overset{\delta^+}{H_3C}-\overset{\delta^-}{\underset{\cdot\cdot}{\overset{\cdot\cdot}{Cl}}}: \quad \longrightarrow \quad H-C\equiv C-CH_3 \quad + \quad :\overset{\cdot\cdot}{\underset{\cdot\cdot}{Cl}}:^-$$

7.12 HYDROGENATION OF ALKENES

● Alkenes react with hydrogen in the presence of a variety of metal catalysts to add one hydrogen atom to each carbon atom of the double bond (Sections 4.16A, 5.10A).

Hydrogenation reactions that involve *insoluble* platinum, palladium, or nickel catalysts (Section 4.16A) proceed by heterogeneous catalysis because the catalyst is not soluble in the reaction mixture. Hydrogenation reactions that involve soluble catalysts occur by homogeneous catalysis. Typical homogeneous hydrogenation catalysts include rhodium and ruthenium complexes that bear various phosphorus and other ligands. One of the most well-known homogeneous hydrogenation catalysts is Wilkinson's catalyst, tris(triphenylphosphine)rhodium chloride, $Rh[(C_6H_5)_3P]_3Cl$ (see Special Topic G.) The following are some examples of hydrogenation reactions under heterogeneous and homogeneous catalysis:

> **Helpful Hint**
>
> These are addition reactions.

$$\diagup\!\!\!\diagup + H_2 \xrightarrow[\substack{\text{Pt, Pd,} \\ \text{or Ni} \\ 25\,°C}]{} \diagup\!\!\!\diagdown$$

$$\diagdown\!\!\!\diagup\!\!\!\diagdown\!\!\!\diagup + H_2 \xrightarrow{Rh[(C_6H_5)_3P]_3Cl} \diagdown\!\!\!\diagup\!\!\!\diagdown\!\!\!\diagup$$

Catalytic hydrogenation reactions, like those shown above, are a type of **addition reaction** (versus substitution or elimination), and they are also a type of reduction. This leads to a distinction between compounds that are saturated versus those that are unsaturated.

- Compounds containing only carbon–carbon single bonds (alkanes and others) are said to be **saturated compounds** because they contain the maximum number of hydrogen atoms that a given formula can possess.
- Compounds containing carbon–carbon multiple bonds (alkenes, alkynes, and aromatic compounds) are said to be **unsaturated compounds** because they contain fewer than the maximum number of hydrogen atoms possible for a given formula.

Unsaturated compounds can be **reduced** to saturated compounds by **catalytic hydrogenation**. The following example shows conversion of an unsaturated triglyceride to a saturated triglyceride (both are fats), in a catalytic hydrogenation reaction as might be done in the food industry to change the physical properties of a fat.

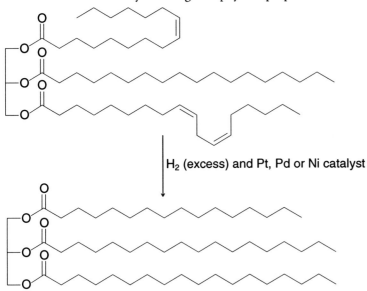

H_2 (excess) and Pt, Pd or Ni catalyst

> **An unsaturated fat can be hydrogenated to form a saturated fat.**

Molecules of a natural unsaturated fat can align less evenly with each other than can molecules of saturated fats due to the "kinks" from the cis double bonds in unsaturated fats. Hence intermolecular forces between unsaturated fat molecules are weaker and they have lower melting points than saturated fats. See "The Chemistry of … Hydrogenation in the Food Industry."

THE CHEMISTRY OF... Hydrogenation in the Food Industry

The food industry makes use of catalytic hydrogenation to convert liquid vegetable oils to semisolid fats in making margarine and solid cooking fats. Examine the labels of many prepared foods and you will find that they contain "partially hydrogenated vegetable oils." There are several reasons why foods contain these oils, but one is that partially hydrogenated vegetable oils have a longer shelf life.

Fats and oils (Section 23.2) are glyceryl esters of carboxylic acids with long carbon chains, called "fatty acids." Fatty acids are saturated (no double bonds), monounsaturated (one double bond), or polyunsaturated (more than one double bond). Oils typically contain a higher proportion of fatty acids with one or more double bonds than fats do. Partial hydrogenation of an oil converts some of its double bonds to single bonds, and this conversion has the effect of producing a fat with the consistency of margarine or a semisolid cooking fat.

One potential problem that arises from using catalytic hydrogenation to produce partially hydrogenated vegetable oils is that the catalysts used for hydrogenation cause isomerization of some of the double bonds of the fatty acids (some of those that do not absorb hydrogen). In most natural fats and oils, the double bonds of the fatty acids have the cis configuration. The catalysts used for hydrogenation convert some of these cis double bonds to the unnatural trans configuration. The health effects of trans fatty acids are still under study, but experiments thus far indicate that they cause an increase in serum levels of cholesterol and triacylglycerols, which in turn increases the risk of cardiovascular disease.

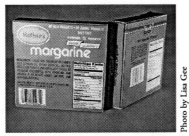

Photo by Lisa Gee

A product used in baking that contains oils and mono- and diacylglycerols that are partially hydrogenated.

Saturated Fat 1g
Trans Fat 0g
Cholesterol 0mg
Sodium 260mg
Carbohydrate

© Jonathan Vasata/iStock photo

No (or zero%) trans fatty acids.

7.13 HYDROGENATION: THE FUNCTION OF THE CATALYST

Hydrogenation of an alkene is an exothermic reaction ($\Delta H° \cong -120$ kJ mol^{-1}):

$$R-CH=CH-R + H_2 \xrightarrow{\text{hydrogenation}} R-CH_2-CH_2-R + \text{heat}$$

Although the process is exothermic, there is usually a high free energy of activation for uncatalyzed alkene hydrogenation, and therefore, the uncatalyzed reaction does not take place at room temperature. However, hydrogenation will take place readily at room temperature in the presence of a catalyst because the catalyst provides a new pathway for the reaction that involves lower free energy of activation (Fig. 7.9).

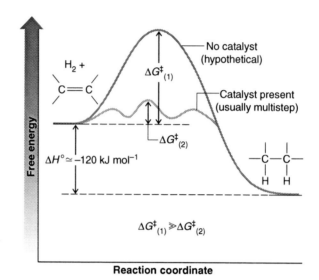

FIGURE 7.9 Free-energy diagram for the hydrogenation of an alkene in the presence of a catalyst and the hypothetical reaction in the absence of a catalyst. The free energy of activation for the uncatalyzed reaction ($\Delta G^{\ddagger}_{(1)}$) is very much larger than the largest free energy of activation for the catalyzed reaction ($\Delta G^{\ddagger}_{(2)}$). The uncatalyzed hydrogenation reaction does not occur.

Heterogeneous hydrogenation catalysts typically involve finely divided platinum, palladium, nickel, or rhodium deposited on the surface of powdered carbon (charcoal). Hydrogen gas introduced into the atmosphere of the reaction vessel adsorbs to the metal by a chemical reaction where unpaired electrons on the surface of the metal *pair* with the electrons of hydrogen (Fig. 7.10*a*) and bind the hydrogen to the surface. The collision of an alkene with the surface bearing adsorbed hydrogen causes adsorption of the alkene as well (Fig. 7.10*b*). A stepwise transfer of hydrogen atoms takes place, and this produces an alkane before the organic molecule leaves the catalyst surface (Figs. 7.10*c, d*). As a consequence, *both hydrogen atoms usually add from the same side of the molecule.* This mode of addition is called a **syn** addition (Section 7.14A):

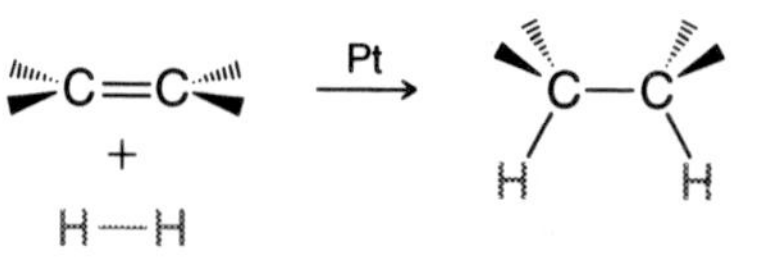

Catalytic hydrogenation is a syn addition.

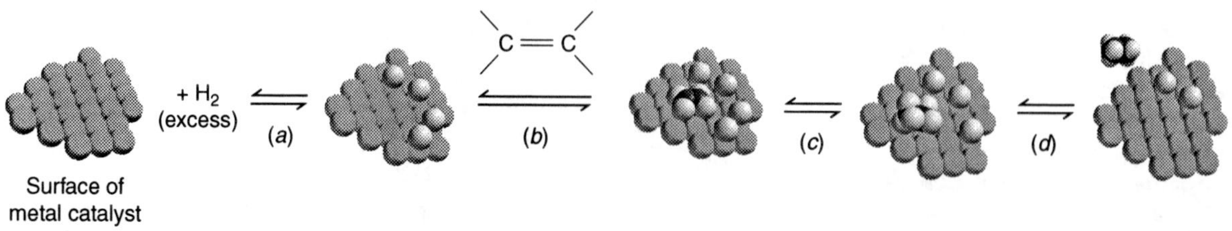

FIGURE 7.10 The mechanism for the hydrogenation of an alkene as catalyzed by finely divided platinum metal: (*a*) hydrogen adsorption; (*b*) adsorption of the alkene; (*c, d*) stepwise transfer of both hydrogen atoms to the same face of the alkene (syn addition).

7.13A Syn and Anti Additions

An addition that places the parts of the adding reagent on the same side (or face) of the reactant is called syn addition. We have just seen that the platinum-catalyzed addition of hydrogen (X = Y = H) is a syn addition:

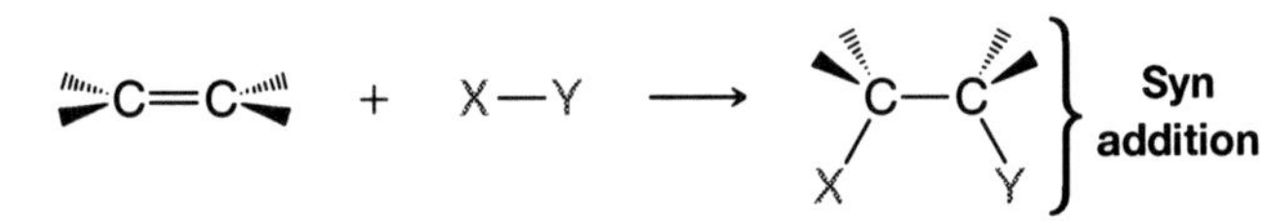

$$\text{C=C} \quad + \quad \text{X—Y} \quad \longrightarrow \quad \text{C—C} \quad \left. \right\} \quad \textbf{Syn addition}$$

The opposite of a syn addition is an anti addition. An anti addition places the parts of the adding reagent on opposite faces of the reactant.

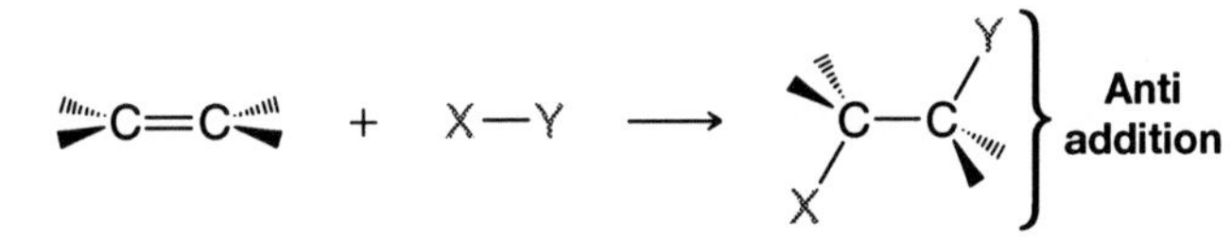

$$\text{C=C} \quad + \quad \text{X—Y} \quad \longrightarrow \quad \text{C—C} \quad \left. \right\} \quad \textbf{Anti addition}$$

In Chapter 8 we shall study a number of important syn and anti additions.

7.14 HYDROGENATION OF ALKYNES

Depending on the conditions and the catalyst employed, one or two molar equivalents of hydrogen will add to a carbon–carbon triple bond. When a platinum catalyst is used, the alkyne generally reacts with two molar equivalents of hydrogen to give an alkane:

$$CH_3C{\equiv}CCH_3 \xrightarrow{\text{Pt, } H_2} [CH_3CH{=}CHCH_3] \xrightarrow{\text{Pt, } H_2} CH_3CH_2CH_2CH_3$$

However, hydrogenation of an alkyne to an alkene can be accomplished through the use of special catalysts or reagents. Moreover, these special methods allow the preparation of either (E)- or (Z)-alkenes from disubstituted alkynes.

7.14A Syn Addition of Hydrogen: Synthesis of *cis*-Alkenes

A heterogeneous catalyst that permits hydrogenation of an alkyne to an alkene is the nickel boride compound called P-2 catalyst. The P-2 catalyst can be prepared by the reduction of nickel acetate with sodium borohydride:

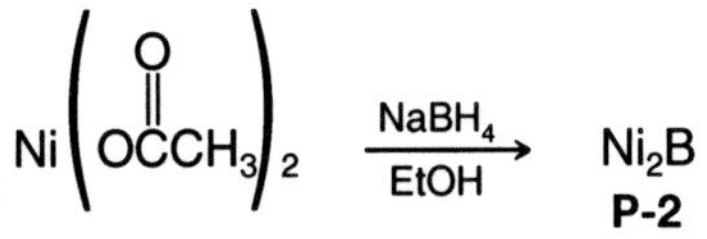

$$Ni\left(\overset{\overset{\displaystyle O}{\displaystyle \|}}{O}CCH_3\right)_2 \xrightarrow[\text{EtOH}]{\text{NaBH}_4} \underset{\textbf{P-2}}{Ni_2B}$$

- Hydrogenation of alkynes in the presence of P-2 catalyst causes **syn addition of hydrogen**. The alkene formed from an internal alkyne has the (Z) or cis configuration.

The hydrogenation of 3-hexyne illustrates this method. The reaction takes place on the surface of the catalyst (Section 7.14), accounting for the syn addition:

Syn addition of hydrogen to an alkyne	3-Hexyne	$\xrightarrow[\text{(syn addition)}]{H_2/Ni_2B \text{ (P-2)}}$	(Z)-3-Hexene (cis-3-hexene) (97%)

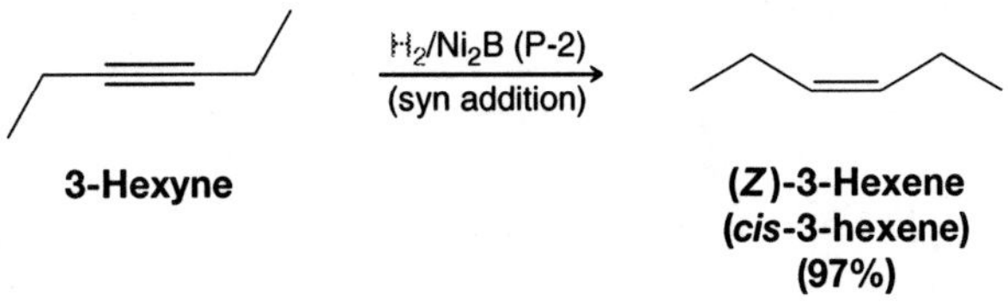

Other specially conditioned catalysts can be used to prepare *cis*-alkenes from disubstituted alkynes. Metallic palladium deposited on calcium carbonate can be used in this way after it has been conditioned with lead acetate and quinoline (an amine, see Section 20.1B). This special catalyst is known as **Lindlar's catalyst:**

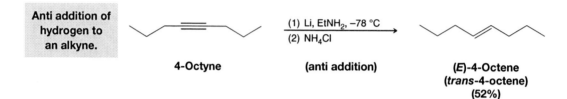

7.14B Anti Addition of Hydrogen: Synthesis of *trans*-Alkenes

● **Anti addition** of hydrogen to the triple bond of alkynes occurs when they are treated with lithium or sodium metal in ammonia or ethylamine at low temperatures.

This reaction, called a **dissolving metal reduction,** takes place in solution and produces an (*E*)- or *trans*-alkene. The mechanism involves radicals, which are molecules that have unpaired electrons (see Chapter 10).

Anti addition of hydrogen to an alkyne.		

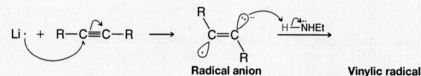

4-Octyne (anti addition) **(*E*)-4-Octene**
(*trans*-4-octene)
(52%)

$$\left[\text{A MECHANISM FOR THE REACTION} \quad \begin{array}{l} \text{The Dissolving Metal Reduction} \\ \text{of an Alkyne} \end{array} \right]$$

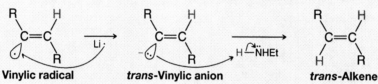

Radical anion **Vinylic radical**

A lithium atom donates an electron to the π bond of the alkyne. An electron pair shifts to one carbon as the hybridization states change to *sp*².

The radical anion acts as a base and removes a proton from a molecule of ethylamine.

Vinylic radical ***trans*-Vinylic anion** ***trans*-Alkene**

A second lithium atom donates an electron to the vinylic radical.

The anion acts as a base and removes a proton from a second molecule of ethylamine.

The mechanism for this reduction, shown in the preceding box, involves successive electron transfers from lithium (or sodium) atoms and proton transfers from amines (or ammonia). In the first step, a lithium atom transfers an electron to the alkyne to produce an intermediate that bears a negative charge and has an unpaired electron, called a **radical anion.** In the second step, an amine transfers a proton to produce a **vinylic radical.** Then, transfer of another electron gives a **vinylic anion.** It is this step that determines the stereochemistry of the reaction. The *trans*-vinylic anion is formed preferentially because it is more stable; the bulky alkyl groups are farther apart. Protonation of the *trans*-vinylic anion leads to the *trans*-alkene.

PRACTICE PROBLEM 7.21

Write the structure of compound **A**, used in this synthesis of the perfume ingredient (*Z*)-jasmone.

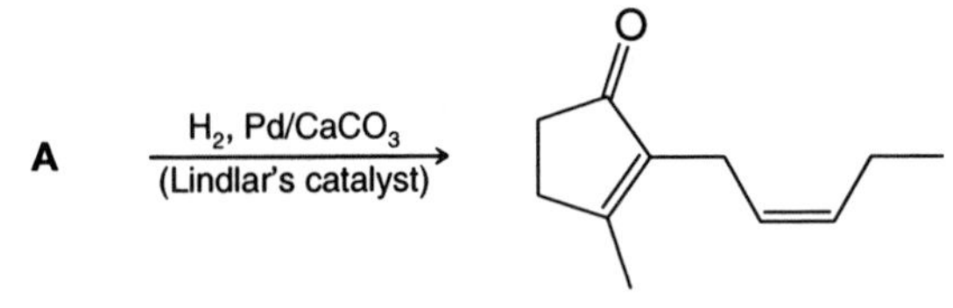

(Z)-Jasmone

PRACTICE PROBLEM 7.22

How would you convert 2-nonyne into (*E*)-2-nonene?

7.15 AN INTRODUCTION TO ORGANIC SYNTHESIS

You have learned quite a few tools that are useful for organic synthesis, including nucleophilic substitution reactions, elimination reactions, and the hydrogenation reactions covered in Sections 7.12–7.14. Now we will consider the logic of organic synthesis and the important process of retrosynthetic analysis. Then we will apply nucleophilic substitution (in the specific case of alkylation of alkynide anions) and hydrogenation reactions to the synthesis of some simple target molecules.

7.15A Why Do Organic Synthesis?

Organic synthesis is the process of building organic molecules from simpler precursors. Syntheses of organic compounds are carried out for many reasons. Chemists who develop new drugs carry out organic syntheses in order to discover molecules with structural attributes that enhance certain medicinal effects or reduce undesired side effects. Crixivan, whose structure is shown below, was designed by small-scale synthesis in a research laboratory and then quickly moved to large-scale synthesis after its approval as a drug. In other situations, organic synthesis may be needed to test a hypothesis about a reaction mechanism or about how a certain organism metabolizes a compound. In cases like these we often will need to synthesize a particular compound "labeled" at a certain position (e.g., with deuterium, tritium, or an isotope of carbon).

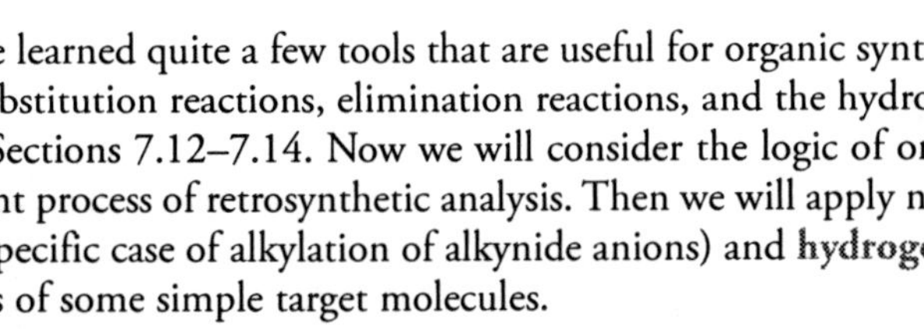

Crixivan (an HIV protease inhibitor)

A carbon–cobalt
σ bond

Vitamin B₁₂

A very simple organic synthesis may involve only one chemical reaction. Others may require from several to 20 or more steps. A landmark example of organic synthesis is that of vitamin B_{12}, announced in 1972 by R. B. Woodward (Harvard) and A. Eschenmoser (Swiss Federal Institute of Technology). Their synthesis of vitamin B_{12} took 11 years, required more than 90 steps, and involved the work of nearly 100 people. We will work with much simpler examples, however.

An organic synthesis typically involves two types of transformations:

1. reactions that convert functional groups from one to another
2. reactions that create new carbon–carbon bonds.

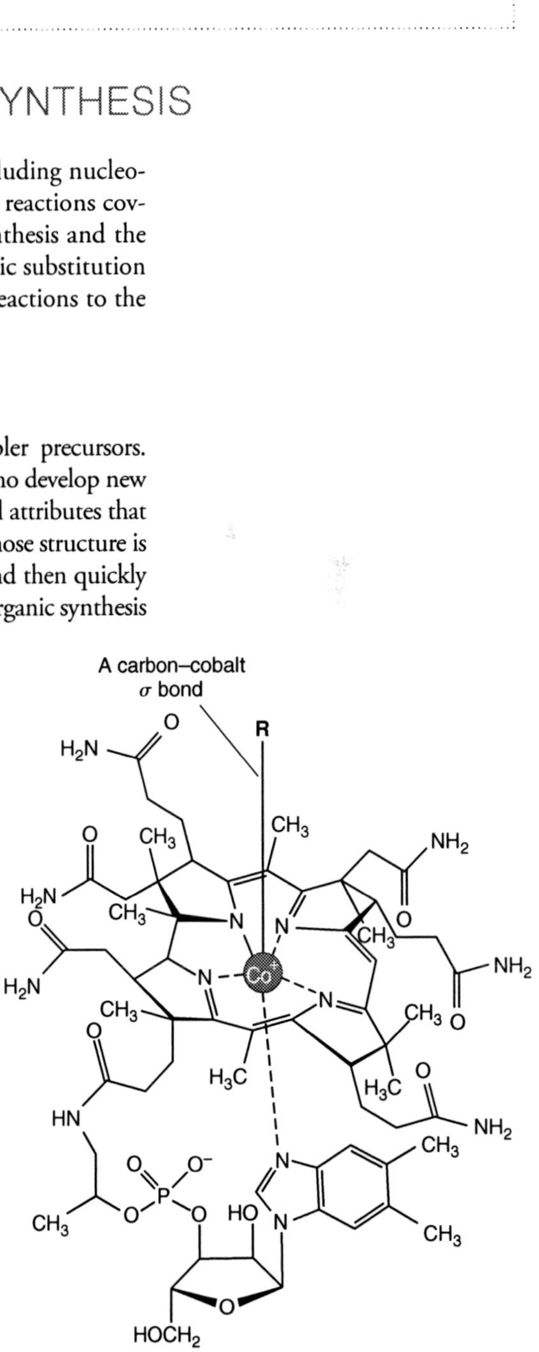

You have studied examples of both types of reactions already. For example, hydrogenation transforms the carbon–carbon double- or triple-bond functional groups in alkenes and alkynes to single bonds (actually removing a functional group in this case), and alkylation of alkynide anions forms carbon–carbon bonds. Ultimately, at the heart of organic synthesis is the orchestration of functional group interconversions and carbon–carbon bond-forming steps. Many methods are available to accomplish both of these things.

7.15B Retrosynthetic Analysis—Planning an Organic Synthesis

Sometimes it is possible to visualize from the start all the steps necessary to synthesize a desired (target) molecule from obvious precursors. Often, however, the sequence of transformations that would lead to the desired compound is too complex for us to "see" a path from the beginning to the end. In this case, since we know where we want to finish (the target molecule) but not where to start, we envision the sequence of steps that is required in a backward fashion, one step at a time. We begin by identifying immediate precursors that could react to make the target molecule. Once these have been chosen, they in turn become new intermediate target molecules, and we identify the next set of precursors that could react to form them, and so on, and so on. This process is repeated until we have worked backward to compounds that are sufficiently simple that they are readily available in a typical laboratory:

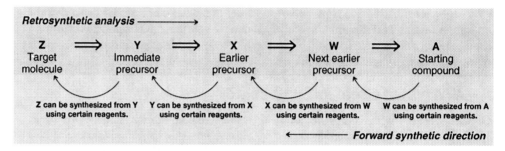

- The process we have just described is called **retrosynthetic analysis.**
- The open arrow is called a **retrosynthesis arrow,** and means that a molecule can be synthesized from its most immediate precursor by some chemical reaction.

Although some of the earliest organic syntheses likely required some type of analytical planning, it was E. J. Corey who first formalized a set of global principles for chemical synthesis, a process which he termed retrosynthetic analysis, that enabled anyone to plan a complex molecule synthesis. Once retrosynthetic analysis has been completed, to actually carry out the synthesis we conduct the sequence of reactions from the beginning, starting with the simplest precursors and working step by step until the target molecule is achieved.

- When doing retrosynthetic analysis it is necessary to generate as many possible precursors, and hence different synthetic routes, as possible (Fig. 7.11).

We evaluate all the possible advantages and disadvantages of each path and in so doing determine the most efficient route for synthesis. The prediction of which route is most feasible is usually based on specific restrictions or limitations of reactions in the sequence, the

 COREY was awarded the Nobel Prize in Chemistry in 1990 for finding new ways of synthesizing organic compounds, which, in the words of the Nobel committee, "have contributed to the high standards of living and health enjoyed ... in the Western world."

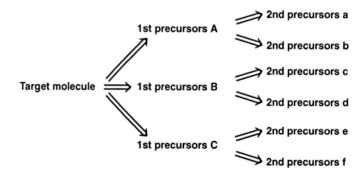

FIGURE 7.11 Retrosynthetic analysis often discloses several routes from the target molecule back to varied precursors.

availability of materials, or other factors. We shall see an example of this in Section 7.16C. In actuality more than one route may work well. In other cases it may be necessary to try several approaches in the laboratory in order to find the most efficient or successful route.

7.15C Identifying Precursors

In the case of functional groups we need to have a toolbox of reactions from which to choose those we know can convert one given functional group into another. You will develop such a toolbox of reactions as you proceed through your study of organic chemistry. Similarly, with regard to making carbon–carbon bonds in synthesis, you will develop a repertoire of reactions for that purpose. In order to choose the appropriate reaction for either purpose, you will inevitably consider basic principles of structure and reactivity.

As we stated in Sections 3.3A and 7.12:

- Many organic reactions depend on the interaction of molecules that have complementary full or partial charges.

One very important aspect of retrosynthetic analysis is being able to identify those atoms in a target molecule that could have had complementary (opposite) charges in synthetic precursors. Consider, for example, the synthesis of 1-cyclohexyl-1-butyne. On the basis of reactions learned in this chapter, you might envision an alkynide anion and an alkyl halide as precursors having complementary polarities that when allowed to react together would lead to this molecule:

Retrosynthetic Analysis

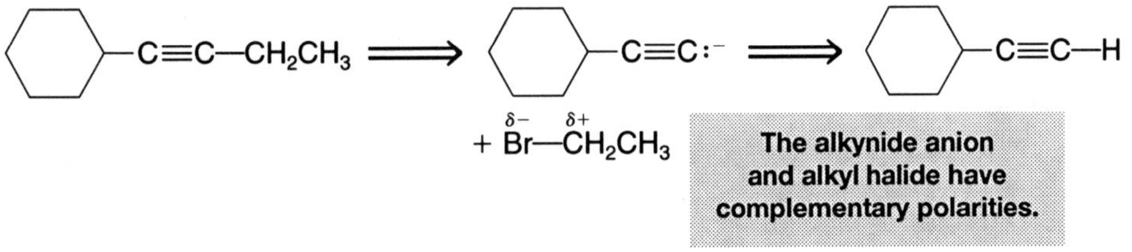

$$\text{Cyclohexyl}-C\equiv C-CH_2CH_3 \Longrightarrow \text{Cyclohexyl}-C\equiv C:^{-} \Longrightarrow \text{Cyclohexyl}-C\equiv C-H$$

$$+ \overset{\delta^-}{Br}-\overset{\delta^+}{CH_2CH_3}$$

The alkynide anion and alkyl halide have complementary polarities.

Synthesis

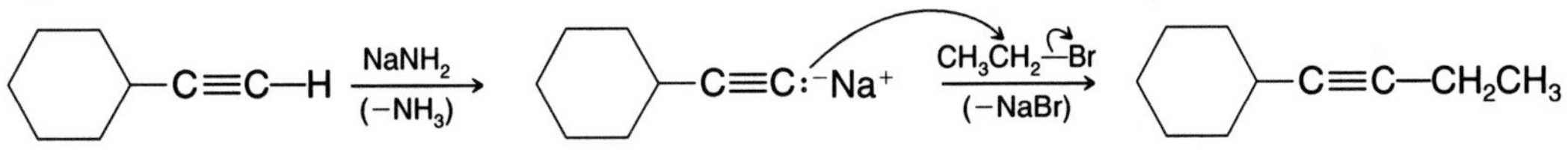

$$\text{Cyclohexyl}-C\equiv C-H \xrightarrow[(-NH_3)]{NaNH_2} \text{Cyclohexyl}-C\equiv C:^{-}Na^+ \xrightarrow[(-NaBr)]{CH_3CH_2-Br} \text{Cyclohexyl}-C\equiv C-CH_2CH_3$$

Sometimes, however, it will not at first be obvious where the retrosynthetic bond disconnections are in a target molecule that would lead to oppositely charged or complementary precursors. The synthesis of an alkane would be such an example. An alkane does not contain carbon atoms that could directly have had opposite charges in precursor molecules. However, if one supposes that certain carbon–carbon single bonds in the alkane could have arisen by hydrogenation of a corresponding alkyne (a functional group interconversion), then, in turn, two atoms of the alkyne could have been joined from precursor molecules that had complementary charges (i.e., an alkynide anion and an alkyl halide).

THE CHEMISTRY OF... From the Inorganic to the Organic

In 1862, Friedrich Wöhler discovered calcium carbide (CaC_2) by heating carbon with an alloy of zinc and calcium. He then synthesized acetylene by allowing the calcium carbide to react with water:

$$C \xrightarrow{\text{zinc-calcium alloy, heat}} CaC_2 \xrightarrow{2H_2O} HC\equiv CH + Ca(OH)_2$$

Acetylene produced this way burned in lamps of some lighthouses and in old-time miners' headlamps. From the standpoint of organic synthesis, it is theoretically possible to synthesize anything using reactions of alkynes to form carbon–carbon bonds and to prepare other functional groups. Thus, while Wöhler's 1828 conversion of ammonium cyanate to urea was the first synthesis of an organic compound from an inorganic precursor (Section 1.1A), his discovery of calcium carbide and its reaction with water to form acetylene gives us a formal link from inorganic materials to the entire realm of organic synthesis.

Consider the following retrosynthetic analysis for **2-methylhexane:**

Retrosynthetic Analysis

Because of steric hindrance in the alkyl halide, this reaction will give a poor yield.

Because of steric hindrance in the alkyl halide, this reaction will give a poor yield.

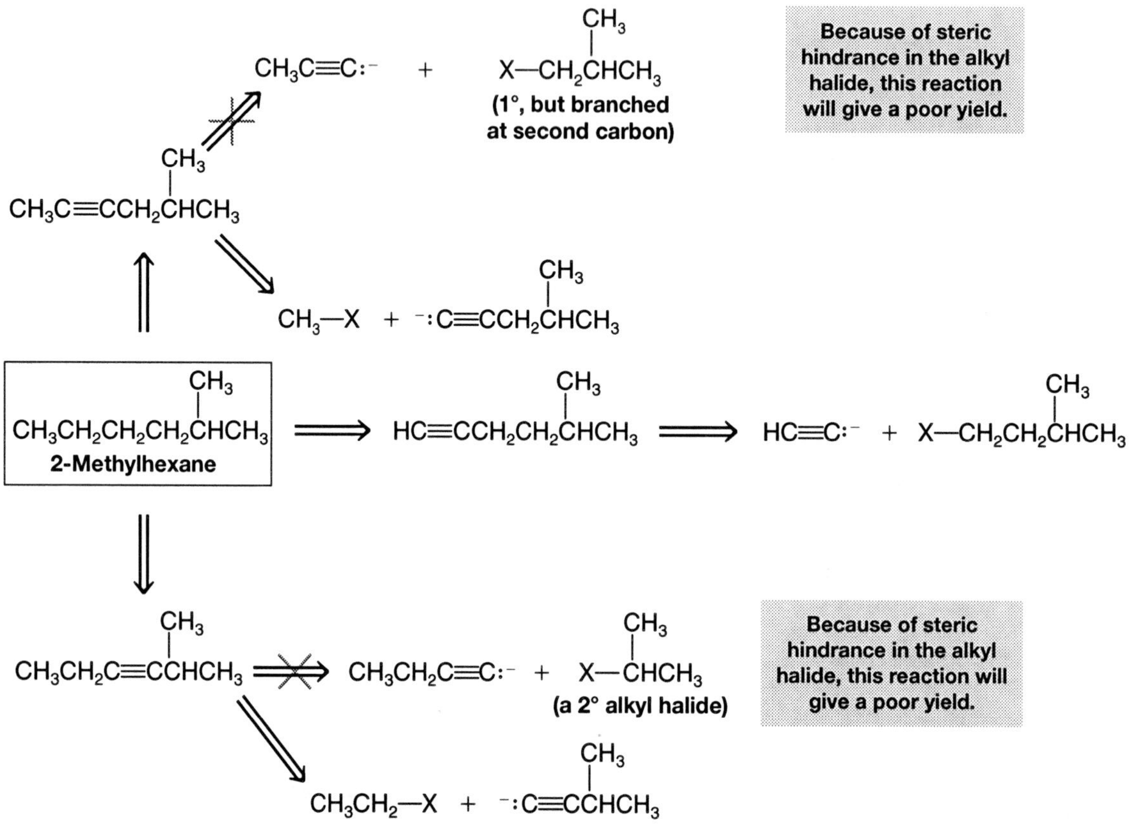

As indicated in the retrosynthetic analysis above, we must bear in mind the limitations that exist for the reactions that would be applied in the synthetic (forward) direction. In the example above, two of the pathways have to be discarded because they involve the use of a 2° alkyl halide or a primary halide branched at the second (beta) carbon (Sections 6.13A, 7.11).

●●● SOLVED PROBLEM 7.9

Outline a retrosynthetic pathway that leads from 'muscalure', the sex attractant pheromone of the common housefly back to the simplest alkyne, ethyne (acetylene). Then show the synthesis. You may use any inorganic compounds, or solvents, you need and alkyl halides of any length necessary.

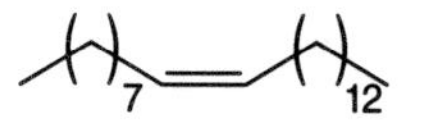

Muscalure

STRATEGY AND ANSWER: We make use of two reactions that we have just studied in this chapter: syn addition of hydrogen to an alkyne, and alkylation of alkynide ions.

Retrosynthetic Analysis

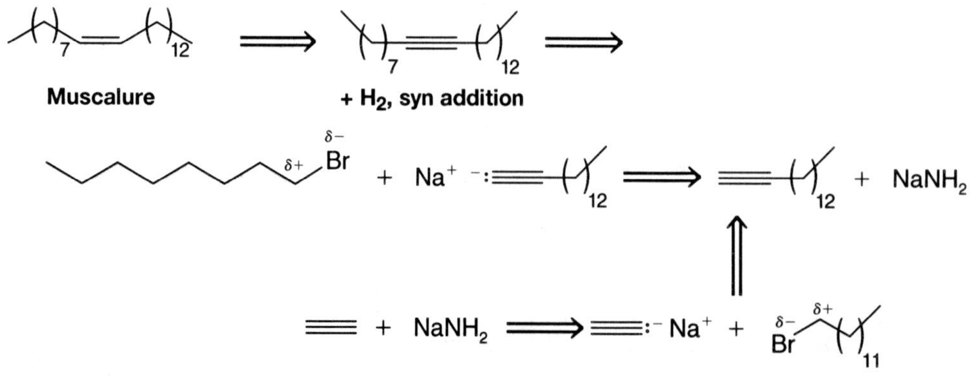

Synthesis

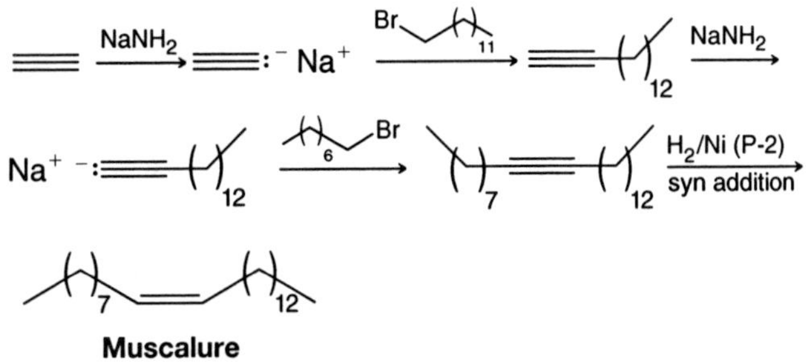

Muscalure

● ● ●

Referring to the retrosynthetic analysis for 2-methylhexane in this section, write reactions for those synthesis routes that are feasible.

PRACTICE PROBLEM 7.23

● ● ◆

(a) Devise retrosynthetic schemes for all conceivable alkynide anion alkylation syntheses of the insect pheromones undecane and 2-methylheptadecane (see "The Chemistry of ... Pheromones" box in Chapter 4). **(b)** Write reactions for two feasible syntheses of each pheromone.

PRACTICE PROBLEM 7.24

7.15D Raison d'Etre

Solving synthetic puzzles by application of retrosynthetic analysis is one of the joys of learning organic chemistry. As you might imagine, there is skill and some artistry involved. Over the years many chemists have set their minds to organic synthesis, and because of this we have all prospered from the fruits of their endeavors.

[WHY Do These Topics Matter?

ALKENE GEOMETRY, RUBBER, AND THE CHEMISTRY OF VISION

The (*E*) or (*Z*) configurations of substituted double bonds is not just a matter for exercise sets and exams. In the real world, they define the properties of many compounds. For example, natural rubber, which can be obtained from the sap of certain trees, has all (*Z*) configurations about its trisubstituted double bonds. Some other trees make the all (*E*) version, a compound known as gutta percha. While gutta percha is also a latex-like material, the change in stereochemistry actually makes it inelastic so that it does not have the same useful properties as natural rubber.

Natural rubber
(Z configuration)

Gutta percha
(E configuration)

Alkene stereochemistry is also critical to our ability to see. In our eyes, the key molecule is a compound called *trans*-retinal, a material that can be synthesized in our bodies and that comes from our diets through foods like carrots.

(continues on next page)

Bjorn Svensson/Photo Researchers, Inc.

In order for retinal to participate in the vision process, one particular double bond within it must first be isomerized from trans to cis through a process that breaks the π-bond, rotates about a single bond, and reforms the π-bond. This new stereochemical orientation places several carbon atoms in a different orientation than they were in the trans configuration. The value of that change, however, is that the new spatial orientation of *cis*-retinal allows it to fit into a receptor in a protein known as opsin in our retinas and merge with it through a general reaction process we will learn more about in Chapter 16; this step generates a new complex known as rhodopsin. The key thing to understand for now, however, is that when rhodopsin is exposed to light of a certain wavelength (of which we will learn more in Chapter 13), the cis double bond isomerizes back to the more stable all trans configuration through a series of steps to become metarho-

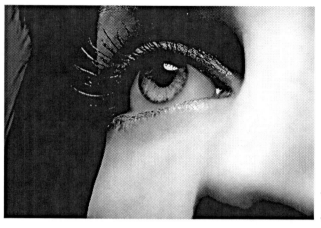

dopsin II as shown below. It is believed that the repositioning of the cyclohexene ring within the retinal portion of metarhodopsin II following this isomerization induces some further conformational changes within the protein. These changes ultimately lead to a nerve impulse that is interpreted by our brains as vision. The picture shown here is but a small part in the overall process, but these initial, critical steps are based solely on alkene stereochemistry. As such, it really does matter whether a double bond is cis or trans, (*E*) or (*Z*)!

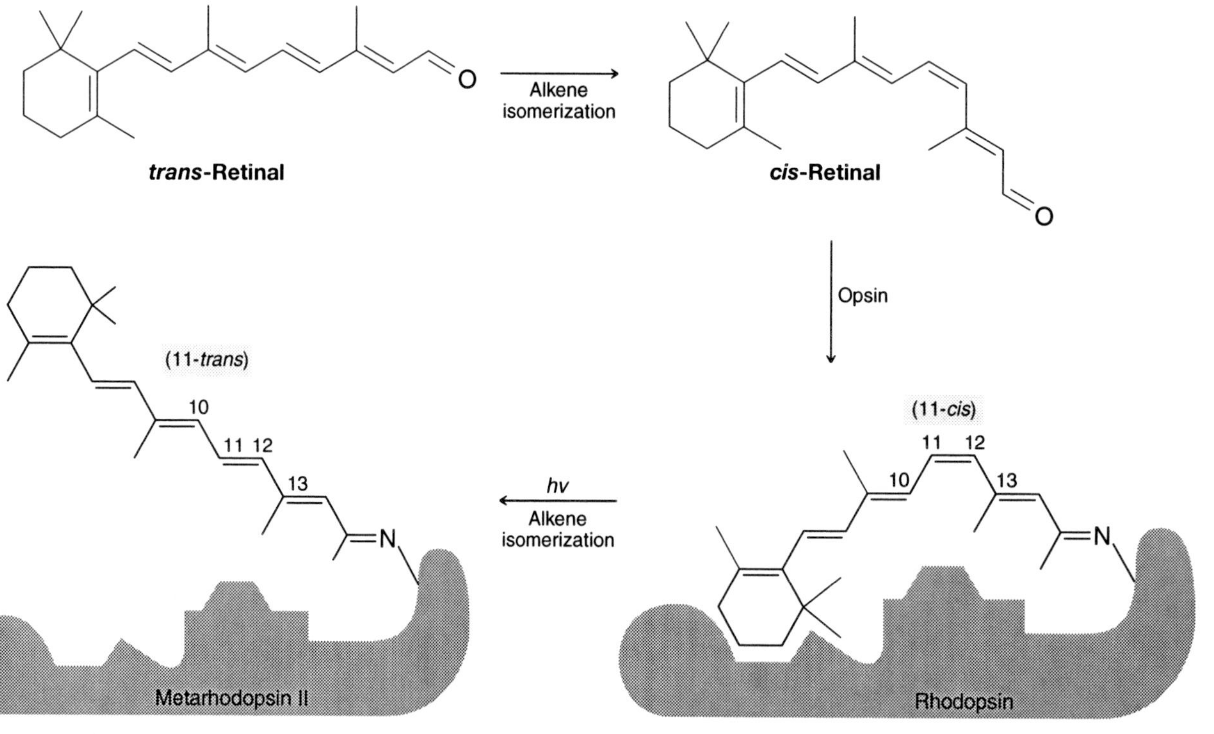

trans-Retinal   → Alkene isomerization →   **cis-Retinal**

↓ Opsin

(11-*trans*)
10
11 12
13

Metarhodopsin II

← *hv* Alkene isomerization

(11-*cis*)
11 12
10 13

Rhodopsin

SUMMARY AND REVIEW TOOLS

In this chapter we described methods for the synthesis of alkenes using dehydrohalogenation, dehydration of alcohols, and reduction of alkynes. We also introduced the alkylation of alkynide anions as a method for forming new carbon–carbon bonds, and we introduced retrosynthetic analysis as a means of logically planning an organic synthesis.

The study aids for this chapter include the list of methods below that we have mentioned for synthesizing alkenes, as well as key terms and concepts (which are hyperlinked to the Glossary from the bold, blue terms in the *WileyPLUS* version of the book at wileyplus.com). Following the end of chapter problems you will find graphical overviews of the mechanisms for E2 and E1 reactions, a Synthetic Connections scheme for alkynes, alkenes, alkyl halides, and alcohols, and a Concept Map regarding organic synthesis involving alkenes.

SUMMARY OF METHODS FOR THE PREPARATION OF ALKENES AND ALKYNES

1. Dehydrohalogenation of alkyl halides (Section 7.6):

General Reaction

$$-\overset{|}{\underset{H}{C}}-\overset{|}{\underset{X}{C}}- \xrightarrow[\text{heat} \atop (-HX)]{\text{base}} \overset{\diagdown}{\diagup}C=C\overset{\diagup}{\diagdown}$$

Specific Examples

$$\text{CH}_3\text{CH}_2\underset{\underset{Br}{|}}{\text{CHCH}_3} \xrightarrow[\text{EtOH}]{\text{EtONa}} \text{CH}_3\text{CH}=\text{CHCH}_3 \;+\; \text{CH}_3\text{CH}_2\text{CH}=\text{CH}_2$$

(cis and trans, 81%)   **(19%)**

$$\text{CH}_3\text{CH}_2\underset{\underset{Br}{|}}{\text{CHCH}_3} \xrightarrow[\text{t-BuOH} \atop 70\,°C]{\text{t-BuOK}} \text{CH}_3\text{CH}=\text{CHCH}_3 \;+\; \text{CH}_3\text{CH}_2\text{CH}=\text{CH}_2$$

Disubstituted alkenes   **Monosubstituted alkene**
(cis and trans, 47%)   **(53%)**

2. Dehydration of alcohols (Sections 7.7 and 7.8):

General Reaction

$$-\overset{|}{\underset{H}{C}}-\overset{|}{\underset{OH}{C}}- \xrightarrow[\text{heat}]{\text{acid}} \overset{\diagdown}{\diagup}C=C\overset{\diagup}{\diagdown} \;+\; \text{H}_2\text{O}$$

Specific Examples

$$\text{CH}_3\text{CH}_2\text{OH} \xrightarrow[180\,°C]{\text{concd H}_2\text{SO}_4} \text{CH}_2=\text{CH}_2 + \text{H}_2\text{O}$$

$$\text{CH}_3\overset{\overset{\text{CH}_3}{|}}{\underset{\underset{\text{CH}_3}{|}}{C}}\text{-OH} \xrightarrow[85\,°C]{20\%\ \text{H}_2\text{SO}_4} \overset{\text{H}_3\text{C}}{\underset{\text{H}_3\text{C}}{}}C=\text{CH}_2 + \text{H}_2\text{O}$$

(83%)

3. Hydrogenation of alkynes (Section 7.15):

General Reaction

$$\text{R}-\text{C}\equiv\text{C}-\text{R}' \begin{cases} \xrightarrow[\text{(syn addition)}]{\text{H}_2\,/\,\text{Ni}_2\text{B (P-2)}} & \underset{\underset{\text{H}}{|}}{\overset{\overset{\text{R}}{|}}{C}}=\underset{\underset{\text{H}}{|}}{\overset{\overset{\text{R}'}{|}}{C} \quad \textbf{(Z)-Alkene}} \\[2em] \xrightarrow[\substack{\text{NH}_3 \text{ or RNH}_2 \\ \text{(anti addition)}}]{\text{Li or Na}} & \underset{\underset{\text{H}}{|}}{\overset{\overset{\text{R}}{|}}{C}}=\underset{\underset{\text{R}'}{|}}{\overset{\overset{\text{H}}{|}}{C} \quad \textbf{(E)-Alkene}} \end{cases}$$

In subsequent chapters we shall see a number of other methods for alkene synthesis.

PROBLEMS *PLUS*

Note to Instructors: Many of the homework problems are available for assignment via *WileyPLUS*, an online teaching and learning solution.

STRUCTURE AND NOMENCLATURE

7.25 Each of the following names is incorrect. Give the correct name and explain your reasoning.

(a) *trans*-3-Pentene

(b) 1,1-Dimethylethene

(c) 2-Methylcyclohexene

(d) 4-Methylcyclobutene

(e) (*Z*)-3-Chloro-2-butene

(f) 5,6-Dichlorocyclohexene

7.26 Write a structural formula for each of the following:

(a) 3-Methylcyclobutene
(b) 1-Methylcyclopentene
(c) 2,3-Dimethyl-2-pentene
(d) (Z)-3-Hexene

(e) (E)-2-Pentene
(f) 3,3,3-Tribromopropene
(g) (Z,4R)-4-Methyl-2-hexene
(h) (E,4S)-4-Chloro-2-pentene

(i) (Z)-1-Cyclopropyl-1-pentene
(j) 5-Cyclobutyl-1-pentene
(k) (R)-4-Chloro-2-pentyne
(l) (E)-4-Methylhex-4-en-1-yne

7.27 Write three-dimensional formulas for and give names using (R)–(S) and (E)–(Z) designations for the isomers of:

(a) 4-Bromo-2-hexene
(b) 3-Chloro-1,4-hexadiene

(c) 2,4-Dichloro-2-pentene
(d) 2-Bromo-4-chlorohex-2-en-5-yne

7.28 Give the IUPAC names for each of the following:

(a)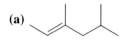

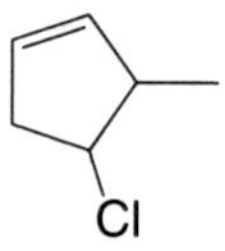

(c)

(e)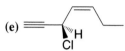

(b)

(d)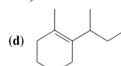

(f)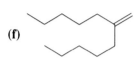

7.29 Without consulting tables, arrange the following compounds in order of decreasing acidity:

Pentane   1-Pentene   1-Pentyne   1-Pentanol

SYNTHESIS

7.30 Outline a synthesis of propene from each of the following:

(a) Propyl chloride
(b) Isopropyl chloride

(c) Propyl alcohol
(d) Isopropyl alcohol

(e) 1,2-Dibromopropane
(f) Propyne

7.31 Outline a synthesis of cyclopentene from each of the following:

(a) Bromocyclopentane

(b) Cyclopentanol

7.32 Starting with ethyne, outline syntheses of each of the following. You may use any other needed reagents, and you need not show the synthesis of compounds prepared in earlier parts of this problem.

(a) Propyne
(b) 1-Butyne
(c) 2-Butyne
(d) cis-2-Butene
(e) trans-2-Butene

(f) 1-Pentyne
(g) 2-Hexyne
(h) (Z)-2-Hexene
(i) (E)-2-Hexene
(j) 3-Hexyne

(k) $CH_3CH_2C \equiv CD$

(l)
$$\underset{D \qquad D}{\overset{H_3C \qquad CH_3}{C=C}}$$

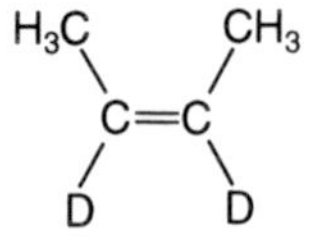

7.33 Starting with 1-methylcyclohexene and using any other needed reagents, outline a synthesis of the following deuterium-labeled compound:

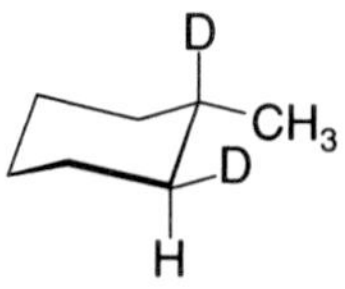

7.34 Outline a synthesis of phenylethyne from each of the following:

(a)

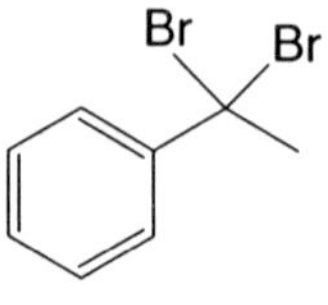

(b)

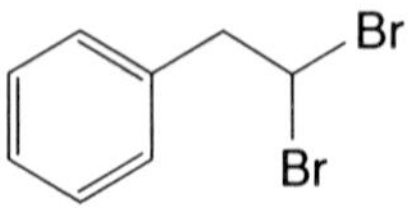

(c)

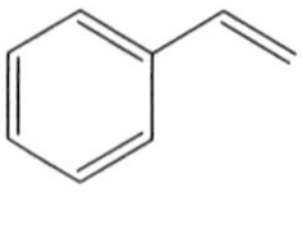

(d)

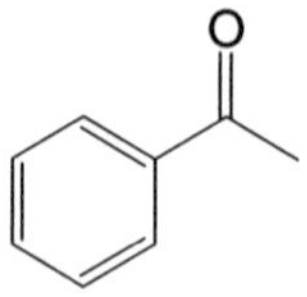

DEHYDROHALOGENATION AND DEHYDRATION

7.35 Write a three-dimensional representation for the transition state structure leading to formation of 2-methyl-2-butene from reaction of 2-bromo-2-methylbutane with sodium ethoxide.

7.36 When *trans*-2-methylcyclohexanol (see the following reaction) is subjected to acid-catalyzed dehydration, the major product is 1-methylcyclohexene:

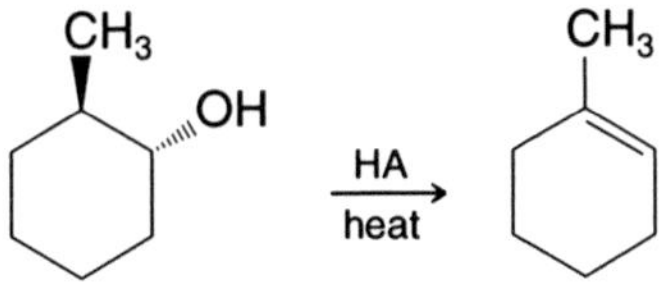

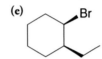

However, when *trans*-1-bromo-2-methylcyclohexane is subjected to dehydrohalogenation, the major product is 3-methylcyclohexene:

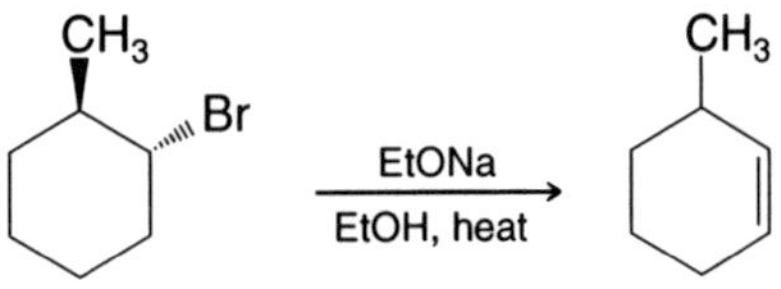

Account for the different products of these two reactions.

7.37 Write structural formulas for all the products that would be obtained when each of the following alkyl halides is heated with sodium ethoxide in ethanol. When more than one product results, you should indicate which would be the major product and which would be the minor product(s). You may neglect cis–trans isomerism of the products when answering this question.

(a)

(c)

(e)

(b)

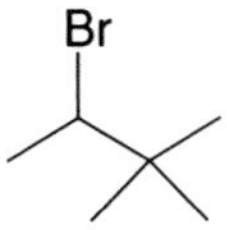

(d)

(f)

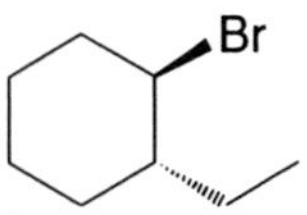

7.38 Write structural formulas for all the products that would be obtained when each of the following alkyl halides is heated with potassium *tert*-butoxide in *tert*-butyl alcohol. When more than one product results, you should indicate which would be the major product and which would be the minor product(s). You may neglect cis–trans isomerism of the products when answering this question.

(a) (b) 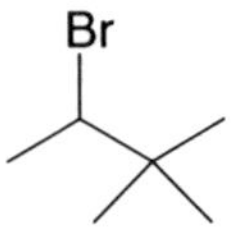 (c) 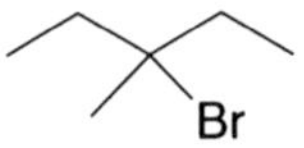 (d) 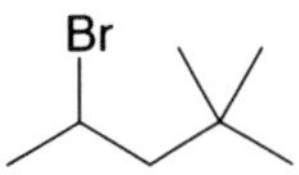 (e)

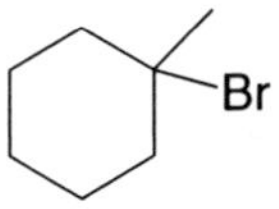

7.39 Starting with an appropriate alkyl halide and base, outline syntheses that would yield each of the following alkenes as the major (or only) product:

(a)  (b) 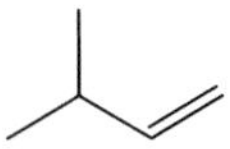 (c) 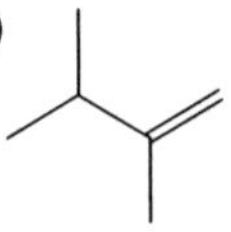 (d) 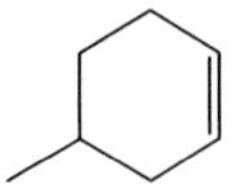 (e)

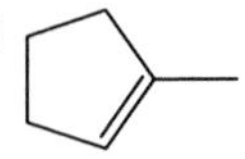

7.40 Arrange the following alcohols in order of their reactivity toward acid-catalyzed dehydration (with the most reactive first):

1-Pentanol   2-Methyl-2-butanol   3-Methyl-2-butanol

7.41 Give the products that would be formed when each of the following alcohols is subjected to acid-catalyzed dehydration. If more than one product would be formed, designate the alkene that would be the major product. (Neglect cis–trans isomerism.)

(a) 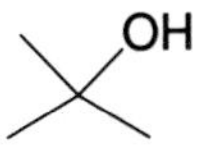 (b) 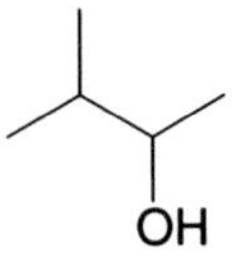 (c) 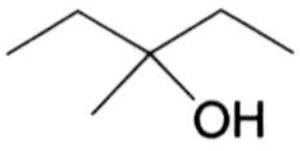 (d) 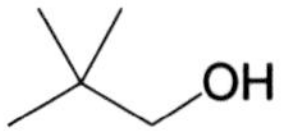 (e)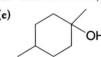

7.42 1-Bromobicyclo[2.2.1]heptane does not undergo elimination (below) when heated with a base. Explain this failure to react. (Construction of molecular models may help.)

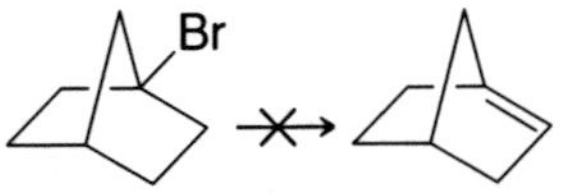

7.43 When the deuterium-labeled compound shown at right is subjected to dehydrohalogenation using sodium ethoxide in ethanol, the only alkene product is 3-methylcyclohexene. (The product contains no deuterium.) Provide an explanation for this result.

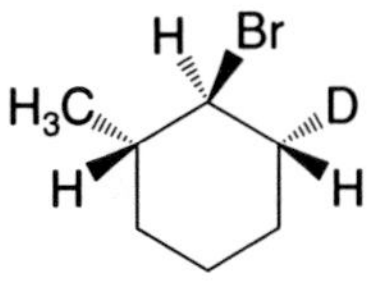

337

7.44 Provide a mechanistic explanation for each of the following reactions:

(a)

(major product)

(c)

(major product)

(b)

(major product)

(d)

(Z only)

INDEX OF HYDROGEN DEFICIENCY

7.45 What is the index of hydrogen deficiency (IHD) (degree of unsaturation) for each of the following compounds?

(a)

(b) $C_6H_8Br_4$

7.46 Caryophyllene, a compound found in oil of cloves, has the molecular formula $C_{15}H_{24}$ and has no triple bonds. Reaction of caryophyllene with an excess of hydrogen in the presence of a platinum catalyst produces a compound with the formula $C_{15}H_{28}$. How many (a) double bonds and (b) rings does a molecule of caryophyllene have?

7.47 Squalene, an important intermediate in the biosynthesis of steroids, has the molecular formula $C_{30}H_{50}$ and has no triple bonds.

(a) What is the index of hydrogen deficiency of squalene?

(b) Squalene undergoes catalytic hydrogenation to yield a compound with the molecular formula $C_{30}H_{62}$. How many double bonds does a molecule of squalene have?

(c) How many rings?

STRUCTURE ELUCIDATION

7.48 Compounds **I** and **J** both have the molecular formula C_7H_{14}. Compounds **I** and **J** are both optically active and both rotate plane-polarized light in the same direction. On catalytic hydrogenation **I** and **J** yield the same compound **K** (C_7H_{16}). Compound **K** is optically active. Propose possible structures for **I**, **J**, and **K**.

$$(+)-I\ (C_7H_{14}) \xrightarrow{\text{H}_2,\ \text{Pt}}$$
$$K\ (C_7H_{16})$$
$$(+)-J\ (C_7H_{14}) \xrightarrow{\text{H}_2,\ \text{Pt}} \text{(Optically active)}$$

7.49 Compounds **L** and **M** have the molecular formula C_7H_{14}. Compounds **L** and **M** are optically inactive, are nonresolvable, and are diastereomers of each other. Catalytic hydrogenation of either **L** or **M** yields **N**. Compound **N** is optically inactive but can be resolved into separate enantiomers. Propose possible structures for **L**, **M**, and **N**.

$$L\ (C_7H_{14})$$
(Optically inactive) $\xrightarrow{\text{H}_2,\ \text{Pt}}$ **N**

$$M\ (C_7H_{14})$$
(Optically inactive) $\xrightarrow{\text{H}_2,\ \text{Pt}}$ **(Optically inactive, resolvable)**
(L and M are diastereomers)

CHALLENGE PROBLEMS

7.50 Propose structures for compounds **E–H**. Compound **E** has the molecular formula C_5H_8 and is optically active. On catalytic hydrogenation **E** yields **F**. Compound **F** has the molecular formula C_5H_{10}, is optically inactive, and cannot be resolved into separate enantiomers. Compound **G** has the molecular formula C_6H_{10} and is optically active. Compound **G** contains no triple bonds. On catalytic hydrogenation **G** yields **H**. Compound **H** has the molecular formula C_6H_{14}, is optically inactive, and cannot be resolved into separate enantiomers.

7.51 Consider the interconversion of *cis*-2-butene and *trans*-2-butene.

(a) What is the value of $\Delta H°$ for the reaction *cis*-2-butene $\rightarrow$ *trans*-2-butene (see Section 7.3A)?

(b) Assume $\Delta H° \cong \Delta G°$. What minimum value of $\Delta G^{\ddagger}$ would you expect for this reaction (see Section 1.13A)?

(c) Sketch a free-energy diagram for the reaction and label $\Delta G°$ and $\Delta G^{\ddagger}$.

7.52 (a) Partial dehydrohalogenation of either (1*R*,2*R*)-1,2-dibromo-1,2-diphenylethane or (1*S*,2*S*)-1,2-dibromo-1,2-diphenylethane enantiomers (or a racemate of the two) produces (*Z*)-1-bromo-1,2-diphenylethene as the product, whereas **(b)** partial dehydrohalogenation of (1*R*,2*S*)-1,2-dibromo-1,2-diphenylethane (the meso compound) gives only (*E*)-1-bromo-1,2-diphenylethene. **(c)** Treating (1*R*,2*S*)-1,2-dibromo-1,2-diphenylethane with sodium iodide in acetone produces only (*E*)-1,2-diphenylethene. Explain these results.

7.53 (a) Using reactions studied in this chapter, show steps by which this alkyne could be converted to the seven-membered ring homolog of the product obtained in Problem 7.44(b).

(b) Could the homologous products obtained in these two cases be relied upon to show infrared absorption in the 1620–1680-cm^{-1} region?

7.54 Predict the structures of compounds **A**, **B**, and **C**:

A is an unbranched C_6 alkyne that is also a primary alcohol.

B is obtained from **A** by use of hydrogen and nickel boride catalyst or dissolving metal reduction.

C is formed from **B** on treatment with aqueous acid at room temperature. Compound **C** has no infrared absorption in either the 1620–1680-cm^{-1} or the 3590–3650-cm^{-1} region. It has an index of hydrogen deficiency of 1 and has one chirality center but forms as the racemate.

7.55 What is the index of hydrogen deficiency for **(a)** $C_7H_{10}O_2$ and **(b)** $C_5H_4N_4$?

LEARNING GROUP PROBLEMS

1. Write the structure(s) of the major product(s) obtained when 2-chloro-2,3-dimethylbutane (either enantiomer) reacts with **(a)** sodium ethoxide (EtONa) in ethanol (EtOH) at 80 °C or (in a separate reaction) with **(b)** potassium *tert*-butoxide (*t*-BuOK) in *tert*-butyl alcohol (*t*-BuOH) at 80 °C. If more than one product is formed, indicate which one would be expected to be the major product. **(c)** Provide a detailed mechanism for formation of the major product from each reaction, including a drawing of the transition state structures.

2. Explain using mechanistic arguments involving Newman projections or other three-dimensional formulas why the reaction of 2-bromo-1,2-diphenylpropane (either enantiomer) with sodium ethoxide (EtONa) in ethanol (EtOH) at 80 °C produces mainly (*E*)-1,2-diphenylpropene [little of the (*Z*) diastereomer is formed].

3. (a) Write the structure of the product(s) formed when 1-methylcyclohexanol reacts with 85% (coned) H_3PO_4 at 150 °C. **(b)** Write a detailed mechanism for the reaction.

4. Consider the reaction of 1-cyclobutylethanol (1-hydroxyethylcyclobutane) with concentrated H_2SO_4 at 120 °C. Write structures of all reasonable organic products. Assuming that methylcyclopentene is one product, write a mechanism that accounts for its formation. Write mechanisms that account for formation of all other products as well.

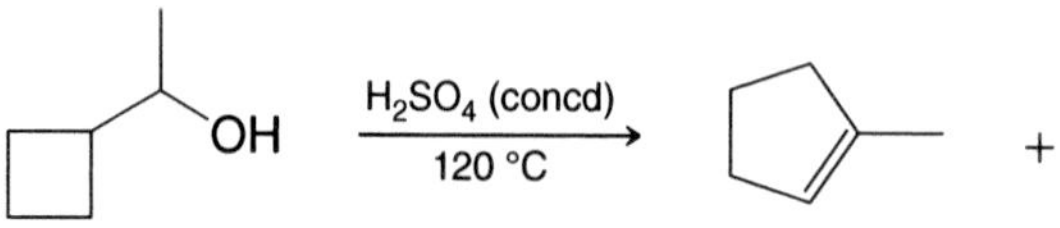

5. Consider the following compound:

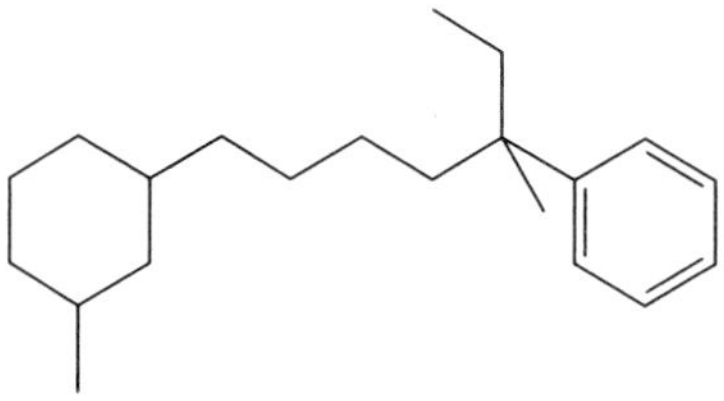

(a) Develop all reasonable retrosynthetic analyses for this compound (any diastereomer) that, at some point, involve carbon–carbon bond formation by alkylation of an alkynide ion.

(b) Write reactions, including reagents and conditions, for syntheses of this compound that correspond to the retrosynthetic analyses you developed above.

(c) Infrared spectroscopy could be used to show the presence of certain impurities in your final product that would result from leftover intermediates in your syntheses. Which of your synthetic intermediates would show IR absorptions that are distinct from those in the final product, and in what regions of the IR spectrum would the absorptions occur?

(d) Draw a three-dimensional structure for either the cis or trans form of the target molecule. Use dashed and solid wedges where appropriate in the alkyl side chain and use a chair conformational structure for the ring. (*Hint:* Draw the structure so that the carbon chain of the most complicated substituent on the cyclohexane ring and the ring carbon where it is attached are all in the plane of the paper. In general, for three-dimensional structures choose an orientation that allows as many carbon atoms as possible to be in the plane of the paper.)

[S U M M A R Y A N D R E V I E W T O O L S]

Reaction Summary of E2 and E1 elimination

E2 via small base

- **Strong unhindered base,** e.g., CH$_3$CH$_2$ONa (EtONa), HO$^-$
- **Predominant formation of most substituted alkene (Zaitsev product)**
- Anti coplanar transition state
- Bimolecular in rate-determining step

E2 via bulky base

- **Strong hindered base,** e.g. (CH$_3$)$_3$COK (t-BuOK)
- **Predominant formation of least substituted alkene (Hofmann product)**
- Anti coplanar transition state
- Bimolecular in rate-determining step

E1 (including Alcohol Dehydration)

- **Absence of strong base (solvent is often the base)**
- **Alcohols require strong acid catalyst**
- Carbocation formation is unimolecular rate-determining step
- Carbocation may rearrange
- **Predominant formation of most substituted alkene (Zaitsev product)**
- Leaving group for alcohols is —OH$_2^+$
- 1° Alcohols react by an E2-type mechanism

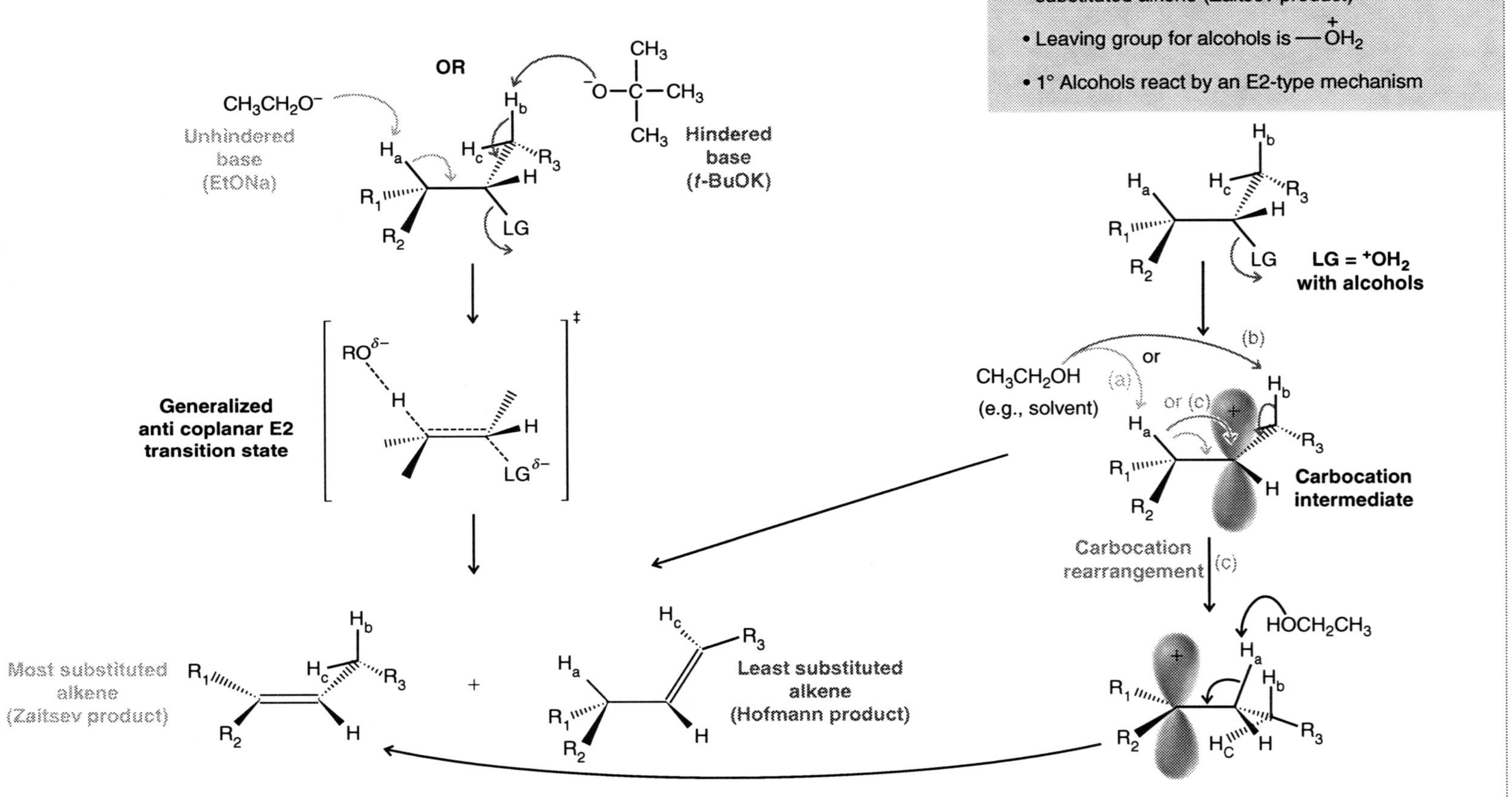

LG = $^+$OH$_2$ with alcohols

Carbocation intermediate

Carbocation rearrangement

Least substituted alkene (Hofmann product)

Most substituted alkene (Zaitsev product)

Generalized anti coplanar E2 transition state

Unhindered base (EtONa)

Hindered base (t-BuOK)

[SUMMARY AND REVIEW TOOLS]

Synthetic Connections of Alkynes, Alkenes, Alkyl Halides, and Alcohols

E2 Elimination
LG
Alkyl halides and alcohols
Alkenes
X_2
Vicinal dihalide
$NaNH_2$ (2 equiv.)
H_2, Lindlar's catalyst or Ni_2B
(Z)-Alkene
H_2, catalyst*
$NaNH_2$
R_2—LG
Terminal alkyne
Alkynide anion
Internal alkyne
Alkane
$NaNH_2$ (2 equiv.)
(1) Li or Na in NH_3 or $EtNH_2$
(2) NH_4Cl
(E)-Alkene
Geminal dichloride
PCl_5
Aldehyde or ketone
*Hydrogenation catalyst = Pt, Pd, Ni (heterogeneous); or Ru or Rh (homogeneous)

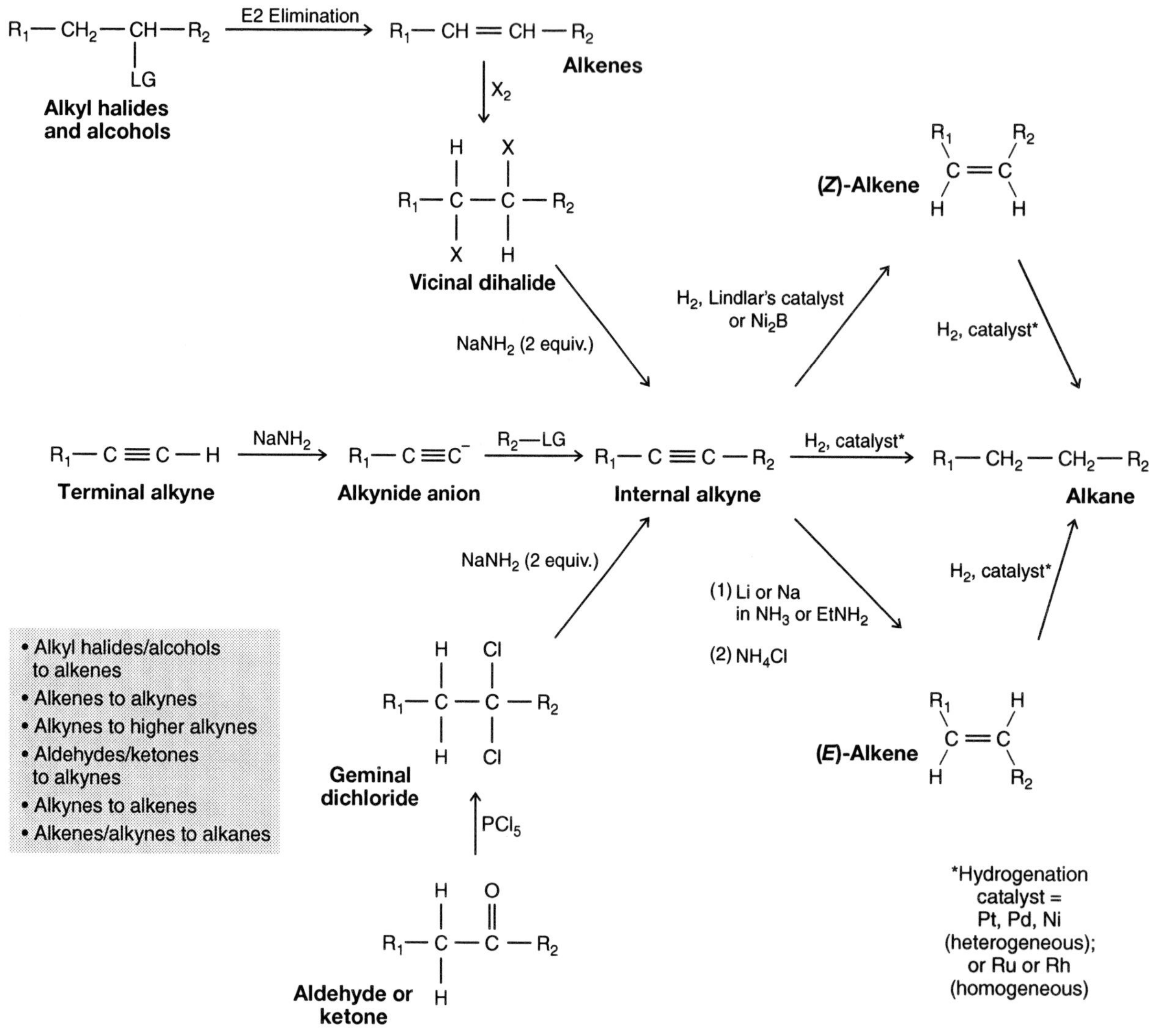

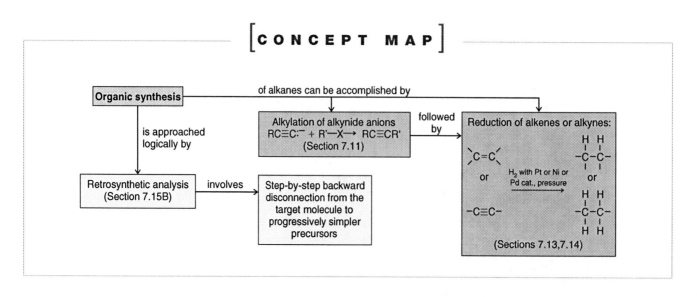

- Alkyl halides/alcohols to alkenes
- Alkenes to alkynes
- Alkynes to higher alkynes
- Aldehydes/ketones to alkynes
- Alkynes to alkenes
- Alkenes/alkynes to alkanes

[CONCEPT MAP]

Organic synthesis
of alkanes can be accomplished by
is approached logically by
Alkylation of alkynide anions
RC≡C:⁻ + R'—X → RC≡CR'
(Section 7.11)
followed by
Reduction of alkenes or alkynes:
or
H_2 with Pt or Ni or Pd cat., pressure
Retrosynthetic analysis (Section 7.15B)
involves
Step-by-step backward disconnection from the target molecule to progressively simpler precursors
(Sections 7.13,7.14)

CHAPTER

8

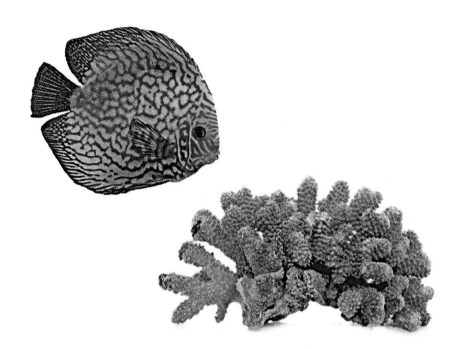

Alkenes and Alkynes II

ADDITION REACTIONS

In recent chapters we have discussed mechanisms that involve electron pairs in bond-forming and bond-breaking steps of substitution and elimination reactions. Nucleophiles and bases served as electron pair donors in these reactions. In this chapter we discuss reactions of **alkenes** and **alkynes** in which a double or triple bond acts as the electron pair donor for bond formation. These reactions are called addition reactions.

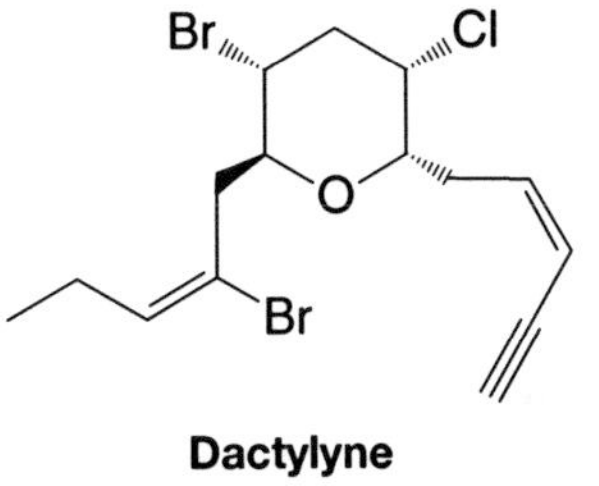

Dactylyne

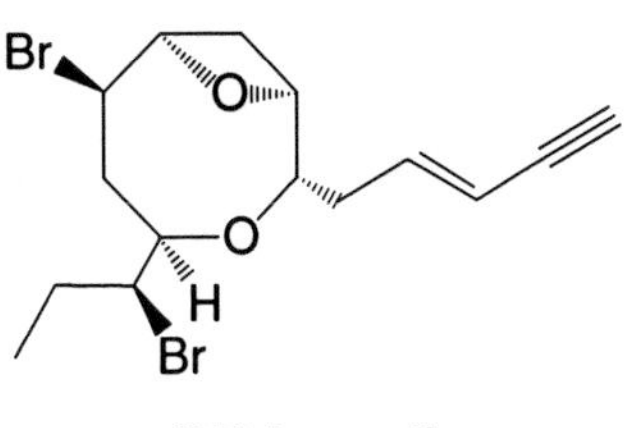

(3E)-Laureatin

Alkenes and alkynes are very common in nature, both on land and in the sea. Examples from the sea include dactylyne and (3E)-laureatin, whose formulas are shown here. These compounds include halogens in their structures, as is the case for many other natural marine compounds. Certain marine organisms may produce compounds like these for the purpose of self-defense, since a number of them have cytotoxic properties. Interestingly, the halogens in these marine compounds are

PHOTO CREDITS: (coral) © Mehmet Torlak/iStockphoto; (discus fish) © cynoclub/iStockphoto

337

incorporated by biological reactions similar to those we shall study in this chapter (Section 8.11). Not only, therefore, do compounds like dactylyne and (3E)-laureatin have intriguing structures and properties, and arise in the beautiful environment of the sea, but they also have fascinating chemistry behind them.

IN THIS CHAPTER WE WILL CONSIDER:

- the regio- and stereochemistry of addition reactions of alkenes

- processes that can add molecules of water, halogens, carbon, and other functionalities across alkenes

- events that cleave double bonds and provide more highly oxidized compounds

- alkyne reactions that are analogous to alkene reactions

[**WHY** DO THESE TOPICS MATTER?] At the end of the chapter, we will show how, in nature, a special class of alkenes is involved in the creation of tens of thousands of bioactive molecules, all through processes that mirror the core reactions discussed in this chapter.

8.1 ADDITION REACTIONS OF ALKENES

We have already studied one addition reaction of alkenes—hydrogenation—in which a hydrogen atom is added at each end of a double (or triple) bond. In this chapter we shall study other alkene addition reactions that do not involve the same mechanism as hydrogenation. We can depict this type of reaction generally, using **E** for an electrophilic portion of a reagent and **Nu** for a nucleophilic portion, as follows.

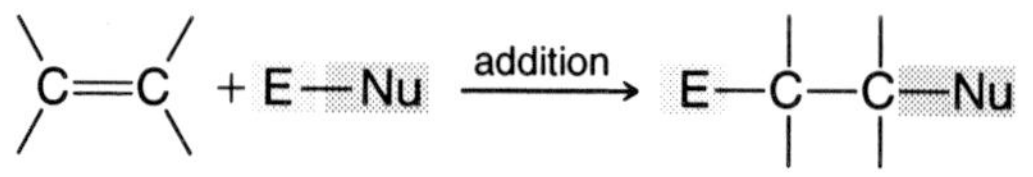

Some specific reactions of this type that we shall study in this chapter include addition of hydrogen halides, sulfuric acid, water (in the presence of an acid catalyst), and halogens. Later we shall also study some specialized reagents that undergo addition reactions with alkenes.

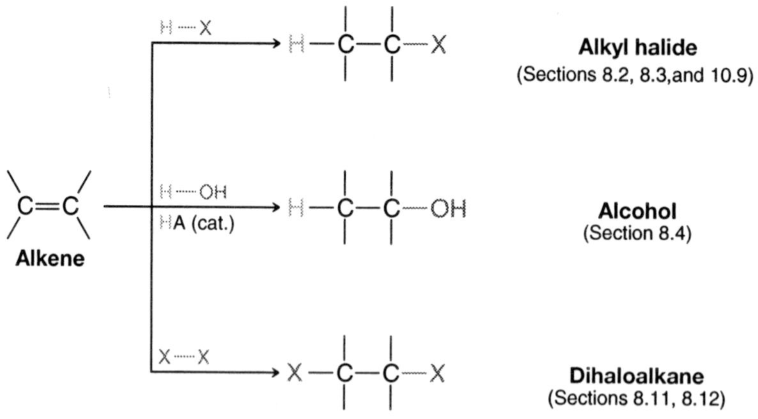

Alkyl halide
(Sections 8.2, 8.3, and 10.9)

Alcohol
(Section 8.4)

Dihaloalkane
(Sections 8.11, 8.12)

8.1A HOW TO Understand Additions to Alkenes

Two characteristics of the double bond help us understand why these addition reactions occur:

1. An addition reaction results in the conversion of one π bond and one σ bond (Sections 1.12 and 1.13) into two σ bonds. The result of this change is usually energetically favorable. The energy released in making two σ bonds exceeds that needed to break

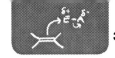

one σ bond and one π bond (because π bonds are weaker), and, therefore, addition reactions are usually exothermic:

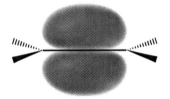

Bonds broken   Bonds formed

2. The electrons of the π bond are exposed. Because the π bond results from overlapping p orbitals, the π electrons lie above and below the plane of the double bond:

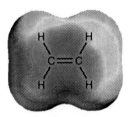

An electrostatic potential map for ethene shows the higher density of negative charge in the region of the π bond.

The electron pair of the π bond is distributed throughout both lobes of the π molecular orbital.

Electrophilic Addition

* Electrons in the π bond of alkenes react with electrophiles.

* **Electrophiles** are electron-seeking reagents. They have the property of being **electrophilic**.

Electrophiles include proton donors such as Brønsted–Lowry acids, neutral reagents such as bromine (because it can be polarized so that one end is positive), and Lewis acids such as BH_3, BF_3, and $AlCl_3$. Metal ions that contain vacant orbitals—the silver ion (Ag^+), the mercuric ion (Hg^{2+}), and the platinum ion (Pt^{2+}), for example—also act as electrophiles.

Hydrogen halides, for example, react with alkenes by accepting a pair of electrons from the π bond to form a σ bond between the hydrogen and one of the carbon atoms, with loss of the halide ion. This leaves a vacant p orbital and a + charge on the other carbon. The overall result is the formation of a carbocation and a halide ion from the alkene and HX:

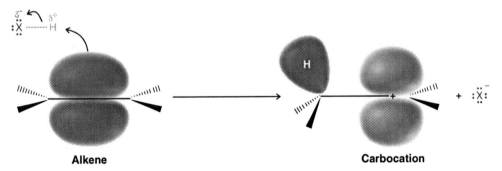

Alkene   **Carbocation**

Being highly reactive, the carbocation may then combine with the halide ion by accepting one of its electron pairs:

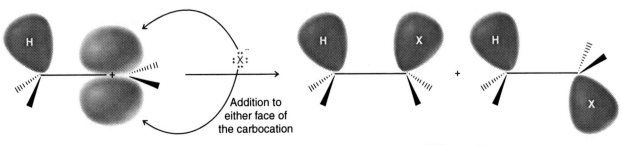

Carbocation   **Addition products**

Electrophiles Are Lewis Acids Electrophiles are molecules or ions that can accept an electron pair. Nucleophiles are molecules or ions that can furnish an electron pair (i.e., Lewis bases). Any reaction of an electrophile also involves a nucleophile. In the protonation of an alkene the electrophile is the proton donated by an acid; the nucleophile is the alkene:

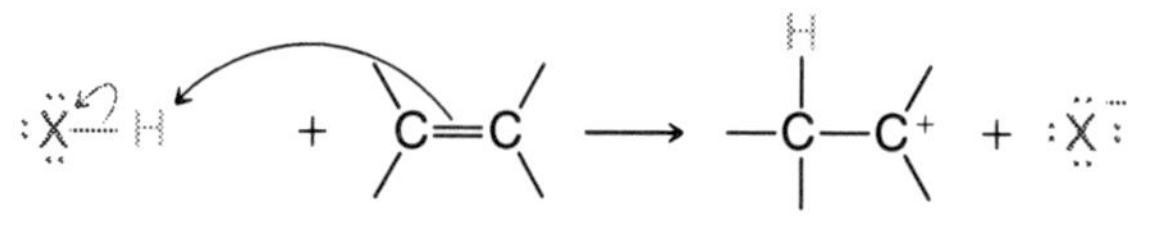

Electrophile   Nucleophile

In the next step, the reaction of the carbocation with a halide ion, the carbocation is the electrophile and the halide ion is the nucleophile:

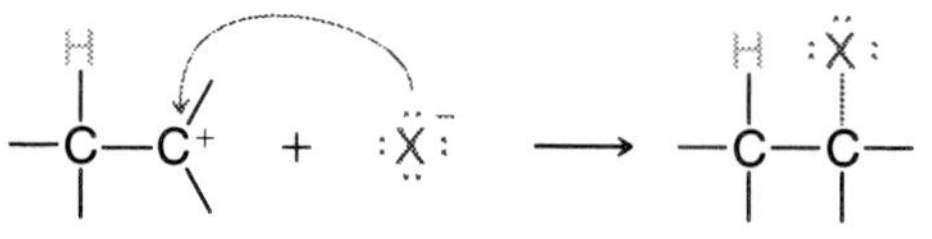

Electrophile   Nucleophile

8.2 ELECTROPHILIC ADDITION OF HYDROGEN HALIDES TO ALKENES: MECHANISM AND MARKOVNIKOV'S RULE

Hydrogen halides (HI, HBr, HCl, and HF) add to the double bond of alkenes:

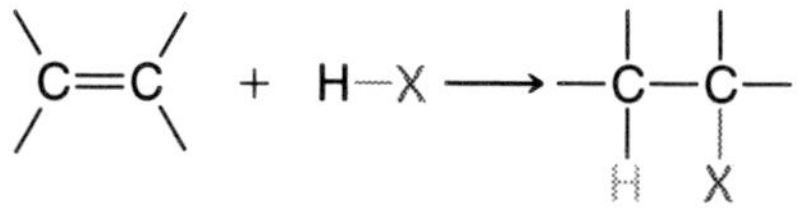

These additions are sometimes carried out by dissolving the hydrogen halide in a solvent, such as acetic acid or CH_2Cl_2, or by bubbling the gaseous hydrogen halide directly into the alkene and using the alkene itself as the solvent. HF is prepared as polyhydrogen fluoride in pyridine.

● The order of reactivity of the hydrogen halides in alkene addition is

$$HI > HBr > HCl > HF$$

Unless the alkene is highly substituted, HCl reacts so slowly that the reaction is not one that is useful as a preparative method. HBr adds readily, but as we shall learn in Section 10.9, unless precautions are taken, the reaction may follow an alternate course.

The addition of HX to an unsymmetrical alkene could conceivably occur in two ways. In practice, however, one product usually predominates. The addition of HBr to propene, for example, could conceivably lead to either 1-bromopropane or 2-bromopropane. The main product, however, is 2-bromopropane:

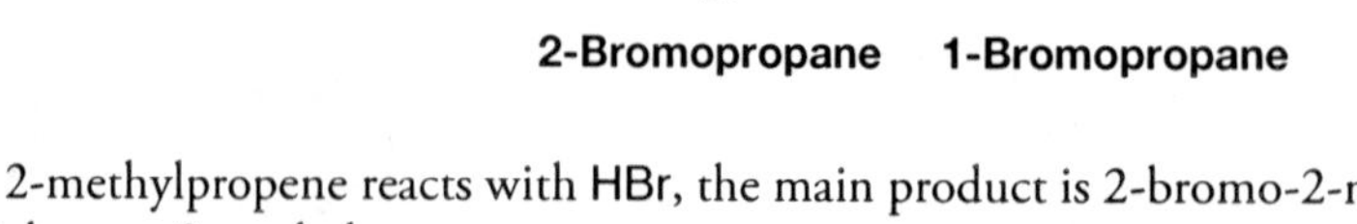

2-Bromopropane   1-Bromopropane

When 2-methylpropene reacts with HBr, the main product is 2-bromo-2-methylpropane, not 1-bromo-2-methylpropane:

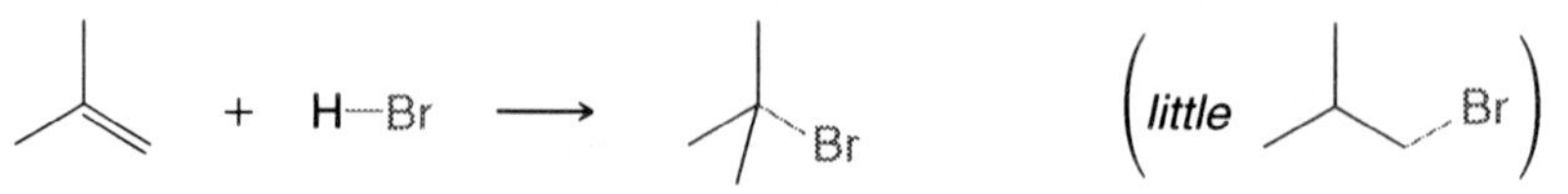

2-Methylpropene   2-Bromo-2-methylpropane   1-Bromo-2-methylpropane

Consideration of many examples like this led the Russian chemist Vladimir Markovnikov in 1870 to formulate what is now known as Markovnikov's rule.

- One way to state **Markovnikov's rule** is to say that *in the addition of HX to an alkene, the hydrogen atom adds to the carbon atom of the double bond that already has the greater number of hydrogen atoms.*[*]

The addition of HBr to propene is an illustration:

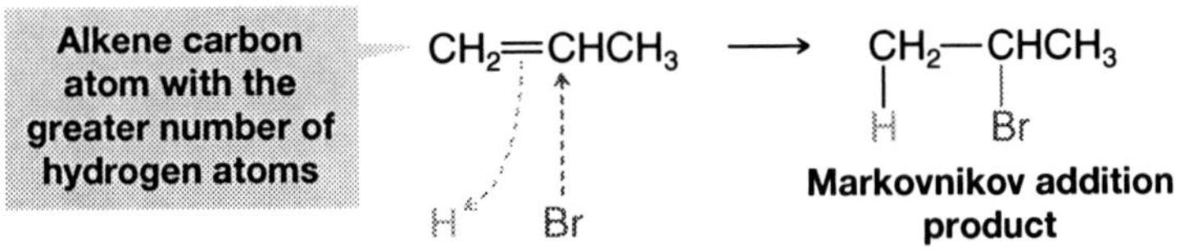

> **Alkene carbon atom with the greater number of hydrogen atoms**
>
> $CH_2=CHCH_3 \longrightarrow CH_2-CHCH_3$
> $\quad\quad\quad\quad | \quad\quad |$
> $\quad\quad\quad\quad H \quad\quad Br$
> $H \quad Br$
>
> **Markovnikov addition product**

Reactions that illustrate Markovnikov's rule are said to be *Markovnikov additions*.

A mechanism for addition of a hydrogen halide to an alkene involves the following two steps:

[A MECHANISM FOR THE REACTION — Addition of a Hydrogen Halide to an Alkene]

Step 1

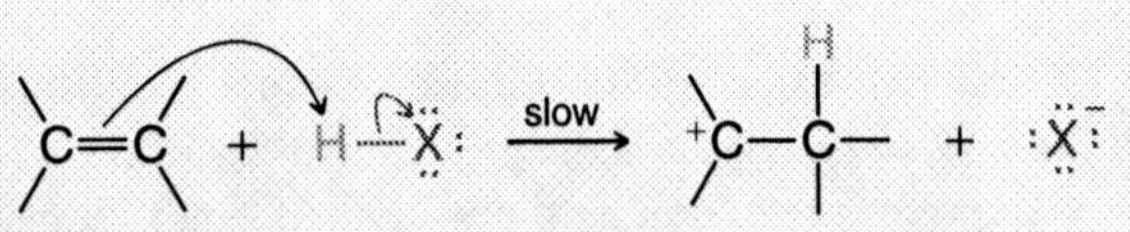

$$\text{C=C} + H-\ddot{X}: \xrightarrow{\text{slow}} {}^+\text{C}-\text{C}- + :\ddot{X}:^-$$

The π electrons of the alkene form a bond with a proton from HX to form a carbocation and a halide ion.

Step 2

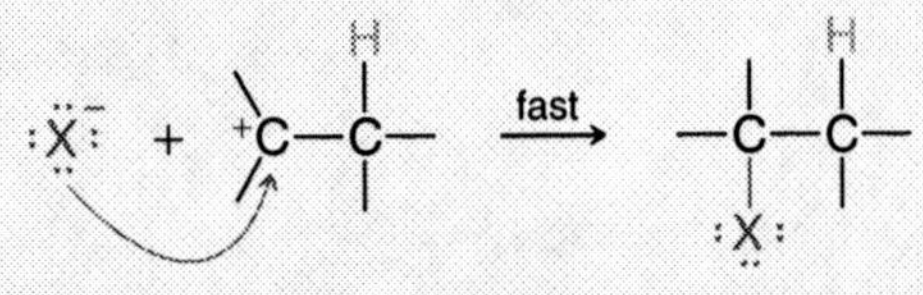

$$:\ddot{X}:^- + {}^+\text{C}-\text{C}- \xrightarrow{\text{fast}} -\text{C}-\text{C}-$$

The halide ion reacts with the carbocation by donating an electron pair; the result is an alkyl halide.

The important step—because it is the **rate-determining step**—is step 1. In step 1 the alkene donates a pair of electrons to the proton of the hydrogen halide and forms a carbocation. This step (Fig. 8.1) is highly endergonic and has a high free energy of activation. Consequently, it takes place slowly. In step 2 the highly reactive carbocation stabilizes itself by combining with a halide ion. This exergonic step has a very low free energy of activation and takes place very rapidly.

8.2A Theoretical Explanation of Markovnikov's Rule

If the alkene that undergoes addition of a hydrogen halide is an unsymmetrical alkene such as propene, then step 1 could conceivably lead to two different carbocations:

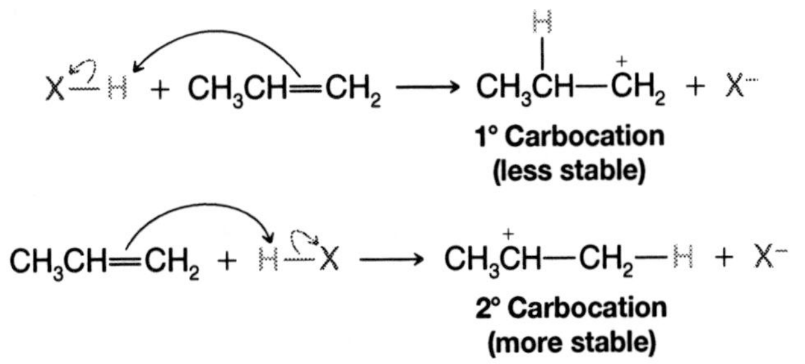

$$X-H + CH_3CH=CH_2 \longrightarrow CH_3CH-{}^+CH_2 + X^-$$

1° Carbocation (less stable)

$$CH_3CH=CH_2 + H-X \longrightarrow CH_3\overset{+}{CH}-CH_2-H + X^-$$

2° Carbocation (more stable)

---

[*]In his original publication, Markovnikov described the rule in terms of the point of attachment of the halogen atom, stating that "if an unsymmetrical alkene combines with a hydrogen halide, the halide ion adds to the carbon atom with the fewer hydrogen atoms."

FIGURE 8.1 Free-energy diagram for the addition of **HX** to an alkene. The free energy of activation for step 1 is much larger than that for step 2.

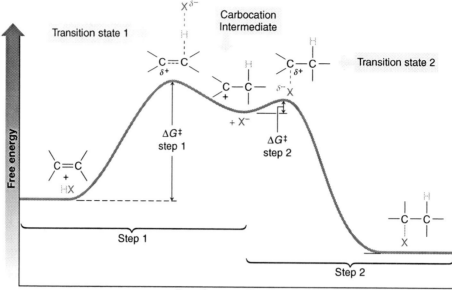

These two carbocations are not of equal stability, however. The secondary carbocation is *more stable*, and it is the greater stability of the secondary carbocation that accounts for the correct prediction of the overall addition by Markovnikov's rule. In the addition of **HBr** to propene, for example, the reaction takes the following course:

These two carbocations are not of equal stability, however. The secondary carbocation is *more stable*, and it is the greater stability of the secondary carbocation that accounts for the correct prediction of the overall addition by Markovnikov's rule. In the addition of **HBr** to propene, for example, the reaction takes the following course:

The chief product of the reaction is 2-bromopropane because the more stable secondary carbocation is formed preferentially in the first step.

- The more stable carbocation predominates because it is formed faster.

We can understand why this is true if we examine the free-energy diagrams in Fig. 8.2.

- The reaction leading to the secondary carbocation (and ultimately to 2-bromopropane) has the lower free energy of activation. This is reasonable because its transition state resembles the more stable carbocation.
- The reaction leading to the primary carbocation (and ultimately to 1-bromopropane) has a higher free energy of activation because its transition state resembles a less stable primary carbocation. This second reaction is much slower and does not compete appreciably with the first reaction.

The reaction of **HBr** with 2-methylpropene produces only 2-bromo-2-methylpropane, for the same reason regarding carbocations stability. Here, in the first step (i.e., the attachment of the proton) the choice is even more pronounced—between a tertiary carbocation and a primary carbocation. Thus, 1-bromo-2-methylpropane is *not* obtained as a product of the reaction because its formation would require the formation of a primary

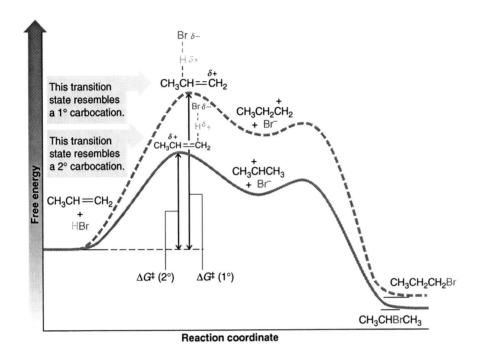

FIGURE 8.2 Free-energy diagrams for the addition of **HBr** to propene. $\Delta G^{\ddagger}(2°)$ is less than $\Delta G^{\ddagger}(1°)$.

carbocation. Such a reaction would have a much higher free energy of activation than that leading to a tertiary carbocation.

- Rearrangements invariably occur when the carbocation initially formed by addition of **HX** to an alkene can rearrange to a more stable one (see Section 7.8 and Practice Problem 8.3).

[A MECHANISM FOR THE REACTION ⎯ Addition of HBr to 2-Methylpropene]

This reaction takes place:

$$\underset{H_3C}{\overset{H_3C}{>}}C=CH_2 \quad H-\ddot{B}r: \longrightarrow \underset{H_3C}{\overset{H_3C}{>}}\overset{+}{C}-CH_2-H \quad :\ddot{B}r: \longrightarrow \underset{:\ddot{B}r:}{\overset{CH_3}{\underset{|}{CH_3-C-CH_3}}} \quad \begin{array}{l}\textbf{Major}\\\textbf{product}\end{array}$$

　　　　　　　　　　　　　　3° Carbocation　　　　　　**2-Bromo-2-methylpropane**
　　　　　　　　　　　(more stable carbocation)

This reaction *does not* occur to any appreciable extent:

$$\underset{H_3C}{\overset{H_3C}{>}}C=CH_2 \quad :\ddot{B}r-H \xrightarrow{\times} \underset{H}{\overset{CH_3}{\underset{|}{CH_3-C-\overset{+}{C}H_2}}} \quad :\ddot{B}r:^- \xrightarrow{\times} \underset{H}{\overset{CH_3}{\underset{|}{CH_3-CH-CH_2-\ddot{B}r:}}} \quad \begin{array}{l}\textbf{Little}\\\textbf{formed}\end{array}$$

　　　　　　　　　　　　　　1° Carbocation　　　　　　**1-Bromo-2-methylpropane**
　　　　　　　　　　　(less stable carbocation)

8.2B General Statement of Markovnikov's Rule

With this understanding of the mechanism for the ionic addition of hydrogen halides to alkenes, we can now generalize about how electrophiles add to alkenes.

- General statement of Markovnikov's rule: In the ionic addition of an unsymmetrical reagent to a double bond, the positive portion of the adding reagent attaches itself to a carbon atom of the double bond so as to yield the more stable carbocation as an intermediate.

• Addition of the electrophile determines the overall orientation of the addition, because it occurs first (before the addition of the nucleophilic portion of the adding reagent).

Notice that this formulation of Markovnikov's rule allows us to predict the outcome of the addition of a reagent such as **ICl**. Because of the greater electronegativity of chlorine, the positive portion of this molecule is iodine. The addition of **ICl** to 2-methylpropene takes place in the following way and produces 2-chloro-1-iodo-2-methylpropane:

2-Methylpropene   **2-Chloro-1-iodo-2-methylpropane**

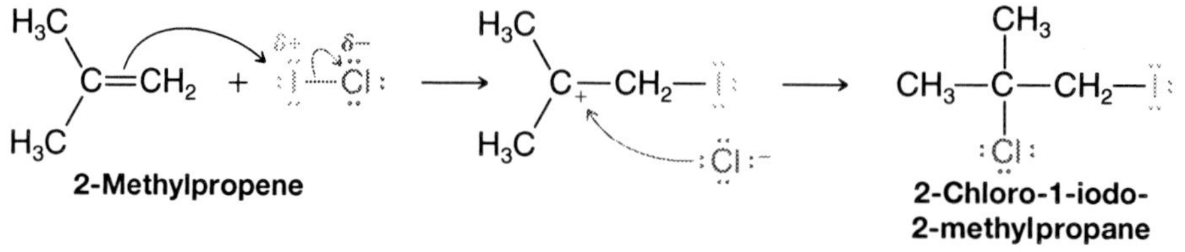

PRACTICE PROBLEM 8.1   Give the structure and name of the product that would be obtained from the ionic addition of **IBr** to propene.

····•◦◦

PRACTICE PROBLEM 8.2   Outline mechanisms for the following addition reactions:

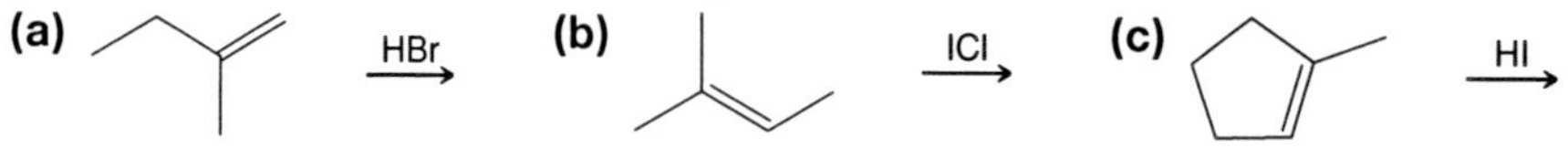

(a) $\xrightarrow{\text{HBr}}$ **(b)** $\xrightarrow{\text{ICl}}$ **(c)** $\xrightarrow{\text{HI}}$

····•◦◦

PRACTICE PROBLEM 8.3   Provide mechanistic explanations for the following observations:

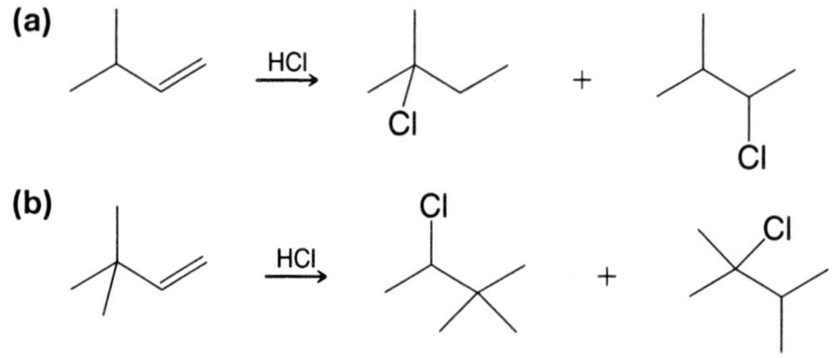

(a)

(b)

8.2C Regioselective Reactions

Chemists describe reactions like the Markovnikov additions of hydrogen halides to alkenes as being **regioselective**. *Regio* comes from the Latin word *regionem* meaning direction.

• When a reaction that can potentially yield two or more constitutional isomers actually produces only one (or a predominance of one), the reaction is said to be a **regioselective reaction**.

The addition of **HX** to an unsymmetrical alkene such as propene could conceivably yield two constitutional isomers, for example. As we have seen, however, the reaction yields only one, and therefore it is regioselective.

8.2D An Exception to Markovnikov's Rule

In Section 10.9 we shall study an exception to Markovnikov's rule. This exception concerns the addition of HBr to alkenes **when the addition is carried out in the presence of peroxides** (i.e., compounds with the general formula ROOR).

- When alkenes are treated with HBr in the presence of peroxides, an anti-Markovnikov addition occurs in the sense that the hydrogen atom becomes attached to the carbon atom with the fewer hydrogen atoms.

With propene, for example, the addition takes place as follows:

$$CH_3CH{=}CH_2 + HBr \xrightarrow{ROOR} CH_3CH_2CH_2Br$$

In Section 10.10 we shall find that this addition occurs by *a radical mechanism*, and not by the ionic mechanism given at the beginning of Section 8.2.

- This anti-Markovnikov addition occurs **only when HBr is used in the presence of peroxides** and does not occur significantly with HF, HCl, and HI even when peroxides are present.

8.3 STEREOCHEMISTRY OF THE IONIC ADDITION TO AN ALKENE

Consider the following addition of HX to 1-butene and notice that the reaction leads to the formation of a 2-halobutane that contains a chirality center:

$$CH_3CH_2CH{=}CH_2 \ + \ HX \longrightarrow CH_3CH_2\overset{*}{C}HCH_3$$
$$\underset{X}{\big|}$$

The product, therefore, can exist as a pair of enantiomers. The question now arises as to how these enantiomers are formed. Is one enantiomer formed in greater amount than the other? The answer is *no*; the carbocation that is formed in the first step of the addition (see the following scheme) is trigonal planar and is **achiral** (a model will show that it has a plane of symmetry). When the halide ion reacts with this achiral carbocation in the second step, **reaction is equally likely at either face.** The reactions leading to the two enantiomers occur at the same rate, and the enantiomers, therefore, are produced in equal amounts **as a racemic mixture.**

[THE STEREOCHEMISTRY OF THE REACTION... — Ionic Addition to an Alkene]

Achiral, trigonal planar carbocation

(S)-2-Halobutane (50%)

(R)-2-Halobutane (50%)

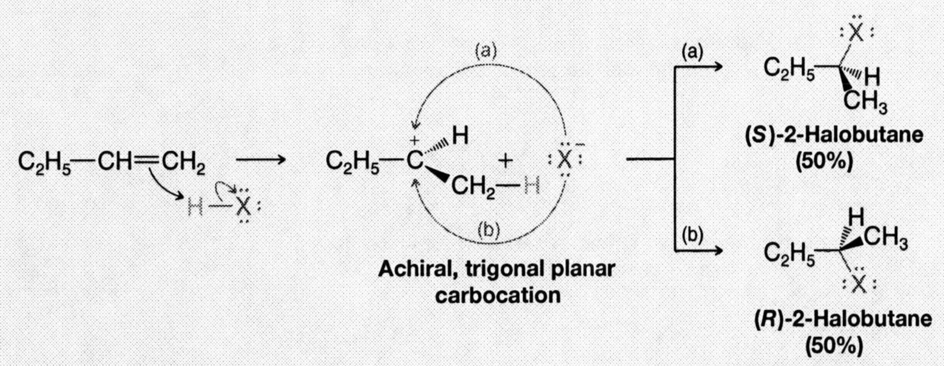

1-Butene donates a pair of electrons to the proton of HX to form an achiral carbocation.

The carbocation reacts with the halide ion at equal rates by path (a) or (b) to form the enantiomers as a racemate.

8.4 ADDITION OF WATER TO ALKENES: ACID-CATALYZED HYDRATION

The acid-catalyzed addition of water to the double bond of an alkene (**hydration** of an alkene) is a method for the preparation of low-molecular-weight alcohols. This reaction has its greatest utility in large-scale industrial processes. The acids most commonly used to catalyze the hydration of alkenes are dilute aqueous solutions of sulfuric acid and phosphoric acid. These reactions, too, are usually regioselective, and the addition of water to the double bond follows Markovnikov's rule. In general, the reaction takes the form that follows:

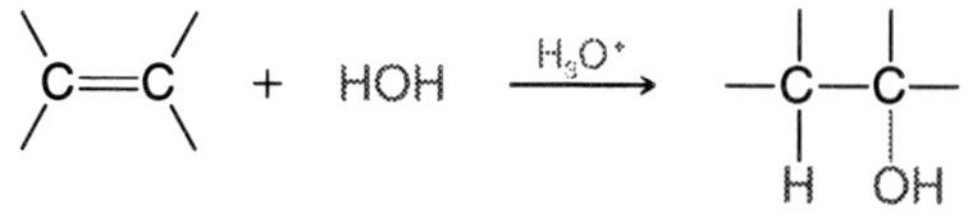

$$\text{C=C} + \text{HOH} \xrightarrow{\text{H}_3\text{O}^+} -\overset{|}{\underset{H}{C}}-\overset{|}{\underset{OH}{C}}-$$

An example is the hydration of 2-methylpropene:

$$\text{+ HOH} \xrightarrow[25\,°C]{\text{H}_3\text{O}^+}$$

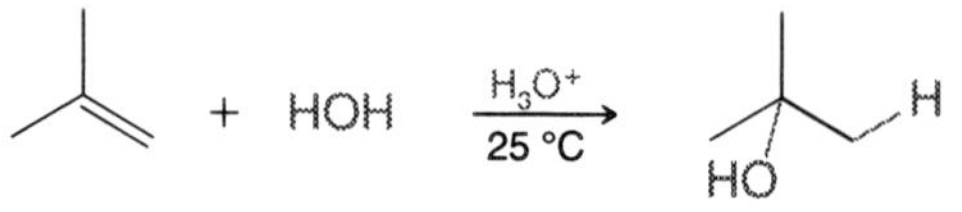

2-Methylpropene
(isobutylene)

2-Methyl-2-propanol
(*tert*-butyl alcohol)

Because the reactions follow Markovnikov's rule, acid-catalyzed hydrations of alkenes do not yield primary alcohols except in the special case of the hydration of ethene:

$$CH_2{=}CH_2 + HOH \xrightarrow[300\,°C]{H_3PO_4} CH_3CH_2OH$$

8.4A Mechanism

The mechanism for the hydration of an alkene is simply the reverse of the mechanism for the dehydration of an alcohol. We can illustrate this by giving the mechanism for the hydration of 2-methylpropene and by comparing it with the mechanism for the **dehydration** of 2-methyl-2-propanol given in Section 7.7A.

[**A MECHANISM FOR THE REACTION** — Acid-Catalyzed Hydration of an Alkene]

Step 1

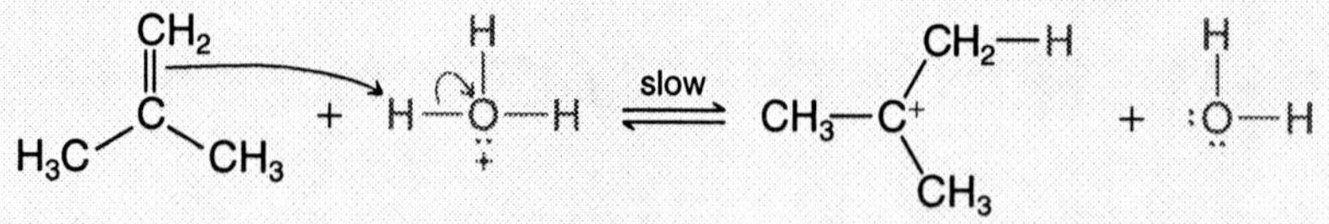

The alkene donates an electron pair to a proton to form the more stable 3° carbocation.

Step 2

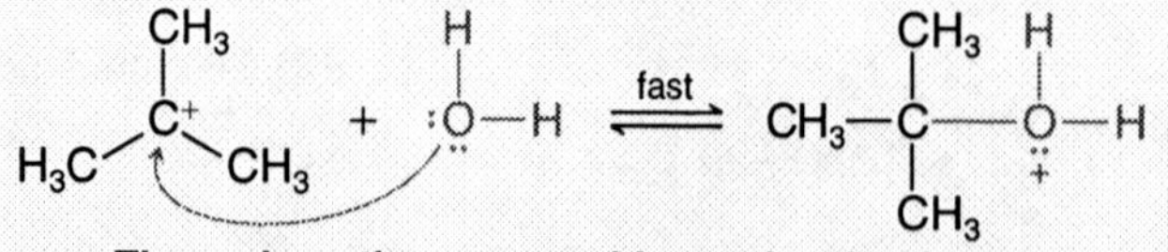

The carbocation reacts with a molecule of water to form a protonated alcohol.

Step 3

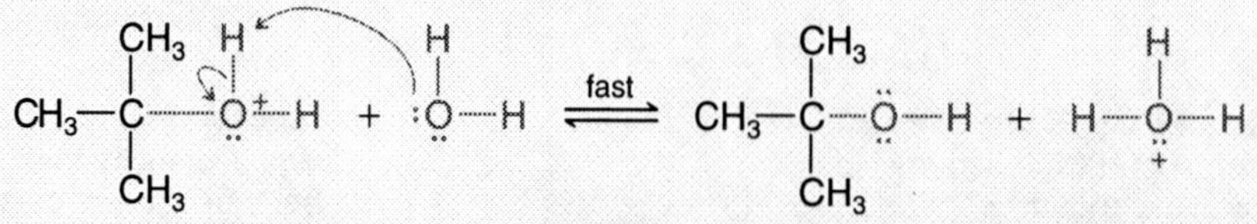

A transfer of a proton to a molecule of water leads to the product.

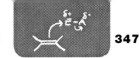

The rate-determining step in the *hydration* mechanism is step 1: the formation of the carbocation. It is this step, too, that accounts for the Markovnikov addition of water to the double bond. The reaction produces 2-methyl-2-propanol because step 1 leads to the formation of the more stable tertiary (3°) cation rather than the much less stable primary (1°) cation:

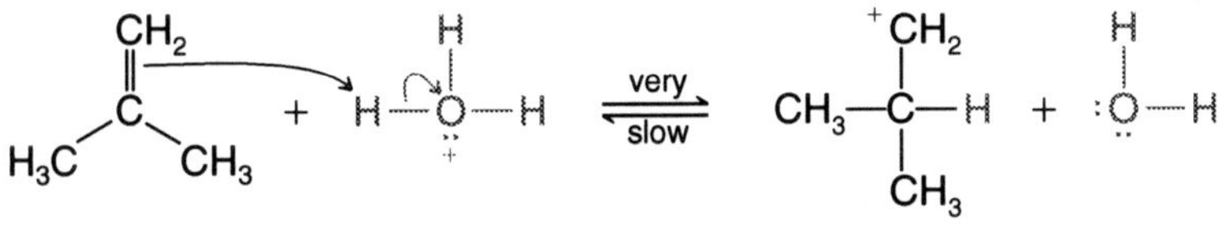

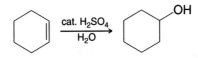

For all practical purposes this reaction does not take place because it produces a 1° carbocation.

The reactions whereby *alkenes are hydrated or alcohols are dehydrated* are reactions in which the ultimate product is governed by the position of an equilibrium. Therefore, in the *dehydration of an alcohol* it is best to use a concentrated acid so that the concentration of water is low. (The water can be removed as it is formed, and it helps to use a high temperature.) In the *hydration of an alkene* it is best to use dilute acid so that the concentration of water is high. It also usually helps to use a lower temperature.

••• SOLVED PROBLEM 8.1

Write a mechanism that explains the following reaction.

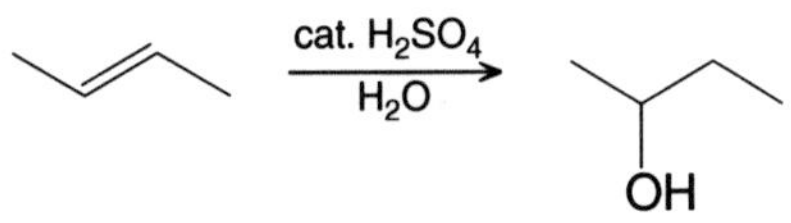

STRATEGY AND ANSWER: We know that a hydronium ion, formed from sulfuric acid and water, can donate a proton to an alkene to form a carbocation. The carbocation can then accept an electon pair from a molecule of water to form a protonated alcohol. The protonated alcohol can donate a proton to water to become an alcohol.

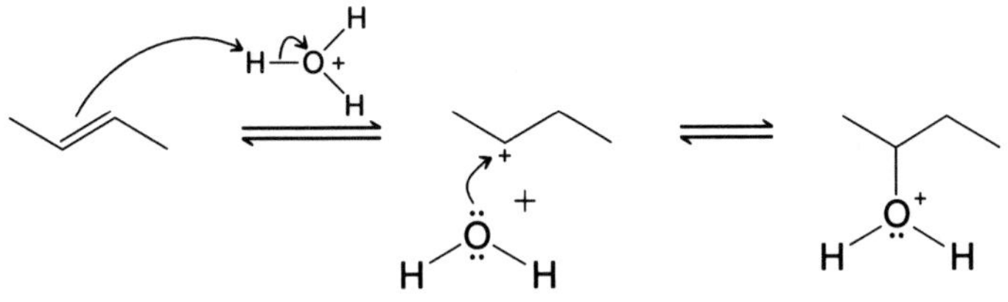

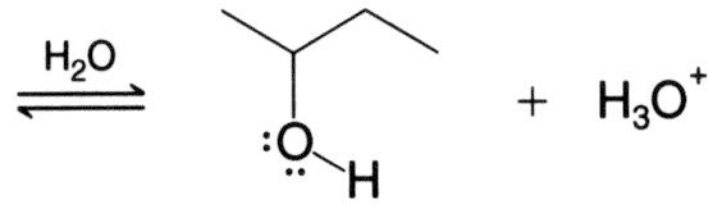

•••

PRACTICE PROBLEM 8.4

(a) Write a mechanism for the following reaction.

(b) What general conditions would you use to ensure a good yield of the product?

(c) What general conditions would you use to carry out the reverse reaction, i.e., the dehydration of cyclohexanol to produce cyclohexene?

(d) What product would you expect to obtain from the acid-catalyzed hydration of 1-methylcyclohexene? Explain your answer.

PRACTICE PROBLEM 8.5   In one industrial synthesis of ethanol, ethene is first dissolved in 95% sulfuric acid. In a second step water is added and the mixture is heated. Outline the reactions involved.

8.4B Rearrangements

• One complication associated with alkene hydrations is the occurrence of **rearrangements**.

Because the reaction involves the formation of a carbocation in the first step, the carbocation formed initially invariably rearranges to a more stable one (or possibly to an isoenergetic one) if such a rearrangement is possible. An illustration is the formation of 2,3-dimethyl-2-butanol as the major product when 3,3-dimethyl-1-butene is hydrated:

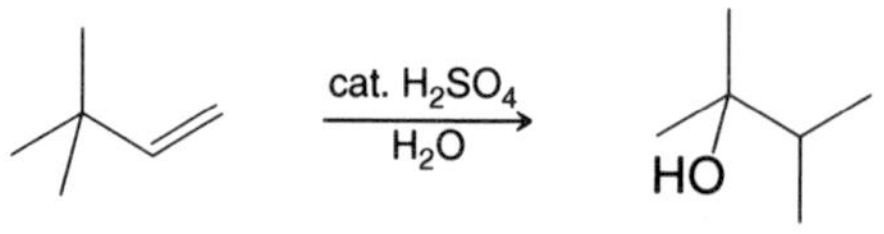

3,3-Dimethyl-1-butene   **2,3-Dimethyl-2-butanol**
                                    (major product)

PRACTICE PROBLEM 8.6   Outline all steps in a mechanism showing how 2,3-dimethyl-2-butanol is formed in the acid-catalyzed hydration of 3,3-dimethyl-1-butene.

PRACTICE PROBLEM 8.7   The following order of reactivity is observed when the following alkenes are subjected to acid-catalyzed hydration:

$$(CH_3)_2C{=}CH_2 > CH_3CH{=}CH_2 > CH_2{=}CH_2$$

Explain this order of reactivity.

PRACTICE PROBLEM 8.8   Write a mechanism for the following reaction.

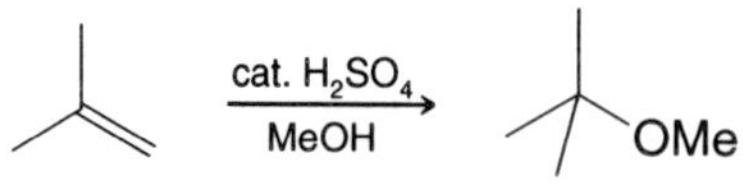

••• SOLVED PROBLEM 8.2

Write a mechanism that will explain the course of the following reaction

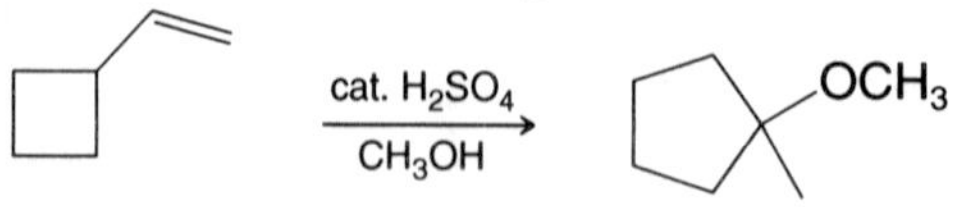

STRATEGY AND ANSWER: As we have learned, in a strongly acidic medium such as methanol containing catalytic sulfuric acid, an alkene can accept a proton to become a carbocation. In the reaction above, the 2° carbocation formed initially can undergo an alkanide shift and a hydride shift as shown below to become a 3° carbocation, which can then react with the solvent (methanol) to form an ether.

The reaction scheme showing the protonation of methanol by sulfuric acid and subsequent carbocation rearrangements:

H—Ö—CH₃ + H—ÖSO₃H ⇌ H—Ö⁺—CH₃ + ⁻ÖSO₃H

(with H above the central oxygen)

Reaction steps showing methylenecyclobutane with protonated methanol, alkanide shift, and hydride shift leading to cyclopentyl cations, followed by CH₃OH addition and demercuration steps yielding the ether product plus CH₃ÖH₂⁺.

8.5 ALCOHOLS FROM ALKENES THROUGH OXYMERCURATION–DEMERCURATION: MARKOVNIKOV ADDITION

A useful laboratory procedure for synthesizing alcohols from alkenes that avoids rearrangement is a two-step method called **oxymercuration–demercuration.**

- Alkenes react with mercuric acetate in a mixture of tetrahydrofuran (THF) and water to produce (hydroxyalkyl)mercury compounds. These (hydroxyalkyl) mercury compounds can be reduced to alcohols with sodium borohydride.

Step 1: Oxymercuration

$$\begin{array}{c} \diagdown \\ C=C \\ \diagup \end{array} + H_2O + Hg\left(\underset{O}{\overset{O}{\underset{\|}{OCCH_3}}}\right)_2 \xrightarrow{\text{THF}} \underset{\underset{HO}{|}}{-C} \underset{\underset{Hg-OCCH_3}{|}}{-C} -O + CH_3\overset{O}{\overset{\|}{C}}OH$$

Step 2: Demercuration

$$\underset{\underset{HO}{|}}{-C}\underset{\underset{Hg-OCCH_3}{|}}{-C}-O + HO^- + NaBH_4 \longrightarrow \underset{\underset{HO}{|}}{-C}\underset{\underset{H}{|}}{-C}- + Hg + CH_3\overset{O}{\overset{\|}{C}}O^-$$

- In the first step, **oxymercuration,** water and mercuric acetate add to the double bond.
- In the second step, **demercuration,** sodium borohydride reduces the acetoxymercury group and replaces it with hydrogen. (The acetate group is often abbreviated —OAc.)

Both steps can be carried out in the same vessel, and both reactions take place very rapidly at room temperature or below. The first step—oxymercuration—usually goes to completion within a period of seconds to minutes. The second step—demercuration—normally requires less than an hour. The overall reaction gives alcohols in very high yields, usually greater than 90%.

8.5A Regioselectivity of Oxymercuration–Demercuration

Oxymercuration–demercuration is also highly regioselective.

- In oxymercuration–demercuration, the net orientation of the addition of the elements of water, H— and —OH, *is in accordance with Markovnikov's rule.* The H— becomes attached to the carbon atom of the double bond with the greater number of hydrogen atoms.

Mercury compounds are extremely hazardous. Before you carry out a reaction involving mercury or its compounds, you should familiarize yourself with current procedures for its use and containment. There are no satisfactory methods for disposal of mercury.

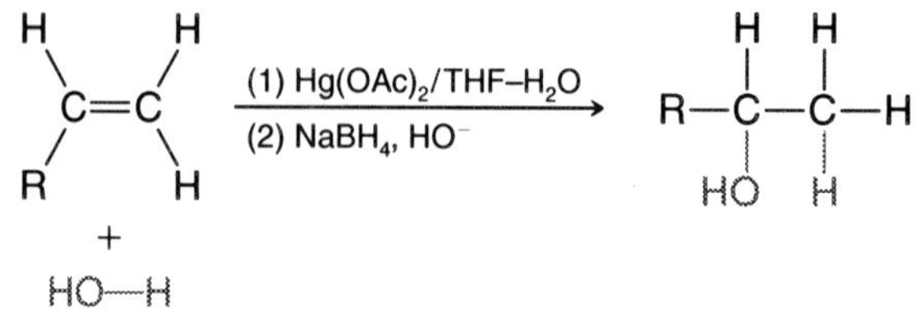

$$H_2C=CH-R + HO-H \xrightarrow[\text{(2) NaBH}_4,\ \text{HO}^-]{\text{(1) Hg(OAc)}_2/\text{THF–H}_2\text{O}} R-CH(OH)-CH_3$$

The following are specific examples:

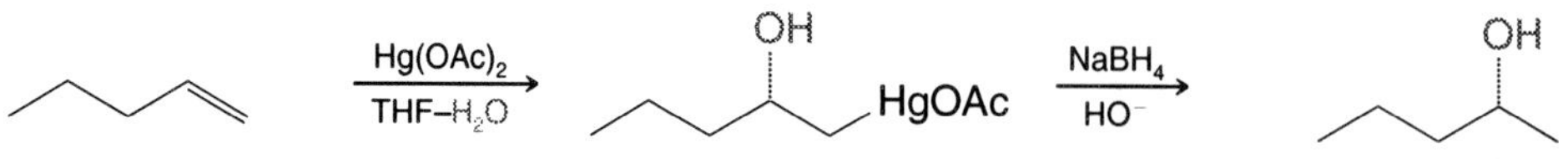

1-Pentene $\xrightarrow[\text{THF–H}_2\text{O}]{\text{Hg(OAc)}_2}$ (2-hydroxy-HgOAc) $\xrightarrow[\text{HO}^-]{\text{NaBH}_4}$ 2-Pentanol (93%)

1-Pentene ... **2-Pentanol (93%)**

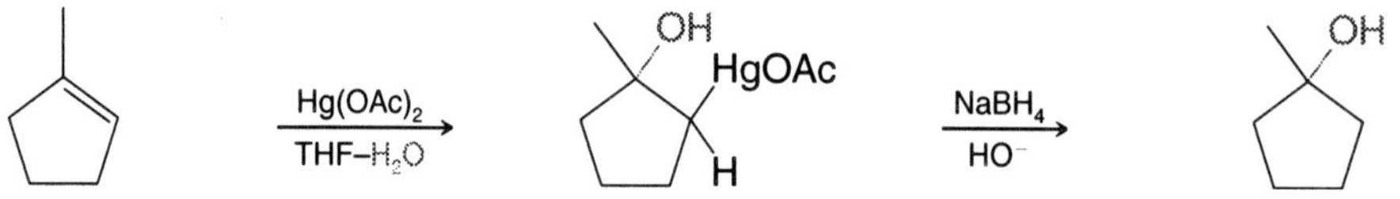

1-Methylcyclopentene $\xrightarrow[\text{THF–H}_2\text{O}]{\text{Hg(OAc)}_2}$ (intermediate) $\xrightarrow[\text{HO}^-]{\text{NaBH}_4}$ **1-Methylcyclopentanol**

8.5B Rearrangements Seldom Occur in Oxymercuration–Demercuration

* Rearrangements of the carbon skeleton seldom occur in oxymercuration–demercuration.

The oxymercuration–demercuration of 3,3-dimethyl-1-butene is a striking example illustrating this feature. It is in direct contrast to the hydration of 3,3-dimethyl-1-butene we studied previously (Section 8.4B).

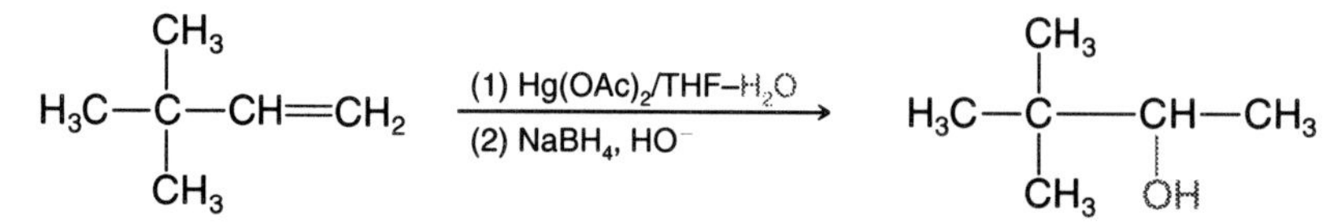

$$H_3C-C(CH_3)(CH_3)-CH=CH_2 \xrightarrow[\text{(2) NaBH}_4,\ \text{HO}^-]{\text{(1) Hg(OAc)}_2/\text{THF–H}_2\text{O}} H_3C-C(CH_3)(CH_3)-CH(OH)-CH_3$$

3,3-Dimethyl-1-butene → **3,3-Dimethyl-2-butanol (94%)**

Analysis of the mixture of products by gas chromatography failed to reveal the presence of any 2,3-dimethyl-2-butanol. The acid-catalyzed hydration of 3,3-dimethyl-1-butene, by contrast, gives 2,3-dimethyl-2-butanol as the major product.

8.5C Mechanism of Oxymercuration

A mechanism that accounts for the orientation of addition in the oxymercuration stage, and one that also explains the general lack of accompanying rearrangements, is shown below.

* Central to this mechanism is an electrophilic attack by the mercury species, $\overset{+}{H}gOAc$, at the less substituted carbon of the double bond (i.e., at the carbon atom that bears the greater number of hydrogen atoms), and the formation of a bridged intermediate.

We illustrate the mechanism using 3,3-dimethyl-1-butene as the example:

[A MECHANISM FOR THE REACTION   Oxymercuration]

Step 1

$$Hg(OAc)_2 \rightleftharpoons \overset{+}{H}gOAc + AcO^-$$

Mercuric acetate dissociates to form a $\overset{+}{H}gOAc$ cation and an acetate anion.

Step 2

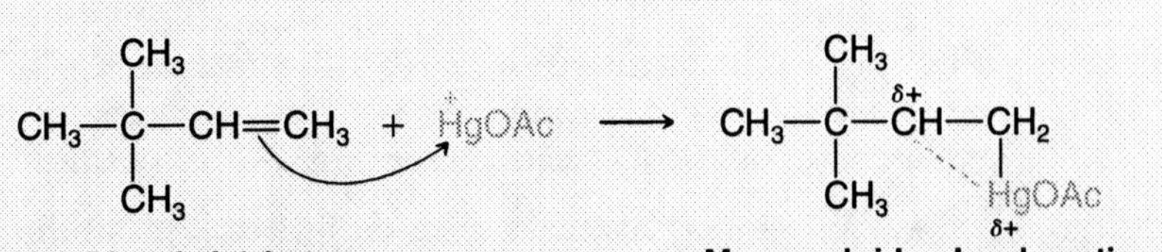

3,3-Dimethyl-1-butene   **Mercury-bridged carbocation**

The alkene donates a pair of electrons to the electrophilic $\overset{+}{H}gOAc$ cation to form a mercury-bridged carbocation. In this carbocation, the positive charge is shared between the 2° (more substituted) carbon atom and the mercury atom. The charge on the carbon atom is large enough to account for the Markovnikov orientation of the addition, but not large enough for a rearrangement to occur.

Step 3

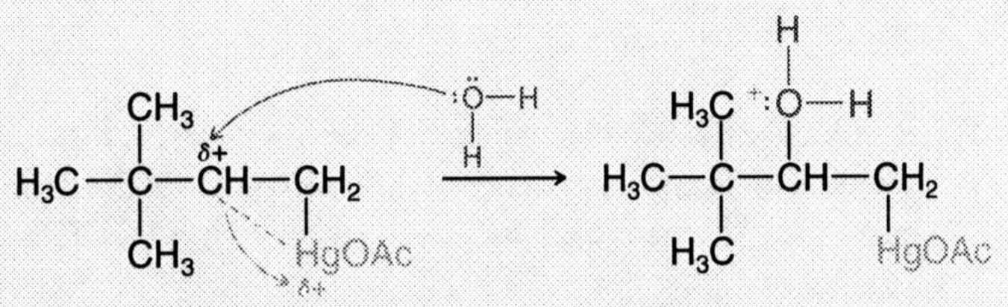

A water molecule attacks the carbon of the bridged mercurinium ion that is better able to bear the partial positive charge.

Step 4

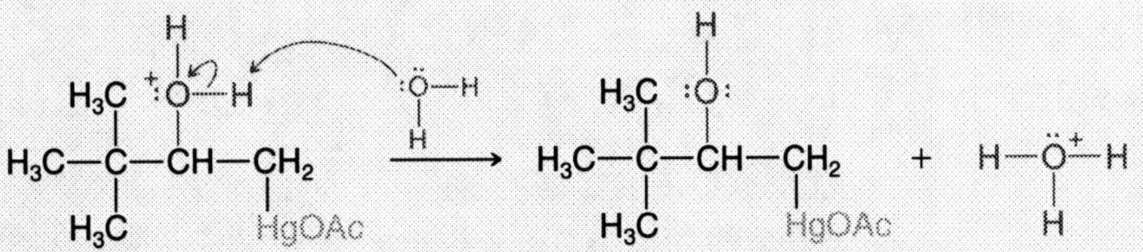

(Hydroxyalkyl)mercury compound

An acid–base reaction transfers a proton to another water molecule (or to an acetate ion). This step produces the (hydroxyalkyl)mercury compound.

Calculations indicate that mercury-bridged carbocations (termed mercurinium ions) such as those formed in this reaction retain much of the positive charge on the mercury moiety. Only a small portion of the positive charge resides on the more substituted carbon atom. The charge is large enough to account for the observed Markovnikov addition, but it is too small to allow the usual rapid carbon skeleton rearrangements that take place with more fully developed carbocations.

Although attack by water on the bridged mercurinium ion leads to anti addition of the hydroxyl and mercury groups, the reaction that replaces mercury with hydrogen is not stereocontrolled (it likely involves radicals; see Chapter 10). This step scrambles the overall stereochemistry.

- The net result of oxymercuration–demercuration is a mixture of syn and anti addition of —H and —OH to the alkene.

- As already noted, oxymercuration–demercuration takes place with Markovnikov regiochemistry.

PRACTICE PROBLEM 8.9 Write the structure of the appropriate alkene and specify the reagents needed for synthesis of the following alcohols by oxymercuration–demercuration:

(a) [structure: OH] **(b)** [structure: OH] **(c)** [structure: OH]

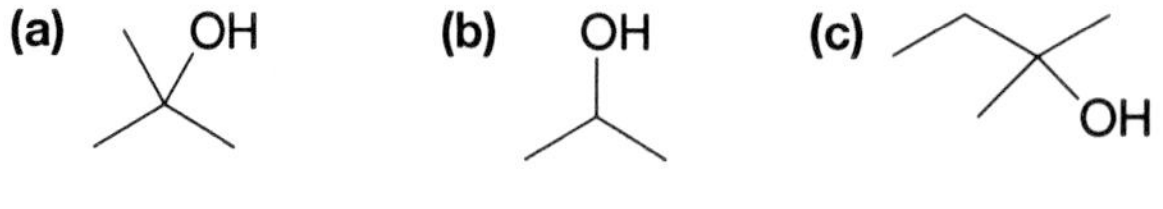

When an alkene is treated with mercuric trifluoroacetate, $Hg(O_2CCF_3)_2$, in THF containing an alcohol, ROH, the product is an (alkoxyalkyl)mercury compound. Treating this product with $NaBH_4/HO^-$ results in the formation of an ether.

● When a solvent molecule acts as the nucleophile in the oxymercuration step the overall process is called *solvomercuration–demercuration*:

| Alkene | (Alkoxyalkyl)mercuric trifluoroacetate | Ether |

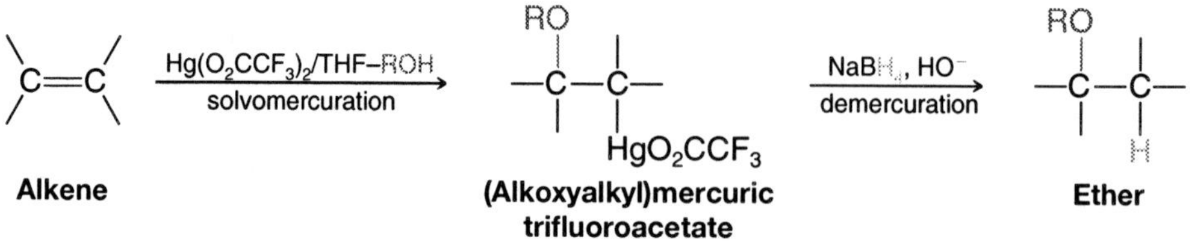

PRACTICE PROBLEM 8.10 **(a)** Outline a likely mechanism for the solvomercuration step of the ether synthesis just shown. **(b)** Show how you would use solvomercuration–demercuration to prepare *tert*-butyl methyl ether. **(c)** Why would one use $Hg(O_2CCF_3)_2$ instead of $Hg(OAc)_2$?

8.6 ALCOHOLS FROM ALKENES THROUGH HYDROBORATION–OXIDATION: ANTI-MARKOVNIKOV SYN HYDRATION

● **Anti-Markovnikov hydration** of a double bond can be achieved through the use of diborane (B_2H_6) or a solution of borane in tetrahydrofuran (BH_3:THF).

The addition of water is indirect in this process, and two reactions are involved. The first is the addition of a boron atom and hydrogen atom to the double bond, called **hydroboration**; the second is **oxidation** and hydrolysis of the alkylborane intermediate to an alcohol and boric acid. The anti-Markovnikov regiochemistry of the addition is illustrated by the hydroboration–oxidation of propene:

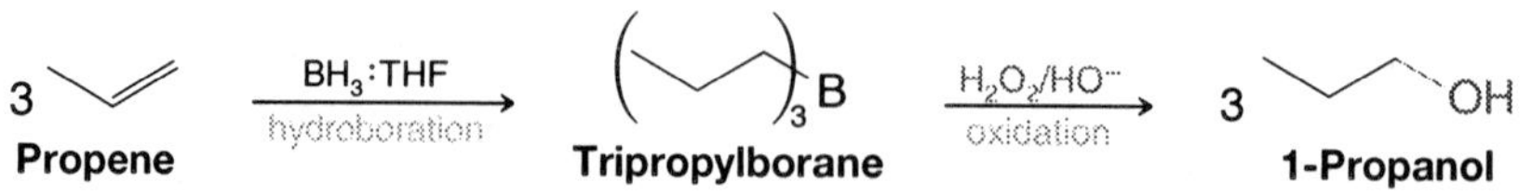

● Hydroboration–oxidation takes place with **syn** stereochemistry, as well as anti-Markovnikov regiochemistry.

This can be seen in the following example with 1-methylcyclopentene:

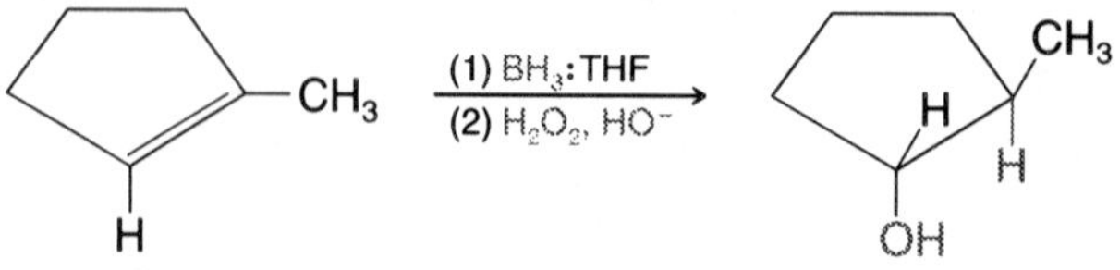

In the following sections we shall consider details of the mechanism that lead to the anti-Markovnikov regiochemistry and syn stereochemistry of hydroboration–oxidation.

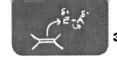

8.7 HYDROBORATION: SYNTHESIS OF ALKYLBORANES

Hydroboration of an alkene is the starting point for a number of useful synthetic procedures, including the anti-Markovnikov syn **hydration** procedure we have just mentioned. Hydroboration was discovered by Herbert C. Brown (Purdue University), and it can be represented in its simplest terms as follows:

BROWN's discovery of hydroboration led to his being named a co-winner of the 1979 Nobel Prize in Chemistry.

Alkene **Boron hydride** **Alkylborane**

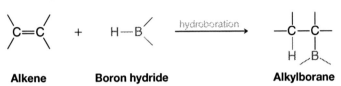

Hydroboration can be accomplished with diborane (B_2H_6), which is a gaseous dimer of borane (BH_3), or more conveniently with a reagent prepared by dissolving diborane in THF. When diborane is introduced to THF, it reacts to form a Lewis acid–base complex of borane (the Lewis acid) and THF. The complex is represented as BH_3:THF.

Diborane **THF (tetrahydrofuran)** **BH_3:THF**

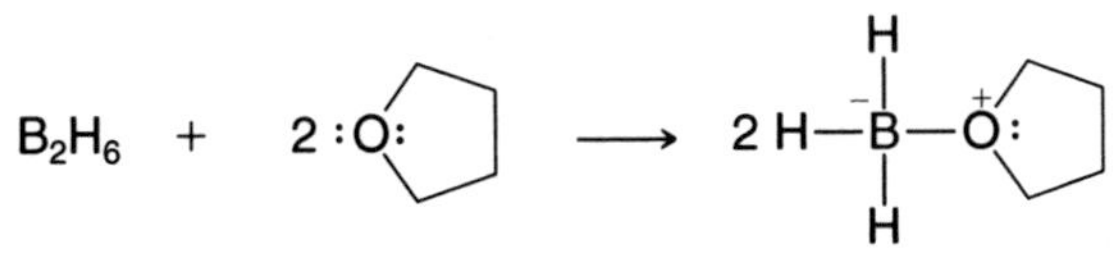

Solutions containing the BH_3:THF complex can be obtained commercially. Hydroboration reactions are usually carried out in ethers: either in diethyl ether, $(CH_3CH_2)_2O$, or in some higher molecular weight ether such as "diglyme" [$(CH_3OCH_2CH_2)_2O$, *di*ethylene *gly*col di*me*thyl ether]. Great care must be used in handling diborane and alkylboranes because they ignite spontaneously in air (with a green flame). The solution of BH_3:THF must be used in an inert atmosphere (e.g., argon or nitrogen) and with care.

8.7A Mechanism of Hydroboration

When a terminal alkene such as propene is treated with a solution containing BH_3:THF, the boron hydride adds successively to the double bonds of three molecules of the alkene to form a trialkylborane:

Tripropylborane

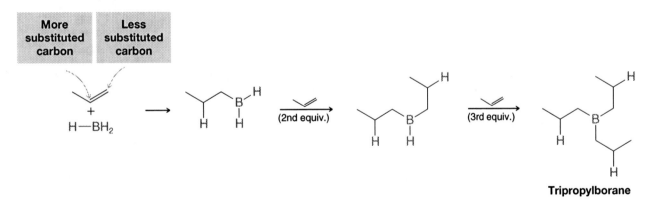

- In each addition step ***the boron atom becomes attached to the less substituted carbon atom of the double bond***, and a hydrogen atom is transferred from the boron atom to the other carbon atom of the double bond.
- Hydroboration is **regioselective** and it is **anti-Markovnikov** (the hydrogen atom becomes attached to the carbon atom with fewer hydrogen atoms).

Other examples that illustrate the tendency for the boron atom to become attached to the less substituted carbon atom are shown here. The percentages designate where the boron atom becomes attached.

These percentages, indicating where boron becomes attached in reactions using these starting materials, illustrate the tendency for boron to bond at the less substituted carbon of the double bond.

This observed attachment of boron to the less substituted carbon atom of the double bond seems to result in part from **steric factors**—the bulky boron-containing group can approach the less substituted carbon atom more easily.

In the mechanism proposed for hydroboration, addition of BH_3 to the double bond begins with a donation of π electrons from the double bond to the vacant p orbital of BH_3 (see the following mechanism). In the next step this complex becomes the addition product by passing through a four-atom transition state in which the boron atom is partially bonded to the less substituted carbon atom of the double bond and one hydrogen atom is partially bonded to the other carbon atom. As this transition state is approached, electrons shift in the direction of the boron atom and away from the more substituted carbon atom of the double bond. This makes the more substituted carbon atom develop a partial positive charge, *and because it bears an electron-releasing alkyl group, it is better able to accommodate this positive charge.* Thus, electronic factors also favor addition of boron at the least substituted carbon.

- Overall, both *electronic* and *steric factors* account for the anti-Markovnikov orientation of the addition.

[A MECHANISM FOR THE REACTION · Hydroboration]

Hydroboration

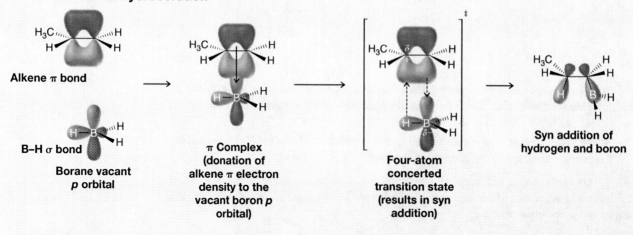

Addition takes place through the initial formation of a π complex, which changes into a cyclic four-atom transition state with the boron adding to the less hindered carbon atom. The dashed bonds in the transition state represent bonds that are partially formed or partially broken. The transition state results in syn addition of the hydrogen and boron group, leading to an alkylborane. The other B–H bonds of the alkylborane can undergo similar additions, leading finally to a trialkylborane.

An orbital view of hydroboration

8.7B Stereochemistry of Hydroboration

● The transition state for hydroboration requires that the boron atom and the hydrogen atom add to the same face of the double bond:

Stereochemistry of Hydroboration

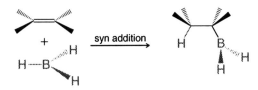

We can see the results of a syn addition in our example involving the hydroboration of 1-methylcyclopentene. Formation of the enantiomer, which is equally likely, results when the boron hydride adds to the top face of the 1-methylcyclopentene ring:

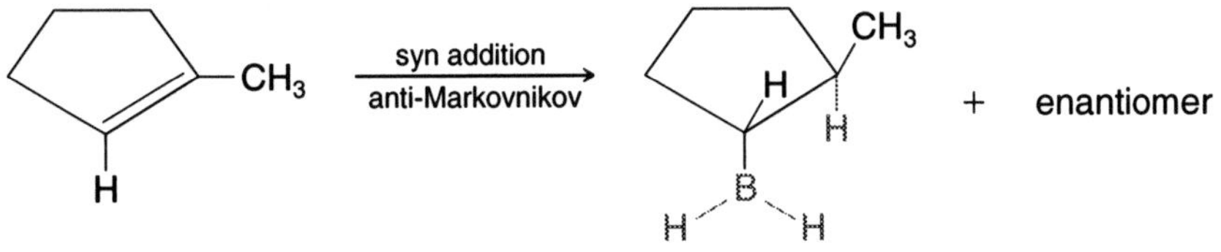

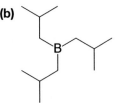

+ enantiomer

● ● ◈ ⋯⋯⋯⋯

PRACTICE PROBLEM 8.11

Specify the alkene needed for synthesis of each of the following alkylboranes by hydroboration:

(a)

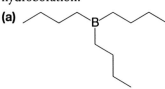

(b)

(c)

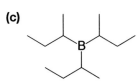

(d) Show the stereochemistry involved in the hydroboration of 1-methylcyclohexene.

● ● ◈ ⋯⋯⋯⋯

PRACTICE PROBLEM 8.12

Treating a hindered alkene such as 2-methyl-2-butene with BH_3:THF leads to the formation of a dialkylborane instead of a trialkylborane. When 2 mol of 2-methyl-2-butene is added to 1 mol of BH_3, the product formed is bis(3-methyl-2-butyl)borane, nicknamed "disiamylborane." Write its structure. Bis(3-methyl-2-butyl)borane is a useful reagent in certain syntheses that require a sterically hindered borane. (The name "disiamyl" comes from "*dis*econdary-*iso-amyl*," a completely unsystematic and unacceptable name. The name "amyl" is an old common name for a five-carbon alkyl group.)

8.8 OXIDATION AND HYDROLYSIS OF ALKYLBORANES

The alkylboranes produced in the hydroboration step are usually not isolated. They are oxidized and hydrolyzed to alcohols in the same reaction vessel by the addition of hydrogen peroxide in an aqueous base:

$$R_3B \xrightarrow[\text{Oxidation and hydrolysis}]{H_2O_2,\ aq.\ NaOH,\ \textbf{25 °C}} 3R\!-\!\!-\!OH + B(ONa)_3$$

* The oxidation and hydrolysis steps take place with retention of configuration at the carbon initially bearing boron and ultimately bearing the hydroxyl group.

We shall see how this occurs by considering the mechanisms of oxidation and hydrolysis.

Alkylborane oxidation begins with addition of a hydroperoxide anion (HOO⁻) to the trivalent boron atom. An unstable intermediate is formed that has a formal negative charge on the boron. Migration of an alkyl group with a pair of electrons from the boron to the adjacent oxygen leads to neutralization of the charge on boron and displacement of a hydroxide anion. The alkyl migration takes place with retention of configuration at the migrating carbon. Repetition of the hydroperoxide anion addition and migration steps occurs twice more until all of the alkyl groups have become attached to oxygen atoms, resulting in a trialkyl borate ester, $B(OR)_3$. The borate ester then undergoes basic hydrolysis to produce three molecules of the alcohol and an inorganic borate anion.

[A MECHANISM FOR THE REACTION — Oxidation of Trialkylboranes]

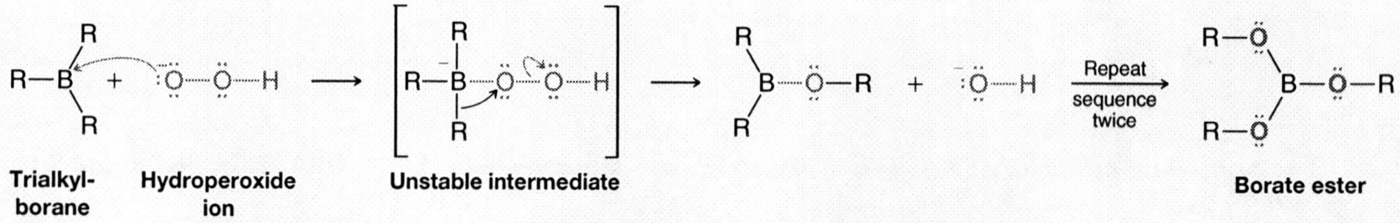

| Trialkyl-borane | Hydroperoxide ion | | Unstable intermediate | | | Borate ester |

The boron atom accepts an electron pair from the hydroperoxide ion to form an unstable intermediate.

An alkyl group migrates from boron to the adjacent oxygen atom as a hydroxide ion departs. The configuration at the migrating carbon remains unchanged.

Hydrolysis of the Borate Ester

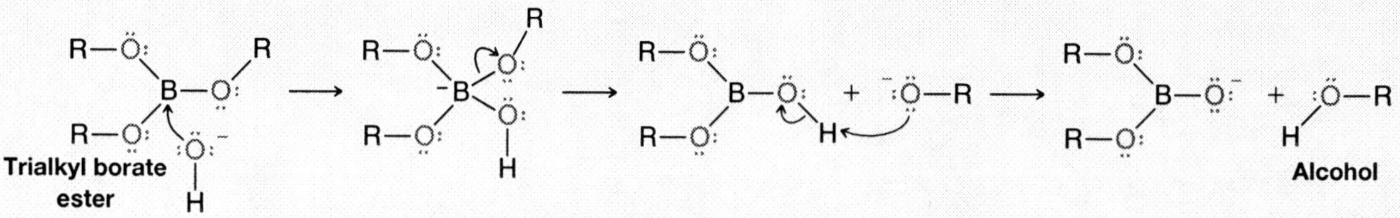

Trialkyl borate ester

Hydroxide anion attacks the boron atom of the borate ester.

An alkoxide anion departs from the borate anion, reducing the formal change on boron to zero.

Proton transfer completes the formation of one alcohol molecule. The sequence repeats until all three alkoxy groups are released as alcohols and inorganic borate remains.

Alcohol

8.8A Regiochemistry and Stereochemistry of Alkylborane Oxidation and Hydrolysis

* Hydroboration–oxidation reactions are **regioselective**; the net result of hydroboration–oxidation is anti-Markovnikov addition of water to an alkene.

* As a consequence, hydroboration–oxidation gives us a method for the preparation of alcohols that cannot normally be obtained through the acid-catalyzed hydration of alkenes or by oxymercuration–demercuration.

For example, the acid-catalyzed hydration (or oxymercuration–demercuration) of 1-hexene yields 2-hexanol, the Markovnikov addition product.

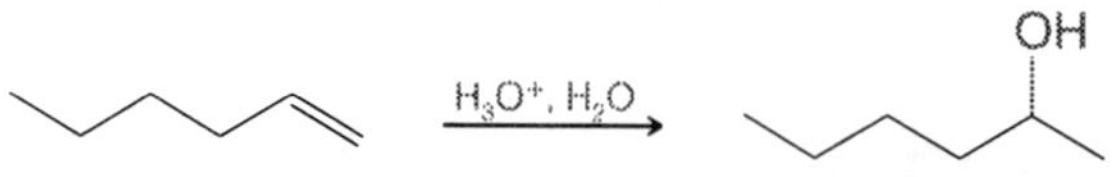

1-Hexene → **2-Hexanol**

Markovnikov addition

In contrast, hydroboration–oxidation of 1-hexene yields 1-hexanol, the anti-Markovnikov product.

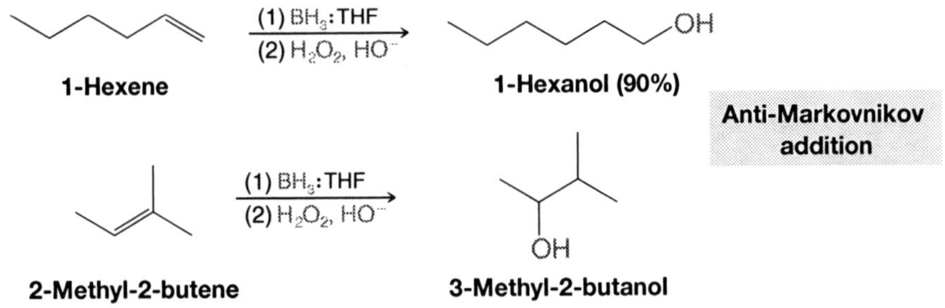

1-Hexene $\xrightarrow[\text{(2) } H_2O_2,\ HO^-]{\text{(1) } BH_3:THF}$ **1-Hexanol (90%)**   Anti-Markovnikov addition

2-Methyl-2-butene $\xrightarrow[\text{(2) } H_2O_2,\ HO^-]{\text{(1) } BH_3:THF}$ **3-Methyl-2-butanol**

- Hydroboration–oxidation reactions are **stereospecific**; the net addition of —H and —OH is **syn**, and if chirality centers are formed, their configuration depends on the stereochemistry of the starting alkene.

Because the oxidation step in the hydroboration–oxidation synthesis of alcohols takes place with retention of configuration, **the hydroxyl group replaces the boron atom where it stands in the alkylboron compound**. The net result of the two steps (hydroboration and oxidation) is the syn addition of —H and —OH. We can review the anti-Markovnikov and syn aspects of hydroboration–oxidation by considering the hydration of 1-methylcyclopentene, as shown in Fig. 8.3.

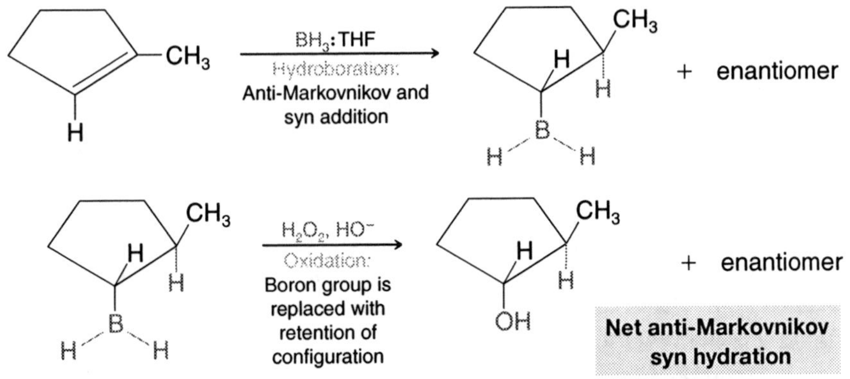

FIGURE 8.3 The hydroboration–oxidation of 1-methylcyclopentene. The first reaction is a syn addition of borane. In this illustration we have shown the boron and hydrogen entering from the bottom side of 1-methylcyclopentene. The reaction also takes place from the top side at an equal rate to produce the enantiomer. In the second reaction the boron atom is replaced by a hydroxyl group with retention of configuration. The product is *trans*-2-methylcyclopentanol, and the overall result is the syn addition of —H and —OH.

Specify the appropriate alkene and reagents for synthesis of each of the following alcohols by hydroboration–oxidation.

PRACTICE PROBLEM 8.13

(a)

(b)

(c)

(d)

(e)

(f)

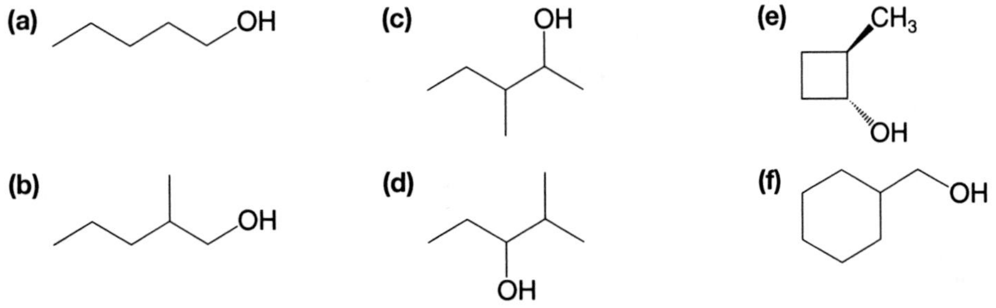

●●● SOLVED PROBLEM 8.3

Outline a method for carrying out the following conversion.

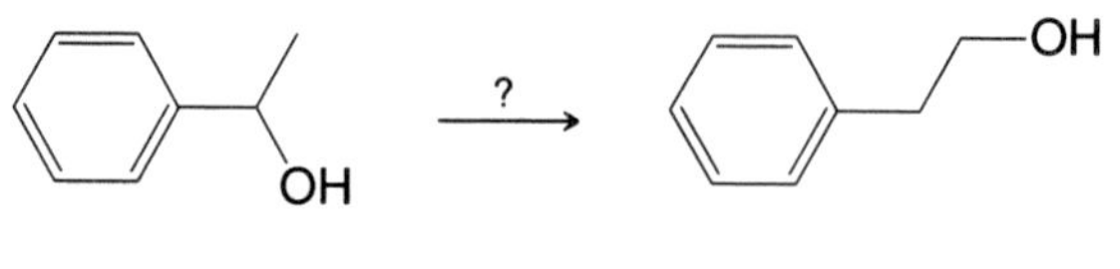

1-Phenylethanol　　　　**2-Phenylethanol**

STRATEGY AND ANSWER: Working backward we realize we could synthesize 2-phenylethanol by hydroboration–oxidation of phenylethene (styrene), and that we could make phenylethene by dehydrating 1-phenylethanol.

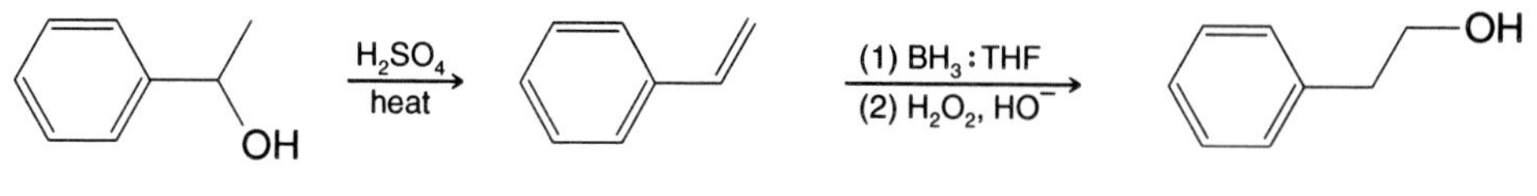

Phenylethene

8.9 SUMMARY OF ALKENE HYDRATION METHODS

The three methods we have studied for alcohol synthesis by addition reactions to alkenes have different regiochemical and stereochemical characteristics.

1. **Acid-catalyzed hydration of alkenes** takes place with Markovnikov regiochemistry but may lead to a mixture of constitutional isomers if the carbocation intermediate in the reaction undergoes rearrangement to a more stable carbocation.

2. **Oxymercuration–demercuration** occurs with Markovnikov regiochemistry and results in hydration of alkenes without complication from carbocation rearrangement. It is often the preferred choice over acid-catalyzed hydration for Markovnikov addition. The overall stereochemistry of addition in acid-catalyzed hydration and oxymercuration–demercuration is not controlled—they both result in a mixture of cis and trans addition products.

3. **Hydroboration–oxidation** results in anti-Markovnikov and syn hydration of an alkene.

The complementary regiochemical and stereochemical aspects of these methods provide useful alternatives when we desire to synthesize a specific alcohol by hydration of an alkene. We summarize them here in Table 8.1.

TABLE 8.1 SUMMARY OF METHODS FOR CONVERTING AN ALKENE TO AN ALCOHOL

Reaction	Conditions	Regiochemistry	Stereochemistry[a]	Occurrence of Rearrangements
Acid-catalyzed hydration	cat. HA, H_2O	Markovnikov addition	Not controlled	Frequent
Oxymercuration–demercuration	(1) $Hg(OAc)_2$, THF — H_2O (2) $NaBH_4$, HO^-	Markovnikov addition	Not controlled	Seldom
Hydroboration–oxidation	(1) BH_3:THF (2) H_2O_2, HO^-	Anti-Markovnikov addition	Stereospecific: syn addition of H— and —OH	Seldom

[a]All of these methods produce racemic mixtures in the absence of a chiral influence.

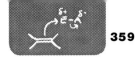

8.10 PROTONOLYSIS OF ALKYLBORANES

Heating an alkylborane with acetic acid causes cleavage of the carbon–boron bond and replacement with hydrogen:

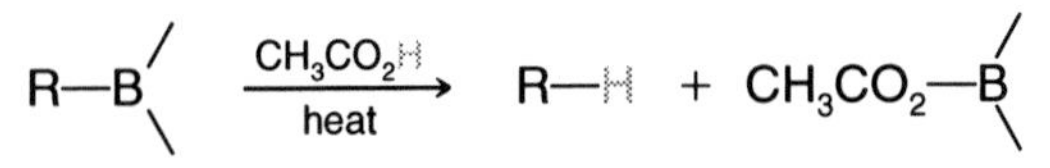

$$R-B \xrightarrow[\text{heat}]{CH_3CO_2H} R-H + CH_3CO_2-B$$

Alkylborane   **Alkane**

- Protonolysis of an alkylborane takes place with retention of configuration; hydrogen replaces boron **where it stands** in the alkylborane.
- The overall stereochemistry of hydroboration–protonolysis, therefore, is **syn** (like that of the oxidation of alkylboranes).

Hydroboration followed by protonolysis of the resulting alkylborane can be used as an alternative method for hydrogenation of alkenes, although catalytic hydrogenation (Section 7.12) is the more common procedure. Reaction of alkylboranes with deuterated or tritiated acetic acid also provides a very useful way to introduce these isotopes into a compound in a specific way.

● ● ◆ ······

PRACTICE PROBLEM 8.14

Starting with any needed alkene (or cycloalkene) and assuming you have deuterioacetic acid (CH_3CO_2D) available, outline syntheses of the following deuterium-labeled compounds.

(a) $(CH_3)_2CHCH_2CH_2D$ **(b)** $(CH_3)_2CHCHDCH_3$ **(c)**

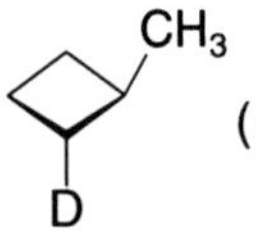

CH₃

(+ enantiomer)

D

(d) Assuming you also have available BD_3:THF and CH_3CO_2T, can you suggest a synthesis of the following?

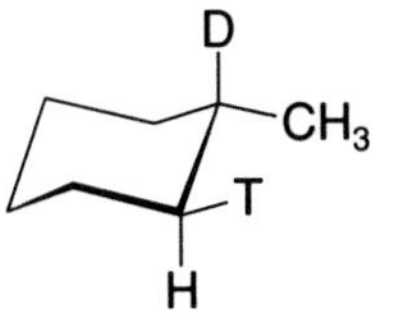

D

CH₃ (+ enantiomer)

T

H

8.11 ELECTROPHILIC ADDITION OF BROMINE AND CHLORINE TO ALKENES

Alkenes react rapidly with bromine and chlorine in nonnucleophilic solvents to form **vicinal dihalides**. An example is the addition of chlorine to ethene.

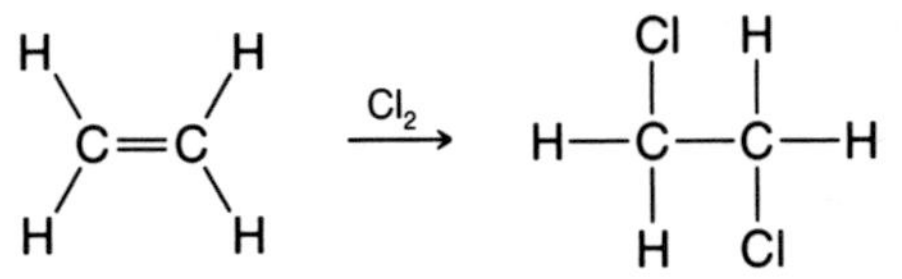

$$\underset{\textbf{Ethene}}{\overset{H}{\underset{H}{>}}C=C\overset{H}{\underset{H}{<}}} \xrightarrow{Cl_2} \underset{\textbf{1,2-Dichloroethane}}{H-\underset{H}{\overset{Cl}{C}}-\underset{Cl}{\overset{H}{C}}-H}$$

This addition is a useful industrial process because 1,2-dichloroethane can be used as a solvent and can be used to make vinyl chloride, the starting material for poly(vinyl chloride).

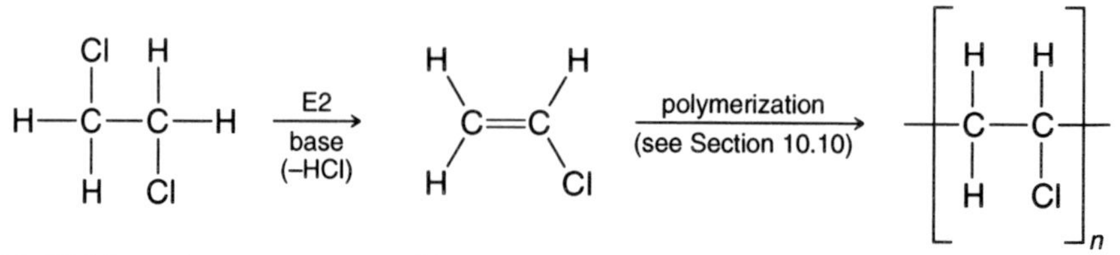

1,2-Dichloroethane　　　　　**Vinyl chloride**　　　　　**Poly(vinyl chloride)**

Other examples of the addition of halogens to a double bond are the following:

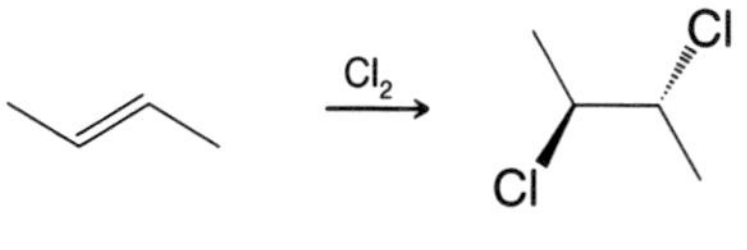

trans-2-Butene　　　*meso*-1,2-Dichlorobutane

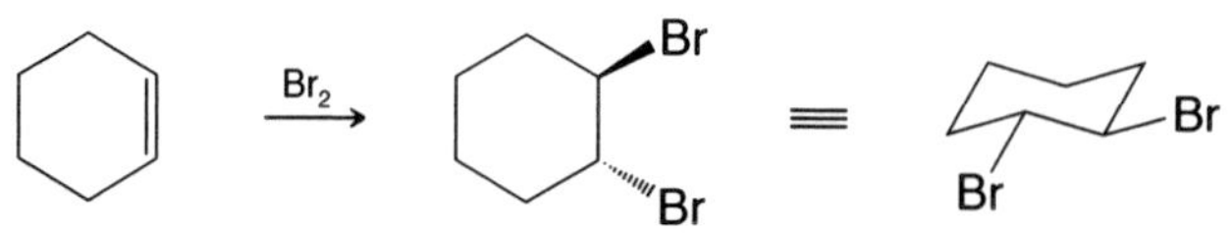

Cyclohexene　　　　　　*trans*-1,2-Dibromocyclohexane
(racemic)

These two examples show an aspect of these additions that we shall address later when we examine a mechanism for the reaction: **the addition of halogens is an anti addition to the double bond**.

When bromine is used for this reaction, it can serve as a test for the presence of carbon–carbon multiple bonds. If we add bromine to an alkene (or alkyne, see Section 8.17), the red-brown color of the bromine disappears almost instantly as long as the alkene (or alkyne) is present in excess:

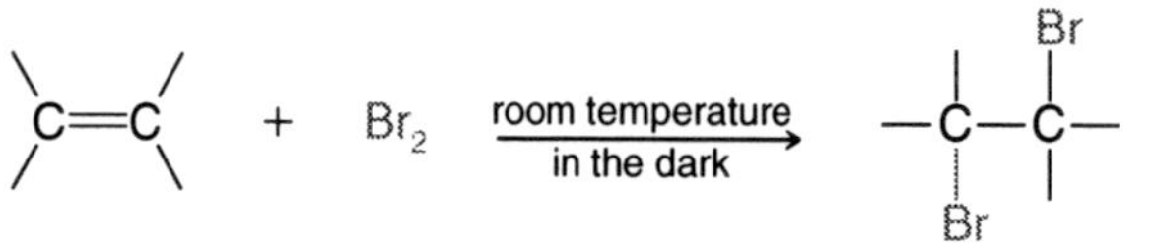

An alkene　　**Bromine**　　　　　　*vic*-**Dibromide**
(colorless)　**(red-brown)**　　　　**(a colorless**
　　　　　　　　　　　　　　　　compound)

> **Rapid decolorization of Br₂ is a positive test for alkenes and alkynes.**

This behavior contrasts markedly with that of **alkanes**. Alkanes do not react appreciably with bromine or chlorine at room temperature and in the absence of light. When alkanes *do* react under those conditions, however, it is by substitution rather than addition and by a mechanism involving radicals that we shall discuss in Chapter 10:

$$\text{R–H} \ + \ \text{Br}_2 \ \xrightarrow[\text{in the dark}]{\text{room temperature}} \ \textbf{No appreciable reaction}$$

Alkane　　**Bromine**
(colorless)　**(red-brown)**

8.11A Mechanism of Halogen Addition

A possible mechanism for the addition of a bromine or chlorine to an alkene is one that involves the formation of a carbocation.

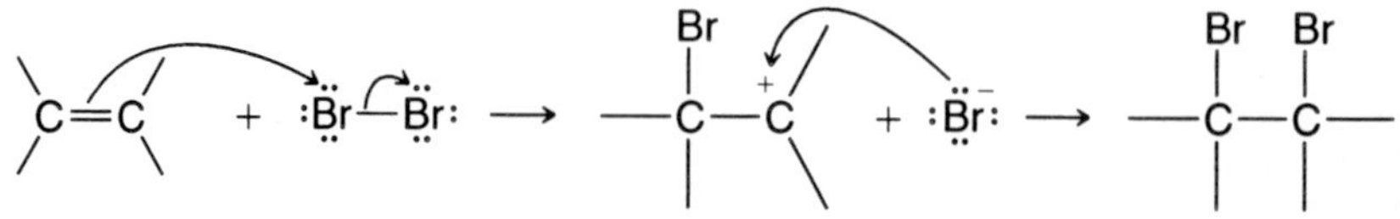

Although this mechanism is similar to ones we have studied earlier, such as the addition of H—X to an alkene, it does not explain an important fact. As we have just seen (in Section 8.11) the addition of bromine or chlorine to an alkene is an **anti addition**.

The addition of bromine to cyclopentene, for example, produces *trans*-1,2-dibromocyclopentane, not *cis*-1,2-dibromocyclopentane.

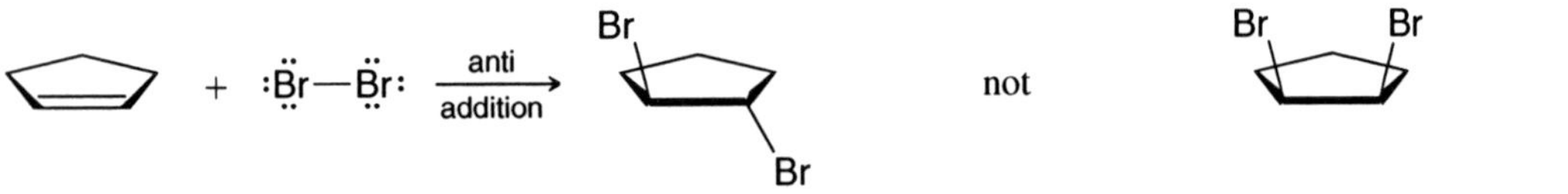

trans-1,2-Dibromocyclopentane
(as a racemic mixture)

cis-1,2-Dibromocyclohexane
(a meso compound)

A mechanism that explains anti addition is one in which a bromine molecule transfers a bromine atom to the alkene to form a cyclic **bromonium ion** and a bromide ion, as shown in step 1 of "A Mechanism for the Reaction" that follows. The cyclic bromonium ion causes net anti addition, as follows.

In step 2, a bromide ion attacks the back side of either carbon 1 or carbon 2 of the bromonium ion (an S_N2 process) to open the ring and produce the *trans*-1,2-dibromide. Attack occurs from the side **opposite the bromine of the bromonium ion** because attack from this direction is unhindered. Attack at the other carbon of the cyclic bromonium ion produces the enantiomer.

[A MECHANISM FOR THE REACTION — Addition of Bromine to an Alkene]

Step 1

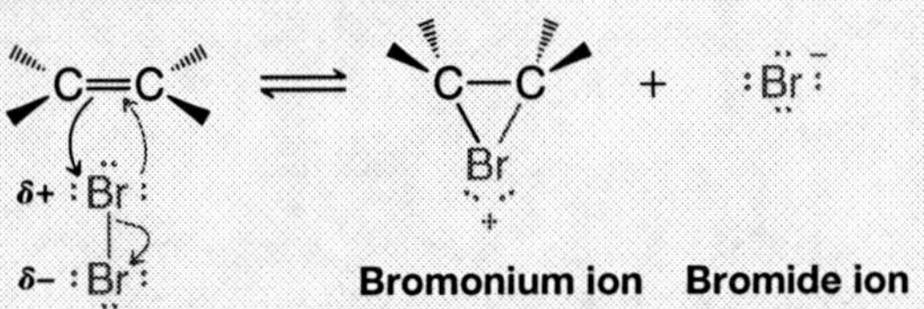

Bromonium ion   Bromide ion

As a bromine molecule approaches an alkene, the electron density of the alkene π bond repels electron density in the closer bromine, polarizing the bromine molecule and making the closer bromine atom electrophilic. The alkene donates a pair of electrons to the closer bromine, causing displacement of the distant bromine atom. As this occurs, the newly bonded bromine atom, due to its size and polarizability, donates an electron pair to the carbon that would otherwise be a carbocation, thereby stabilizing the positive charge by delocalization. The result is a bridged bromonium ion intermediate.

Step 2

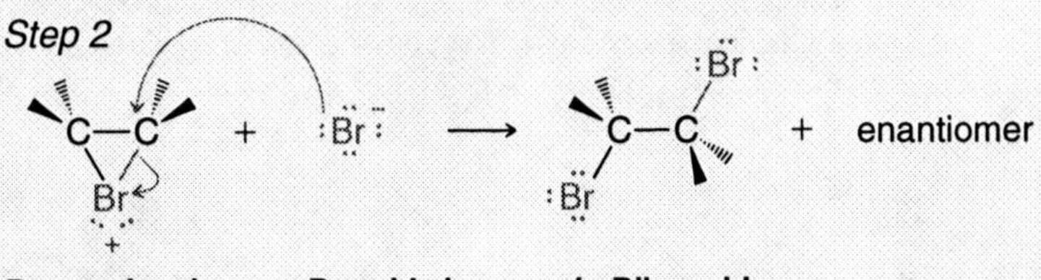

Bromonium ion   Bromide ion   vic-Dibromide

A bromide anion attacks at the back side of one carbon (or the other) of the bromonium ion in an S_N2 reaction, causing the ring to open and resulting in the formation of a *vic*-dibromide.

This process is shown for the addition of bromine to cyclopentene below.

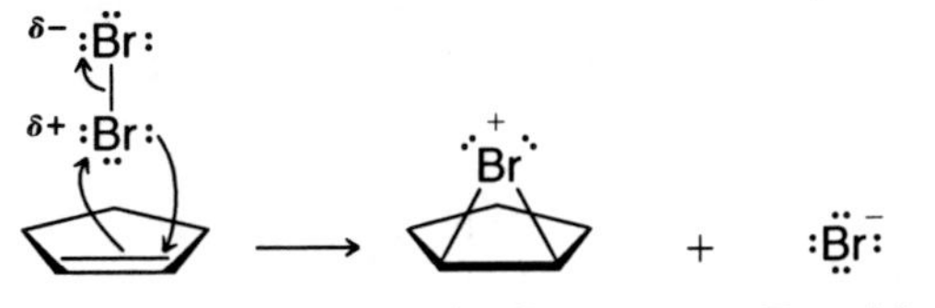

**Cyclic
bromonium ion**

**Bromide
ion**

Plane of symmetry	Enantiomers

Cyclic bromonium ion

trans-1,2-Dibromocyclopentane (as a racemic mixture)

Attack at either carbon of the cyclopentene bromonium ion is equally likely because the cyclic bromonium ion is symmetric. It has a vertical plane of symmetry passing through the bromine atom and halfway between carbons 1 and 2. The *trans*-dibromide, therefore, is formed as a racemic mixture.

THE CHEMISTRY OF... The Sea: A Treasury of Biologically Active Natural Products

The world's oceans are a vast storehouse of dissolved halide ions. The concentration of halides in the ocean is approximately 0.5 M in chloride, 1 mM in bromide, and 1 μM in iodide ions. Perhaps it is not surprising, then, that marine organisms have incorporated halogen atoms into the structures of many of their metabolites. Among these are such intriguing polyhalogenated compounds as halomon, dactylyne, tetrachloromertensene, (3E)-laureatin, peyssonol A, azamerone, and a structurally complex member of the polychlorinated sulfolipid family of natural products. Just the sheer number of halogen atoms in these metabolites is cause for wonder. For the organisms that make them, some of these molecules are part of defense mechanisms that serve to promote the species' survival by deterring predators or inhibiting the growth of competing organisms. For humans, the vast resource of marine natural products shows ever-greater potential as a source of new therapeutic agents. Halomon, for example, is in preclinical evaluation as a cytotoxic agent against certain tumor cell types, dactylyne is an inhibitor of pentobarbital metabolism, and peyssonol A is a modest allosteric inhibitor of the reverse transcriptases of the human immunodeficiency virus.

Image Source

Halomon **Tetrachloromertensene** **A polychlorinated sulfolipid**

Dactylyne **(3E)-Laureatin** **Peyssonol A** **Azamerone**

The biosynthesis of certain halogenated marine natural products is intriguing. Some of their halogens appear to have been introduced as *electrophiles* rather than as Lewis bases or nucleophiles, which is their character when they are solutes in seawater. But how do marine organisms transform nucleophilic halide anions into *electrophilic* species for incorporation into their metabolites? It happens that many marine organisms have enzymes called haloperoxidases that convert nucleophilic iodide, bromide, or chloride anions into electrophilic species that react like I$^+$, Br$^+$, or Cl$^+$. In the biosynthetic schemes proposed for some halogenated natural products, positive halogen intermediates are attacked by electrons from the π bond of an alkene or alkyne in an addition reaction.

The final Learning Group Problem for this chapter asks you to propose a scheme for biosynthesis of the marine natural product kumepaloxane by electrophilic halogen addition. Kumepaloxane is a fish antifeedant synthesized by the Guam bubble snail *Haminoea cymbalum*, presumably as a defense mechanism for the snail. In later chapters we shall see other examples of truly remarkable marine natural products, such as brevetoxin B, associated with deadly "red tides," and eleutherobin, a promising anticancer agent.

The mechanisms for addition of Cl_2 and I_2 to alkenes are similar to that for Br_2, involving formation and ring opening of their respective **halonium ions**.

As with bridged mercurinium ions, the bromonium ion does not necessarily have symmetrical charge distribution at its two carbon atoms. If one carbon of the bromonium ion is more highly substituted than the other, and therefore able to stabilize positive charge better, it may bear a greater fraction of positive charge than the other carbon (i.e., the positively charged bromine draws electron density from the two carbon atoms of the ring, but not equally if they are of different substitution). Consequently, the more positively charged carbon may be attacked by the reaction nucleophile more often than the other carbon. However, in reactions with symmetrical reagents (e.g., Br_2, Cl_2, and I_2) there is no observed difference. We shall discuss this point further in Section 8.13, where we will study a reaction where we can discern regioselectivity of attack on a halonium ion by the nucleophile.

8.12 STEREOSPECIFIC REACTIONS

The anti addition of a halogen to an alkene provides us with an example of what is called a **stereospecific reaction**.

- A **stereospecific reaction** is one where a particular stereoisomer of the starting material yields a specific stereoisomeric form of the product.

Consider the reactions of *cis*- and *trans*-2-butene with bromine shown below. When *trans*-2-butene adds bromine, the product is the meso compound, (2R,3S)-2,3-dibromobutane. When *cis*-2-butene adds bromine, the product is a *racemic mixture* of (2R,3R)-2,3-dibromobutane and (2S,3S)-2,3-dibromobutane:

Reaction 1

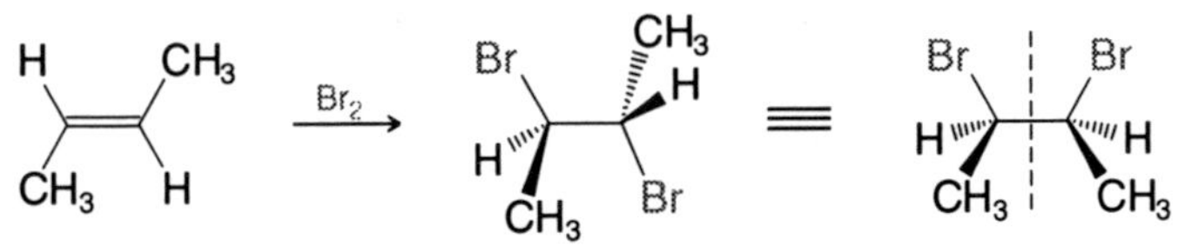

trans-2-Butene → (2R,3S)-2,3-Dibromobutane (a meso compound)

Reaction 2

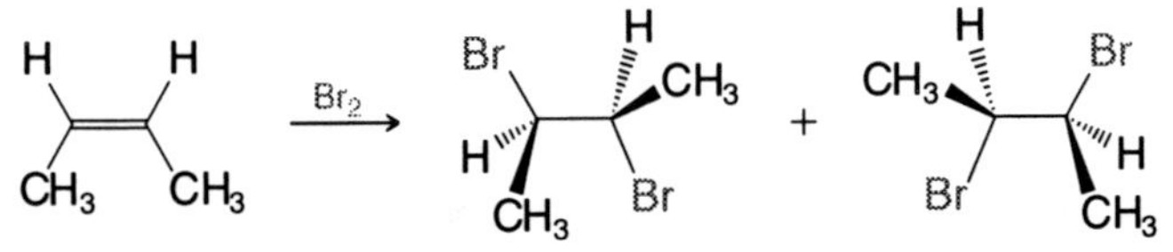

cis-2-Butene → (2R,3R) + (2S,3S) (a pair of enantiomers)

The reactants *cis*-2-butene and *trans*-2-butene are stereoisomers; they are *diastereomers*. The product of reaction 1, (2R,3S)-2,3-dibromobutane, is a meso compound, and it is a stereoisomer of both of the products of reaction 2 (the enantiomeric 2,3-dibromobutanes). Thus, by definition, both reactions are stereospecific. One stereoisomeric form of the reactant (e.g., *trans*-2-butene) gives one product (the meso compound), whereas the other stereoisomeric form of the reactant (*cis*-2-butene) gives a stereoisomerically different product (the enantiomers).

We can better understand the results of these two reactions if we examine their mechanisms. The first mechanism in the following box shows how *cis*-2-butene adds bromine to yield intermediate bromonium ions that are achiral. (The bromonium ion has a plane of symmetry.) These bromonium ions can then react with bromide ions by either path (a) or path (b). Reaction by path (a) yields one 2,3-dibromobutane enantiomer; reaction by path (b) yields the other enantiomer. The reaction occurs at the same rate by either path; therefore, the two enantiomers are produced in equal amounts (as a racemic form).

The second mechanism in the box shows how *trans*-2-butene reacts at the bottom face to yield an intermediate bromonium ion that is chiral. (Reaction at the other face would produce the enantiomeric bromonium ion.) Reaction of this chiral bromonium ion (or its enantiomer) with a bromide ion either by path (a) or by path (b) yields the same achiral product, *meso*-2,3-dibromobutane.

[THE STEREOCHEMISTRY OF THE REACTION... Addition of Bromine to *cis*- and *trans*-2-Butene]

cis-2-Butene reacts with bromine to yield the enantiomeric 2,3-dibromobutanes by the following mechanism:

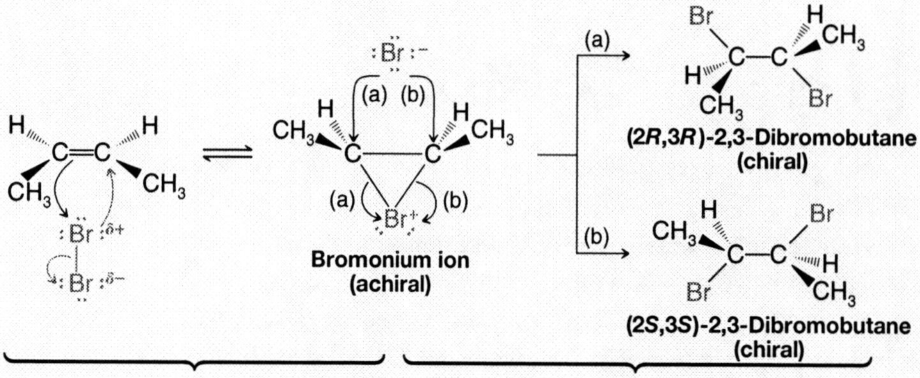

(2R,3R)-2,3-Dibromobutane (chiral)

(2S,3S)-2,3-Dibromobutane (chiral)

Bromonium ion (achiral)

cis-2-Butene reacts with bromine to yield an achiral bromonium ion and a bromide ion. [Reaction at the other face of the alkene (top) would yield the same bromonium ion.]

The bromonium ion reacts with the bromide ions at equal rates by paths (a) and (b) to yield the two enantiomers in equal amounts (i.e., as the racemic form).

trans-2-Butene reacts with bromine to yield *meso*-2,3-dibromobutane.

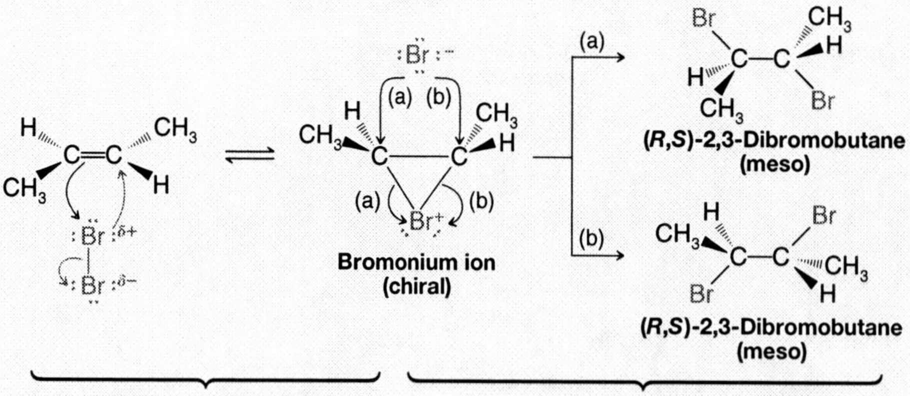

(R,S)-2,3-Dibromobutane (meso)

(R,S)-2,3-Dibromobutane (meso)

Bromonium ion (chiral)

trans-2-Butene reacts with bromine to yield chiral bromonium ions and bromide ions. [Reaction at the other face (top) would yield the enantiomer of the bromonium ion as shown here.]

When the bromonium ions react by either path (a) or path (b), they yield the *same* achiral meso compound. (Reaction of the enantiomer of the intermediate bromonium ion would produce the same result.)

8.13 HALOHYDRIN FORMATION

* When the halogenation of an alkene is carried out in aqueous solution, rather than in a non-nucleophilic solvent, the major product is a **halohydrin** (also called a halo alcohol) instead of a *vic*-dihalide.

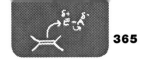

Molecules of water react with the halonium ion intermediate as the predominant nucleophile because they are in high concentration (as the solvent). The result is formation of a halohydrin as the major product. If the halogen is bromine, it is called a **bromohydrin**, and if chlorine, a **chlorohydrin**.

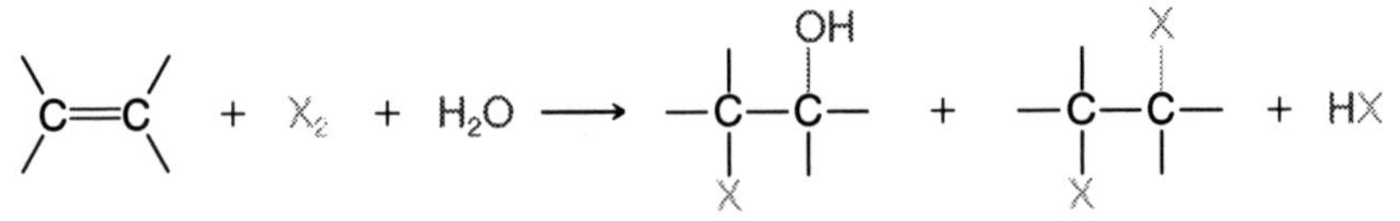

$$\text{C=C} \ + \ X_2 \ + \ H_2O \longrightarrow -\text{C}-\text{C}- \ + \ -\text{C}-\text{C}- \ + \ HX$$

X = Cl or Br	Halohydrin (major)	*vic*-Dihalide (minor)

Halohydrin formation can be described by the following mechanism.

[A MECHANISM FOR THE REACTION ⋯ Halohydrin Formation from an Alkene]

Step 1

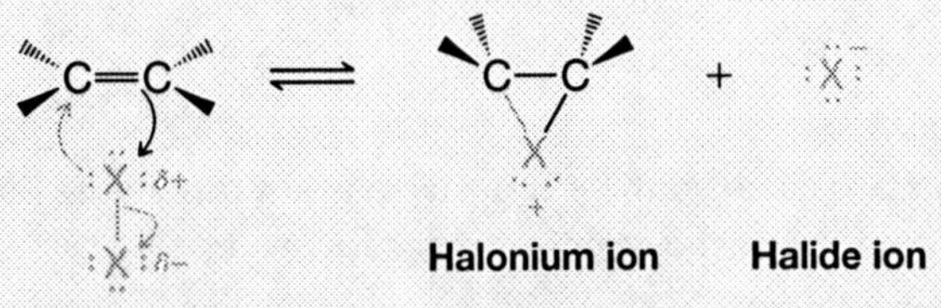

Halonium ion   Halide ion

This step is the same as for halogen addition to an alkene (see Section 8.11A).

Steps 2 and 3

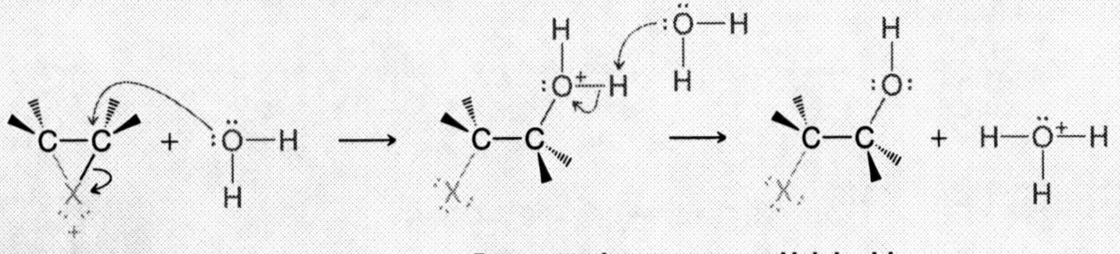

Halonium ion   Protonated halohydrin   Halohydrin

Here, however, a water molecule acts as the nucleophile and attacks a carbon of the ring, causing the formation of a protonated halohydrin.

The protonated halohydrin loses a proton (it is transferred to a molecule of water). This step produces the halohydrin and hydronium ion.

The first step is the same as that for halogen addition. In the second step, however, the two mechanisms differ. In halohydrin formation, water acts as the nucleophile and attacks one carbon atom of the halonium ion. The three-membered ring opens, and a protonated halohydrin is produced. Loss of a proton then leads to the formation of the halohydrin itself.

Write a mechanism to explain the following reaction.

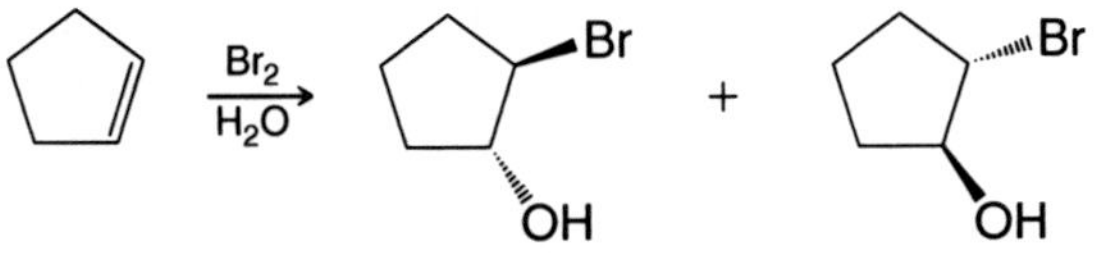

PRACTICE PROBLEM 8.15

$$\xrightarrow[\text{H}_2\text{O}]{\text{Br}_2}$$

(as a racemic mixture)

● If the alkene is unsymmetrical, the halogen ends up on the carbon atom with the greater number of hydrogen atoms.

Bonding in the intermediate bromonium ion is *unsymmetrical*. The more highly substituted carbon atom bears the greater positive charge because it resembles the more stable carbocation. Consequently, water attacks this carbon atom preferentially. The greater positive charge on the tertiary carbon permits a pathway with a lower free energy of activation even though attack at the primary carbon atom is less hindered:

> **This bromonium ion is bridged asymmetrically because the 3° carbon can accommodate more positive charge than the 1° carbon.**

(73%)

········

PRACTICE PROBLEM 8.16 When ethene gas is passed into an aqueous solution containing bromine and sodium chloride, the products of the reaction are the following:

Write mechanisms showing how each product is formed.

THE CHEMISTRY OF... Citrus-Flavored Soft Drinks

In Chapter 7 we discussed how double bonds within unsaturated fats could be hydrogenated to change their physical properties to convert materials like butter into margarine. It turns out that similar unsaturated fats can be used in the food industry in other ways, as well! For example, the properties of some unsaturated emulsifying agents can be enhanced if just a small percentage of their double bonds are brominated using Br_2, via the chemistry in this chapter. The increased density of these emulsifying agents, due to the bromine atoms, helps match the density of water more closely and creates a more stable, cloudy, colloidal-like mixture. The real value of this process, however, lies in what can now occur: other lipid-soluble molecules, such as many citrus flavors, can be used in aqueous foods due to the solubilizing action of these higher-density emulsifiers. The results are seen in beverages such as Mountain Dew, Squirt, or Fresca, soft drinks that all take advantage of this chemistry and that can be identified by the presence of "brominated vegetable oil" in the listing of ingredients.

© Donald Erickson/iStockphoto

8.14 DIVALENT CARBON COMPOUNDS: CARBENES

There are compounds in which a carbon has an unshared electron pair and only *two bonds*. These divalent carbon compounds are called **carbenes**. Carbenes are neutral and have no formal charge. Most carbenes are highly unstable compounds that have only a fleeting existence. Soon after carbenes are formed, they usually react with another molecule. The reactions of carbenes are especially interesting because, in many instances, the reactions show a remarkable degree of stereospecificity. The reactions of carbenes are also of great synthetic use in the preparation of compounds that have three-membered rings such as bicyclo[4.1.0]heptane, shown on the next page.

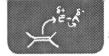

8.14A Structure and Reactions of Methylene

The simplest carbene is the compound called methylene (:CH₂). Methylene can be prepared by the decomposition of diazomethane (CH_2N_2), a very poisonous yellow gas. This decomposition can be accomplished by heating diazomethane (thermolysis) or by irradiating it with light of a wavelength that it can absorb (photolysis):

$$:\overset{-}{C}H_2 \!-\! \overset{+}{N} \!\equiv\! N\!: \quad \xrightarrow[\text{or light}]{\text{heat}} \quad :CH_2 \;+\; :N \!\equiv\! N\!:$$

| **Diazomethane** | **Methylene** | **Nitrogen** |

Bicyclo[4.1.0]heptane

The structure of diazomethane is actually a resonance hybrid of three structures:

$$:\overset{-}{C}H_2 \!-\! \overset{+}{N} \!\equiv\! N\!: \longleftrightarrow CH_2 \!=\! \overset{+}{N} \!=\! \overset{-}{N}\!: \longleftrightarrow :\overset{-}{C}H_2 \!-\! \overset{..}{N} \!=\! \overset{+}{N}\!:$$
$$\textbf{I} \qquad\qquad\qquad \textbf{II} \qquad\qquad\qquad \textbf{III}$$

We have chosen resonance structure **I** to illustrate the decomposition of diazomethane because with **I** it is readily apparent that heterolytic cleavage of the carbon–nitrogen bond results in the formation of methylene and molecular nitrogen.

Methylene reacts with alkenes by adding to the double bond to form cyclopropanes:

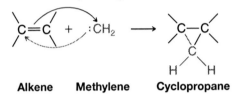

| **Alkene** | **Methylene** | **Cyclopropane** |

8.14B Reactions of Other Carbenes: Dihalocarbenes

Dihalocarbenes are also frequently employed in the synthesis of cyclopropane derivatives from alkenes. Most reactions of dihalocarbenes are **stereospecific**:

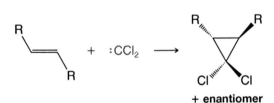

> The addition of :CX_2 is stereospecific. If the R groups of the alkene are trans, they will be trans in the product. (If the R groups were initially cis, they would be cis in the product.)

Dichlorocarbene can be synthesized by an *α elimination* of hydrogen chloride from chloroform. [The hydrogen of chloroform is mildly acidic ($pK_a \approx 24$) due to the inductive effect of the chlorine atoms.] This reaction resembles the β-elimination reactions by which alkenes are synthesized from alkyl halides (Section 6.15), except that the leaving group is on the same carbon as the proton that is removed.

$$R \!-\! \overset{..}{\underset{..}{O}}\!:^{-}K^{+} + H\!:\!CCl_3 \rightleftharpoons R \!-\! \overset{..}{\underset{..}{O}}\!:\!H + {}^{-}\!:\!CCl_3 + K^{+} \xrightarrow{\text{slow}} :CCl_2 + :\overset{..}{\underset{..}{Cl}}\!:^{-}$$

Dichlorocarbene

Compounds *with a β hydrogen* react by β elimination preferentially. Compounds with no β hydrogen but with an α hydrogen (such as chloroform) react by α elimination.

A variety of cyclopropane derivatives have been prepared by generating dichlorocarbene in the presence of alkenes. Cyclohexene, for example, reacts with dichlorocarbene generated by treating chloroform with potassium *tert*-butoxide to give a bicyclic product:

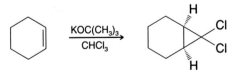

7,7-Dichlorobicyclo[4.1.0]heptane
(59%)

8.14C Carbenoids: The Simmons–Smith Cyclopropane Synthesis

A useful cyclopropane synthesis was developed by H. E. Simmons and R. D. Smith of the DuPont Company. In this synthesis diiodomethane and a zinc–copper couple are stirred together with an alkene. The diiodomethane and zinc react to produce a carbene-like species called a carbenoid:

$$CH_2I_2 + Zn(Cu) \longrightarrow ICH_2ZnI$$
A carbenoid

The carbenoid then brings about the stereospecific addition of a CH_2 group directly to the double bond.

PRACTICE PROBLEM 8.17 What products would you expect from each of the following reactions?

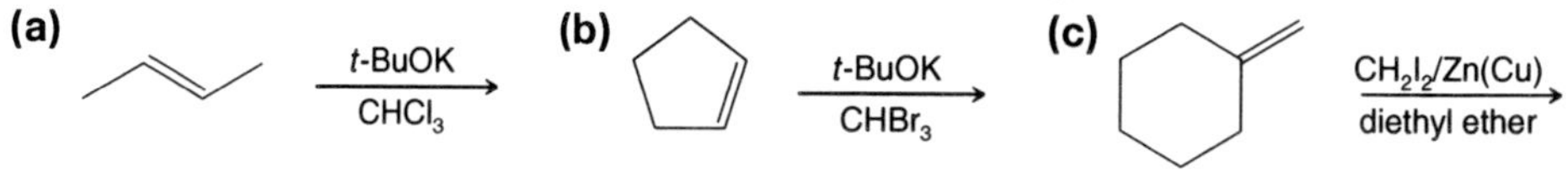

(a)

$$\xrightarrow[\text{CHCl}_3]{t\text{-BuOK}}$$

(b)

$$\xrightarrow[\text{CHBr}_3]{t\text{-BuOK}}$$

(c)

$$\xrightarrow[\text{diethyl ether}]{\text{CH}_2\text{I}_2/\text{Zn(Cu)}}$$

PRACTICE PROBLEM 8.18 Starting with cyclohexene and using any other needed reagents, outline a synthesis of 7,7-dibromobicyclo[4.1.0]heptane.

PRACTICE PROBLEM 8.19 Treating cyclohexene with 1,1-diiodoethane and a zinc–copper couple leads to two isomeric products. What are their structures?

8.15 OXIDATION OF ALKENES: SYN 1,2-DIHYDROXYLATION

Alkenes undergo a number of reactions in which the carbon–carbon double bond is oxidized.

- **1,2-Dihydroxylation** is an important oxidative addition reaction of alkenes.

Osmium tetroxide is widely used to synthesize **1,2-diols** (the products of 1,2-dihydroxylation, sometimes also called **glycols**). Potassium permanganate can also be used, although because it is a stronger oxidizing agent it is prone to cleave the diol through further oxidation (Section 8.15).

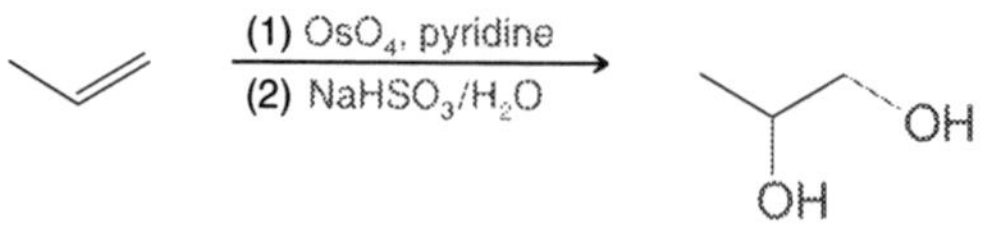

$$\xrightarrow[\text{(2) NaHSO}_3/\text{H}_2\text{O}]{\text{(1) OsO}_4, \text{ pyridine}}$$

Propene → **1,2-Propanediol (propylene glycol)**

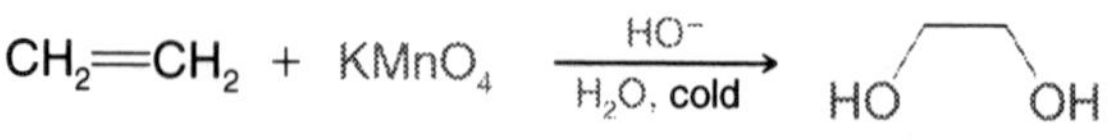

$$CH_2{=}CH_2 + KMnO_4 \xrightarrow[\text{H}_2\text{O, cold}]{\text{HO}^-}$$

Ethene → **1,2-Ethanediol (ethylene glycol)**

8.15A Mechanism for Syn Dihydroxylation of Alkenes

- The mechanism for the formation of a 1,2-diol by osmium tetroxide involves a cyclic intermediate that results in **syn addition** of the oxygen atoms (see below).

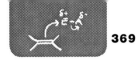

After formation of the cyclic intermediate with osmium, cleavage at the oxygen–metal bonds takes place without altering the stereochemistry of the two new C—O bonds.

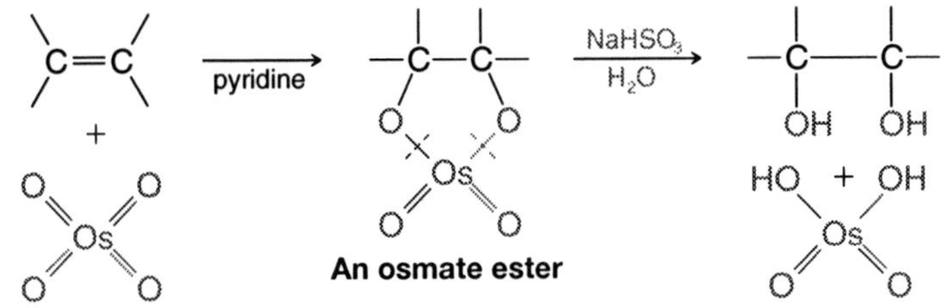

The syn stereochemistry of this dihydroxylation can readily be observed by the reaction of cyclopentene with osmium tetroxide. The product is *cis*-1,2-cyclopentanediol.

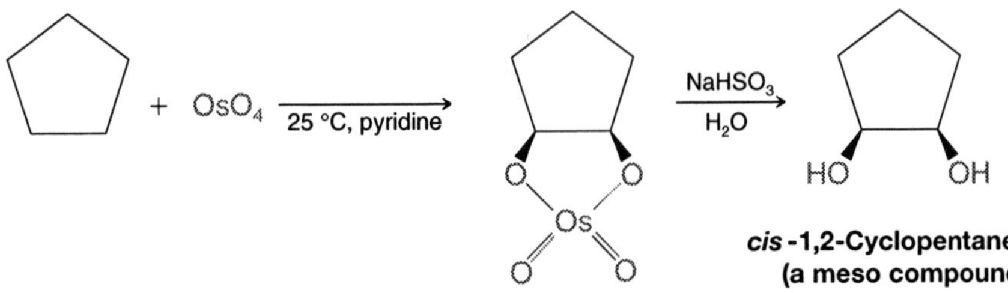

cis-1,2-Cyclopentanediol
(a meso compound)

Osmium tetroxide is highly toxic, volatile, and very expensive. For these reasons, methods have been developed that permit OsO_4 to be used *catalytically* in conjunction with a co-oxidant.[*] A very small molar percentage of OsO_4 is placed in the reaction mixture to do the dihydroxylation step, while a stoichiometric amount of co-oxidant reoxidizes the OsO_4 as it is used in each cycle, allowing oxidation of the alkene to continue until all has been converted to the diol. *N*-Methylmorpholine *N*-oxide (NMO) is one of the most commonly used co-oxidants with catalytic OsO_4. The method was discovered at Upjohn Corporation in the context of reactions for synthesis of a prostaglandin[†] (Section 23.5):

Catalytic OsO₄ 1,2-Dihydroxylation

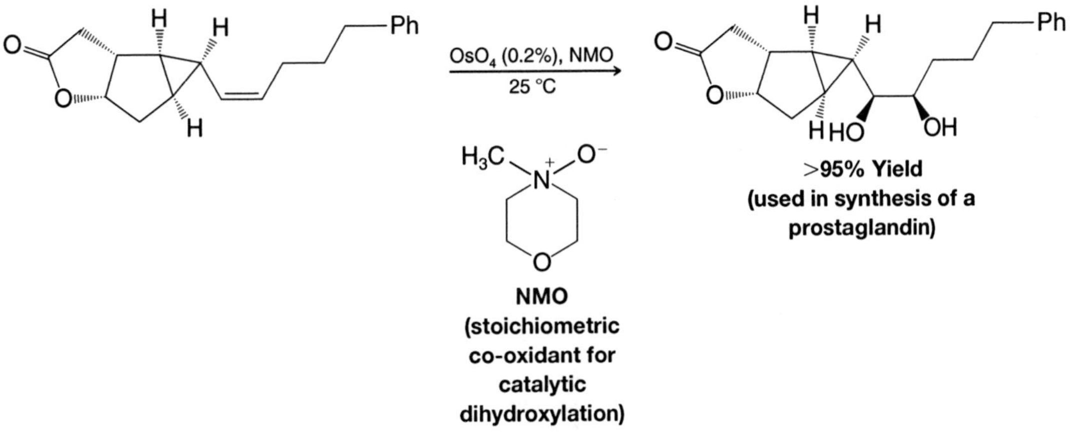

OsO_4 (0.2%), NMO
25 °C

NMO
(stoichiometric
co-oxidant for
catalytic
dihydroxylation)

>95% Yield
(used in synthesis of a
prostaglandin)

Specify the alkene and reagents needed to synthesize each of the following diols.

PRACTICE PROBLEM 8.20

(a)

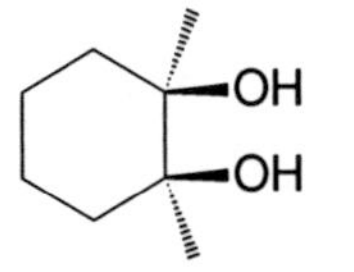

(b)

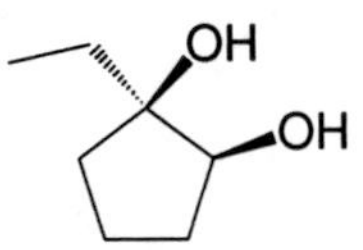

(racemic)

(c)

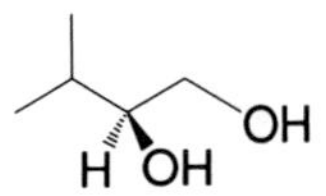

(racemic)

---

[*]See Nelson, D. W., et al., *J. Am. Chem. Soc.* **1997**, *119*, 1840–1858; and Corey, E. J., et al., *J. Am. Chem. Soc.* **1996**, *118*, 319–329.

[†]Van Rheenan, V., Kelley, R. C., and Cha, D. Y., *Tetrahedron Lett.* **1976**, *25*, 1973.

●●● SOLVED PROBLEM 8.4

Explain the following facts: Treating (Z)-2-butene with OsO$_4$ in pyridine and then NaHSO$_3$ in water gives a diol that is optically inactive and cannot be resolved. Treating (E)-2-butene with the same reagents gives a diol that is optically inactive but can be resolved into enantiomers.

STRATEGY AND ANSWER: Recall that the reaction in either instance results in syn dihydroxylation of the double bond of each compound. Syn dihydroxylation of (E)-2-butene gives a pair of enantiomers, while syn dihydroxylation of (Z)-2-butene gives a single product that is a meso compound.

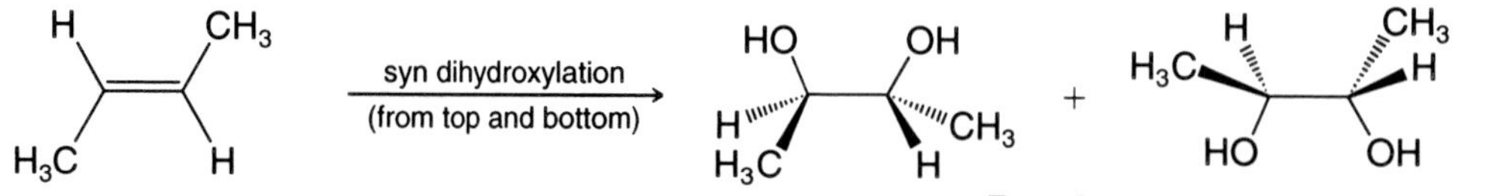

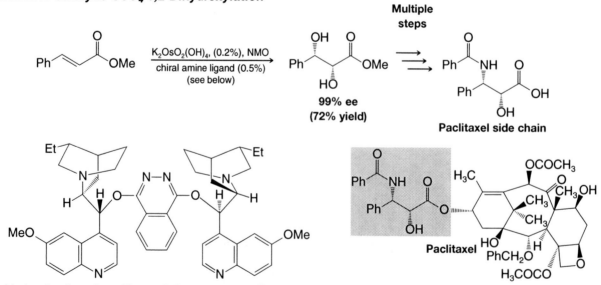

THE CHEMISTRY OF... Catalytic Asymmetric Dihydroxylation

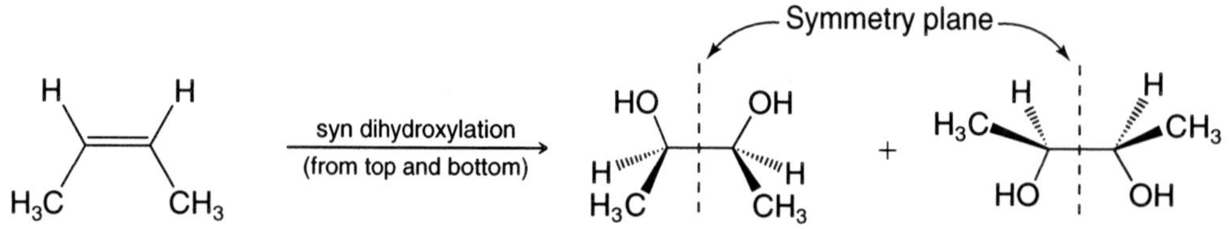

SHARPLESS shared the 2001 Nobel Prize in Chemistry for his development of asymmetric oxidation methods.

Methods for catalytic *asymmetric syn dihydroxylation* have been developed that significantly extend the synthetic utility of dihydroxylation. K. B. Sharpless (The Scripps Research Institute) and co-workers discovered that addition of a chiral amine to the oxidizing mixture leads to enantioselective catalytic syn dihydroxylation. Asymmetric dihydroxylation has become an important and widely used tool in the synthesis of complex organic molecules. In recognition of this and other advances in asymmetric oxidation procedures developed by his group (Section 11.13), Sharpless was awarded half of the 2001 Nobel Prize in Chemistry. (The other half of the 2001 prize was awarded to W. Knowles and R. Noyori for their development of catalytic asymmetric reduction reactions; see Section 7.13A.) The following reaction, involved in an enantioselective synthesis of the side chain of the anticancer drug paclitaxel (Taxol), serves to illustrate Sharpless's catalytic asymmetric dihydroxylation. The example utilizes a catalytic amount of K$_2$OsO$_2$(OH)$_4$, an OsO$_4$ equivalent, a chiral amine ligand to induce enantioselectivity, and NMO as the stoichiometric co-oxidant. The product is obtained in 99% enantiomeric excess (ee):

*Asymmetric Catalytic OsO$_4$ 1,2-Dihydroxylation**

A chiral amine ligand used in catalytic asymmetric dihydroxylation

(*Adapted with permission from Sharpless et al., *The Journal of Organic Chemistry*, Vol. 59, p. 5104, 1994. Copyright 1994 American Chemical Society.)

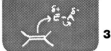

8.16 OXIDATIVE CLEAVAGE OF ALKENES

Alkenes can be **oxidatively cleaved** using potassium permanganate or ozone (as well as by other reagents). Potassium permanganate ($KMnO_4$) is used when strong oxidation is needed. Ozone (O_3) is used when mild oxidation is desired. [Alkynes and aromatic rings are also oxidized by $KMnO_4$ and O_3 (Sections 8.19 and 15.13D).]

8.16A Cleavage with Hot Basic Potassium Permanganate

- Treatment with hot basic potassium permanganate oxidatively cleaves the double bond of an alkene.

Cleavage is believed to occur via a cyclic intermediate similar to the one formed with osmium tetroxide (Section 8.15A) and intermediate formation of a 1,2-diol.

- Alkenes with monosubstituted carbon atoms are oxidatively cleaved to salts of carboxylic acids.
- Disubstituted alkene carbons are oxidatively cleaved to ketones.
- Unsubstituted alkene carbons are oxidized to carbon dioxide.

The following examples illustrate the results of potassium permanganate cleavage of alkenes with different substitution patterns. In the case where the product is a carboxylate salt, an acidification step is required to obtain the carboxylic acid.

$$CH_3CH{=}CHCH_3 \xrightarrow[\text{heat}]{KMnO_4,\ HO^-,\ H_2O} 2\ \underset{\textbf{Acetate ion}}{H_3C-\overset{O}{\overset{\|}{C}}-O^-} \xrightarrow{H_3O^+} 2\ \underset{\textbf{Acetic acid}}{H_3C-\overset{O}{\overset{\|}{C}}-OH}$$

(cis or trans)

$$\underset{CH_2}{\underset{||}{\diagup}} \xrightarrow[\text{(2) } H_3O^+]{\substack{\text{(1) } KMnO_4,\ HO^- \\ \text{heat}}} \diagdown\!\!\diagup{=}O\ +\ O{=}C{=}O\ +\ H_2O$$

One of the uses of potassium permanganate, other than for oxidative cleavage, is as a **chemical test for unsaturation** in an unknown compound.

- If an alkene is present (or an alkyne, Section 8.19), the purple color of a potassium permanganate solution is discharged and a brown precipitate of manganese dioxide (MnO_2) forms as the oxidation takes place.

The oxidative cleavage of alkenes has also been used to establish the location of the double bond in an alkene chain or ring. The reasoning process requires us to think backward much as we do with retrosynthetic analysis. Here we are required to work backward from the products to the reactant that might have led to those products. We can see how this might be done with the following example.

●●● SOLVED PROBLEM 8.5

An unknown alkene with the formula C_8H_{16} was found, on oxidation with hot basic permanganate, to yield a three-carbon carboxylic acid (propanoic acid) and a five-carbon carboxylic acid (pentanoic acid). What was the structure of this alkene?

$$C_8H_{16} \xrightarrow[\text{(2) } H_3O^+]{\substack{\text{(1) } KMnO_4,\ H_2O, \\ HO^-,\ \text{heat}}} \underset{\textbf{Propanoic acid}}{\diagup\!\!\diagdown\overset{O}{\overset{\|}{\diagup}}\!\!OH}\ +\ \underset{\textbf{Pentanoic acid}}{HO\overset{O}{\overset{\|}{\diagdown}}\!\!\diagup\!\!\diagdown}$$

(continues on next page)

STRATEGY AND ANSWER: The carbonyl groups in the products are the key to seeing where the oxidative cleavage occurred. Therefore, oxidative cleavage must have occurred as follows, and the unknown alkene must have been *cis-* or *trans*-3-octene, which is consistent with the molecular formula given.

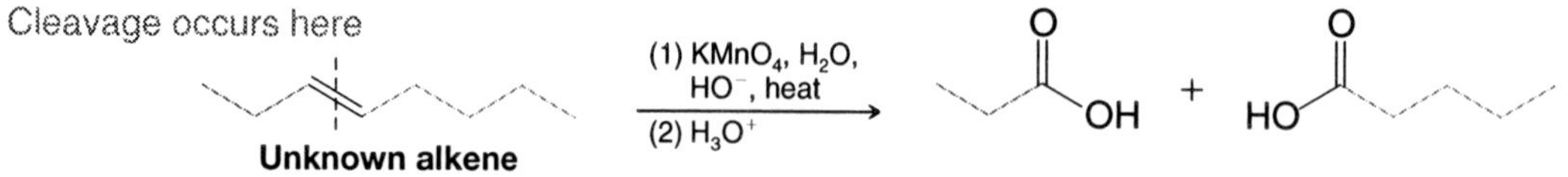

Cleavage occurs here

Unknown alkene
(either *cis-* or *trans*-3-octene)

8.16B Cleavage with Ozone

* The most useful method for cleaving alkenes is to use ozone (O_3).

Ozonolysis consists of bubbling ozone into a very cold (−78°C) solution of the alkene in CH_2Cl_2, followed by treatment of the solution with dimethyl sulfide (or zinc and acetic acid). The overall result is as follows:

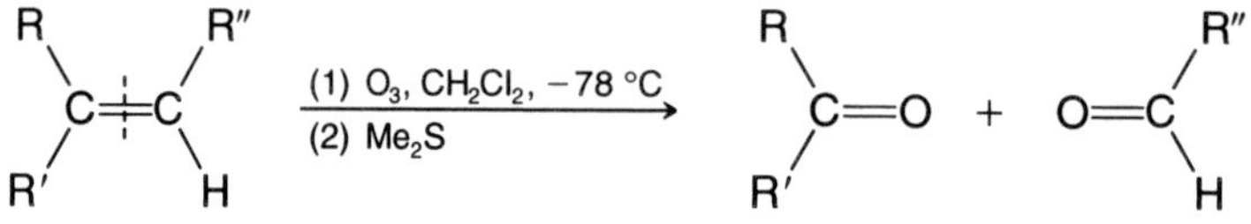

The reaction is useful as a synthetic tool, as well as a method for determining the location of a double bond in an alkene by reasoning backward from the structures of the products.

* The overall process (above) results in alkene cleavage at the double bond, with each carbon of the double bond becoming doubly bonded to an oxygen atom.

The following examples illustrate the results for each type of alkene carbon.

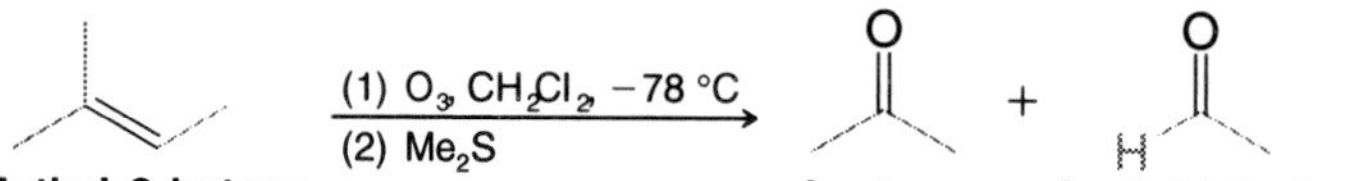

2-Methyl-2-butene   **Acetone**   **Acetaldehyde**

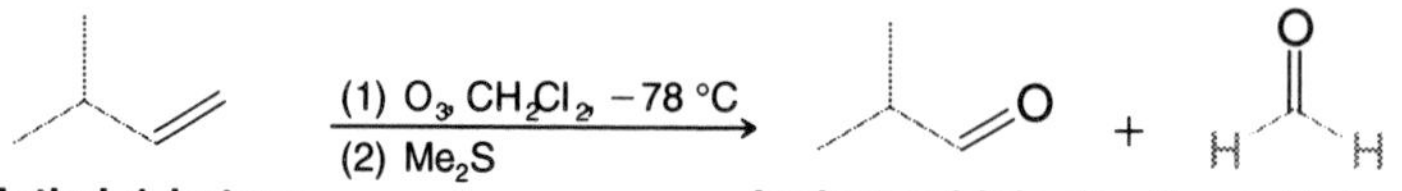

3-Methyl-1-butene   **Isobutyraldehyde Formaldehyde**

●●● SOLVED PROBLEM 8.6

Give the structure of an unknown alkene with the formula C_7H_{12} that undergoes ozonolysis to yield, after acidification, *only the following product*:

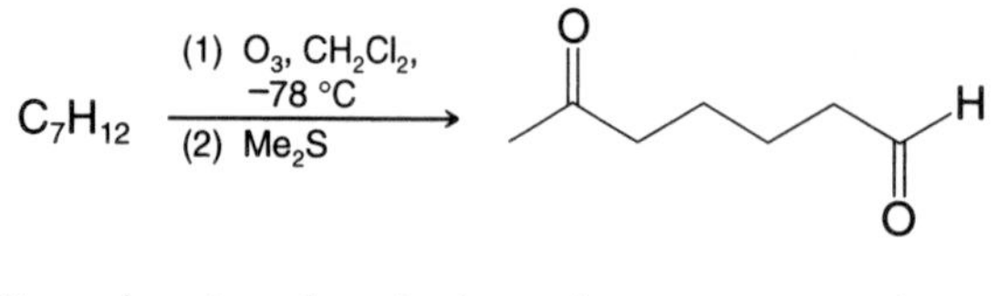

STRATEGY AND ANSWER: Since there is only a single product containing the same number of carbon atoms as the reactant, the only reasonable explanation is that the reactant has a double bond contained in a ring. Ozonolysis of the double bond opens the ring:

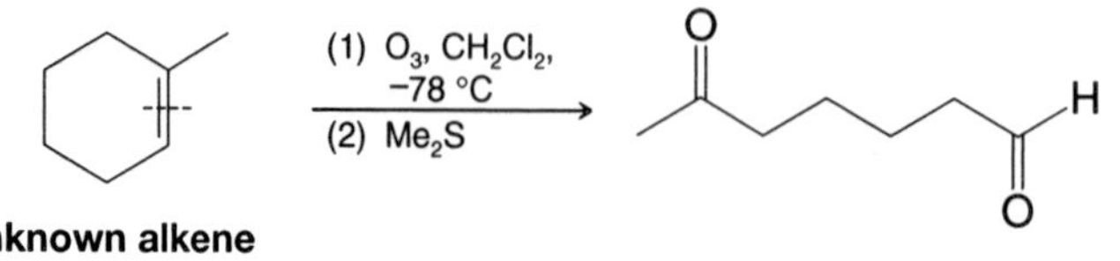

Unknown alkene
(1-methylcyclohexene)

••• ⋯⋯

Predict the products of the following ozonolysis reactions.   **PRACTICE PROBLEM 8.21**

(a)

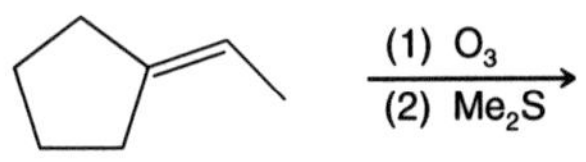

$\xrightarrow[\text{(2) Me}_2\text{S}]{\text{(1) O}_3}$

(c)

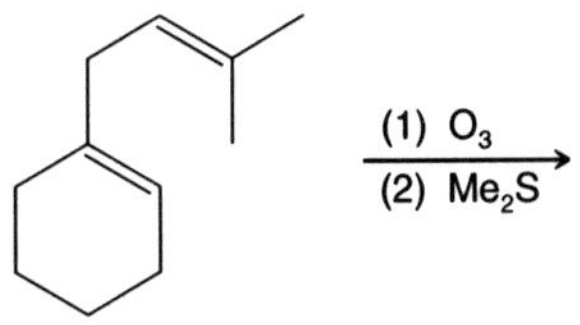

$\xrightarrow[\text{(2) Me}_2\text{S}]{\text{(1) O}_3}$

(b)

$\xrightarrow[\text{(2) Me}_2\text{S}]{\text{(1) O}_3}$

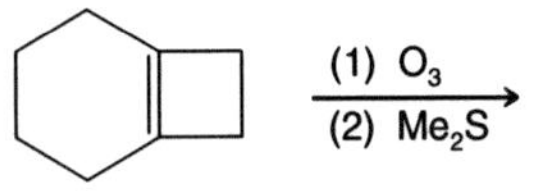

The mechanism of ozone addition to alkenes begins with formation of unstable compounds called *initial ozonides* (sometimes called molozonides). The process occurs vigorously and leads to spontaneous (and sometimes noisy) rearrangement to compounds known as **ozonides.** The rearrangement is believed to occur with dissociation of the initial ozonide into reactive fragments that recombine to yield the ozonide. Ozonides are very unstable compounds, and low-molecular-weight ozonides often explode violently.

A MECHANISM FOR THE REACTION — Ozonolysis of an Alkene

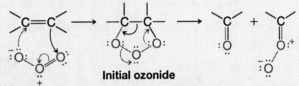

Ozone adds to the alkene to form an initial ozonide.   **Initial ozonide**   **The initial ozonide fragments.**

The fragments recombine to form the ozonide.   **Ozonide**   Me₂S → **Aldehydes and/or ketones**   **Dimethyl sulfoxide**

••• ⋯⋯

Write the structures of the alkenes that would yield the following carbonyl compounds when treated with ozone and then with dimethyl sulfide.   **PRACTICE PROBLEM 8.22**

(a)   and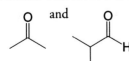

(c) and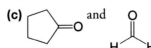

(b) 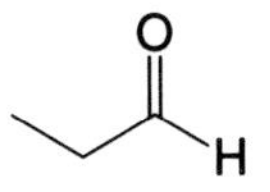   (2 mol is produced from 1 mol of alkene)

8.17 ELECTROPHILIC ADDITION OF BROMINE AND CHLORINE TO ALKYNES

- Alkynes show the same kind of addition reactions with chlorine and bromine that alkenes do.
- With alkynes **the addition may occur once or twice**, depending on the number of molar equivalents of halogen we employ:

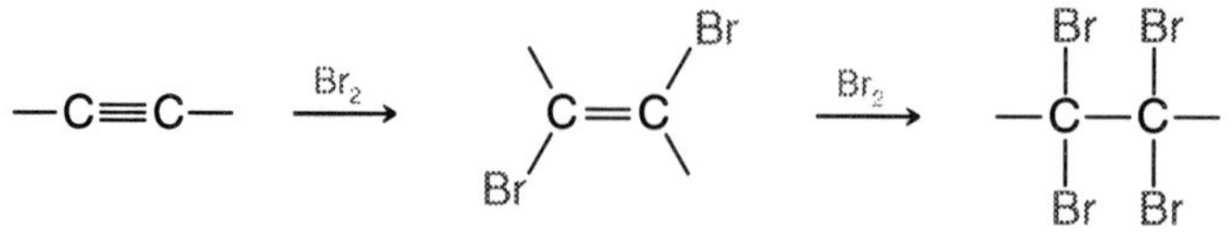

Dibromoalkene **Tetrabromoalkane**

Dichloroalkene **Tetrachloroalkane**

It is usually possible to prepare a dihaloalkene by simply adding one molar equivalent of the halogen:

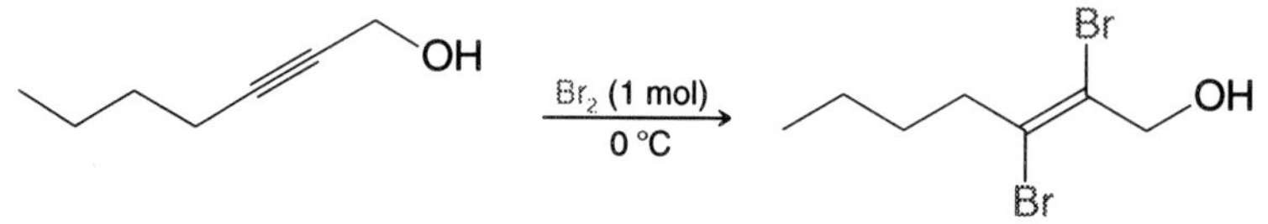

- Addition of one molar equivalent of chlorine or bromine to an alkyne generally results in anti addition and yields a *trans*-dihaloalkene.

Addition of bromine to acetylenedicarboxylic acid, for example, gives the trans isomer in 70% yield:

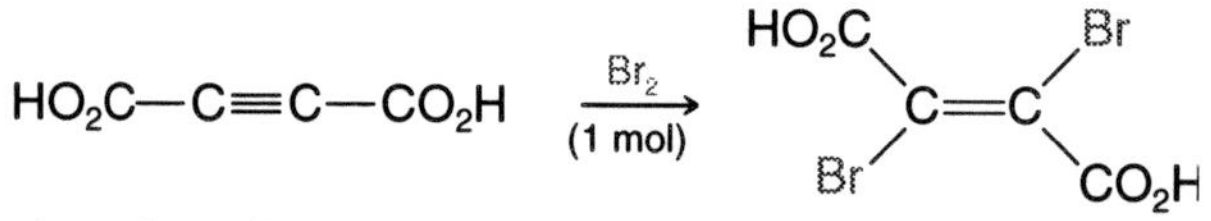

Acetylenedicarboxylic acid **(70%)**

···•◦•···

PRACTICE PROBLEM 8.23 Alkenes are more reactive than alkynes toward addition of electrophilic reagents (i.e., Br_2, Cl_2, or HCl). Yet when alkynes are treated with one molar equivalent of these same electrophilic reagents, it is easy to stop the addition at the "alkene stage." This appears to be a paradox and yet it is not. Explain.

8.18 ADDITION OF HYDROGEN HALIDES TO ALKYNES

- Alkynes react with one molar equivalent of hydrogen chloride or hydrogen bromide to form haloalkenes, and with two molar equivalents to form geminal dihalides.
- Both additions are **regioselective** and follow **Markovnikov's rule**:

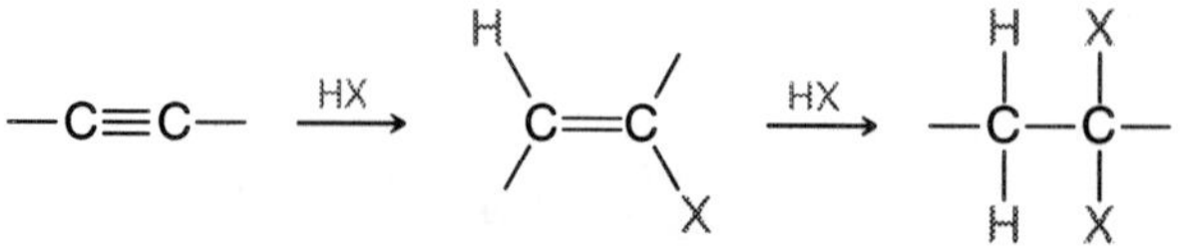

Haloalkene *gem*-**Dihalide**

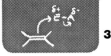

The hydrogen atom of the hydrogen halide becomes attached to the carbon atom that has the greater number of hydrogen atoms. 1-Hexyne, for example, reacts slowly with one molar equivalent of hydrogen bromide to yield 2-bromo-1-hexene and with two molar equivalents to yield 2,2-dibromohexane:

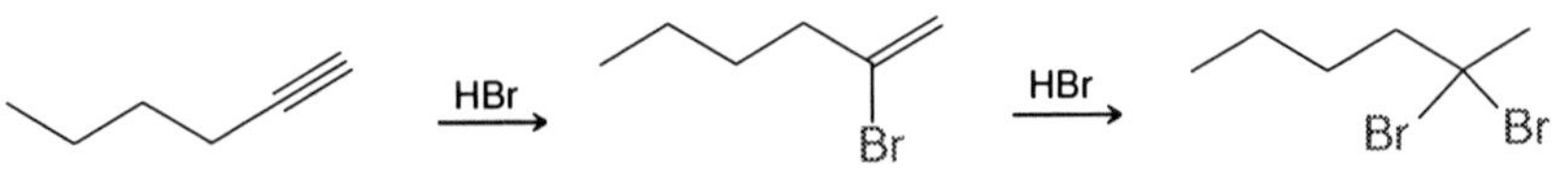

2-Bromo-1-hexene   **2,2-Dibromohexane**

The addition of HBr to an alkyne can be facilitated by using acetyl bromide (CH₃COBr) and alumina instead of aqueous HBr. Acetyl bromide acts as an HBr precursor by reacting with the alumina to generate HBr. For example, 1-heptyne can be converted to 2-bromo-1-heptene in good yield using this method:

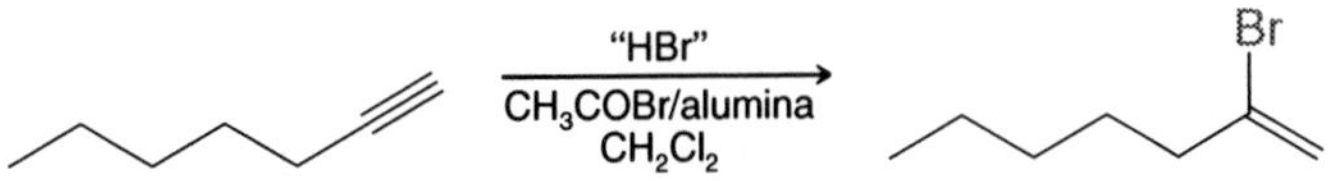

(82%)

Anti-Markovnikov addition of hydrogen bromide to alkynes occurs when peroxides are present in the reaction mixture. These reactions take place through a free-radical mechanism (Section 10.10):

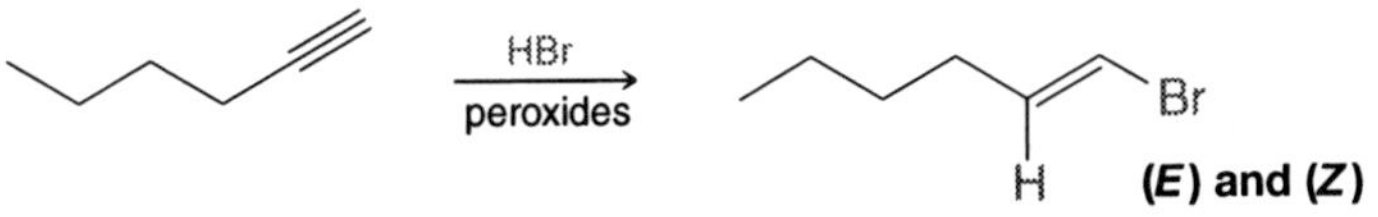

(E) and (Z)

(74%)

8.19 OXIDATIVE CLEAVAGE OF ALKYNES

Treating alkynes with ozone followed by acetic acid, or with basic potassium permanganate followed by acid, leads to cleavage at the carbon–carbon triple bond. The products are carboxylic acids:

$$R—C \equiv C—R' \xrightarrow[\text{(2) HOAc}]{\text{(1) O}_3} RCO_2H + R'CO_2H$$

or

$$R—C \equiv C—R' \xrightarrow[\text{(2) H}_3O^+]{\text{(1) KMnO}_4, \text{ HO}^-} RCO_2H + R'CO_2H$$

●●● SOLVED PROBLEM 8.7

Three alkynes, **X**, **Y**, and **Z**, each have the formula C_6H_{10}. When allowed to react with excess hydrogen in the presence of a platinum catalyst each alkyne yields only hexane as a product.

(1) The IR spectrum of compound **X** shows, among others, a peak near 3320 cm⁻¹, several peaks in the 2800–3000-cm⁻¹ region, and a peak near 2100 cm⁻¹. On oxidation with hot, basic potassium permanganate followed by acidification, **X** produces a five-carbon carboxylic acid and a gas.

(2) Compound **Y** has no IR peak in the 3300-cm⁻¹ region and when oxidized with hot, basic KMnO₄ produces on acidification a three-carbon carboxylic acid only. Compound **Y** has peaks in the 2800–3000-cm⁻¹ region, but no peak near 2100 cm⁻¹.

(3) On treatment with hot basic KMnO₄ followed by acid, **Z** produces a two-carbon carboxylic acid and a four-carbon one. In its IR spectrum, **Z** has peaks in the 2800–3000-cm⁻¹ region and a peak near 2100 cm⁻¹, but no peaks near the 3300-cm⁻¹ region. Consult Section 2.16A and propose structures for each alkyne.

(continues on next page)

STRATEGY AND ANSWER: That all three alkynes yield hexane on catalytic hydrogenation shows that they are all unbranched hexynes.

(1) That compound **X** has a peak near 3200 cm^{-1} indicates that it has a terminal triple bond. The peak near 2100 cm^{-1} is also associated with that triple bond. These facts suggest that compound **X** is 1-hexyne, something that is confirmed by the results of its oxidation to a five-carbon carboxylic acid and carbon dioxide.

(2) That compound **Y**, on oxidative cleavage, yields only a three-carbon carboxylic acid strongly suggests that it is 3-hexyne; this is confirmed by the absence of a peak near 2100 cm^{-1}. (The triple bond of 3-hexyne is symmetrically substituted and, therefore, the absence of an IR peak in this region is consistent with there being no dipole moment change associated with its vibration.)

(3) That compound **Z** has a peak near 2100 cm^{-1} indicates the presence of an unsymmetrically substituted triple bond, and this is consistent with the formation of two different carboxylic acids (one with two carbons and one with four) when it is oxidized. **Z**, therefore, is 2-hexyne.

PRACTICE PROBLEM 8.24 **A**, **B**, and **C** are alkynes. Elucidate their structures and that of **D** using the following reaction roadmap.

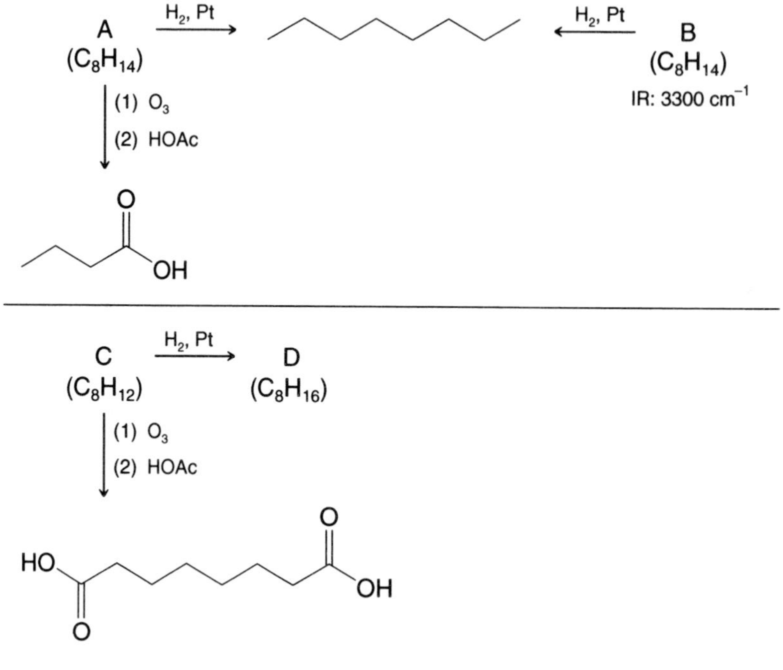

8.20 HOW TO PLAN A SYNTHESIS: SOME APPROACHES AND EXAMPLES

In planning a synthesis we often have to consider four interrelated aspects:

1. construction of the carbon skeleton,

2. functional group interconversions,

3. control of regiochemistry, and

4. control of stereochemistry.

You have had some experience with certain aspects of synthetic strategies in earlier sections.

* In Section 7.15B you learned about *retrosynthetic analysis* and how this kind of thinking could be applied to the construction of carbon skeletons of alkanes and cycloalkanes.

* In Section 6.14 you learned the meaning of a *functional group interconversion* and how nucleophilic substitution reactions could be used for this purpose.

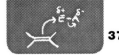

In other sections, perhaps without realizing it, you have begun adding to your basic store of methods for construction of carbon skeletons and for making functional group interconversions. This is the time to begin keeping a card file for all the reactions that you have learned, noting especially their applications to synthesis. This file will become your **Tool Kit for Organic Synthesis**. Now is also the time to look at some new examples and to see how we integrate all four aspects of synthesis into our planning.

8.20A Retrosynthetic Analysis

Consider a problem in which we are asked to outline a synthesis of 2-bromobutane from compounds of two carbon atoms or fewer. This synthesis, as we shall see, involves construction of the carbon skeleton, functional group interconversion, and control of regiochemistry.

HOW TO Apply Retrosynthetic Analysis to 2-Bromobutane

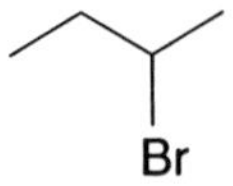

We begin by thinking backward. The final target, 2-bromobutane, can be made in one step from 1-butene by addition of hydrogen bromide. The regiochemistry of this functional group interconversion must be Markovnikov addition:

Retrosynthetic Analysis

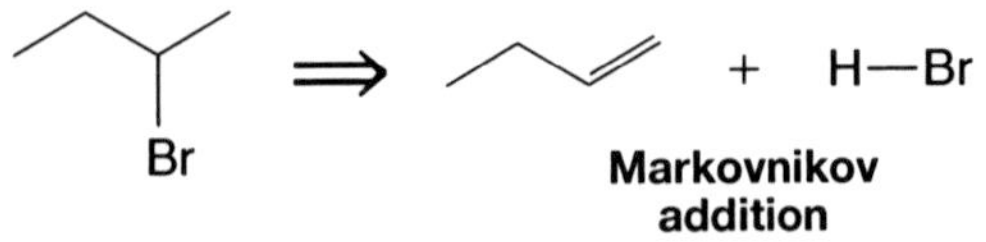

Synthesis

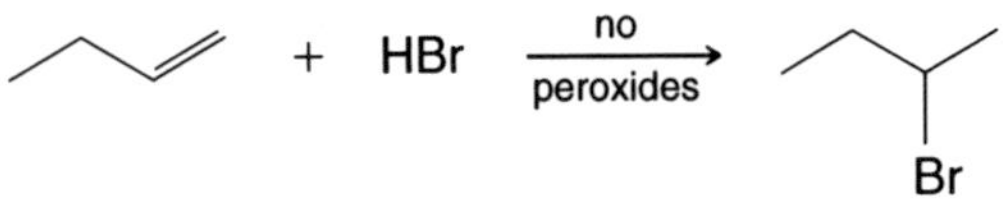

Remember: The open arrow is a symbol used to show a retrosynthetic process that relates the target molecule to its precursors:

Target molecule $\Longrightarrow$ precursors

Continuing to work backward one hypothetical reaction at a time, we realize that a synthetic precursor of 1-butene is 1-butyne. Addition of 1 mol of hydrogen to 1-butyne would lead to 1-butene. With 1-butyne as our new target, and bearing in mind that we are told that we have to construct the carbon skeleton from compounds with two carbons or fewer, we realize that 1-butyne can be formed in one step from ethyl bromide and acetylene by an alkynide anion alkylation.

* The **key to retrosynthetic analysis** is to think of how to synthesize each target molecule in one reaction from an immediate precursor, considering first the ultimate target molecule and working backward.

Retrosynthetic Analysis

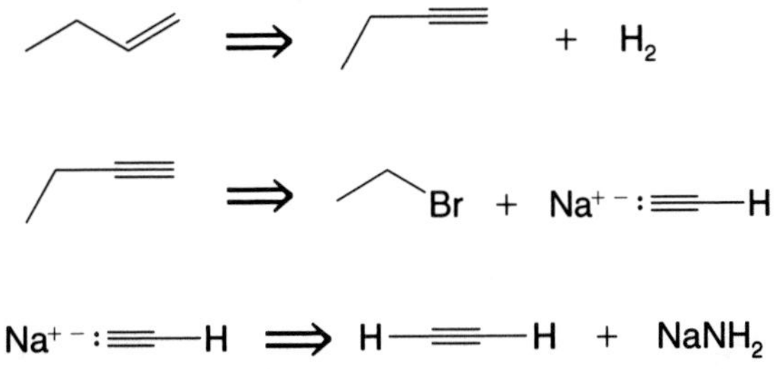

Synthesis

$$H\!\!-\!\!\!\equiv\!\!\!-\!\!H \; + \; Na^+ \; ^-NH_2 \xrightarrow[\text{liq. } NH_3, \, -33\,°C]{} Na^+ \; ^- :\!\!\equiv\!\!\!-\!\!H$$

$$\overset{Br}{\diagup} \; + \; Na^+ \; ^-:\!\!\equiv\!\!\!-\!\!H \xrightarrow[\text{liq. } NH_3, \, -33\,°C]{} \diagup\!\!\!\equiv$$

$$\diagup\!\!\!\equiv \; + \; H_2 \xrightarrow{Ni_2B\,(P\text{-}2)} \diagup\!\!\!\diagdown$$

8.20B Disconnections, Synthons, and Synthetic Equivalents

● One approach to retrosynthetic analysis is to consider a retrosynthetic step as a "disconnection" of one of the bonds (Section 7.15).*

For example, an important step in the synthesis that we have just given is the one in which a new carbon–carbon bond is formed. Retrosynthetically, it can be shown in the following way:

$$\diagup\!\!\!\equiv \;\Longrightarrow\; \diagup^+ \; + \; ^- :\!\!\equiv\!\!\!-\!\!H$$

The hypothetical fragments of this disconnection are an ethyl cation and an ethynide anion.

● In general, we call the fragments of a hypothetical retrosynthetic disconnection **synthons**.

Seeing the synthons above may help us to reason that we could, in theory, synthesize a molecule of 1-butyne by combining an ethyl cation with an ethynide anion. We know, however, that bottles of carbocations and carbanions are not to be found on our laboratory shelves and that even as a reaction intermediate, it is not reasonable to consider an ethyl carbocation. What we need are the **synthetic equivalents** of these synthons. The synthetic equivalent of an ethynide ion is sodium ethynide, because sodium ethynide contains an ethynide ion (and a sodium cation). The synthetic equivalent of an ethyl cation is ethyl bromide. To understand how this is true, we reason as follows: if ethyl bromide were to react by an S_N1 reaction, it would produce an ethyl cation and a bromide ion. However, we know that, being a primary halide, ethyl bromide is unlikely to react by an S_N1 reaction. Ethyl bromide, however, will react readily with a strong nucleophile such as sodium ethynide by an S_N2 reaction, and when it reacts, the product that is obtained is the same as the product that would have been obtained from the reaction of an ethyl cation with sodium ethynide. Thus, ethyl bromide, in this reaction, functions as the synthetic equivalent of an ethyl cation.

2-Bromobutane could also be synthesized from compounds of two carbons or fewer by a route in which (*E*)- or (*Z*)-2-butene is an intermediate. You may wish to work out the details of that synthesis for yourself.

8.20C Stereochemical Considerations

Consider another example, a synthesis that requires stereochemical control: the synthesis of the enantiomeric 2,3-butanediols, (2*R*,3*R*)-2,3-butanediol and (2*S*,3*S*)-2,3-butanediol, from compounds of two carbon atoms or fewer, and in a way that does not produce the meso stereoisomer.

---

*For an excellent detailed treatment of this approach you may want to read the following: Warren, S., and Wyatt, P., *Organic Synthesis, The Disconnection Approach*, 2nd Ed. Wiley: New York, 2009; and Warren, S., and Wyatt, P., *Workbook for Organic Synthesis, The Disconnection Approach*, 2nd Ed. Wiley: New York, 2009.

HOW TO Apply Stereochemical Considerations in Planning a Synthesis of 2,3-Butanediol Enantiomers

Here we see that a possible final step to the enantiomers is syn dihydroxylation of *trans*-2-butene. This reaction is stereospecific and produces the desired enantiomeric 2,3-butanediols as a racemic form. Here we have made the key choice **not** to use *cis*-2-butene. Had we chosen *cis*-2-butene, our product would have been the meso 2,3-butanediol stereoisomer.

Retrosynthetic Analysis

Enantiomeric 2,3-butanediols

(R,R)

(S,S)

syn dihydroxylation at either face of the alkene

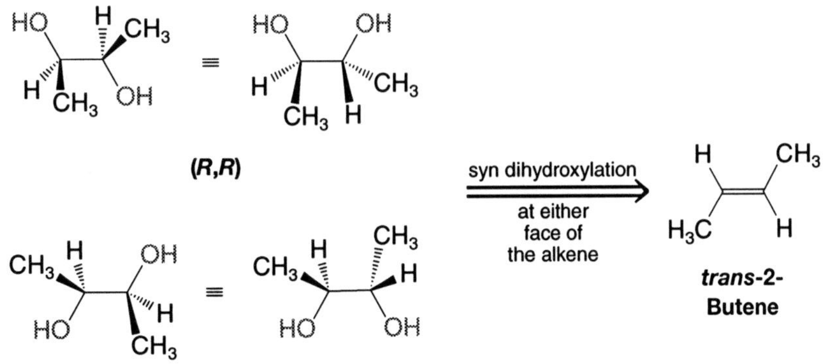

trans-2-Butene

Synthesis

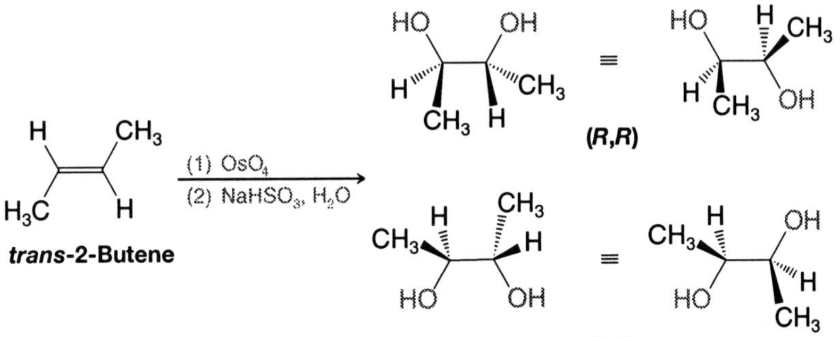

trans-2-Butene

(1) OsO$_4$
(2) NaHSO$_3$, H$_2$O

(R,R)

(S,S)

Enantiomeric 2,3-butanediols

Synthesis of *trans*-2-butene can be accomplished by treating 2-butyne with lithium in liquid ammonia. The anti addition of hydrogen by this reaction gives us the trans product that we need.

Retrosynthetic Analysis

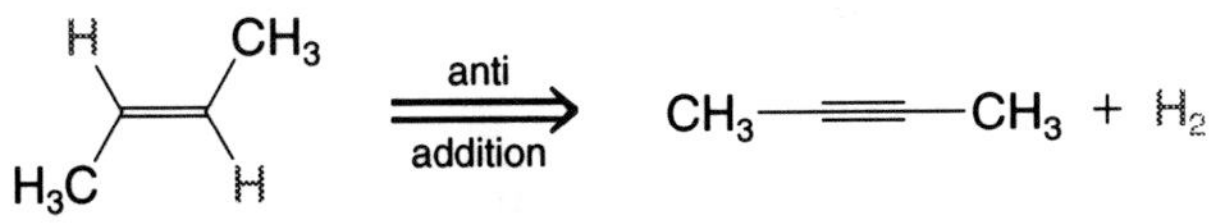

trans-2-Butene

anti addition

CH$_3$——≡——CH$_3$ + H$_2$

2-Butyne

Synthesis

CH$_3$——≡——CH$_3$

(1) Li, EtNH$_2$
(2) NH$_4$Cl
(anti addition of H$_2$)

trans-2-Butene

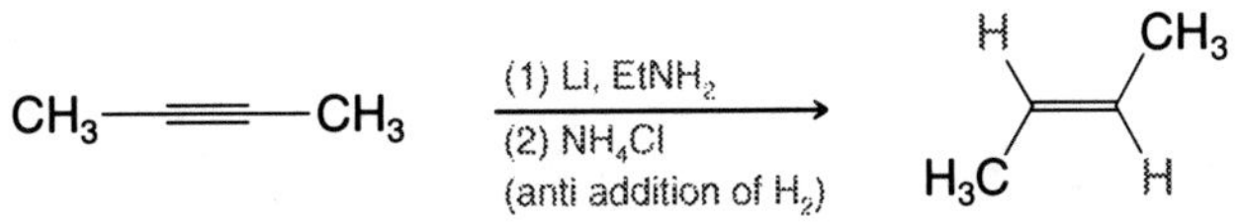

2-Butyne

trans-2-Butene

* The reaction above is an example of a **stereoselective reaction**. A stereoselective reaction is one in which the reactant is not necessarily chiral (as in the case of an alkyne) but in which the reaction produces predominantly or exclusively one stereoisomeric form of the product (or a certain subset of stereoisomers from among all those that are possible).

* Note the difference between stereoselective and stereospecific. A stereospecific reaction is one that produces predominantly or exclusively one stereoisomer of the product when a specific stereoisomeric form of the reactant is used. (All stereospecific reactions are stereoselective, but the reverse is not necessarily true.)

We can synthesize 2-butyne from propyne by first converting it to sodium propynide and then alkylating sodium propynide with methyl iodide:

Retrosynthetic Analysis

$$CH_3 \equiv\!\!\xi\,CH_3 \implies CH_3 \equiv\!:^-Na^+ + CH_3 \!\!-\!\!I$$

$$CH_3 \equiv\!:^-Na^+ \implies CH_3 \equiv\!\!-H + NaNH_2$$

Synthesis

$$CH_3 \equiv\!\!-H \xrightarrow[\text{(2) } CH_3I]{\text{(1) } NaNH_2/\text{liq. } NH_3} CH_3 \equiv\!\!-CH_3$$

And to get propyne, we synthesize it from ethyne:

Retrosynthetic Analysis

$$H \equiv\!\!\xi\,CH_3 \implies H \equiv\!:^-Na^+ + CH_3 \!\!-\!\!I$$

Synthesis

$$H \equiv\!\!-H \xrightarrow[\text{(2) } CH_3I]{\text{(1) } NaNH_2/\text{liq. } NH_3} CH_3 \equiv\!\!-H$$

●●● SOLVED PROBLEM 8.8

ILLUSTRATING A STEREOSPECIFIC MULTISTEP SYNTHESIS: Starting with compounds of two carbon atoms or fewer, outline a stereospecific synthesis of *meso*-3,4-dibromohexane.

STRATEGY AND ANSWER: We begin by working backward from the target molecule. Since the target molecule is a meso compound, it is convenient to start by drawing a formula that illustrates its internal plane of symmetry, as shown below. But since we also know that a vicinal dibromide can be formed by anti addition of bromine to an alkene, we redraw the target molecule formula in a conformation that shows the bromine atoms anti to each other, as they would be after addition to an alkene. Then, retaining the relative spatial relationship of the alkyl groups, we draw the alkene precursor to the 1,2-dibromide, and find that this compound is (*E*)-3-hexene. Knowing that an (*E*) alkene can be formed by anti addition of hydrogen to an alkyne using lithium in ethylamine or ammonia (Section 7.14B), we see that 3-hexyne is a suitable synthetic precursor to (*E*)-3-hexene. Last, because we know it is possible to alkylate terminal alkynes, we recognize that 3-hexyne could be synthesized from acetylene by two successive alkylations with an ethyl halide. The following is a retrosynthetic analysis.

Retrosynthetic Analysis

meso-3,4-Dibromohexane

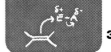

The synthesis could be written as follows:

$$H—\!\!\equiv\!\!—H \xrightarrow[\text{(2) CH}_3\text{CH}_2\text{Br}]{\text{(1) NaNH}_2,\ \text{liq. NH}_3}\quad \text{----}\!\!\equiv\!\!—H \xrightarrow[\text{(2) CH}_3\text{CH}_2\text{Br}]{\text{(1) NaNH}_2,\ \text{liq. NH}_3}\quad \text{----}\!\!\equiv\!\!—\text{----}$$

then

$$\text{----}\!\!\equiv\!\!—\text{----} \xrightarrow[\text{(2) NH}_4\text{Cl}]{\text{(1) Li, EtNH}_2}$$

and finally

***meso*-3,4-Dibromohexane**

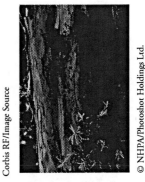

● ● ● ·········

How would you modify the procedure given in Solved Problem 8.8 so as to synthesize a racemic form of (3*R*,4*R*)- and (3*S*,4*S*)-3,4-dibromohexane? **PRACTICE PROBLEM 8.25**

[WHY Do These Topics Matter?

ALKENES IN NATURAL CHEMICAL SYNTHESES

As illustrated in Chapters 7 and 8, unsaturation within molecules provides numerous possibilities for the addition of functional groups and the creation of C—C bonds. Thus, it should probably come as no surprise that the synthesis of complex molecules in nature also involves sites of unsaturation. Alkenes, not alkynes, are the main players in such processes, often in the form of isoprene building blocks. The five-carbon isoprene unit is easily recognized as an unsaturated four carbon chain with a methyl branch. In nature, several isoprene units combine to make long carbon chains that terminate with a reactive pyrophosphate group, such as geranylgeranyl pyrophosphate (GGPP). Such compounds take part in highly controlled reaction processes that generate tens of thousands of distinct natural products—compounds that serve as critical hormones and signaling molecules, among a myriad of other functions.

A eucalyptus tree, the source of eucalyptol.

A Pacific yew tree, the source of Taxol.

Corbis RF/Image Source

© NHPA/Photoshot Holdings Ltd.

Isoprene building block   **Geranylgeranyl pyrophosphate (GGPP)**

$$PP = \begin{array}{c} O \\ \| \\ -P-O-P-O^- \\ | \qquad | \\ O_- \qquad O_- \end{array}$$

This chemistry begins with an enzyme that folds the isoprene-containing building block into a distinct conformation, one meant to trigger specific C—C bond formations where the OPP group will serve as a departing group in S_N2 or S_N1 processes. In some

(continues on next page)

cases, the leaving group initially helps to reposition the site of C—C bond formation through chemistry such as that shown below for the synthesis of eucalyptol. After that key step, though, it is all chemistry of the type you have seen in this chapter where alkenes are attacking electrophilic species, with the OPP group serving to shuttle around protons (try filling in the missing proton transfer steps for yourself).

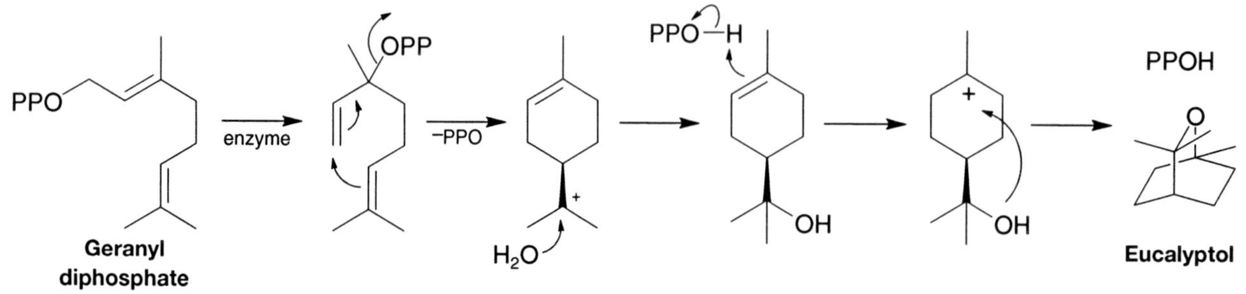

Geranyl diphosphate

Eucalyptol

In other cases, the OPP group is replaced directly. For example, following enzymatic organization of GGPP as shown below, removal of the indicated proton by a base can cause the neighboring alkene to displace the OPP group, leading to a molecule known as cembrene A. Then, through a series of further alkene-based C—C bond formation reactions (using more of the standard principles of nucleophiles and electrophiles as we have discussed), and oxidations, and again controlled by specific enzymes, this carbon core can be converted into materials like kempene-2. For termites, this and related molecules serve as critical protective agents against invading species.

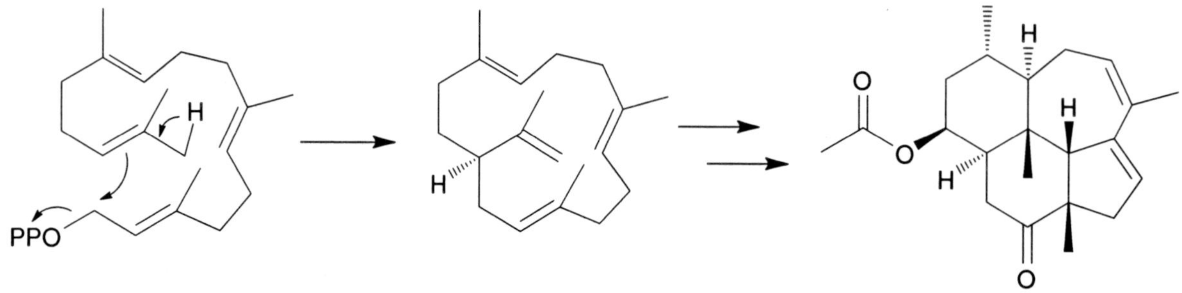

GGPP   **Cembrene A**   **Kempene-2**

What is amazing, however, is that other organisms can take the same starting piece and make completely different molecules through exactly the same processes (folding and oxidation). In the Pacific yew tree, for example, GGPP is converted into Taxol, a compound that is currently one of the world's leading cancer therapies. Several other plant species and fungi, by contrast, turn GGPP into a signaling molecule known as gibberellic acid 3. There is a lot of complex organic chemistry going on in these processes, but the key take-home message is both simple and elegant: from one single set of starting materials a large number of diverse compounds can be synthesized, all through the power of alkenes, one additional reactive group, and some very specialized and highly evolved enzymes.

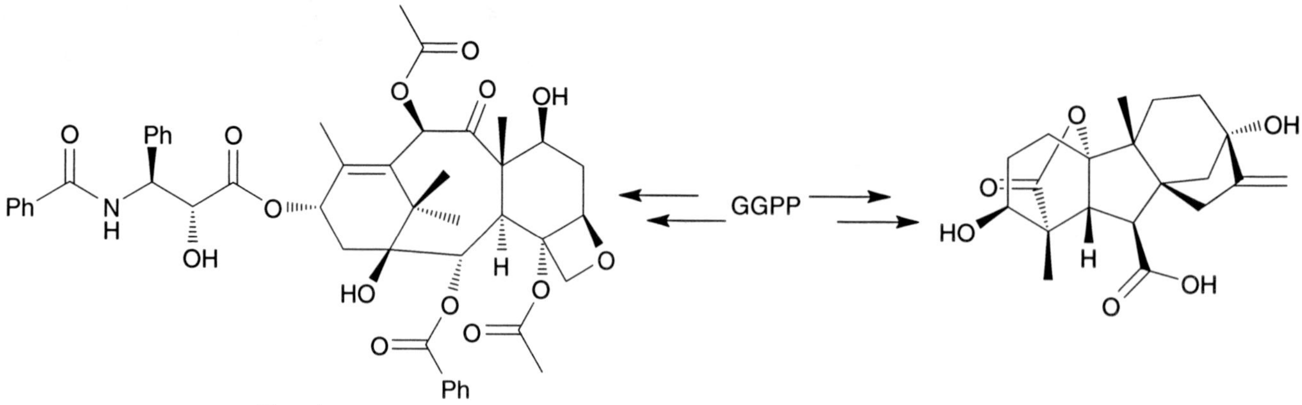

Taxol   **Gibberellic acid 3**

To learn more about these topics, see:

1. Fischbach, M. A.; Clardy, J. "One pathway, many products" in *Nature: Chem. Bio.* **2007**, *3*, 353–355.
2. Ishihara, Y.; Baran, P.S. "Two-Phase Terpene Total Synthesis: Historical Perspective and Application to the Taxol® Problem" in *Synlett* **2010**, *12*, 1733–1745.

SUMMARY AND REVIEW TOOLS

The study aids for this chapter include key terms and concepts (which are hyperlinked to the Glossary from the bold, blue terms in the *WileyPLUS* version of the book at wileyplus.com), a Mechanism Review of Alkene Addition Reactions, and a Synthetic Connections roadmap involving alkenes and alkynes.

PROBLEMS PLUS

Note to Instructors: Many of the homework problems are available for assignment via *WileyPLUS*, an online teaching and learning solution.

ALKENES AND ALKYNES REACTION TOOLKIT

8.26 Write structural formulas for the products that form when 1-butene reacts with each of the following reagents:

(a) HI

(b) H_2, Pt

(c) Dilute H_2SO_4, warm

(d) Cold concentrated H_2SO_4

(e) Cold concentrated H_2SO_4, then H_2O and heat

(f) HBr

(g) Br_2 in CCl_4

(h) Br_2 in H_2O

(i) HCl

(j) O_3, then Me_2S

(k) OsO_4, then $NaHSO_3/H_2O$

(l) $KMnO_4$, HO^-, heat, then H_3O^+

(m) $Hg(OAc)_2$ in THF and H_2O, then $NaBH_4$, HO^-

(n) BH_3:THF, then H_2O_2, HO^-

8.27 Repeat Exercise 8.26 using 1-methylcyclopentene instead of 1-butene.

8.28 Write structures for the major organic products from the following reactions. Show stereoisomers where applicable.

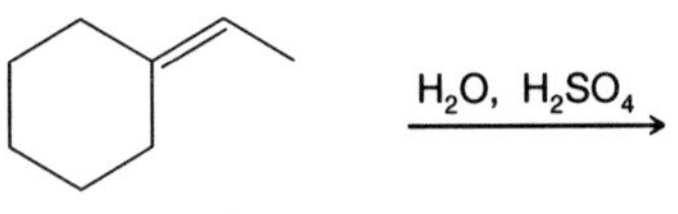

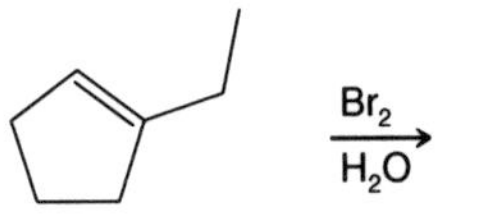

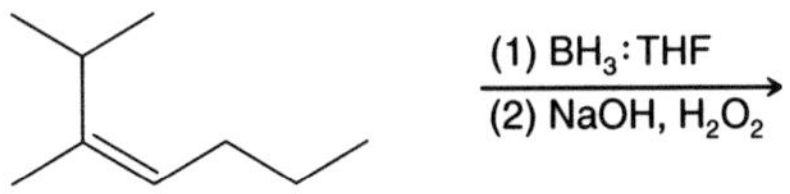

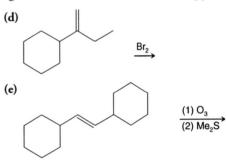

8.29 Give the structure of the products that you would expect from the reaction of 1-butyne with:

(a) One molar equivalent of Br_2

(b) One molar equivalent of HBr

(c) Two molar equivalents of HBr

(d) H_2 (in excess)/Pt

(e) H_2, Ni_2B (P-2)

(f) $NaNH_2$ in liquid NH_3, then CH_3I

(g) $NaNH_2$ in liquid NH_3, then $(CH_3)_3CBr$

8.30 Give the structure of the products you would expect from the reaction (if any) of 2-butyne with:

(a) One molar equivalent of HBr

(b) Two molar equivalents of HBr

(c) One molar equivalent of Br_2

(d) Two molar equivalents of Br_2

(e) H_2, Ni_2B (P-2)

(f) One molar equivalent of HCl

(g) Li/liquid NH_3

(h) H_2 (in excess), Pt

(i) Two molar equivalents of H_2, Pt

(j) Hot $KMnO_4$, HO^-, then H_3O^+

(k) O_3, then HOAc

(l) $NaNH_2$, liquid NH_3

8.31 Write structures for the major organic products from the following reactions. Show stereoisomers where applicable.

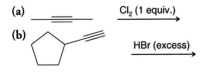

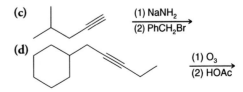

8.32 Show how 1-butyne could be synthesized from each of the following:

(a) 1-Butene   (b) 1-Chlorobutane   (c) 1-Chloro-1-butene   (d) 1,1-Dichlorobutane   (e) Ethyne and ethyl bromide

8.33 Starting with 2-methylpropene (isobutylene) and using any other needed reagents, outline a synthesis of each of the following:

(a)

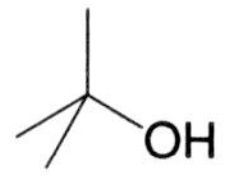

(b)

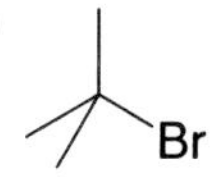

(c)

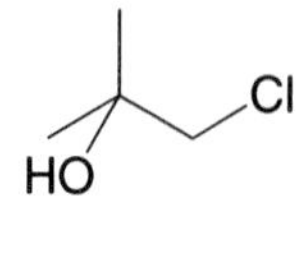

(d)

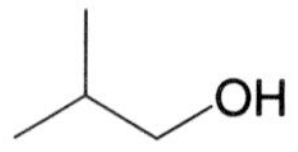

MECHANISMS

8.34 Write a three-dimensional formula for the product formed when 1-methylcyclohexene is treated with each of the following reagents. In each case, designate the location of deuterium or tritium atoms.

(a) (1) BH_3:THF, (2) CH_3CO_2T (c) (1) BD_3:THF, (2) NaOH, H_2O_2, H_2O

(b) (1) BD_3:THF, (2) CH_3CO_2D

8.35 Write a mechanism that accounts for the formation of ethyl isopropyl ether in the following reaction.

$$\xrightarrow[\text{EtOH}]{\text{HCl}}$$

Cl   +   OEt

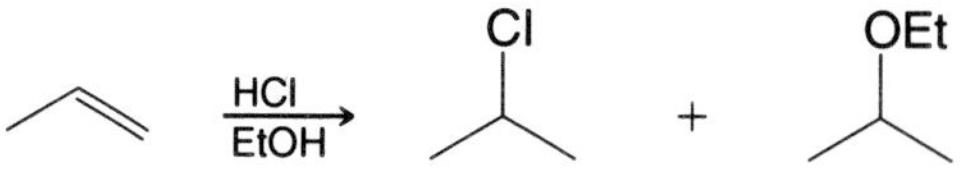

8.36 When, in separate reactions, 2-methylpropene, propene, and ethene are allowed to react with HI under the same conditions (i.e., identical concentration and temperature), 2-methylpropene is found to react fastest and ethene slowest. Provide an explanation for these relative rates.

8.37 Propose a mechanism that accounts for the following reaction.

$$\xrightarrow{\text{HI}}$$

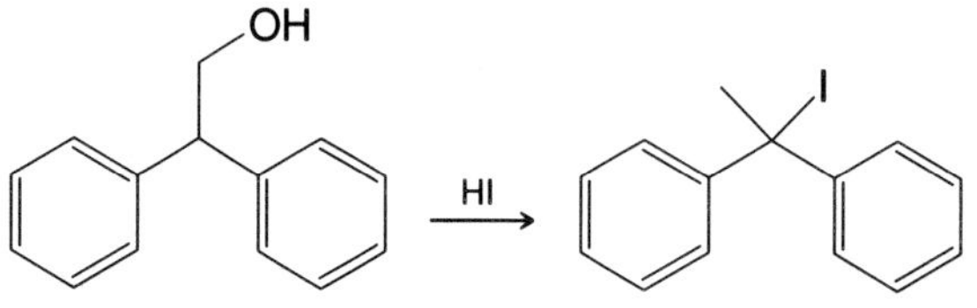

8.38 When 3,3-dimethyl-2-butanol is treated with concentrated HI, a rearrangement takes place. Which alkyl iodide would you expect from the reaction? (Show the mechanism by which it is formed.)

8.39 Write stereochemical formulas for all of the products that you would expect from each of the following reactions. (You may find models helpful.)

(a) 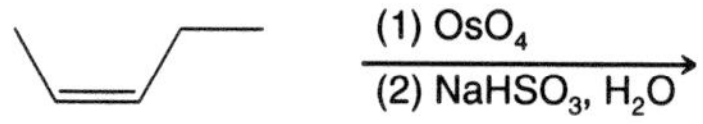 $\xrightarrow[\text{(2) NaHSO}_3\text{, H}_2\text{O}]{\text{(1) OsO}_4}$

(c)  $\xrightarrow{\text{Br}_2}$

(b) 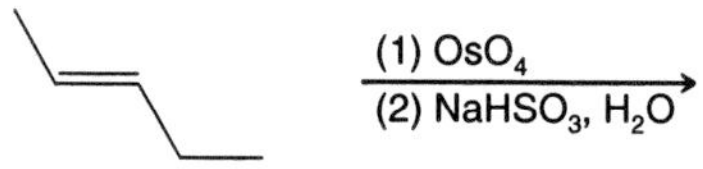 $\xrightarrow[\text{(2) NaHSO}_3\text{, H}_2\text{O}]{\text{(1) OsO}_4}$

(d)  $\xrightarrow{\text{Br}_2}$

8.40 Give (R, S) designations for each different compound given as an answer to Problem 8.39.

8.41 The double bond of tetrachloroethene is undetectable in the bromine test for unsaturation. Give a plausible explanation for this behavior.

8.42 The reaction of bromine with cyclohexene involves anti addition, which generates, initially, the diaxial confor-mation of the addition product that then undergoes a ring flip to the diequatorial conformation of *trans*-1,2-dibromo-cyclohexane. However, when the unsaturated bicyclic compound **I** is the alkene, instead of cyclohexene, the addition product is exclusively in a stable diaxial conformation. Account for this. (You may find it helpful to build handheld molecular models.)

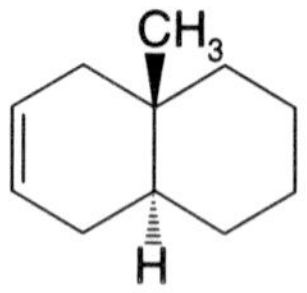

8.43 Propose a mechanism that explains formation of the products from the following reaction, including the distri-bution of the products as major and minor.

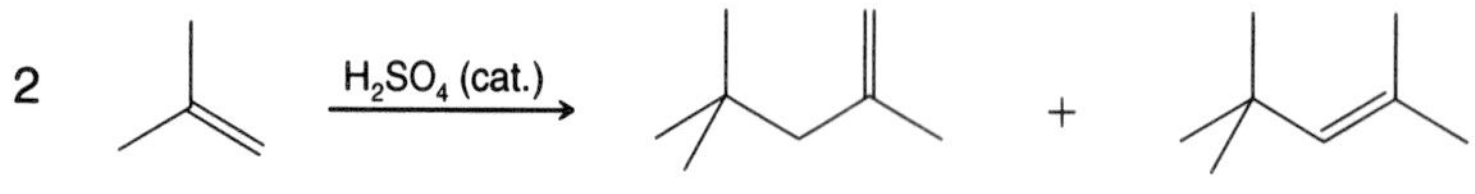

$$2 \quad \xrightarrow{\text{H}_2\text{SO}_4\text{ (cat.)}} \quad + $$

Major   **Minor**

8.44 Internal alkynes can be isomerized to terminal alkynes on treatment with $NaNH_2$. The process is much less successful when NaOH is used. Why is there this difference?

8.45 Write a mechanism that explains the following reaction.

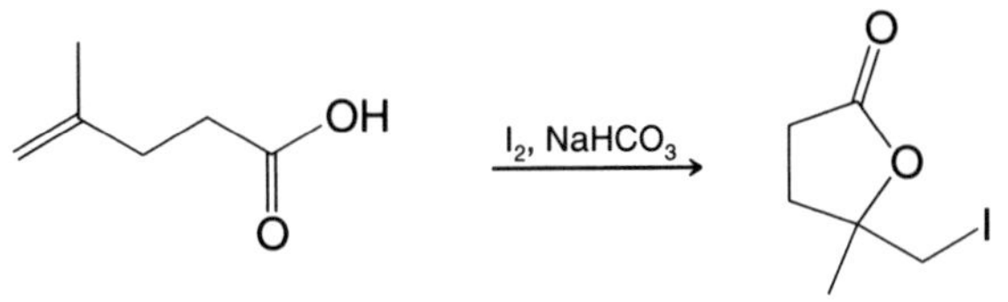

8.46 Write a mechanism for the following reaction.

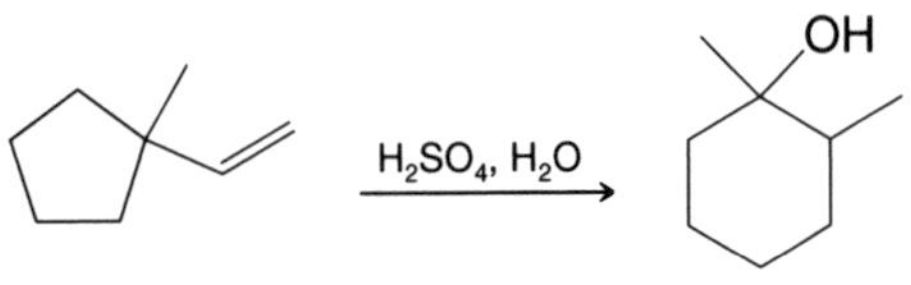

8.47 Write a mechanism that explains formation of the products shown in the following reaction.

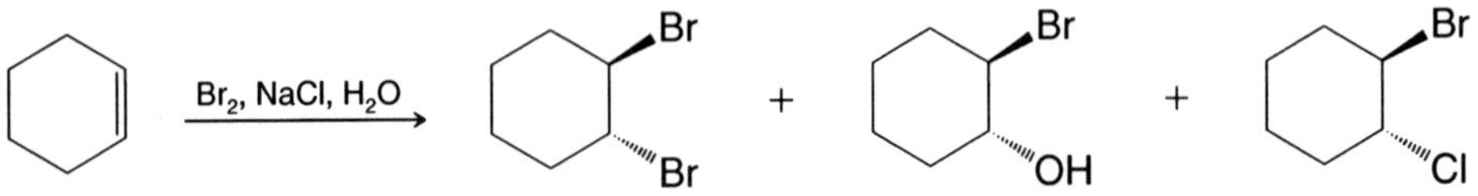

STRUCTURE ELUCIDATION

8.48 Myrcene, a fragrant compound found in bayberry wax, has the formula $C_{10}H_{16}$ and is known not to contain any triple bonds.

(a) What is the index of hydrogen deficiency of myrcene? When treated with excess hydrogen and a platinum catalyst, myrcene is converted to a compound **(A)** with the formula $C_{10}H_{22}$.

(b) How many rings does myrcene contain?

(c) How many double bonds? Compound **A** can be identified as 2,6-dimethyloctane. Ozonolysis of myrcene followed by treatment with dimethyl sulfide yields 2 mol of formaldehyde (HCHO), 1 mol of acetone (CH_3COCH_3), and a third compound **(B)** with the formula $C_5H_6O_3$.

(d) What is the structure of compound **B**?

(e) What is the structure of myrcene?

8.49 Farnesene (below) is a compound found in the waxy coating of apples. **(a)** Give the structure and IUPAC name of the product formed when farnesene is allowed to react with excess hydrogen in the presence of a platinum catalyst. **(b)** How many stereoisomers of the product are possible?

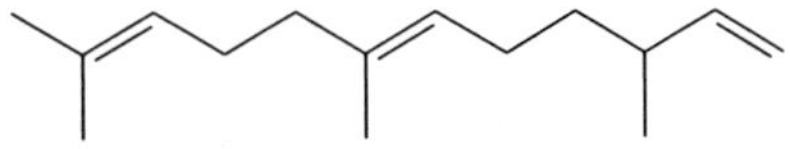

Farnesene

8.50 Write structural formulas for the products that would be formed when geranial, a component of lemongrass oil, is treated with ozone and then with dimethyl sulfide (Me_2S).

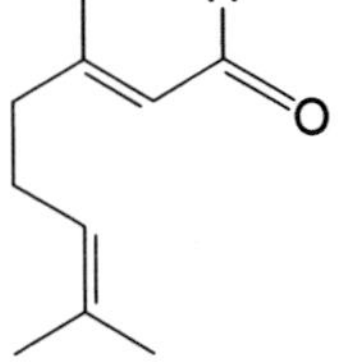

Geranial

8.51 Limonene is a compound found in orange oil and lemon oil. When limonene is treated with excess hydrogen and a platinum catalyst, the product of the reaction is 1-isopropyl-4-methylcyclohexane. When limonene is treated with ozone and then with dimethyl sulfide (Me_2S), the products of the reaction are formaldehyde (HCHO) and the following compound. Write a structural formula for limonene.

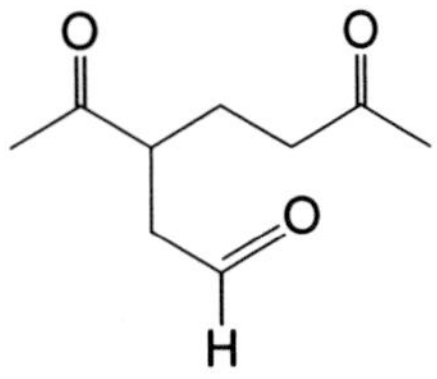

8.52 Pheromones (Section 4.7) are substances secreted by animals that produce a specific behavioral response in other members of the same species. Pheromones are effective at very low concentrations and include sex attractants, warning substances, and "aggregation" compounds. The sex attractant pheromone of the codling moth has the molecular formula $C_{13}H_{24}O$. Using information you can glean from the following reaction diagram, deduce the structure of the codling moth sex pheromone. The double bonds are known (on the basis of other evidence) to be (2Z,6E).

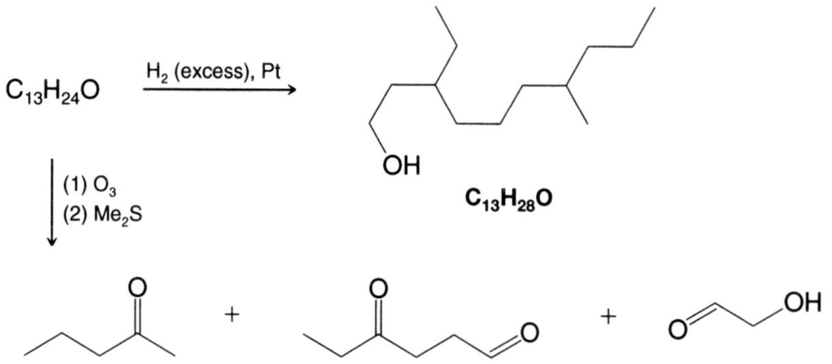

GENERAL PROBLEMS

8.53 Synthesize the following compound starting with ethyne and 1-bromopentane as your only organic reagents (except for solvents) and using any needed inorganic compounds.

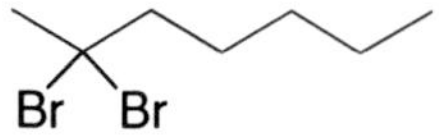

8.54 Shown below is the final step in a synthesis of an important perfume constituent, *cis*-jasmone. Which reagents would you choose to carry out this last step?

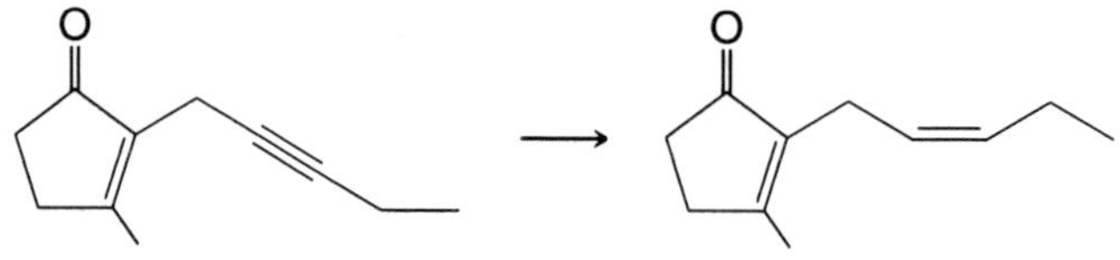

cis-**Jasmone**

8.55 Predict features of their IR spectra that you could use to distinguish between the members of the following pairs of compounds. You may find the IR chart in the endpapers of the book and Table 2.1 useful.

(a) Pentane and 1-pentyne
(b) Pentane and 1-pentene
(c) 1-Pentene and 1-pentyne
(d) Pentane and 1-bromopentane
(e) 2-Pentyne and 1-pentyne

(f) 1-Pentene and 1-pentanol
(g) Pentane and 1-pentanol
(h) 1-Bromo-2-pentene and 1-bromopentane
(i) 1-Pentanol and 2-penten-1-ol

8.56 Deduce the structures of compounds **A**, **B**, and **C**, which all have the formula C_6H_{10}. As you read the information that follows, draw reaction flowcharts (roadmaps) like those in Problems 8.24 and 8.52. This approach will help you solve the problem. All three compounds rapidly decolorize bromine; all three are soluble in cold concentrated sulfuric acid. Compound **A** has an absorption in its IR spectrum at about 3300 cm^{-1}, but compounds **B** and **C** do not. Compounds **A** and **B** both yield hexane when they are treated with excess hydrogen in the presence of a platinum catalyst. Under these conditions **C** absorbs only one molar equivalent of hydrogen and gives a product with the formula C_6H_{12}. When **A** is oxidized with hot basic potassium permanganate and the resulting solution acidified,

the only organic product that can be isolated is 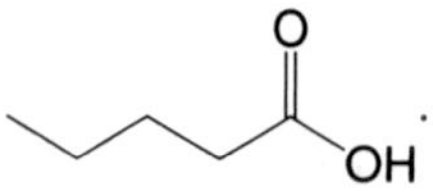 . Similar oxidation of **B** gives only 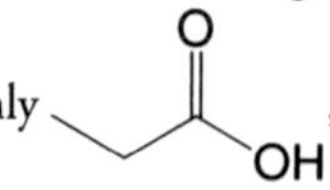 , and similar

treatment of **C** gives only

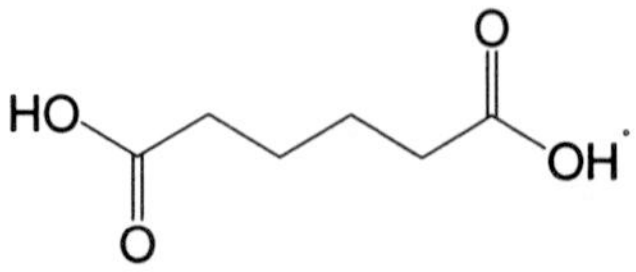

8.57 Ricinoleic acid, a compound that can be isolated from castor oil, has the structure $CH_3(CH_2)_5CHOHCH_2CH=CH(CH_2)_7CO_2H$.

(a) How many stereoisomers of this structure are possible?   (b) Write these structures.

8.58 There are two dicarboxylic acids with the general formula $HO_2CCH=CHCO_2H$. One dicarboxylic acid is called maleic acid; the other is called fumaric acid. When treated with OsO_4, followed by $NaHSO_3/H_2O$, maleic acid yields *meso*-tartaric acid and fumaric acid yields (±)-tartaric acid. Show how this information allows one to write stereochemical formulas for maleic acid and fumaric acid.

8.59 Use your answers to the preceding problem to predict the stereochemical outcome of the addition of bromine to maleic acid and to fumaric acid. **(a)** Which dicarboxylic acid would add bromine to yield a meso compound? **(b)** Which would yield a racemic form?

8.60 Alkyl halides add to alkenes in the presence of $AlCl_3$; yields are the highest when tertiary halides are used. Predict the outcome of the reaction of *tert*-pentyl chloride (1-chloro-2,2-dimethylpropane) with propene and specify the mechanistic steps.

8.61 Explain the stereochemical results observed in this catalytic hydrogenation. (You may find it helpful to build hand-held molecular models.)

I (70%)   **II (30%)**

8.62 Make a reaction flowchart (roadmap diagram), as in previous problems, to organize the information provided to solve this problem. An optically active compound **A** (assume that it is dextrorotatory) has the molecular formula $C_7H_{11}Br$. **A** reacts with hydrogen bromide, in the absence of peroxides, to yield isomeric products, **B** and **C**, with the molecular formula $C_7H_{12}Br_2$. Compound **B** is optically active; **C** is not. Treating **B** with 1 mol of potassium *tert*-butoxide yields (+)-**A**. Treating **C** with 1 mol of potassium *tert*-butoxide yields (±)-**A**. Treating **A** with potassium *tert*-butoxide yields **D** (C_7H_{10}). Subjecting 1 mol of **D** to ozonolysis followed by treatment with dimethyl sulfide (Me_2S) yields 2 mol of formaldehyde and 1 mol of 1,3-cyclopentanedione. Propose stereochemical formulas for **A**, **B**, **C**, and **D** and outline the reactions involved in these transformations.

1,3-Cyclopentanedione

8.63 A naturally occurring antibiotic called mycomycin has the structure shown here. Mycomycin is optically active. Explain this by writing structures for the enantiomeric forms of mycomycin.

$$HC\equiv C-C\equiv C-CH=C=CH-(CH=CH)_2CH_2CO_2H$$

Mycomycin

8.64 An optically active compound **D** has the molecular formula C_6H_{10} and shows a peak at about 3300 cm^{-1} in its IR spectrum. On catalytic hydrogenation **D** yields **E** (C_6H_{14}). Compound **E** is optically inactive and cannot be resolved. Propose structures for **D** and **E**.

8.65 (a) Based on the following information, draw three-dimensional formulas for **A**, **B**, and **C**.

Reaction of cyclopentene with bromine in water gives **A**.

Reaction of **A** with aqueous NaOH (1 equivalent, cold) gives **B**, C_5H_8O (no 3590–3650-cm^{-1} infrared absorption). (See the squalene cyclization discussion in "The Chemistry of…Cholesterol Biosynthesis" in *WileyPLUS* for a hint.)

Heating of **B** in methanol containing a catalytic amount of strong acid gives **C**, $C_6H_{12}O_2$, which does show 3590–3650-cm^{-1} infrared absorption.

(b) Specify the (*R*) or (*S*) configuration of the chirality centers in your predicted structures for **C**. Would **C** be formed as a single stereoisomer or as a racemate?

(c) How could you experimentally confirm your predictions about the stereochemistry of **C**?

CHALLENGE PROBLEMS

8.66 Propose a mechanism that explains the following transformation. (Note its similarity to the cyclization of squalene oxide to lanosterol, as shown in "The Chemistry of…Cholesterol Biosynthesis." in *WileyPLUS*.)

8.67 Triethylamine, $(C_2H_5)_3N$, like all amines, has a nitrogen atom with an unshared pair of electrons. Dichlorocarbene also has an unshared pair of electrons. Both can be represented as shown below. Draw the structures of compounds **D**, **E**, and **F**.

$$(C_2H_5)_3N: + :CCl_2 \longrightarrow D \qquad \text{(an unstable adduct)}$$

$$D \longrightarrow E + C_2H_4 \qquad \text{(by an intramolecular E2 reaction)}$$

$$E \xrightarrow{H_2O} F \qquad \text{(Water effects a replacement that is the reverse of that used to make } \textit{gem}\text{-dichlorides.)}$$

LEARNING GROUP PROBLEMS

1. (a) Synthesize (3S,4R)-3,4-dibromo-1-cyclohexylpentane (and its enantiomer, since a racemic mixture will be formed) from ethyne, 1-chloro-2-cyclohexylethane, bromomethane, and any other reagents necessary. (Use ethyne, 1-chloro-2-cyclohexylethane, and bromomethane as the sole sources of carbon atoms.) Start the problem by showing a retrosynthetic analysis. In the process, decide which atoms of the target molecule will come from which atoms of the starting reagents. Also, bear in mind how the stereospecificity of the reactions you employ can be used to achieve the required stereochemical form of the final product.

(b) Explain why a racemic mixture of products results from this synthesis.

(c) How could the synthesis be modified to produce a racemic mixture of the (3R,4R) and (3S,4S) isomers instead?

2. Write a reasonable and detailed mechanism for the following transformation:

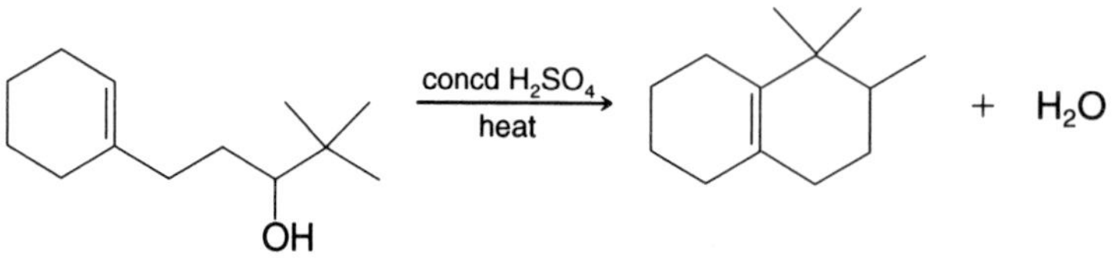

3. Deduce the structures of compounds **A–D**. Draw structures that show stereochemistry where appropriate:

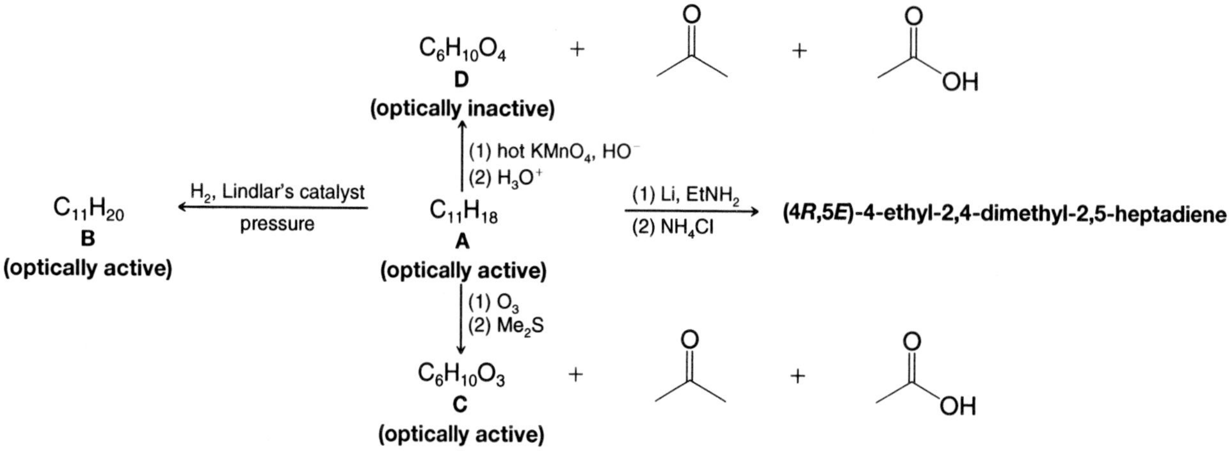

4. The Guam bubble snail (*Haminoea cymbalum*) contains kumepaloxane (shown below), a chemical signal agent discharged when this mollusk is disturbed by predatory carnivorous fish. The biosynthesis of bromoethers like kumepaloxane is thought to occur via the enzymatic intermediacy of a "Br$^+$" agent. Draw the structure of a possible biosynthetic precursor (*hint:* an alkene alcohol) to kumepaloxane and write a plausible and detailed mechanism by which it could be converted to kumepaloxane using Br$^+$ and some generic proton acceptor Y$^-$.

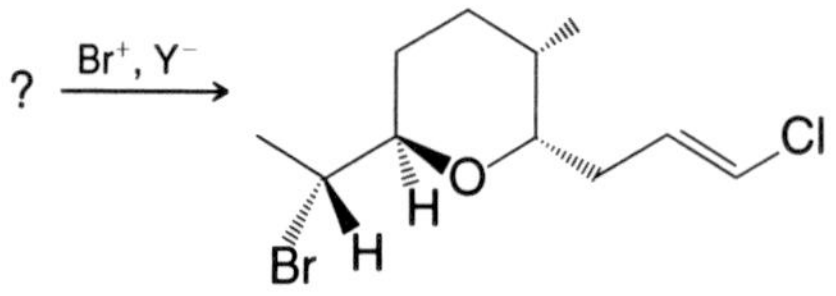

Kumepaloxane

[SUMMARY AND REVIEW TOOLS]

Summary of Alkene Addition Reactions

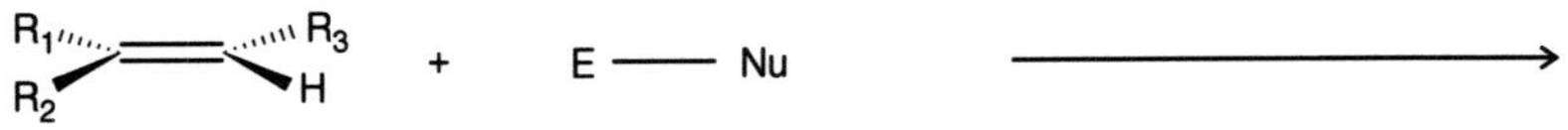

$$R_1\text{—}R_2\text{C}=\text{CR}_3\text{H} \quad + \quad E\text{—}Nu$$

	Reaction Conditions	Electrophile	Nucleophile	Key Intermediates or Transition State	Regiochemistry	Stereochemistry of Addition	Product*
Hydrohalogenation	H—X	$\overset{\delta+}{H}\text{—}\overset{\delta-}{X}$	:$\ddot{\text{X}}$:⁻	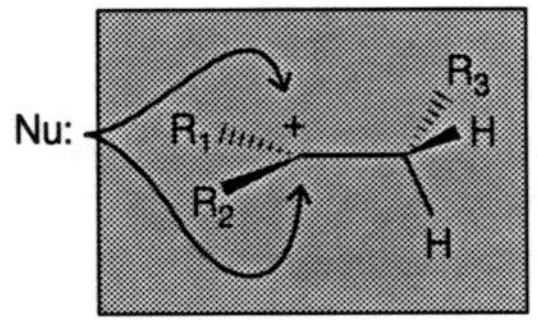	Markovnikov	Not controlled	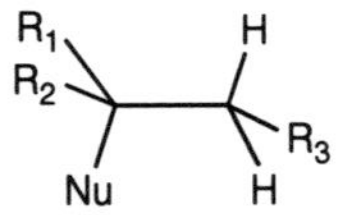 Nu = X or OH
Hydration (acid cat.)	Cat. HA, H_2O	$H\text{—}\overset{+}{\underset{H}{O}}\text{—}H$	$H\text{—}\ddot{O}\text{—}H$		Markovnikov	Not controlled	
Halogenation	X_2 (nonnucleophilic solvent)	$\overset{\delta+}{X}\text{—}\overset{\delta-}{X}$	:$\ddot{\text{X}}$:⁻	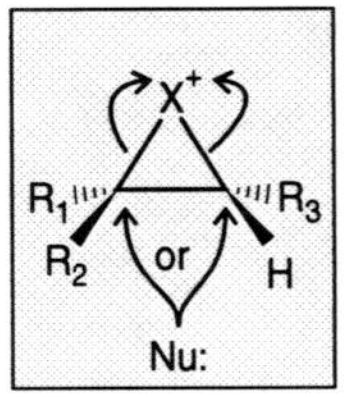	Not applicable	Anti	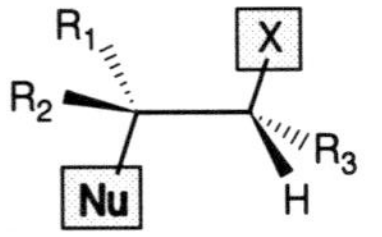
Halohydrin Formation	X_2, ROH; R = H or C (nucleophilic solvent)	$\overset{\delta+}{X}\text{—}\overset{\delta-}{X}$	$H\text{—}\ddot{O}\text{—}R$		Markovnikov	Anti	Nu = X or OR
Oxymercuration–Demercuration	(1) Hg(OAc)₂, HOR: THF (R = H or C); (2) NaBH₄, HO⁻	⁺HgOAc	$H\text{—}\ddot{O}\text{—}R$	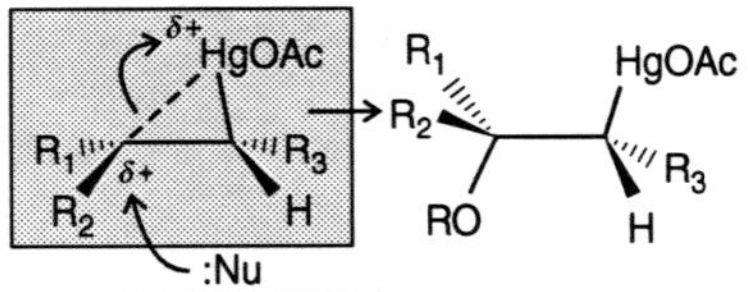	Markovnikov	Not controlled	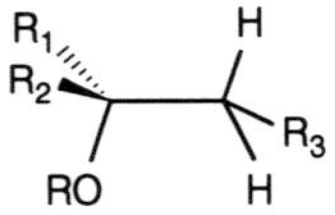
Hydroboration–Oxidation	(1) BH₃:THF; (2) H₂O₂, HO⁻		$H\text{—}\underset{H}{B}\text{—}H$	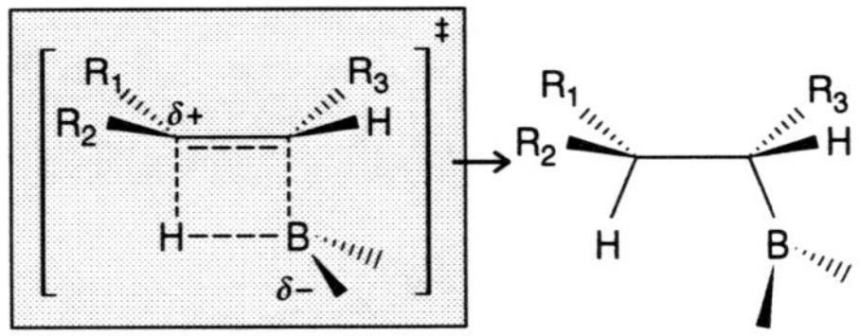	anti-Markovnikov	Net anti-Markovnikov / Syn	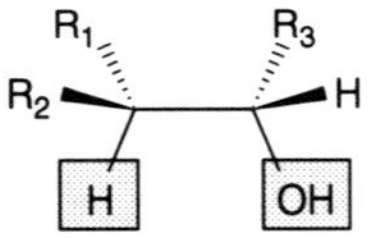
1,2-Dihydroxylation	(1) OsO₄; (2) aq NaHSO₃			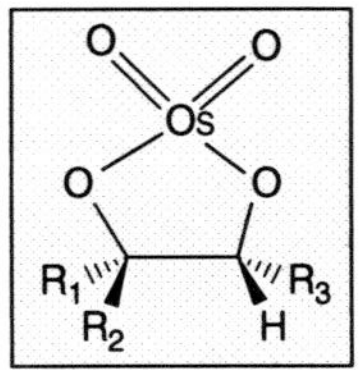		Syn	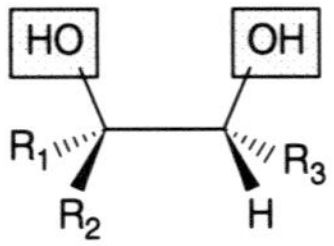

*The products are formed as a mixture of enantiomers in each case.

*The generic alkene chosen has a substitution pattern that allows both regiochemistry and stereochemistry of the products to be discerned.

[S U M M A R Y A N D R E V I E W T O O L S]

Synthetic Connections of Alkynes and Alkenes: II

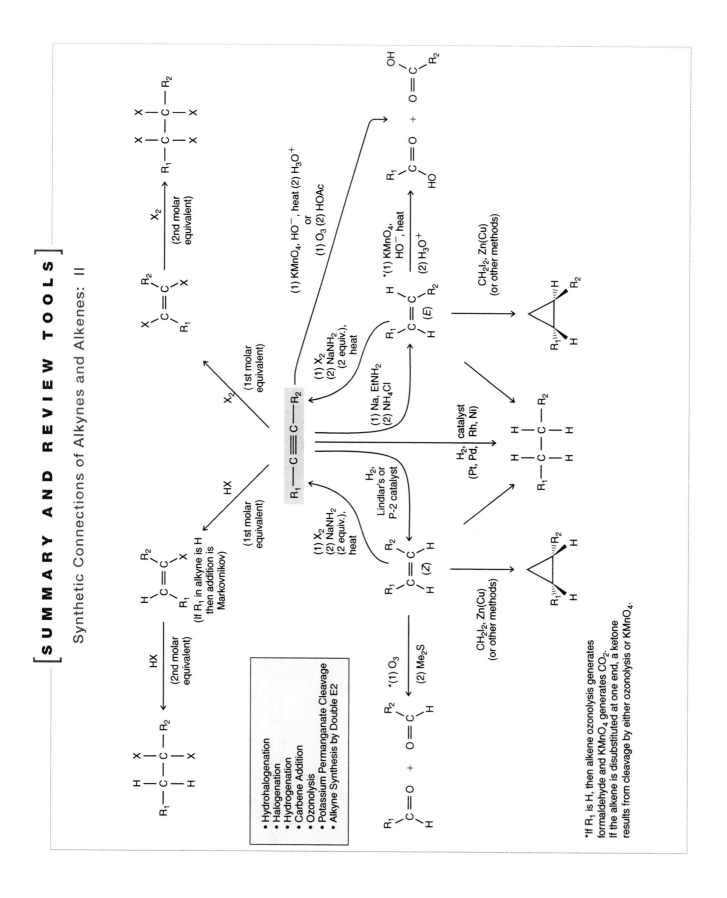

*If R₁ is H, then alkene ozonolysis generates formaldehyde and KMnO₄ generates CO₂. If the alkene is disubstituted at one end, a ketone results from cleavage by either ozonolysis or KMnO₄.

- Hydrohalogenation
- Halogenation
- Hydrogenation
- Carbene Addition
- Ozonolysis
- Potassium Permanganate Cleavage
- Alkyne Synthesis by Double E2

CHAPTER

10

Radical Reactions

Unpaired electrons lead to many burning questions about radical types of reactivity. In fact, species with unpaired electrons are called radicals, and they are involved in the chemistry of burning, aging, disease, as well as in reactions related to destruction of the ozone layer and the synthesis of products that enhance our everyday lives. For example, polyethylene, which can have a molecular weight from the thousands to the millions, and practical uses ranging from plastic films and wraps to water bottles, bulletproof vests, and hip and knee replacements, is made by a reaction involving radicals. Oxygen that we breathe and nitric oxide that serves as a chemical signaling agent for some fundamental biological processes are both molecules with unpaired electrons. Highly colored natural compounds like those found in blueberries and carrots react with radicals and may protect us from undesirable biological radical reactions. Large portions of the economy hinge on radicals, as well, from reactions used to make polymers like polyethylene, to the target action of pharmaceuticals like Cialis, Levitra, and Viagra, which act on a nitric oxide biological signaling pathway.

IN THIS CHAPTER WE WILL CONSIDER:

- the properties of radicals, their formation, and their reactivity
- significant radical-based reactions in nature

[**WHY** DO THESE TOPICS MATTER?] At the end of the chapter, we will show that there is a natural molecule that combines radical chemistry and molecular shape in a way that can cause cell death. Chemists have used this knowledge to fashion a few anticancer drugs.

10.1 INTRODUCTION: HOW RADICALS FORM AND HOW THEY REACT

So far almost all of the reactions whose mechanisms we have studied have been *ionic reactions*. Ionic reactions are those in which covalent bonds break **heterolytically** and in which ions are involved as reactants, intermediates, or products.

Another broad category of reactions has mechanisms that involve *homolysis* of covalent bonds with the production of intermediates possessing unpaired electrons called **radicals** (or **free radicals**):

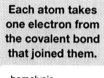

Each atom takes one electron from the covalent bond that joined them.

$$A \overset{\frown}{:} B \xrightarrow{\text{homolysis}} A\cdot + \cdot B$$
Radicals

Helpful Hint

A single-barbed curved arrow shows movement of one electron.

This simple example illustrates the way we use **single-barbed** curved arrows to show the movement of **a single electron** (not of an electron pair as we have done earlier). In this instance, each group, A and B, comes away with one of the electrons of the covalent bond that joined them.

10.1A Production of Radicals

● Energy in the form of heat or light must be supplied to cause homolysis of covalent bonds (Section 10.2).

For example, compounds with an oxygen–oxygen single bond, called *peroxides*, undergo homolysis readily when heated, because the oxygen–oxygen bond is weak. The products are two radicals, called alkoxyl radicals:

$$R-\ddot{\underset{..}{O}} \overset{\frown}{:} \ddot{\underset{..}{O}}-R \xrightarrow{\text{heat}} 2\ R-\ddot{\underset{..}{O}}\cdot$$

Dialkyl peroxide   **Alkoxyl radicals**

Homolysis of a dialkyl peroxide.

Halogen molecules (X_2) also contain a relatively weak bond. As we shall soon see, halogens undergo homolysis readily when heated or when irradiated with light of a wavelength that can be absorbed by the halogen molecule:

$$:\ddot{\underset{..}{X}} \overset{\frown}{:} \ddot{\underset{..}{X}}: \xrightarrow[\substack{\text{heat} \\ \text{or light }(h\nu)}]{\text{homolysis}} 2\ :\ddot{\underset{..}{X}}\cdot$$

Homolysis of a halogen molecule.

The products of this homolysis are halogen atoms, and because halogen atoms contain an unpaired electron, they are radicals.

10.1B Reactions of Radicals

● Almost all small radicals are short-lived, highly reactive species.

When radicals collide with other molecules, they tend to react in a way that leads to pairing of their unpaired electron. One way they can do this is by abstracting an atom from another molecule. To abstract an atom means to remove an atom by homolytic bond cleavage as the atom forms a bond with another radical. For example, a halogen atom may abstract a hydrogen atom from an alkane. This **hydrogen abstraction** gives the halogen atom an electron (from the hydrogen atom) to pair with its unpaired electron. Notice, however, that the other product of this abstraction *is another radical intermediate*, in this case, an alkyl radical, $R\cdot$, which goes on to react further, as we shall see in this chapter.

[A MECHANISM FOR THE REACTION — Hydrogen Atom Abstraction]

General Reaction

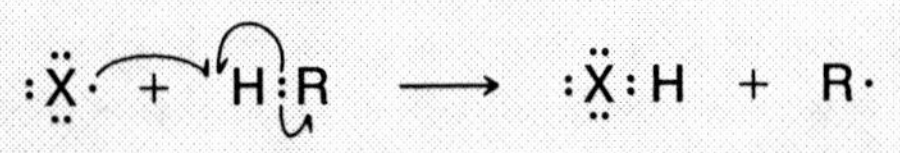

$$:\ddot{X}\cdot \; + \; H{:}R \longrightarrow :\ddot{X}{:}H \; + \; R\cdot$$

| Reactive radical intermediate | Alkane | Alkyl radical intermediate (reacts further) |

Specific Example

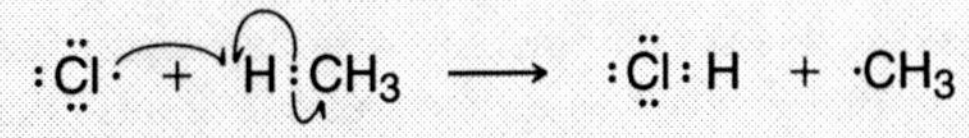

$$:\ddot{Cl}\cdot \; + \; H{:}CH_3 \longrightarrow :\ddot{Cl}{:}H \; + \; \cdot CH_3$$

| Chlorine atom (a radical) | Methane | Methyl radical intermediate (reacts further) |

This behavior is characteristic of radical reactions. Consider another example, one that shows another way in which radicals can react: they can combine with a compound containing a multiple bond to produce a new radical, which goes on to react further. (We shall study reactions of this type in Section 10.10.)

[A MECHANISM FOR THE REACTION — Radical Addition to a π Bond]

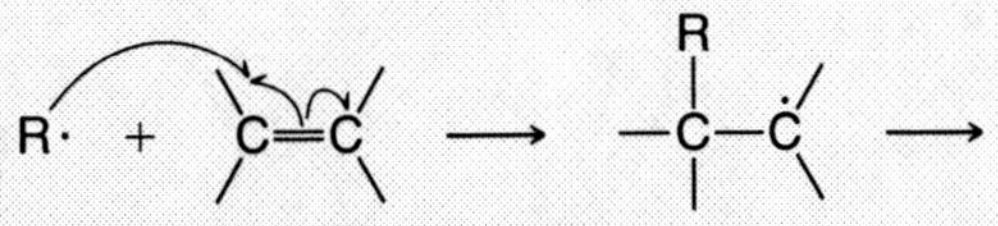

$$R\cdot \; + \; C{=}C \longrightarrow -\overset{\underset{R}{|}}{C}-\overset{\cdot}{C} \longrightarrow \text{Further reaction (Section 10.11)}$$

| Reactive alkyl radical intermediate | Alkene | New radical intermediate |

THE CHEMISTRY OF... Acne Medications

It turns out that although certain peroxides are great at initiating radical reactions, peroxy radicals also have many valuable uses on their own. For example, benzoyl peroxide is an active ingredient typically found in many acne medications that breaks apart and forms radicals through the warmth of our skin and exposure to light. These radicals can then kill the bacteria that cause break-outs.

The same compound is also used as a whitening and bleaching agent. As we will see in Chapter 13, many colored compounds possess double bonds in conjugation; the benzoyl peroxide radicals can add to those bonds, break their conjugation, and remove their color to leave behind new white materials. If you have ever wiped your face after using an acne medication with a colored towel, you may already have seen these effects!

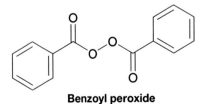

Benzoyl peroxide

10.2 HOMOLYTIC BOND DISSOCIATION ENERGIES (*DH°*)

When atoms combine to form molecules, energy is released as covalent bonds form. The molecules of the products have lower enthalpy than the separate atoms. When hydrogen atoms combine to form hydrogen molecules, for example, the reaction is *exothermic*; it evolves 436 kJ of heat for every mole of hydrogen that is produced. Similarly, when chlorine atoms combine to form chlorine molecules, the reaction evolves 243 kJ mol^{-1} of chlorine produced:

$$H\cdot \; + \; H\cdot \; \longrightarrow \; H—H \qquad \Delta H° = -436 \text{ kJ mol}^{-1}$$
$$Cl\cdot \; + \; Cl\cdot \; \longrightarrow \; Cl—Cl \qquad \Delta H° = -243 \text{ kJ mol}^{-1}$$

Bond formation is an exothermic process: $\Delta H°$ is negative.

Reactions in which only bond breaking occurs are always endothermic. The energy required to break the covalent bonds of hydrogen or chlorine homolytically is exactly equal to that evolved when the separate atoms combine to form molecules. In the bond cleavage reaction, however, $\Delta H°$ is positive:

$$H—H \; \longrightarrow \; H\cdot \; + \; H\cdot \qquad \Delta H° = +436 \text{ kJ mol}^{-1}$$
$$Cl—Cl \; \longrightarrow \; Cl\cdot \; + \; Cl\cdot \qquad \Delta H° = +243 \text{ kJ mol}^{-1}$$

Bond breaking is an endothermic process: $\Delta H°$ is positive.

- Energy must be supplied to break covalent bonds.
- The energies required to break covalent bonds homolytically are called **homolytic bond dissociation energies**, and they are usually abbreviated by the symbol *DH°*.

The homolytic bond dissociation energies of hydrogen and chlorine, for example, can be written in the following way:

$$H—H \qquad\qquad Cl—Cl$$
$$(\textbf{\textit{DH}}° = \textbf{436 kJ mol}^{-1}) \qquad (\textbf{\textit{DH}}° = \textbf{243 kJ mol}^{-1})$$

The homolytic bond dissociation energies of a variety of covalent bonds have been determined experimentally or calculated from related data. Some of these *DH°* values are listed in Table 10.1.

10.2A HOW TO Use Homolytic Bond Dissociation Energies to Determine the Relative Stabilities of Radicals

Homolytic bond dissociation energies also provide us with a convenient way to estimate the relative stabilities of radicals. If we examine the data given in Table 10.1, we find the following values of *DH°* for the primary and secondary C—H bonds of propane:

$$(\textbf{\textit{DH}}° = \textbf{423 kJ mol}^{-1}) \qquad (\textbf{\textit{DH}}° = \textbf{413 kJ mol}^{-1})$$

This means that for the reaction in which the designated C—H bonds are broken homolytically, the values of $\Delta H°$ are those given here.

$$\Delta H° = +423 \text{ kJ mol}^{-1}$$

Propyl radical (a 1° radical)

$$\Delta H° = +413 \text{ kJ mol}^{-1}$$

Isopropyl radical (a 2° radical)

These reactions resemble each other in two respects: they both begin with the same alkane (propane), and they both produce an alkyl radical and a hydrogen atom. They differ, however, in the amount of energy required and in the type of carbon radical produced. These two differences are related to each other.

* Alkyl radicals are classified as being 1°, 2°, or 3° based on the carbon atom that has the unpaired electron, the same way that we classify carbocations based on the carbon atom with the positive charge.

More energy must be supplied to produce a primary alkyl radical (the propyl radical) from propane than is required to produce a secondary carbon radical (the isopropyl radical) from the same compound. This must mean that the primary radical has absorbed more energy and thus has greater *potential energy*. Because the relative stability of a chemical species is inversely related to its potential energy, the secondary radical must be the *more stable* radical (Fig. 10.1a). In fact, the secondary isopropyl radical is more stable than the primary propyl radical by 10 kJ mol^{-1}.

TABLE 10.1 SINGLE-BOND HOMOLYTIC DISSOCIATION ENERGIES (DH°) AT 25 °C[a]

$$A{:}B \longrightarrow A{\cdot} + B{\cdot}$$

Bond Broken (shown in red)	kJ mol^{-1}	Bond Broken (shown in red)	kJ mol^{-1}	Bond Broken (shown in red)	kJ mol^{-1}
H—H	436	CH_3CH_2—OCH_3	352	$CH_2{=}CHCH_2$—H	369
D—D	443	$CH_3CH_2CH_2$—H	423	$CH_2{=}CH$—H	465
F—F	159	$CH_3CH_2CH_2$—F	444	C_6H_5—H	474
Cl—Cl	243	$CH_3CH_2CH_2$—Cl	354	HC≡C—H	547
Br—Br	193	$CH_3CH_2CH_2$—Br	294	CH_3—CH_3	378
I—I	151	$CH_3CH_2CH_2$—I	239	CH_3CH_2—CH_3	371
H—F	570	$CH_3CH_2CH_2$—OH	395	$CH_3CH_2CH_2$—CH_3	374
H—Cl	432	$CH_3CH_2CH_2$—OCH_3	355	CH_3CH_2—CH_2CH_3	343
H—Br	366	$(CH_3)_2CH$—H	413	$(CH_3)_2CH$—CH_3	371
H—I	298	$(CH_3)_2CH$—F	439	$(CH_3)_3C$—CH_3	363
CH_3—H	440	$(CH_3)_2CH$—Cl	355	HO—H	499
CH_3—F	461	$(CH_3)_2CH$—Br	298	HOO—H	356
CH_3—Cl	352	$(CH_3)_2CH$—I	222	HO—OH	214
CH_3—Br	293	$(CH_3)_2CH$—OH	402	$(CH_3)_3CO$—$OC(CH_3)_3$	157
CH_3—I	240	$(CH_3)_2CH$—OCH_3	359	$C_6H_5\overset{O}{\overset{\|}{C}}O$—$O\overset{O}{\overset{\|}{C}}C_6H_5$	139
CH_3—OH	387	$(CH_3)_2CHCH_2$—H	422	CH_3CH_2O—OCH_3	184
CH_3—OCH_3	348	$(CH_3)_3C$—H	400	CH_3CH_2O—H	431
CH_3CH_2—H	421	$(CH_3)_3C$—Cl	349		
CH_3CH_2—F	444	$(CH_3)_3C$—Br	292	$CH_3\overset{O}{\overset{\|}{C}}$—H	364
CH_3CH_2—Cl	353	$(CH_3)_3C$—I	227		
CH_3CH_2—Br	295	$(CH_3)_3C$—OH	400		
CH_3CH_2—I	233	$(CH_3)_3C$—OCH_3	348		
CH_3CH_2—OH	393	$C_6H_5CH_2$—H	375		

[a]Data compiled from the National Institute of Standards (NIST) Standard Reference Database Number 69, July 2001 Release, Accessed via NIST Chemistry WebBook (http://webbook.nist.gov/chemistry/) Copyright 2000. Data from CRC Handbook of Chemistry and Physics, Updated 3rd Electronic Edition; Lide, David R., ed. DH° values were obtained directly or calculated from heat of formation (H$_f$) data using the equation DH° [A-B]= H$_f$ [A.] + H$_f$ [B.] - H$_f$ [A-B].

We can use the data in Table 10.1 to make a similar comparison of the *tert*-butyl radical (a 3° radical) and the isobutyl radical (a 1° radical) relative to isobutane:

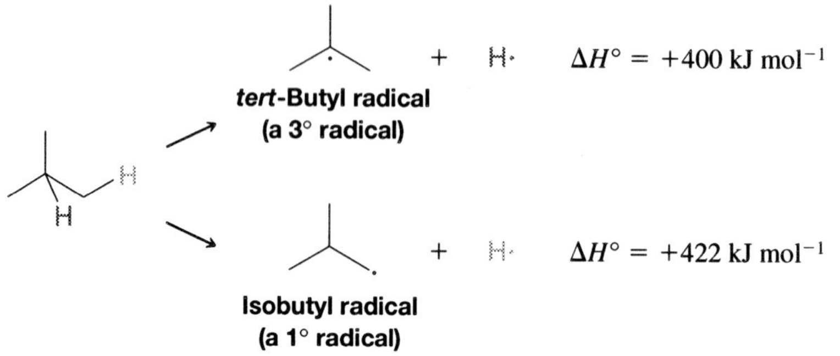

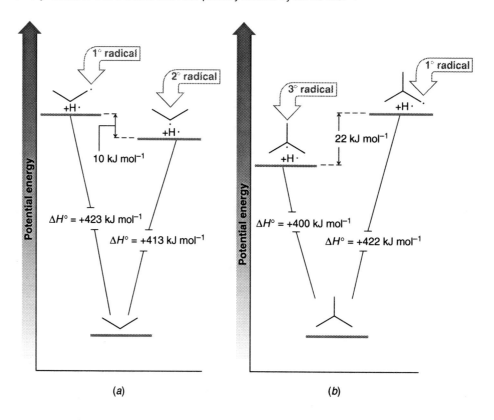

Here we find (Fig. 10.1*b*) that the difference in stability of the two radicals is even larger. The tertiary radical is more stable than the primary radical by 22 kJ mol⁻¹.

FIGURE 10.1 (*a*) Comparison of the potential energies of the propyl radical (+H·) and the isopropyl radical (+H·) relative to propane. The isopropyl radical (a 2° radical) is more stable than the 1° radical by 10 kJ mol⁻¹. (*b*) Comparison of the potential energies of the *tert*-butyl radical (+H·) and the isobutyl radical (+H·) relative to isobutane. The 3° radical is more stable than the 1° radical by 22 kJ mol⁻¹.

The kind of pattern that we find in these examples is found with alkyl radicals generally.

* **Overall, the relative stabilities of radicals are 3° > 2° > 1° > methyl.**

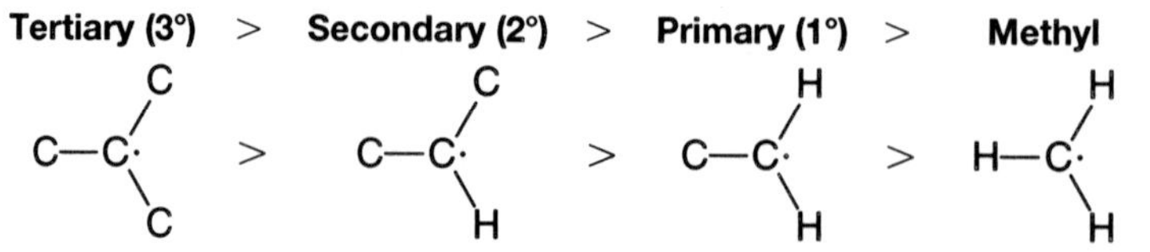

* **The order of stability of alkyl radicals is the same as for carbocations** (Section 6.11B).

Although alkyl radicals are uncharged, the carbon that bears the odd electron is *electron deficient*. Therefore, alkyl groups attached to this carbon provide a stabilizing effect through hyperconjugation, and the more alkyl groups bonded to it, the more stable the radical is. Thus, the reasons for the relative stabilities of radicals and carbocations are similar.

Helpful Hint

Knowing the relative stability of radicals is important for predicting reaction pathways.

Classify each of the following radicals as being 1°, 2°, or 3°, and rank them in order of decreasing stability.

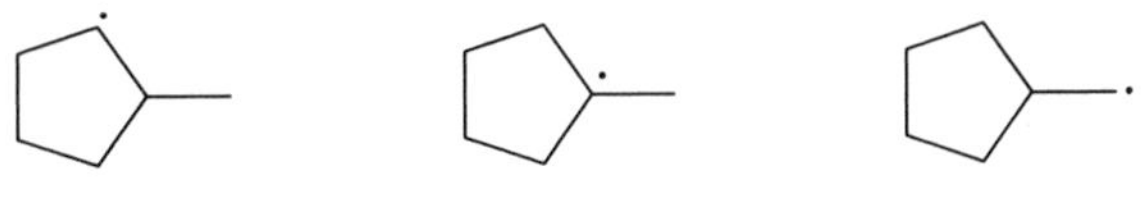

A   **B**   **C**

STRATEGY AND ANSWER: We examine the carbon bearing the unpaired electron in each radical to classify the radical as to its type. **B** is a tertiary radical (the carbon bearing the unpaired electron is tertiary) and is, therefore, most stable. **C** is a primary radical and is least stable. **A**, being a secondary radical, falls in between. The order of stability is **B > A > C**.

●●●

List the following radicals in order of decreasing stability: **PRACTICE PROBLEM 10.1**

·CH₃

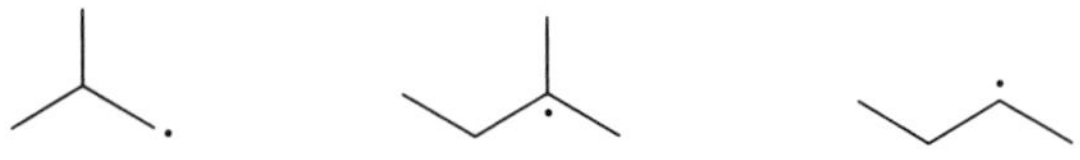

10.3 REACTIONS OF ALKANES WITH HALOGENS

- Alkanes react with molecular halogens to produce alkyl halides by a **substitution reaction called radical halogenation.**

A general reaction showing formation of a monohaloalkane by radical halogenation is shown below. It is called radical halogenation because, as we shall see, the mechanism involves species with unpaired electrons called radicals. This reaction is not a nucleophilic substitution reaction.

$$R{-}H + X_2 \longrightarrow R{-}X + HX$$

- A halogen atom replaces one or more of the hydrogen atoms of the alkane, and the corresponding hydrogen halide is formed as a by-product.

Only fluorine, chlorine, and bromine react this way with alkanes. Iodine is essentially unreactive due to unfavorable reaction energetics.

10.3A Multiple Halogen Substitution

One complicating factor of alkane halogenations is that multiple substitutions almost always occur unless we use an excess of the alkane (see Solved Problem 10.2). The following example illustrates this phenomenon. If we mix an equimolar ratio of methane and chlorine (both substances are gases at room temperature) and then either heat the mixture or irradiate it with light of the appropriate wavelength, a reaction begins to occur vigorously and ultimately produces the following mixture of products:

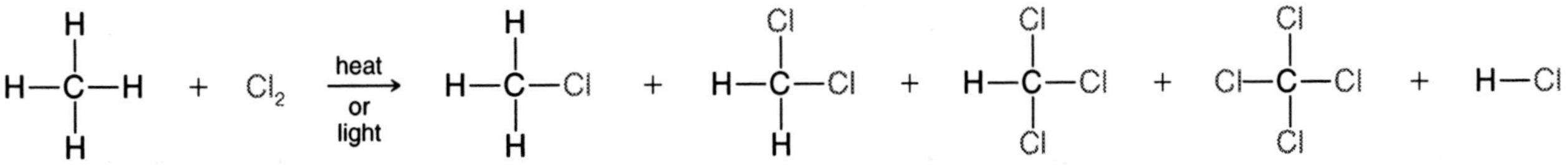

| Methane | Chlorine | | Chloromethane | Dichloromethane | Trichloromethane | Tetrachloromethane | Hydrogen chloride |

(The sum of the number of moles of each chlorinated methane produced equals the number of moles of methane that reacted.)

To understand the formation of this mixture, we need to consider how the concentration of reactants and products changes as the reaction proceeds. At the outset, the only compounds that are present in the mixture are chlorine and methane, and the only reaction that can take place is one that produces chloromethane and hydrogen chloride:

$$
\underset{\substack{H\\|\\H-\overset{\displaystyle H}{\underset{\displaystyle H}{C}}-H}}{} + Cl_2 \longrightarrow \underset{\substack{H\\|\\H-\overset{\displaystyle H}{\underset{\displaystyle H}{C}}-Cl}}{} + H-Cl
$$

As the reaction progresses, however, the concentration of chloromethane in the mixture increases, and a second substitution reaction begins to occur. Chloromethane reacts with chlorine to produce dichloromethane:

$$
\underset{\substack{H\\|\\H-\overset{\displaystyle H}{\underset{\displaystyle H}{C}}-Cl}}{} + Cl_2 \longrightarrow \underset{\substack{Cl\\|\\H-\overset{\displaystyle Cl}{\underset{\displaystyle H}{C}}-Cl}}{} + H-Cl
$$

The dichloromethane produced can then react to form trichloromethane, and trichloromethane, as it accumulates in the mixture, can react with chlorine to produce tetrachloromethane. Each time a substitution of —Cl for —H takes place, a molecule of H—Cl is produced.

●●● SOLVED PROBLEM 10.2

If the goal of a synthesis is to prepare chloromethane (CH_3Cl), its formation can be maximized and the formation of CH_2Cl_2, $CHCl_3$, and CCl_4 minimized by using a large excess of methane in the reaction mixture. Explain why this is possible.

ANSWER: The use of a large excess of methane maximizes the probability that chlorine will attack methane molecules because the concentration of methane in the mixture will always be relatively large. It also minimizes the probability that chlorine will attack molecules of CH_3Cl, CH_2Cl_2, and $CHCl_3$, because their concentrations will always be relatively small. After the reaction is over, the unreacted excess methane can be recovered and recycled.

10.3B Lack of Chlorine Selectivity

Chlorination of most higher alkanes gives a mixture of isomeric monochlorinated products as well as more highly halogenated compounds.

- Chlorine is relatively **unselective**; it does not discriminate greatly among the different types of hydrogen atoms (primary, secondary, and tertiary) in an alkane.

An example is the light-promoted chlorination of isobutane:

| Isobutane | $\xrightarrow[\text{light}]{Cl_2}$ | Isobutyl chloride (48%) | + | *tert*-Butyl chloride (29%) | + | Polychlorinated products (23%) | + | HCl |

- Because alkane chlorinations usually yield a complex mixture of products, they are not useful as synthetic methods when the goal is preparation of a specific alkyl chloride.
- An exception is the halogenation of an alkane (or cycloalkane) whose hydrogen atoms *are all equivalent* (i.e., homotopic). [Homotopic hydrogen atoms are defined as those that on replacement by some other group (e.g., chlorine) yield the same compound (Section 9.8).]

Helpful Hint

Chlorination is unselective.

Neopentane, for example, can form only one monohalogenation product, and the use of a large excess of neopentane minimizes polychlorination:

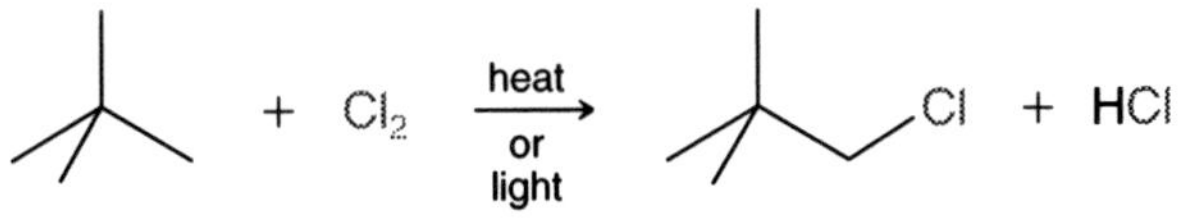

Neopentane   **Neopentyl chloride**
(excess)

- Bromine is generally less reactive toward alkanes than chlorine, and bromine is *more selective* in the site of attack when it does react.

We shall examine the selectivity of bromination further in Section 10.5A.

10.4 CHLORINATION OF METHANE: MECHANISM OF REACTION

The reaction of methane with chlorine (in the gas phase) provides a good example for studying the mechanism of radical halogenation.

$$CH_4 + Cl_2 \longrightarrow CH_3Cl + HCl \ (+ \ CH_2Cl_2, \ CHCl_3, \ and \ CCl_4)$$

Several experimental observations help in understanding the mechanism of this reaction:

1. **The reaction is promoted by heat or light.** At room temperature methane and chlorine do not react at a perceptible rate as long as the mixture is kept away from light. Methane and chlorine do react, however, at room temperature if the gaseous reaction mixture is irradiated with UV light at a wavelength absorbed by Cl_2, and they react in the dark if the gaseous mixture is heated to temperatures greater than 100 °C.

2. **The light-promoted reaction is highly efficient.** A relatively small number of light photons permits the formation of relatively large amounts of chlorinated product.

   A mechanism that is consistent with these observations has several steps, shown below. The first step involves the dissociation of a chlorine molecule, by heat or light, into two chlorine atoms. The second step involves hydrogen abstraction by a chlorine atom.

[A MECHANISM FOR THE REACTION – Radical Chlorination of Methane]

Reaction

$$CH_4 + Cl_2 \xrightarrow[\text{or light}]{\text{heat}} CH_3Cl + HCl$$

Mechanism

Chain Initiation

Step 1: Halogen dissociation

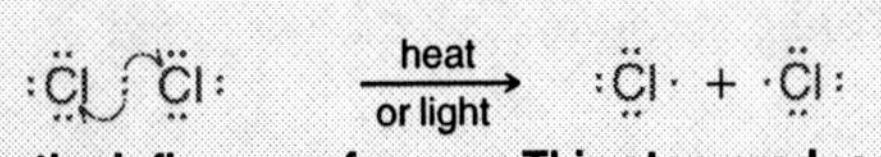

$$:\ddot{C}l \overset{\frown}{} \ddot{C}l: \xrightarrow[\text{or light}]{\text{heat}} :\ddot{C}l\cdot \ + \ \cdot\ddot{C}l:$$

Under the influence of heat or light a molecule of chlorine dissociates; each atom takes one of the bonding electrons.

This step produces two highly reactive chlorine atoms.

(mechanism continues on the next page)

Chain Propagation

Step 2: Hydrogen abstraction

A chlorine atom abstracts a hydrogen atom from a methane molecule.

This step produces a molecule of hydrogen chloride and a methyl radical.

Step 3: Halogen abstraction

A methyl radical abstracts a chlorine atom from a chlorine molecule.

This step produces a molecule of chloromethane and a chlorine atom. The chlorine atom can now cause a repetition of step 2.

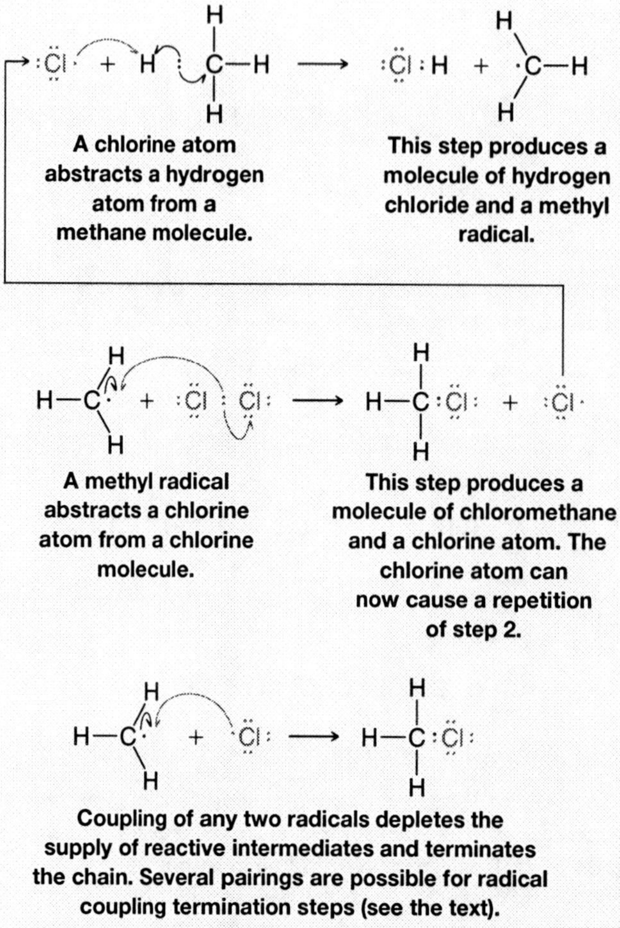

Helpful Hint

Remember: These conventions are used in illustrating reaction mechanisms in this text.

1. Curved arrows ⌢ or ⌢ always show the direction of movement of electrons.

2. Single-barbed arrows ⌢ show the attack (or movement) of an unpaired electron.

3. Double-barbed arrows ⌢ show the attack (or movement) of an electron pair.

Chain Termination

Coupling of any two radicals depletes the supply of reactive intermediates and terminates the chain. Several pairings are possible for radical coupling termination steps (see the text).

In step 3 the highly reactive methyl radical reacts with a chlorine molecule by abstracting a chlorine atom. This results in the formation of a molecule of chloromethane (one of the ultimate products of the reaction) and a *chlorine atom*. The latter product is particularly significant, for the chlorine atom formed in step 3 can attack another methane molecule and cause a repetition of step 2. Then, step 3 is repeated, and so forth, for hundreds or thousands of times. (With each repetition of step 3 a molecule of chloromethane is produced.)

● This type of sequential, stepwise mechanism, in which each step generates the reactive intermediate that causes the next cycle of the reaction to occur, is called a **chain reaction**.

Step 1 is called the **chain-initiating step**. In the chain-initiating step *radicals are created*. Steps 2 and 3 are called **chain-propagating steps**. In chain-propagating steps *one radical generates another*.

Chain Initiation: *creation of radicals*

$$\textit{Step 1} \qquad Cl_2 \xrightarrow[\text{or light}]{\text{heat}} 2\ Cl\cdot$$

Chain Propagation: *reaction and regeneration of radicals*

$$\textit{Step 2} \qquad CH_4 + Cl\cdot \longrightarrow \cdot CH_3 + H\!-\!Cl$$

$$\textit{Step 3} \qquad \cdot CH_3 + Cl_2 \longrightarrow CH_3Cl + Cl\cdot$$

The chain nature of the reaction accounts for the observation that the light-promoted reaction is highly efficient. The presence of a relatively few atoms of chlorine at any given moment is all that is needed to cause the formation of many thousands of molecules of chloromethane.

What causes the chain reaction to terminate? Why does one photon of light not promote the **chlorination** of all of the methane molecules present? We know that this does not happen because we find that, at low temperatures, continuous irradiation is required or the reaction slows and stops. The answer to these questions is the existence of **chain-terminating steps**: steps that happen infrequently but occur often enough to *use up one or both of the reactive intermediates*. The continuous replacement of intermediates used up by chain-terminating steps requires continuous irradiation. Plausible chain-terminating steps are as follows.

Chain Termination: *consumption of radicals (e.g., by coupling)*

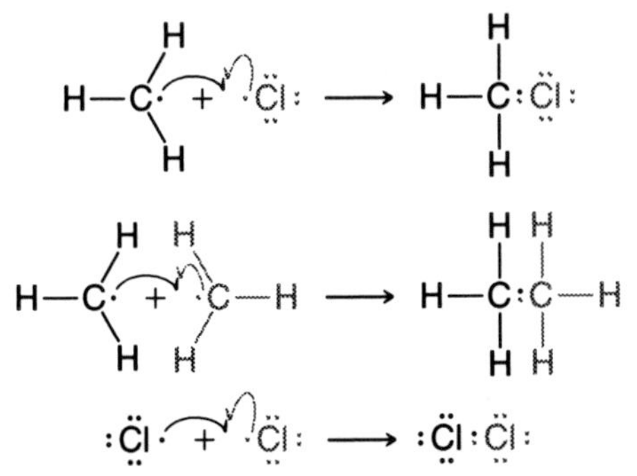

(Ethane by-product)

Our radical mechanism also explains how the reaction of methane with chlorine produces the more highly halogenated products, CH_2Cl_2, $CHCl_3$, and CCl_4 (as well as additional HCl). As the reaction progresses, chloromethane (CH_3Cl) accumulates in the mixture and its hydrogen atoms, too, are susceptible to abstraction by chlorine. Thus chloromethyl radicals are produced that lead to dichloromethane (CH_2Cl_2).

Side Reactions: *multihalogenated by-product formation*

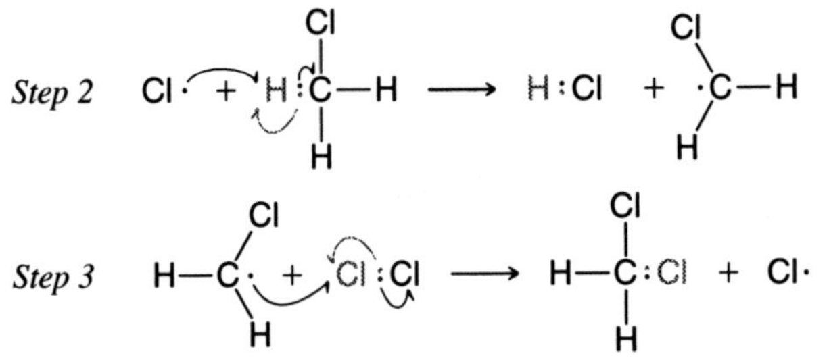

(Dichloromethane)

Then step 2 is repeated, then step 3 is repeated, and so on. Each repetition of step 2 yields a molecule of HCl, and each repetition of step 3 yields a molecule of CH_2Cl_2.

●●● SOLVED PROBLEM 10.3

When methane is chlorinated, among the products found are traces of chloroethane. How is it formed? Of what significance is its formation?

STRATEGY AND ANSWER: A small amount of ethane is formed by the combination of two methyl radicals:

$$2 \cdot CH_3 \longrightarrow CH_3 : CH_3$$

The ethane byproduct formed by coupling then reacts with chlorine in a radical halogenation reaction (see Section 10.5) to form chloroethane.

The significance of this observation is that it is evidence for the proposal that the combination of two methyl radicals is one of the chain-terminating steps in the chlorination of methane.

PRACTICE PROBLEM 10.2 Suggest a method for separating and isolating the CH_3Cl, CH_2Cl_2, $CHCl_3$, and CCl_4 that may be formed as a mixture when methane is chlorinated. (You may want to consult a handbook.) What analytical method could be used to separate this mixture and give structural information about each component?

PRACTICE PROBLEM 10.3 How would the molecular ion peaks in the respective mass spectra of CH_3Cl, CH_2Cl_2, $CHCl_3$, and CCl_4 differ on the basis of the number of chlorines? (Remember that chlorine has isotopes ^{35}Cl and ^{37}Cl found in a $3:1$ ratio.)

PRACTICE PROBLEM 10.4 If the goal is to synthesize CCl_4 in maximum yield, this can be accomplished by using a large excess of chlorine. Explain.

10.5 HALOGENATION OF HIGHER ALKANES

Higher alkanes react with halogens by the same kind of chain mechanism as those that we have just seen. Ethane, for example, reacts with chlorine to produce chloroethane (ethyl chloride). The mechanism is as follows:

[**A MECHANISM FOR THE REACTION** ⎯ **Radical Halogenation of Ethane**]

Chain Initiation

Step 1

$$Cl_2 \xrightarrow[\text{or}]{\text{light}} 2\,Cl\cdot$$
$$\text{heat}$$

Chain Propagation

Step 2

$$CH_3CH_2{:}\overset{\frown}{H} + \cdot Cl \longrightarrow CH_3CH_2\cdot + H{:}Cl$$

Step 3

$$CH_3CH_2\cdot + \overset{\frown}{Cl}{:}Cl \longrightarrow CH_3CH_2{:}Cl + Cl\cdot$$

Chain propagation continues with steps 2, 3, 2, 3, and so on.

Chain Termination

$$CH_3CH_2\cdot + \cdot Cl \longrightarrow CH_3CH_2{:}Cl$$

$$CH_3CH_2\cdot + \cdot CH_2CH_3 \longrightarrow CH_3CH_2{:}CH_2CH_3$$

$$Cl\cdot + \cdot Cl \longrightarrow Cl{:}Cl$$

PRACTICE PROBLEM 10.5 When ethane is chlorinated, 1,1-dichloroethane and 1,2-dichloroethane, as well as more highly chlorinated ethanes, are formed in the mixture (see Section 10.3A). Write chain reaction mechanisms accounting for the formation of 1,1-dichloroethane and 1,2-dichloroethane.

Chlorination of most alkanes whose molecules contain more than two carbon atoms gives a mixture of isomeric monochloro products (as well as more highly chlorinated compounds). Several examples follow. The percentages given are based on the total amount of monochloro products formed in each reaction.

These examples show the nonselectivity of chlorination.

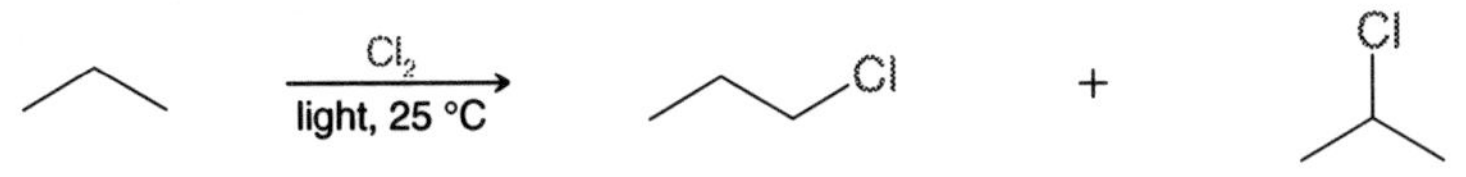

| Propane | 1-Chloropropane (45%) | 2-Chloropropane (55%) |

| 2-Methylpropane | 1-Chloro-2-methyl propane (63%) | 2-Chloro-2-methyl propane (37%) |

| 2-Methylbutane | 1-Chloro-2-methylbutane (30%) | 2-Chloro-2-methyl butane (22%) |

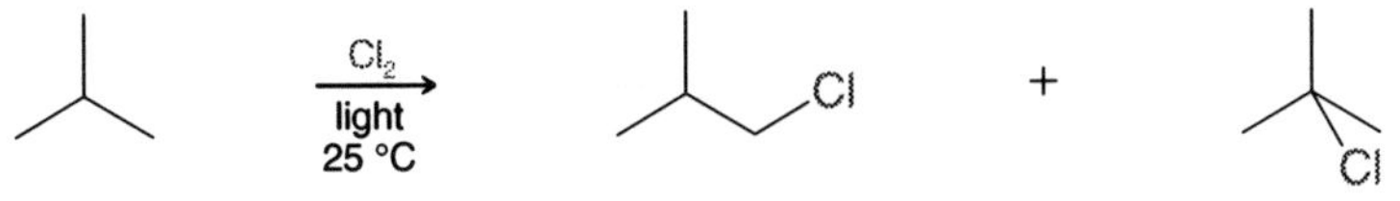

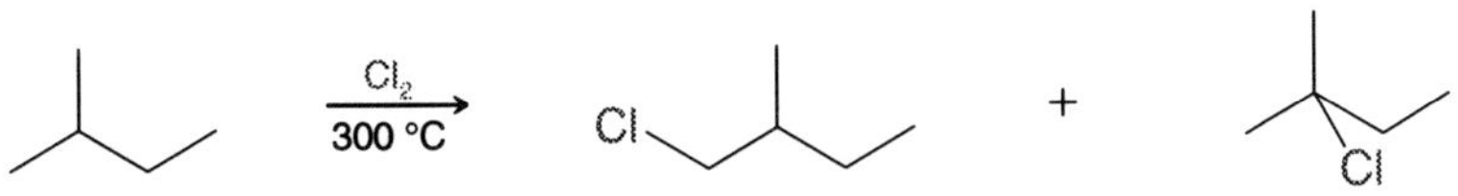

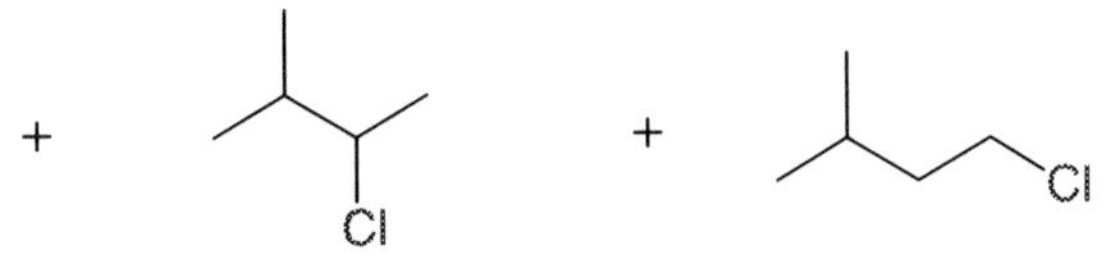

2-Chloro-3-methyl-butane (33%)   1-Chloro-3-methyl butane (15%)

> **Helpful Hint**
>
> Chlorination is not selective.

The ratios of products that we obtain from chlorination reactions of higher alkanes are not identical to what we would expect if all the hydrogen atoms of the alkane were equally reactive. We find that there is a correlation between reactivity of different hydrogen atoms and the type of hydrogen atom (1°, 2°, or 3°) being replaced. The tertiary hydrogen atoms of an alkane are most reactive, secondary hydrogen atoms are next most reactive, and primary hydrogen atoms are the least reactive (see Practice Problem 10.6).

PRACTICE PROBLEM 10.6

(a) What percentages of 1-chloropropane and 2-chloropropane would you expect to obtain from the chlorination of propane if 1° and 2° hydrogen atoms were equally reactive?

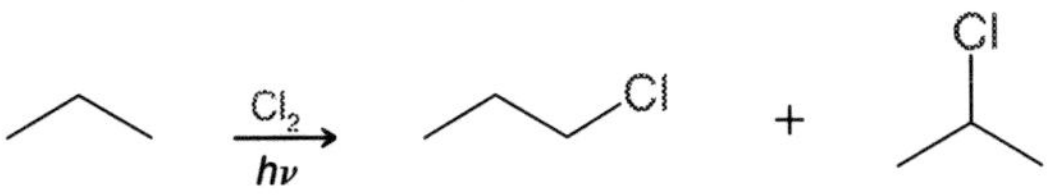

(b) What percentages of 1-chloro-2-methylpropane and 2-chloro-2-methylpropane would you expect from the chlorination of 2-methylpropane if the 1° and 3° hydrogen atoms were equally reactive?

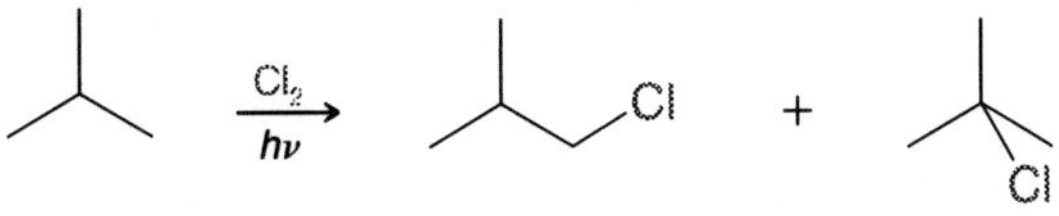

(c) Compare these calculated answers with the results actually obtained (above in Section 10.5) and justify the assertion that the order of reactivity of the hydrogen atoms is 3° > 2° > 1°.

We can account for the relative reactivities of the primary, secondary, and tertiary hydrogen atoms in a chlorination reaction on the basis of the homolytic bond dissociation energies we saw earlier (Table 10.1). Of the three types, breaking a tertiary C—H bond requires the least energy, and breaking a primary C—H bond requires the most. Since the step in which the C—H bond is broken (i.e., the hydrogen atom–abstraction step) determines the location or orientation of the chlorination, we would expect the E_{act} for abstracting a tertiary hydrogen atom to be least and the E_{act} for abstracting a primary hydrogen atom to be greatest. Thus tertiary hydrogen atoms should be most reactive, secondary hydrogen atoms should be the next most reactive, and primary hydrogen atoms should be the least reactive.

The differences in the rates with which primary, secondary, and tertiary hydrogen atoms are replaced by chlorine are not large, however.

- Chlorine does not discriminate among the different types of hydrogen atoms in a way that makes chlorination of higher alkanes a generally useful laboratory synthesis.

●●● SOLVED PROBLEM 10.4

An alkane with the formula C_5H_{12} undergoes chlorination to give only one product with the formula $C_5H_{11}Cl$. What is the structure of this alkane?

STRATEGY AND ANSWER: The hydrogen atoms of the alkane must all be equivalent (homotopic), so that replacing any one of them leads to the same product. The only five-carbon alkane for which this is true is neopentane.

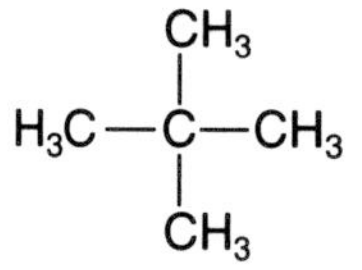

$$
\begin{array}{c}
CH_3 \\
| \\
H_3C-C-CH_3 \\
| \\
CH_3
\end{array}
$$

●●●

PRACTICE PROBLEM 10.7 Chlorination reactions of certain alkanes can be used for laboratory preparations. Examples are the preparation of chlorocyclopropane from cyclopropane and chlorocyclobutane from cyclobutane.

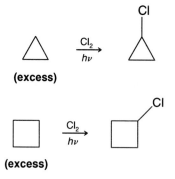

What structural feature of these molecules makes this possible?

●●●

PRACTICE PROBLEM 10.8 Each of the following alkanes reacts with chlorine to give a single monochloro substitution product. On the basis of this information, deduce the structure of each alkane.

(a) C_5H_{10} **(b)** C_8H_{18}

10.5A Selectivity of Bromine

Bromine shows a much greater ability to discriminate among the different types of hydrogen atoms.

- Bromine is less reactive than chlorine toward alkanes in general but bromine is more *selective* in the site of attack.

- Bromination is selective for substitution where the most stable radical intermediate can be formed.

The reaction of 2-methylpropane and bromine, for example, gives almost exclusive replacement of the tertiary hydrogen atom:

$$\text{2-methylpropane} \xrightarrow[hv,\ 127\ °C]{Br_2} \text{(>99\%)} + \text{(trace)}$$

A very different result is obtained when 2-methylpropane reacts with chlorine:

$$\text{2-methylpropane} \xrightarrow[hv,\ 25\ °C]{Cl_2} \text{(37\%)} + \text{(63\%)}$$

Fluorine, being much more reactive than chlorine, *is even less selective than chlorine.* Because the energy of activation for the abstraction of any type of hydrogen by a fluorine atom is low, there is very little difference in the rate at which a 1°, 2°, or 3° hydrogen reacts with fluorine. Reactions of alkanes with fluorine give (almost) the distribution of products that we would expect if all of the hydrogens of the alkane were equally reactive.

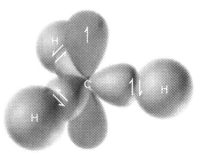

(a)

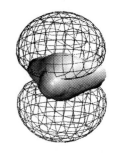

(b)

FIGURE 10.2 (a) Drawing of a methyl radical showing the sp^2-hybridized carbon atom at the center, the unpaired electron in the half-filled p orbital, and the three pairs of electrons involved in covalent bonding. The unpaired electron could be shown in either lobe. (b) Calculated structure for the methyl radical showing the highest occupied molecular orbital, where the unpaired electron resides, in red and blue. The region of bonding electron density around the carbons and hydrogens is in gray.

10.6 THE GEOMETRY OF ALKYL RADICALS

Experimental evidence indicates that the geometric structure of most alkyl radicals is trigonal planar at the carbon having the unpaired electron. This structure can be accommodated by an sp^2-hybridized central carbon. In an alkyl radical, the p orbital contains the unpaired electron (Fig. 10.2).

10.7 REACTIONS THAT GENERATE TETRAHEDRAL CHIRALITY CENTERS

- When achiral molecules react to produce a compound with a single tetrahedral chirality center, the product will be a racemic form.

This will always be true in the absence of any chiral influence on the reaction such as an enzyme or the use of a chiral reagent or solvent.

Let us examine a reaction that illustrates this principle, the radical chlorination of pentane:

$$\text{Pentane} \xrightarrow[\text{(achiral)}]{Cl_2} \text{1-Chloropentane} + (\pm)\text{-2-Chloropentane} + \text{3-Chloropentane}$$

| Pentane (achiral) | 1-Chloropentane (achiral) | (±)-2-Chloropentane (a racemic form) | 3-Chloropentane (achiral) |

The reaction will lead to the products shown here, as well as more highly chlorinated products. (We can use an excess of pentane to minimize multiple chlorinations.) Neither 1-chloropentane nor 3-chloropentane contains a chirality center, but 2-chloropentane does, and it is *obtained as a racemic form.* If we examine the mechanism we shall see why.

[A MECHANISM FOR THE REACTION | The Stereochemistry of Chlorination at C2 of Pentane]

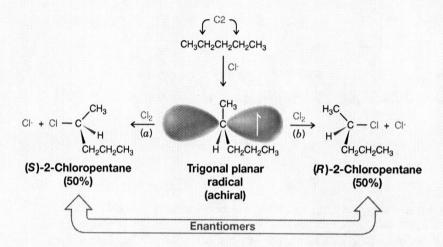

(S)-2-Chloropentane (50%)

Trigonal planar radical (achiral)

(R)-2-Chloropentane (50%)

Enantiomers

Abstraction of a hydrogen atom from C2 produces a trigonal planar radical that is achiral. This radical then reacts with chlorine at either face [by path (a) or path (b)]. Because the radical is achiral, the probability of reaction by either path is the same; therefore, the two enantiomers are produced in equal amounts, and a racemic form of 2-chloropentane results.

We can also say that the C2 hydrogens of pentane are **enantiotopic** because enantiomers are formed by reaction at each C2 hydrogen.

10.7A Generation of a Second Chirality Center in a Radical Halogenation

Let us now examine what happens when a chiral molecule (containing one chirality center) reacts so as to yield a product with a second chirality center. As an example consider what happens when (S)-2-chloropentane undergoes chlorination at C3 (other products are formed, of course, by chlorination at other carbon atoms). The results of chlorination at C3 are shown in the box below.

The products of the reactions are (2S,3S)-2,3-dichloropentane and (2S,3R)-2,3-dichloropentane. These two compounds are **diastereomers**. (They are stereoisomers but they are not mirror images of each other.) They each resulted by substitution of one of the **diastereotopic** hydrogens at C3. The two diastereomers are *not* produced in equal amounts. Because the intermediate radical itself is chiral, reactions at the two faces are not equally likely. The radical reacts with chlorine to a greater extent at one face than

the other (although we cannot easily predict which). That is, the presence of a chirality center in the radical (at C2) influences the reaction that introduces the new chirality center (at C3).

Both of the 2,3-dichloropentane diastereomers are chiral and, therefore, each exhibits optical activity. Moreover, because the two compounds are *diastereomers*, they have different physical properties (e.g., different melting points and boiling points) and are separable by conventional means (by gas chromatography or by careful fractional distillation).

[A MECHANISM FOR THE REACTION ⋮ The Stereochemistry of Chlorination at C3 of (S)-2-Chloropentane]

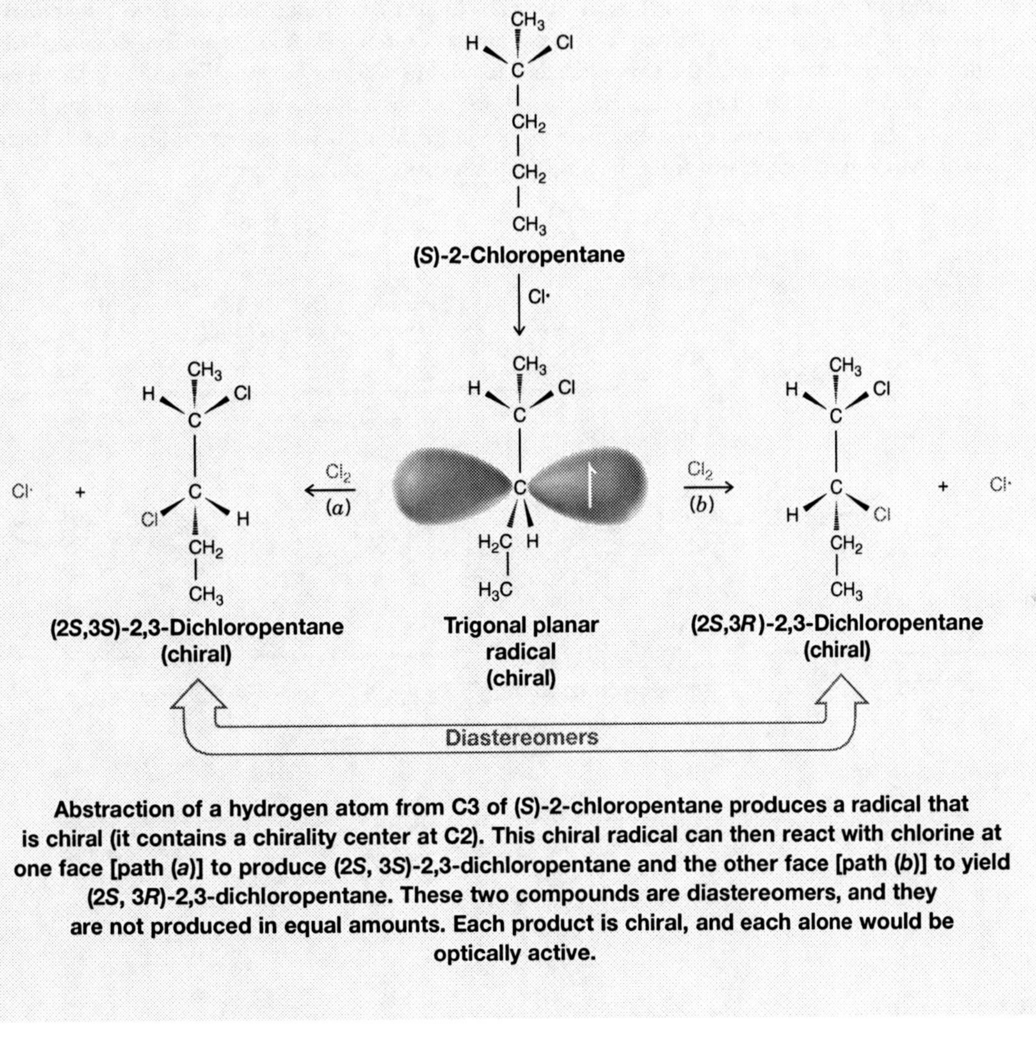

CH₃
H—C—Cl
|
CH₂
|
CH₂
|
CH₃

(S)-2-Chloropentane

↓ Cl·

(2S,3S)-2,3-Dichloropentane (chiral) ←(a) Cl₂ Trigonal planar radical (chiral) (b) Cl₂→ (2S,3R)-2,3-Dichloropentane (chiral)

Diastereomers

Abstraction of a hydrogen atom from C3 of (S)-2-chloropentane produces a radical that is chiral (it contains a chirality center at C2). This chiral radical can then react with chlorine at one face [path (a)] to produce (2S, 3S)-2,3-dichloropentane and the other face [path (b)] to yield (2S, 3R)-2,3-dichloropentane. These two compounds are diastereomers, and they are not produced in equal amounts. Each product is chiral, and each alone would be optically active.

Consider the chlorination of (S)-2-chloropentane at **C4**. **(a)** Write structural formulas for the products, showing three dimensions at all chirality centers. Give each its proper (R,S) designation. **(b)** What is the stereoisomeric relationship between these products? **(c)** Are both products chiral? **(d)** Are both optically active? **(e)** Could the products be separated by conventional means? **(f)** What other dichloropentanes would be obtained by chlorination of (S)-2-chloropentane? **(g)** Which of these are optically active?

PRACTICE PROBLEM 10.9

●●● **SOLVED PROBLEM 10.5**

Consider the bromination of butane using sufficient bromine to cause dibromination. After the reaction is over, you separate all the dibromobutane isomers by gas chromatography or by fractional distillation. How many fractions would you obtain, and what compounds would the individual fractions contain? Which if any of the fractions would be optically active?

STRATEGY AND ANSWER: The construction of handheld models will help in solving this problem. First, decide how many constitutional isomers are possible by replacing two hydrogens of butane with two bromine atoms. There are six: 1,1-dibromobutane, 1,2-dibromobutane, 2,2-dibromobutane, 2,3-dibromobutane, 1,3-dibromobutane, and 1,4-dibromobutane. Then recall that constitutional isomers have different physical properties (i.e., boiling points and retention times in a gas chromatograph), so there should be at least six fractions. In actuality there are seven. See fractions **(a)–(g)** below. We soon see why there are seven fractions if we examine each constitutional isomer looking for chirality centers and stereoisomers. Isomers **(a)**, **(c)**, and **(g)** have no chirality centers and are, therefore, achiral and are optically inactive. 1,2-Dibromobutane in fraction **(b)** and 1,4-dibromobutane in fraction **(f)** each have one chirality center and, because there is no chiral influence on the reaction, they will be formed as a 50:50 mixture of enantiomers (a racemate). A racemate cannot be separated by distillation or conventional gas chromatography; therefore, fractions **(b)** and **(f)** will not be optically active. 2,3-Dibromobutane has two chirality centers and will be formed as a racemate [fraction **(d)**] and as a meso compound, fraction **(e)**. Both fractions will be optically inactive. The meso compound is a diastereomer of the enantiomers in fraction **(d)** (and has different physical properties from them); therefore, it is separated from them by distillation or gas chromatography.

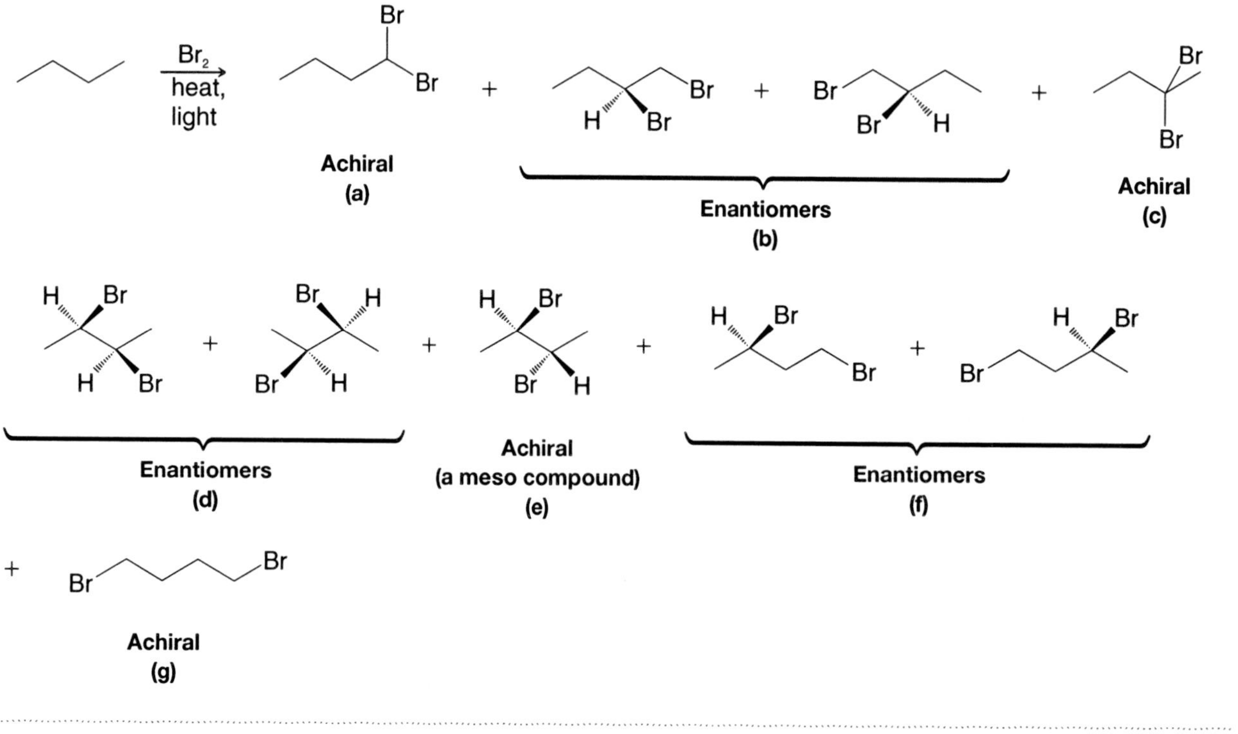

●●●

PRACTICE PROBLEM 10.10 Consider the monochlorination of 2-methylbutane.

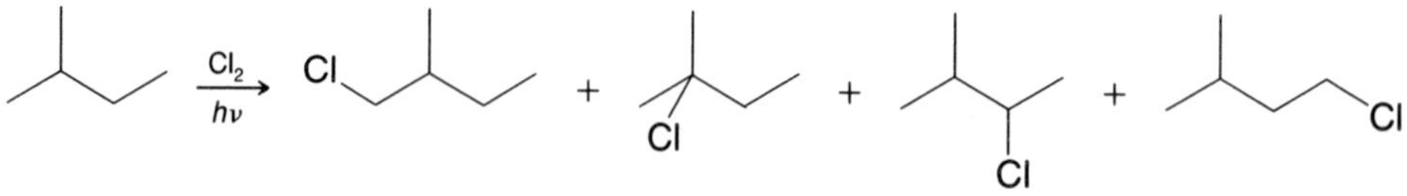

(a) Assuming that the product mixture was subjected to fractional distillation, which fractions, if any, would show optical activity? (b) Could any of these fractions be resolved, theoretically, into enantiomers? (c) Could the components of each fraction from the distillation be identified on the basis of ^{1}H NMR spectroscopy? What specific characteristics in a ^{1}H NMR spectrum of each fraction would indicate the identity of the component(s) in that fraction?

10.8 ALLYLIC SUBSTITUTION AND ALLYLIC RADICALS

- An atom or group that is bonded to an sp^3-hybridized carbon adjacent to an alkene double bond is called an **allylic group**. The group is said to be bonded at the **allylic position**.

The following are some examples.

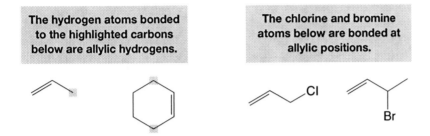

| The hydrogen atoms bonded to the highlighted carbons below are allylic hydrogens. | The chlorine and bromine atoms below are bonded at allylic positions. |

Allylic hydrogens are especially reactive in radical substitution reactions. We can synthesize allylic halides by substitution of allylic hydrogens. For example, when propene reacts with bromine or chlorine at high temperatures or under radical conditions where the concentration of the halogen is small, the result is **allylic substitution**.

Propene + X_2 $\xrightarrow[\text{and low concentration of } X_2]{\text{high temperature}}$ ⟍⟍⟍X + HX

> At high temperature (or in the presence of a radical initiator) and low concentration of X_2 a substitution reaction occurs.

On the other hand, when propene reacts with bromine or chlorine at low temperatures, an addition reaction of the type we studied in Chapter 8 occurs.

⟍⟍ + X_2 $\xrightarrow[\text{CCl}_4]{\text{low temperature}}$

> At low temperature an addition reaction occurs.

To bias the reaction toward allylic substitution we need to use reaction conditions that favor formation of radicals and that provide a low but steady concentration of halogen.

10.8A Allylic Chlorination (High Temperature)

Propene undergoes allylic chlorination when propene and chlorine react in the gas phase at 400 °C.

Propene + Cl_2 $\xrightarrow[\text{gas phase}]{400\ °C}$ ⟍⟍⟍Cl + HCl

3-Chloropropene
(allyl chloride)

The mechanism for allylic substitution is the same as the chain mechanism for alkane halogenations that we saw earlier in the chapter. In the chain-initiating step, the chlorine molecule dissociates into chlorine atoms.

Chain-Initiating Step

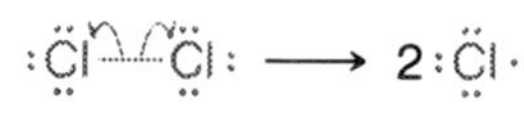

$$:\ddot{C}l\frown\frown\ddot{C}l: \longrightarrow 2:\ddot{C}l\cdot$$

In the first chain-propagating step the chlorine atom abstracts one of the allylic hydrogen atoms. The radical that is produced in this step is called an **allylic radical**.

First Chain-Propagating Step

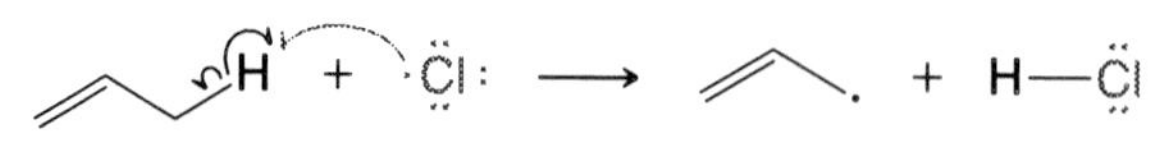

An allylic radical

In the second chain-propagating step the allyl radical reacts with a molecule of chlorine.

Second Chain-Propagating Step

Allyl chloride

This step results in the formation of a molecule of allyl chloride (2-chloro-1-propene) and a chlorine atom. The chlorine atom then brings about a repetition of the first chain-propagating step. The chain reaction continues until the usual chain-terminating steps (see Section 10.4) consume the radicals.

10.8B Allylic Bromination with *N*-Bromosuccinimide (Low Concentration of Br₂)

Propene undergoes allylic bromination when it is treated with *N*-bromosuccinimide (NBS) in the presence of peroxides or light:

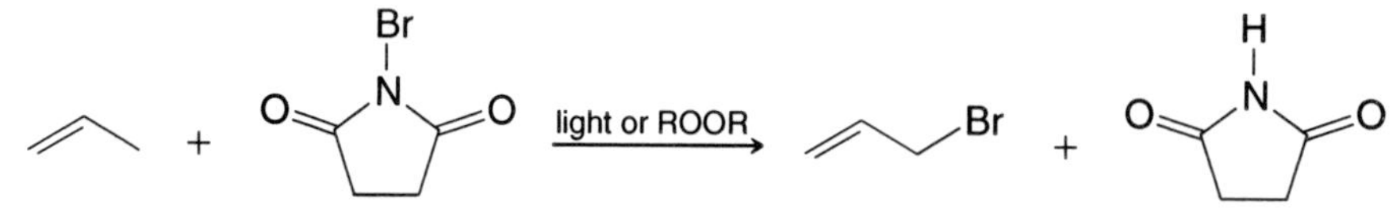

| *N*-Bromosuccinimide (NBS) | 3-Bromopropene (allyl bromide) | Succinimide |

The reaction is initiated by the formation of a small amount of Br· (possibly formed by dissociation of the N—Br bond of the NBS). The main propagation steps for this reaction are the same as for allylic chlorination (Section 10.2A):

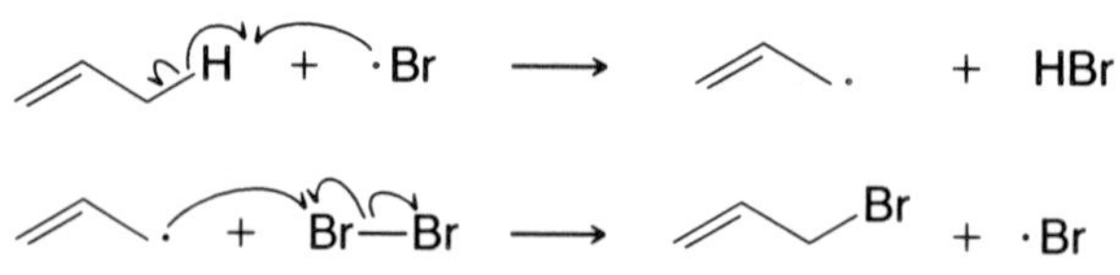

N-Bromosuccinimide is a solid that provides a constant but very low concentration of bromine in the reaction mixture. It does this by reacting very rapidly with the HBr formed in the substitution reaction. Each molecule of HBr is replaced by one molecule of Br₂.

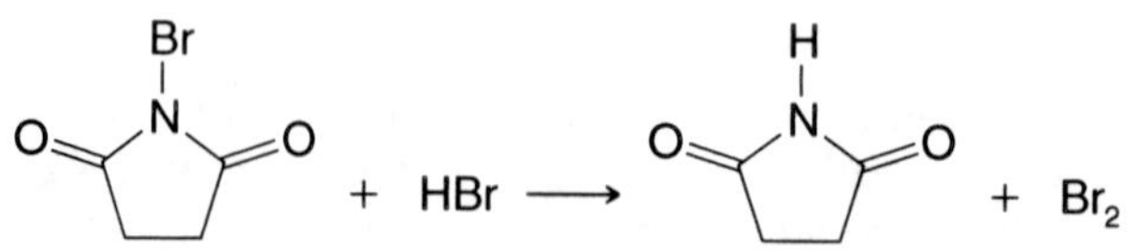

Under these conditions, that is, *in a nonpolar solvent and with a very low concentration of bromine*, very little bromine adds to the double bond; it reacts by substitution and replaces an allylic hydrogen atom instead.

The following reaction with cyclohexene is another example of allylic bromination with NBS:

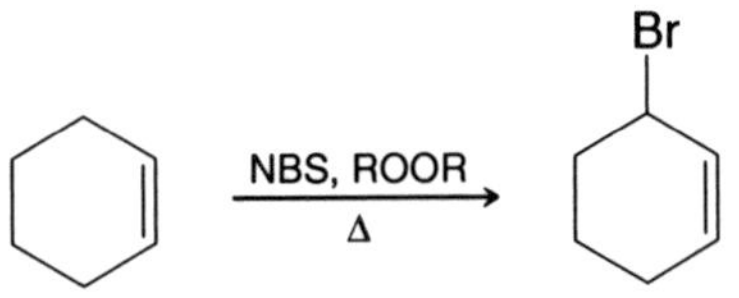

82–87%

* In general, NBS is a good reagent to use for allylic bromination.

10.8C Allylic Radicals Are Stabilized by Electron Delocalization

Let us examine the bond dissociation energy of an allylic carbon–hydrogen bond and compare it with the bond dissociation energies of other carbon–hydrogen bonds.

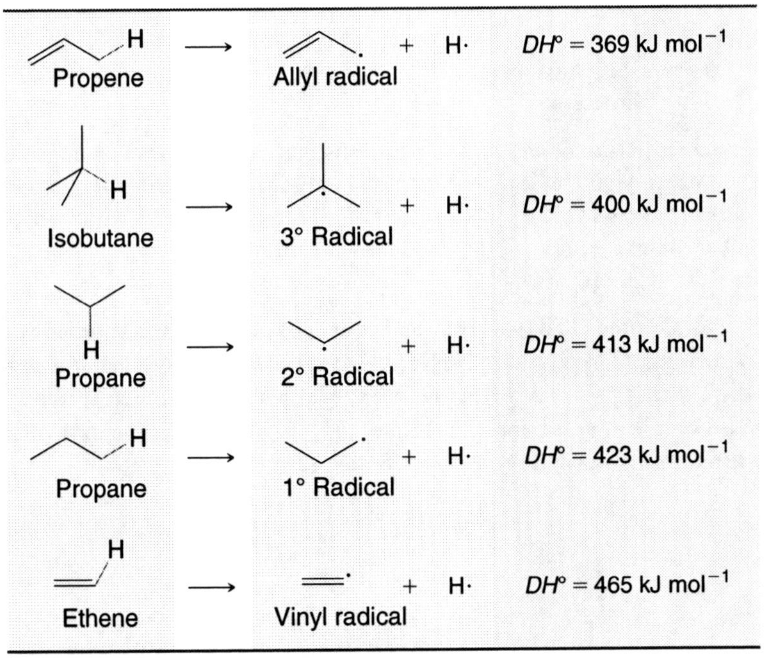

See Table 10.1 for a list of additional bond dissociation energies.

We see that an allylic carbon–hydrogen bond of propene is broken with greater ease than even the tertiary carbon–hydrogen bond of isobutane and with far greater ease than a vinylic carbon–hydrogen bond:

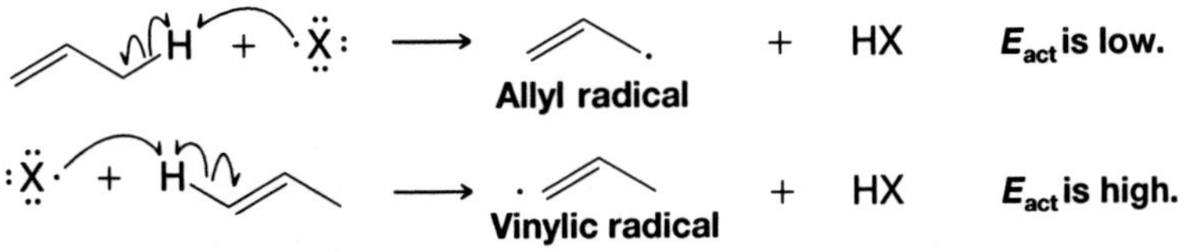

* The ease with which an allylic carbon–hydrogen bond is broken means that relative to primary, secondary, tertiary, and vinyl free radicals an allylic radical is the *most stable* (Fig. 10.3):

Relative stability: allylic or allyl > 3° > 2° > 1° > vinyl or vinylic

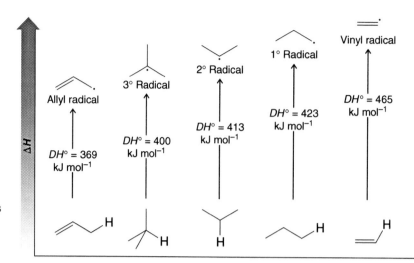

FIGURE 10.3 The relative stability of the allyl radical compared to 1°, 2°, 3°, and vinyl radicals. (The stabilities of the radicals are relative to the hydrocarbon from which each was formed, and the overall order of stability is allyl > 3° > 2° > 1° > vinyl.)

The reason that allylic radicals are more stable than alkyl radicals is due to electron delocalization. For example, we can draw the following contributing resonance structures and the corresponding resonance hybrid for the allylic radical from propene.

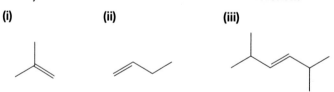

Contributing Resonance
Structures

Resonance Hybrid

Resonance delocalization of allylic radicals means that bonding of the halogen can occur at either end of an allylic radical. With the allylic radical from propene the two possible substitutions are the same, but unsymmetrical allylic radicals lead to products that are constitutional isomers.

PRACTICE PROBLEM 10.11   **(a)** What monobromo allylic substitution products would result from reaction of each of the following compounds with NBS in the presence of peroxides and/or light? **(b)** In the case of isomeric products for any reaction, which would you predict to be the most stable based on the double bond in the product? **(c)** Draw the resonance hybrid(s) for the allylic radical that would be involved in each reaction.

(i)   **(ii)**   **(iii)**

10.9 BENZYLIC SUBSTITUTION AND BENZYLIC RADICALS

● An atom or group bonded to an sp^3-hybridized carbon adjacent to a benzene ring is called a **benzylic group**. The group is said to be bonded at the **benzylic position**.

The following are some examples.

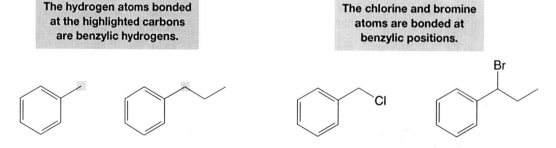

| The hydrogen atoms bonded at the highlighted carbons are benzylic hydrogens. | | The chlorine and bromine atoms are bonded at benzylic positions. | |

Benzylic hydrogens are even more reactive than allylic hydrogens in radical substitution reactions due to the additional delocalization that is possible for a benzylic radical intermediate (see Practice Problem 10.12).

When methylbenzene (toluene) reacts with N-bromosuccinimide (NBS) in the presence of light, for example, the major product is benzyl bromide. N-Bromosuccinimide furnishes a low concentration of Br_2, and the reaction is analogous to that for allylic bromination that we studied in Section 10.8B.

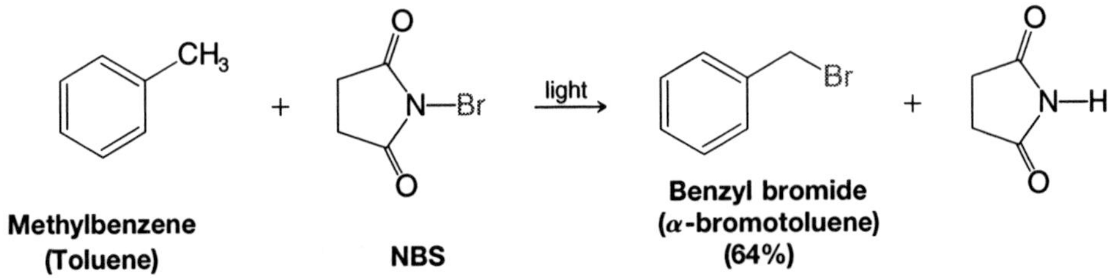

Methylbenzene (Toluene) + **NBS** →light→ **Benzyl bromide** (α-bromotoluene) (64%) +

Benzylic chlorination of methylbenzene takes place in the gas phase at 400–600 °C or in the presence of UV light. When an excess of chlorine is used, multiple chlorinations of the side chain occur:

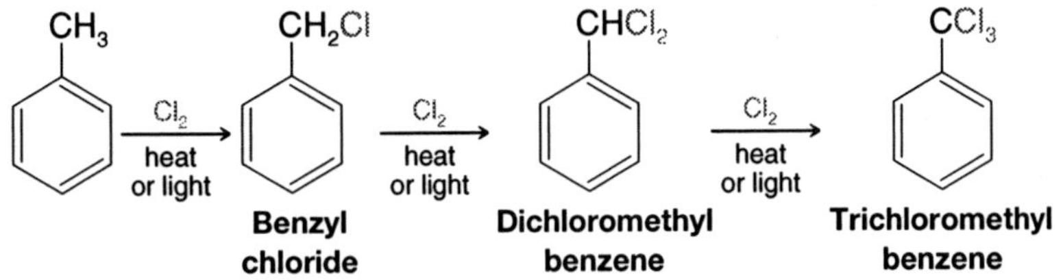

These halogenations take place through the same radical mechanism we saw for alkanes in Section 10.4. The halogens dissociate to produce halogen atoms and then the halogen atoms initiate chain reactions by abstracting hydrogens of the methyl group.

PRACTICE PROBLEM 10.12

Benzylic radicals, due to the adjacent benzene ring, have even greater possibility for delocalization than allylic radicals. Draw contributing resonance structures that show this delocalization for the benzylic radical derived from methylbenzene. (*Hint:* There are four contributing resonance structures for this benzylic radical.)

The greater stability of benzylic radicals accounts for the fact that when ethylbenzene is halogenated, the major product is the 1-halo-1-phenylethane. The benzylic radical is formed much faster than the 1° radical:

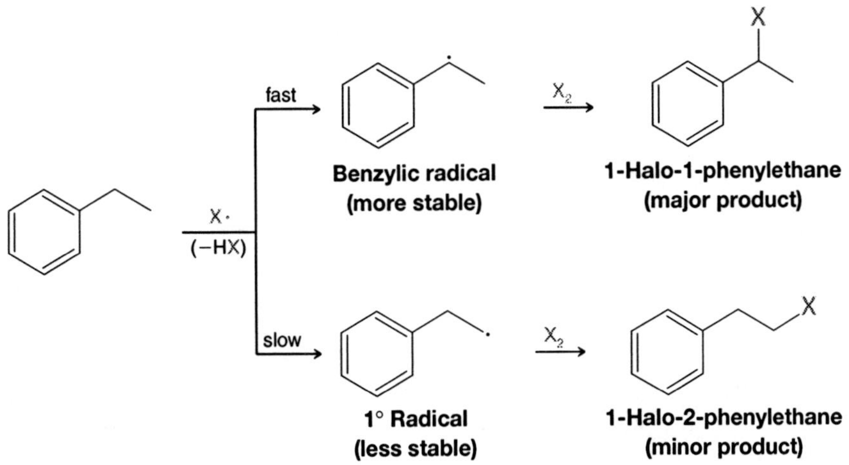

Benzylic radical (more stable)   **1-Halo-1-phenylethane** (major product)

1° Radical (less stable)   **1-Halo-2-phenylethane** (minor product)

PRACTICE PROBLEM 10.13 When propylbenzene reacts with chlorine in the presence of UV radiation, the major product is 1-chloro-1-phenylpropane. Both 2-chloro-1-phenylpropane and 3-chloro-1-phenylpropane are minor products. Write the structure of the radical leading to each product and account for the fact that 1-chloro-1-phenylpropane is the major product.

Benzylic halogenation is useful for introducing a leaving group where none may have been present before. Consider the following solved problem regarding multistep synthesis, where introduction of a leaving group is a necessary step.

●●● SOLVED PROBLEM 10.6

ILLUSTRATING A MULTISTEP SYNTHESIS: Show how phenylacetylene ($C_6H_5C\equiv CH$) could be synthesized from ethylbenzene (phenylethane). Begin by writing a retrosynthetic analysis, and then write reactions needed for the synthesis.

ANSWER: Working backward, that is, using *retrosynthetic analysis*, we find that we can easily envision two syntheses of phenylacetylene. We can make phenylacetylene by dehydrohalogenation of 1,1-dibromo-1-phenylethane, which could have been prepared by allowing ethylbenzene (phenylethane) to react with 2 mol of NBS. Alternatively, we can prepare phenylacetylene from 1,2-dibromo-1-phenylethane, which could be prepared from styrene (phenylethene). Styrene can be made from 1-bromo-1-phenylethane, which can be made from ethylbenzene.

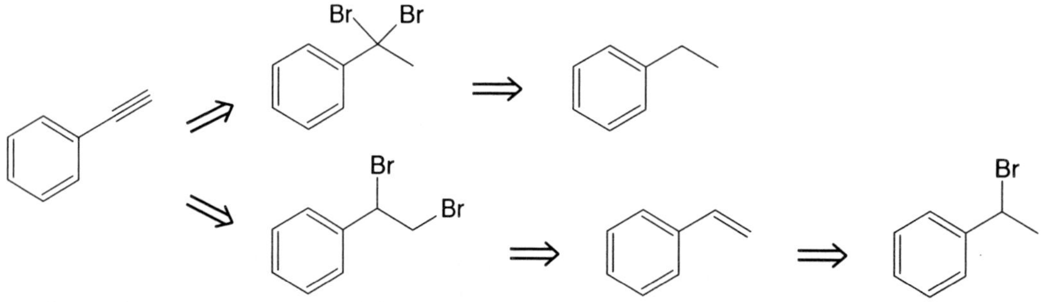

Following are the synthetic reactions we need for the two retrosynthetic analyses above:

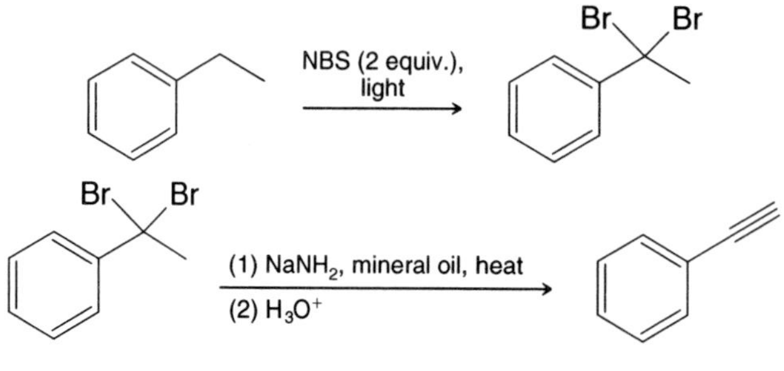

or

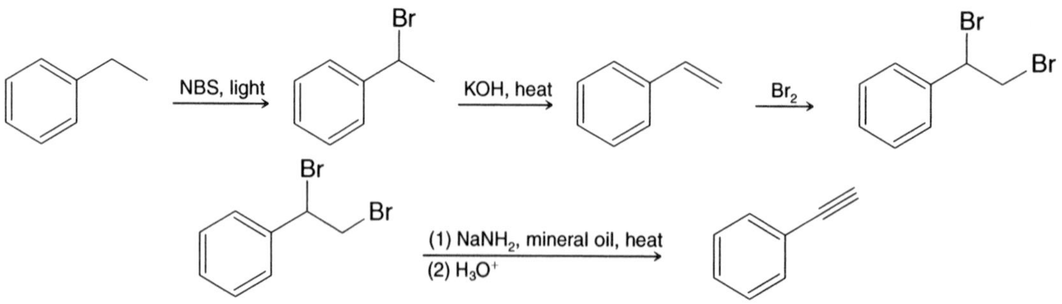

PRACTICE PROBLEM 10.14 Show how the following compounds could be synthesized from phenylacetylene ($C_6H_5C\equiv CH$): **(a)** 1-phenylpropyne, **(b)** 1-phenyl-1-butyne, **(c)** (*Z*)-1-phenylpropene, and **(d)** (*E*)-1-phenylpropene. Begin each synthesis by writing a retrosynthetic analysis.

10.10 RADICAL ADDITION TO ALKENES: THE ANTI-MARKOVNIKOV ADDITION OF HYDROGEN BROMIDE

Before 1933, the orientation of the addition of hydrogen bromide to alkenes was the subject of much confusion. At times addition occurred in accordance with Markovnikov's rule; at other times it occurred in just the opposite manner. Many instances were reported where, under what seemed to be the same experimental conditions, Markovnikov additions were obtained in one laboratory and anti-Markovnikov additions in another. At times even the same chemist would obtain different results using the same conditions but on different occasions.

The mystery was solved in 1933 by the research of M. S. Kharasch and F. R. Mayo (of the University of Chicago). The explanatory factor turned out to be organic peroxides present in the alkenes—peroxides that were formed by the action of atmospheric oxygen on the alkenes (Section 10.12D).

$$R—\ddot{O}—\ddot{O}—R \qquad\qquad R—\ddot{O}—\ddot{O}—H$$

An organic peroxide   **An organic hydroperoxide**

- When alkenes containing peroxides or hydroperoxides react with hydrogen bromide, anti-Markovnikov addition of HBr occurs.

For example, in the *presence* of peroxides propene yields 1-bromopropane. In the *absence* of peroxides, or in the presence of compounds that "trap" radicals, normal Markovnikov addition occurs.

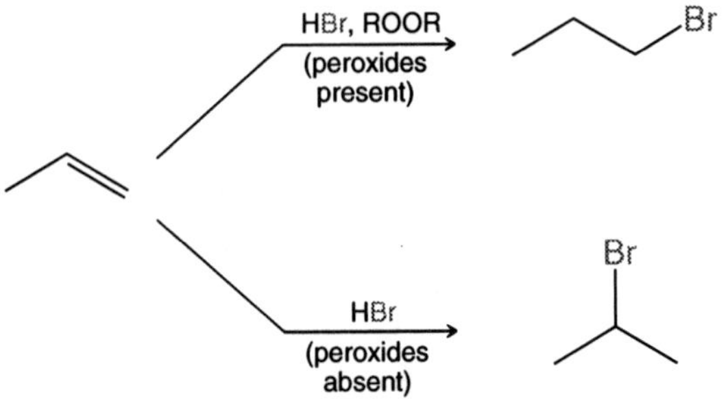

HBr, ROOR
(peroxides present) → ⟋⟍Br   **Anti-Markovnikov addition**

HBr
(peroxides absent) → (Br on central carbon)   **Markovnikov addition**

- Hydrogen bromide is the only hydrogen halide that gives anti-Markovnikov addition when peroxides are present.

Hydrogen fluoride, hydrogen chloride, and hydrogen iodide *do not* give anti-Markovnikov addition even when peroxides are present.

The mechanism for anti-Markovnikov addition of hydrogen bromide is a **radical chain reaction** initiated by peroxides.

[A MECHANISM FOR THE REACTION ─ Anti-Markovnikov Addition of HBr]

Chain Initiation

Step 1

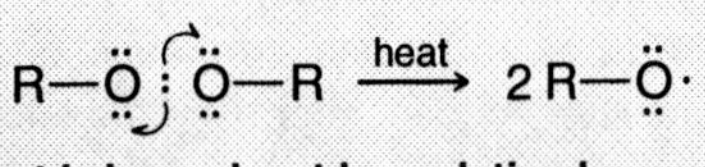

$$R—\ddot{O} \,\vdots\, \ddot{O}—R \xrightarrow{\text{heat}} 2\,R—\ddot{O}\cdot$$

Heat brings about homolytic cleavage of the weak oxygen–oxygen bond.

Step 2

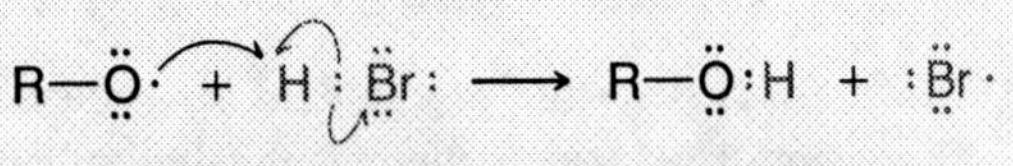

$$R—\ddot{O}\cdot \; + \; H \vdots \ddot{B}r\vdots \longrightarrow R—\ddot{O}\colon H \; + \; \vdots \ddot{B}r\cdot$$

The alkoxyl radical abstracts a hydrogen atom from HBr, producing a bromine radical.

(mechanism continues on the next page)

Chain Propagation

Step 3

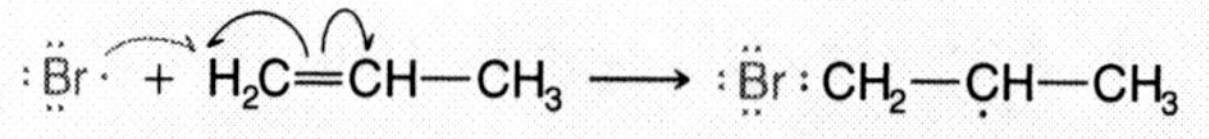

$$:\ddot{Br}\cdot\ +\ H_2C=CH-CH_3\ \longrightarrow\ :\ddot{Br}:CH_2-\dot{C}H-CH_3$$

2° Radical

**A bromine radical adds to the double bond
to produce the more stable 2° alkyl radical.**

Step 4

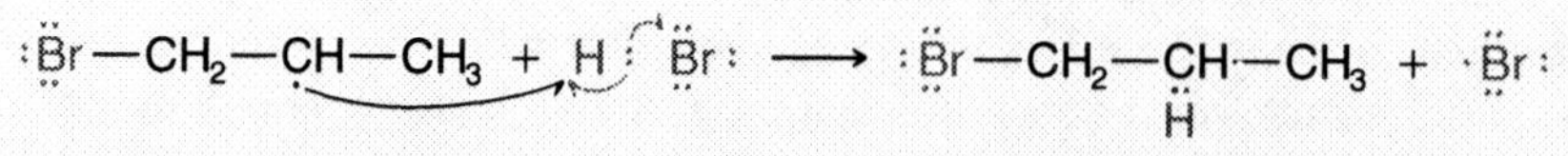

$$:\ddot{Br}-CH_2-\dot{C}H-CH_3\ +\ H:\ddot{Br}:\ \longrightarrow\ :\ddot{Br}-CH_2-\underset{\underset{H}{|}}{CH}-CH_3\ +\ \cdot\ddot{Br}:$$

1-Bromopropane

**The alkyl radical abstracts a hydrogen atom from HBr.
This leads to the product and regenerates a bromine radical.
Then repetitions of steps 3 and 4 lead to a chain reaction.**

Step 1 is the simple homolytic cleavage of the peroxide molecule to produce two alkoxyl radicals. The oxygen–oxygen bond of peroxides is weak, and such reactions are known to occur readily:

$$R-\ddot{O}:\ddot{O}-R\ \longrightarrow\ 2\ R-\ddot{O}\cdot \qquad \Delta H° \cong +150\ kJ\ mol^{-1}$$

Peroxide　　　**Alkoxyl radical**

Step 2 of the mechanism, abstraction of a hydrogen atom by the radical, is exothermic and has a low energy of activation:

$$R-\ddot{O}\cdot\ +\ H:\ddot{Br}:\ \longrightarrow\ R-\ddot{O}:H\ +\ :\ddot{Br}\cdot \qquad \Delta H° \cong -96\ kJ\ mol^{-1}$$

$$E_{act}\ is\ low$$

Step 3 of the mechanism determines the final orientation of bromine in the product. It occurs as it does because a *more stable secondary radical* is produced and because *attack at the primary carbon atom is less hindered.* Had the bromine attacked propene at the secondary carbon atom, a less stable, primary radical would have been the result,

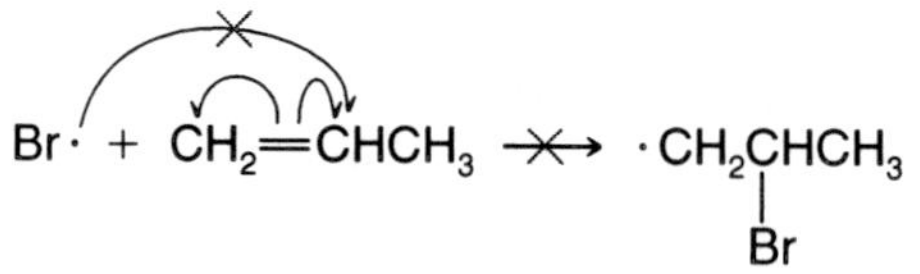

$$Br\cdot\ +\ CH_2=CHCH_3\ \xrightarrow{\;\;\times\;\;}\ \cdot CH_2\underset{\underset{Br}{|}}{CHCH_3}$$

**1° Radical
(less stable)**

and attack at the secondary carbon atom would have been more hindered.

Step 4 of the mechanism is simply the abstraction of a hydrogen atom from hydrogen bromide by the radical produced in step 3. This hydrogen atom abstraction produces a bromine atom (which, of course, is a radical due to its unpaired electron) that can bring about step 3 again; then step 4 occurs again—a chain reaction.

Helpful Hint

How to achieve regioselective alkyl halide synthesis through alkene addition.

10.10A Summary of Markovnikov versus Anti-Markovnikov Addition of HBr to Alkenes

We can now see the contrast between the two ways that HBr can add to an alkene. In the *absence* of peroxides, the reagent that attacks the double bond first is a proton. Because a proton is small, steric effects are unimportant. It attaches itself to a carbon atom by an

ionic mechanism so as to form the more stable carbocation. The result is Markovnikov addition. Polar, protic solvents favor this process.

Ionic Addition

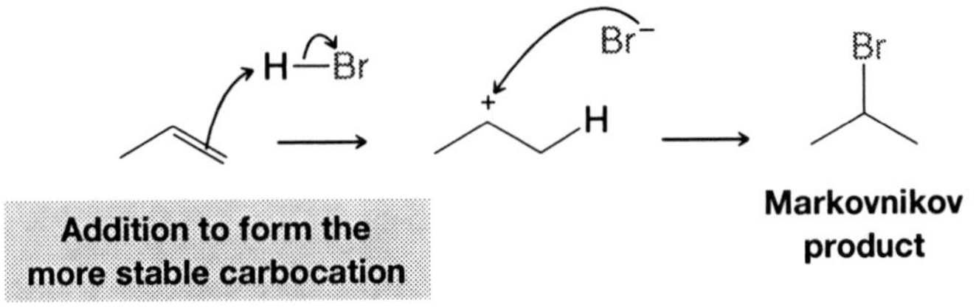

Addition to form the more stable carbocation

Markovnikov product

In the *presence* of peroxides, the reagent that attacks the double bond first is the larger bromine atom. It attaches itself to the less hindered carbon atom by a radical mechanism, so as to form the more stable radical intermediate. The result is anti-Markovnikov addition. Nonpolar solvents are preferable for reactions involving radicals.

Radical Addition

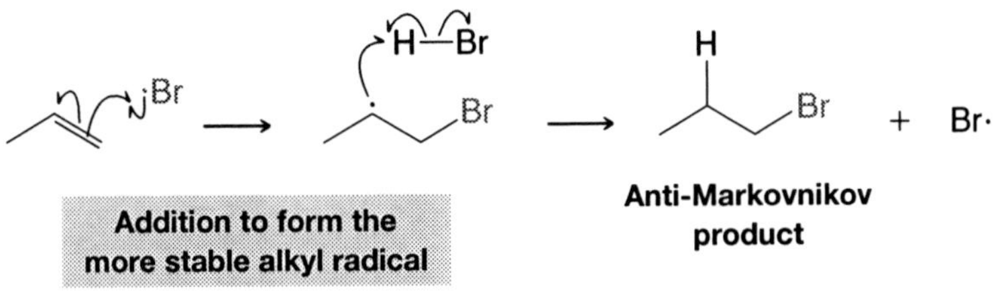

Addition to form the more stable alkyl radical

Anti-Markovnikov product

10.11 RADICAL POLYMERIZATION OF ALKENES: CHAIN-GROWTH POLYMERS

Polymers are substances that consist of very large molecules called **macromolecules** that are made up of many repeating subunits. The molecular subunits that are used to synthesize polymers are called **monomers**, and the reactions by which monomers are joined together are called **polymerizations**. Many polymerizations can be initiated by radicals.

Ethylene (ethene), for example, is the monomer that is used to synthesize the familiar polymer called *polyethylene*.

Monomeric units

$$m\,CH_2{=}CH_2 \xrightarrow{\text{polymerization}} {-}CH_2CH_2{\left(CH_2CH_2\right)_n}CH_2CH_2{-}$$

Ethylene monomer   **Polyethylene polymer**

(*m* and *n* are large numbers)

Because polymers such as polyethylene are made by addition reactions, they are often called **chain-growth polymers** or **addition polymers**. Let us now examine in some detail how polyethylene is made.

Ethene (ethylene) polymerizes by a radical mechanism when it is heated at a pressure of 1000 atm with a small amount of an organic peroxide (called a diacyl peroxide).

[A MECHANISM FOR THE REACTION

Radical Polymerization of Ethene (Ethylene)]

Chain Initiation

Step 1

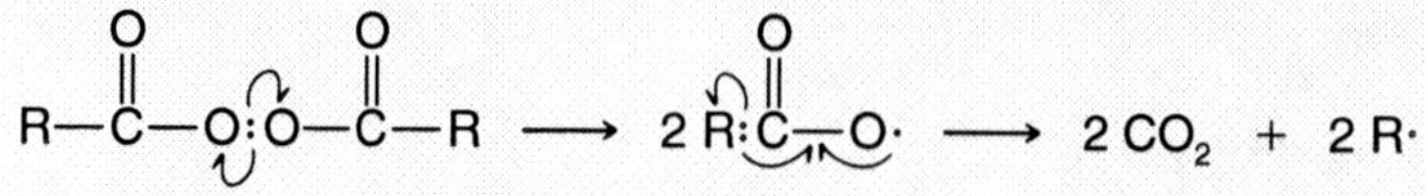

$$R-\overset{O}{\underset{}{C}}-O:O-\overset{O}{\underset{}{C}}-R \longrightarrow 2\ R:\overset{O}{\underset{}{C}}-O\cdot \longrightarrow 2\ CO_2\ +\ 2\ R\cdot$$

Diacyl peroxide

Step 2

$$R\cdot\ +\ CH_2=CH_2 \longrightarrow R:CH_2-CH_2\cdot$$

The diacyl peroxide dissociates and releases carbon dioxide gas. Alkyl radicals are produced, which in turn initiate chains.

Chain Propagation

Step 3

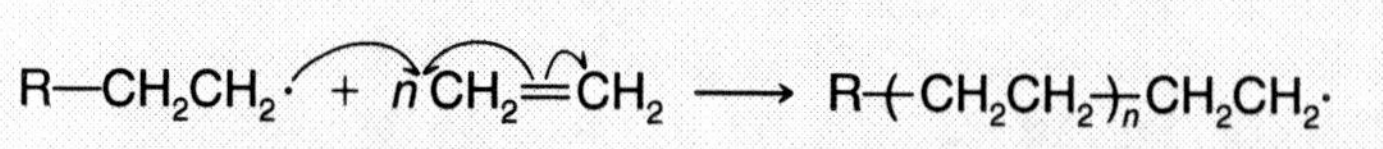

$$R-CH_2CH_2\cdot\ +\ n\ CH_2=CH_2 \longrightarrow R(CH_2CH_2)_n CH_2CH_2\cdot$$

Chains propagate by adding successive ethylene units, until their growth is stopped by combination or disproportionation.

Chain Termination

Step 4

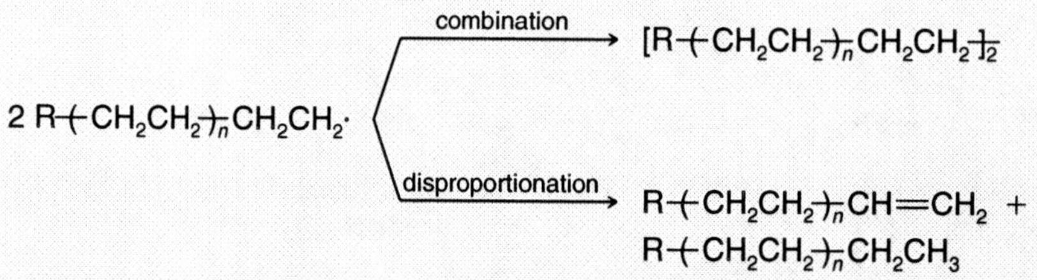

$$2\ R(CH_2CH_2)_n CH_2CH_2\cdot$$

combination $\longrightarrow [R(CH_2CH_2)_n CH_2CH_2]_2$

disproportionation $\longrightarrow R(CH_2CH_2)_n CH=CH_2\ +$
$R(CH_2CH_2)_n CH_2CH_3$

The radical at the end of the growing polymer chain can also abstract a hydrogen atom from itself by what is called "black biting." This leads to chain branching.

Chain Branching

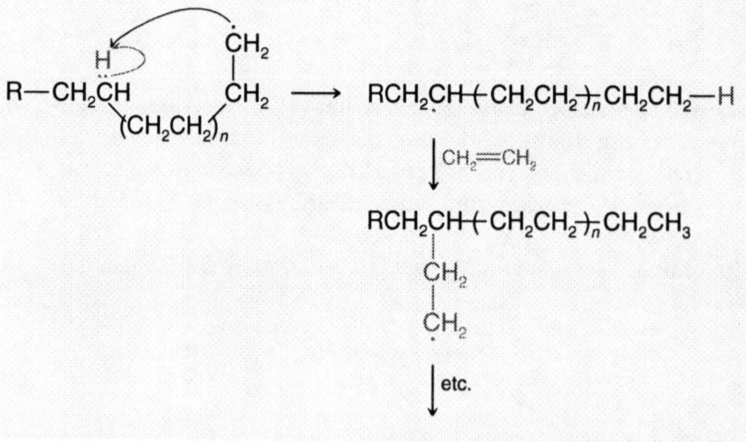

$$R-CH_2\overset{H}{\underset{(CH_2CH_2)_n}{CH}} \overset{\dot{C}H_2}{\underset{CH_2}{}} \longrightarrow RCH_2\dot{C}H(CH_2CH_2)_n CH_2CH_2-H$$

$$\downarrow CH_2=CH_2$$

$$RCH_2\overset{|}{\underset{\overset{|}{CH_2}}{CH}}(CH_2CH_2)_n CH_2CH_3$$
$$\underset{\dot{C}H_2}{}$$

$$\downarrow \text{etc.}$$

The polyethylene produced by radical polymerization is not generally useful unless it has a molecular weight of nearly 1,000,000. Very high molecular weight polyethylene can be obtained by using a low concentration of the initiator. This initiates the growth of only a few chains and ensures that each chain will have a large excess of the monomer available. More initiator may be added as chains terminate during the polymerization, and, in this way, new chains are begun.

Polyethylene has been produced commercially since 1943. It is used in manufacturing flexible bottles, films, sheets, and insulation for electric wires. Polyethylene produced by radical polymerization has a softening point of about 110 °C.

Polyethylene can be produced in a different way using (see Special Topic B in *WileyPLUS*) catalysts called **Ziegler–Natta catalysts** that are organometallic complexes

The 1963 Nobel Prize was awarded to Karl Ziegler and Guilio Natta for their research in polymers.

of transition metals. In this process no radicals are produced, no back biting occurs, and, consequently, there is no chain branching. The polyethylene that is produced is of higher density, has a higher melting point, and has greater strength.

Another familiar polymer is *polystyrene*. The monomer used in making polystyrene is phenylethene, a compound commonly known as *styrene*.

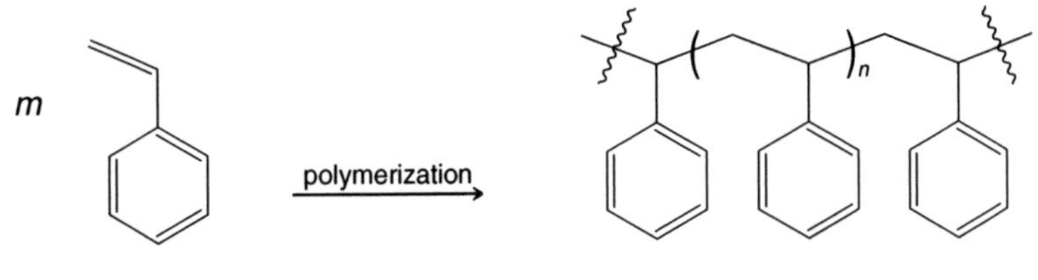

Styrene   **Polystyrene**

Table 10.2 lists several other common chain-growth polymers. Further information on each is provided in Special Topic B.

TABLE 10.2 OTHER COMMON CHAIN-GROWTH POLYMERS

Monomer	Polymer	Names
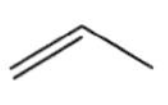	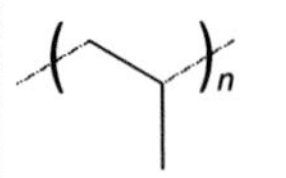	Polypropylene
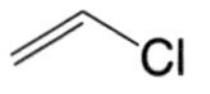	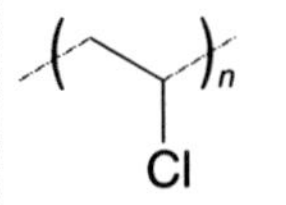	Poly(vinyl chloride), PVC
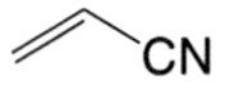	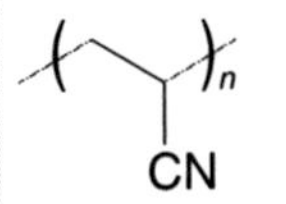	Polyacrylonitrile, Orlon
	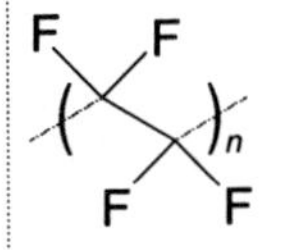	Poly(tetrafluoroethene), Teflon
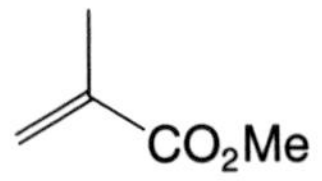	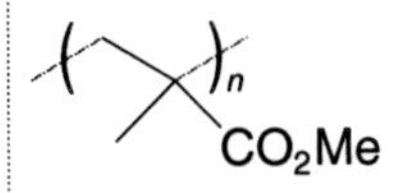	Poly(methyl methacrylate), Lucite, Plexiglas, Perspex

Can you suggest an explanation that accounts for the fact that the radical polymerization of styrene ($C_6H_5CH{=}CH_2$) to produce polystyrene occurs in a head-to-tail fashion, **PRACTICE PROBLEM 10.15**

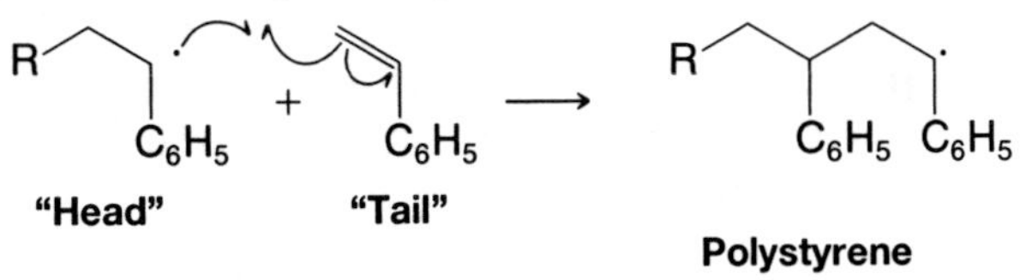

rather than the head-to-head manner shown here?

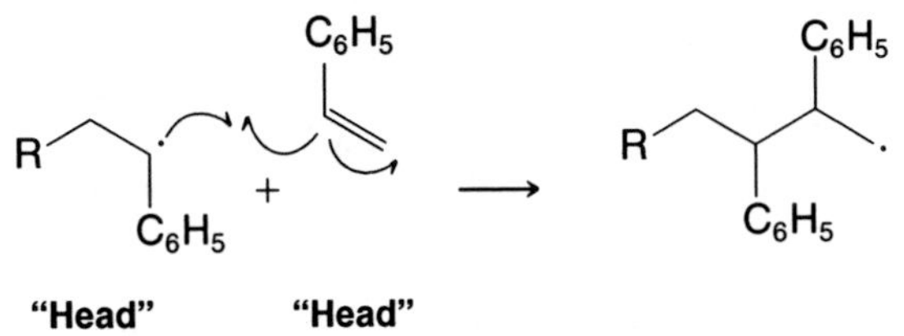

PRACTICE PROBLEM 10.16 Outline a general method for the synthesis of each of the following polymers by radical polymerization. Show the monomers that you would use.

(a)

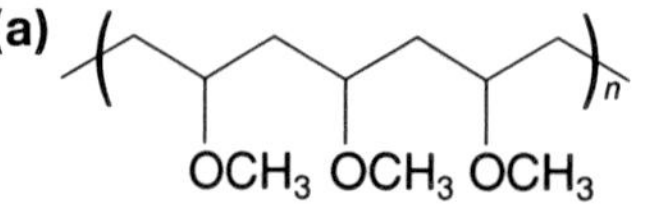

OCH$_3$ OCH$_3$ OCH$_3$

(b)

Cl Cl Cl Cl Cl Cl

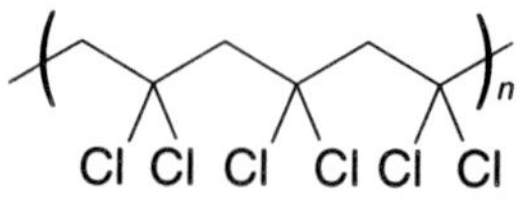

Alkenes also polymerize when they are treated with strong acids. The growing chains in acid-catalyzed polymerizations are *cations* rather than radicals. The following reactions illustrate the cationic polymerization of isobutylene:

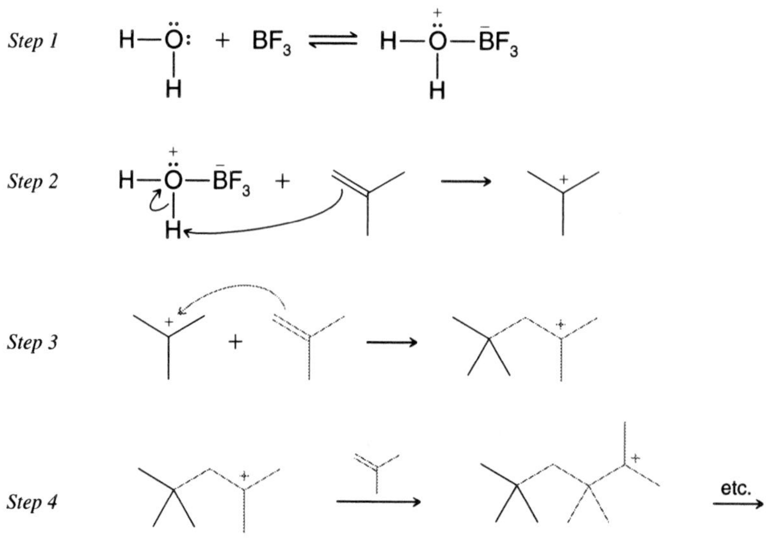

The catalysts used for cationic polymerizations are usually Lewis acids that contain a small amount of water. The polymerization of isobutylene illustrates how the catalyst (BF$_3$ and H$_2$O) functions to produce growing cationic chains.

PRACTICE PROBLEM 10.17 Alkenes such as ethene, vinyl chloride, and acrylonitrile do not undergo cationic polymerization very readily. On the other hand, isobutylene undergoes cationic polymerization rapidly. Provide an explanation for this behavior.

Alkenes containing electron-withdrawing groups polymerize in the presence of strong bases. Acrylonitrile, for example, polymerizes when it is treated with sodium amide (NaNH$_2$) in liquid ammonia. The growing chains in this polymerization are anions:

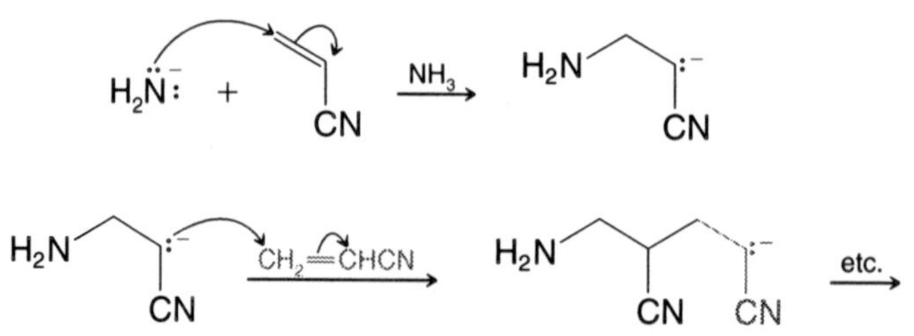

Anionic polymerization of acrylonitrile is less important in commercial production than the radical process illustrated in Special Topic B.

The remarkable adhesive called "superglue" is a result of anionic polymerization. Superglue is a solution containing methyl cyanoacrylate:

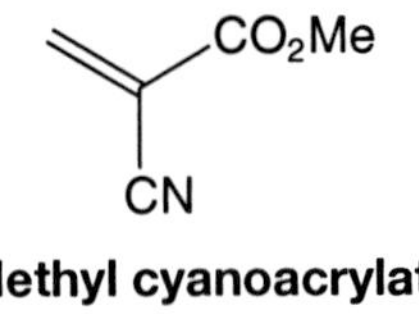

Methyl cyanoacrylate

Methyl cyanoacrylate can be polymerized by anions such as hydroxide ion, but it is even polymerized by traces of water found on the surfaces of the two objects being glued together. (These two objects, unfortunately, have often been two fingers of the person doing the gluing.) Show how methyl cyanoacrylate would undergo anionic polymerization.

STRATEGY AND ANSWER:

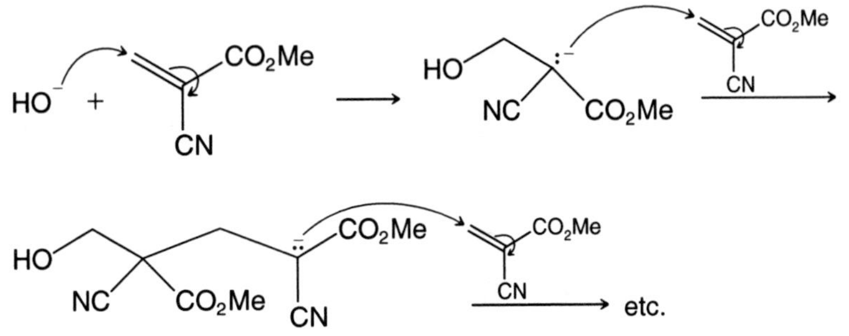

10.12 OTHER IMPORTANT RADICAL REACTIONS

Radical mechanisms are important in understanding many other organic reactions. We shall see other examples in later chapters, but let us examine a few important radicals and radical reactions here: oxygen and superoxide, the combustion of alkanes, DNA cleavage, autoxidation, antioxidants, and some reactions of chlorofluoromethanes that have threatened the protective layer of ozone in the stratosphere.

10.12A Molecular Oxygen and Superoxide

One of the most important radicals (and one that we encounter every moment of our lives) is molecular oxygen. Molecular oxygen in the ground state is a diradical with one unpaired electron on each oxygen. As a radical, oxygen can abstract hydrogen atoms just like other radicals we have seen. This is one way oxygen is involved in autoxidation (Section 10.12C) and combustion reactions (Section 10.12D). In biological systems, oxygen is an electron acceptor. When molecular oxygen accepts one electron, it becomes a radical anion called superoxide (O_2^-). Superoxide is involved in both positive and negative physiological roles. The immune system uses superoxide in its defense against pathogens, yet superoxide is also suspected of being involved in degenerative disease processes associated with aging and oxidative damage to healthy cells. The enzyme superoxide dismutase regulates the level of superoxide by catalyzing conversion of superoxide to hydrogen peroxide and molecular oxygen. Hydrogen peroxide, however, is also harmful because it can produce hydroxyl ($HO\cdot$) radicals. The enzyme catalase helps to prevent release of hydroxyl radicals by converting hydrogen peroxide to water and oxygen:

 The 1998 Nobel Prize in Physiology or Medicine was awarded to R. F. Furchgott, L. J. Ignarro, and F. Murad for their discovery that NO is an important signaling molecule.

$$2\,O_2^- + 2\,H^+ \xrightarrow{\text{superoxide dismutase}} H_2O_2 + O_2$$

$$2\,H_2O_2 \xrightarrow{\text{catalase}} 2\,H_2O + O_2$$

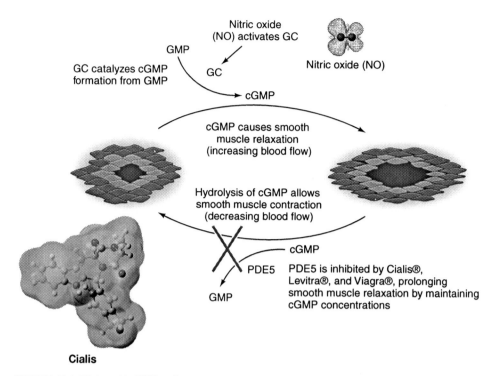

Cialis

FIGURE 10.4 Nitric oxide (NO) activates guanylate cyclase (GC), leading to production of cyclic guanosine monophosphate (cGMP). cGMP signals processes that cause smooth muscle relaxation, ultimately resulting in increased blood flow to certain tissues. Phosphodiesterase V (PDE5) degrades cGMP, leading to smooth muscle contraction and a reduction of blood flow. Cialis, Levitra, and Viagra take their effect by inhibiting PDE5, thus maintaining concentrations of cGMP and sustaining smooth muscle relaxation and tissue engorgement. (Reprinted with permission from Christianson, *Accounts of Chemical Research, 38*, p197, Figure 6b 2005. Copyright 2005 American Chemical Society.)

10.12B Nitric Oxide

Nitric oxide, synthesized in the body from the amino acid arginine, serves as a chemical messenger in a variety of biological processes, including blood pressure regulation and the immune response. Its role in relaxation of smooth muscle in vascular tissues is shown in Fig. 10.4.

10.12C Autoxidation

Linoleic acid is an example of a *polyunsaturated fatty acid*, the kind of polyunsaturated acid that occurs as an ester in **polyunsaturated fats** (Section 7.13, "The Chemistry of . . . Hydrogenation in the Food Industry," and Chapter 23). By polyunsaturated, we mean that the compound contains two or more double bonds:

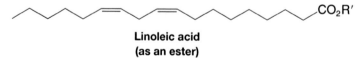

Linoleic acid
(as an ester)

Polyunsaturated fats occur widely in the fats and oils that are components of our diets. They are also widespread in the tissues of the body where they perform numerous vital functions.

The hydrogen atoms of the —CH$_2$— group located between the two double bonds of linoleic ester (Lin—H) are especially susceptible to abstraction by radicals (we shall see why in Chapter 13). Abstraction of one of these hydrogen atoms produces a new radical (Lin·) that can react with oxygen in a chain reaction that belongs to a general type of reaction called **autoxidation** (Fig. 10.5). The result of autoxidation is the formation of a hydroperoxide. Autoxidation is a process that occurs in many substances; for example, autoxidation is responsible for the development of the rancidity that occurs when fats and oils spoil and for the spontaneous combustion of oily rags left open to the air. Autoxidation also occurs in the body, and here it may cause irreversible damage.

Chain Initiation
Step 1

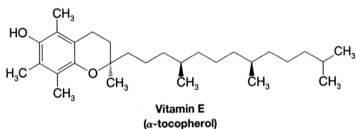

FIGURE 10.5 Autoxidation of a linoleic acid ester. In step 1 the reaction is initiated by the attack of a radical on one of the hydrogen atoms of the $-CH_2-$ group between the two double bonds; this hydrogen abstraction produces a radical that is a resonance hybrid. In step 2 this radical reacts with oxygen in the first of two chain-propagating steps to produce an oxygen-containing radical, which in step 3 can abstract a hydrogen from another molecule of the linoleic ester (**Lin—H**). The result of this second chain-propagating step is the formation of a hydroperoxide and a radical (**Lin·**) that can bring about a repetition of step 2.

Chain Propagation
Step 2

Another radical

Step 3

**Hydrogen abstraction from
another molecule of
the linoleic ester**

A hydroperoxide

THE CHEMISTRY OF... Antioxidants

If you want to stop the ability of radicals to generate more of themselves, especially in scenarios where they could be damaging like autoxidation, one needs to find a suitable trapping reagent. Such materials, known as antioxidants, succeed when they can lead to a new, and more stable, radical species that terminates the chain by no longer reacting, or by further consuming reactive radicals to generate additional nonradical species. Two such compounds are vitamin E (also known as α-tocopherol) and BHT (butylated hydroxytoluene), shown further below:

**Vitamin E
(α-tocopherol)**

Vitamin E is found in vegetable oils.

In both cases, reaction with a radical species initially leads to a phenoxy radical, shown below with BHT in its reaction with a peroxy radical (**ROO·**). This event is the key for antioxidant behavior, in that it turns a highly reactive radical species into a fully covalent molecule that is less reactive (here a hydroperoxide, **ROOH**), with the newly formed phenoxy radical stabilized by the neighboring aromatic ring and attendant steric bulk of the *tert*-butyl groups.

$$\xrightarrow{ROO\cdot}$$

**BHT
(Butylated hydroxytoluene)**

BHT radical

$+\ ROOH$

Worth noting is that vitamin E could be considered a natural antioxidant, since it is found in many foods and may work in our bodies to scavenge potentially damaging radical species, while BHT is a synthetic material that is added to many foods as a preservative.

10.12D Combustion of Alkanes

When alkanes react with oxygen (e.g., in oil and gas furnaces and in internal combustion engines) a complex series of reactions takes place, ultimately converting the alkane to carbon dioxide and water. Although our understanding of the detailed mechanism of combustion is incomplete, we do know that the important reactions occur by radical chain mechanisms with chain-initiating and chain-propagating steps such as the following reactions:

$$RH + O_2 \longrightarrow R\cdot + \cdot OOH \quad \textbf{Initiating}$$

$$R\cdot + O_2 \longrightarrow R{-}OO\cdot$$

$$R{-}OO\cdot + R{-}H \longrightarrow R{-}OOH + R\cdot \quad \textbf{Propagating}$$

One product of the second chain-propagating step is $R{-}OOH$, called an alkyl hydroperoxide. The oxygen–oxygen bond of an alkyl hydroperoxide is quite weak, and it can break and produce radicals that can initiate other chains:

$$RO{-}OH \longrightarrow RO\cdot + \cdot OH$$

THE CHEMISTRY OF... Ozone Depletion and Chlorofluorocarbons (CFCs)

In the stratosphere at altitudes of about 25 km, very high-energy (very short wavelength) UV light converts diatomic oxygen (O_2) into ozone (O_3). The reactions that take place may be represented as follows:

Step 1 $O_2 + h\nu \longrightarrow O + O$

Step 2 $O + O_2 + M \longrightarrow O_3 + M + \text{heat}$

where M is some other particle that can absorb some of the energy released in the second step.

The ozone produced in step 2 can also interact with high-energy UV light in the following way:

Step 3 $O_3 + h\nu \longrightarrow O_2 + O + \text{heat}$

The oxygen atom formed in step 3 can cause a repetition of step 2, and so forth. The net result of these steps is to convert highly energetic UV light into heat. This is important because the existence of this cycle shields Earth from radiation that is destructive to living organisms. This shield makes life possible on Earth's surface. Even a relatively small increase in high-energy UV radiation at Earth's surface would cause a large increase in the incidence of skin cancers.

Production of chlorofluoromethanes (and of chlorofluoroethanes) called chlorofluorocarbons (CFCs) or **freons** began in 1930. These compounds have been used as refrigerants, solvents, and propellants in aerosol cans. Typical freons are trichlorofluoromethane, $CFCl_3$ (called Freon-11), and dichlorodifluoromethane, CF_2Cl_2 (called Freon-12).

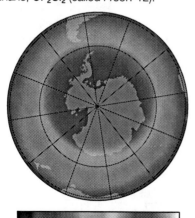

0 100 200 300 400 500 600 700
Total Ozone (Dobson units)

Chain Initiation

Step 1 $CF_2Cl_2 + h\nu \longrightarrow CF_2Cl\cdot + Cl\cdot$

Chain Propagation

Step 2 $Cl\cdot + O_3 \longrightarrow ClO\cdot + O_2$

Step 3 $ClO\cdot + O \longrightarrow O_2 + Cl\cdot$

In the chain-initiating step, UV light causes homolytic cleavage of one $C{-}Cl$ bond of the freon. The chlorine atom thus produced is the real villain; it can set off a chain reaction that destroys thousands of molecules of ozone before it diffuses out of the stratosphere or reacts with some other substance.

In 1975 a study by the National Academy of Sciences supported the predictions of Rowland and Molina, and since January 1978 the use of freons in aerosol cans in the United States has been banned.

In 1985 a hole was discovered in the ozone layer above Antarctica. Studies done since then strongly suggest that chlorine atom destruction of the ozone is a factor in the formation of the hole. This ozone hole has continued to grow in size, and such a hole has also been discovered in the Arctic ozone layer. Should the ozone layer be depleted, more of the sun's damaging rays would penetrate to the surface of Earth.

 By 1974 world freon production was about 2 billion pounds annually. Most freon, even that used in refrigeration, eventually makes its way into the atmosphere where it diffuses unchanged into the stratosphere. In June 1974 F. S. Rowland and M. J. Molina published an article indicating, for the first time, that in the stratosphere freon is able to initiate radical chain reactions that can upset the natural ozone balance. The 1995 Nobel Prize in Chemistry was awarded to P. J. Crutzen, M. J. Molina, and F. S. Rowland for their combined work in this area. The reactions that take place are the following. (Freon-12 is used as an example.)

Recognizing the global nature of the problem, the "Montreal Protocol" was initiated in 1987. This treaty required the signing nations to reduce their production and consumption of chlorofluorocarbons. Accordingly, the industrialized nations of the world ceased production of chlorofluorocarbons as of 1996, and over 120 nations have signed the Montreal Protocol. Increased worldwide understanding of stratospheric ozone depletion, in general, has accelerated the phasing out of chlorofluorocarbons.

[WHY Do These Topics Matter?

RADICALS FROM THE BERGMAN CYCLOAROMATIZATION REACTION

In 1972, chemists at the University of California at Berkeley under the direction of Robert Bergman discovered a new chemical reaction that could be used to synthesize a benzene ring from starting materials that contained two alkyne triple bonds connected by a cis double bond, an array of atoms also known as an enediyne. This process, known as a cycloaromatization since it makes a ring that is aromatic, involves radicals as shown below both in making new bonds as well as in adding the final hydrogen atoms needed to make a benzene ring system.

Equally interesting, it was discovered on further exploration that the temperature needed to make the reaction occur was directly correlated to the distance between the termini of the two alkynes. For most molecules, that distance is greater than 3.6 Å and temperatures in excess of 200 °C are required to initiate the event. However, if that length can be made shorter, for example by placing the alkynes within a constrained ring, then these processes can occur at lower temperatures. Typically, distances between 3.2 to 3.3 Å allow for the cycloaromatization at ambient temperature (i.e., 37 °C), while even shorter distances, such as 3.0 Å, allow the reaction to proceed at room temperature (i.e., 25 °C).

Globally, such studies highlight the ability of chemists to discover new reactivity and understand molecular processes at a very sophisticated level. In this case, however, it turns out that the process occurs in nature, a fact that chemists just did not know until the natural product calicheamicin γ_1^I was isolated from a bacterial strain!

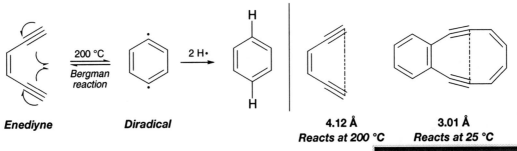

Enediyne   **Diradical**   **4.12 Å**   **3.01 Å**
                                                 Reacts at 200 °C   *Reacts at 25 °C*

As you can see from its structure below, calicheamicin γ_1^I is highly complex. It has an enediyne motif, one that is stable at 37 °C (body temperature) since the distance between the ends of the two alkyne units in its natural form is calculated to be just longer than 3.3 Å. However, when this compound is brought into a cell's nucleus, the unique trisulfide portion of the molecule can be converted into a sulfide nucleophile. Once unveiled, this reactive group can then attack a neighboring group of atoms through a chemical reaction we will learn more about in Chapter 19. What is important to know for now, however, is that this event changes the conformation of the entire right-hand half of the molecule, bringing the ends of the two alkynes closer together, to a distance of ~3.2 Å. As a result, a Bergman cycloaromatization can now occur at 37 °C, immediately generating a diradical that can abstract hydrogen from DNA, creating new DNA radicals that lead to cell death.

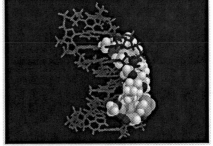

Calicheamicin bound to DNA. (PDB ID: 2PIK. Kumar, R. A.; Ikemoto, N., and Patel, D. J., Solution structure of the calicheamicin γ_1^I–DNA complex, J. Mol. Biol. 1997, 265, 187.) [Calicheamicin γ_1^I structure from Chemistry and Biology, 1994, 1(1). Nicolaou, K.C., Pitsinos, E.N., Theodorakis, A., Saimoto, H., and Wrasidio, W., Chemistry and Biology of the Calicheamicins, pp. 25-30. Copyright Elsevier 1994.

(continues on next page)

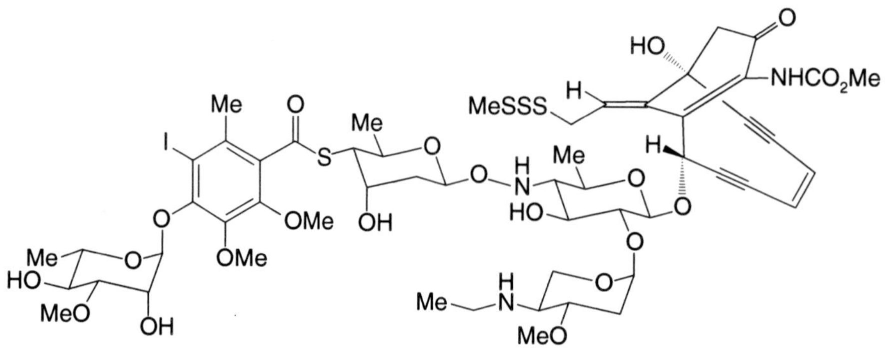

Calicheamicin γ₁ᴵ

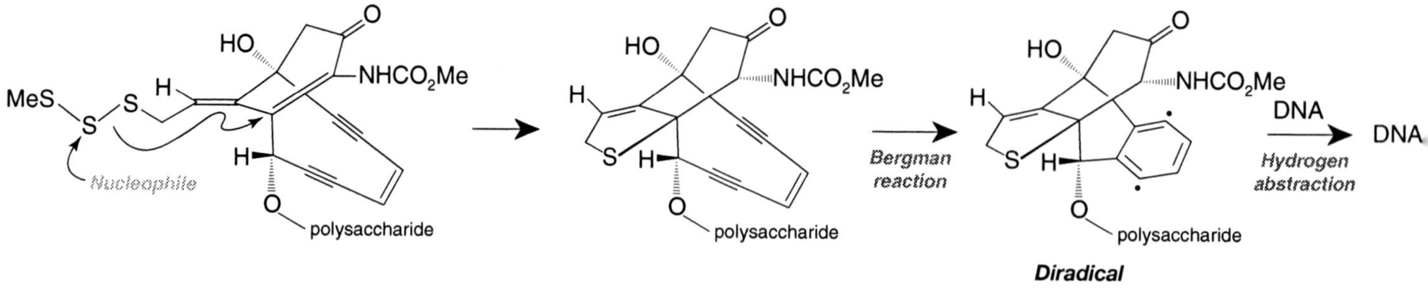

Diradical

   This chemistry shows that the Bergman reaction can occur naturally and that it functions in the formation of a molecule with a special triggering system that takes advantage of the differences in reactivity between different enediynes. Scientists in the pharmaceutical industry have since used this trigger system, as well as those of other related enediyne molecules from Nature, to create new drugs that have undergone clinical testing targeting a number of cancers such as acute forms of leukemia.

To learn more about these topics, see:

1. Bergman, R. G. "Reactive 1,4-Dehydroaromatics" in *Acc. Chem. Res.* **1973**, *6*, 25–31.
2. Nicolaou, K. C.; Smith, A. L.; Yue, E. W. "Chemistry and biology of natural and designed enediynes" in *Proc. Natl. Acad. Sci. USA* **1993**, *90*, 5881–5888 and references therein.

SUMMARY AND REVIEW TOOLS

The study aids for this chapter include key terms and concepts (which are hyperlinked to the Glossary from the bold, blue terms in the *WileyPLUS* version of the book at wileyplus.com) and a Mechanism Review regarding radical reactions.

PROBLEMS PLUS

Note to Instructors: Many of the homework problems are available for assignment via *WileyPLUS*, an online teaching and learning solution.

RADICAL MECHANISMS AND PROPERTIES

10.18 Write a mechanism for the following radical halogenation reaction.

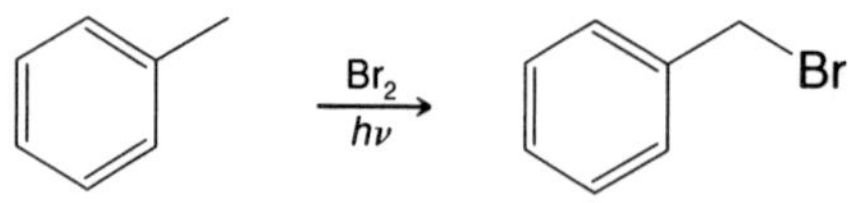

10.19 Explain the relative distribution of products below using reaction energy diagrams for the hydrogen abstraction step that leads to each product. (The rate-determining step in radical halogenation is the hydrogen abstraction step.) In energy diagrams for the two pathways, show the relative energies of the transition states and of the alkyl radical intermediate that results in each case.

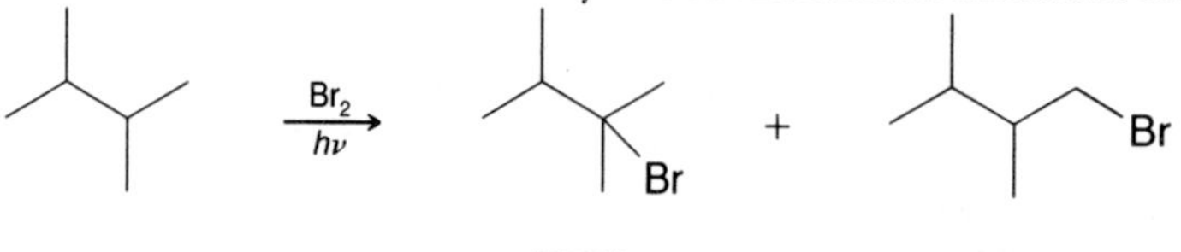

10.20 Which of the following compounds can be prepared by radical halogenation with little complication by formation of isomeric by-products?

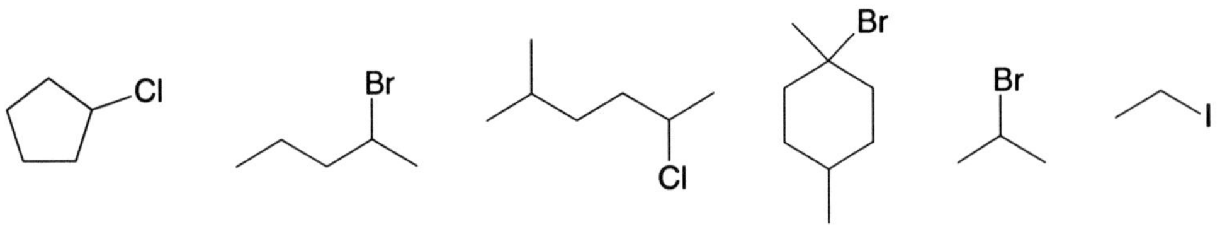

10.21 The radical reaction of propane with chlorine yields (in addition to more highly halogenated compounds) 1-chloropropane and 2-chloropropane.

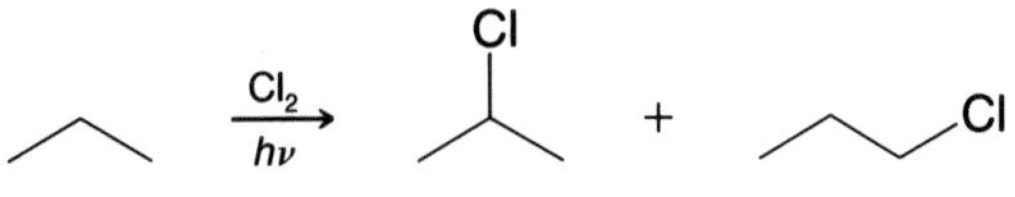

Write chain-initiating and chain-propagating steps showing how each of the products above is formed.

10.22 In addition to more highly chlorinated products, chlorination of butane yields a mixture of compounds with the formula C_4H_9Cl.

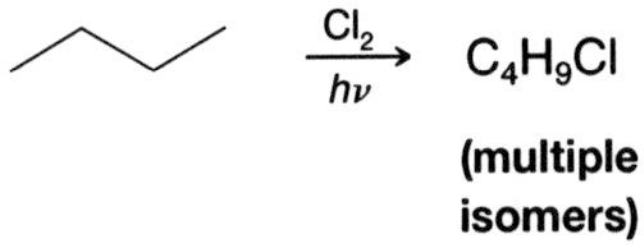

(a) Taking stereochemistry into account, how many different isomers with the formula C_4H_9Cl would you expect?

(b) If the mixture of C_4H_9Cl isomers were subjected to fractional distillation (or gas chromatography), how many fractions (or peaks) would you expect?

(c) Which fractions would be optically *inactive*?

(d) Which fractions could theoretically be resolved into enantiomers?

(e) Predict features in the ^1H and ^{13}C DEPT NMR spectra for each that would differentiate among the isomers separated by distillation or GC.

(f) How could fragmentation in their mass spectra be used to differentiate the isomers?

10.23 Chlorination of (R)-2-chlorobutane yields a mixture of dichloro isomers.

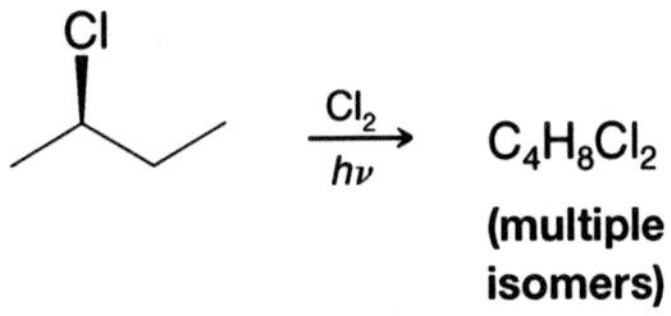

(a) Taking into account stereochemistry, how many different isomers would you expect? Write their structures.

(b) How many fractions would be obtained upon fractional distillation?

(c) Which of these fractions would be optically active?

10.24 Peroxides are often used to initiate radical chain reactions such as in the following radical halogenation.

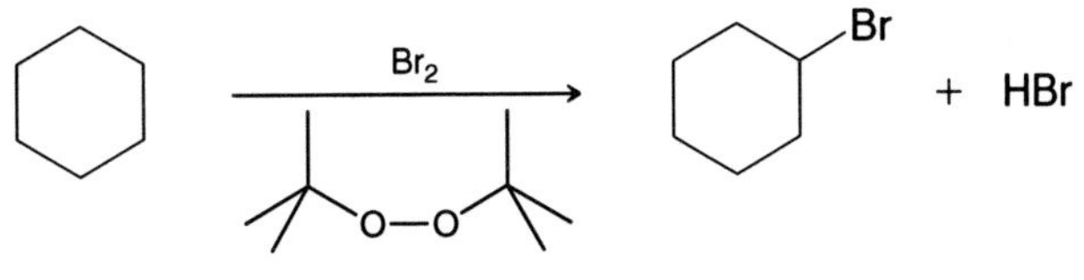

(Di-*tert*-butyl peroxide)

(a) Using bond dissociation energies in Table 10.1, explain why peroxides are especially effective as radical initiators.

(b) Write a mechanism for the reaction above showing how it could be initiated by di-*tert*-butyl peroxide.

10.25 List in order of decreasing stability all of the radicals that can be obtained by abstraction of a hydrogen atom from 2-methylbutane.

10.26 Draw mechanism arrows to show electron movements in the Bergman cycloaromatization reaction that leads to the diradical believed responsible for the DNA-cleaving action of the antitumor agent calicheamicin (see "Why Do These Topics Matter?" after Section 10.12).

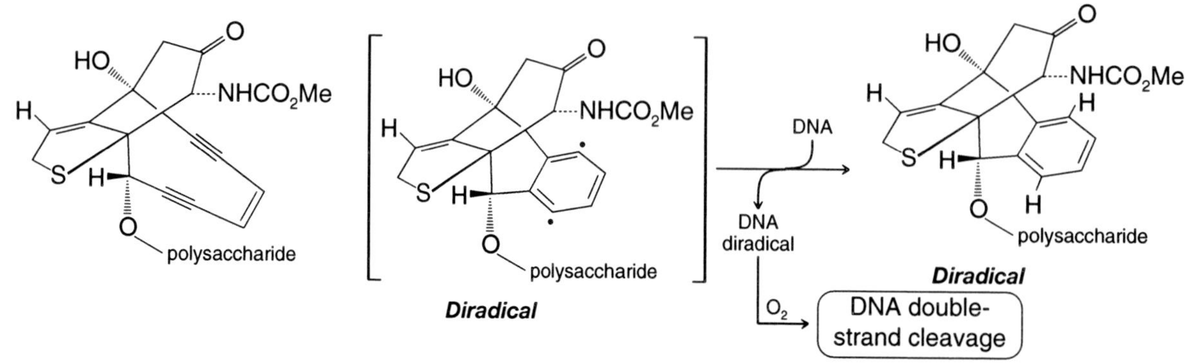

10.27 Find examples of C—H bond dissociation energies in Table 10.1 that are as closely related as possible to the bonds to H_a, H_b, and H_c in the molecule at right. Use these values to answer the questions below.

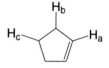

(a) What can you conclude about the relative ease of radical halogenation at H_a?

(b) Comparing H_b and H_c, which would more readily undergo substitution by radical halogenation?

10.28 Write a radical chain mechanism for the following reaction (a reaction called the Hunsdiecker reaction).

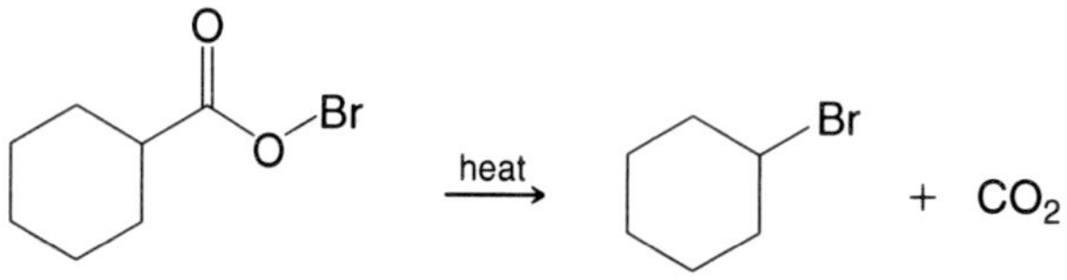

SYNTHESIS

10.29 Starting with the compound or compounds indicated in each part and using any other needed reagents, outline syntheses of each of the following compounds. (You need not repeat steps carried out in earlier parts of this problem.)

(a) $CH_3CH_3 \longrightarrow$

(b) $CH_3CH_3 \longrightarrow$

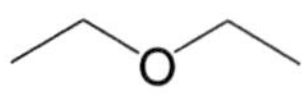

(c)

(d)

(e) $CH_4 + HC\equiv CH \longrightarrow$

(f) $CH_3CH_3 + HC\equiv CH \longrightarrow$

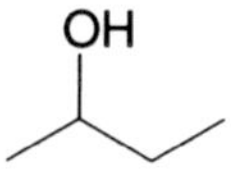

(g) $CH_3CH_3 \longrightarrow$

10.30 Provide the reagents necessary for the following synthetic transformations. More than one step may be required.

(a)

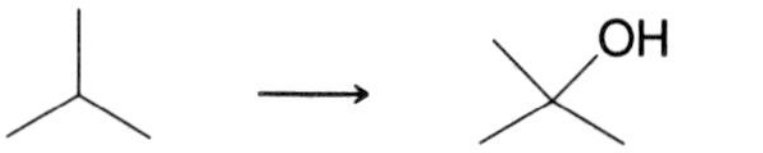

(b)

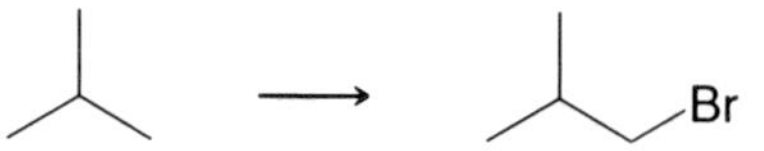

(c)

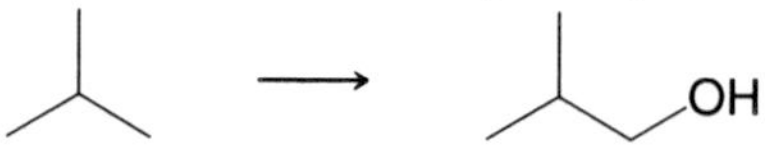

(d)

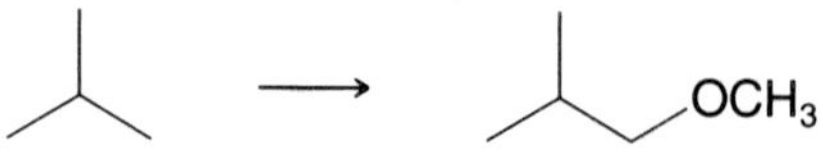

(e)

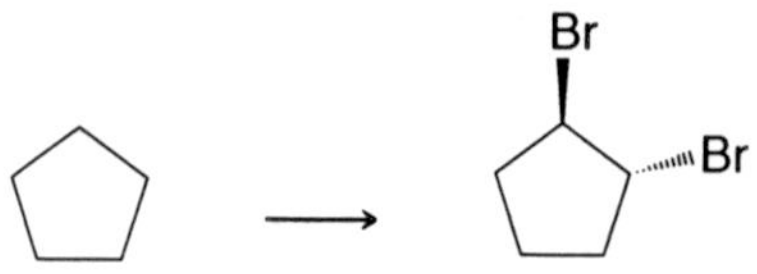

(f)

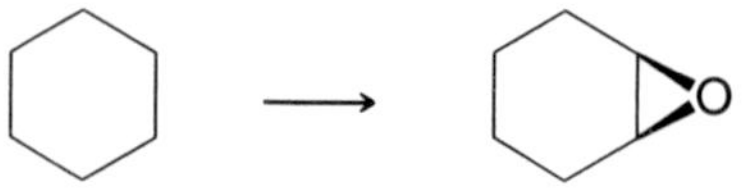

10.31 Synthesize each of the following compounds by routes that involve allylic bromination by NBS. Use starting materials having four carbons or fewer. Begin by writing a retrosynthetic analysis.

(a)

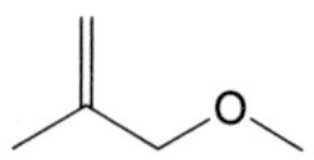

(b)

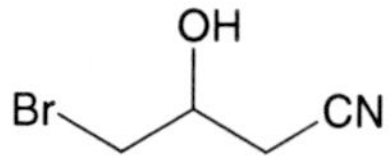

(c)

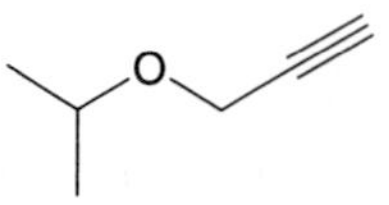

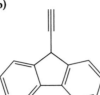

10.32 Synthesize each of the following compounds by routes that involve benzylic bromination by NBS and any other synthetic steps necessary. Begin by writing a retrosynthetic analysis.

(a)

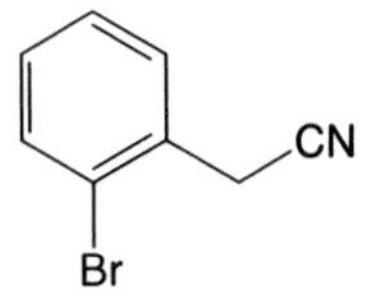

(b)

(c)

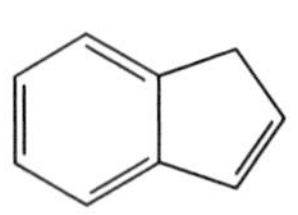

10.33 Synthesize each of the following compounds by routes that involve both allylic and benzylic bromination by NBS.

(a)

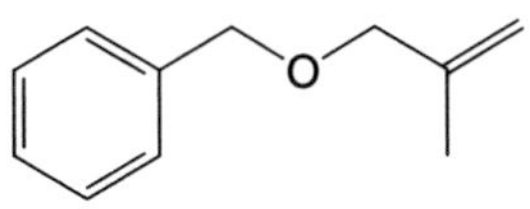

(b)

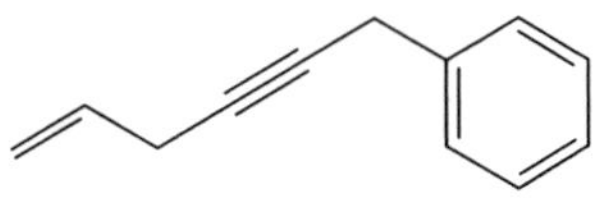

CHALLENGE PROBLEMS

10.34 The following reaction is the first step in the industrial synthesis of acetone and phenol (C_6H_5OH). AIBN (2,2′-azobisisobutyronitrile) initiates radical reactions by breaking down upon heating to form two isobutyronitrile radicals and nitrogen gas. Using an isobutyronitrile radical to initiate the reaction, write a mechanism for the following process.

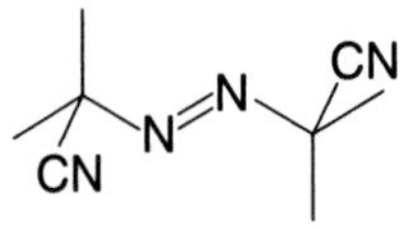

$$\xrightarrow{\text{O}_2,\ \text{AIBN}\quad \Delta}$$

AIBN

10.35 In the radical chlorination of 2,2-dimethylhexane, chlorine substitution occurs much more rapidly at **C5** than it does at a typical secondary carbon (e.g., **C2** in butane). Consider the mechanism of radical polymerization and then suggest an explanation for the enhanced rate of substitution at **C5** in 2,2-dimethylhexane.

10.36 Write a mechanism for the following reaction.

$$\xrightarrow{(\text{PhCO}_2)_2,\ \text{heat}} \quad + \quad \text{CO}$$

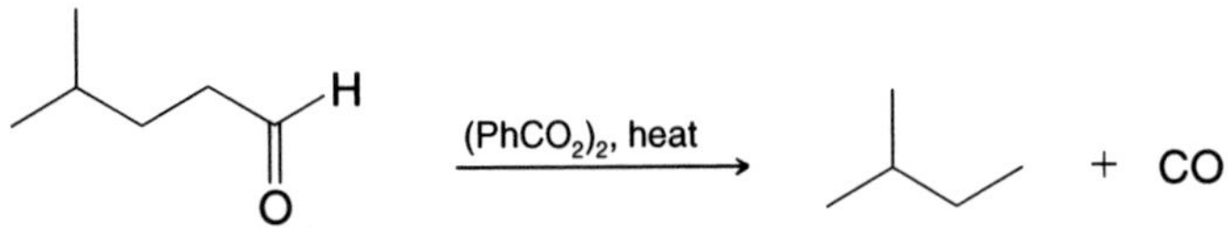

10.37 Hydrogen peroxide and ferrous sulfate react to produce hydroxyl radical (HO·), as reported in 1894 by English chemist H. J. H. Fenton. When *tert*-butyl alcohol is treated with HO· generated this way, it affords a crystalline reaction product **X**, mp 92 °C, which has these spectral properties:

> **MS:** heaviest mass peak is at *m/z* 131
> **IR:** 3620, 3350 (broad), 2980, 2940, 1385, 1370 cm^{-1}
> **^{1}H NMR:** sharp singlets at δ 1.22, 1.58, and 2.95 (6:2:1 area ratio)
> **^{13}C NMR:** δ 28 (CH_3), 35 (CH_2), 68 (C)

Draw the structure of **X** and write a mechanism for its formation.

10.38 The halogen atom of an alkyl halide can be replaced by the hydrogen atom bonded to tin in tributyltin hydride (Bu_3SnH). The process, called dehalogenation, is a radical reaction, and it can be initiated by AIBN (2,2′-azobisisobutyronitrile). AIBN decomposes to form nitrogen gas and two isobutyronitrile radicals, which initiate the reaction. Write a mechanism for the reaction.

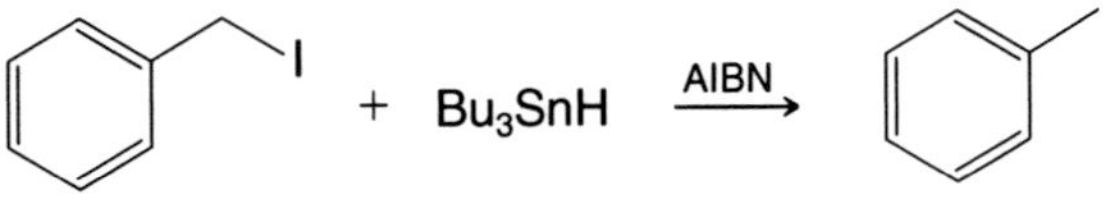

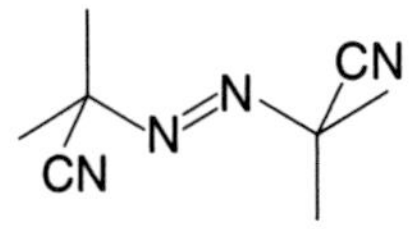

$$+ \quad \text{Bu}_3\text{SnH} \quad \xrightarrow{\text{AIBN}}$$

AIBN

10.39 Write a mechanism that accounts for the following reaction. Note that the hydrogen atom bonded to tin in tributyltin hydride is readily transferred in radical mechanisms.

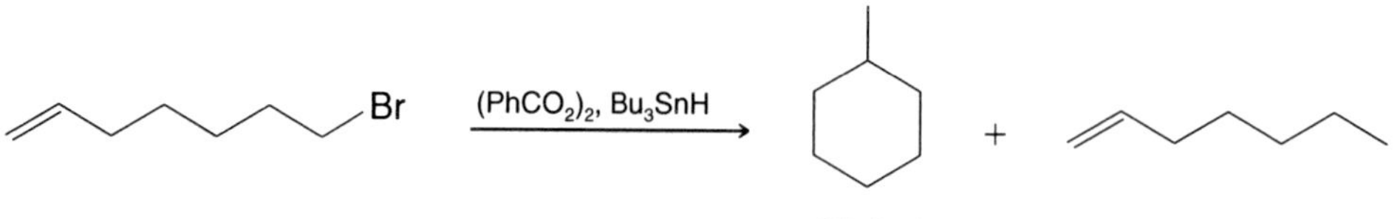

(Major)

10.40 Molecular orbital calculations can be used to model the location of electron density from unpaired electrons in a radical. Open the molecular models on the book's website for the methyl, ethyl, and *tert*-butyl radicals. The gray wire mesh surfaces in these models represent volumes enclosing electron density from unpaired electrons. What do you notice about the distribution of unpaired electron density in the ethyl radical and *tert*-butyl radical, as compared to the methyl radical? What bearing does this have on the relative stabilities of the radicals in this series?

10.41 If one were to try to draw the simplest Lewis structure for molecular oxygen, the result might be the following $\left(\ddot{\underset{..}{O}} = \ddot{\underset{..}{O}} \right)$.

However, it is known from the properties of molecular oxygen and experiments that O_2 contains two unpaired electrons, and therefore, the Lewis structure above is incorrect. To understand the structure of O_2, it is necessary to employ a molecular orbital representation. To do so, we will need to recall (1) the shapes of bonding and antibonding σ and π molecular orbitals, (2) that each orbital can contain a maximum of two electrons, (3) that molecular oxygen has 16 electrons in total, and (4) that the two unpaired electrons in oxygen occupy separate degenerate (equal-energy) orbitals. Now, open the molecular model on the book's website for oxygen and examine its molecular orbitals in sequence from the HOMO-7 orbital to the LUMO. [HOMO-7 means the seventh orbital in energy below the highest occupied molecular orbital (HOMO), HOMO-6 means the sixth below the HOMO, and so forth.] Orbitals HOMO-7 through HOMO-4 represent the $\sigma 1s$, $\sigma 1s^*$, $\sigma 2s$, and $\sigma 2s^*$ orbitals, respectively, each containing a pair of electrons.

(a) What type of orbital is represented by HOMO-3 and HOMO-2? (*Hint*: What types of orbitals are possible for second-row elements like oxygen, and which orbitals have already been used?)

(b) What type of orbital is HOMO-1? [*Hint*: The $\sigma 2s$ and $\sigma 2s^*$ orbitals are already filled, as are the HOMO-3 and HOMO-2 orbitals identified in part (a). What bonding orbital remains?]

(c) The orbitals designated HOMO and LUMO in O_2 have the same energy (they are degenerate), and each contains one of the unpaired electrons of the oxygen molecule. What type of orbitals are these?

LEARNING GROUP PROBLEMS

1. (a) Draw structures for all organic products that would result when an *excess* of *cis*-1,3-dimethylcyclohexane reacts with Br_2 in the presence of heat and light. Use three-dimensional formulas to show stereochemistry.

(b) Draw structures for all organic products that would result when an *excess* of *cis*-1,3-dimethylcyclohexane reacts with Cl_2 in the presence of heat and light. Use three-dimensional formulas to show stereochemistry.

(c) As an alternative, use *cis*-1,2-dimethylcyclohexane to answer parts (a) and (b) above.

2. (a) Propose a synthesis of 2-methoxypropene starting with propane and methane as the sole source for carbon atoms. You may use any other reagents necessary. Devise a retrosynthetic analysis first.

(b) 2-Methoxypropene will form a polymer when treated with a radical initiator. Write the structure of this polymer and a mechanism for the polymerization reaction assuming a radical mechanism initiated by a diacyl peroxide.

[CONCEPT MAP]

Mechanism Review of Radical Reactions

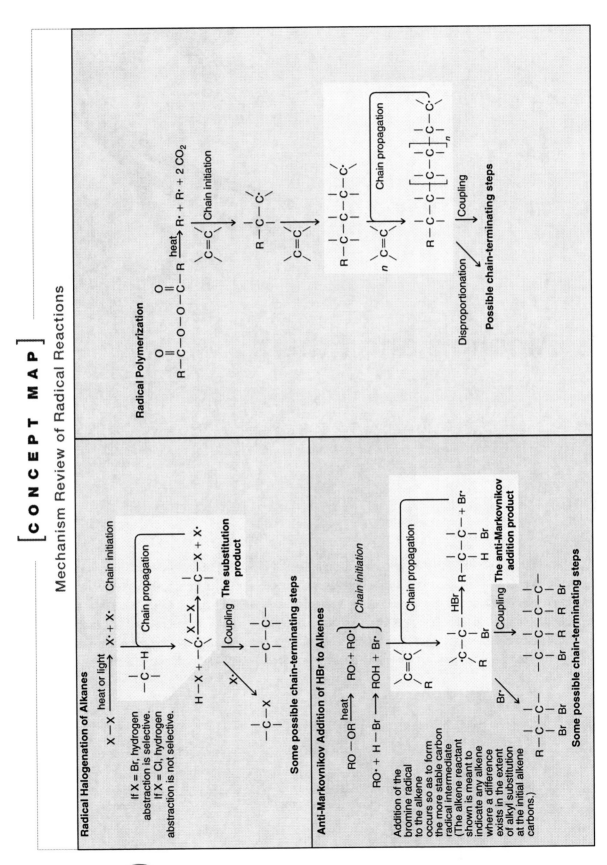

Radical Halogenation of Alkanes

If X = Br, hydrogen abstraction is selective.
If X = Cl, hydrogen abstraction is not selective.

Radical Polymerization

Anti-Markovnikov Addition of HBr to Alkenes

Addition of the bromine radical to the alkene occurs so as to form the more stable carbon radical intermediate (The alkene reactant shown is meant to indicate any alkene where a difference exists in the extent of alkyl substitution at the initial alkene carbons.)

PLUS See Special Topic B in *WileyPLUS*

Alcohols and Ethers

SYNTHESIS AND REACTIONS

Have you ever walked into a bakery and caught a whiff of vanilla or peppermint emanating from a cake or pastry? Maybe you like to snack on licorice. These smells and flavors, as well as many others that you encounter in daily life, arise from naturally occurring molecules that contain either an alcohol or an ether functional group. Hundreds of such molecules are known, and in addition to their use as flavorings, some have other kinds of commercial roles, for example, as antifreezes or pharmaceuticals. An understanding of the physical properties and reactivity of these compounds will enable you to see how they can be used to create new materials with different and even more valuable characteristics.

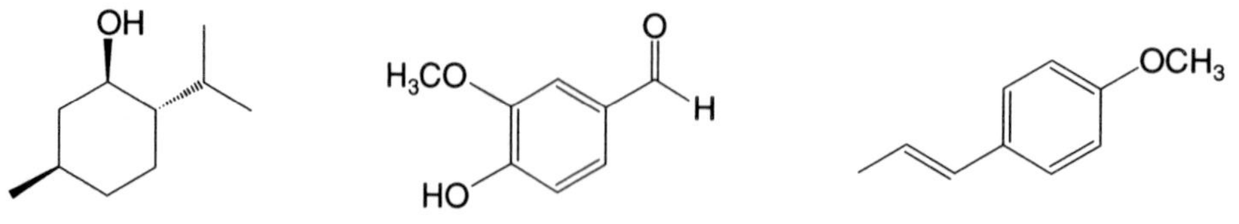

(–)-Menthol
(from peppermint)

Vanillin
(from vanilla beans)

Anethole
(from fennel)

PHOTO CREDITS: (peppermint plant) © Alexey Ilyashenko/iStockphoto; (licorice roots) © Fabrizio Troiani/Age Fotostock America, Inc.; (vanilla pods and seeds) © STOCKFOOD LBRF/Age Fotostock America, Inc.

498

IN THIS CHAPTER WE WILL CONSIDER:

- the structures, properties, and nomenclature of common alcohols and ethers
- key molecules that contain such groups
- the reactivity of alcohols, ethers, and a special group of ethers known as epoxides

[**WHY** DO THESE TOPICS MATTER?] At the end of the chapter, we will see how the reactivity of epoxides can not only make highly complex molecules containing dozens of rings from acyclic precursors in a single step, but also help detoxify cancer-causing compounds from grilled meat, cigarettes, and peanuts.

11.1 STRUCTURE AND NOMENCLATURE

Alcohols have a hydroxyl (—OH) group bonded to a *saturated* carbon atom. The alcohol carbon atom may be part of a simple alkyl group, as in some of the following examples, or it may be part of a more complex molecule, such as cholesterol. Alcohols are also classified as 1°, 2°, or 3°, depending on the number of carbons bonded to the alcohol carbon.

CH_3OH

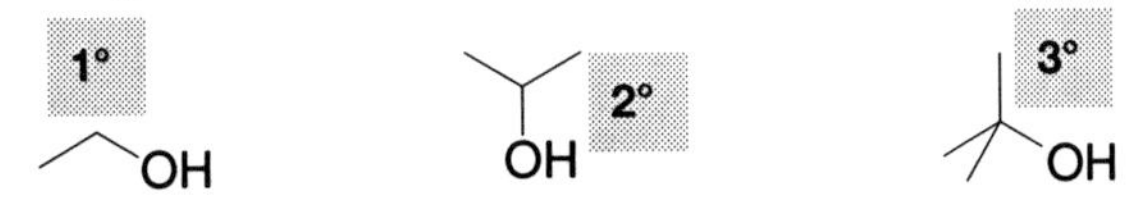

Methanol
(methyl alcohol)

1°

Ethanol
(ethyl alcohol),
a 1° alcohol

2°

2-Propanol
(isopropyl alcohol),
a 2° alcohol

3°

2-Methyl-2-propanol
(*tert*-butyl alcohol),
a 3° alcohol

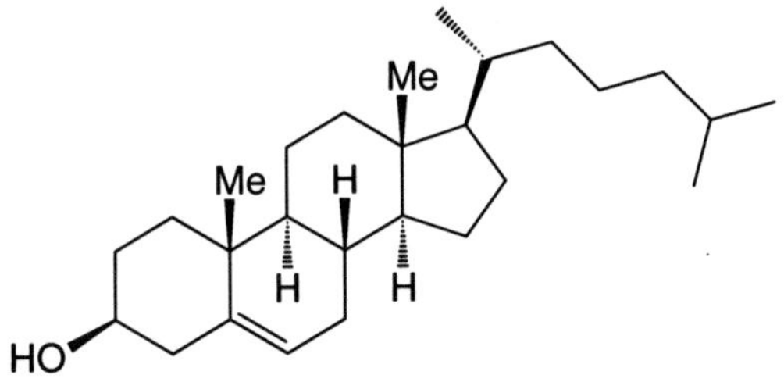

Cholesterol

The alcohol carbon atom may also be a saturated carbon atom adjacent to an alkenyl or alkynyl group, or the carbon atom may be a saturated carbon atom that is attached to a benzene ring:

allylic, 1° position

benzylic, 1° position

2-Propenol
(or prop-2-en-1-ol,
or allyl alcohol),
an allylic alcohol

2-Propynol
(or prop-2-yn-1-ol,
or propargyl alcohol)

Benzyl alcohol
(*a benzylic alcohol*)

Compounds that have a hydroxyl group attached *directly* to a benzene ring are called **phenols**. (Phenols are discussed in detail in Chapter 21.)

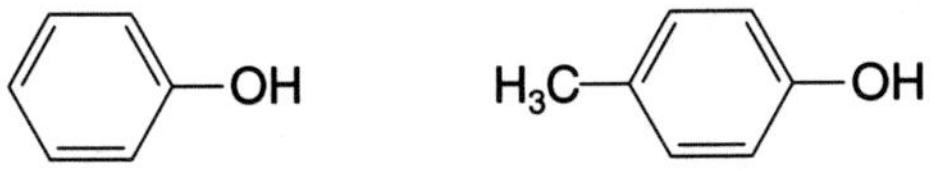

Phenol

p-Methylphenol,
a substituted phenol

Ar—OH

General formula
for a phenol

Ethers differ from alcohols in that the oxygen atom of an ether is bonded to two carbon atoms. The hydrocarbon groups may be alkyl, alkenyl, vinyl, alkynyl, or aryl. Several examples are shown here:

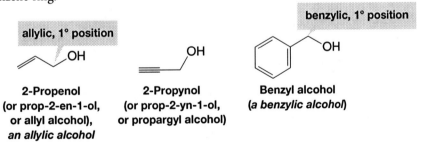

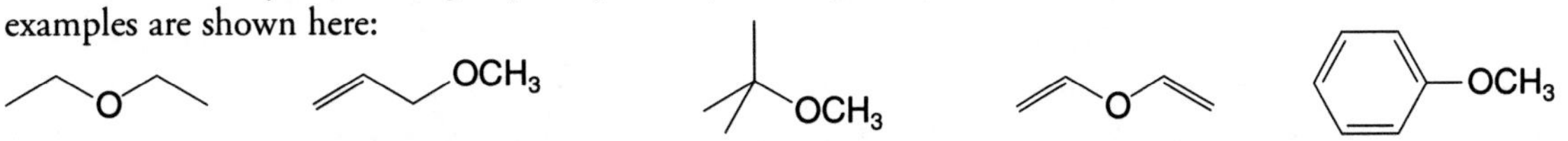

Diethyl ether

Allyl methyl ether

tert-Butyl methyl ether

Divinyl ether

Methyl phenyl ether

11.1A Nomenclature of Alcohols

We studied the IUPAC system of nomenclature for alcohols in Sections 2.6 and 4.3F. As a review consider the following problem.

●●● SOLVED PROBLEM 11.1

Give IUPAC substitutive names for the following alcohols:

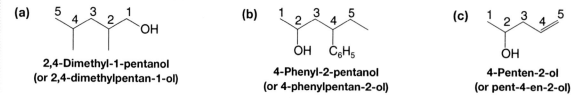

(a)   OH   **(b)**   OH C_6H_5 **(c)**   OH

ANSWER: The longest chain *to which the hydroxyl group is attached* gives us the *base name*. The ending is **-ol**. We then number *the longest chain from the end that gives the carbon bearing the hydroxyl group the lower number*. Thus, the names, in both of the accepted IUPAC formats, are

(a)
$$\overset{5}{}\ \overset{4}{}\ \overset{3}{}\ \overset{2}{}\ \overset{1}{}\text{OH}$$

2,4-Dimethyl-1-pentanol
(or 2,4-dimethylpentan-1-ol)

(b)
$$\overset{1}{}\ \overset{2}{}\ \overset{3}{}\ \overset{4}{}\ \overset{5}{}$$
OH C_6H_5

4-Phenyl-2-pentanol
(or 4-phenylpentan-2-ol)

(c)
$$\overset{1}{}\ \overset{2}{}\ \overset{3}{}\ \overset{4}{}\ \overset{5}{}$$
OH

4-Penten-2-ol
(or pent-4-en-2-ol)

- The hydroxyl group has precedence over double bonds and triple bonds in deciding which functional group to name as the suffix [see example (c) above].

In common functional class nomenclature (Section 2.6) alcohols are called **alkyl alcohols** such as methyl alcohol, ethyl alcohol, and so on.

●●●

PRACTICE PROBLEM 11.1   What is wrong with the use of such names as "isopropanol" and "*tert*-butanol"?

11.1B Nomenclature of Ethers

Simple ethers are frequently given common functional class names. One simply lists (in alphabetical order) both groups that are attached to the oxygen atom and adds the word *ether*.

    OCH_3 O OC_6H_5

Ethyl methyl ether   **Diethyl ether**   ***tert*-Butyl phenyl ether**

IUPAC substitutive names should be used for complicated ethers, however, and for compounds with more than one ether linkage. In this IUPAC style, ethers are named as alkoxyalkanes, alkoxyalkenes, and alkoxyarenes. The RO— group is an **alkoxy** group.

    OCH_3 O H_3C H_3CO OCH_3

2-Methoxypentane   **1-Ethoxy-4-methylbenzene**   **1,2-Dimethoxyethane (DME)**

Cyclic ethers can be named in several ways. One simple way is to use **replacement nomenclature**, in which we relate the cyclic ether to the corresponding hydrocarbon ring system and use the prefix **oxa-** to indicate that an oxygen atom replaces a CH_2 group. In another system, a cyclic three-membered ether is named **oxirane** and a four-membered ether is called **oxetane**. Several simple cyclic ethers also have common names; in the examples below, these common names are given in parentheses. Tetrahydrofuran (THF) and 1,4-dioxane are useful solvents:

Oxacyclopropane or oxirane (ethylene oxide) 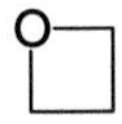 **Oxacyclobutane or oxetane**  **Oxacyclopentane (tetrahydrofuran or THF)** 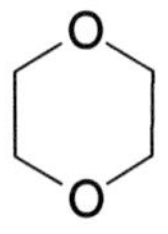 **1,4-Dioxacyclohexane (1,4-dioxane)**

Polyethylene oxide (PEO) (a water-soluble polymer made from ethylene oxide)

Polyethylene oxide is used in some skin creams.

Ethylene oxide is the starting material for polyethylene oxide (PEO, also called polyethylene glycol, PEG). Polyethylene oxide has many practical uses, including covalent attachment to therapeutic proteins such as interferon, a use that has been found to increase the circulatory lifetime of the drug. PEO is also used in some skin creams, and as a laxative prior to digestive tract procedures.

••• SOLVED PROBLEM 11.2

Albuterol (used in some commonly prescribed respiratory medications) and vanillin (from vanilla beans) each contain several functional groups. Name the functional groups in albuterol and vanillin and, if appropriate for a given group, classify them as primary (1°), secondary (2°), or tertiary (3°).

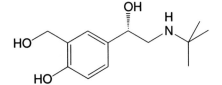 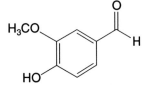

Albuterol (an asthma medication) **Vanillin (from vanilla beans)**

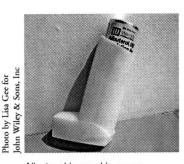

Albuterol is used in some respiratory medications.

STRATEGY AND ANSWER: Albuterol has the following functional groups: 1° alcohol, 2° alcohol, phenol, and 2° amine. Vanillin has aldehyde, ether, and phenol functional groups. See Chapter 2 for a review of how to classify alcohol and amine functional groups as 1°, 2°, or 3°.

••• PRACTICE PROBLEM 11.2

Give bond-line formulas and appropriate names for all of the alcohols and ethers with the formulas **(a)** C_3H_8O and **(b)** $C_4H_{10}O$.

11.2 PHYSICAL PROPERTIES OF ALCOHOLS AND ETHERS

The physical properties of a number of alcohols and ethers are given in Tables 11.1 and 11.2.

- Ethers have boiling points that are roughly comparable with those of hydrocarbons of the same molecular weight (MW).

For example, the boiling point of diethyl ether (MW = 74) is 34.6 °C; that of pentane (MW = 72) is 36 °C.

- Alcohols have much higher boiling points than comparable ethers or hydrocarbons.

The boiling point of butyl alcohol (MW = 74) is 117.7 °C. We learned the reason for this behavior in Section 2.13C.

TABLE 11.1 PHYSICAL PROPERTIES OF SOME COMMON ALCOHOLS

Name	Formula	mp (°C)	bp (°C) (1 atm)	Water Solubility (g/100 mL H₂O)
Monohydroxy Alcohols				
Methanol	CH_3OH	−97	64.7	∞
Ethanol	CH_3CH_2OH	−117	78.3	∞
Propyl alcohol	$CH_3CH_2CH_2OH$	−126	97.2	∞
Isopropyl alcohol	$CH_3CH(OH)CH_3$	−88	82.3	∞
Butyl alcohol	$CH_3CH_2CH_2CH_2OH$	−90	117.7	8.3
Isobutyl alcohol	$CH_3CH(CH_3)CH_2OH$	−108	108.0	10.0
sec-Butyl alcohol	$CH_3CH_2CH(OH)CH_3$	−114	99.5	26.0
tert-Butyl alcohol	$(CH_3)_3COH$	25	82.5	∞
Diols and Triols				
Ethylene glycol	CH_2OHCH_2OH	−12.6	197	∞
Propylene glycol	$CH_3CHOHCH_2OH$	−59	187	∞
Trimethylene glycol	$CH_2OHCH_2CH_2OH$	−30	215	∞
Glycerol	$CH_2OHCHOHCH_2OH$	18	290	∞

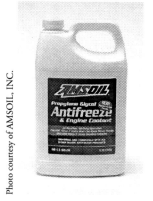

Photo courtesy of AMSOIL, INC.

Propylene glycol (1,2-propanediol) is used as an environmentally friendly engine coolant because it is biodegradable, has a high boiling point, and is miscible with water.

- Alcohol molecules can associate with each other through **hydrogen bonding**, whereas those of ethers and hydrocarbons cannot.

Hydrogen bonding between molecules of methanol

Ethers, however, *are* able to form hydrogen bonds with compounds such as water. Ethers, therefore, have solubilities in water that are similar to those of alcohols of the same molecular weight and that are very different from those of hydrocarbons.

TABLE 11.2 PHYSICAL PROPERTIES OF SOME COMMON ETHERS

Name	Formula	mp (°C)	bp (°C) (1 atm)
Dimethyl ether	CH_3OCH_3	−138	−24.9
Ethyl methyl ether	$CH_3OCH_2CH_3$		10.8
Diethyl ether	$CH_3CH_2OCH_2CH_3$	−116	34.6
1,2-Dimethoxyethane (DME)	$CH_3OCH_2CH_2OCH_3$	−68	83
Oxirane		−112	12
Tetrahydrofuran (THF)		−108	65.4
1,4-Dioxane		11	101

Diethyl ether and 1-butanol, for example, have the same solubility in water, approximately 8 g per 100 mL at room temperature. Pentane, by contrast, is virtually insoluble in water.

Methanol, ethanol, both propyl alcohols, and *tert*-butyl alcohol are completely miscible with water (Table 11.1). The solubility of alcohols in water gradually decreases as the hydrocarbon portion of the molecule lengthens; long-chain alcohols are more "alkane-like" and are, therefore, less like water.

●●● SOLVED PROBLEM 11.3

1,2-Propanediol (propylene glycol) and 1,3-propanediol (trimethylene glycol) have higher boiling points than any of the butyl alcohols (see Table 11.1), even though they all have roughly the same molecular weight. Propose an explanation.

STRATEGY AND ANSWER: The presence of two hydroxyl groups in each of the diols allows their molecules to form more hydrogen bonds than the butyl alcohols. Greater hydrogen-bond formation means that the molecules of 1,2-propanediol and 1,3-propanediol are more highly associated and, consequently, their boiling points are higher.

11.3 IMPORTANT ALCOHOLS AND ETHERS

11.3A Methanol

At one time, most methanol was produced by the destructive distillation of wood (i.e., heating wood to a high temperature in the absence of air). It was because of this method of preparation that methanol came to be called "wood alcohol." Today, most methanol is prepared by the catalytic hydrogenation of carbon monoxide. This reaction takes place under high pressure and at a temperature of 300–400°C:

$$CO \ + \ 2\,H_2 \ \xrightarrow[\substack{200-300\ atm \\ ZnO-Cr_2O_3}]{300-400\ °C} \ CH_3OH$$

Methanol is highly toxic. Ingestion of even small quantities of methanol can cause blindness; large quantities cause death. Methanol poisoning can also occur by inhalation of the vapors or by prolonged exposure to the skin.

11.3B Ethanol

Ethanol can be made by the fermentation of sugars, and it is the alcohol of all alcoholic beverages. The synthesis of ethanol in the form of wine by the fermentation of the sugars of fruit juices was among our first accomplishments in the field of organic synthesis. Sugars from a wide variety of sources can be used in the preparation of alcoholic beverages. Often, these sugars are from grains, and it is this derivation that accounts for ethanol having the synonym "grain alcohol."

Fermentation is usually carried out by adding yeast to a mixture of sugars and water. Yeast contains enzymes that promote a long series of reactions that ultimately convert a simple sugar ($C_6H_{12}O_6$) to ethanol and carbon dioxide:

$$C_6H_{12}O_6 \ \xrightarrow{\text{yeast}} \ 2\,CH_3CH_2OH \ + \ 2\,CO_2$$
$$\text{(~95\% yield)}$$

Fermentation alone does not produce beverages with an ethanol content greater than 12–15% because the enzymes of the yeast are deactivated at higher concentrations. To produce beverages of higher alcohol content, the aqueous solution must be distilled.

Ethanol is an important industrial chemical. Most ethanol for industrial purposes is produced by the acid-catalyzed hydration of ethene:

$$\diagequals \ + \ H_2O \ \xrightarrow{\text{acid}} \ \diagup\diagdown_{OH}$$

About 5% of the world's ethanol supply is produced this way.

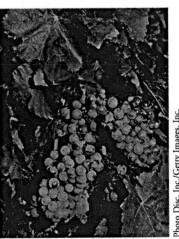

Vineyard grapes for use in fermentation.

Photo Disc, Inc./Getty Images, Inc.

THE CHEMISTRY OF... Ethanol as a Biofuel

Ethanol is said to be a renewable energy source because it can be made by fermentation of grains and other agricultural sources such as switchgrass and sugarcane. The crops themselves grow, of course, by converting light energy from the sun to chemical energy through photosynthesis. Once obtained, the ethanol can be combined with gasoline in varying proportions and used in internal combustion engines. During the year 2007, the United States led the world in ethanol production with 6.5 billion U.S. gallons, followed closely by Brazil with 5 billion gallons.

When used as a replacement for gasoline, ethanol has a lower energy content, by about 34% per unit volume. This, and other factors, such as costs in energy required to produce the agricultural feedstock, especially corn, have created doubts about the wisdom of an ethanol-based program as a renewable energy source. Production of ethanol from corn is 5 to 6 times less efficient than producing it from sugarcane, and it also diverts production of a food crop into an energy source. World food shortages may be a result.

Media Bakery

Ethanol is a *hypnotic* (sleep producer). It depresses activity in the upper brain even though it gives the illusion of being a stimulant. Ethanol is also toxic, but it is much less toxic than methanol. In rats the lethal dose of ethanol is 13.7 g kg^{-1} of body weight.

11.3C Ethylene and Propylene Glycols

Ethylene glycol ($HOCH_2CH_2OH$) has a low molecular weight, a high boiling point, and is miscible with water (Table 11.1). These properties made ethylene glycol a good automobile antifreeze. Unfortunately, however, ethylene glycol is toxic. Propylene glycol (1,2-propanediol) is now widely used as a low-toxicity, environmentally friendly alternative to ethylene glycol.

11.3D Diethyl Ether

Diethyl ether is a very low boiling, highly flammable liquid. Care should always be taken when diethyl ether is used in the laboratory, because open flames or sparks from light switches can cause explosive combustion of mixtures of diethyl ether and air.

Most ethers react slowly with oxygen by a radical process called **autoxidation** (see Section 10.12D) to form hydroperoxides and peroxides:

Step 1

> **Hydrogen abstraction adjacent to the ether oxygen occurs readily.**

Step 2

Step 3a

A hydroperoxide

or

Step 3b

> **Hydroperoxides and peroxides can be explosive.**

A peroxide

THE CHEMISTRY OF... Cholesterol and Heart Disease

Cholesterol (below, see also Section 23.4B) is an alcohol that is a precursor of steroid hormones and a vital constituent of cell membranes. It is essential to life. On the other hand, deposition of cholesterol in arteries is a cause of heart disease and atherosclerosis, two leading causes of death in humans. For an organism to remain healthy, there has to be a delicate balance between the biosynthesis of cholesterol and its utilization, so that arterial deposition is kept at a minimum.

a drug called a *statin*, a drug designed to interfere with the biosynthesis of cholesterol.

In the body, the biosynthesis of cholesterol takes place through a series of steps, one of which is catalyzed by the enzyme *HMG-CoA reductase* and which uses mevalonate ion as a substrate. The statin interferes with this step and thereby reduces blood cholesterol levels.

Cholesterol

Lovastatin　　　**Mevalonate ion**

Lovastatin, a compound isolated from the fungus *Apergillus terreus*, was the first statin to be marketed. Now many others are in use.

Lovastatin, because a part of its structure resembles mevalonate ion, can apparently bind at the active site of HMGA-CoA-reductase and act as a competitive inhibitor of this enzyme and thereby reduce cholesterol biosynthesis.

For some individuals with high blood levels of cholesterol, the remedy is as simple as following a diet low in cholesterol and fat. For those who suffer from elevated blood cholesterol levels for genetic reasons, other means of cholesterol reduction are required. One remedy involves taking

---

These hydroperoxides and peroxides, which often accumulate in ethers that have been stored for months or longer in contact with air (the air in the top of the bottle is enough), are dangerously explosive. They often detonate without warning when ether solutions are distilled to near dryness. Since ethers are used frequently in extractions, one should take care to test for and decompose any peroxides present in the ether before a distillation is carried out. (Consult a laboratory manual for instructions.)

Diethyl ether was at one time used as a surgical anesthetic. The most popular modern anesthetic is halothane ($CF_3CHBrCl$). Unlike diethyl ether, halothane is not flammable. (See "The Chemistry of... Ethers as General Anesthetics," Section 2.7, for more information.)

11.4 SYNTHESIS OF ALCOHOLS FROM ALKENES

We have already studied the acid-catalyzed hydration of alkenes, oxymercuration–demercuration, and hydroboration–oxidation as methods for the synthesis of alcohols from alkenes (see Sections 8.4, 8.5, and 8.6, respectively). Below, we briefly summarize these methods.

1. **Acid-Catalyzed Hydration of Alkenes** Alkenes add water in the presence of an acid catalyst to yield alcohols (Section 8.5). The addition takes place with **Markovnikov regioselectivity**. The reaction is reversible, and the mechanism for the acid-catalyzed hydration of an alkene is simply the reverse of that for the dehydration of an alcohol (Section 7.7).

Alkene　　　　　　　　　　　　　　　　　　　　　　　　　　　　　**Alcohol**

445

Acid-catalyzed hydration of alkenes has limited synthetic utility, however, because the carbocation intermediate may rearrange if a more stable or isoenergetic carbocation is possible by hydride or alkanide migration. Thus, a mixture of isomeric alcohol products may result.

2. **Oxymercuration–Demercuration** Alkenes react with mercuric acetate in a mixture of water and tetrahydrofuran (THF) to produce (hydroxyalkyl)mercury compounds. These can be reduced to alcohols with sodium borohydride and water (Section 8.5).

Oxymercuration

In the margin:
Mercury compounds are hazardous. Before you carry out a reaction involving mercury or its compounds, you should familiarize yourself with current procedures for its use and disposal.

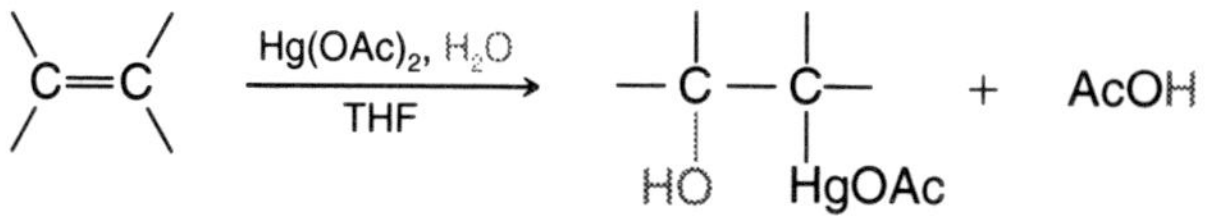

Demercuration

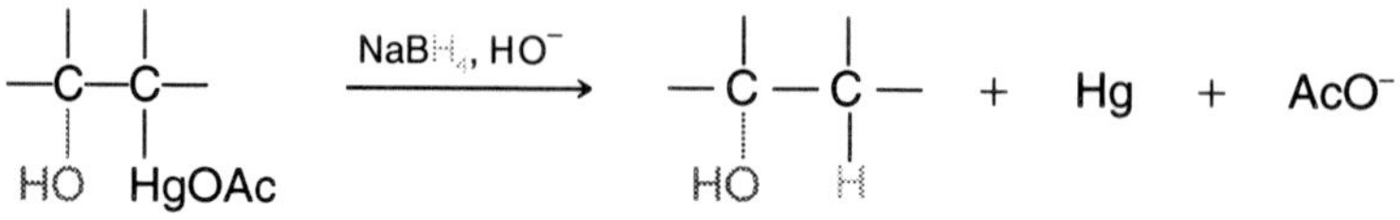

In the oxymercuration step, water and mercuric acetate add to the double bond; in the demercuration step, sodium borohydride reduces the acetoxymercury group and replaces it with hydrogen. The net addition of H— and —OH takes place with **Markovnikov regioselectivity** and **generally takes place without the complication of rearrangements**, as sometimes occurs with acid-catalyzed hydration of alkenes. The overall alkene hydration is not stereoselective because even though the oxymercuration step occurs with anti addition, the demercuration step is not stereoselective (radicals are thought to be involved), and hence a mixture of syn and anti products results.

Helpful Hint

Oxymercuration–demercuration and hydroboration–oxidation have complementary regioselectivity.

3. **Hydroboration–Oxidation** An alkene reacts with BH₃:THF or diborane to produce an alkylborane. Oxidation and hydrolysis of the alkylborane with hydrogen peroxide and base yield an alcohol (Section 8.6).

Hydroboration

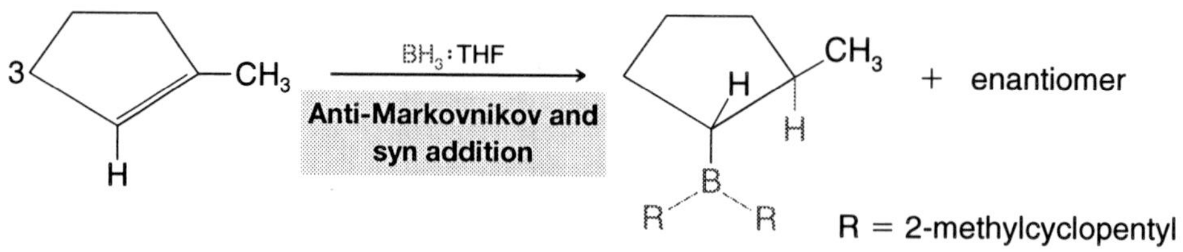

Oxidation

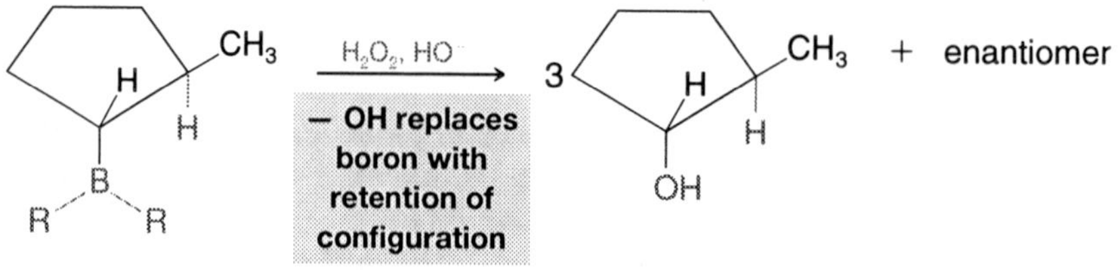

In the first step, boron and hydrogen undergo syn addition to the alkene; in the second step, treatment with hydrogen peroxide and base replaces the boron with —OH with retention of configuration. The net addition of —H and —OH occurs with **anti-Markovnikov regioselectivity** and **syn stereoselectivity.** Hydroboration–oxidation, therefore, serves as a useful regiochemical complement to oxymercuration–demercuration.

SOLVED PROBLEM 11.4

What conditions would you use for each reaction?

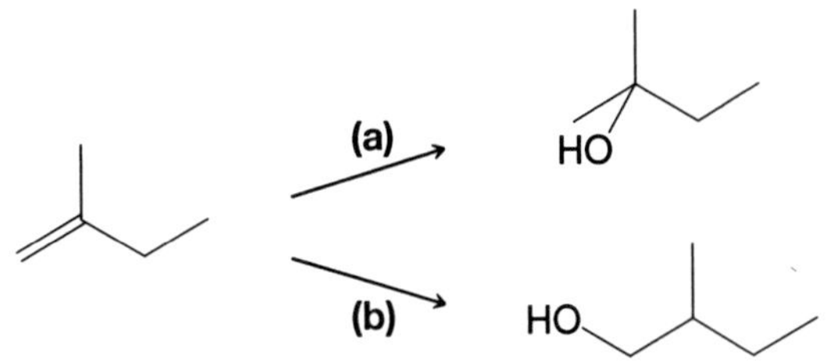
(a)
HO
(b)
HO

STRATEGY AND ANSWER: We recognize that synthesis by path (a) would require a Markovnikov addition of water to the alkene. So, we could use either acid-catalyzed hydration or oxymercuration–demercuration.

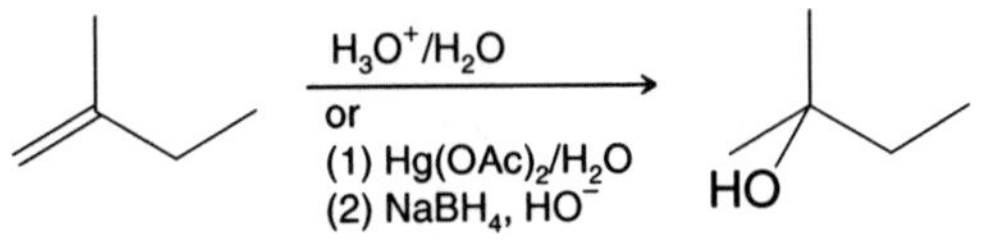
H_3O^+/H_2O
or
(1) $Hg(OAc)_2/H_2O$
(2) $NaBH_4$, HO^-
HO

Markovnikov addition of H— and —OH

Synthesis by path (b) requires an anti-Markovnikov addition, so we would choose hydroboration–oxidation.

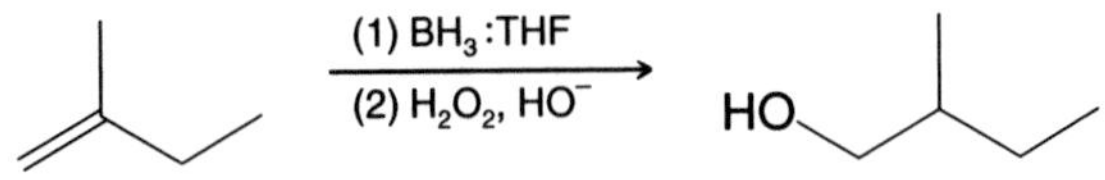
(1) BH_3:THF
(2) H_2O_2, HO^-
HO

anti-Markovnikov addition of H— and —OH

PRACTICE PROBLEM 11.3

Predict the major products of the following reactions:

(a) 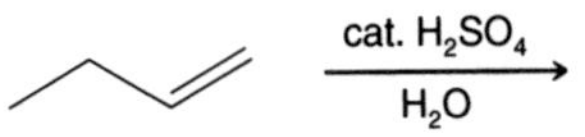
cat. H_2SO_4
H_2O

(b) 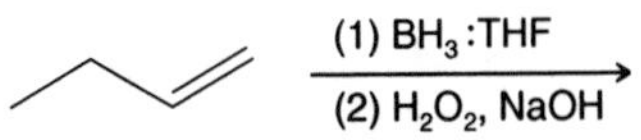
(1) BH_3:THF
(2) H_2O_2, NaOH

(c) 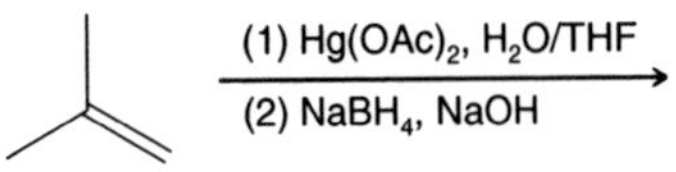
(1) $Hg(OAc)_2$, H_2O/THF
(2) $NaBH_4$, NaOH

PRACTICE PROBLEM 11.4

The following reaction does not produce the product shown.

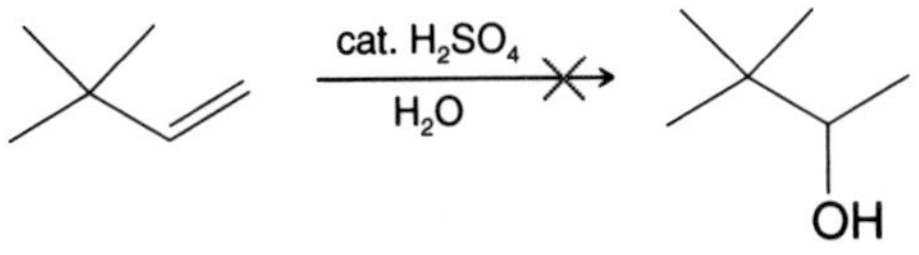
cat. H_2SO_4
H_2O
OH

(a) Predict the major product from the conditions shown above, and write a detailed mechanism for its formation.

(b) What reaction conditions would you use to successfully synthesize the product shown above (3,3-dimethyl-2-butanol).

11.5 REACTIONS OF ALCOHOLS

The reactions of alcohols have mainly to do with the following:

- The oxygen atom of the hydroxyl group is nucleophilic and weakly basic.
- The hydrogen atom of the hydroxyl group is weakly acidic.
- The hydroxyl group can be converted to a leaving group so as to allow substitution or elimination reactions.

Our understanding of the reactions of alcohols will be aided by an initial examination of the electron distribution in the alcohol functional group and of how this distribution affects its reactivity. The oxygen atom of an alcohol polarizes both the C—O bond and the O—H bond of an alcohol:

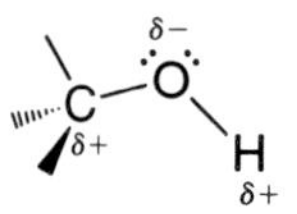

The C—O and O—H bonds of an alcohol are polarized

An electrostatic potential map for methanol shows partial negative charge at the oxygen and partial positive charge at the hydroxyl proton.

Polarization of the O—H bond makes the hydrogen partially positive and explains why alcohols are weak acids (Section 11.6). Polarization of the C—O bond makes the carbon atom partially positive, and if it were not for the fact that HO^- is a strong base and, therefore, a very poor leaving group, this carbon would be susceptible to nucleophilic attack.

The electron pairs on the oxygen atom make it both *basic* and *nucleophilic*. In the presence of strong acids, alcohols act as bases and accept protons in the following way:

Protonation of an alcohol

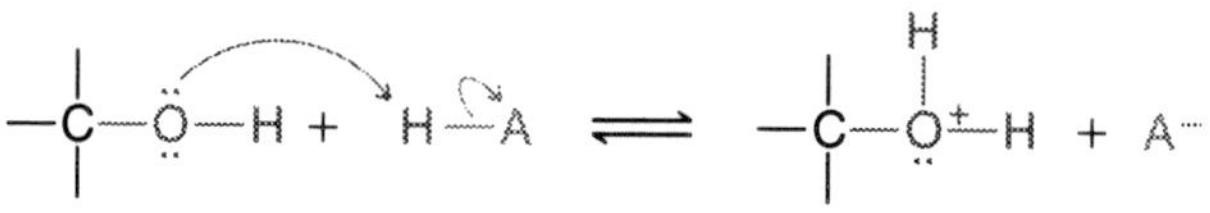

$$-\overset{|}{\underset{|}{C}}-\ddot{O}-H + H-A \rightleftharpoons -\overset{|}{\underset{|}{C}}-\overset{H}{\underset{}{\overset{+}{O}}}-H + A^-$$

Alcohol · · · **Strong acid** · · · **Protonated alcohol**

- Protonation of the alcohol converts a poor leaving group (HO^-) into a good one (H_2O).

Protonation also makes the carbon atom even more positive (because $-\overset{+}{O}H_2$ is more electron withdrawing than $-OH$) and, therefore, even more susceptible to nucleophilic attack.

- Once the alcohol is protonated substitution reactions become possible (S_N2 or S_N1, depending on the class of alcohol, Section 11.8).

The protonated hydroxyl group is a good leaving group (H_2O)

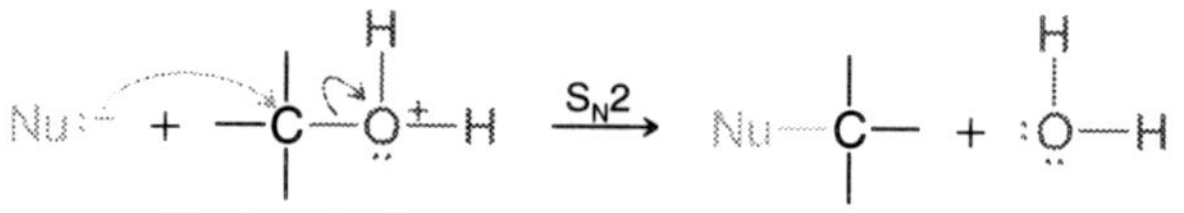

$$Nu:^- + -\overset{|}{\underset{|}{C}}-\overset{H}{\underset{}{\overset{+}{O}}}-H \xrightarrow{S_N2} Nu-\overset{|}{\underset{|}{C}}- + :\overset{H}{\underset{}{O}}-H$$

Protonated alcohol

Because alcohols are nucleophiles, they, too, can react with protonated alcohols. This, as we shall see in Section 11.11A, is an important step in one synthesis of ethers:

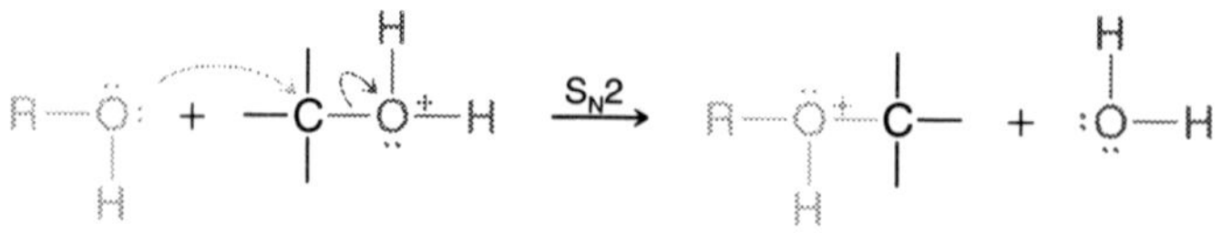

$$R-\overset{}{\underset{H}{\ddot{O}}} + -\overset{|}{\underset{|}{C}}-\overset{H}{\underset{}{\overset{+}{O}}}-H \xrightarrow{S_N2} R-\overset{+}{\underset{H}{\ddot{O}}}-\overset{|}{\underset{|}{C}}- + :\overset{H}{\underset{}{O}}-H$$

Protonated ether

At a high enough temperature and in the absence of a good nucleophile, protonated alcohols are capable of undergoing E1 or E2 reactions. This is what happens in alcohol dehydrations (Section 7.7).

Alcohols also react with PBr_3 and $SOCl_2$ to yield alkyl bromides and alkyl chlorides. These reactions, as we shall see in Section 11.9, are initiated by the alcohol using its unshared electron pairs to act as a nucleophile.

11.6 ALCOHOLS AS ACIDS

TABLE 11.3 pK_a VALUES FOR SOME WEAK ACIDS	
Acid	pK_a
CH_3OH	15.5
H_2O	15.74
CH_3CH_2OH	15.9
$(CH_3)_3COH$	18.0

● Alcohols have acidities similar to that of water.

Methanol is a slightly stronger acid than water ($pK_a = 15.7$) but most alcohols are somewhat weaker acids. Values of pK_a for several alcohols are listed in Table 11.3.

Alcohol   **Alkoxide ion**

(If R is bulky, there is less stabilization of the alkoxide by solvation and greater destabilization due to inductive effects. Consequently, the equilibrium lies even further toward the alcohol.)

● Sterically hindered alcohols such as *tert*-butyl alcohol are less acidic, and hence their conjugate bases more basic, than unhindered alcohols such as ethanol or methanol.

One reason for this difference in acidity has to do with the effect of solvation. With an unhindered alcohol, water molecules can easily surround, solvate, and hence stabilize the alkoxide anion that would form by loss of the alcohol proton to a base. As a consequence of this stabilization, formation of the alcohol's conjugate base is easier, and therefore its acidity is increased. If the R group of the alcohol is bulky, solvation of the alkoxide anion is hindered. Stabilization of the conjugate base is not as effective, and consequently the hindered alcohol is a weaker acid. Another reason that hindered alcohols are less acidic has to do with the inductive electron-donating effect of alkyl groups. The alkyl groups of a hindered alcohol donate electron density, making formation of an alkoxide anion more difficult than with a less hindered alcohol.

● All alcohols are much stronger acids than terminal alkynes, and they are very much stronger acids than hydrogen, ammonia, and alkanes (see Table 3.1).

Helpful Hint

Remember: Any factor that stabilizes the conjugate base of an acid increases its acidity.

Relative Acidity

Water and alcohols are the strongest acids in this series.	$H_2O > ROH > RC{\equiv}CH > H_2 > NH_3 > RH$

Sodium and potassium alkoxides can be prepared by treating alcohols with sodium or potassium metal or with the metal hydride (Section 6.15B). Because most alcohols are weaker acids than water, most alkoxide ions are stronger bases than the hydroxide ion.

● Conjugate bases of compounds with higher pK_a values than an alcohol will deprotonate an alcohol.

Relative Basicity

$R^- > H_2N^- > H^- > RC{\equiv}C^- > RO^- > HO^-$

Hydroxide is the weakest base in this series.

Write equations for the acid–base reactions that would occur (if any) if ethanol were added to solutions of each of the following compounds. In each reaction, label the stronger acid, the stronger base, and so forth (consult Table 3.1).

PRACTICE PROBLEM 11.5

(a) $NaNH_2$ **(b)** $H{-\!\!\!\equiv}\!:^-Na^+$ **(c)** (structure: acetate with ONa)   **(d)** $NaOH$

Sodium and potassium alkoxides are often used as bases in organic syntheses (Section 6.15B). We use alkoxides, such as ethoxide and *tert*-butoxide, when we carry out reactions that require stronger bases than hydroxide ion but do not require exceptionally powerful bases, such as the amide ion or the anion of an alkane. We also use alkoxide ions when, for reasons of solubility, we need to carry out a reaction in an alcohol solvent rather than in water.

11.7 CONVERSION OF ALCOHOLS INTO ALKYL HALIDES

In this and several following sections we will be concerned with reactions that involve substitution of the alcohol hydroxyl group.

- A hydroxyl group is such a poor leaving group (it would depart as hydroxide) that a common theme of these reactions will be conversion of the hydroxyl to a group that can depart as a weak base.

These processes begin by reaction of the alcohol oxygen as a base or nucleophile, after which the modified oxygen group undergoes substitution. First, we shall consider reactions that convert alcohols to alkyl halides.

The most commonly used reagents for conversion of alcohols to alkyl halides are the following:

- Hydrogen halides (HCl, HBr, HI)
- Phosphorus tribromide (PBr_3)
- Thionyl chloride ($SOCl_2$)

Examples of the use of these reagents are the following. All of these reactions result in cleavage of the C—O bond of the alcohol. In each case, the hydroxyl group is first converted to a suitable leaving group. We will see how this is accomplished when we study each type of reaction.

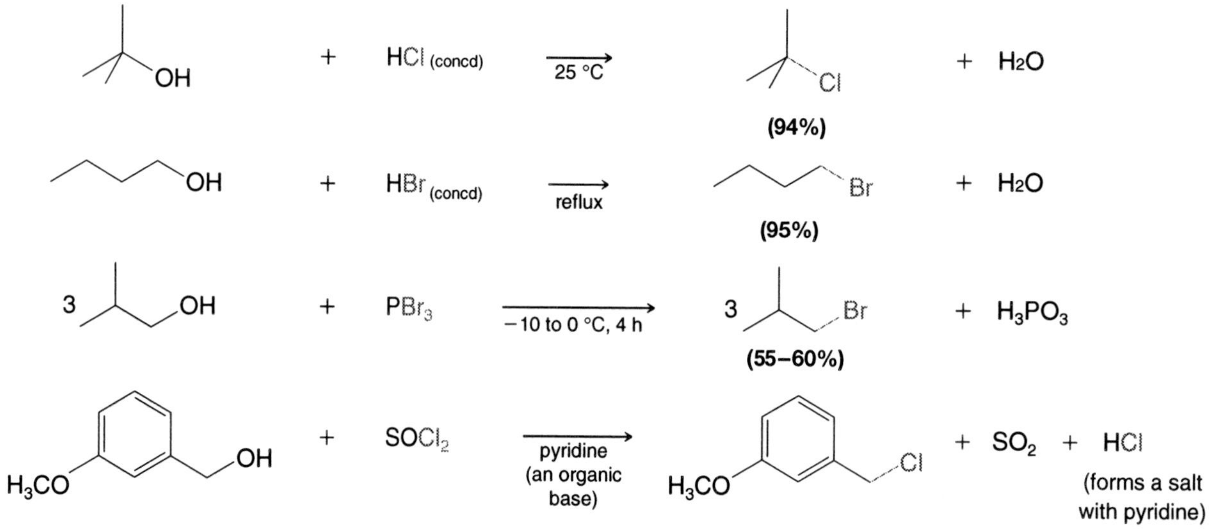

11.8 ALKYL HALIDES FROM THE REACTION OF ALCOHOLS WITH HYDROGEN HALIDES

When alcohols react with a hydrogen halide, a substitution takes place producing an alkyl halide and water:

$$R{-}OH \ + \ HX \longrightarrow R{-}X \ + \ H_2O$$

- The order of reactivity of alcohols is 3° > 2° > 1° < methyl.
- The order of reactivity of the hydrogen halides is HI > HBr > HCl (HF is generally unreactive).

The reaction is *acid catalyzed.* Alcohols react with the strongly acidic hydrogen halides HCl, HBr, and HI, but they do not react with nonacidic NaCl, NaBr, or NaI. Primary and secondary alcohols can be converted to alkyl chlorides and bromides by allowing them to react with a mixture of a sodium halide and sulfuric acid:

$$ROH \ + \ NaX \ \xrightarrow{H_2SO_4} \ RX \ + \ NaHSO_4 \ + \ H_2O$$

11.8A Mechanisms of the Reactions of Alcohols with HX

- Secondary, tertiary, allylic, and benzylic alcohols appear to react by a mechanism that involves the formation of a carbocation—a mechanism that we first saw in Section 3.13 and that you should now recognize *as an S_N1 reaction with the protonated alcohol acting as the substrate.*

We again illustrate this mechanism with the reaction of *tert*-butyl alcohol and aqueous hydrochloric acid (H_3O^+, Cl^-).

The first two steps in this S_N1 substitution mechanism are the same as in the mechanism for the dehydration of an alcohol (Section 7.7).

Step 1

The alcohol accepts a proton.

Step 2

The protonated hydroxyl group departs as a leaving group to form a carbocation and water.

In step 3 the mechanisms for the dehydration of an alcohol and the formation of an alkyl halide differ. In dehydration reactions the carbocation loses a proton in an E1 reaction to form an alkene. In the formation of an alkyl halide, the carbocation reacts with a nucleophile (a halide ion) in an S_N1 reaction.

Step 3

A halide anion reacts with the carbocation.

How can we account for S_N1 substitution in this case versus elimination in others?

When we dehydrate alcohols, we usually carry out the reaction in concentrated sulfuric acid and at high temperature. The hydrogen sulfate (HSO_4^-) present after protonation of the alcohol is a weak nucleophile, and at high temperature the highly reactive carbocation forms a more stable species by losing a proton and becoming an alkene. Furthermore, the alkene is usually volatile and distills from the reaction mixture as it is formed, thus drawing the equilibrium toward alkene formation. The net result is *an E1 reaction.*

In the reverse reaction, that is, the hydration of an alkene (Section 8.5), the carbocation *does* react with a nucleophile. It reacts with water. Alkene hydrations are carried out in dilute sulfuric acid, where the water concentration is high. In some instances, too, carbocations may react with HSO_4^- ions or with sulfuric acid, itself. When they do, they form alkyl hydrogen sulfates ($R—OSO_2OH$).

When we convert an alcohol to an alkyl halide, we carry out the reaction in the presence of acid and *in the presence of halide ions*, and not at elevated temperature. Halide ions are good nucleophiles (they are much stronger nucleophiles than water), and since halide ions are present in high concentration, most of the carbocations react with an electron pair of a halide ion to form a more stable species, the alkyl halide product. The overall result is an S_N1 reaction.

These two reactions, dehydration and the formation of an alkyl halide, also furnish another example of the competition between nucleophilic substitution and elimination (see Section 6.18). Very often, in conversions of alcohols to alkyl halides, we find that the reaction is accompanied by the formation of some alkene (i.e., by elimination). The free energies of activation for these two reactions of carbocations are not very different from one another. Thus, not all of the carbocations become stable products by reacting with nucleophiles; some lose a β proton to form an alkene.

Primary Alcohols Not all acid-catalyzed conversions of alcohols to alkyl halides proceed through the formation of carbocations.

- Primary alcohols and methanol react to form alkyl halides under acidic conditions by an S_N2 mechanism.

In these reactions the function of the acid is to produce *a protonated alcohol*. The halide ion then displaces a molecule of water (a good leaving group) from carbon; this produces an alkyl halide:

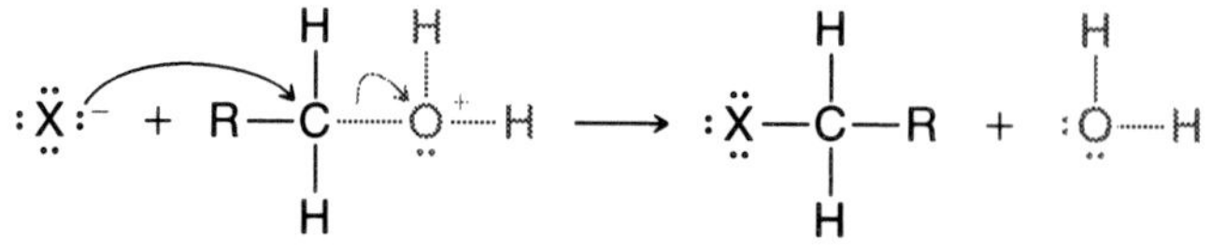

(Protonated 1° alcohol or methanol) **(A good leaving group)**

Acid Is Required Although halide ions (particularly iodide and bromide ions) are strong nucleophiles, they are not strong enough to carry out substitution reactions with alcohols themselves.

- Reactions like the following do not occur because the leaving group would have to be a strongly basic hydroxide ion:

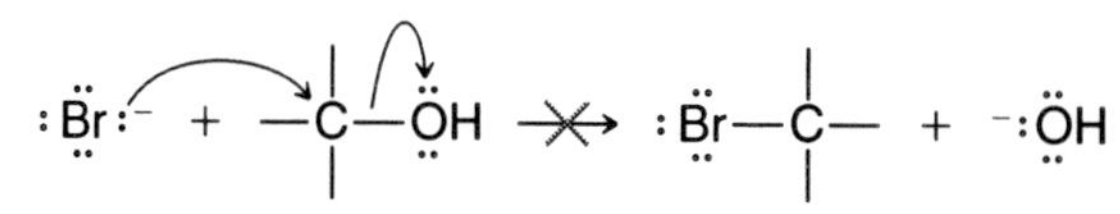

Helpful Hint

The reverse reaction, that is, the reaction of an alkyl halide with hydroxide ion, does occur and is a method for the synthesis of alcohols. We saw this reaction in Chapter 6.

We can see now why the reactions of alcohols with hydrogen halides are acid-promoted.

- Acid protonates the alcohol hydroxyl group, making it a good leaving group.

Because the chloride ion is a weaker nucleophile than bromide or iodide ions, hydrogen chloride does not react with primary or secondary alcohols unless zinc chloride or some similar Lewis acid is added to the reaction mixture as well. Zinc chloride, a good Lewis acid, forms a complex with the alcohol through association with an unshared pair of electrons on the oxygen atom. This enhances the hydroxyl group's leaving potential sufficiently that chloride can displace it.

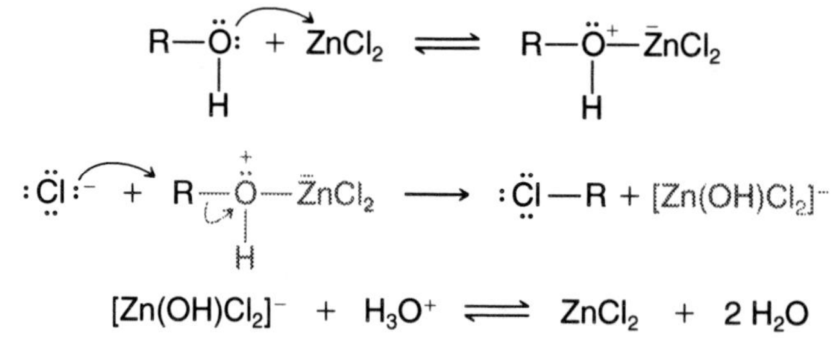

$$[Zn(OH)Cl_2]^- \ + \ H_3O^+ \ \rightleftharpoons \ ZnCl_2 \ + \ 2\,H_2O$$

- As we might expect, many reactions of alcohols with hydrogen halides, particularly those in which carbocations are formed, *are accompanied by rearrangements*.

How do we know that rearrangements can occur when secondary alcohols are treated with a hydrogen halide? Results like that in Solved Problem 11.5 indicate this to be the case.

●●● SOLVED PROBLEM 11.5

Treating 3-methyl-2-butanol (see the following reaction) yields 2-bromo-2-methylbutane as the sole product. Propose a mechanism that explains the course of the reaction.

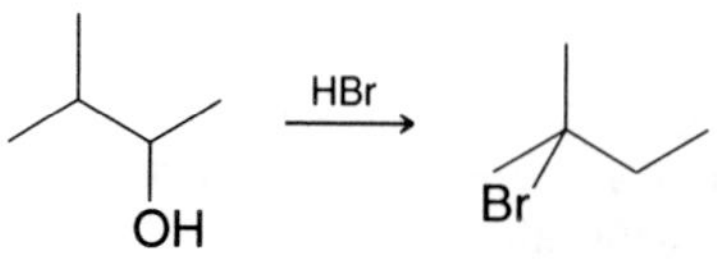

STRATEGY AND ANSWER: The reaction must involve a rearrangement by a hydride shift from the initially formed carbocation.

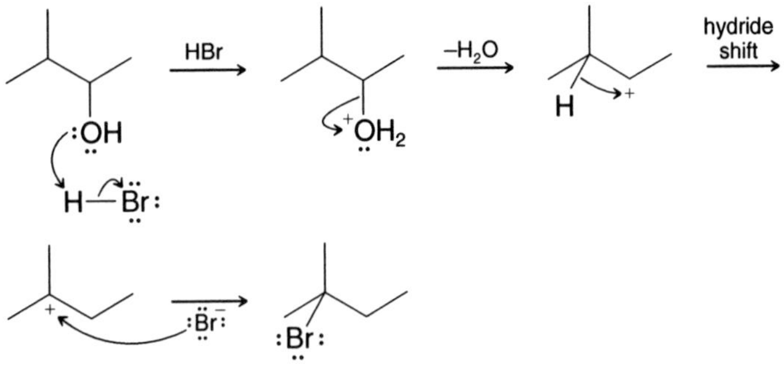

Write a detailed mechanism for the following reaction.

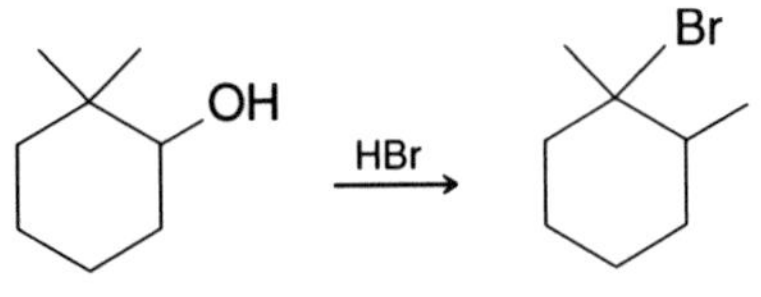

PRACTICE PROBLEM 11.6

(a) What factor explains the observation that tertiary alcohols react with HX faster than secondary alcohols? **(b)** What factor explains the observation that methanol reacts with HX faster than a primary alcohol?

PRACTICE PROBLEM 11.7

Since rearrangements can occur when some alcohols are treated with hydrogen halides, how can we successfully convert a secondary alcohol to an alkyl halide without rearrangement? The answer to this question comes in the next section, where we discuss the use of reagents such as thionyl chloride ($SOCl_2$) and phosphorus tribromide (PBr_3).

11.9 ALKYL HALIDES FROM THE REACTION OF ALCOHOLS WITH PBr₃ OR SOCl₂

Primary and secondary alcohols react with phosphorus tribromide to yield alkyl bromides.

$$3\,R\!\!-\!\!OH + PBr_3 \longrightarrow 3\,R\!-\!Br + H_3PO_3$$
(1° or 2°)

> **Helpful Hint**
>
> PBr_3: A reagent for synthesizing 1° and 2° alkyl bromides.

- The reaction of an alcohol with PBr_3 does not involve the formation of a carbocation and *usually occurs without rearrangement* of the carbon skeleton (especially if the temperature is kept below 0 °C).
- Phosphorus tribromide is often preferred as a reagent for the transformation of an alcohol to the corresponding alkyl bromide.

The mechanism for the reaction involves sequential replacement of the bromine atom in PBr_3 by three molecules of the alcohol to form a trialkylphosphite, $P(OR)_3$, and three molecules of HBr.

$$ROH + PBr_3 \longrightarrow P(OR)_3 + 3\,HBr$$

The trialkylphosphite goes on to react with three molecules of HBr to form three molecules of the alkyl bromide and a molecule of phosphonic acid.

$$P(OR)_3 + 3\,HBr \longrightarrow 3\,RBr + H_3PO_3$$

Helpful Hint

SOCl$_2$: A reagent for synthesizing 1° and 2° alkyl chlorides.

Thionyl chloride (SOCl$_2$) converts primary and secondary alcohols to alkyl chlorides. Pyridine (C$_5$H$_5$N) is often included to promote the reaction. The alcohol substrate attacks thionyl chloride as shown below, releasing a chloride anion and losing its proton to a molecule of pyridine. The result is an alkylchlorosulfite.

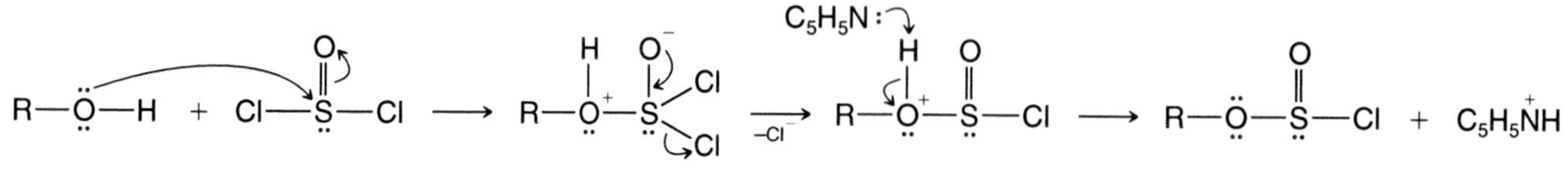

The alkylchlorosulfite intermediate then reacts rapidly with another molecule of pyridine, in the same fashion as the original alcohol, to give a pyridinium alkylsulfite intermediate, with release of the second chloride anion. A chloride anion then attacks the substrate carbon, displacing the sulfite leaving group, which in turn decomposes to release gaseous SO$_2$ and pyridine. (In the absence of pyridine the reaction occurs with retention of configuration. See Problem 11.55.)

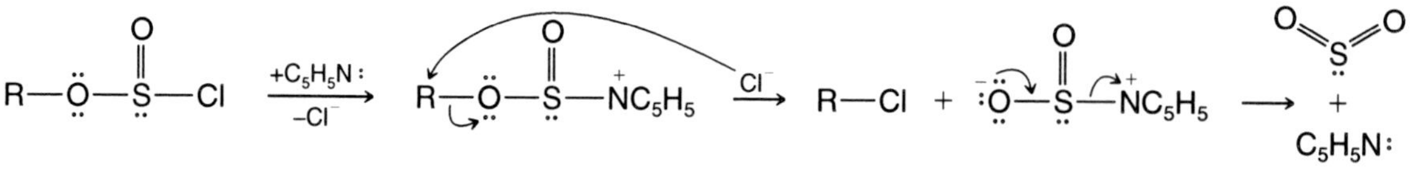

● ● ● **SOLVED PROBLEM 11.6**

Starting with alcohols, outline a synthesis of each of the following: **(a)** benzyl bromide, **(b)** cyclohexyl chloride, and **(c)** butyl bromide.

POSSIBLE ANSWERS:

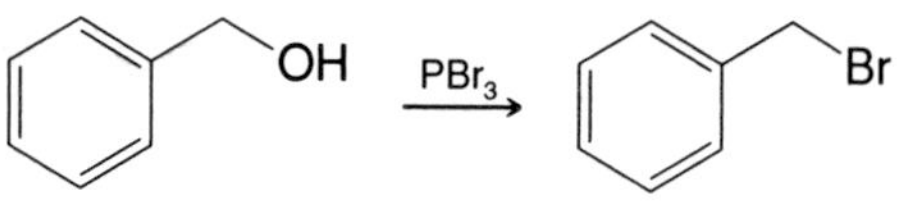

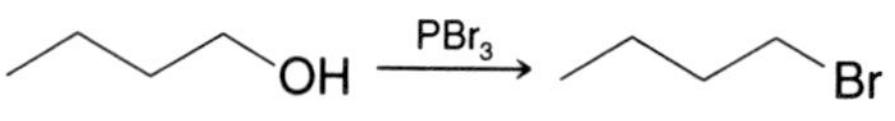

11.10 TOSYLATES, MESYLATES, AND TRIFLATES: LEAVING GROUP DERIVATIVES OF ALCOHOLS

The hydroxyl group of an alcohol can be converted to a good leaving group by conversion to a sulfonate ester derivative. The most common sulfonate esters used for this purpose are methanesulfonate esters ("mesylates"), p-toluenesulfonate esters ("tosylates"), and trifluoromethanesulfonates ("triflates").

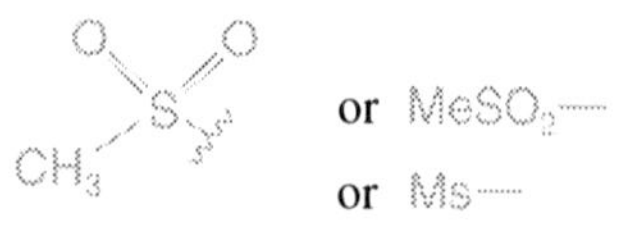

The mesyl group 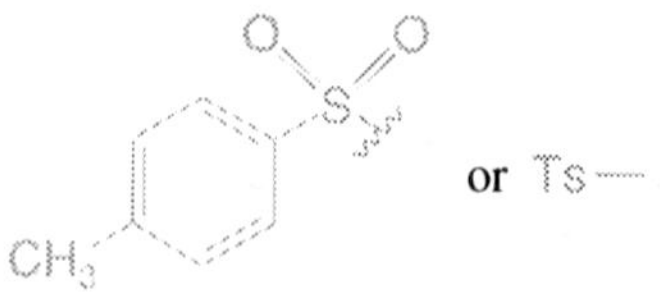   The tosyl group 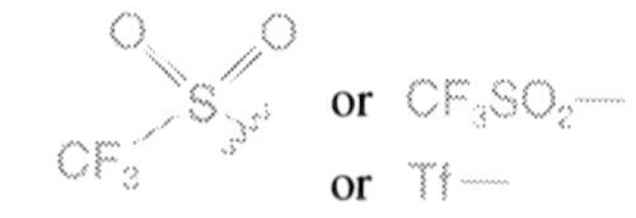   The trifyl group

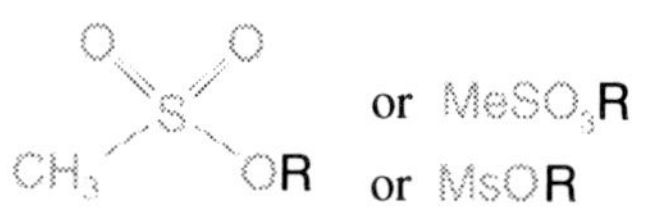

An alkyl mesylate 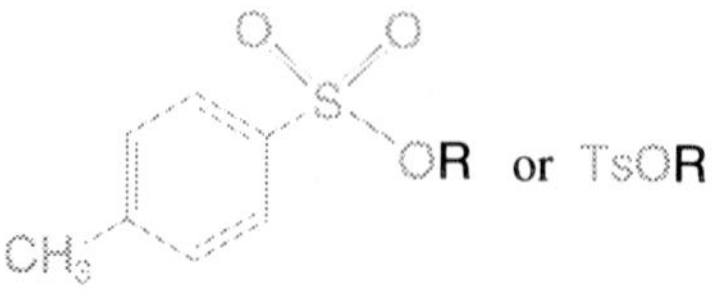   An alkyl tosylate 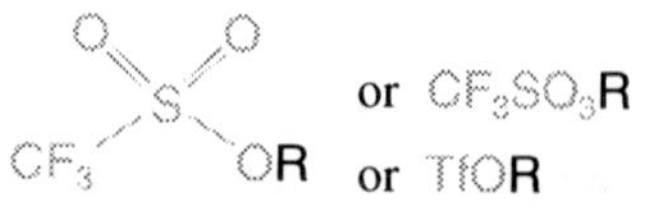   An alkyl triflate

The desired sulfonate ester is usually prepared by reaction of the alcohol in pyridine with the appropriate sulfonyl chloride, that is, methanesulfonyl chloride (mesyl chloride) for a mesylate, p-toluenesulfonyl chloride (tosyl chloride) for a tosylate, or trifluoromethane-sulfonyl chloride [or trifluoromethanesulfonic anhydride (triflic anhydride)] for a triflate. Pyridine (C_5H_5N, pyr) serves as the solvent and to neutralize the HCl formed. Ethanol, for example, reacts with methanesulfonyl chloride to form ethyl methanesulfonate and with p-toluenesulfonyl chloride to form ethyl p-toluenesulfonate:

Helpful Hint

A method for making an alcohol hydroxyl group into a leaving group.

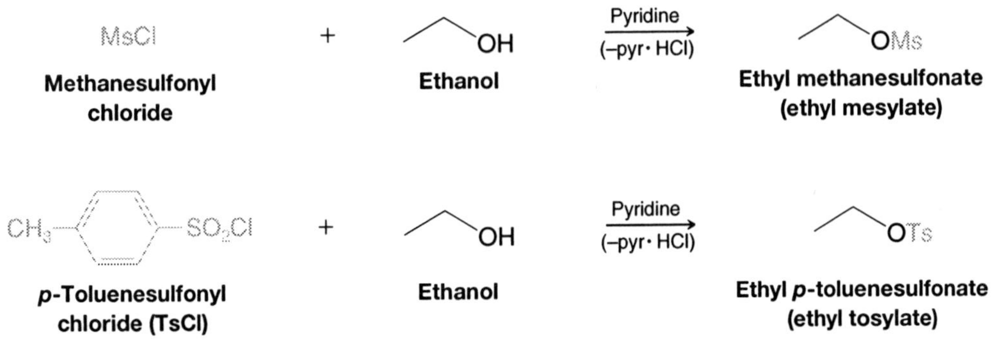

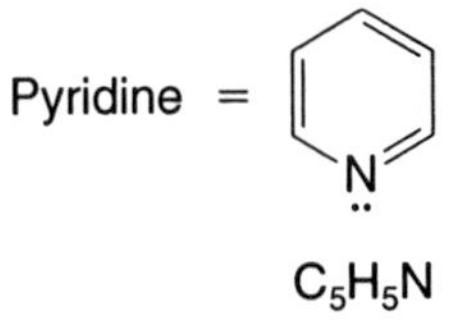

It is important to note that formation of the sulfonate ester does not affect the stereochemistry of the alcohol carbon, because the C—O bond is not involved in this step. Thus, if the alcohol carbon is a chirality center, no change in configuration occurs on making the sulfonate ester—the reaction proceeds with **retention of configuration.** On reaction of the sulfonate ester with a nucleophile, the usual parameters of nucleophilic substitution reactions become involved.

Substrates for Nucleophilic Substitution Mesylates, tosylates, and triflates, because they are good leaving groups, are frequently used as substrates for nucleophilic substitution reactions. They are good leaving groups because the sulfonate anions they become when they depart are very weak bases. The triflate anion is the weakest base in this series, and is thus the best leaving group among them.

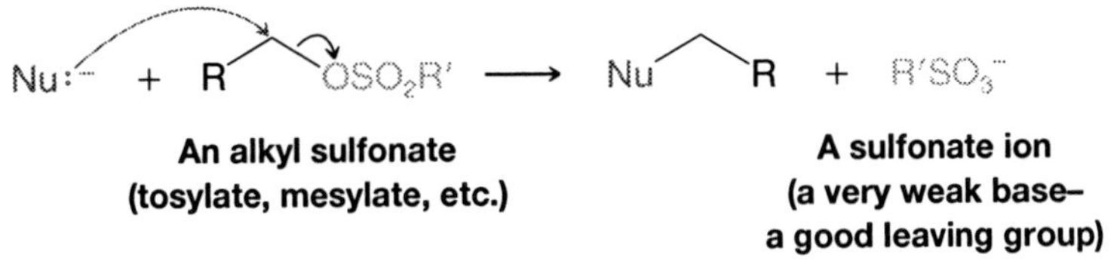

- To carry out a nucleophilic substitution on an alcohol, we first convert the alcohol to an alkyl sulfonate and then, in a second reaction, allow it to react with a nucleophile.
- If the mechanism is S_N2, as shown in the second reaction of the following example, **inversion of configuration** takes place at the carbon that originally bore the alcohol hydroxyl group:

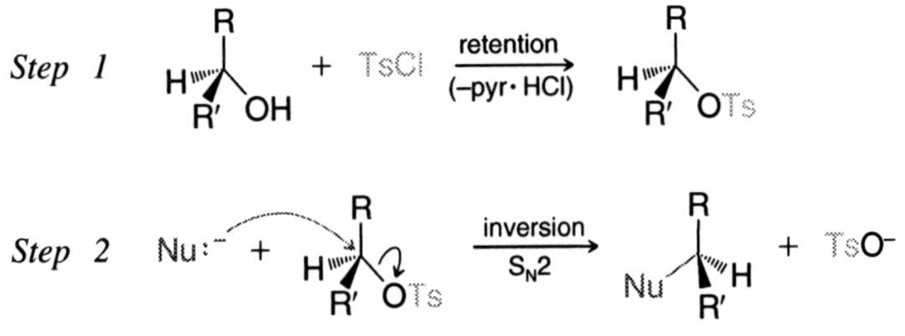

The fact that the C—O bond of the alcohol does not break during formation of the sulfonate ester is accounted for by the following mechanism. Methanesulfonyl chloride is used in the example.

[A MECHANISM FOR THE REACTION | Conversion of an Alcohol into a Mesylate (an Alkyl Methanesulfonate)]

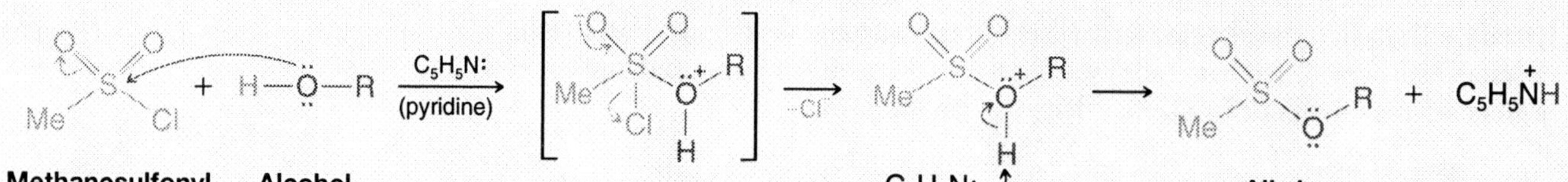

Methanesulfonyl chloride   **Alcohol**

The alcohol oxygen attacks the sulfur atom of the sulfonyl chloride.

The intermediate loses a chloride ion.

Loss of a proton leads to the product.

Alkyl methanesulfonate

●●● SOLVED PROBLEM 11.7

Supply the missing reagents.

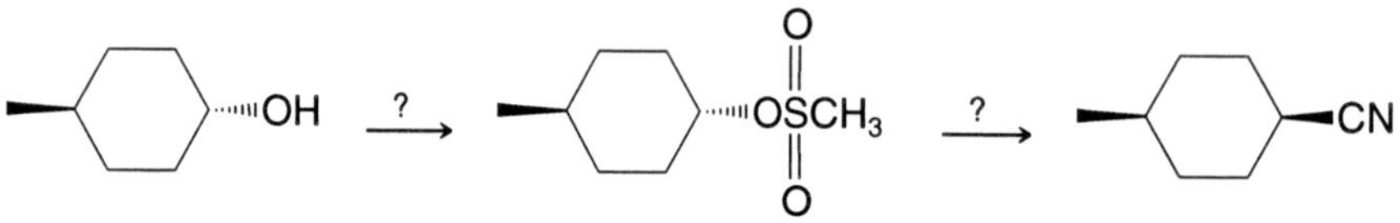

STRATEGY AND ANSWER: The overall transformation over two steps involves replacing an alcohol hydroxyl group by a cyano group with inversion of configuration. To accomplish this, we need to convert the alcohol hydroxyl to a good leaving group in the first step, which we do by making it a methanesulfonate ester (a mesylate) using methanesulfonyl chloride in pyridine. The second step is an S_N2 substitution of the methanesulfonate (mesyl) group, which we do using potassium or sodium cyanide in a polar aprotic solvent such as dimethylformamide (DMF).

●●● PRACTICE PROBLEM 11.8 Show how you would prepare the following compounds from the appropriate sulfonyl chlorides.

(a)   **(b)** 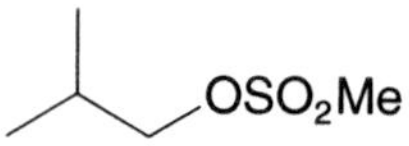   **(c)**

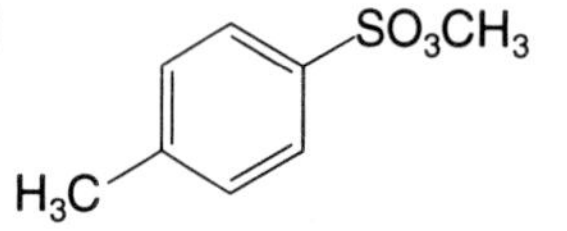

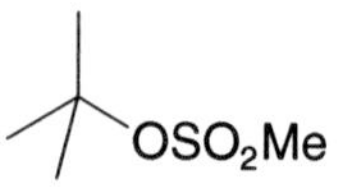

●●● PRACTICE PROBLEM 11.9 Write structures for products **X, Y, A,** and **B**, showing stereochemistry.

(a)   (R)-2-Butanol   Pyridine   **X**   NaOH (S_N2)   **Y**

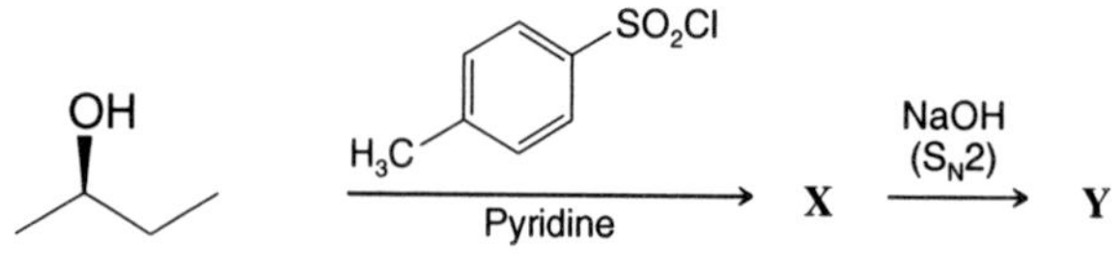

(b)   Pyridine   **A**   LiCl   **B**

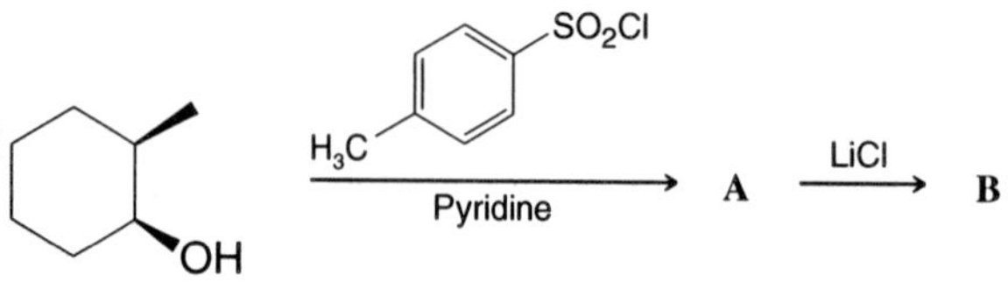

●●● PRACTICE PROBLEM 11.10 Suggest an experiment using an isotopically labeled alcohol that would prove that the formation of an alkyl sulfonate does not cause cleavage at the C—O bond of the alcohol.

11.11 SYNTHESIS OF ETHERS

11.11A Ethers by Intermolecular Dehydration of Alcohols

Two alcohol molecules can form an ether by loss of water through an acid-catalyzed substitution reaction.

$$R{-}OH + HO{-}R \xrightarrow[-H_2O]{HA} R{-}O{-}R$$

This reaction competes with the formation of alkenes by acid-catalyzed alcohol dehydration (Sections 7.7 and 7.8). Intermolecular dehydration of alcohols usually takes place at lower temperature than dehydration to an alkene, and dehydration to the ether can be aided by distilling the ether as it is formed. For example, diethyl ether is made commercially by dehydration of ethanol. Diethyl ether is the predominant product at 140 °C; ethene is the predominant product at 180 °C.

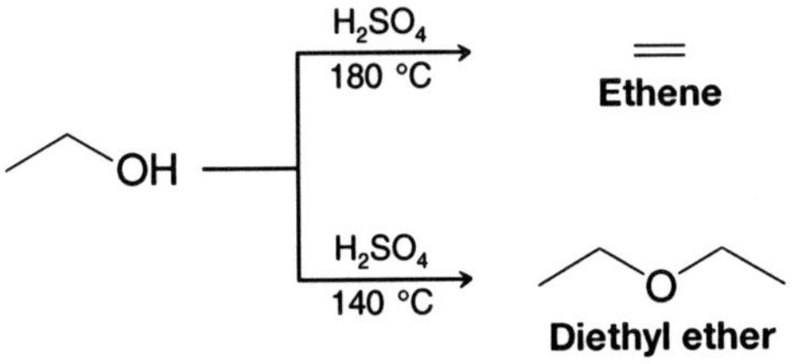

Ethene

Diethyl ether

The formation of the ether occurs by an S_N2 mechanism with one molecule of the alcohol acting as the nucleophile and another protonated molecule of the alcohol acting as the substrate (see Section 11.5).

[**A MECHANISM FOR THE REACTION** — **Intermolecular Dehydration of Alcohols to Form an Ether**]

Step 1

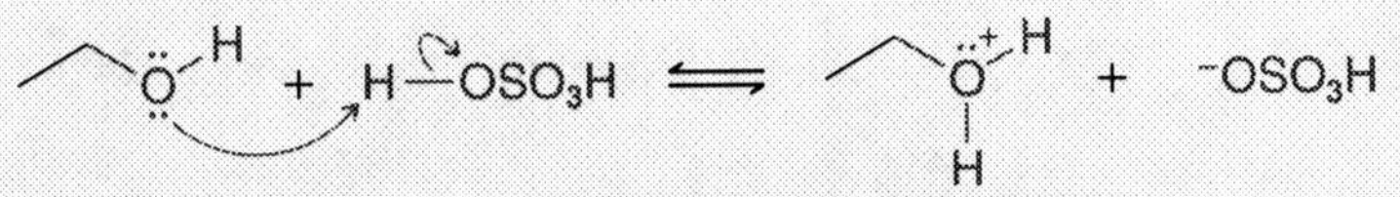

This is an acid–base reaction in which the alcohol accepts a proton from the sulfuric acid.

Step 2

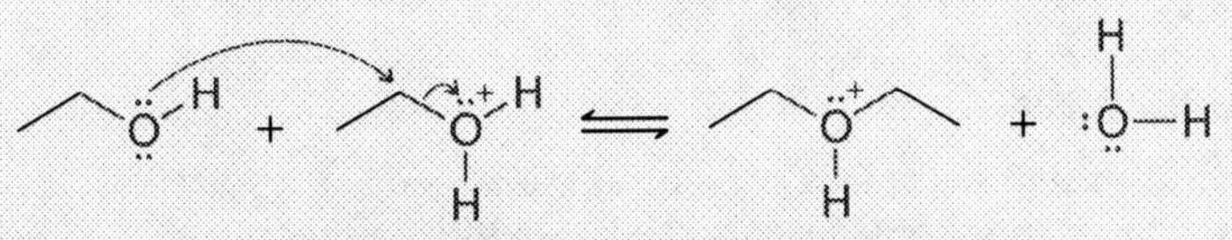

Another molecule of the alcohol acts as a nucleophile and attacks the protonated alcohol in an S_N2 reaction.

Step 3

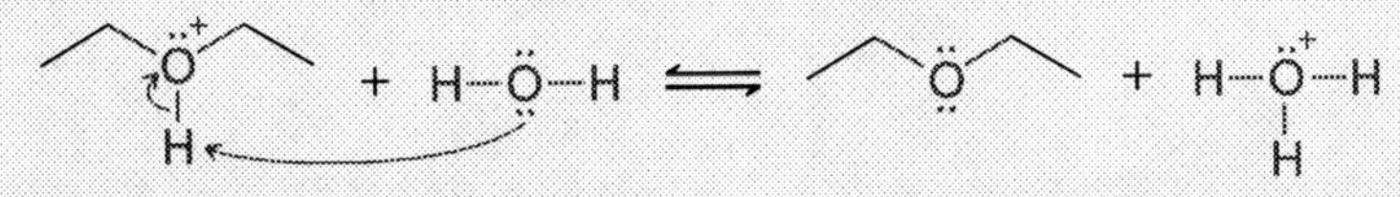

Another acid–base reaction converts the protonated ether to an ether by transferring a proton to a molecule of water (or to another molecule of the alcohol).

Complications of Intermolecular Dehydration   The method of synthesizing ethers by intermolecular dehydration has some important limitations.

- Attempts to synthesize ethers by intermolecular dehydration of secondary alcohols are usually unsuccessful because alkenes form too easily.

- Attempts to make ethers with tertiary alkyl groups lead predominantly to alkenes.

• Intermolecular dehydration is not useful for the preparation of unsymmetrical ethers from primary alcohols because the reaction leads to a mixture of products:

$$\underbrace{ROH + R'OH}_{1° \text{ Alcohols}} \underset{}{\overset{H_2SO_4}{\rightleftarrows}} \begin{array}{c} ROR \\ + \\ ROR' \\ + \\ R'OR' \end{array} + H_2O$$

PRACTICE PROBLEM 11.11 An exception to what we have just said has to do with syntheses of unsymmetrical ethers in which one alkyl group is a *tert*-butyl group and the other group is primary. For example, this synthesis can be accomplished by adding *tert*-butyl alcohol to a mixture of the primary alcohol and H_2SO_4 at room temperature.

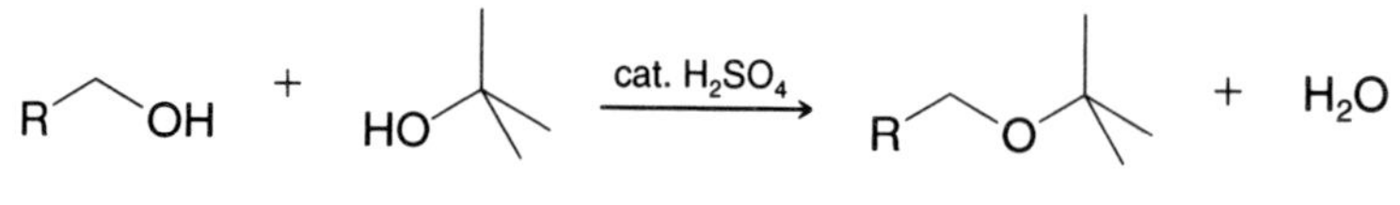

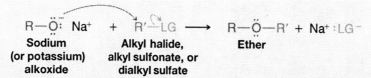

Give a likely mechanism for this reaction and explain why it is successful.

11.11B The Williamson Ether Synthesis

An important route to unsymmetrical ethers is a nucleophilic substitution reaction known as the **Williamson ether synthesis**.

• The Williamson ether synthesis consists of an S_N2 reaction of a sodium alkoxide with an alkyl halide, alkyl sulfonate, or alkyl sulfate.

[A MECHANISM FOR THE REACTION | The Williamson Ether Synthesis]

$$R-\overset{..}{\underset{..}{O}}{:} \ Na^+ \ + \ R'-LG \longrightarrow R-\overset{..}{\underset{..}{O}}-R' + Na^+ {:}LG^-$$

Sodium   **Alkyl halide,**   **Ether**
(or potassium)   **alkyl sulfonate, or**
alkoxide   **dialkyl sulfate**

The alkoxide ion reacts with the substrate in an S_N2 reaction, with the resulting formation of an ether. The substrate must be unhindered and bear a good leaving group. Typical substrates are 1° or 2° alkyl halides, alkyl sulfonates, and dialkyl sulfates:

$$-LG = -\overset{..}{\underset{..}{Br}}{:}, \ -\overset{..}{\underset{..}{I}}{:}, \ -OSO_2R', \text{ or } -OSO_2OR''$$

The following reaction is a specific example of the Williamson ether synthesis. The sodium alkoxide can be prepared by allowing an alcohol to react with NaH:

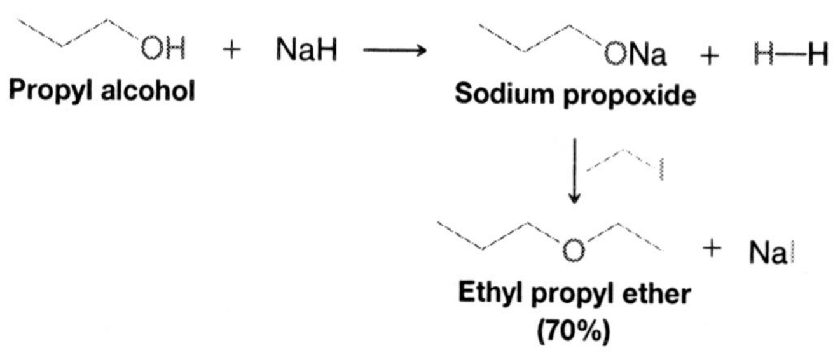

$$\text{OH} + NaH \longrightarrow \text{ONa} + H-H$$

Propyl alcohol   **Sodium propoxide**

$$\downarrow$$

$$\text{O} + Na\overset{..}{\underset{..}{I}}{:}$$

Ethyl propyl ether
(70%)

The usual limitations of S_N2 reactions apply here.

● Best results are obtained when the alkyl halide, sulfonate, or sulfate is primary (or methyl). **If the substrate is tertiary, elimination is the exclusive result.** Substitution is also favored over elimination at lower temperatures.

PRACTICE PROBLEM 11.12

(a) Outline two methods for preparing isopropyl methyl ether by a Williamson ether synthesis.

(b) One method gives a much better yield of the ether than the other. Explain which is the better method and why.

●●● **SOLVED PROBLEM 11.8**

The cyclic ether tetrahydrofuran (THF) can be synthesized by treating 4-chloro-1-butanol with aqueous sodium hydroxide (see below). Propose a mechanism for this reaction.

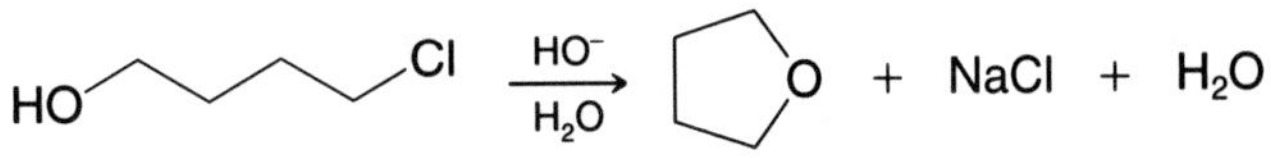

Tetrahydrofuran

STRATEGY AND ANSWER: Removal of a proton from the hydroxyl group of 4-chloro-1-butanol gives an alkoxide ion that can then react with itself in an intramolecular S_N2 reaction to form a ring.

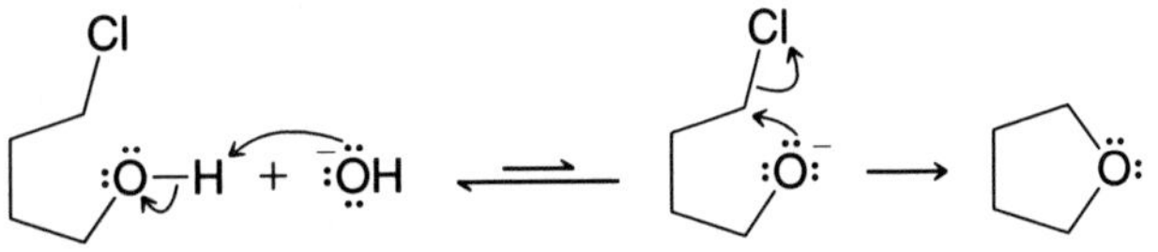

Even though treatment of the alcohol with hydroxide does not favor a large equilibrium concentration of the alkoxide, the alkoxide anions that are present react rapidly by the intramolecular S_N2 reaction. As alkoxide anions are consumed by the substitution reaction, their equilibrium concentration is replenished by deprotonation of additional alcohol molecules, and the reaction is drawn to completion.

●●● **PRACTICE PROBLEM 11.13**

Epoxides can be synthesized by treating halohydrins with aqueous base. Propose a mechanism for reactions **(a)** and **(b)**, and explain why no epoxide formation is observed in **(c)**.

(a)

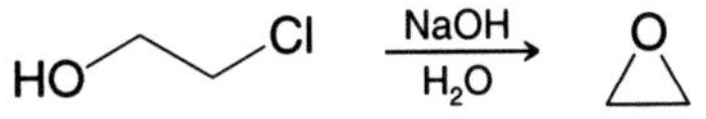

(c)

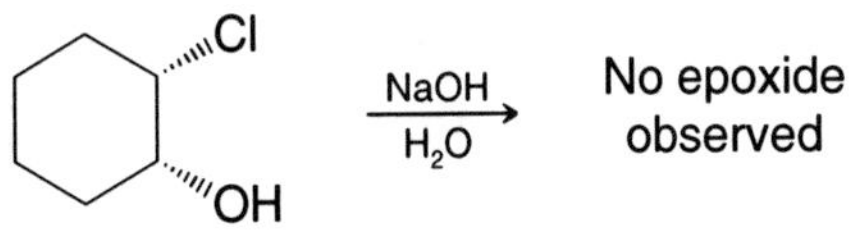

No epoxide observed

(b)

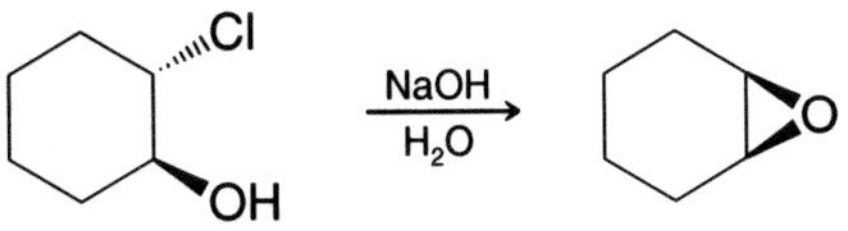

●●● **PRACTICE PROBLEM 11.14**

Write structures for products **A, B, C,** and **D**, showing stereochemistry. (*Hint:* **B** and **D** are stereoisomers.)

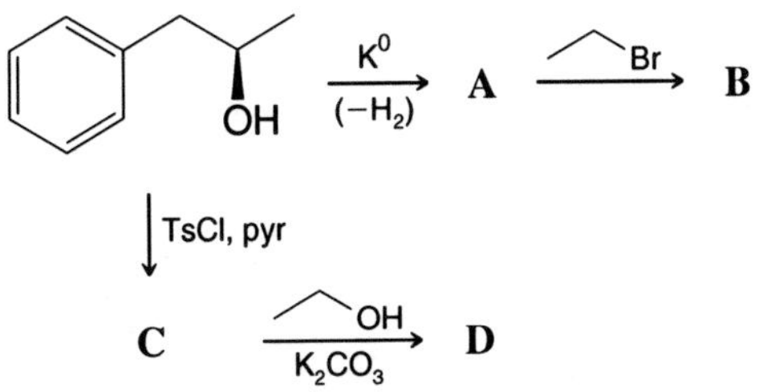

11.11C Synthesis of Ethers by Alkoxymercuration–Demercuration

Alkoxymercuration–demercuration is another method for synthesizing ethers.

* The reaction of an alkene with an alcohol in the presence of a mercury salt such as mercuric acetate or trifluoroacetate leads to an alkoxymercury intermediate, which on reaction with sodium borohydride yields an ether.

When the alcohol reactant is also the solvent, the method is called solvomercuration–demercuration. This method directly parallels hydration by oxymercuration–demercuration (Section 8.5):

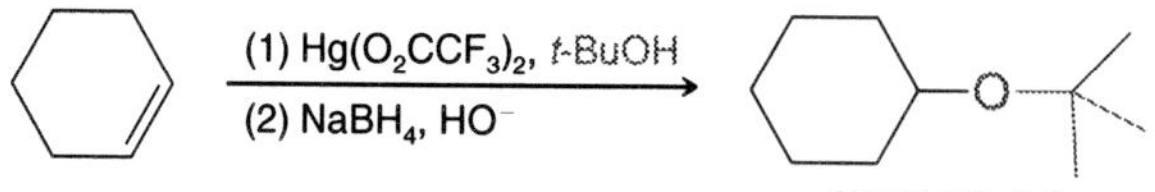

(98% Yield)

11.11D *tert*-Butyl Ethers by Alkylation of Alcohols: Protecting Groups

Primary alcohols can be converted to *tert*-butyl ethers by dissolving them in a strong acid such as sulfuric acid and then adding isobutylene to the mixture. (This procedure minimizes dimerization and polymerization of the isobutylene.)

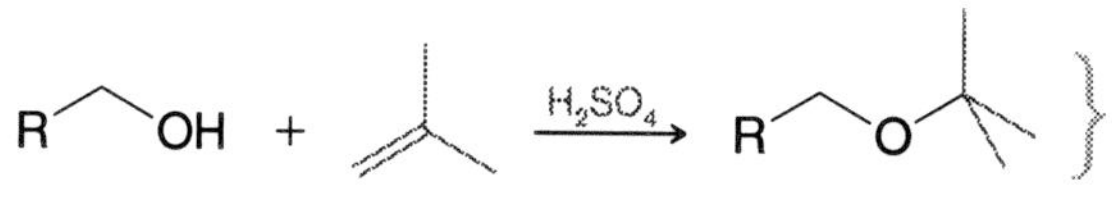

tert-Butyl protecting group

* A *tert*-butyl ether can be used to "protect" the hydroxyl group of a primary alcohol while another reaction is carried out on some other part of the molecule.
* A *tert*-butyl protecting group can be removed easily by treating the ether with dilute aqueous acid.

Suppose, for example, we wanted to prepare 4-pentyn-1-ol from 3-bromo-1-propanol and sodium acetylide. If we allow them to react directly, the strongly basic sodium acetylide will react first with the hydroxyl group, making the alkylation unsuccessful:

3-Bromo-1-propanol

Unsuccessful alkylation due to competing acid–base reaction.

However, if we protect the —OH group first, the synthesis becomes feasible:

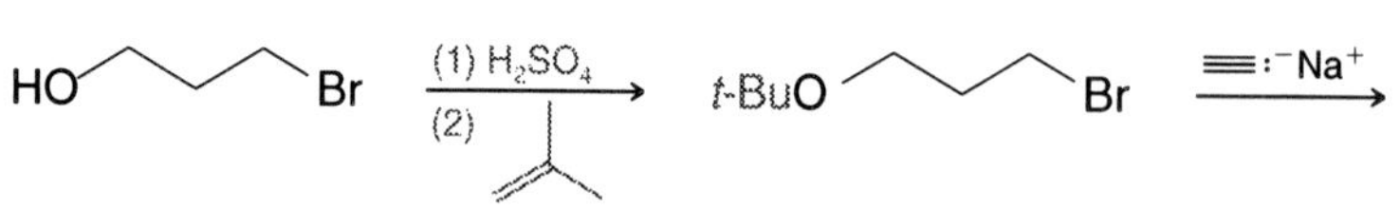

Successful alkylation with protection of the acidic group first.

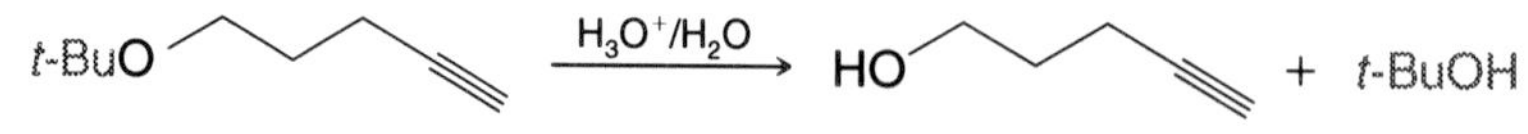

4-Pentyn-1-ol

• • •

PRACTICE PROBLEM 11.15 Propose mechanisms for the following reactions.

(a)

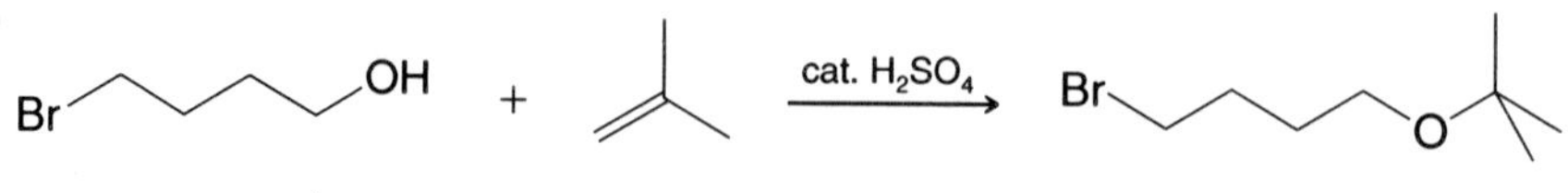

(b)

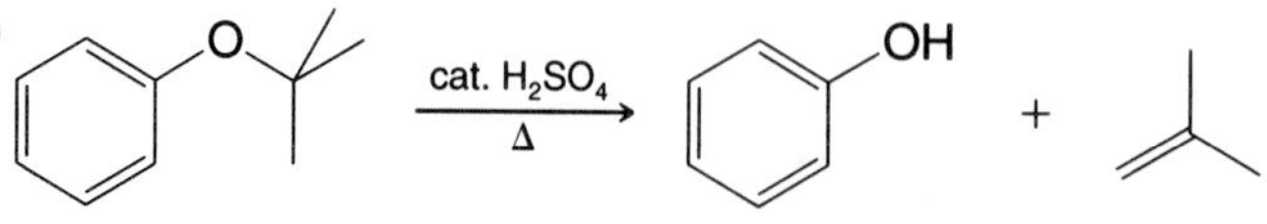

11.11E Silyl Ether Protecting Groups

- A hydroxyl group can be protected from acid–base reactions by converting it to a silyl ether group.

One of the most common silyl ether protecting groups is the *tert*-butyldimethylsilyl ether group [*tert*-butyl $(Me)_2Si$—O—R, or TBS—O—R], although triethylsilyl, triisopropylsilyl, *tert*-butyldiphenylsilyl, and others can be used. The *tert*-butyldimethylsilyl ether is stable over a pH range of roughly 4–12. A TBS group can be added by allowing the alcohol to react with *tert*-butyldimethylsilyl chloride in the presence of an aromatic amine (a base) such as imidazole or pyridine:

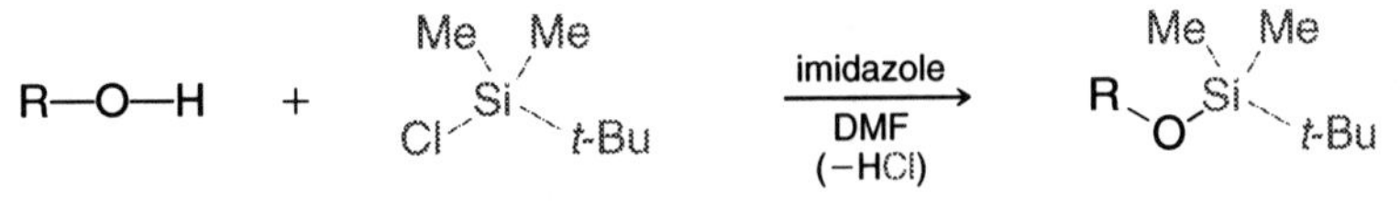

tert-Butylchlorodimethylsilane (TBSCl)

(R—O—TBS)

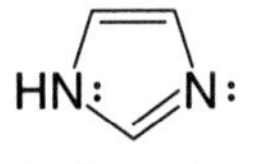

Imidazole

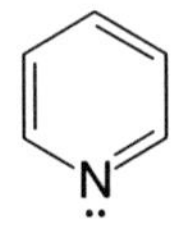

Pyridine

- The TBS group can be removed by treatment with fluoride ion (tetrabutylammonium fluoride or aqueous HF is frequently used). These conditions tend not to affect other functional groups, which is why TBS ethers are such good protecting groups.

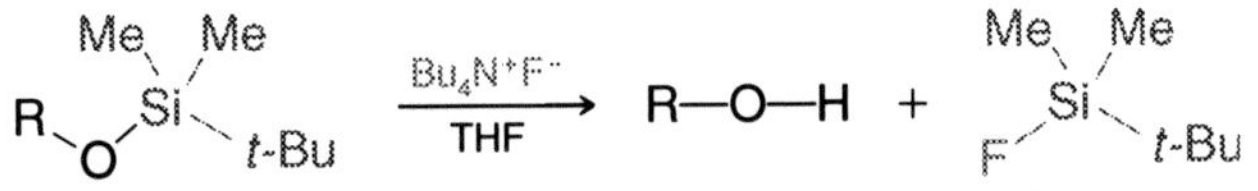

(R—O—TBS)

Converting an alcohol to a silyl ether also makes it much more volatile. This increased volatility makes the alcohol (as a silyl ether) much more amenable to analysis by gas chromatography. Trimethylsilyl ethers are often used for this purpose. The trimethylsilyl ether group is too labile to use as a protecting group in most reactions, however.

●●● SOLVED PROBLEM 11.9

Supply the missing reagents and intermediates **A–E**.

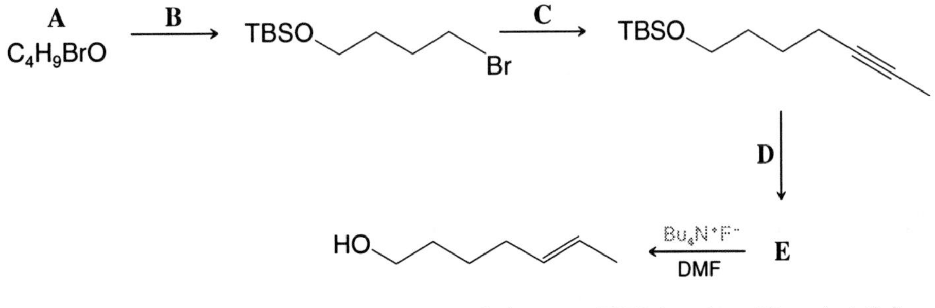

STRATEGY AND ANSWER: We start by noticing several things: a TBS (*tert*-butyldimethylsilyl) protecting group is involved, the carbon chain increases from four carbons in **A** to seven in the final product, and an alkyne is reduced to a trans alkene. **A** does not contain any silicon atoms, whereas the product after the reaction under conditions **B** does. Therefore, **A** must be an alcohol that is protected as a TBS ether by conditions specified as **B**. **A** is therefore 4-bromo-1-butanol, and conditions **B** are TBSCl (*tert*-butyldimethylsilyl chloride) with imidazole in DMF. Conditions **C** involve loss of the bromine and chain extension by three carbons with incorporation of an alkyne. Thus, the reaction conditions for **C** must involve sodium propynide, which would come from deprotonation of propyne using an appropriate base, such as $NaNH_2$ or CH_3MgBr. The conditions leading from **E** to the final product are those for removal of a TBS group, and not those for converting an alkyne to a trans alkene; thus, **E** must still contain the TBS ether but already contain the trans alkene. Conditions **D**, therefore, must be (1) Li, Et_2NH, (2) NH_4Cl, which are those required for converting the alkyne to a trans alkene. **E**, therefore, must be the TBS ether of 5-heptyn-1-ol (which can also be named 1-*tert*-butyldimethylsiloxy-5-heptynol).

11.12 REACTIONS OF ETHERS

Dialkyl ethers react with very few reagents other than acids. The only reactive sites that molecules of a dialkyl ether present to another reactive substance are the C—H bonds of the alkyl groups and the —Ö— group of the ether linkage. Ethers resist attack by nucleophiles (why?) and by bases. This lack of reactivity coupled with the ability of ethers to solvate cations (by donating an electron pair from their oxygen atom) makes ethers especially useful as solvents for many reactions.

Ethers are like alkanes in that they undergo halogenation reactions (Chapter 10), but these reactions are of little synthetic importance. They also undergo slow autoxidation to form explosive peroxides (see Section 11.3D).

The oxygen of the ether linkage makes ethers weakly basic. Ethers can react with proton donors to form **oxonium salts**:

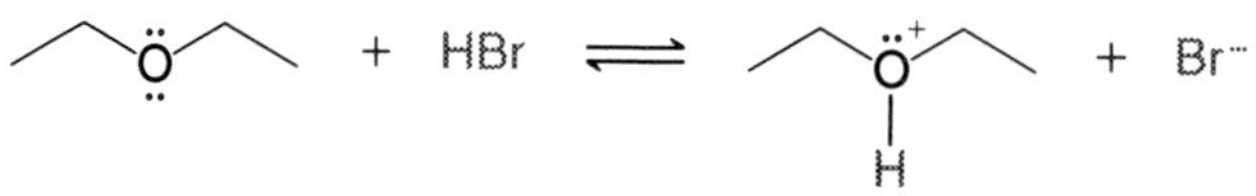

An oxonium salt

11.12A Cleavage of Ethers

Heating dialkyl ethers with very strong acids (HI, HBr, and H_2SO_4) causes them to undergo reactions in which the carbon–oxygen bond breaks. Diethyl ether, for example, reacts with hot concentrated hydrobromic acid to give two molecular equivalents of bromoethane:

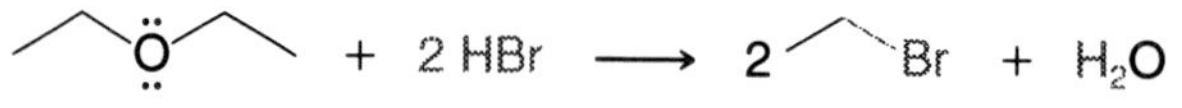

Cleavage of an ether

The mechanism for this reaction begins with formation of an oxonium cation. Then, an S_N2 reaction with a bromide ion acting as the nucleophile produces ethanol and bromoethane. Excess **HBr** reacts with the ethanol produced to form the second molar equivalent of bromoethane.

[**A MECHANISM FOR THE REACTION** ‒ **Ether Cleavage by Strong Acids**]

Step 1

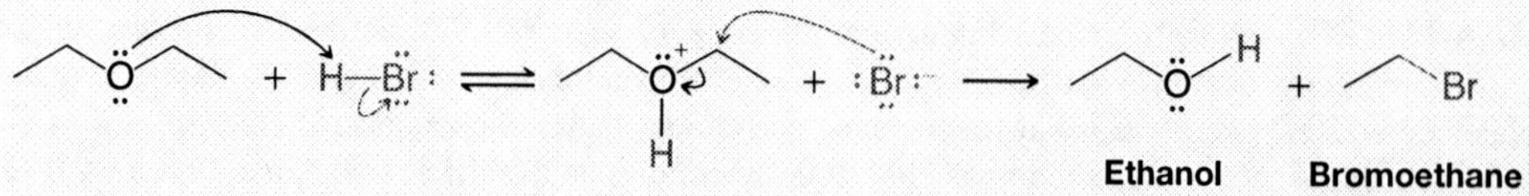

Ethanol   Bromoethane

Step 2   In step 2 the ethanol (just formed) reacts with HBr (present in excess) to form a second molar equivalent of bromoethane

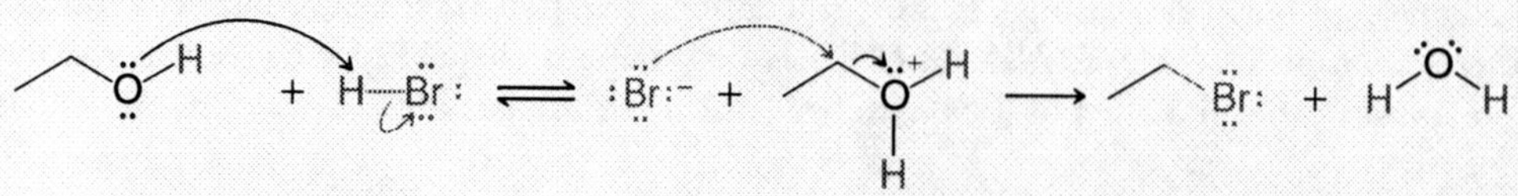

When an ether is treated with *cold* concentrated HI, cleavage occurs as follows:

PRACTICE PROBLEM 11.16

$$R—O—R + HI \longrightarrow ROH + RI$$

When mixed ethers are used, the alcohol and alkyl iodide that form depend on the nature of the alkyl groups. Use mechanisms to explain the following observations:

(a)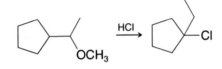

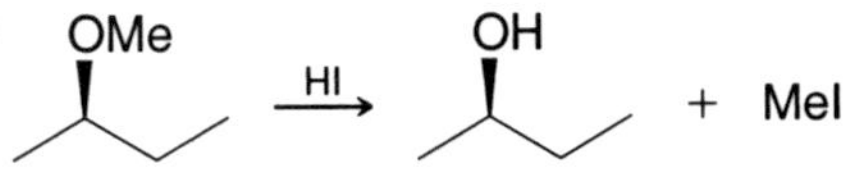

(b)

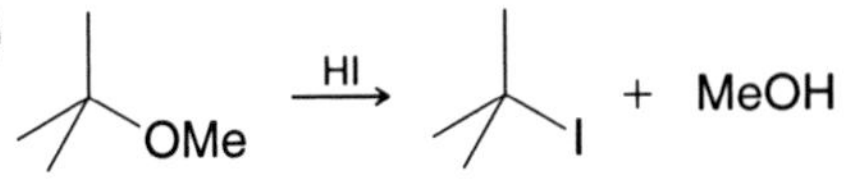

Write a detailed mechanism for the following reaction.

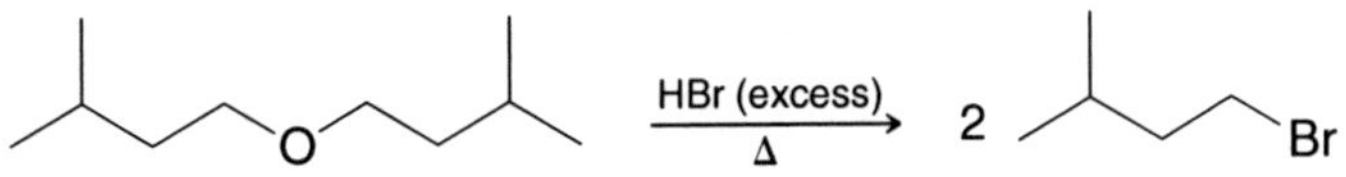

PRACTICE PROBLEM 11.17

Provide a mechanism for the following reaction.

PRACTICE PROBLEM 11.18

11.13 EPOXIDES

Epoxides are cyclic ethers with three-membered rings. In IUPAC nomenclature epoxides are called **oxiranes**. The simplest epoxide has the common name ethylene oxide:

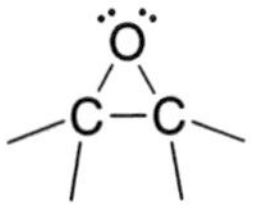

An epoxide

IUPAC name: oxirane
Common name: ethylene oxide

11.13A Synthesis of Epoxides: Epoxidation

Epoxides can be synthesized by the reaction of an alkene with an organic **peroxy acid** (RCO₃H—sometimes called simply a **peracid**), a process that is called **epoxidation**. *meta*-Chloroperoxybenzoic acid (mCPBA) is one peroxy acid reagent commonly used for epoxidation. The following reaction is an example.

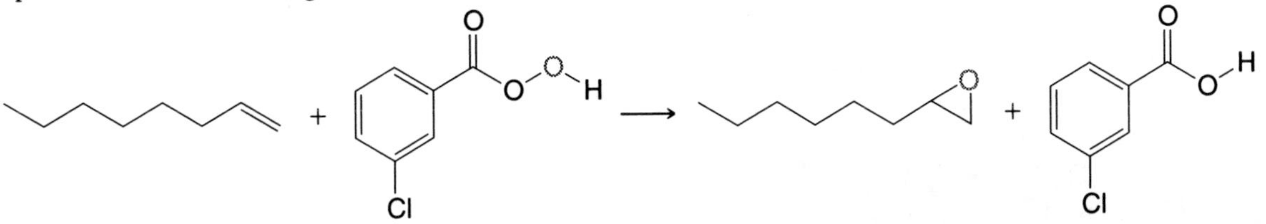

1-Octene   **mCPBA**   **(81%)**   ***meta*-Chlorobenzoic acid**

meta-Chlorobenzoic acid is a by-product of the reaction. Often it is not written in the chemical equation, as the following example illustrates.

(77%)

As the first example illustrates, the peroxy acid transfers an oxygen atom to the alkene. The following mechanism has been proposed.

[A MECHANISM FOR THE REACTION ⋯ Alkene Epoxidation]

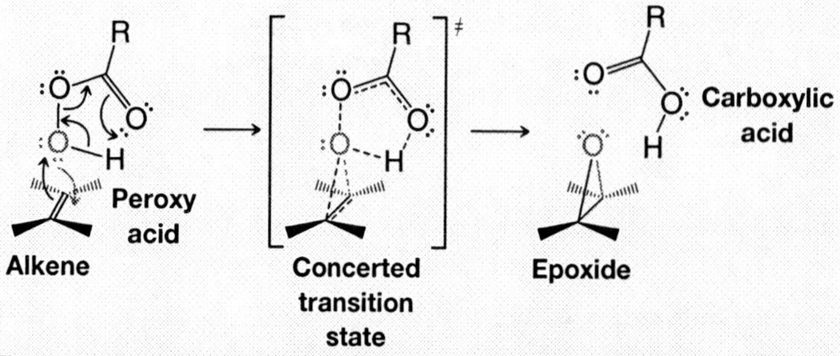

The peroxy acid transfers an oxygen atom to the alkene in a cyclic, single-step mechanism. The result is the syn addition of the oxygen to the alkene, with the formation of an epoxide and a carboxylic acid.

THE CHEMISTRY OF... The Sharpless Asymmetric Epoxidation

In 1980, K. B. Sharpless (then at the Massachusetts Institute of Technology, presently at The Scripps Research Institute) and co-workers reported a method that has since become one of the most valuable tools for chiral synthesis. The Sharpless asymmetric epoxidation is a method for converting allylic alcohols (Section 11.1) to chiral epoxy alcohols with very high enantioselectivity (i.e., with preference for one enantiomer rather than formation of a racemic mixture). In recognition of this and other work in asymmetric oxidation methods (see Section 8.16A), Sharpless received half of the 2001 Nobel Prize in Chemistry (the other half was awarded to W. S. Knowles and R. Noyori; see Section 7.14). The Sharpless asymmetric epoxidation involves treating the allylic alcohol with *tert*-butyl hydroperoxide, titanium(IV) tetraisopropoxide [Ti(O—*i*-Pr)$_4$], and a specific stereoisomer of a tartrate ester. (The tartrate stereoisomer that is chosen depends on the specific enantiomer of the epoxide desired). The following is an example:

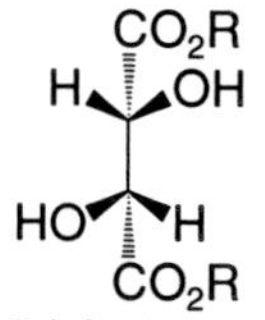

A (+)-dialkyl tartrate ester

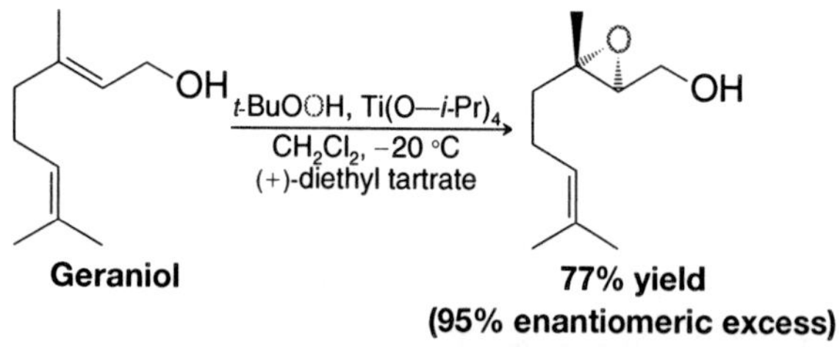

The oxygen that is transferred to the allylic alcohol to form the epoxide is derived from *tert*-butyl hydroperoxide. The enantioselectivity of the reaction results from a titanium complex among the reagents that includes the enantiomerically pure tartrate ester as one of the ligands. The choice of whether to use the (+)- or (−)-tartrate ester for stereochemical control depends on which enantiomer of the epoxide is desired. [The (+)- and (−)-tartrates are either diethyl or diisopropyl esters.] The stereochemical preferences of the reaction have been well studied, such that it is possible to prepare either enantiomer of a chiral epoxide in high enantiomeric excess, simply by choosing the appropriate (+)- or (−)-tartrate stereoisomer as the chiral ligand:

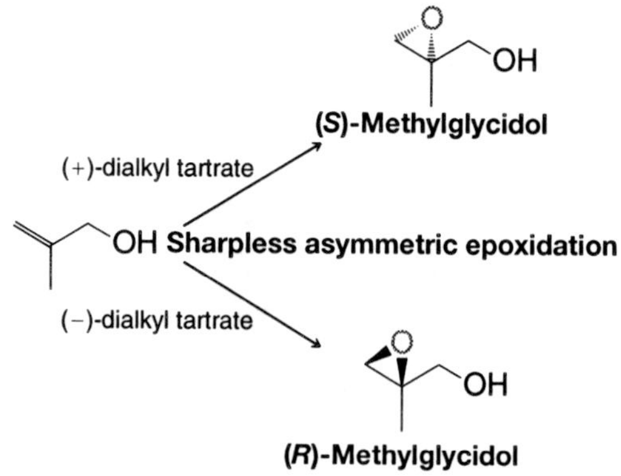

(S)-Methylglycidol

(+)-dialkyl tartrate

Sharpless asymmetric epoxidation

(−)-dialkyl tartrate

(R)-Methylglycidol

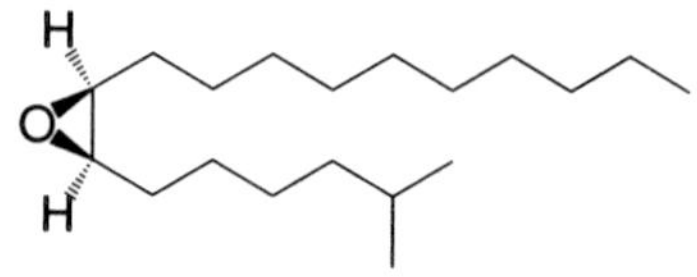

(7R,8S)-Disparlure

Compounds of this general structure are extremely useful and versatile synthons because combined in one molecule are an epoxide functional group (a highly reactive electrophilic site), an alcohol functional group (a potentially nucleophilic site), and at least one chirality center that is present in high enantiomeric purity. The synthetic utility of chiral epoxy alcohol synthons produced by the Sharpless asymmetric epoxidation has been demonstrated over and over in enantioselective syntheses of many important compounds. Some examples include the synthesis

Geraniol

t-BuOOH, Ti(O—*i*-Pr)$_4$
CH$_2$Cl$_2$, −20 °C
(+)-diethyl tartrate

**77% yield
(95% enantiomeric excess)**

of the polyether antibiotic X-206 by E. J. Corey (Harvard), the J. T. Baker commercial synthesis of the gypsy moth pheromone (7R,8S)-disparlure, and synthesis by K. C. Nicolaou (University of California San Diego and Scripps Research Institute) of zaragozic acid A (which is also called squalestatin S1 and has been shown to lower serum cholesterol levels in test animals by inhibition of squalene biosynthesis; see "The Chemistry of... Cholesterol Biosynthesis," online in *WileyPLUS* after Chapter 8).

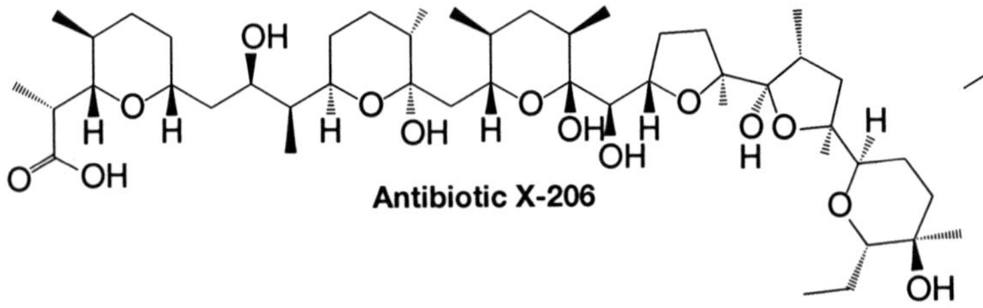

Antibiotic X-206

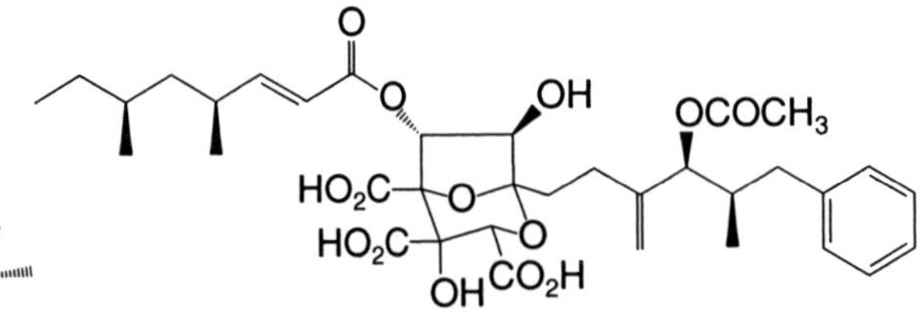

Zaragozic acid A (squalestatin S1)

11.13B Stereochemistry of Epoxidation

- The reaction of alkenes with peroxy acids is, of necessity, a **syn** addition, and it is **stereospecific**. Furthermore, the oxygen atom can add to either face of the alkene.

For example, *trans*-2-butene yields racemic *trans*-2,3-dimethyloxirane, because addition of oxygen to each face of the alkene generates an enantiomer. *cis*-2-Butene, on the other hand, yields only *cis*-2,3-dimethyloxirane, no matter which face of the alkene accepts the oxygen atom, due to the plane of symmetry in both the reactant and the product. If additional chirality centers are present in a substrate, then diastereomers would result.

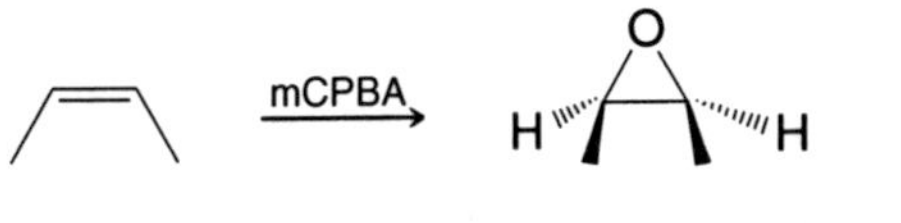

cis-2-Butene   **cis-2,3-Dimethyloxirane**
(a meso compound)

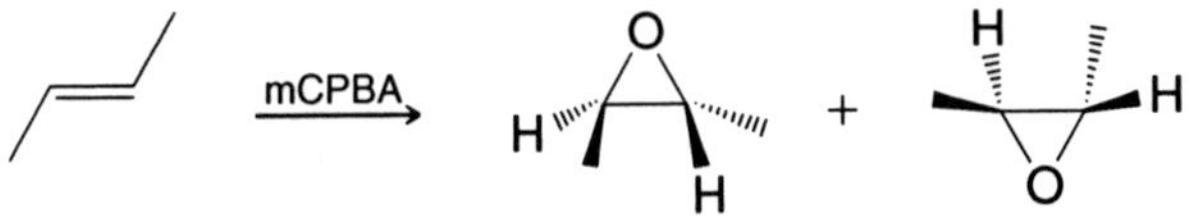

trans-2-Butene   **Enantiomeric trans-2,3-dimethyloxiranes**

In Special Topic D (Section D.3, in *WileyPLUS*) we present a method for synthesizing epoxides from aldehydes and ketones.

11.14 REACTIONS OF EPOXIDES

- The highly strained three-membered ring of epoxides makes them much more reactive toward nucleophilic substitution than other ethers.

Acid catalysis assists epoxide ring opening by providing a better leaving group (an alcohol) at the carbon atom undergoing nucleophilic attack. This catalysis is especially important if the nucleophile is a weak nucleophile such as water or an alcohol. An example is the acid-catalyzed hydrolysis of an epoxide.

[**A MECHANISM FOR THE REACTION**   Acid-Catalyzed Ring Opening of an Epoxide]

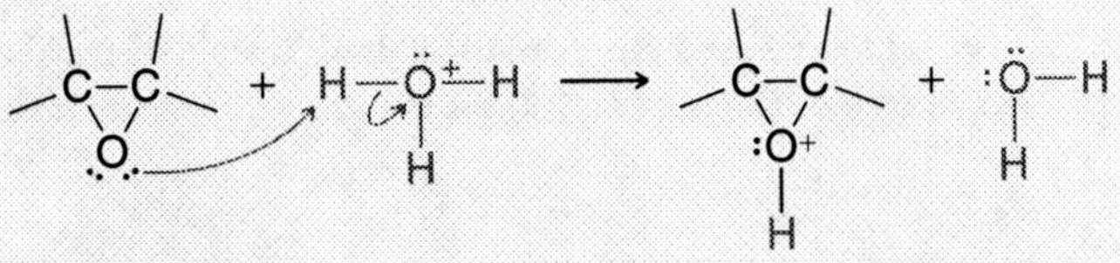

Epoxide   **Protonated epoxide**
The acid reacts with the epoxide to produce a protonated epoxide.

(mechanism continues on the next page)

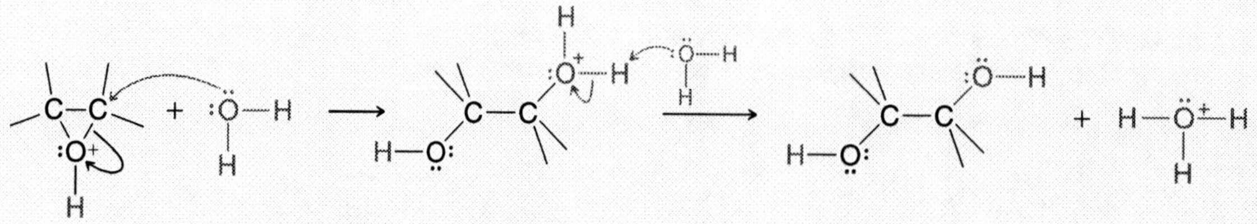

Protonated epoxide   **Weak nucleophile**   **Protonated 1,2-diol**   **1,2-Diol**

The protonated epoxide reacts with the weak nucleophile (water) to form a protonated 1,2-diol, which then transfers a proton to a molecule of water to form the 1,2-diol and a hydronium ion.

Epoxides can also undergo base-catalyzed ring opening. Such reactions do not occur with other ethers, but they are possible with epoxides (because of ring strain), provided that the attacking nucleophile is also a strong base such as an alkoxide ion or hydroxide ion.

[A MECHANISM FOR THE REACTION — Base-Catalyzed Ring Opening of an Epoxide]

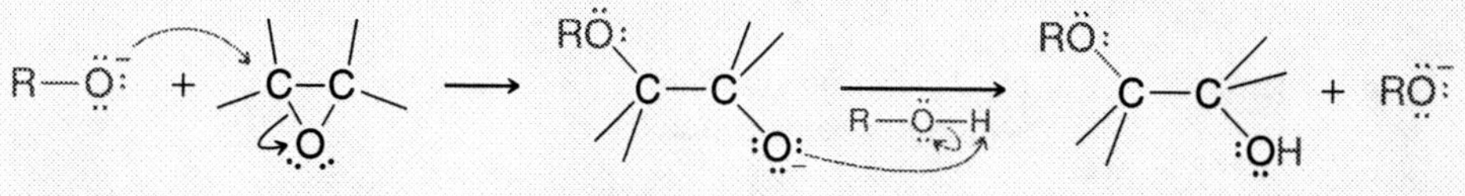

Strong nucleophile   **Epoxide**   **An alkoxide ion**

A strong nucleophile such as an alkoxide ion or a hydroxide ion is able to open the strained epoxide ring in a direct S_N2 reaction.

Helpful Hint

Regioselectivity in the opening of epoxides.

● **Base-catalyzed ring opening** of an unsymmetrical epoxide occurs primarily by attack of the nucleophile *at the less substituted carbon atom.*

For example, methyloxirane reacts with an alkoxide ion mainly at its primary carbon atom:

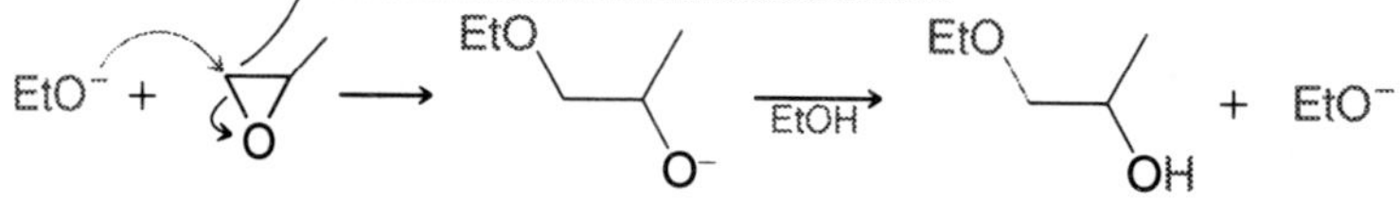

1° Carbon atom is less hindered.

Methyloxirane   **1-Ethoxy-2-propanol**

This is just what we should expect: the reaction is, after all, an S_N2 reaction, and, as we learned earlier (Section 6.13A), primary substrates react more rapidly in S_N2 reactions because they are less sterically hindered.

● **Acid-catalyzed ring opening** of an unsymmetrical epoxide occurs primarily by attack of the nucleophile *at the more substituted carbon atom.*

For example,

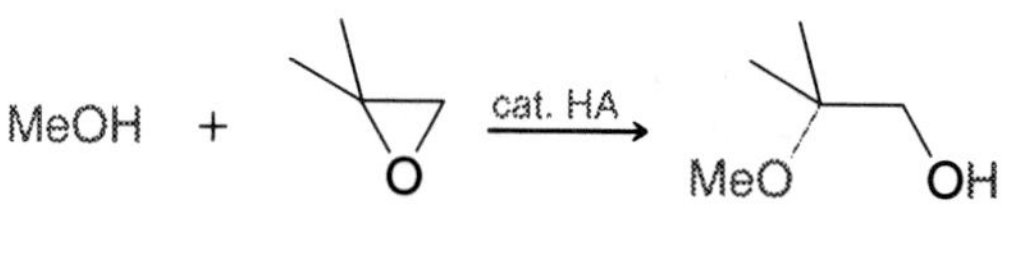

The reason: bonding in the protonated epoxide (see the following reaction) is unsymmetrical, with the more highly substituted carbon atom bearing a considerable positive charge; the reaction is S_N1 like. The nucleophile, therefore, attacks this carbon atom even though it is more highly substituted:

This carbon resembles a 3° carbocation.

MeOH +   ⟶

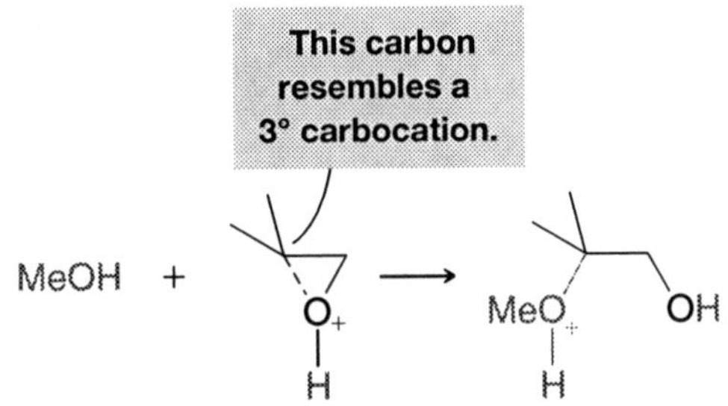

Protonated epoxide

The more highly substituted carbon atom bears a greater positive charge because it resembles a more stable tertiary carbocation. [Notice how this reaction (and its explanation) resembles that given for halohydrin formation from unsymmetrical alkenes in Section 8.14 and attack on mercurinium ions.]

PRACTICE PROBLEM 11.19

Propose structures for each of the following products derived from oxirane (ethylene oxide):

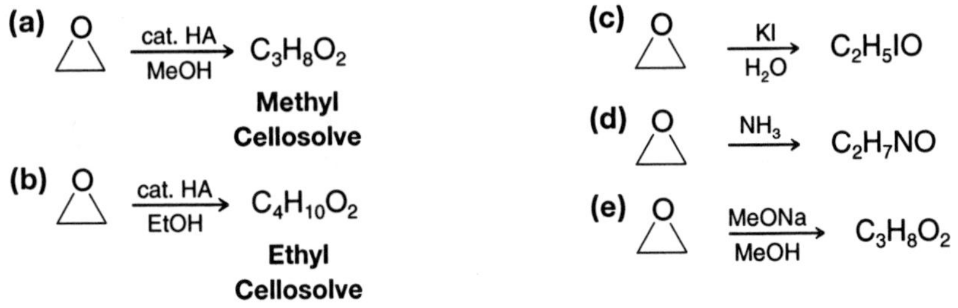

(a) $\xrightarrow[\text{MeOH}]{\text{cat. HA}}$ $C_3H_8O_2$
Methyl Cellosolve

(b) $\xrightarrow[\text{EtOH}]{\text{cat. HA}}$ $C_4H_{10}O_2$
Ethyl Cellosolve

(c) $\xrightarrow[\text{H}_2\text{O}]{\text{KI}}$ C_2H_5IO

(d) $\xrightarrow{\text{NH}_3}$ C_2H_7NO

(e) $\xrightarrow[\text{MeOH}]{\text{MeONa}}$ $C_3H_8O_2$

PRACTICE PROBLEM 11.20

Provide a mechanistic explanation for the following observation.

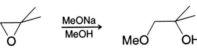

$\xrightarrow[\text{MeOH}]{\text{MeONa}}$

PRACTICE PROBLEM 11.21

When sodium ethoxide reacts with 1-(chloromethyl)oxirane (also called epichlorohydrin), labeled with ^{14}C as shown by the asterisk in **I**, the major product is **II**. Provide a mechanistic explanation for this result.

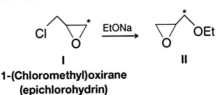

I

**1-(Chloromethyl)oxirane
(epichlorohydrin)**

II

11.14A Polyethers from Epoxides

Treating ethylene oxide with sodium methoxide (in the presence of a small amount of methanol) can result in the formation of a **polyether**:

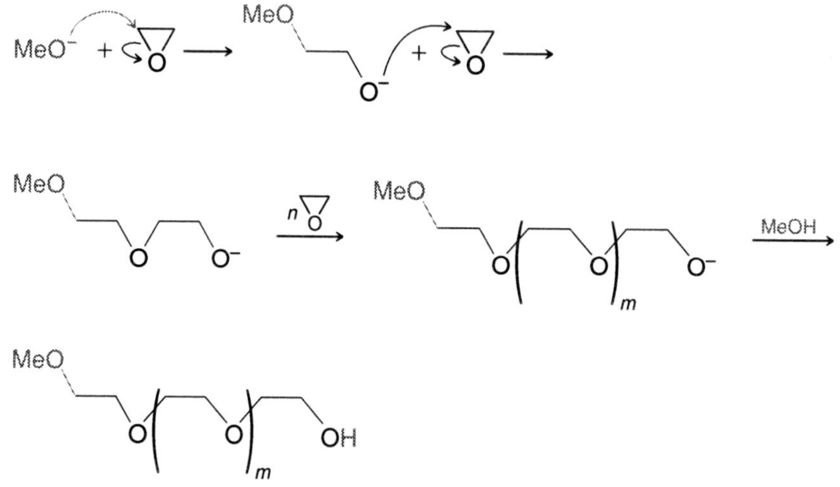

Poly(ethylene glycol)
(a polyether)

This is an example of **anionic polymerization** (Section 10.11). The polymer chains continue to grow until methanol protonates the alkoxide group at the end of the chain. The average length of the growing chains and, therefore, the average molecular weight of the polymer can be controlled by the amount of methanol present. The physical properties of the polymer depend on its average molecular weight.

Polyethers have high water solubilities because of their ability to form multiple hydrogen bonds to water molecules. Marketed commercially as **carbowaxes**, these polymers have a variety of uses, ranging from use in gas chromatography columns to applications in cosmetics.

11.15 ANTI 1,2-DIHYDROXYLATION OF ALKENES VIA EPOXIDES

Epoxidation of cyclopentene with a peroxycarboxylic acid produces 1,2-epoxycyclopentane:

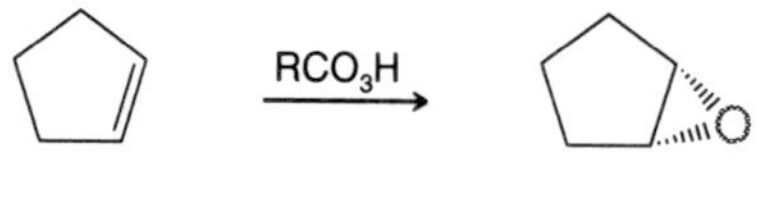

Cyclopentene   **1,2-Epoxycyclopentane**

Helpful Hint

A synthetic method for anti 1,2-dihydroxylation.

Acid-catalyzed hydrolysis of 1,2-epoxycyclopentane, shown below, yields a trans diol, *trans*-1,2-cyclopentanediol. Water acting as a nucleophile attacks the protonated epoxide from the side opposite the epoxide group. The carbon atom being attacked undergoes an inversion of configuration. We show here only one carbon atom being attacked. Attack at the other carbon atom of this symmetrical system is equally likely and produces the enantiomeric form of *trans*-1,2-cyclopentanediol:

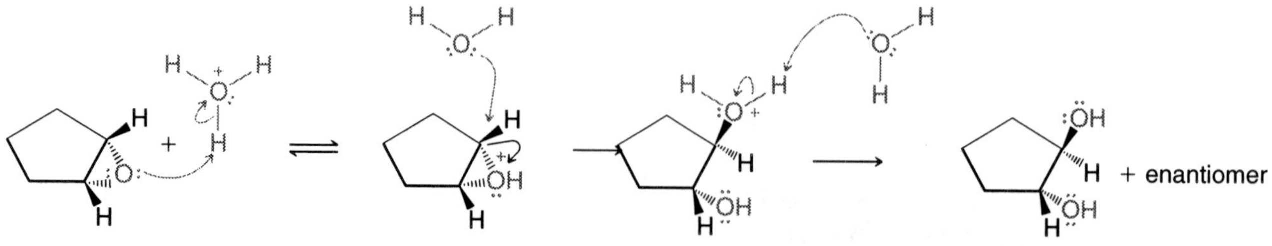

trans-1,2-Cyclopentanediol

Epoxidation followed by acid-catalyzed hydrolysis gives us, therefore, a method for **anti 1,2-dihydroxylation** of a double bond (as opposed to syn 1,2-dihydroxylation, Section 8.16). The stereochemistry of this technique parallels closely the stereochemistry of the bromination of cyclopentene given earlier (Section 8.13).

● ● ●

PRACTICE PROBLEM 11.22

Outline a mechanism similar to the one just given that shows how the enantiomeric form of *trans*-1,2-cyclopentanediol is produced.

●●● **SOLVED PROBLEM 11.10**

In Section 11.13B we showed the epoxidation of *cis*-2-butene to yield *cis*-2,3-dimethyloxirane and epoxidation of *trans*-2-butene to yield *trans*-2,3-dimethyloxirane. Now consider acid-catalyzed hydrolysis of these two epoxides and show what product or products would result from each. Are these reactions stereospecific?

ANSWER: (a) The meso compound, *cis*-2,3-dimethyloxirane (Fig. 11.1), yields on hydrolysis (2R,3R)-2,3-butanediol and (2S,3S)-2,3-butanediol. These products are enantiomers. Since the attack by water at either carbon [path **(a)** or path **(b)** in Fig. 11.1] occurs at the same rate, the product is obtained in a racemic form.

When either of the *trans*-2,3-dimethyloxirane enantiomers undergoes acid-catalyzed hydrolysis, the only product that is obtained is the meso compound, (2R,3S)-2,3-butanediol. The hydrolysis of one enantiomer is shown in Fig. 11.2. (You might construct a similar diagram showing the hydrolysis of the other enantiomer to convince yourself that it, too, yields the same product.)

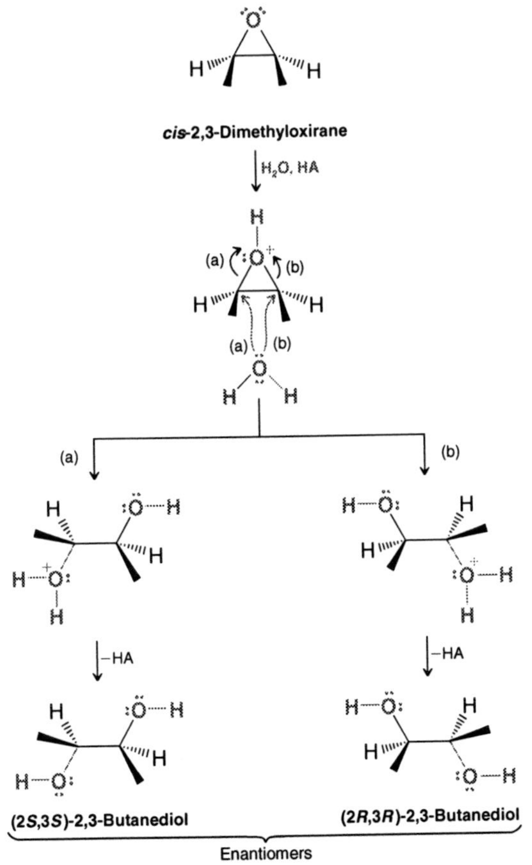

FIGURE 11.1 Acid-catalyzed hydrolysis of *cis*-2,3-dimethyloxirane yields (2S,3S)-2,3-butanediol by path (a) and (2R,3R)-2,3-butanediol by path (b). (Use models to convince yourself.)

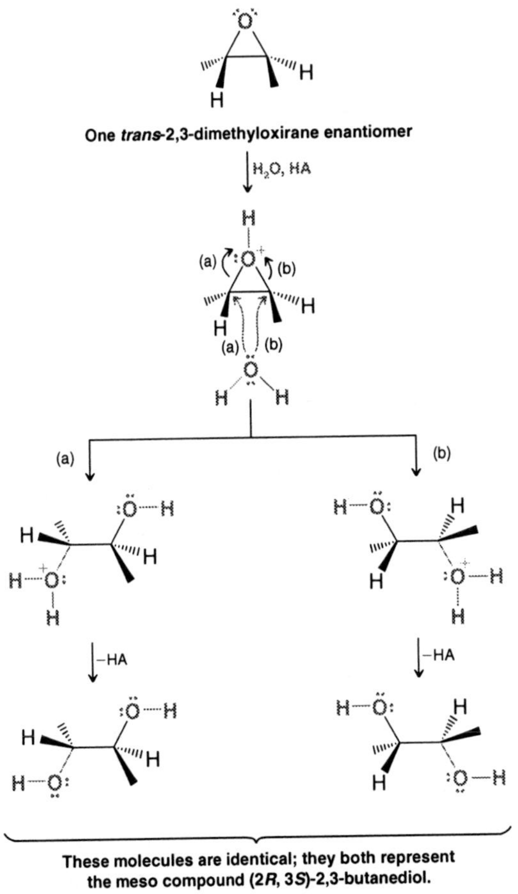

FIGURE 11.2 The acid-catalyzed hydrolysis of one *trans*-2,3-dimethyloxirane enantiomer produces the meso compound, (2R,3S)-2,3-butanediol, by path (a) or by path (b). Hydrolysis of the other enantiomer (or the racemic modification) would yield the same product. (You should use models to convince yourself that the two structures given for the products do represent the same compound.)

(continues on next page)

(b) Since both steps in this method for the conversion of an alkene to a 1,2-diol (glycol) are stereospecific (i.e., both the epoxidation step and the acid-catalyzed hydrolysis), the net result is a stereospecific anti 1,2-dihydroxylation of the double bond (Fig. 11.3).

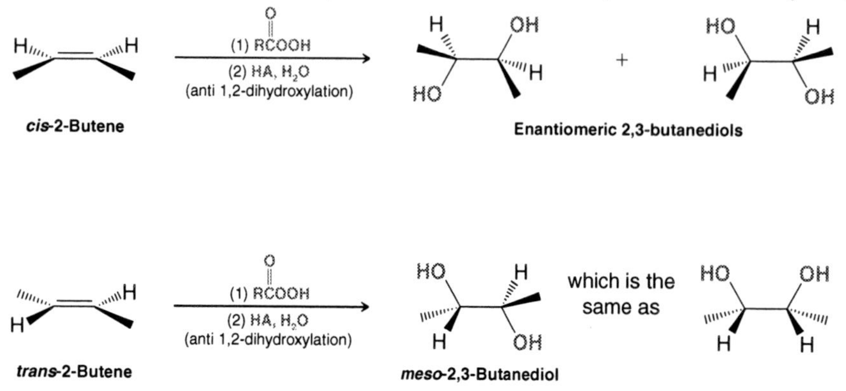

FIGURE 11.3 The overall result of epoxidation followed by acid-catalyzed hydrolysis is a stereospecific anti 1,2-dihydroxylation of the double bond. *cis*-2-Butene yields the enantiomeric 2,3-butanediols; *trans*-2-butene yields the meso compound.

PRACTICE PROBLEM 11.23 Supply the missing reagents and intermediates **A–E.**

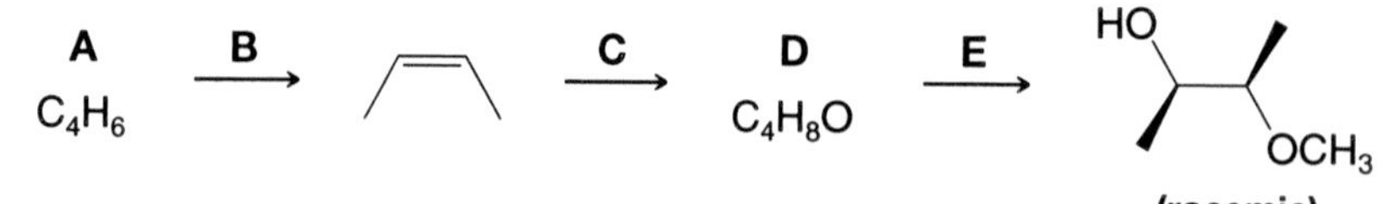

THE CHEMISTRY OF... Environmentally Friendly Alkene Oxidation Methods

The effort to develop synthetic methods that are environmentally friendly is a very active area of chemistry research. The push to devise "green chemistry" procedures includes not only replacing the use of potentially hazardous or toxic reagents with ones that are more friendly to the environment but also developing catalytic procedures that use smaller quantities of potentially harmful reagents when other alternatives are not available. The catalytic syn 1,2-dihydroxylation methods that we described in Section 8.16 (including the Sharpless asymmetric dihydroxylation procedure) are environmentally friendly modifications of the original procedures because they require only a small amount of OsO_4 or other heavy metal oxidant.

Nature has provided hints for ways to carry out environmentally sound oxidations as well. The enzyme methane monooxygenase (MMO) uses iron to catalyze hydrogen peroxide oxidation of small hydrocarbons, yielding alcohols or epoxides, and this example has inspired development of new laboratory methods for alkene oxidation. A 1,2-dihydroxylation procedure developed by L. Que (University of Minnesota) yields a mixture of 1,2-diols and epoxides by action of an iron catalyst and hydrogen peroxide on an alkene. (The ratio of diol to epoxide formed depends on the reaction conditions, and in the case of dihydroxylation, the procedure shows some enantioselectivity.) Another green reaction is the epoxidation method developed by E. Jacobsen (Harvard University). Jacobsen's procedure uses hydrogen peroxide and a similar iron catalyst to epoxidize alkenes (without the complication of diol formation). Que's and Jacobsen's methods are environmentally friendly because their procedures employ catalysts containing a nontoxic metal, and an inexpensive, relatively safe oxidizing reagent is used that is converted to water in the course of the reaction.

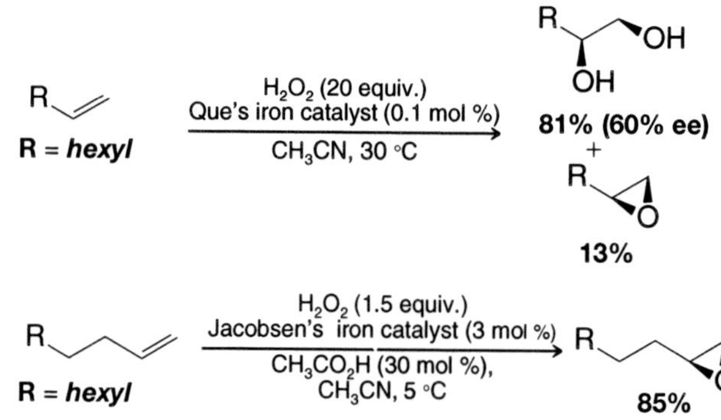

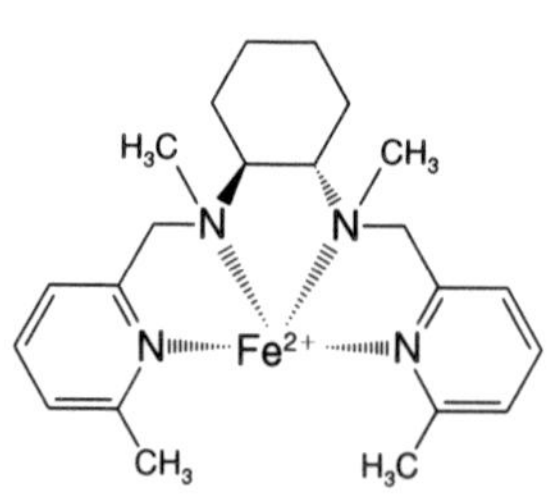

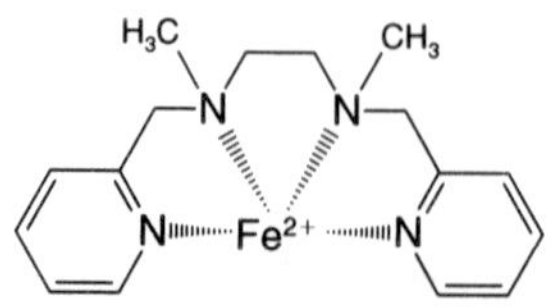

The quest for more methods in green chemistry, with benign reagents and by-products, catalytic cycles, and high yields, will no doubt drive further research by present and future chemists. In coming chapters we shall see more examples of green chemistry in use or under development.

11.16 CROWN ETHERS

Crown ethers are compounds having structures like that of 18-crown-6, below. 18-Crown-6 is a cyclic oligomer of ethylene glycol. Crown ethers are named as *x*-crown-*y*, where *x* is the total number of atoms in the ring and *y* is the number of oxygen atoms. A key property of crown ethers is that they are able to bind cations, as shown below for 18-crown-6 and a potassium ion.

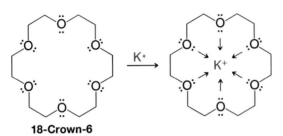

18-Crown-6

Crown ethers render many salts soluble in nonpolar solvents. For this reason they are called **phase transfer catalysts**. When a crown ether coordinates with a metal cation it masks the ion with a hydrocarbon-like exterior. 18-Crown-6 coordinates very effectively with potassium ions because the cavity size is correct and because the six oxygen atoms are ideally situated to donate their electron pairs to the central ion in a Lewis acid–base complex.

● The relationship between a crown ether and the ion it binds is called a **host–guest relationship**.

Salts such as KF, KCN, and potassium acetate can be transferred into aprotic solvents using catalytic amounts of 18-crown-6. Use of a crown ether with a nonpolar solvent can be very favorable for an S_N2 reaction because the nucleophile (such as F⁻, CN⁻, or acetate from the compounds just listed) is unencumbered by solvent in an aprotic solvent, while at the same time the cation is prevented by the crown ether from associating with the nucleophile. Dicyclohexano-18-crown-6 is another example of a phase transfer catalyst. It is even more soluble in nonpolar solvents than 18-crown-6 due to its additional hydrocarbon groups. Phase transfer catalysts can also be used for reactions such as oxidations. (There are phase transfer catalysts that are not crown ethers, as well.)

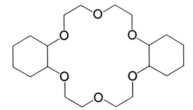

Dicyclohexano-18-crown-6

The development of crown ethers and other molecules "with structure specific interactions of high selectivity" led to awarding of the 1987 Nobel Prize in Chemistry to Charles J. Pedersen (DuPont Company, deceased), Donald J. Cram (University of California, Los Angeles, deceased), and Jean-Marie Lehn (Louis Pasteur University, Strasbourg, France). Their contributions to our understanding of what is now called "molecular recognition" have implications for how enzymes recognize their substrates, how hormones cause their effects, how antibodies recognize antigens, how neurotransmitters propagate their signals, and many other aspects of biochemistry.

 The 1987 Nobel Prize in Chemistry was awarded to Pedersen, Cram, and Lehn for their work relating to crown ethers.

Write structures for **(a)** 15-crown-5 and **(b)** 12-crown-4.

PRACTICE PROBLEM 11.24

◆● THE CHEMISTRY OF... Transport Antibiotics and Crown Ethers

There are several antibiotics called ionophores. Some notable examples are monensin, nonactin, gramicidin, and valinomycin. The structures of monensin and nonactin are shown below. Ionophore antibiotics like monensin and nonactin coordinate with metal cations in a manner similar to crown ethers. Their mode of action has to do with disrupting the natural gradient of ions on each side of the cell membrane.

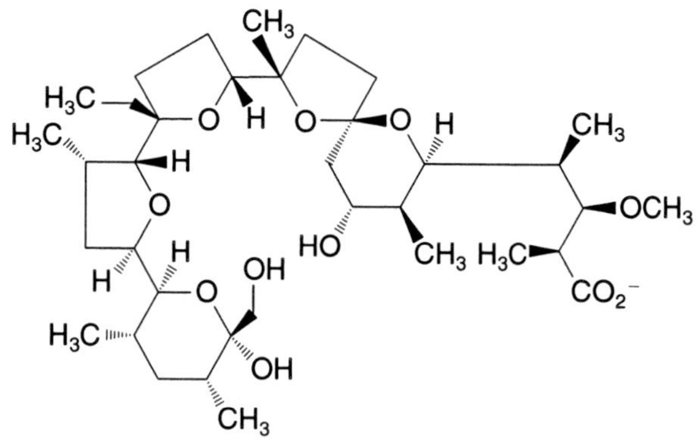

Monensin

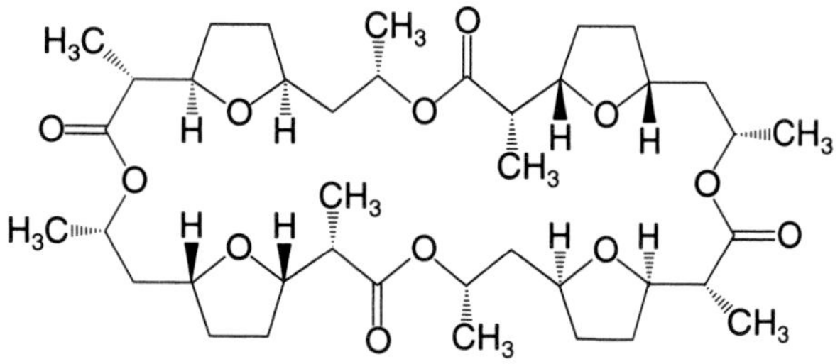

Nonactin

through the cell membrane is slow, and requires an expenditure of energy by the cell. (The 1997 Nobel Prize in Chemistry was awarded in part for work regarding sodium and potassium cell membrane transport.*)

Monensin is called a carrier ionophore because it binds with sodium ions and carries them across the cell membrane. Gramicidin and valinomycin are channel-forming antibiotics because they open pores that extend through the membrane. The ion-trapping ability of monensin results principally from its many ether functional groups, and as such, it is an example of a polyether antibiotic. Its oxygen atoms bind with sodium ions by Lewis acid–base interactions, forming the octahedral complex shown here in the molecular model. The complex is a hydrophobic "host" for the cation that allows it to be carried as a "guest" of monensin from one side of the cell membrane to the other. The transport process destroys the critical sodium concentration gradient needed for cell function. Nonactin is another ionophore that upsets the concentration gradient by binding strongly to potassium ions, allowing the membrane to be permeable to potassium ions, also destroying the essential concentration gradient.

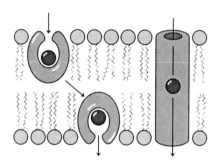

The ionophore antibiotic monensin complexed with a sodium cation.

The cell membrane, in its interior, is like a hydrocarbon because it consists in this region primarily of the hydrocarbon portions of lipids (Chapter 23). Normally, cells must maintain a gradient between the concentrations of sodium and potassium ions inside and outside the cell membrane. Potassium ions are "pumped" in, and sodium ions are pumped out. This gradient is essential to the functions of nerves, transport of nutrients into the cell, and maintenance of proper cell volume. The biochemical transport of sodium and potassium ions

Carrier (left) and channel-forming modes of transport ionophores. (Reprinted with permission of John Wiley & Sons, Inc. from Voet, D. and Voet, J. G. *Biochemistry*, Second Edition. Copyright 1995 Voet, D., and Voet, J. G.)

 *Discovery and characterization of the actual molecular pump that establishes the sodium and potassium concentration gradient (Na+, K+ -ATPase) earned Jens Skou (Aarhus University, Denmark) half of the 1997 Nobel Prize in Chemistry. The other half went to Paul D. Boyer (UCLA) and John E. Walker (Cambridge) for elucidating the enzymatic mechanism of ATP synthesis.

11.17 SUMMARY OF REACTIONS OF ALKENES, ALCOHOLS, AND ETHERS

Helpful Hint

Some tools for synthesis.

We have studied reactions in this chapter and in Chapter 8 that can be extremely useful in designing syntheses. Most of these reactions involving alcohols and ethers are summarized in the Summary Review Tools at the end of the chapter.

- We can use alcohols to make alkyl halides, sulfonate esters, ethers, and alkenes.

- We can oxidize alkenes to make epoxides, diols, aldehydes, ketones, and carboxylic acids (depending on the specific alkene and conditions).

- We can use alkenes to make alkanes, alcohols, and alkyl halides.

- If we have a terminal alkyne, such as could be made from an appropriate vicinal dihalide, we can use the alkynide anion derived from it to form carbon–carbon bonds by nucleophilic substitution.

All together, we have a repertoire of reactions that can be used to directly or indirectly interconvert almost all of the functional groups we have studied so far. In Section 11.17A we summarize some reactions of alkenes.

11.17A HOW TO Use Alkenes in Synthesis

- Alkenes are an entry point to virtually all of the other functional groups that we have studied.

For this reason, and because many of the reactions afford us some degree of control over the regiochemical and/or stereochemical form of the products, alkenes are versatile intermediates for synthesis.

- We have two methods to **hydrate a double bond in a Markovnikov orientation**: (1) *oxymercuration–demercuration* (Section 8.5), and (2) *acid-catalyzed hydration* (Section 8.4).

Of these methods oxymercuration–demercuration is the most useful in the laboratory because it is easy to carry out and *is not accompanied by rearrangements*.

- We can **hydrate a double bond in an anti-Markovnikov orientation** by *hydroboration–oxidation* (Section 8.6). With hydroboration–oxidation we can also achieve a *syn addition of the* H— *and* —OH *groups*.

Remember, too, **the boron group of an organoborane can be replaced by hydrogen, deuterium, or tritium** (Section 8.11), and that hydroboration, itself, involves a *syn addition of* H— *and* —B—.

- We can **add HX to a double bond in a Markovnikov sense** (Section 8.2) using HF, HCl, HBr, or HI.

- We can **add HBr in an anti-Markovnikov orientation** (Section 10.9), by treating an alkene with HBr *and a peroxide*. (The other hydrogen halides do not undergo anti-Markovnikov addition when peroxides are present.)

- We can **add bromine or chlorine to a double bond** (Section 8.12) and the addition is an *anti addition* (Section 8.13).

- We can also **add X— and** —OH to a double bond (i.e., synthesize a halohydrin) by carrying out a bromination or chlorination in water (Section 8.14). This addition, too, is an *anti addition*.

- We can carry out a **syn 1,2-dihydroxylation of a double bond** using either $KMnO_4$ in cold, dilute, and basic solution or OsO_4 followed by $NaHSO_3$ (Section 8.16). Of these two methods, the latter is preferable because of the tendency of $KMnO_4$ to overoxidize the alkene and cause cleavage at the double bond.

- We can carry out **anti 1,2-dihydroxylation of a double bond** by converting the alkene to an *epoxide* and then carrying out an acid-catalyzed hydrolysis (Section 11.15).

Equations for most of these reactions are given in the Synthetic Connections reviews for Chapters 7 and 8 and this chapter.

WHY Do These Topics Matter?]

IMPORTANT, BUT HIDDEN, EPOXIDES

Because of the strain and reactivity of epoxides, it is quite rare to isolate a compound from nature that actually contains an epoxide ring. That does not mean that this functional group does not serve diverse purposes. In fact, there are many instances where epoxides appear to play a critical role in the formation of new bonds within complex natural products. For example, if a long chain of alkenes such as that shown below could be epoxidized at every double bond in a stereocontrolled way (likely using enzymes), then subsequent activation of the terminal epoxide with a proton could potentially initiate a cascade, or domino-like, set of cyclizations leading to many new ring systems with complete stereocontrol. This process is shown here specifically for gymnocin B, one member of a large class of marine-based natural products known as cyclic polyethers. These compounds are potent neurotoxins.

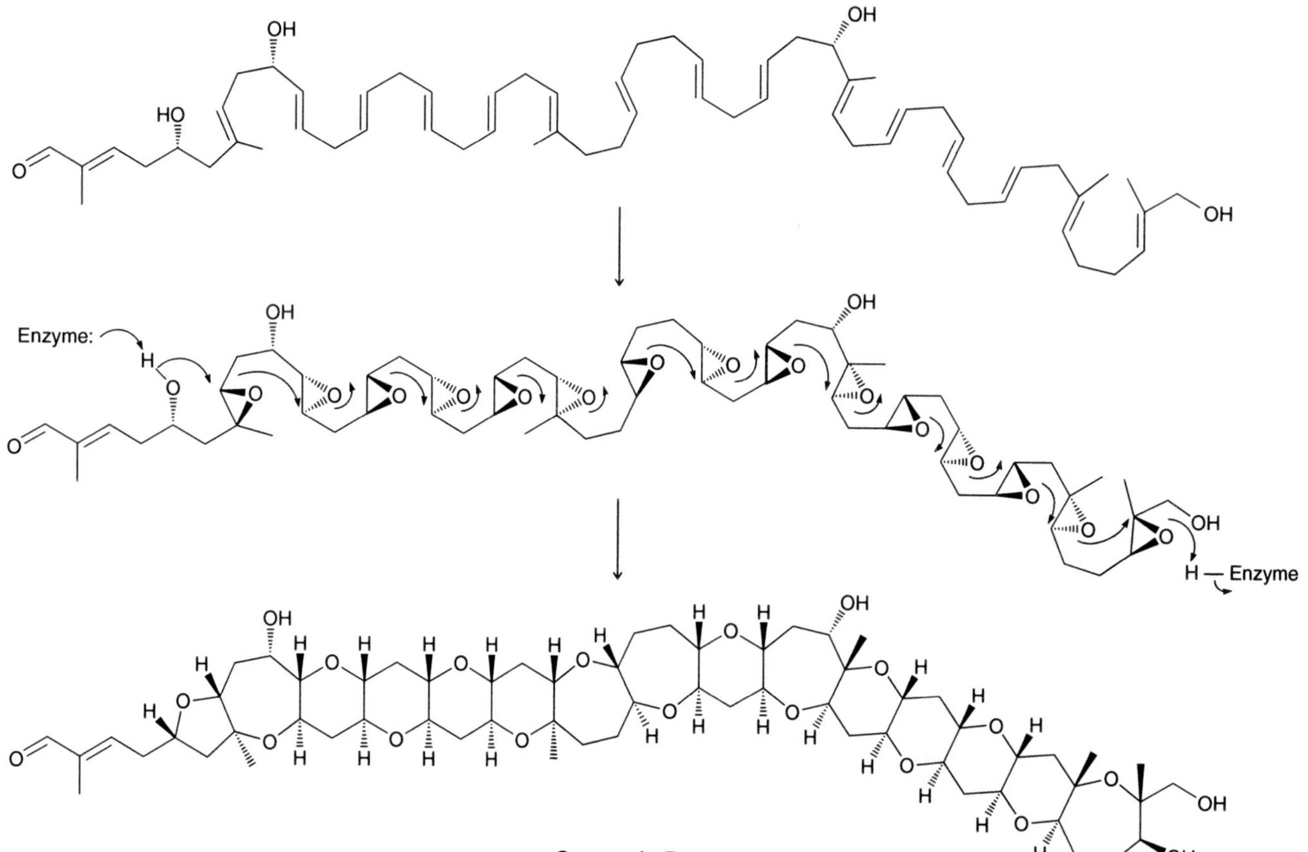

Gymnocin B

Above structure from Vilotijevic, I.; Jamison, T.F.: Epoxide-Opening Cascades Promoted by Water. SCIENCE 317:1189 (2007). Reprinted with permission from AAAS.

Epoxides also play a critical role in eliminating some dangerous molecules we might ingest, a role that again is hidden if we only look at starting materials and products. We will consider two compounds. The first is aflatoxin B₁, a compound that can contaminate peanuts and some cereal grains depending on the soil conditions where the crop was grown. The second is benzo[a]pyrene, a substance found in cigarette smoke and grilled meat (it is a component of the char marks). Aflatoxin B₁ is a carcinogen and benzo[a]pyrene can intercalate with DNA and prevent gene transcription (a topic we will discuss in more detail in Chapter 25).

Michael Patrick O'Neill/Photo Researchers, Inc.

Image Source

The body's system to eliminate these toxic chemicals begins by oxidizing their carbon frameworks using enzymes known as cytochrome P450s; these enzymes are found in the liver and intestines. For both aflatoxin B₁ and benzo[a]pyrene, at least one of their double bonds can be converted into an epoxide, as shown below. The next step is for a highly polar nucleophile, such as glutathione, to add to that reactive ring system and make the resulting molecule water soluble so it can be excreted quickly. However, these reactions are risky because other nucleophiles can attack as well. For example, nucleotide bases within DNA can also react with these epoxides. If that happens, as shown for the epoxidized form of benzo[a]pyrene, cancer can result. Thus, the epoxide in these instances is a two-edged sword—it serves as a way to remove a potentially toxic molecule while also creating a species that is sometimes even more dangerous and reactive than the original material. As a challenge question with this closing essay, why do you think the two nucleophile additions shown below occur only at the indicated positions?

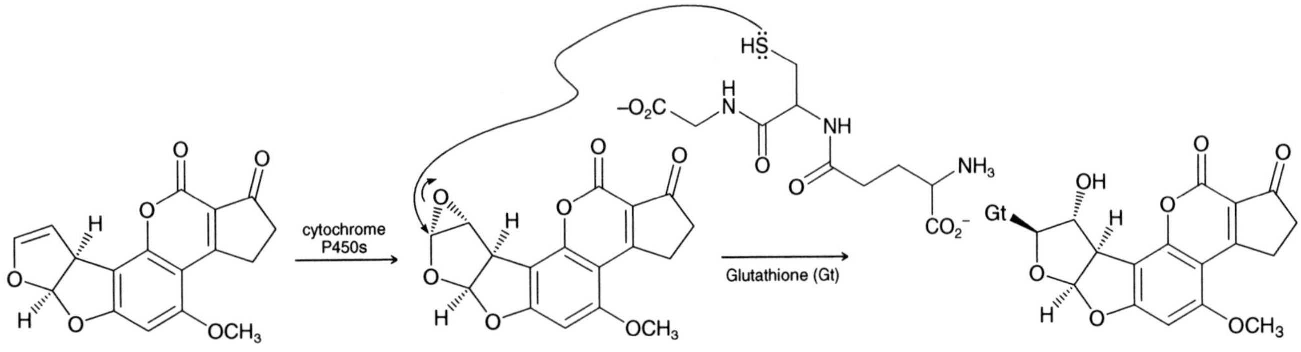

Aflatoxin B₁ ... **[can be excreted]**

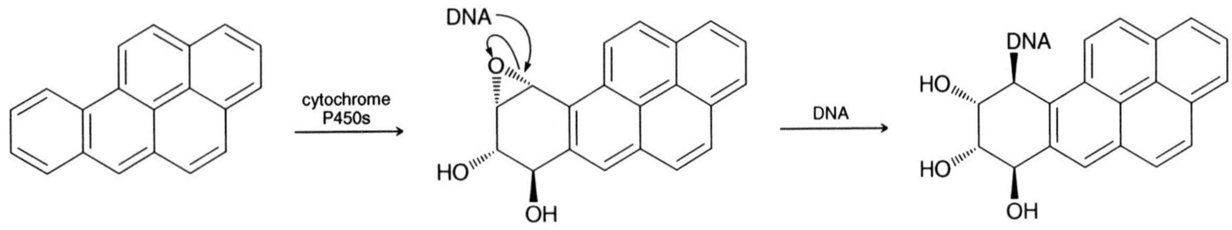

Benzo[a]pyrene ... **[carcinogenic]**

To learn more about these topics, see:

1. Vilotijevic, I.; Jamison, T. F. "Epoxide–Opening Cascades Promoted by Water" in *Science* **2007**, *317*, 1189 and references therein.
2. Nakanishi, K. "The Chemistry of Brevetoxins: A Review" in *Toxicon* **1985**, *23*, 473–479.

SUMMARY AND REVIEW TOOLS

In addition to Section 11.17, which summarizes many of the reactions of alkenes, alcohols, and ethers, the study aids for this chapter also include key terms and concepts (which are hyperlinked to the Glossary from the bold, blue terms in the *WileyPLUS* version of the book at wileyplus.com) and a Synthetic Connections chart.

PROBLEMS PLUS

Note to Instructors: Many of the homework problems are available for assignment via *WileyPLUS*, an online teaching and learning solution.

NOMENCLATURE

11.25 Give an IUPAC substitutive name for each of the following alcohols:

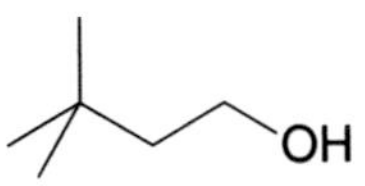

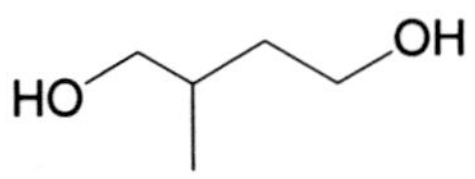

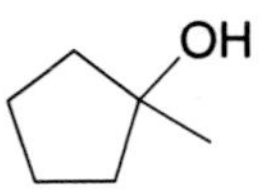

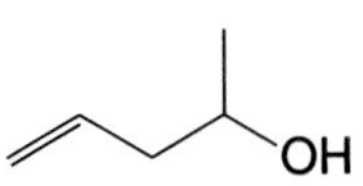

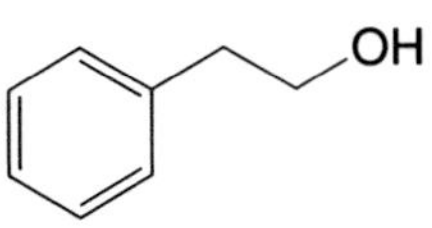

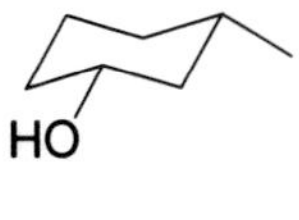

11.26 Write structural formulas for each of the following:

(a) (Z)-But-2-en-1-ol
(b) (R)-Butane-1,2,4-triol
(c) (1R,2R)-Cyclopentane-1,2-diol

(d) 1-Ethylcyclobutanol
(e) 2-Chlorohex-3-yn-1-ol
(f) Tetrahydrofuran

(g) 2-Ethoxypentane
(h) Ethyl phenyl ether
(i) Diisopropyl ether

(j) 2-Ethoxyethanol

REACTIONS AND SYNTHESIS

11.27 Provide the alkene needed to synthesize each of the following by oxymercuration–demercuration.

(a)
(b)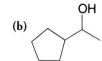
(c)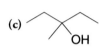
(d)

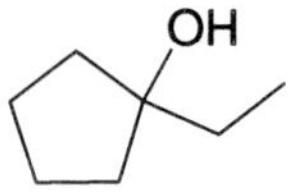

11.28 Provide the alkene needed to synthesize each of the following by hydroboration–oxidation.

(a)
(b)
(c)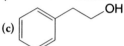
(d)

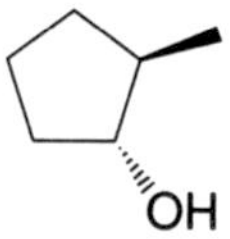

11.29 Starting with each of the following, outline a practical synthesis of 1-butanol:

(a) 1-Butene
(b) 1-Chlorobutane
(c) 2-Chlorobutane
(d) 1-Butyne

11.30 Show how you might prepare 2-bromobutane from

(a) 2-Butanol
(b) 1-Butanol
(c) 1-Butene
(d) 1-Butyne

11.31 Starting with 2-methylpropene (isobutylene) and using any other needed reagents, outline a synthesis of each of the following (T = tritium, D = deuterium):

(a)
(b)
(c)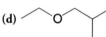
(d)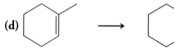

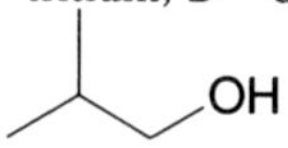

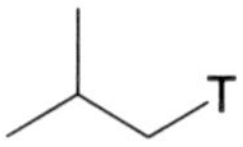

11.32 Show how you might carry out the following transformations:

(a)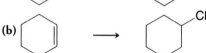
(b)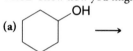
(c)
(d)
(e)

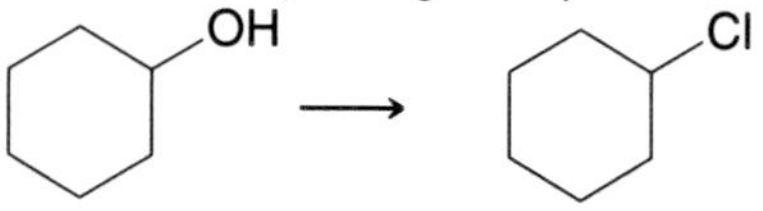

11.33 What compounds would you expect to be formed when each of the following ethers is refluxed with excess concentrated hydrobromic acid?

(a)

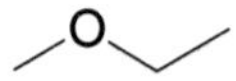

(b)

(c) 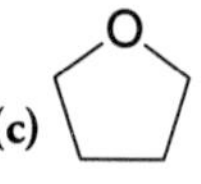 **(THF)**

(d) 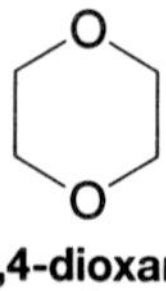 **(1,4-dioxane)**

11.34 Considering **A–L** to represent the major products formed in each of the following reactions, provide a structure for each of **A** through **L**. If more than one product can reasonably be conceived from a given reaction, include those as well.

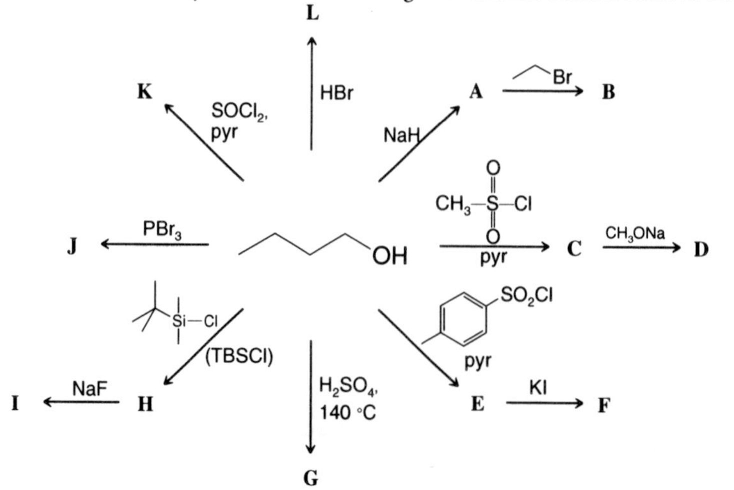

L

K ← SOCl₂, pyr   HBr   **A** ─Br→ **B**

J ← PBr₃   NaH

CH₃—S—Cl, pyr → **C** ─CH₃ONa→ **D**

Si—Cl (TBSCl)

I ← NaF **H**

H₂SO₄, 140 °C

SO₂Cl, pyr → **E** ─KI→ **F**

G

11.35 Write structures for the products that would be formed under the conditions in Problem 11.34 if cyclopentanol had been used as the starting material. If more than one product can reasonably be conceived from a given reaction, include those as well.

11.36 Starting with isobutane, show how each of the following could be synthesized. (You need not repeat the synthesis of a compound prepared in an earlier part of this problem.)

(a) *tert*-Butyl bromide   (g) Isobutyl methyl ether   (i) [structure] CN   (k) [structure]   (m) [structure] NH₂ HO

(b) 2-Methylpropene

(c) Isobutyl bromide   (h) [structure]   (j) CH₃S [structure]   (l) [structure] OH OH   (n) [structure] HO

(d) Isobutyl iodide

(e) Isobutyl alcohol (two ways)

(f) *tert*-Butyl bromide

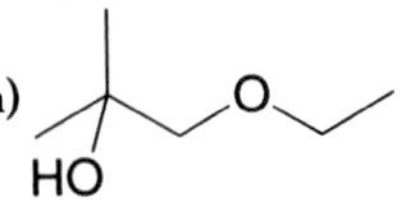

11.37 Outlined below is a synthesis of the gypsy moth sex attractant disparlure (a pheromone). Give the structure of disparlure and intermediates **A–D**.

HC≡CNa $\xrightarrow[\text{liq. NH}_3]{\text{1-bromo-5-methylhexane}}$ **A** (C₉H₁₆) $\xrightarrow[\text{liq. NH}_3]{\text{NaNH}_2}$ **B** (C₉H₁₅Na) $\xrightarrow{\text{1-bromodecane}}$ **C** (C₁₉H₃₆) $\xrightarrow[\text{Ni}_2\text{B(P-2)}]{\text{H}_2}$ **D** (C₁₉H₃₈) $\xrightarrow{\text{mCPBA}}$ **Disparlure** (C₁₉H₃₈O)

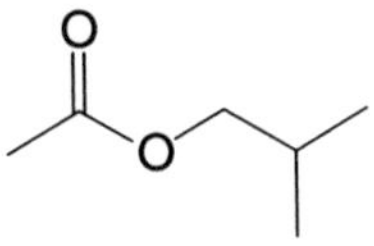

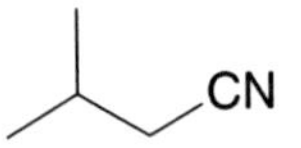

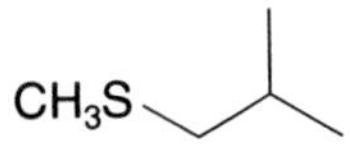

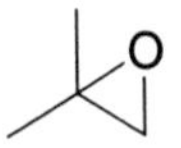

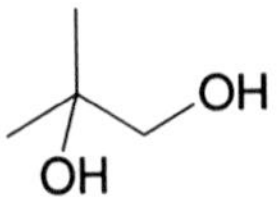

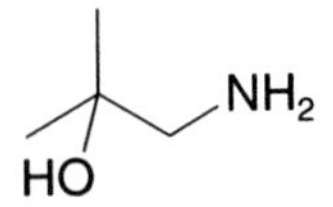

11.38 Provide the reagents necessary for the following syntheses. More than one step may be required.

(a) 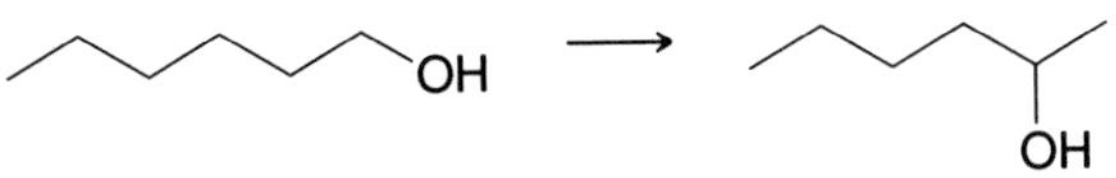 [structure] OH → [structure] OH

(b)  [structure with Br] → [epoxide structure]

(c) 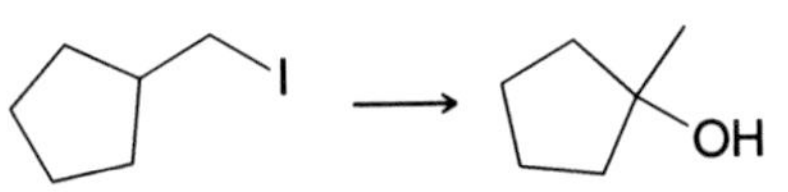 [structure with I] → [structure with OH]

(d) 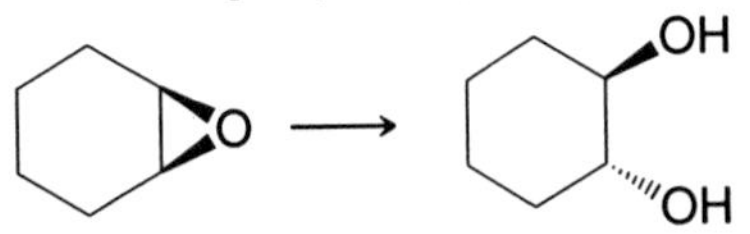 [epoxide structure] → [structure with OH, OH]

(e)  [cyclohexene] → [epoxide structure]

(f) 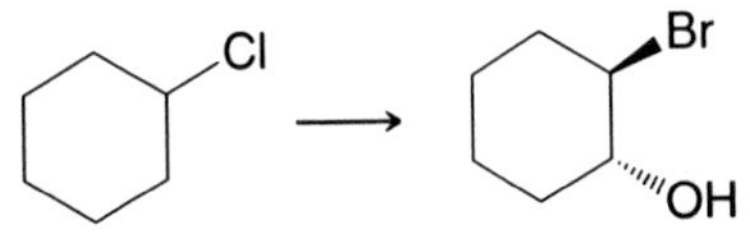 [structure with Cl] → [structure with Br, OH]

11.39 Predict the major product from each of the following reactions.

(a) 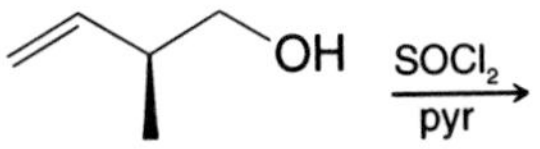 [structure] OH $\xrightarrow[\text{pyr}]{\text{SOCl}_2}$

(b) 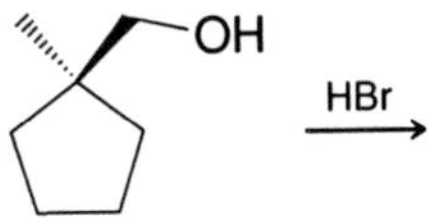 [structure] OH $\xrightarrow{\text{HBr}}$

(c) 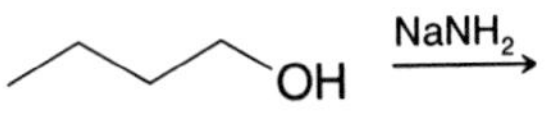 [structure] OH $\xrightarrow{\text{NaNH}_2}$

(d) 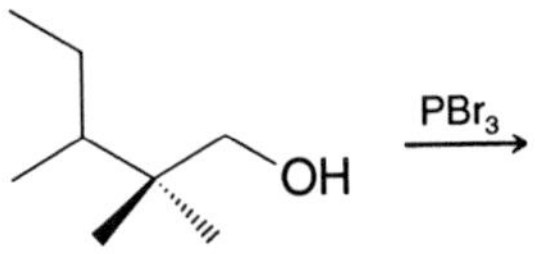 [structure] OH $\xrightarrow{\text{PBr}_3}$

(e) 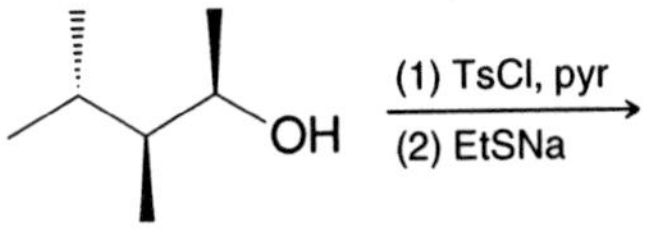 [structure] OH $\xrightarrow[\text{(2) EtSNa}]{\text{(1) TsCl, pyr}}$

(f) 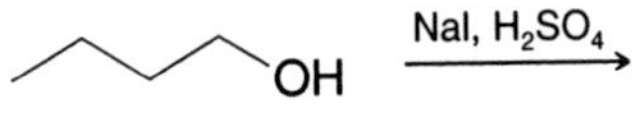 [structure] OH $\xrightarrow{\text{NaI, H}_2\text{SO}_4}$

11.40 Predict the products from each of the following reactions.

(a) 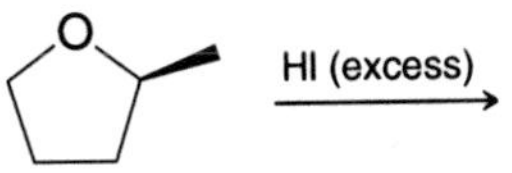 [structure] $\xrightarrow{\text{HI (excess)}}$

(b) 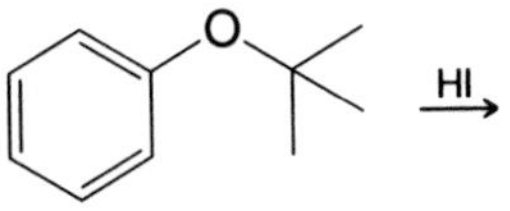 [structure] $\xrightarrow{\text{HI}}$

(c) 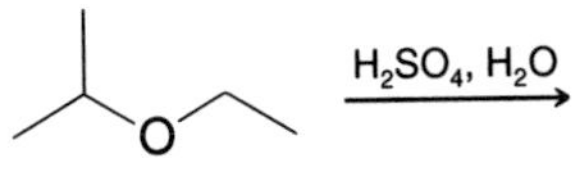 [structure] $\xrightarrow{\text{H}_2\text{SO}_4, \text{H}_2\text{O}}$

(d) 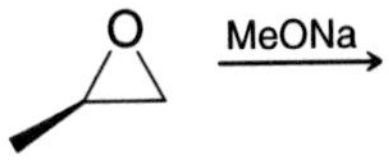 [epoxide structure] $\xrightarrow{\text{MeONa}}$

(e) 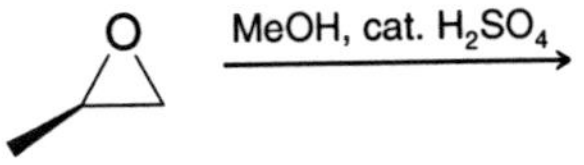 [epoxide structure] $\xrightarrow{\text{MeOH, cat. H}_2\text{SO}_4}$

(f) 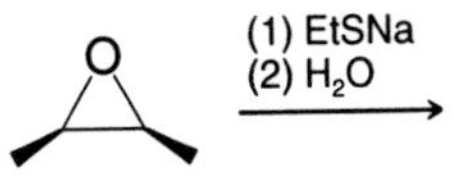 [epoxide structure] $\xrightarrow[\text{(2) H}_2\text{O}]{\text{(1) EtSNa}}$

(g) 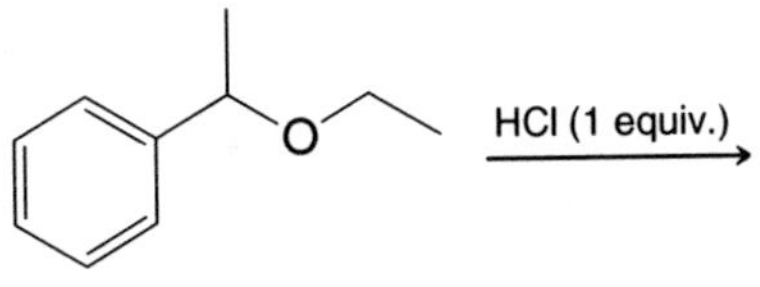 [structure] $\xrightarrow{\text{HCl (1 equiv.)}}$

(h) [structure] $\xrightarrow{\text{MeONa}}$

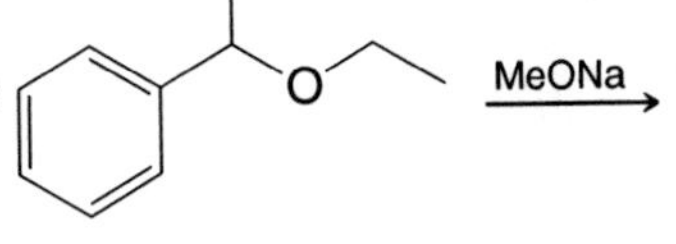

(i) 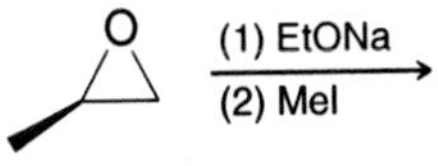 [epoxide structure] $\xrightarrow[\text{(2) MeI}]{\text{(1) EtONa}}$

(j)  [epoxide structure] $\xrightarrow{\text{HI}}$

477

11.41 Provide the reagents necessary to accomplish the following syntheses.

(a)

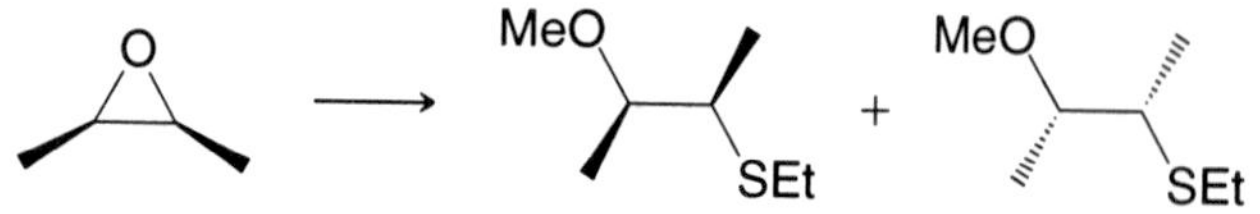

(c)

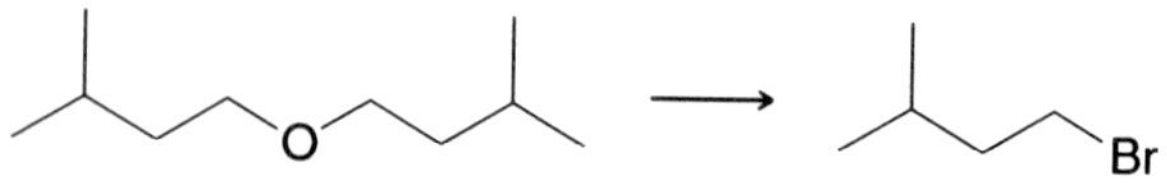

(b)

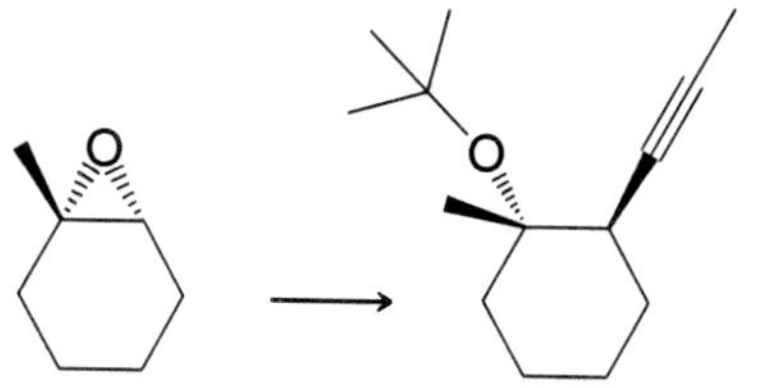

(d)

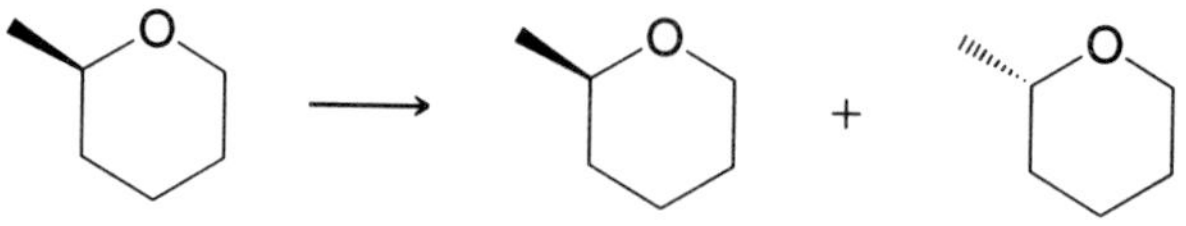

11.42 Provide reagents that would accomplish the follwing syntheses.

(a)

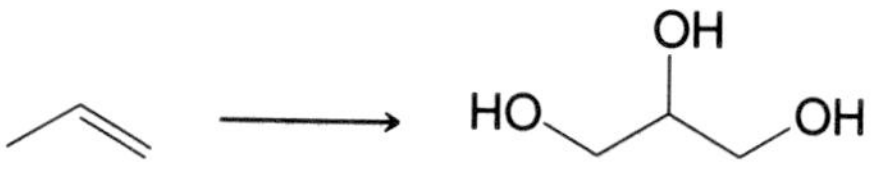

Glycerol

(b)

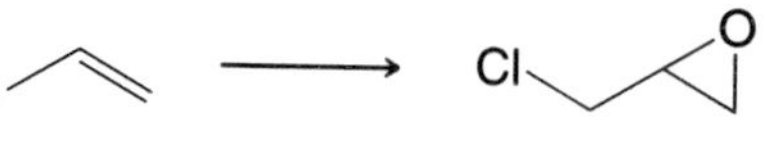

Epichlorohydrin

11.43 Write structures for compounds **A–J** showing stereochemistry where appropriate.

(a)

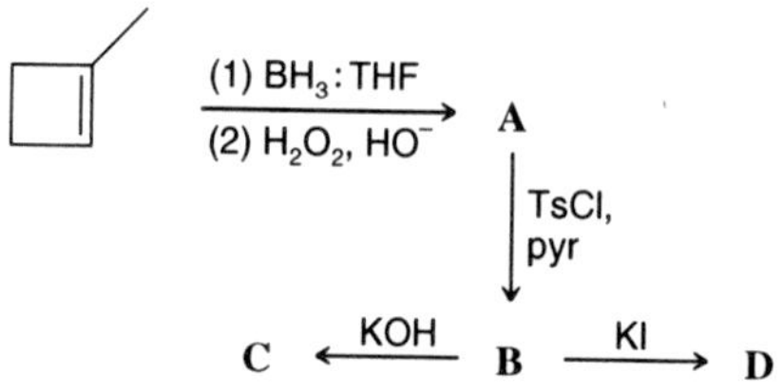

(1) BH₃ : THF
(2) H₂O₂, HO⁻ → **A**

TsCl, pyr

C ←KOH— **B** —KI→ **D**

What is the stereochemical relationship between **A** and **C**?

(b)

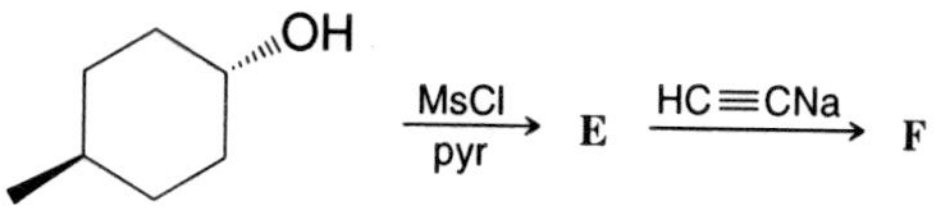

MsCl/pyr → **E** —HC≡CNa→ **F**

(c)

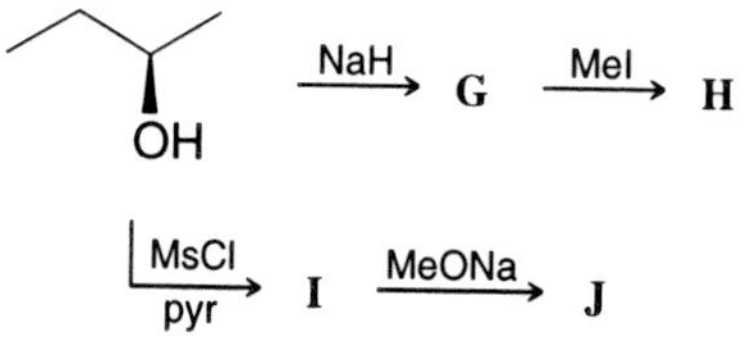

NaH → **G** —MeI→ **H**

MsCl/pyr → **I** —MeONa→ **J**

What is the stereochemical relationship between **H** and **J**?

MECHANISMS

11.44 Write a mechanism that accounts for the following reaction:

HA → + HOH

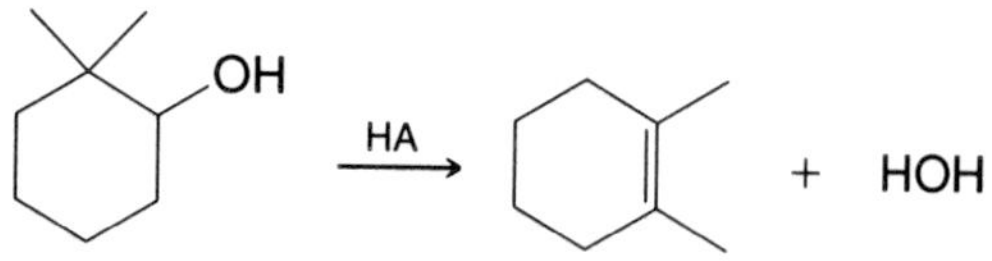

11.45 Propose a reasonable mechanism for the following reaction.

cat. H₂SO₄ →

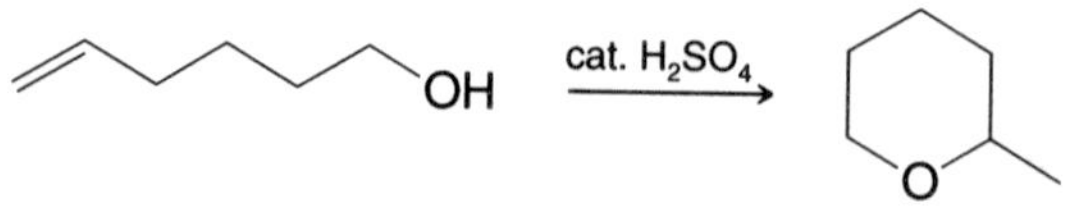

11.46 Propose a reasonable mechanism for the following reaction.

Br₂ → + HBr

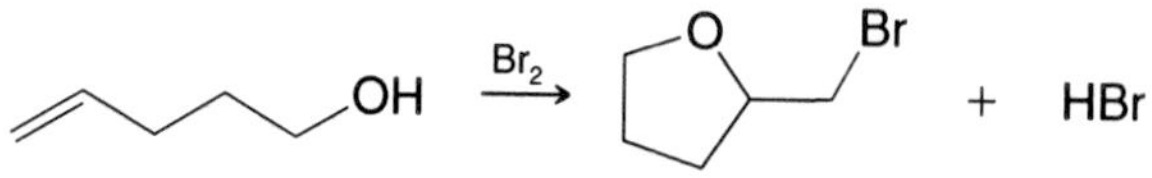

11.47 Propose a reasonable mechanism for the following reaction.

cat. H₃PO₄, EtOH →

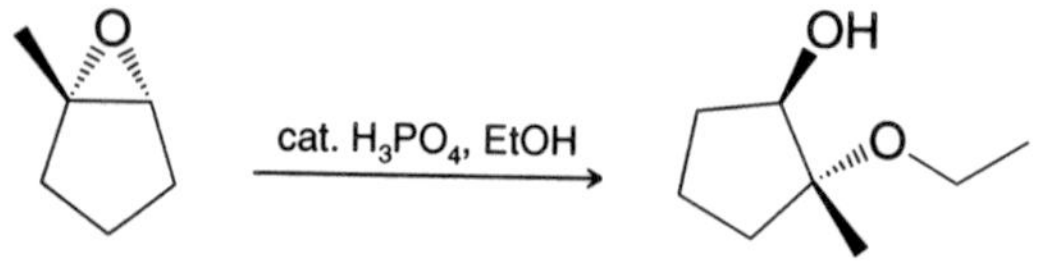

11.48 Vicinal halo alcohols (halohydrins) can be synthesized by treating epoxides with HX. (**a**) Show how you would use this method to synthesize 2-chlorocyclopentanol from cyclopentene. (**b**) Would you expect the product to be *cis*-2-chlorocyclopentanol or *trans*-2-chlorocyclopentanol; that is, would you expect a net syn addition or a net anti addition of —Cl and —OH? Explain.

11.49 Base-catalyzed hydrolysis of the 1,2-chlorohydrin **1** is found to give a chiral glycol **2** with retention of configuration. Propose a reasonable mechanism that would account for this transformation. Include all formal charges and arrows showing the movement of electrons.

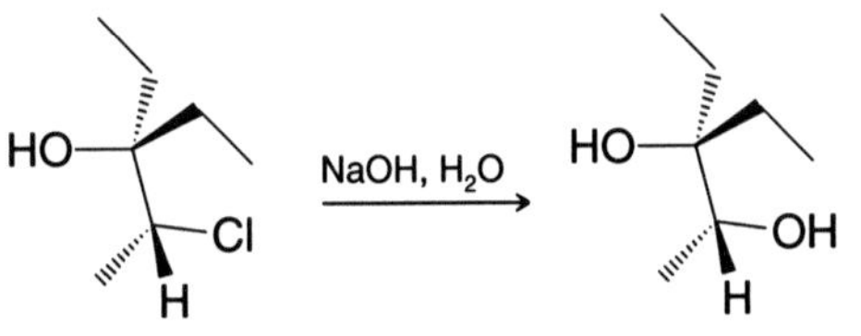

1 **2**

11.50 Compounds of the type 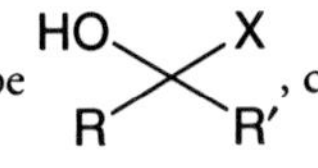

, called α-haloalcohols, are unstable and cannot be isolated. Propose a mechanistic explanation for why this is so.

11.51 While simple alcohols yield alkenes on reaction with dehydrating acids, diols form carbonyl compounds. Rationalize mechanistically the outcome of the following reaction:

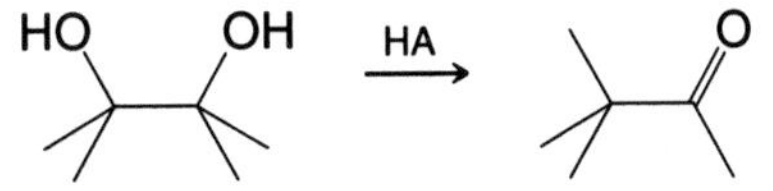

11.52 When the bicyclic alkene **I**, a *trans*-decalin derivative, reacts with a peroxy acid, **II** is the major product. What factor favors the formation of **II** in preference to **III**? (You may find it helpful to build a handheld molecular model.)

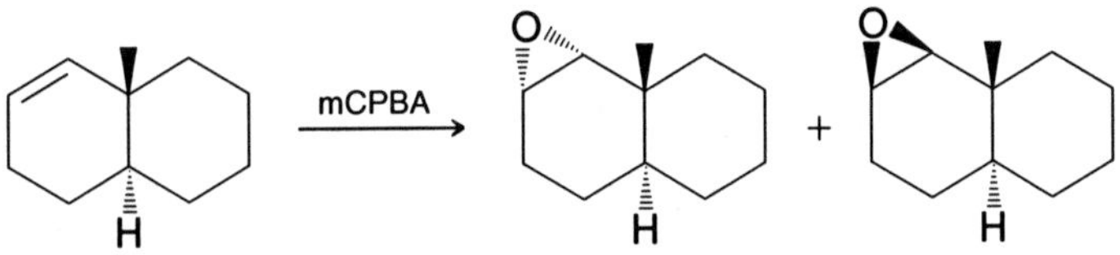

I **II (major)** **III (minor)**

11.53 Use Newman projection formulas for ethylene glycol (1,2-ethanediol) and butane to explain why the gauche conformer of ethylene glycol is expected to contribute more to its ensemble of conformers than would the gauche conformer of butane to its respective set of conformers.

CHALLENGE PROBLEMS

11.54 When the 3-bromo-2-butanol with the stereochemical structure **A** is treated with concentrated HBr, it yields *meso*-2,3-dibromobutane; a similar reaction of the 3-bromo-2-butanol **B** yields (±)-2,3-dibromobutane. This classic experiment performed in 1939 by S. Winstein and H. J. Lucas was the starting point for a series of investigations of what are called *neighboring group effects.* Propose mechanisms that will account for the stereochemistry of these reactions.

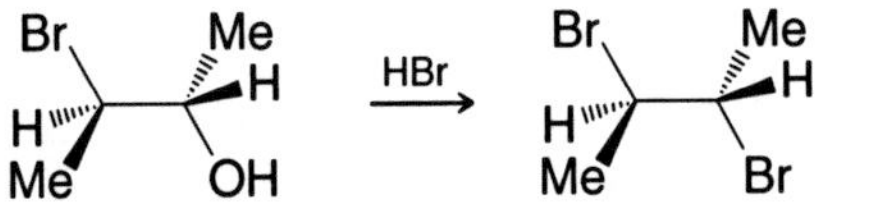

A **2,3-Dibromobutane (meso)**

versus

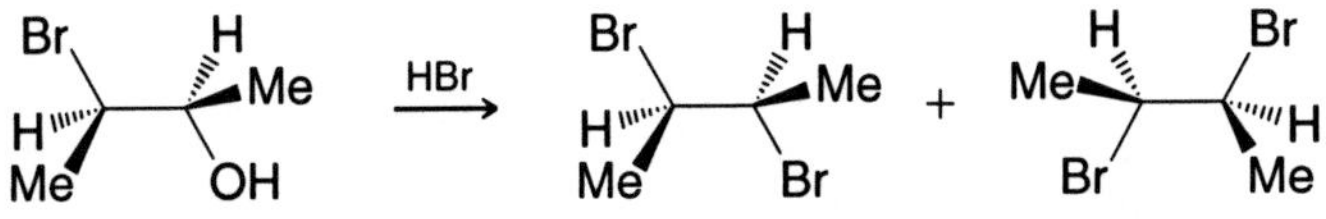

B **2,3-Dibromobutane (racemic)**

11.55 Reaction of an alcohol with thionyl chloride in the presence of a tertiary amine (e.g., pyridine) affords replacement of the OH group by Cl *with inversion of configuration* (Section 11.9). However, if the amine is omitted, the result is usually replacement with retention of configuration. The same chlorosulfite intermediate is involved in both cases. Suggest a mechanism by which this intermediate can give the chlorinated product without inversion.

11.56 Draw all of the stereoisomers that are possible for 1,2,3-cyclopentanetriol. Label their chirality centers and say which are enantiomers and which are diastereomers.

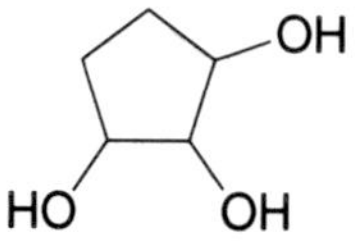

(*Hint*: Some of the isomers contain a "pseudoasymmetric center," one that has two possible configurations, each affording a different stereoisomer, each of which is identical to its mirror image. Such stereoisomers can only be distinguished by the order of attachment of **R** versus **S** groups at the pseudoasymmetric center. Of these the **R** group is given higher priority than the **S**, and this permits assignment of configuration as **r** or **s**, lowercase letters being used to designate the pseudoasymmetry.)

11.57 Dimethyldioxirane (DMDO), whose structure is shown below, is another reagent commonly used for alkene epoxidation. Write a mechanism for the epoxidation of (Z)-2-butene by DMDO, including a possible transition state structure. What is the by-product of a DMDO epoxidation?

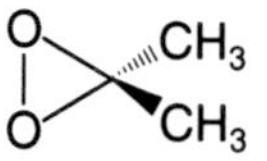

Dimethyldioxirane
(DMDO)

11.58 Two configurations can actually be envisioned for the transition state in the DMDO epoxidation of (Z)-2-butene, based on analogy with geometric possibilities fitting within the general outline for the transition state in a peroxycarboxylic acid epoxidation of (Z)-2-butene. Draw these geometries for the DMDO epoxidation of (Z)-2-butene. Then, open the molecular models on the book's website for these two possible transition state geometries in the DMDO epoxidation of (Z)-2-butene and speculate as to which transition state would be lower in energy.

LEARNING GROUP PROBLEMS

1. Devise two syntheses for *meso*-2,3-butanediol starting with acetylene (ethyne) and methane. Your two pathways should take different approaches during the course of the reactions for controlling the origin of the stereochemistry required in the product.

2. (a) Write as many chemically reasonable syntheses as you can think of for ethyl 2-methylpropyl ether (ethyl isobutyl ether). Be sure that at some point in one or more of your syntheses you utilize the following reagents (not all in the same synthesis, however): PBr_3, $SOCl_2$, *p*-toluenesulfonyl chloride (tosyl chloride), NaH, ethanol, 2-methyl-1-propanol (isobutyl alcohol), concentrated H_2SO_4, $Hg(OAc)_2$, ethene (ethylene).
(b) Evaluate the relative merits of your syntheses on the basis of selectivity and efficiency. (Decide which ones could be argued to be the "best" syntheses and which might be "poorer" syntheses.)

3. Synthesize the compound shown below from methylcyclopentane and 2-methylpropane using those compounds as the source of the carbon atoms and any other reagents necessary. Synthetic tools you might need include Markovnikov or anti-Markovnikov hydration, Markovnikov or anti-Markovnikov hydrobromination, radical halogenation, elimination, and nucleophilic substitution reactions.

[S U M M A R Y   A N D   R E V I E W   T O O L S]

Some Synthetic Connections of Alkenes, Alkynes, Alcohols, Alkyl Halides, and Ethers

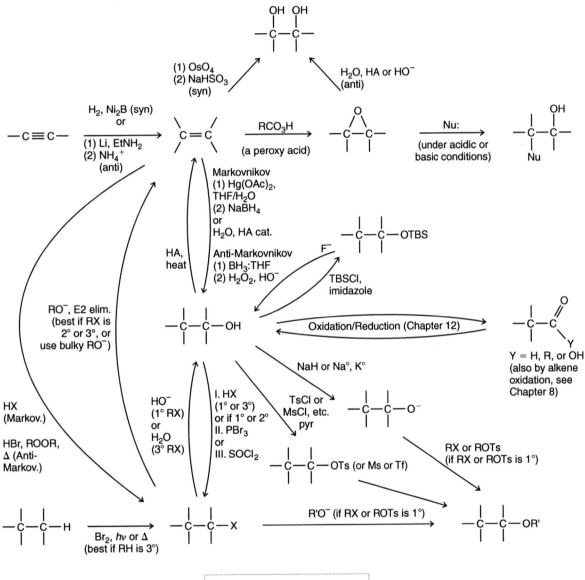

- Alkynes to alkenes
- Alkenes and alcohols
- Alcohols and alkyl halides
- Alkenes and alkyl halides
- Alcohols and ethers
- Alkenes, epoxides, and 1,2-diols
- Alkanes to alkyl halides
- Alcohol silyl protecting group
- Alcohols to carbonyl compounds

481

[ANSWERS TO SELECTED PROBLEMS]

CHAPTER 1

1.15 (a) and (d); (b) and (e); and (c) and (f).

1.27 (a), (c), (d), (f), (g), and (h) have tetrahedral geometry; (b) is linear; (e) is trigonal planar.

1.35 (a), (g), (i), (l), represent different compounds that are not isomeric; (b–e), (h), (j), (m), (n), (o) represent the same compound; (f), (k), (p) represent constitutional isomers.

1.42 (a) The structures differ in the positions of the nuclei. (b) The anions are resonance structures.

1.44 (a) A negative charge; (b) a negative charge; (c) trigonal pyramidal.

CHAPTER 2

2.11 (c) Propyl bromide; (d) isopropyl fluoride; (e) phenyl iodide.

2.14 (a) (b)
(e) diisopropyl ether.

2.25 (a) (b)
(c)

2.29 (a) ketone; (c) 2° alcohol; (e) 2° alcohol.

2.30 (a) 3 alkene groups, and a 2° alcohol; (c) phenyl and 1° amine; (e) phenyl, ester and 3° amine; (g) alkene and 2 ester groups.

2.35 (f)

2.53 Ester

CHAPTER 3

3.3 (a), (c), (d), and (f) are Lewis bases; (b) and (e) are Lewis acids.

3.5 (a) $[H_3O^+] = [HCO_2^-] = .0042\ M$; (b) Ionization = 4.2%.

3.6 (a) $pK_a = 7$; (b) $pK_a = -0.7$; (c) Because the acid with a $pK_a = 5$ has a larger K_a, it is the stronger acid.

3.8 The pK_a of the methylaminium ion is equal to 10.6 (Section 3.6B). Because the pK_a of the anilinium ion is equal to 4.6, the anilinium ion is a stronger acid than the methylaminium ion, and aniline ($C_6H_5NH_2$) is a weaker base than methylamine (CH_3NH_2).

3.14 (a) $CHCl_2CO_2H$ would be the stronger acid because the electron-withdrawing inductive effect of two chlorine atoms would make its hydroxyl proton more positive. (c) CH_2FCO_2H would be the stronger acid because a fluorine atom is more electronegative than a bromine atom and would be more electron withdrawing.

3.28 (a) $pK_a = 3.752$; (b) $K_a = 10^{-13}$.

CHAPTER 4

4.8 (a) (1,1-dimethylethyl)cyclopentane or *tert*-butyl-cyclopentane; (c) butylcyclohexane; (e) 2-chlorocyclopentanol.

4.9 (a) 2-Chlorobicyclo[1.1.0]butane; (c) bicyclo[2.1.1]hexane; (e) 2-methylbicyclo[2.2.2]octane.

4.10 (a) *trans*-3-Heptene; (c) 4-ethyl-2-methyl-1-hexene

4.11

(a)

(c)

(e)

(g) (i)

4.12 1-Hexyne, 2-Hexyne, 3-Hexyne, 4-Methyl-1-pentyne, 4-Methyl-2-pentyne 3,3-Dimethyl-1-butyne

(*R*)-3-Methyl-1-pentyne   (*S*)-3-Methyl-1-pentyne

4.24 (a) 5-ethyl-7-isopropyl-2,3-dimethyldecane; (c) 4-bromo-6-chloro-3-methyloctane; (e) 2-Bromobicyclo[3.3.1]nonane; (g) 5,6-dimethyl-2-heptene

4.39 (a) Pentane would boil higher because its chain is unbranched. (c) 2-Chloropropane because it is more polar and has a higher molecular weight. (e) CH_3COCH_3 because it is more polar.

4.43

(a)

More stable conformation because both alkyl groups are equatorial

(b)

More stable because larger group is equatorial

(c)

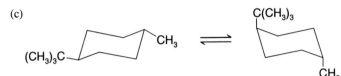

More stable conformation because
both alkyl groups are equatorial

(d)

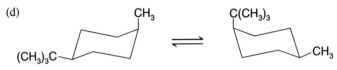

More stable because larger group
is equatorial

CHAPTER 5

5.1 (a) achiral; (c) chiral; (e) chiral.

5.2 (a) Yes; (c) no.

5.3 (a) They are the same. (b) They are enantiomers.

5.7 The following possess a plane of symmetry and are, therefore, achiral: screwdriver, baseball bat, hammer.

5.11

(a) $-Cl > -SH > -OH > -H$

(c) $-OH > -CHO > -CH_3 > -H$

(e) $-OCH_3 > -N(CH_3)_2 > -CH_3 > -H$

5.13 (a) enantiomers; (c) enantiomers.

5.19 (a) diastereomers; (c) no; (e) no.

5.21 (a) represents **A**; (b) represents **C**; (c) represents **B**.

5.23 **B** (2S,3S)-2,3-Dibromobutane; **C** (2R,3S)-2,3-Dibromobutane.

5.40 (a) same; (c) diastereomers; (e) same; (g) diastereomers; (i) same; (k) diastereomers; (m) diastereomers; (o) diastereomers; (q) same.

CHAPTER 6

6.6 (a) The reaction is S_N2 and, therefore, occurs with inversion of configuration. Consequently, the configuration of (+)-2-chlorobutane is opposite [i.e., (S)] to that of (−)-2-butanol [i.e., (R)]. (b) The configuration of (−)-2-iodobutane is (R).

6.14 Protic solvents are formic acid, formamide, ammonia, and ethylene glycol. The others are aprotic.

6.16 (a) CH_3O^-; (c) $(CH_3)_3P$.

6.20 (a) 1-Bromopropane would react more rapidly, because, being a primary halide, it is less hindered. (c) 1-Chlorobutane, because the carbon bearing the leaving group is less hindered than in 1-chloro-2-methylpropane. (e) 1-Chlorohexane because it is a primary halide. Phenyl halides are unreactive in S_N2 reactions.

6.21 (a) Reaction (1) because ethoxide ion is a stronger nucleophile than ethanol; (c) reaction (2) because triphenylphosphine, $(C_6H_5)_3P$, is a stronger nucleophile than triphenylamine. (Phosphorus atoms are larger than nitrogen atoms.)

6.22 (a) Reaction (2) because bromide ion is a better leaving group than chloride ion; (c) reaction (2) because the concentration of the substrate is twice that of reaction (1).

6.26 The better yield is obtained by using the secondary halide, 1-bromo-1-phenylethane, because the desired reaction is E2. Using the primary halide will result in substantial S_N2 reaction as well, producing the alcohol instead of the desired alkene.

6.38 (a) You should use a strong base, such as RO^-, at a higher temperature to bring about an E2 reaction. (b) Here we want an S_N1 reaction. We use ethanol as the solvent *and as the nucleophile*, and we carry out the reaction at a low temperature so that elimination is minimized.

CHAPTER 7

7.4 (a) 2,3-Dimethyl-2-butene would be the more stable because the double bond is tetrasubstituted. (c) *cis*-3-Hexene would be more stable because its double bond is disubstituted.

7.7 (a)

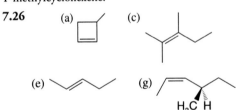

(trisubstituted,   **(monosubstituted,**
more stable)   **less stable)**

Major product   **Minor product**

7.25 (a) We designate the position of the double bond by using the *lower* of the two numbers of the doubly bonded carbon atoms, and the chain is numbered from the end nearer the double bond. The correct name is *trans*-2-pentene. (c) We use the lower number of the two doubly bonded carbon atoms to designate the position of the double bond. The correct name is 1-methylcyclohexene.

7.26

(a)   (c)

(e)   (g)

H_3C H

7.28 (a) (E)-3,5-Dimethyl-2-hexene; (c) 6-methyl-3-heptyne; (e) (3Z,5R)-5-chloro-3-hepten-6-yne.

7.43 Only the deuterium atom can assume the anti coplanar orientation necessary for an E2 reaction to occur.

CHAPTER 8

8.1 2-Bromo-1-iodopropane.

8.8 The order reflects the relative ease with which these alkenes accept a proton and form a carbocation. 2-Methylpropene reacts fastest because it leads to a 3° cation; ethene reacts slowest because it leads to a 1° cation.

8.25 By converting the 3-hexyne to *cis*-3-hexene using H₂/Ni₂B (P-2).

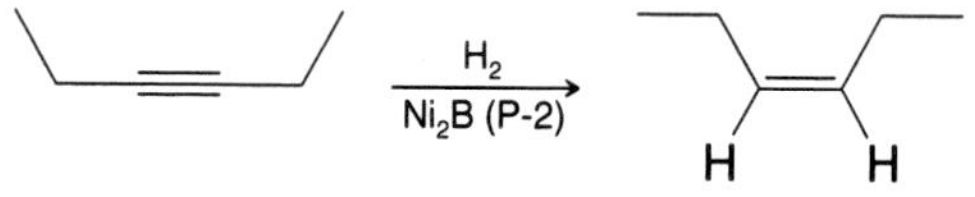

Then, addition of bromine to *cis*-3-hexene will yield (3R,4R), and (3S,4S)-3,4-dibromohexane as a racemic form.

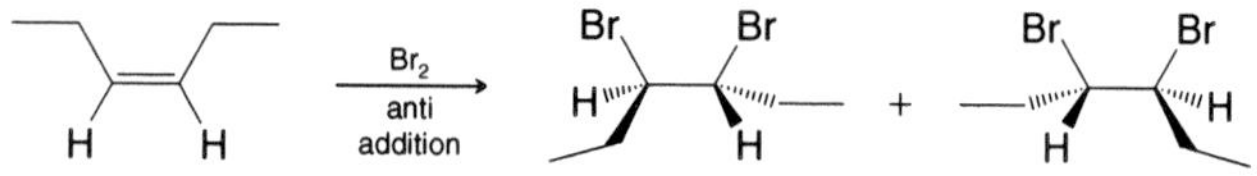

8.26 (a) 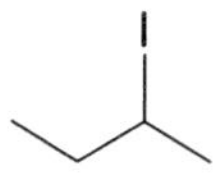 I (b)  (e) 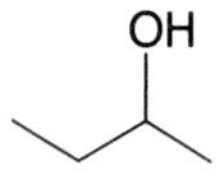 OH

(i) 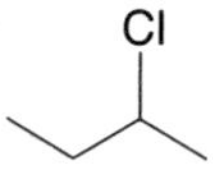 Cl (j) 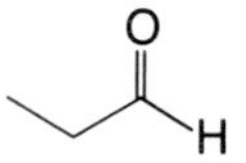 O + HCHO

8.29 (a) 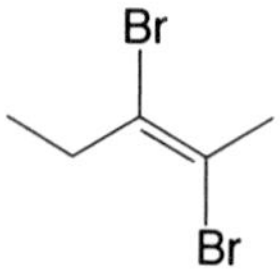 Br (c) 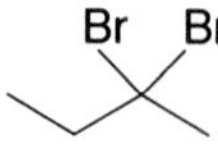 Br Br (e)

8.33 (a) 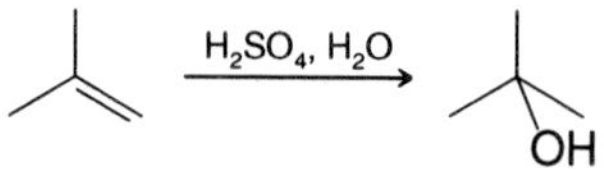 H₂SO₄, H₂O → OH

(c) 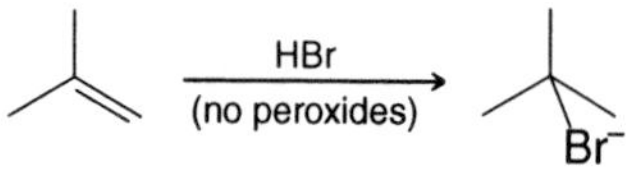 HBr (no peroxides) → Br⁻

(d) 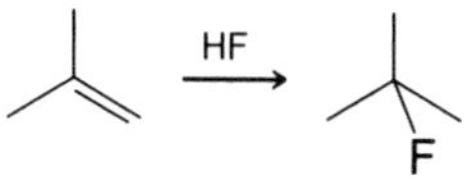 HF → F

8.34 (a)

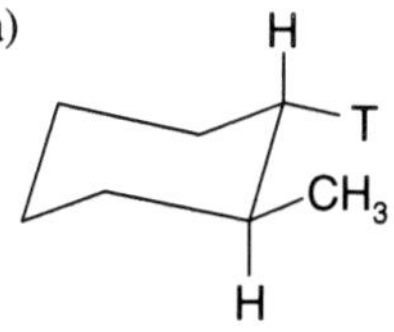

(c)

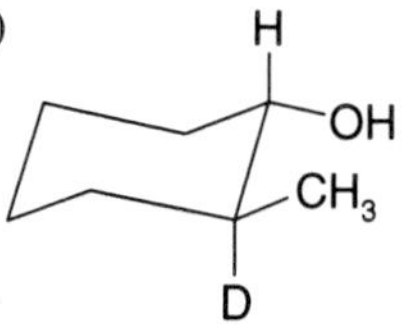

8.64

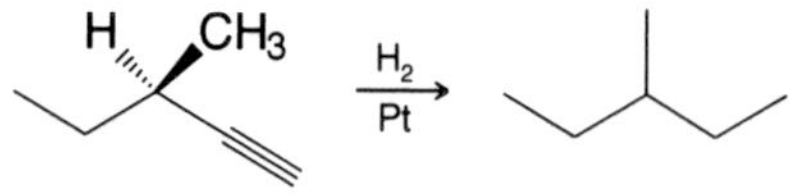

D → H₂/Pt → E

CHAPTER 9

9.4 (a) One; (b) two; (c) two; (d) one; (e) two; (f) two.

9.9 A doublet (3H) at relatively higher frequency; a quartet (1H) at relatively lower frequency.

9.10 A, CH₃CHICH₃; B, CH₃CHCl₂; C, CH₂ClCH₂CH₂Cl

9.25 G, Br

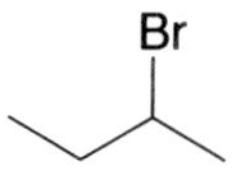

H, Br Br

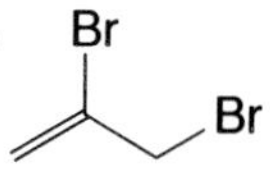

9.28 Q is bicyclo[2.2.1]hepta-2,5-diene.
R is bicyclo[2.2.1]heptane.

9.39 E is phenylacetylene.

CHAPTER 10

10.1

3° > 2° 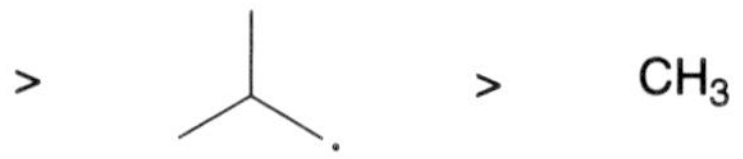 > 1° > CH₃ Methyl

10.8 (a) Cyclopentane; (b) 2,2,3,3-tetramethylbutane

10.9 (a)

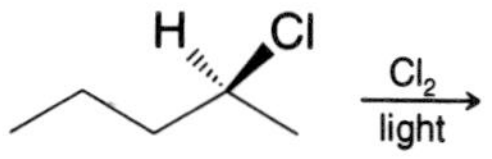

Cl₂/light →

(2S,4S)-2,4-Dichloropentane + (2R,4S)-2,4-Dichloropentane

(c) No, (2R,4S)-2,4-dichloropentane is achiral because it is a meso compound. (It has a plane of symmetry passing through C3.)

(e) Yes, by fractional distillation or by gas–liquid chromatography. (Diastereomers have different physical properties. Therefore, the two isomers would have different vapor pressures.)

10.10 (a) The only fractions that would contain chiral molecules (as enantiomers) would be those containing 1-chloro-2-methylbutane and the two diastereomers of 2-chloro-3-methylbutane. These fractions would not show optical activity, however, because they would contain racemic forms of the enantiomers.

(b) Yes, the fractions containing 1-chloro-2-methylbutane and the two containing the 2-chloro-3-methylbutane diastereomers.

10.25

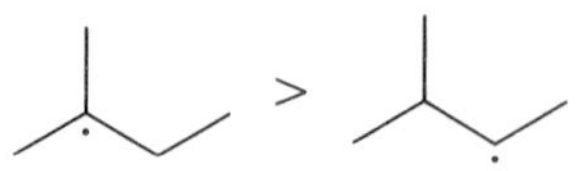

(3°) > (2°)  > (1°) ~ (1°)

484

CHAPTER 11

11.3 (a) [structure: 2-butanol with OH] (b) [structure: 1-butanol with OH] (b) [structure: tert-butanol with OH]

(c) [structure: 1,1-diphenyl-1-propanol] $\Rightarrow$ [structure: methyl propanoate, MeO–C(=O)] + 2 [structure: C₆H₅MgBr]

11.10 Use an alcohol containing labeled oxygen. If all of the labeled oxygen appears in the sulfonate ester, then it can be concluded that the alcohol C—O bond does not break during the reaction.

11.25 (a) 3,3-Dimethyl-1-butanol; (c) 2-methyl-1,4-butanediol; (e) 1-methyl-2-cyclopenten-1-ol.

[structure: methyl propanoate] $\xrightarrow[\text{ether}]{2\ C_6H_5MgBr}$ [structure with OMgBr]

11.26 (a) [structure: cis-CH=CH–CH₂OH]

(c) [cyclopentane structure with H, HO, OH, H]

[structure with OMgBr] $\xrightarrow[H_2O]{NH_4^+}$ [structure with OH]

(e) [structure: pentynyl chain with OH and Cl]

12.11 (a) CH_3CH_3; (b) CH_3CH_2D;

(g) [structure: ether with OEt and propyl]

(c) C_6H_5 [structure with OH] (g) CH_3CH_3 + [structure: hexynyl with OH]

(i) [structure: isopropyl ether]

11.33 (a) CH_3Br + [structure with Br]

12.12 (a) [structure with OH] (b) [structure with OH]

(c) Br [structure] Br

(e) [structure with D]

CHAPTER 12

12.3 (a) $LiAlH_4$; (c) $NaBH_4$

12.4 (a) [pyridinium structure] $\overset{+}{N}HCrO_3Cl^-$ (PCC)/CH_2Cl_2

(c) H_2CrO_4/acetone

12.10
(a) [structure: 1-phenyl-1-propanol with OH] $\Rightarrow$ [structure: propanal, O=CH] +

[structure: C₆H₅MgBr] $\Rightarrow$ [structure: 1-propanol with OH]

[structure: 1-propanol] $\xrightarrow[CH_2Cl_2]{PCC}$ [structure: propanal] [structure: C₆H₅MgBr] $\longrightarrow$

[structure with O⁻] $\xrightarrow[H_2O]{H_3O^+}$ [structure with OH]

CHAPTER 13

13.2 (a) [structure: 2-butene cation] $\longrightarrow$ [structure: allyl cation]

(c) [structure: 1-chloro-2-butene] and [structure: 3-chloro-1-butene with Cl] (racemic)

13.6 (b) 1,4-Cyclohexadiene and 1,4-pentadiene are isolated dienes.

13.18 (a) 1,4-Dibromobutane + *t*-BuOK, and heat; (g) $HC\equiv CCH=CH_2$ + H_2, Ni_2B (P-2).

13.22 (a) 1-Butene + *N*-bromosuccinimide, then *t*-BuOK and heat; (e) cyclopentane + Br_2, *hv*, then *t*-BuOK and heat, then *N*-bromosuccinimide.

13.45 The endo adduct is less stable than the exo, but is produced at a faster rate at 25 °C. At 90 °C the Diels-Alder reaction becomes reversible; an equilibrium is established, and the more stable exo adduct predominates.

CHAPTER 14

14.1 (a) 4-Bromobenzoic acid (or *p*-bromobenzoic acid)
(b) 2-Benzyl-1,3-cyclohexadiene
(c) (2-chloro-2-pentyl) benzene
(d) Phenyl propyl ether

14.7 (a)

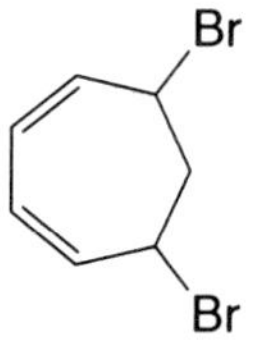

(b)

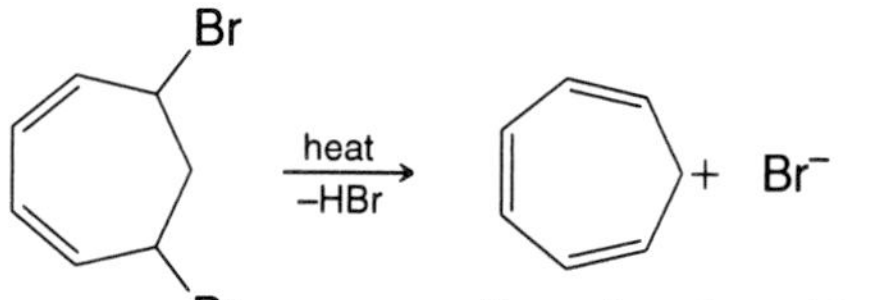

Tropylium bromide

These results suggest that the bonding in tropylium bromide is ionic; that is, it consists of a positive tropylium ion and a negative bromide ion.

14.9 The cyclopropenyl cation.

14.15 A, *o*-bromotoluene; **B**, *p*-bromotoluene; **C**, *m*-bromotoluene; **D**, benzyl bromide.

14.23 Hückel's rule should apply to both pentalene and heptalene. Pentalene's antiaromaticity can be attributed to its having 8 π electrons. Heptalene's lack of aromaticity can be attributed to its having 12 π electrons. Neither 8 nor 12 is a Hückel number.

14.25 The bridging —CH$_2$— group causes the 10 π electron ring system to become planar. This allows the ring to become aromatic.

14.28 (a) The cyclononatetraenyl anion, with 10 π electrons, obeys Hückel's rule.

14.31 A,   **B**, 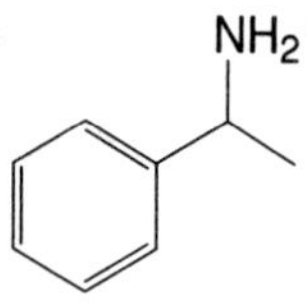   **C**,

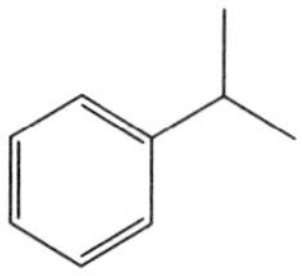

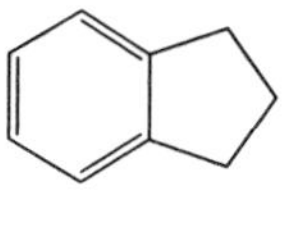

14.33 F,

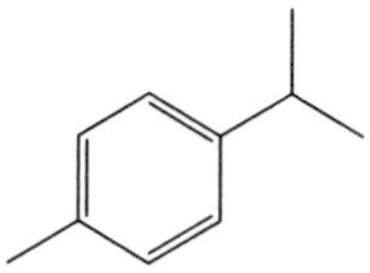

CHAPTER 15

15.6 If the methyl group had no directive effect on the incoming electrophile, we would expect to obtain the products in purely statistical amounts. Since there are two ortho hydrogen atoms, two meta hydrogen atoms, and one para hydrogen, we would expect to get 40% ortho (2/5), 40% meta (2/5), and 20% para (1/5). Thus, we would expect that only 60% of the mixture of mononitrotoluenes would have the nitro group in the ortho or para position. And, we would expect to obtain 40% of *m*-nitrotoluene. In actuality, we get 96% of combined *o*- and *p*-nitrotoluene and only 4% *m*-nitrotoluene. This result shows the ortho–para directive effect of the methyl group.

15.9 (b) Structures such as the following compete with the benzene ring for the oxygen electrons, making them less available to the benzene ring.

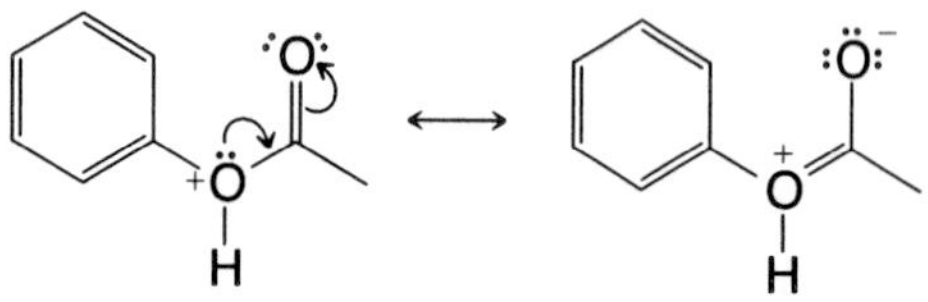

(d) Structures such as the following compete with the benzene ring for the nitrogen electrons, making them less available to the benzene ring.

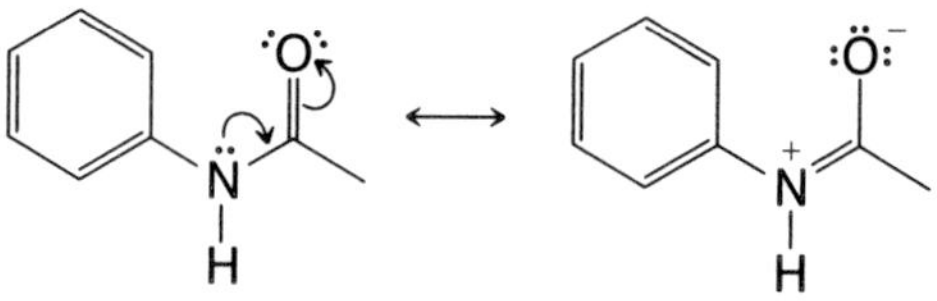

15.32

(a)

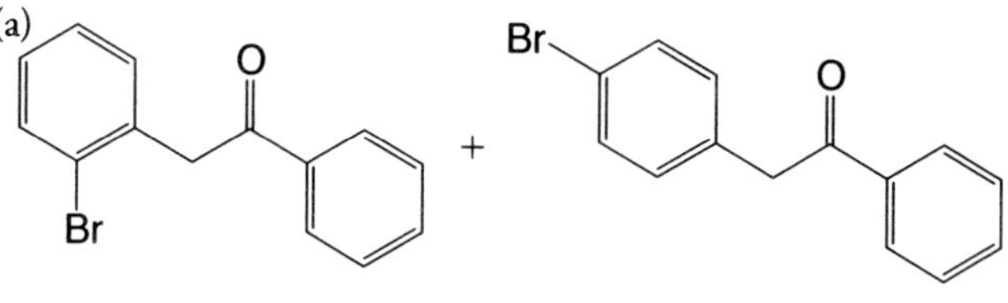

(c)

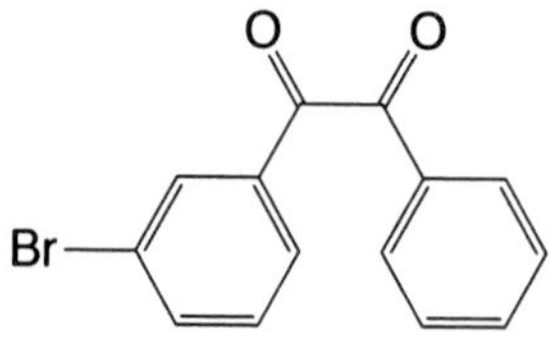

15.33 (a)

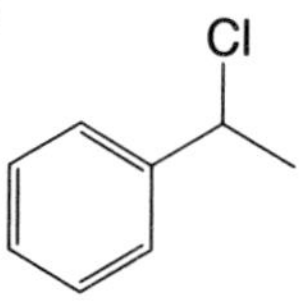

(c)

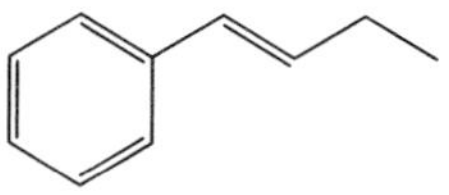

(e)

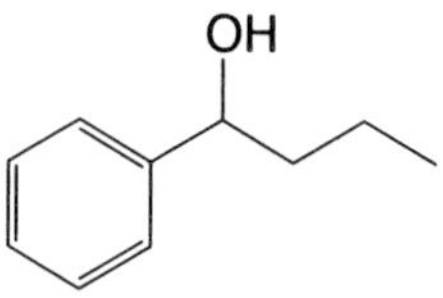

(g)

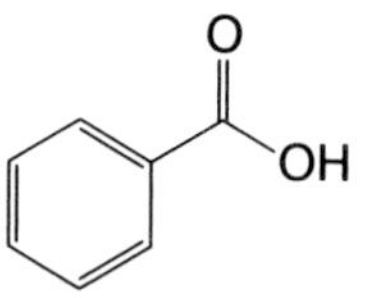

CHAPTER 16

16.2 (a) 1-Pentanol; **(c)** pentanal; **(e)** benzyl alcohol.

16.6 A hydride ion.

16.17 (b) CH$_3$CH$_2$Br + (C$_6$H$_5$)$_3$P, then strong base, then C$_6$H$_5$COCH$_3$; **(d)** CH$_3$I + (C$_6$H$_5$)$_3$P, then strong base, then cyclopentanone; **(f)** CH$_2$=CHCH$_2$Br + (C$_6$H$_5$)$_3$P, then strong base, then C$_6$H$_5$CHO.

16.23 (a) CH$_3$CH$_2$CH$_2$OH; **(c)** CH$_3$CH$_2$CH$_2$OH **(h)** CH$_3$CH$_2$CH=CHCH$_3$; **(j)** CH$_3$CH$_2$CO$_2^-$NH$_4^+$ + Ag↓ **(l)** CH$_3$CH$_2$CH=NNHCONH$_2$; **(n)** CH$_3$CH$_2$CO$_2^-$

16.49 X is

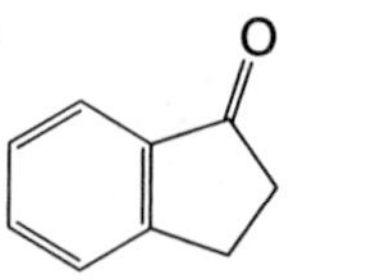

16.50 Y is 1-phenyl-2-butanone; **Z** is 4-phenyl-2-butanone.

CHAPTER 17

17.3 (a) CH$_2$FCO$_2$H; (c) CH$_3$CH$_2$CHFCO$_2$H;

(e)

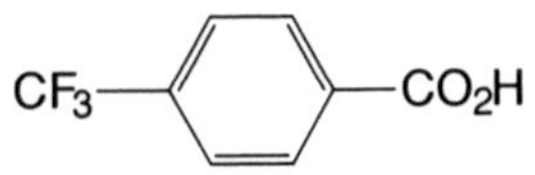

17.6 (a) C$_6$H$_5$CH$_2$Br + Mg in diethyl ether, then CO$_2$, then H$_3$O$^+$;
(c) CH$_2$=CHCH$_2$Br + Mg in diethyl ether, then CO$_2$, then H$_3$O$^+$.

17.7 (a), (c), and (e).

17.9 In the carboxyl group of benzoic acid.

17.14 (a) (CH$_3$)$_3$CCO$_2$H + SOCl$_2$, then NH$_3$, then P$_4$O$_{10}$, heat;
(b)

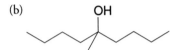

17.22 (a)

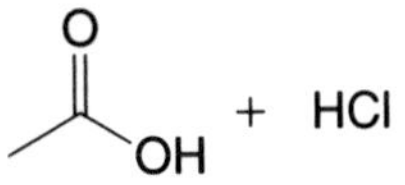

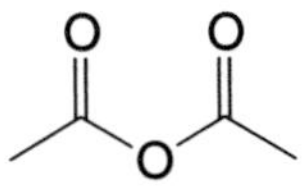

17.46 (a) Diethyl succinate; (c) ethyl phenylacetate; (e) ethyl chloroacetate.

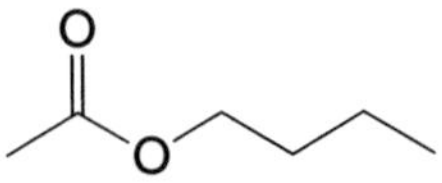

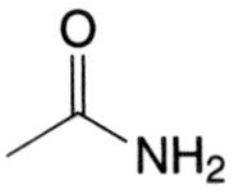

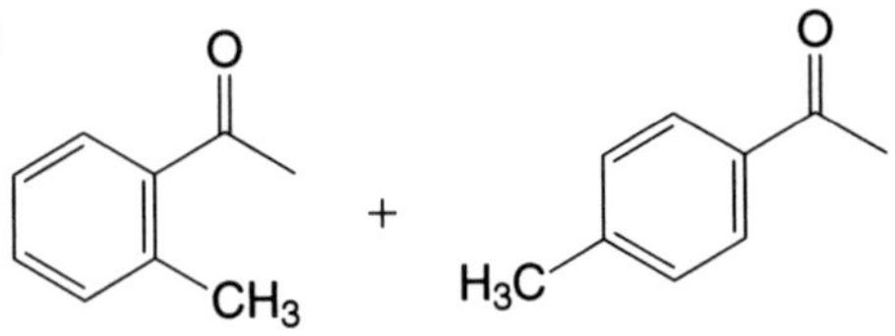

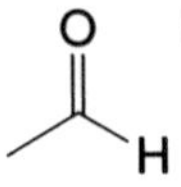

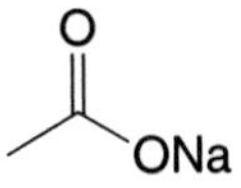

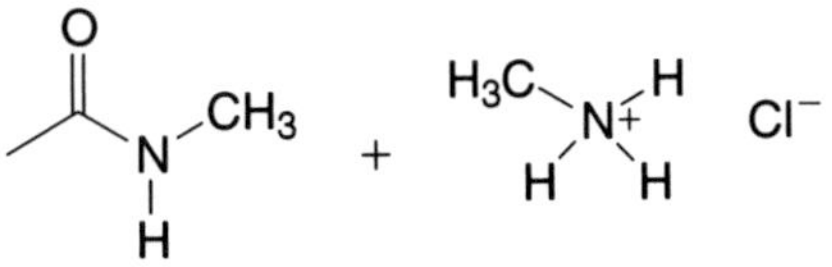

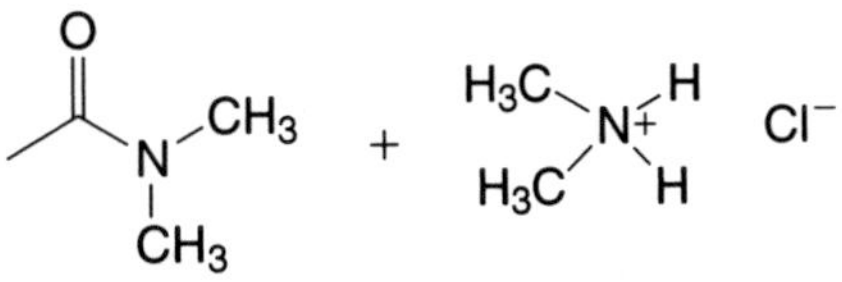

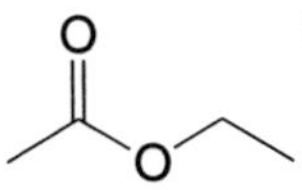

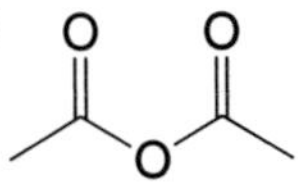

17.47 **X** is diethyl malonate.

CHAPTER 18

18.1 The enol form is phenol. It is especially stable because it is aromatic.

18.2 No. does not have a hydrogen attached to its α-carbon atom (which is a chirality center) and thus enol formation involving the chirality center is not possible.

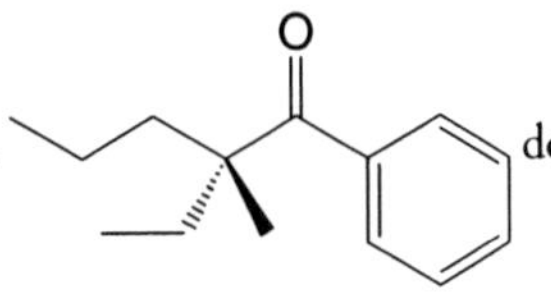

With the chirality center is a β carbon and thus enol formation does not affect it.

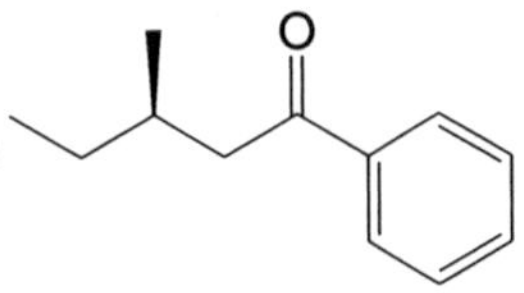

18.5 Base is consumed as the reaction takes place. A catalyst, by definition, is not consumed.

18.8 (a) Reactivity is the same as with any S$_N$2 reaction. With primary halides substitution is highly favored, with secondary halides elimination competes with substitution, and with tertiary halides elimination is the exclusive course of the reaction.
(b) Acetoacetic ester and 2-methylpropene. (c) Bromobenzene is unreactive toward nucleophilic substitution.

18.10 Working backward

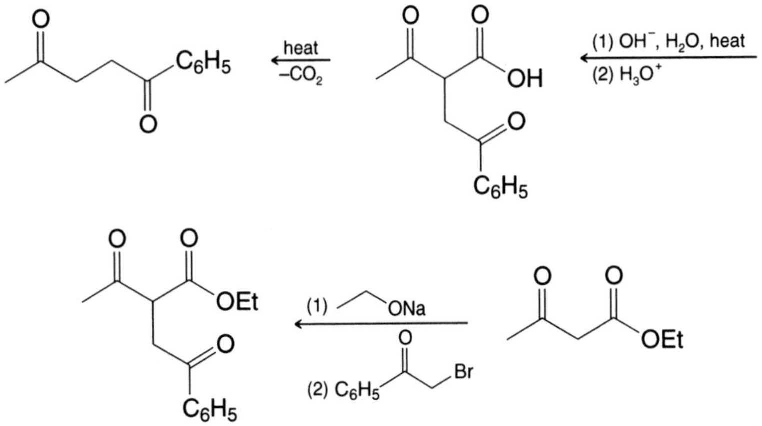

18.17 In a polar solvent, such as water, the keto form is stabilized by solvation. When the interaction with the solvent becomes minimal, the enol form achieves stability by internal hydrogen bonding.

18.25 (b) **D** is racemic *trans*-1,2-cyclopentanedicarboxylic acid, **E** is *cis*-1,2-cyclopentanedicarboxylic acid, a meso compound.

CHAPTER 19

19.3 (a)

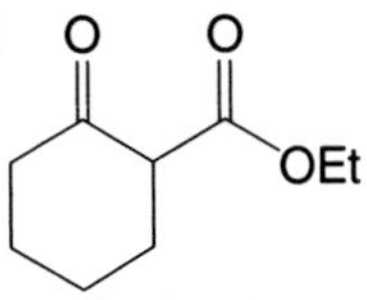

(b) To undergo a Dieckmann condensation, diethyl 1,5-pentanedioate would have to form a highly strained four-membered ring.

19.5 (a)

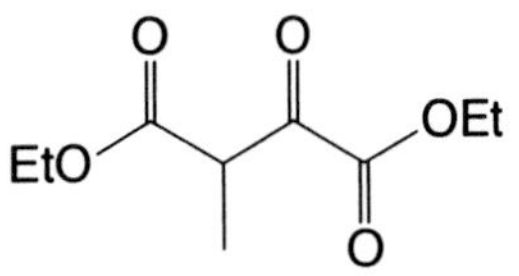

(b)

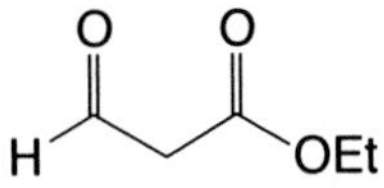

19.11

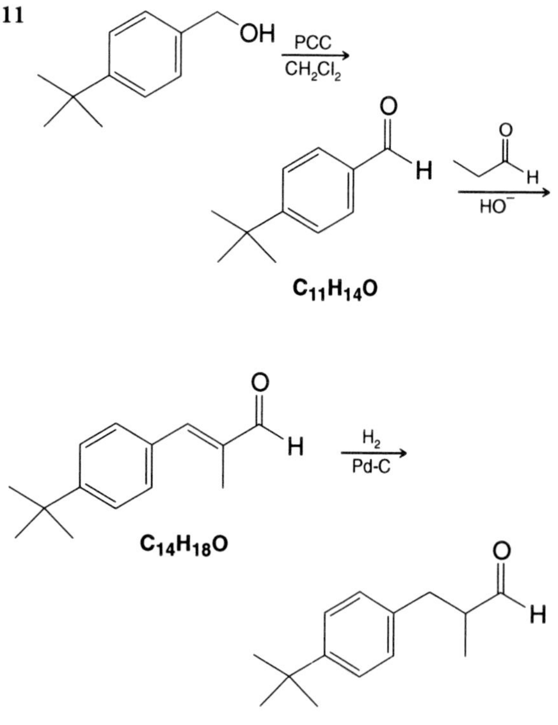

$C_{11}H_{14}O$

$C_{14}H_{18}O$

Lily aldehyde ($C_{14}H_{20}O$)

19.17

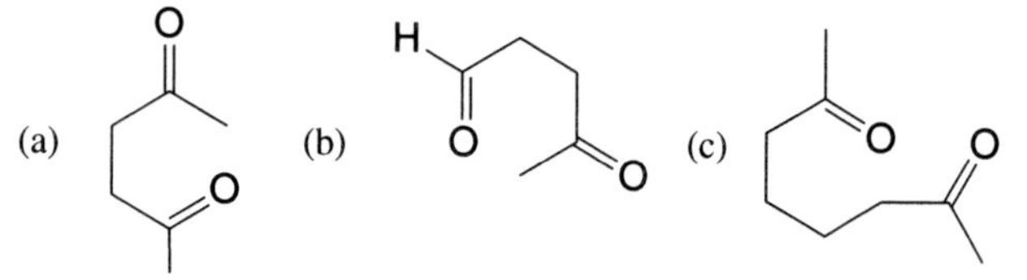

(a) (b) (c)

Notice that starting compounds are drawn so as to indicate which atoms are involved in the cyclization reaction.

19.19

(a)

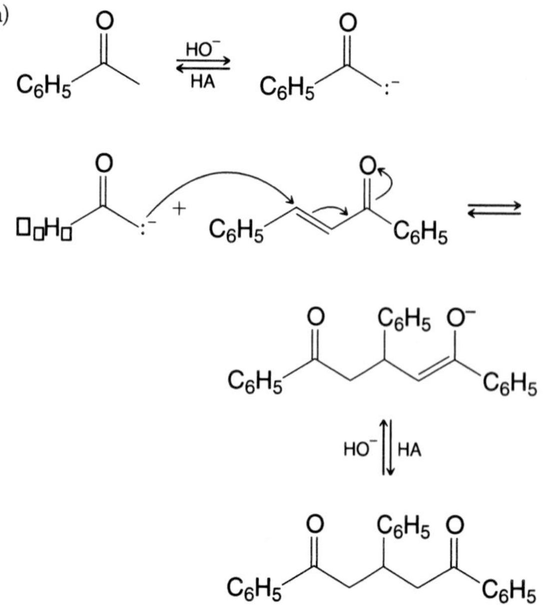

(b)

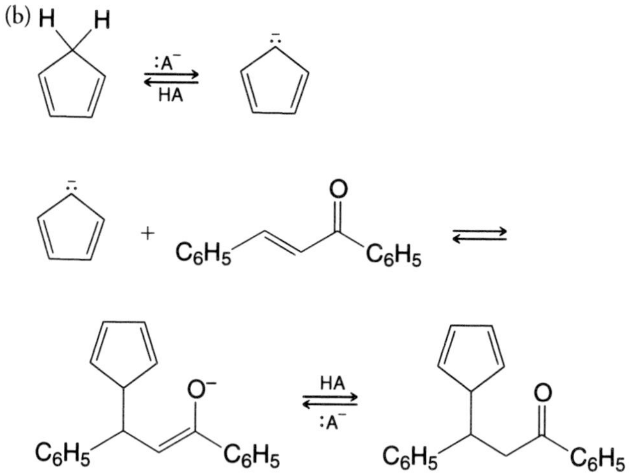

19.50 (a) CH_2=$C(CH_3)CO_2CH_3$; (b) $KMnO_4$, HO^-; H_3O^+; (c) CH_3OH, HA; (d) CH_3ONa, then H_3O^+

(e) and (f)

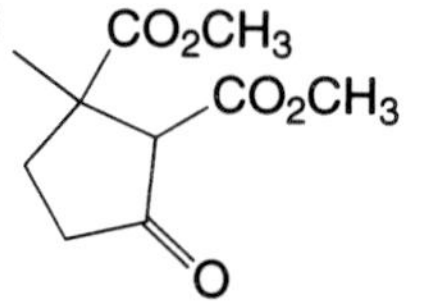

and

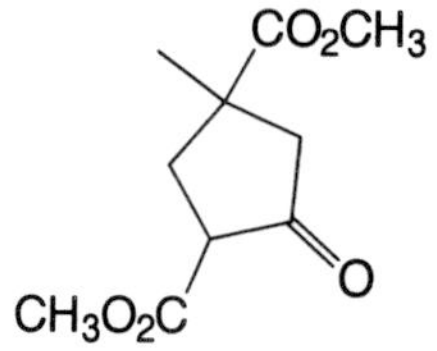

(g) HO^-, H_2O, then H_3O^+; (h) heat ($-CO_2$); (i) CH_3OH, HA;

(j)

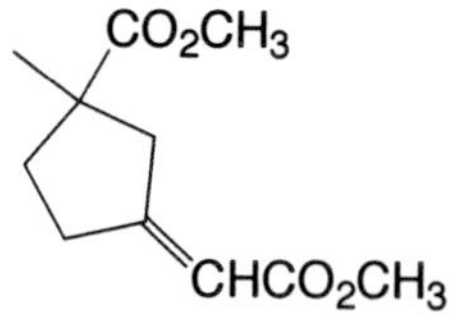

(k) H_2, Pt; (m) CH_3ONa, then H_3O^+; (n) 2 $NaNH_2$ + 2 CH_3I

CHAPTER 20

20.5 (a) $CH_3(CH_2)_3CHO + NH_3 \xrightarrow[LiBH_3CN]{H_2, Ni} CH_3(CH_2)_3CH_2NH_2$
(c) $CH_3(CH_2)_4CHO + C_6H_5NH_2 \longrightarrow$

$CH_3(CH_2)_4CH_2NHC_6H_5$

20.6 The reaction of a secondary halide with ammonia is almost always accompanied by some elimination.

20.7 (a) Methoxybenzene + HNO_3 + H_2SO_4, then Fe + HCl;
(b) Methoxybenzene + CH_3COCl + $AlCl_3$, then NH_3 + H_2 + Ni;
(c) toluene + Cl_2 and light, then $(CH_3)_3N$; (d) p-nitrotoluene + $KMnO_4$ + HO^-, then H_3O^+, then $SOCl_2$ followed by NH_3, then NaOBr (Br_2 in NaOH); (e) toluene + N-bromosuccinimide then KCN, then $LiAlH_4$.

20.12 p-Nitroaniline + Br_2 + Fe, followed by $H_2SO_4/NaNO_2$ followed by CuBr, then H2/Pt, then $H_2SO_4/NaNO_2$ followed by H_3PO_2.

20.45 **W** is N-benzyl-N-ethylaniline.

CHAPTER 21

21.1 The electron-releasing group (i.e., —CH$_3$) changes the charge distribution in the molecule so as to make the hydroxyl oxygen less positive, causing the proton to be held more strongly; it also destabilizes the phenoxide anion by intensifying its negative charge. These effects make the substituted phenol less acidic than phenol itself.

Electron-releasing — CH$_3$ destabilizes the anion more than the acid. pKa is larger than for phenol.

21.4 (a) The para-sulfonated phenol. (b) For ortho sulfonation.

21.9 (a) (b)

21.10 That *o*-chlorotoluene leads to the formation of two products (*o*-cresol and *m*-cresol), when submitted to the conditions used in the Dow process, suggests that an elimination-addition mechanism takes place.

21.11 2-Bromo-1,3-dimethylbenzene, because it has no *o*-hydrogen atom, cannot undergo an elimination. Its lack of reactivity toward sodium amide in liquid ammonia suggests that those compounds (e.g., bromobenzene) that do react, react by a mechanism that begins with an elimination.

21.14 (a) 4-Fluorophenol because a fluorine substituent is more electron withdrawing than a methyl group. (e) 4-Fluorophenol because fluorine is more electronegative than bromine.

21.16 (a) 4-Chlorophenol will dissolve in aqueous NaOH; 4-chloro-1-methylbenzene will not. (c) Phenyl vinyl ether will react with bromine by addition (thus decolorizing the solution); ethyl phenyl ether will not. (e) 4-Ethylphenol will dissolve in aqueous NaOH; ethyl phenyl ether will not.

CHAPTER 22

22.1 (a) Two; (b) two; (c) four.

22.5 Acid catalyzes hydrolysis of the glycosidic (acetal) group.

22.9 (a) 2 CH$_3$CHO, one molar equivalent HIO$_4$; (b) HCHO + HCO$_2$H + CH$_3$CHO, two molar equivalents HIO$_4$; (c) HCHO + OHCCH(OCH$_3$)$_2$, one molar equivalent HIO$_4$; (d) HCHO + HCO$_2$H + CH$_3$CO$_2$H, two molar equivalents HIO$_4$; (e) 2 CH$_3$CO$_2$H + HCO$_2$H, two molar equivalents HIO$_4$

22.18 D-(+)-Glucose.

22.23 One anomeric form of D-mannose is dextrorotatory ($[\alpha]_D = +29.3$), the other is levorotatory ($[\alpha]_D = -17.0$).

22.24 The microorganism selectively oxidizes the —CHOH group of D-glucitol that corresponds to C5 of D-glucose.

22.27 **A** is D-altrose; **B** is D-talose, **C** is D-galactose

CHAPTER 23

23.5 Br$_2$ would react with geraniol (discharging the bromine color) but would not react with menthol.

23.12 (a) C$_2$H$_5$OH, HA, heat; or SOCl$_2$, then C$_2$H$_5$OH; (d) SOCl$_2$, then (CH$_3$)$_2$NH; (g) SOCl$_2$, then LiAlH[OC(CH$_3$)$_3$]$_3$

23.15 Elaidic acid is *trans*-9-octadecenoic acid.

23.19 **A** is CH$_3$(CH$_2$)$_5$C≡CNa

B is CH$_3$(CH$_2$)$_5$C≡CCH$_2$(CH$_2$)$_7$CH$_2$Cl

C is CH$_3$(CH$_2$)$_5$C≡CCH$_2$(CH$_2$)$_7$CH$_2$CN

E is CH$_3$(CH$_2$)$_5$C≡CCH$_2$(CH$_2$)$_7$CH$_2$CO$_2$H

Vaccenic acid is

23.20 **F** is FCH$_2$(CH$_2$)$_6$CH$_2$C≡CH

G is FCH$_2$(CH$_2$)$_6$CH$_2$C≡C(CH$_2$)$_7$Cl

H is FCH$_2$(CH$_2$)$_6$CH$_2$C≡C(CH$_2$)$_7$CN

I is FCH$_2$(CH$_2$)$_7$C≡C(CH$_2$)$_7$CO$_2$H

CHAPTER 24

24.5 The labeled amino acid no longer has a basic —NH$_2$ group; it is, therefore, insoluble in aqueous acid.

24.8 Glutathione is

24.22 Arg·Pro·Pro·Gly·Phe·Ser·Pro·Phe·Arg

24.23 Val·Leu·Lys·Phe·Ala·Glu·Ala

CHAPTER 25

25.2 (a) The nucleosides have an *N*-glycosidic linkage that (like an *O*-glycosidic linkage) is rapidly hydrolyzed by aqueous acid, but one that is stable in aqueous base.

25.4 (a) The isopropylidene group is part of a cyclic acetal. (b) By treating the nucleoside with acetone and a trace of acid.

25.7 (b) Thymine would pair with adenine, and, therefore, adenine would be introduced into the complementary strand where guanine should occur.

25.9

Uracil (in mRNA)   **Adenine (in DNA)**

25.10 (a) ACC CCC AAA AUG UCC *m*RNA

(b) T P K M S Amino acids

(c) UGC GGC UUU UAC AGC Anticodons

[GLOSSARY]

A

Absolute configuration (Section 5.15A): The actual arrangement of groups in a molecule. The absolute configuration of a molecule can be determined by X-ray analysis or by relating the configuration of a molecule, using reactions of known stereochemistry, to another molecule whose absolute configuration is known.

Absorption spectrum (Section 13.8B): A plot of the wavelength (λ) of a region of the spectrum versus the absorbance (A) at each wavelength. The absorbance at a particular wavelength (A_λ) is defined by the equation $A_\lambda = \log(I_R/I_S)$, where I_R is the intensity of the reference beam and I_S is the intensity of the sample beam.

Acetal (Section 16.7B): A functional group, consisting of a carbon bonded to alkoxy groups [i.e., $RCH(OR')_2$ or $R_2C(OR')_2$], derived by adding 2 molar equivalents of an alcohol to an aldehyde or ketone. An acetal synthesized from a ketone is sometimes called a ketal.

Acetoacetic ester synthesis (Section 18.6): A sequence of reactions involving removal of the α-hydrogen of ethyl 3-oxobutanoate (ethyl acetoacetate, also called "acetoacetic ester"), creating a resonance-stabilized anion which then can serve as a nucleophile in an S_N2 reaction. The α-carbon can be substituted twice; the ester functionality can be converted into α carboxylic acid which, after decarboxylation, yields a substituted ketone.

Acetonide (Section 22.5E): A cyclic acetal formed from acetone.

Acetylene (Sections 1.14, 7.1, and 7.11): A common name for ethyne.

Acetylenic hydrogen atom (Sections 4.6, and 7.9): A hydrogen atom attached to a carbon atom that is bonded to another carbon atom by a triple bond.

Achiral molecule (Sections 5.3 and 5.4): A molecule that is superposable on its mirror image. Achiral molecules lack handedness and are incapable of existing as a pair of enantiomers.

Acid strength (Section 3.5): The strength of an acid is related to its acidity constant, K_a or to its pK_a. The larger the value of its K_a or the smaller the value of its pK_a, the stronger is the acid.

Acidity constant, K_a (Section 3.5A): An equilibrium constant related to the strength of an acid. For the reaction,

$$HA + H_2O \rightleftharpoons H_3O^+ + A^-$$

$$K_a = \frac{[H_3O^+][A^-]}{[HA]}$$

Activating group (Sections 15.10, 15.10D): A group that when present on a benzene ring causes the ring to be more reactive in electrophilic substitution than benzene itself.

Activation energy, E_{act} (See **Energy of activation** and Section 10.5A)

Active hydrogen compounds or *active methylene compounds* (Section 18.8): Compounds in which two electron-withdrawing groups are attached to the same carbon atom (a methylene or methane carbon). The electron-withdrawing groups enhance the acidity of the hydrogens on carbon; these hydrogens are easily removed, creating a resonance-stabilized nucleophilic anion.

Active site (Section 24.9): The location in an enzyme where a substrate binds.

Acylation (Section 15.7): The introduction of an acyl group into a molecule.

Acyl compounds (Section 17.1): A compound containing the group $(R-C=O)-$, usually derived from a carboxylic acid, such as an ester, acid halide (acyl halide), amide, or carboxylic acid anhydride.

Acyl group (Section 15.7): The general name for groups with the structure $RCO-$ or $ArCO-$.

Acyl halide (Section 15.7): Also called an *acid halide*. A general name for compounds with the structure $RCOX$ or $ArCOX$.

Acylium ion (Sections 9.16C and 15.7): The resonance-stabilized cation:

$$R-\overset{+}{C}=\overset{..}{O}: \longleftrightarrow R-C\equiv\overset{+}{O}:$$

Acyl transfer reactions (Section 17.4): A reaction in which a new acyl compound is formed by a nucleophilic addition-elimination reaction at a carbonyl carbon bearing a leaving group.

Addition polymer (Section 10.11 and Special Topic B in *WileyPLUS*): A polymer that results from a stepwise addition of monomers to a chain (usually through a chain reaction) with no loss of other atoms or molecules in the process. Also called a chain-growth polymer.

Addition reaction (Sections Chapter 8 intro, 8.1–8.9, 8.11, 8.12, 12.1A, 16.6B, and 17.4): A reaction that results in an increase in the number of groups attached to a pair of atoms joined by a double or triple bond. An addition reaction is the opposite of an elimination reaction.

Adduct (Section 13.10): The product formed by a Diels-Alder [4 + 2] cycloaddition reaction, so called because two compounds (a *diene* and a *dienophile*) are added together to form the product.

Aglycone (Section 22.4): The alcohol obtained by hydrolysis of a glycoside.

Aldaric acid (Section 22.6C): An α,ω-dicarboxylic acid that results from oxidation of the aldehyde group and the terminal 1° alcohol group of an aldose.

Alditol (Section 22.7): The alcohol that results from the reduction of the aldehyde or keto group of an aldose or ketose.

Aldol (Section 19.4): A common name for 3-hydroxybutanal, which contains both *ald*ehyde and an alco*hol* functional groups. Aldol is formed from the *aldol reaction* (see below) of ethanal (acetaldehyde) with itself.

GL-1

Aldol additions (Section 19.4): See **Aldol reaction** and **Aldol condensation**.

Aldol condensation (Sections 19.1 and 19.4): An aldol reaction that forms an α,β-unsaturated product by dehydration of the β-hydroxy aldehyde or ketone aldol product.

Aldol reactions (Sections 19.4–19.6): Reactions in which the enol or enolate ion of an aldehyde or ketone reacts with the carbonyl group of the same or a different aldehyde or ketone, creating a β-hydroxy aldehyde or ketone and a new carbon-carbon σ-bond.

Aldonic acid (Section 22.6C): A monocarboxylic acid that results from oxidation of the aldehyde group of an aldose.

Aliphatic compound (Section 14.1): A nonaromatic compound such as an alkane, cycloalkane, alkene, or alkyne.

Alkaloid (Special Topic F in *WileyPLUS*): A naturally occurring basic compound that contains an amino group. Most alkaloids have profound physiological effects.

Alkanes (Sections 2.1, 2.1A, 4.1–4.3, 4.7, and 4.16): Hydrocarbons having only single (σ) bonds between carbon atoms. Acyclic alkanes have the general formula C_nH_{2n+2}. Monocyclic alkanes have the general formula of C_nH_{2n}. Alkanes are said to be "saturated" because $C—C$ single bonds cannot react to add hydrogen to the molecule.

Alkanide (Section 7.8A): An alkyl anion, $R{:}^-$, or alkyl species that reacts as though it were an alkyl anion.

Alkenes (Sections 2.1, 2.1B, 4.1, and 4.5): Hydrocarbons having at least one double bond between carbon atoms. Acyclic alkenes have the general formula C_nH_{2n}. Monocyclic alkenes have the general formula of C_nH_{2n-2}. Alkenes are said to be "unsaturated" because their $C{=}C$ double bonds can react to add hydrogen to the molecule, yielding an alkane.

Alkenyl halides (Section 6.1): An organic halide in which the halogen atom is bonded to an alkene carbon.

Alkylation (Sections 7.11A, 15.6, and 18.4C): The introduction of an alkyl group into a molecule.

Alkyl group (See **R**) (Sections 2.4A and 4.3A): The designation given to a fragment of a molecule hypothetically derived from an alkane by removing a hydrogen atom. Alkyl group names end in "yl." Example: the methyl group, $CH_3—$, is derived from methane, CH_4.

Alkyl halide (Section 6.1): An organic halide in which the halogen atom is bonded to an alkyl carbon.

Alkynes (Sections 2.1, 2.1C, 4.1, and 4.6): Hydrocarbons having at least one triple bond between carbon atoms. Acyclic alkynes have the general formula C_nH_{2n-2}. Monocyclic alkynes have the general formula of C_nH_{2n+4}. Alkynes are said to be "unsaturated" because $C{\equiv}C$ triple bonds can react to add two molecules of hydrogen to the molecule, yielding an alkane.

Allyl group (Section 4.5): The $CH_2—CHCH_2—$ group.

Allylic carbocation (Sections 13.1, 13.9, and 15.15): A substructure involving a three-carbon delocalized carbocation in which the positively charged carbon is adjacent to a carbon-carbon double bond in each of two contributing resonance structures.

Allylic group (Section 10.8): An atom or group that is bonded to an sp^3-hybridized carbon adjacent to an alkene double bond.

Allylic position (Section 10.8): The location of a group that is bonded to an sp^3-hybridized carbon adjacent to an alkene double bond.

Allylic substitution (Section 10.8): The replacement of a group at an allylic position.

Allyl (propenyl cation) (Section 13.3): The carbocation formally related to propene by removal of a proton from its methyl group. The two contributing resonance structures of the delocalized carbocation each include a positive charge on a carbon adjacent to the double bond, such that a p orbital on each of the three carbons overlaps to delocalize positive charge to each end of the allyl system.

Allyl radical (Sections 10.8A and 13.3): The radical formally related to propene by removal of a hydrogen atom from its methyl group. The two contributing resonance structures of the delocalized radical each include an unpaired electron on a carbon adjacent to the double bond, such that a p orbital on each of the three carbons overlaps to delocalize the radical to each end of the allyl system, in which the radical carbon is adjacent to a carbon-carbon double bond.

Alpha (α) anomer (Section 22.2C): In the standard Haworth formula representation for a D-hexopyranose, the α anomer has the hemiacetal hydroxyl or acetal alkoxyl group trans to C6. Similar usage applies to other carbohydrate forms regarding the stereochemical relationship of the anomeric hydroxyl or alkoxyl group and the configuration at the carbon bearing the ring oxygen that forms the hemiacetal or acetal.

Alpha (α) carbon (Section 18.1): A carbon adjacent to a carbonyl ($C{=}O$) group.

Alpha (α) helix (Section 24.8A): A secondary structure in proteins where the polypeptide chain is coiled in a right-handed helix.

Alpha (α) hydrogens (Sections 18.1 and 18.5D): A hydrogen atom bonded to an α carbon. These hydrogens are significantly more acidic than the typical alkane hydrogen.

Aminium salt (Section 20.3D): The product of the reaction of an amine, acting as a Bronsted-Lowry base, with an acid. The amine can be primary, secondary, or tertiary. The positively charged nitrogen in an aminium salt is attached to at least one hydrogen atom. (An ammonium salt has no hydrogen atoms bonded directly to the nitrogen.)

Amino acid residue (Section 24.4): An amino acid that is part of a peptide.

Angle strain (Section 4.10): The increased potential energy of a molecule (usually a cyclic one) caused by deformation of a bond angle away from its lowest energy value.

Annulene (Section 14.7B): Monocyclic hydrocarbon that can be represented by a structure having alternating single and double bonds. The ring size of an annulene is represented by a number in brackets, e.g., benzene is [6]annulene and cyclooctatetraene is [8]annulene.

Anomeric carbon (Section 22.2C): The hemiacetal or acetal carbon in the cyclic form of a carbohydrate. The anomeric carbon can have either the α or β stereochemical configuration (using carbohydrate nomenclature), resulting in diastereomeric forms of the carbohydrate called anomers (α-anomers and β-anomers). Anomers differ *only* in the stereochemistry at the anomeric carbon.

Anomers (Section 22.2C): A term used in carbohydrate chemistry. Anomers are diastereomers that differ only in configuration at the acetal or hemiacetal carbon of a sugar in its cyclic form.

Anti 1,2-dihydroxylation (Section 11.15): The installation of hydroxyl groups at adjacent carbons and on opposite faces of an alkene, often accomplished by ring-opening of an epoxide.

Anti addition (Sections 7.13A, 7.14B, and 8.11A): An addition that places the parts of the adding reagent on opposite faces of the reactant.

Antiaromatic compound (Section 14.7E): A cyclic conjugated system whose π electron energy is greater than that of the corresponding open-chain compound.

Antibonding molecular orbital (antibonding MO) (Sections 1.11, 1.13, and 1.15): A molecular orbital whose energy is higher than that of the isolated atomic orbitals from which it is constructed. Electrons in an antibonding molecular orbital destabilize the bond between the atoms that the orbital encompasses.

Anticodon (Section 25.5C): A sequence of three bases on transfer RNA (tRNA) that associates with a codon of messenger RNA (mRNA).

Anti conformation (Section 4.9): An anti conformation of butane, for example, has the methyl groups at an angle of 180° to each other:

CH3

CH3

**Anti
conformation
of butane**

Anti coplanar (Section 7.6D): The relative position of two groups that have a 180º dihedral angle between them.

anti-Markovnikov addition (Sections 8.2D, 8.6–8.9, 8.18, and 10.10): An addition reaction where the hydrogen atom of a reagent becomes bonded to an alkene or alkyne at the carbon having the fewer hydrogen atoms initially. This orientation is the opposite of that predicted by Markovnikov's rule.

Arenium ion (Section 15.2): A general name for the cyclohexadienyl carbocations that form as intermediates in electrophilic aromatic substitution reactions.

Aromatic compound (Sections 2.1, 2.1D, 14.1–14.8, and 14.11): A cyclic conjugated unsaturated molecule or ion that is stabilized by π electron delocalization. Aromatic compounds are characterized by having large resonance energies, by reacting by substitution rather than addition, and by deshielding of protons exterior to the ring in their ^{1}H NMR spectra caused by the presence of an induced ring current.

Aromatic ions (Section 14.7D): Cations and anions that fulfill the criteria for aromaticity (planarity, electron delocalization, and a Hückel number of π-electrons) and thus have additional (aromatic) stability.

Arylamines (Section 20.1A): A compound in which the carbon of an aromatic ring bears the amine nitrogen atom. Aryl amines can be primary, secondary, or tertiary.

Aryl halide (Sections 2.5 and 6.1): An organic halide in which the halogen atom is attached to an aromatic ring, such as a benzene ring.

Atactic polymer (Special Topic B.1 in *WileyPLUS*): A polymer in which the configuration at the stereogenic centers along the chain is random.

Atomic orbital (AO) (Sections 1.10, 1.11, and 1.15): A volume of space about the nucleus of an atom where there is a high probability of finding an electron. An atomic orbital can be described mathematically by its wave function. Atomic orbitals have characteristic quantum numbers; the *principal quantum number, n,* is related to the energy of the electron in an atomic orbital and can have the values 1, 2, 3,.... The *azimuthal quantum number, l,* determines the angular momentum of the electron that results from its motion around the nucleus, and can have the values 0, 1, 2,..., $(n-1)$. The *magnetic quantum number, m,* determines the orientation in space of the angular momentum and can have values from $+l$ to $-l$. The *spin quantum number, s,* specifies the intrinsic angular momentum of an electron and can have the values of $+\frac{1}{2}$ and $-\frac{1}{2}$ only.

Atropisomers (Section 5.18): Conformational isomers that are stable, isolable compounds.

Aufbau principle (Section 1.10A): A principle that guides us in assigning electrons to orbitals of an atom or molecule in its lowest energy state or ground state. The aufbau principle states that electrons are added so that orbitals of lowest energy are filled first.

Autoxidation (Section 10.12C): The reaction of an organic compound with oxygen to form a hydroperoxide.

Axial bond (Section 4.12): The six bonds of a cyclohexane ring (below) that are perpendicular to the general plane of the ring, and that alternate up and down around the ring.

B

Base peak (Section 9.13): The most intense peak in a mass spectrum.

Base strength (Sections 3.5C and 20.3): The strength of a base is inversely related to the strength of its conjugate acid; the weaker the conjugate acid, the stronger is the base. In other words, if the conjugate acid has a large pK_a, the base will be strong.

Benzene (Section 2.1D): The prototypical aromatic compound having the formula C_6H_6. Aromatic compounds are planar, cyclic, and contain 4n + 2 π electrons *delocalized* in contiguous fashion about a ring of electron density in the molecule. Electron delocalization gives aromatic compounds a high degree of stability.

Benzenoid aromatic compound (Section 14.8A): An aromatic compound whose molecules have one or more benzene rings.

Benzyl group (Sections 2.4B and 10.9): The $C_6H_5CH_2-$ group.

Benzylic carbocation (Section 15.15): A carbocation located adjacent to a benzene ring.

Benzylic cation (Section 15.12A): A carbocation where the positive charge is on a carbon bonded to a benzene ring. The positive charge is delocalized into the benzene ring through conjugation, resulting in a relatively stable carbocation.

Benzylic position (Section 10.9): The location of a group that is bonded to an sp^3-hybridized carbon adjacent to a benzene ring.

Benzylic radical (Section 15.12A): The radical comprised of a methylene (CH_2) group bonded to a benzene ring, wherein the unpaired electron is *delocalized* over the methylene group and the ring. As a highly *conjugated* system, the benzylic radical has greatly enhanced stability.

Benzylic substituent (Sections 15.12A): Refers to a substituent on a carbon atom adjacent to a benzene ring.

Benzyne (Section 21.11B): An unstable, highly reactive intermediate consisting of a benzene ring with an additional bond resulting from sideways overlap of sp^2 orbitals on adjacent atoms of the ring.

Beta (β) anomer (Section 22.2C): In the standard Haworth formula representation for a D-hexopyranose, the β anomer has the hemiacetal hydroxyl or acetal alkoxyl group cis to C6. Similar usage applies to other carbohydrate forms regarding the stereochemical relationship of the anomeric hydroxyl or alkoxyl group and the configuration at the carbon bearing the ring oxygen that forms the hemiacetal or acetal.

Beta (β)-carbonyl compound (Section 18.5C): A compound having two carbonyl groups separated by an intervening carbon atom.

Beta (β)-pleated sheet (Section 24.8A): A type of protein secondary structure involving alignment of two polypeptide regions alongside each other through hydrogen bonding of their amide groups.

Bicyclic compounds (Section 4.4B): Compounds with two fused or bridged rings.

Bimolecular reaction (Section 6.5B): A reaction whose rate-determining step involves two initially separate species.

Boat conformation (Section 4.11): A conformation of cyclohexane that resembles a boat and that has eclipsed bonds along its two sides:

It is of higher energy than the chair conformation.

Boiling point (Sections 2.13A and 2.13C): The temperature at which the vapor pressure of a liquid is equal to the pressure above the surface of the liquid.

Bond angle (Section 1.7A): The angle between two bonds originating at the same atom.

Bond dissociation energy (See **Homolytic bond dissociation energy** and Section 10.2)

Bonding molecular orbital (bonding MO) (Sections 1.11, 1 .12, and 1.15): The energy of a bonding molecular orbital is lower than the energy of the isolated atomic orbitals from which it arises. When electrons occupy a bonding molecular orbital they help hold together the atoms that the molecular orbital encompasses.

Bond length (Sections 1.11 and 1.14A): The equilibrium distance between two bonded atoms or groups.

Bond-line formula (Section 1.7C): A formula that shows the carbon skeleton of a molecule with lines. The number of hydrogen atoms necessary to fulfill each carbon's valence is assumed to be present but not written in. Other atoms (e.g., O, Cl, N) are written in.

Broadband (BB) proton decoupling (see **Proton decoupling**) (Section 9.11B): A method of eliminating carbon-proton coupling by irradiating the sample with a wide-frequency ("broadband") energy input in the frequencies in which protons absorb energy. This energy input causes the protons to remain in the high energy state, eliminating coupling with carbon nuclei.

Bromohydrin (Section 8.13): A compound bearing a bromine atom and a hydroxyl group on adjacent (vicinal) carbons.

Bromonium ion (Section 8.11A): An ion containing a positive bromine atom bonded to two carbon atoms.

Brønsted–Lowry theory of acid–base (Section 3.1A): An acid is a substance that can donate (or lose) a proton; a base is a substance that can accept (or remove) a proton. The *conjugate acid* of a base is the molecule or ion that forms when a base accepts a proton. The *conjugate base* of an acid is the molecule or ion that forms when an acid loses its proton.

C

Carbanion (Sections 3.4 and 12.1A): A chemical species in which a carbon atom bears a formal negative charge.

Carbene (Section 8.14): An uncharged species in which a carbon atom is divalent. The species :CH_2, called methylene, is a carbene.

Carbenoid (Section 8.14C): A carbene-like species. A species such as the reagent formed when diiodomethane reacts with a zinc–copper couple. This reagent, called the Simmons–Smith reagent, reacts with alkenes to add methylene to the double bond in a stereospecific way.

Carbocation (Sections 3.4, 6.11, and 6.12): A chemical species in which a trivalent carbon atom bears a formal positive charge.

Carbohydrate (Section 22.1A): A group of naturally occurring compounds that are usually defined as polyhydroxyaldehydes or polyhydroxyketones, or as substances that undergo hydrolysis to yield such compounds. In actuality, the aldehyde and ketone groups of carbohydrates are often present as hemiacetals and acetals. The name comes from the fact that many carbohydrates possess the empirical formula $C_x(H_2O)_y$.

Carbon-carbon double bond (Section 1.3B): A bond between two carbon atoms comprised of four electrons; two of the electrons are in a sigma bond and two of the electrons are in a pi bond.

Carbon-carbon single bond (Section 1.3B): A bond between two carbon atoms comprised of two electrons shared in a sigma bond.

Carbon-carbon triple bond (Section 1.3B): A bond between two carbon atoms comprised of six electrons; two of the electrons are in a sigma bond and four of the electrons are as pairs in each of two pi bonds.

Carbon-13 NMR spectroscopy (Section 9.11): NMR spectroscopy applied to carbon. Carbon-13 is NMR active, whereas carbon-12 is not and therefore cannot be studied by NMR. Only 1.1% of all naturally occurring carbon is carbon-13.

Carbonyl group (Section 16.1): A functional group consisting of a carbon atom doubly bonded to an oxygen atom. The carbonyl group is found in aldehydes, ketones, esters, anhydrides, amides, acyl halides, and so on. Collectively these compounds are referred to as carbonyl compounds.

Carboxylic acid derivatives (Section 17.1): Acyl compounds that can be synthesized from a carboxylic acid or another carboxylic acid derivative. Examples include esters, amides, acid halides, anhydrides, etc.

CFC (see **Freon**): A chlorofluorocarbon.

Chain-growth polymer (See **Addition polymer** and Special Topic B in *WileyPLUS*): Polymers (macromolecules with repeating units) formed by adding subunits (called *monomers*) repeatedly to form a chain.

Chain reaction (Sections 10.4 and 10.10): A reaction that proceeds by a sequential, stepwise mechanism, in which each step generates the reactive intermediate that causes the next step to occur. Chain reactions have *chain-initiating steps, chain-propagating steps,* and *chain-terminating steps.*

Chain-terminating (dideoxynucleotide) method (Section 25.6): A method of sequencing DNA that involves replicating DNA in a way that generates a family of partial copies, each differing in length by one base pair and containing a nucleotide-specific fluorescent tag on the terminal base. The partial copies of the parent DNA are separated by length, usually using capillary electrophoresis, and the terminal base on each strand is identified by the covalently attached fluorescent marker.

Chair conformation (Section 4.11): The all-staggered conformation of cyclohexane that has no angle strain or torsional strain and is, therefore, the lowest energy conformation:

Chemical exchange (Section 9.10): In the context of NMR, transfer of protons bonded to heteroatoms from one molecule to another, broadening their signal and eliminating spin-spin coupling.

Chemical shift, δ (Sections 9.2A, 9.7, and 9.11C): The position in an NMR spectrum, relative to a reference compound, at which a nucleus absorbs. The reference compound most often used is tetramethylsilane (TMS), and its absorption point is arbitrarily designated zero. The chemical shift of a given nucleus is proportional to the strength of the magnetic field of the spectrometer. The chemical shift in delta units, δ, is determined by dividing the observed shift from TMS in hertz multiplied by 10^6 by the operating frequency of the spectrometer in hertz.

Chirality (Sections 5.1, 5.4, and 5.6): The property of having handedness.

Chirality center (Sections 5.4 and 5.17): An atom bearing groups of such nature that an interchange of any two groups will produce a stereoisomer.

Chiral molecule (Sections 5.3 and 5.12): A molecule that is not superposable on its mirror image. Chiral molecules have handedness and are capable of existing as a pair of enantiomers.

Chlorination (Sections 8.12, 10.3B, 10.4, and 10.5): A reaction in which one or more chlorine atoms are introduced into a molecule.

Chlorohydrin (Section 8.13): A compound bearing a chlorine atom and a hydroxyl group on adjacent (vicinal) carbons.

Cis–trans isomers (Sections 1.13B, 4.13, and 7.2): Diastereomers that differ in their stereochemistry at adjacent atoms of a double bond or on different atoms of a ring. Cis groups are on the same side of a double bond or ring. Trans groups are on opposite sides of a double bond or ring.

Claisen condensation (Section 19.1): A reaction in which an enolate anion from one ester attacks the carbonyl function of another ester, forming a new carbon-carbon σ-bond. A tetrahedral intermediate is involved that, with expulsion of an alkoxyl group, collapses to a β-ketoester. The two esters are said to "condense" into a larger product with loss of an alcohol molecule.

Claisen rearrangement (Section 21.9): A [3,3] sigmatropic rearrangement reaction involving an allyl vinyl ether, in which the allyl group of migrates to the other end of the vinyl system, with bond reorganization leading to a γ,δ-unsaturated carbonyl compound.

Codon (Section 25.5C): A sequence of three bases on messenger RNA (mRNA) that contains the genetic information for one amino acid. The codon associates, by hydrogen bonding, with an anticodon of a transfer RNA (tRNA) that carries the particular amino acid for protein synthesis on the ribosome.

Coenzyme (Section 24.9): A small organic molecule that participates in the mechanism of an enzyme and which is bound at the active site of the enzyme.

Cofactor (Section 24.9): A metal ion or organic molecule whose presence is required in order for an enzyme to function.

Concerted reaction (Section 6.6): A reaction where bond forming and bond breaking occur simultaneously (in concert) through a single transition state.

Condensation polymer (See **Step-growth polymer**, Section 17.12, and Special Topic C in *WileyPLUS*): A polymer produced when bifunctional monomers (or potentially bifunctional monomers) react with each other through the intermolecular elimination of water or an alcohol. Polyesters, polyamides, and polyurethanes are all condensation polymers.

Condensation reaction (Section 19.1): A reaction in which molecules become joined through the intermolecular elimination of water or an alcohol.

Condensed structural formula (Section 1.7B): A chemical formula written using letters of the elemental symbols for the atoms involved, listed in sequence for the connections of the central chain of atoms and without showing the bonds between them. In organic compounds, all of the substituent atoms that are bonded to a given carbon atom are written immediately after the symbol for that carbon atom, then the next carbon atom in the chain is written, and so on.

Configuration (Sections 5.7, 5.15, and 6.8): The particular arrangement of atoms (or groups) in space that is characteristic of a given stereoisomer.

Conformation (Section 4.8): A particular temporary orientation of a molecule that results from rotations about its single bonds.

Conformational analysis (Sections 4.8, 4.9, 4.11, and 4.12): An analysis of the energy changes that a molecule undergoes as its groups undergo rotation (sometimes only partial) about the single bonds that join them.

Conformational stereoisomers (Section 4.9A): Stereoisomers differing in space only due to rotations about single (σ) bonds.

Conformations of cyclohexane (Sections 4.11 and 4.13): Rotations about the carbon-carbon single bonds of cyclohexane can produce different conformations which are interconvertible. The most important are the chair conformation, the boat conformation, and the twist conformation.

Conformer (Section 4.8): A particular staggered conformation of a molecule.

Conjugate acid (Section 3.1A): The molecule or ion that forms when a base accepts a proton.

Conjugate addition (Sections 19.1 and 19.7): A form of nucleophilic addition to an α,β-unsaturated carbonyl compound in which the nucleophile adds to the β carbon. Also called Michael addition.

Conjugate base (Sections 3.1A and 3.5C): The molecule or ion that forms when an acid loses its proton.

Conjugated protein (Section 24.12): A protein that contains a nonprotein group (called a prosthetic group) as part of its structure.

Connectivity (Sections 1.6 and 1.7A): The sequence, or order, in which the atoms of a molecule are attached to each other.

Constitutional isomers (Sections 1.6, 4.2, and 5.2A): Compounds that have the same molecular formula but that differ in their connectivity (i.e., molecules that have the same molecular formula but have their atoms connected in different ways).

Coplanar (Section 7.6D): A conformation in which vicinal groups lie in the same plane.

Copolymer (Special Topic B in *WileyPLUS*): A polymer synthesized by polymerizing two monomers.

COSY (Correlation Spectroscopy) (Section 9.12): A two-dimensional NMR method that displays coupling relationships between protons in a molecule.

Coupling (Section 9.2C): In NMR, the splitting of the energy levels of a nucleus under observation by the energy levels of nearby NMR-active nuclei, causing characteristic splitting patterns for the signal of the nucleus being observed. The signal from an NMR-active nucleus will be split into (2nI + 1) peaks, where n = the number of equivalent neighboring magnetic nuclei and I = the spin quantum number. For hydrogen (I = 1/2) this rule devolves to (n + 1), where n = the number of equivalent neighboring hydrogen nuclei.

Coupling constant, J_{ab} (Section 9.9C): The separation in frequency units (hertz) of the peaks of a multiplet caused by spin–spin coupling between atoms a and b.

Covalent bond (Section 1.3B): The type of bond that results when atoms share electrons.

Cracking (Section 4.1A): A process used in the petroleum industry for breaking down the molecules of larger alkanes into smaller ones. Cracking may be accomplished with heat (thermal cracking), or with a catalyst (catalytic cracking).

Crossed-aldol reaction (Section 19.5): An aldol reaction involving two different aldehyde or ketone reactants. If both aldol reactants have α hydrogens, four products can result. Crossed aldol reactions are synthetically useful when one reactant has no α hydrogens, such that it can serve only as an electrophile that is subject to attack by the enolate from the other reactant.

Crown ether (Section 11.16): Cyclic polyethers that have the ability to form complexes with metal ions. Crown ethers are named as *x*-crown-*y* where *x* is the total number of atoms in the ring and *y* is the number of oxygen atoms in the ring.

Curved arrows (Sections 1.8, 3.2, and 10.1): Curved arrows show the direction of electron flow in a reaction mechanism. They point from the source of an electron pair to the atom receiving the pair. Double-barbed curved arrows are used to indicate the movement of a pair of electrons; single-barbed curved arrows are used to indicate the movement of a single electron. Curved arrows are never used to show the movement of atoms.

Cyanohydrin (Sections 16.9 and 17.3): A functional group consisting of a carbon atom bonded to a cyano group and to a hydroxyl group, i.e., RHC(OH)(CN) or R₂C(OH)(CN), derived by adding HCN to an aldehyde or ketone.

1,4-Cycloaddition (Section 13.10): A ring-forming reaction where new bonds are formed to the first and fourth atoms of a molecular moiety, as at the ends of a 1,3-diene in a Diels-Alder reaction.

Cycloaddition (Section 13.10): A reaction, like the Diels–Alder reaction, in which two connected groups add to the end of a π system to generate a new ring. Also called 1,4-cycloaddition.

Cycloalkanes (Sections 4.1, 4.4, 4.7, 4.10, and 4.11): Alkanes in which some or all of the carbon atoms are arranged in a ring. Saturated cycloalkanes have the general formula C_nH_{2n}.

D

1,3-Diaxial interaction (Section 4.12): The interaction between two axial groups that are on adjacent carbon atoms.

1,2-Dihydroxylation (Section 8.15): The installation of hydroxyl groups on adjacent carbons, such as by the reaction of OsO_4 or $KMnO_4$ with an alkene.

D and L nomenclature (Section 22.2B): A method for designating the configuration of monosaccharides and other compounds in which the reference compound is (+)- or (−)-glyceraldehyde. According to this system, (+)-glyceraldehyde is designated D-(+)-glyceraldehyde and (−)-glyceraldehyde is designated L-(−)-glyceraldehyde. Therefore, a monosaccharide whose highest numbered stereogenic center has the same general configuration as D-(+)-glyceraldehyde is designated a D-sugar; one whose highest numbered stereogenic center has the same general configuration as L-(+)-glyceraldehyde is designated an L-sugar.

Dash structural formulas (Sections 1.3B and 1.7A): Structural formulas in which atom symbols are drawn and a line or "dash" represents each pair of electrons (a covalent bond). These formulas show connectivities between atoms but do not represent the true geometries of the species.

Deactivating group (Sections 15.10, 15.10E, 15.10F, and 15.11A): A group that when present on a benzene ring causes the ring to be less reactive in electrophilic substitution than benzene itself.

Debye (Section 2.2): The unit in which dipole moments are stated. One debye, D, equals 1×10^{-18} esu cm.

Decarboxylation (Section 17.10): A reaction whereby a carboxylic acid loses CO_2.

Degenerate orbitals (Section 1.10A): Orbitals of equal energy. For example, the three 2*p* orbitals are degenerate.

Dehydration (Sections 7.7 and 7.8): An elimination that involves the loss of a molecule of water from the substrate.

Dehydrohalogenation (Sections 6.15A and 7.6): An elimination reaction that results in the loss of HX from adjacent carbons of the substrate and the formation of a π bond.

Delocalization effect (Sections 3.10A and 6.11B): The dispersal of electrons (or of electrical charge). Delocalization of charge always stabilizes a system.

Deoxyribonucleic acid (DNA) (Sections 25.1 and 25.4A): One of the two molecules (the other is RNA) that carry genetic information in cells. Two molecular strands held together by hydrogen bonds give DNA a "twisted ladder"-like structure, with four types of heterocyclic bases (adenine, cytosine, thymine, and guanine) making up the "rungs" of the ladder.

DEPT ¹³**C NMR spectra** (Section 9.11D): Distortionless enhanced polarization transfer (DEPT) ¹³C NMR spectra indicate how many hydrogen atoms are bonded to a given carbon atom.

Deshielded (Section 9.7): See Shielding.

Dextrorotatory (Section 5.8B): A compound that rotates plane-polarized light clockwise.

Diastereomers (Section 5.2C): Stereoisomers that are not mirror images of each other.

Diastereoselective reaction (see **Stereoselective reaction** and Sections 5.10B and 12.3D)

Diastereotopic hydrogens (or *ligands*) (Section 9.8B): If replacement of each of two hydrogens (or ligands) by the same groups yields compounds that are diastereomers, the two hydrogen atoms (or ligands) are said to be diastereotopic.

Diazonium salts (Sections 20.6A, 20.6B, and 20.7): Salts synthesized from the reaction of primary amines with nitrous acid. Diazonium salts have the structure $[R–N\equiv N]^+ X^-$. Diazonium salts of primary aliphatic amines are unstable and decompose rapidly; those from primary aromatic amines decompose slowly when cold, and are useful in the synthesis of substituted aromatics and *azo* compounds.

Dieckmann condensation (Section 19.2A): An intramolecular Claisen condensation of a diester; the enolate from one ester group attacks the carbonyl of another ester function in the same molecule, leading to a cyclic product.

Dielectric constant (Section 6.13C): A measure of a solvent's ability to insulate opposite charges from each other. The dielectric constant of a solvent roughly measures its polarity. Solvents with high dielectric constants are better solvents for ions than are solvents with low dielectric constants.

Diels-Alder reaction (Section 13.10): In general terms, a reaction between a conjugated diene (a 4-π-electron system) and a compound containing a double bond (a 2-π-electron system), called a dienophile, to form a cyclohexene ring.

Diene (Section 13.10): A molecule containing two double bonds (*di* = two, *ene* = alkene or double bonds). In a Diels-Alder reaction, a *conjugated* diene in the *s-cis* conformation reacts with a dienophile.

Dienophile (Section 13.10): The diene-seeking component of a Diels–Alder reaction.

Dihedral angle (Sections 4.8A and 9.9D): See Fig. 4.4. The angle between two atoms (or groups) bonded to adjacent atoms, when viewed as a projection down the bond between the adjacent atoms.

Dihydroxylation (Section 8.15): A process by which a starting material is converted into a product containing adjacent alcohol functionalities (called a "1,2-diol" or "glycol").

Dipeptide (Section 24.4): A peptide comprised of two amino acids.

Dipolar ion (Section 24.2C): The charge-separated form of an amino acid that results from the transfer of a proton from a carboxyl group to a basic group.

Dipole–dipole force (Section 2.13B): An interaction between molecules having permanent dipole moments.

Dipole moment, μ (Section 2.2): A physical property associated with a polar molecule that can be measured experimentally. It is defined as the product of the charge in electrostatic units (esu) and the distance that separates them in centimeters: $\mu = e \times d$.

Direct alkylation (Section 18.4C): A synthetic process in which the α-hydrogen of an ester is removed by a strong, bulky base such as LDA, creating a resonance-stabilized anion which will act as a nucleophile in an S_N2 reaction.

Directed aldol reaction (Section 19.5B): A crossed aldol reaction in which the desired enolate anion is generated first and rapidly using a strong base (e.g., LDA) after which the carbonyl reactant to be attacked by the enolate is added. If both a *kinetic enolate anion* and a *thermodynamic enolate anion* are possible, this process favors generation of the kinetic enolate anion.

Disaccharide (Sections 22.1A and 22.12): A carbohydrate that, on a molecular basis, undergoes hydrolytic cleavage to yield two molecules of a monosaccharide.

Dispersion force (or *London force*) (Sections 2.13B and 4.12B): Weak forces that act between nonpolar molecules or between parts of the same molecule. Bringing two groups (or molecules) together first results in an attractive force between them because a temporary unsymmetrical distribution of electrons in one group induces an opposite polarity in the other. When groups are brought closer than

their *van der Waals radii*, the force between them becomes repulsive because their electron clouds begin to interpenetrate each other.

Distortionless enhanced polarization transfer (DEPT) spectra (Section 9.11D): A technique in ^{13}C NMR spectroscopy by which the number of hydrogens at each carbon, e.g., C, CH, CH_2, and CH_3 can be determined.

Disulfide linkage (Section 24.2A): A sulfur-sulfur single bond in a peptide or protein formed by an oxidative reaction between the thiol groups of two cysteine amino acid residues.

Double bonds (Sections 1.4A and 1.13A): Bonds composed of four electrons: two electrons in a sigma (σ) bond and two electrons in a pi (π) bond.

Doublet (Section 9.2C): An NMR signal comprised of two peaks with equal intensity, caused by signal splitting from one neighboring NMR-active nucleus.

Downfield (Section 9.3): Any area or signal in an NMR spectrum that is to the left relative to another. (See **Upfield** for comparison.) A signal that is downfield of another occurs at higher frequency (and higher δ and ppm values) than the other signal.

E

E1 reaction (Sections 6.15C, 6.17, and 6.18B): A unimolecular elimination in which, in a slow, rate-determining step, a leaving group departs from the substrate to form a carbocation. The carbocation then in a fast step loses a proton with the resulting formation of a π bond.

E2 reaction (Sections 6.15C, 6.16, and 6.18B): A bimolecular 1,2 elimination in which, in a single step, a base removes a proton and a leaving group departs from the substrate, resulting in the formation of a π bond.

Eclipsed conformation (Section 4.8A): A temporary orientation of groups around two atoms joined by a single bond such that the groups directly oppose each other.

An eclipsed conformation

Edman degradation (Section 24.5A): A method for determining the *N*-terminal amino acid in a peptide. The peptide is treated with phenylisothiocyanate ($C_6H_5-N=C=S$), which reacts with the *N*-terminal residue to form a derivative that is then cleaved from the peptide with acid and identified. Automated sequencers use the Edman degradation method.

Electromagnetic spectrum (Section 13.8A): The full range of energies propagated by wave fluctuations in an electromagnetic field.

Electron density surface (Section 1.12B): An electron density surface shows points in space that happen to have the same electron density. An electron density surface can be calculated for any chosen value of electron density. A "high" electron density surface (also called a "bond" electron density surface) shows the *core* of electron density around each atomic nucleus and regions where neighboring atoms share electrons (bonding regions). A "low" electron density surface roughly shows the *outline* of a molecule's electron cloud. This surface gives information about molecular shape and volume, and usually looks the same as a van der Waals or space-filling model of the molecule. (Contributed by Alan Shusterman, Reed College, and Warren Hehre, Wavefunction, Inc.)

Electronegativity (Sections 1.3A and 2.2): A measure of the ability of an atom to attract electrons it is sharing with another and thereby polarize the bond.

Electron impact (EI) (Sections 9.14 and 9.16A): A method of ion formation in mass spectrometry whereby the sample to be analyzed (analyte) is placed in a high vacuum and, when in the gas phase, bombarded with a beam of high-energy electrons. A valence electron is displaced by the impact of the electron beam, yielding a species called the *molecular ion* (if there has been no fragmentation), with a +1 charge and an unshared electron (a radical cation).

Electron probability density (Section 1.10): The likelihood of finding an electron in a given volume of space. If the electron probability density is large, then the probability of finding an electron in a given volume of space is high, and the corresponding volume of space defines an orbital.

Electrophile (Sections 3.4A and 8.1A): A Lewis acid, an electron-pair acceptor, an electron-seeking reagent.

Electrophilic aromatic substitutions (Sections 15.1, 15.2, and 21.8): A reaction of aromatic compounds in which an *electrophile* ("electron-seeker" – a positive ion or other electron-deficient species with a full or large partial positive charge) replaces a hydrogen bonded to the carbon of an aromatic ring.

Electrophoresis (Section 25.6A): A technique for separating charged molecules based on their different mobilities in an electric field.

Electrospray ionization (ESI) (Section 9.19): A method of ion formation in mass spectrometry whereby a solution of the sample to be analyzed (analyte) is sprayed into the vacuum chamber of the mass spectrometer from the tip of a high-voltage needle, imparting charge to the mixture. Evaporation of the solvent in the vacuum chamber yields charged species of the analyte; some of which may have charges greater than +1. A family of *m/z* peaks unique to the formula weight of the analyte results, from which the formula weight itself can be calculated by computer.

Elimination-addition (via benzyne) (Section 21.11B): A substitution reaction in which a base, under highly forcing conditions, deprotonates an aromatic carbon that is adjacent to a carbon bearing a leaving group. Loss of the leaving group and overlap of the adjacent *p* orbitals creates a species, called *benzyne*, with a π-bond in the plane of the ring (separate from the aromatic π-system). Attack by a nucleophile on this π-bond followed by protonation yields a substituted aromatic compound.

Elimination reaction (Sections 3.1, 6.15–6.17, 7.5, 7.7): A reaction that results in the loss of two groups from the substrate and the formation of a π bond. The most common elimination is a 1,2 elimination or β elimination, in which the two groups are lost from adjacent atoms.

Enamines (Sections 16.8 and 18.9): An *enamine* group consists of an amine function bonded to the sp^2 carbon of an alkene.

Enantiomeric excess (or *enantiomeric purity*) (Section 5.9B): A percentage calculated for a mixture of enantiomers by dividing the moles of one enantiomer minus the moles of the other enantiomer by the moles of both enantiomers and multiplying by 100. The enantiomeric excess equals the percentage optical purity.

Enantiomers (Sections 5.2C, 5.3, 5.7, 5.8, and 5.16): Stereoisomers that are mirror images of each other.

Enantioselective reaction (see **Stereoselective reaction** and Sections 5.10B and 12.3D)

Enantiotopic hydrogens (or *ligands*) (Section 9.8B): If replacement of each of two hydrogens (or ligands) by the same group yields compounds that are enantiomers, the two hydrogen atoms (or ligands) are said to be enantiotopic.

Endergonic reaction (Section 6.7): A reaction that proceeds with a positive free-energy change.

Endo group (Section 13.10B): A group on a bicyclic compound that is on the same side (syn) as the longest bridge in the compound.

Endothermic reaction (Section 3.8A): A reaction that absorbs heat. For an endothermic reaction D$H°$ is positive.

Energy (Section 3.8): Energy is the capacity to do work.

Energy of activation, E_{act} (Section 10.5A): A measure of the difference in potential energy between the reactants and the transition state of a reaction. It is related to, but not the same as, the free energy of activation, $\Delta G^{\ddagger}$.

Enol (Section 18.1): An alkene alcohol, where the hydroxyl group is bonded to an alkene carbon. A generally minor tautomeric equilibrium contributor to the keto form of a carbonyl group that has at least one alpha hydrogen.

Enolate (Sections 18.1, 18.3, and 18.4): The delocalized anion formed when an enol loses its hydroxylic proton or when the carbonyl tautomer that is in equilibrium with the enol loses an α proton.

Enthalpy change (Sections 3.8A, 3.9, and 3.16): Also called the heat of reaction. The *standard enthalpy change*, $\Delta H°$, is the change in enthalpy after a system in its standard state has undergone a transformation to another system, also in its standard state. For a reaction, $\Delta H°$ is a measure of the difference in the total bond energy of the reactants and products. It is one way of expressing the change in potential energy of molecules as they undergo reaction. The enthalpy change is related to the free-energy change, $\Delta G°$, and to the entropy change, $\Delta S°$, through the expression:

$$\Delta H° = \Delta G° + T\Delta S°$$

Entropy change (Section 3.9): The standard entropy change, $\Delta S°$, is the change in entropy between two systems in their standard states. Entropy changes have to do with changes in the relative order of a system. The more random a system is, the greater is its entropy. When a system becomes more disorderly its entropy change is positive.

Enzyme (Section 24.9): A protein or polypeptide that is a catalyst for biochemical reactions.

Enzyme-substrate complex (Section 24.9): The species formed when a substrate (reactant) binds at the active site of an enzyme.

Epimers, epimerization (Sections 18.3A and 22.8): Diastereomers that differ in configuration at only a single tetrahedral chirality center. Epimerization is the interconversion of epimers.

Epoxidation (Section 11.13A): The process of synthesizing an epoxide. Peroxycarboxylic acids (RCO_3H) are reagents commonly used for epoxidation.

Epoxide (Sections 11.13 and 11.14): An oxirane. A three-membered ring containing one oxygen and two carbon atoms.

Equatorial bond (Section 4.12): The six bonds of a cyclohexane ring that lie generally around the "equator" of the molecule:

497

Equilibrium constant, K_{eq} (Section 3.5A): A constant that expresses the position of an equilibrium. The equilibrium constant is calculated by multiplying the molar concentrations of the products together and then dividing this number by the number obtained by multiplying together the molar concentrations of the reactants.

Equilibrium control (see **Thermodynamic control**)

Essential amino acid (Section 24.2B) An amino acid that cannot be synthesized by the body and must be ingested as part of the diet. For adult humans there are eight essential amino acids ($RCH(NH_2)$ CO_2H): valine (R = isopropyl), Leucine (R = isobutyl), isoleucine (R = *sec*-butyl), phenylalanine (R = benzyl), threonine (R = 1-hydroxyethyl), methionine (R = 2-(methylthio)ethyl), lysine (R = 4-aminobutyl), and tryptophen (R = 3-methyleneindole).

Essential oil (Section 23.3): A volatile odoriferous compound obtained by steam distillation of plant material.

Esterification (Section 17.7A): The synthesis of an ester, usually involving reactions of carboxylic acids, acid chlorides or acid anhydrides with alcohols.

Exchangeable protons (Section 9.10): Protons that can be transferred rapidly from one molecule to another. These protons are often attached to electronegative elements such as oxygen or nitrogen.

Exergonic reaction (Section 6.7): A reaction that proceeds with a negative free-energy change.

Exo group (Section 13.10B): A group on a bicyclic compound that is on the opposite side (anti) to the longest bridge in the compound.

Exon (Section 25.5A): Short for "expressed sequence," an exon is a segment of DNA that is used when a protein is expressed. (See **Intron**).

Exothermic reaction (Section 3.8A): A reaction that evolves heat. For an exothermic reaction, $\Delta H°$ is negative.

(E)–(Z) system (Section 7.2): A system for designating the stereochemistry of alkene diastereomers based on the priorities of groups in the Cahn–Ingold–Prelog convention. An *E* isomer has the highest priority groups on opposites sides of the double bond, a *Z* isomer has the highest priority groups on the same side of the double bond.

F

Fat (Section 23.2): A triacylglycerol. The triester of glycerol with carboxylic acids.

Fatty acid (Section 23.2): A long-chained carboxylic acid (usually with an even number of carbon atoms) that is isolated by the hydrolysis of a fat.

Fischer projection (Sections 5.13 and 22.2C): A two-dimensional formula for representing the configuration of a chiral molecule. By convention, Fischer projection formulas are written with the main carbon chain extending from top to bottom with all groups eclipsed. Vertical lines represent bonds that project behind the plane of the page (or that lie in it). Horizontal lines represent bonds that project out of the plane of the page.

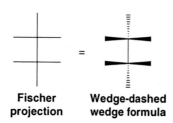

Fischer   Wedge-dashed
projection   wedge formula

Formal charge (Section 1.5): The difference between the number of electrons assigned to an atom in a molecule and the number of electrons it has in its outer shell in its elemental state. Formal charge can be calculated using the formula: $F = Z - S/2 - U$, where F is the formal charge, Z is the group number of the atom (i.e., the number of electrons the atom has in its outer shell in its elemental state), S is the number of electrons the atom is sharing with other atoms, and U is the number of unshared electrons the atom possesses.

Fourier transform NMR (Section 9.5): An NMR method in which a pulse of energy in the radiofrequency region of the electromagnetic spectrum is applied to nuclei whose nuclear magnetic moment is precessing about the axis of a magnetic field. This pulse of energy causes the nuclear magnetic moment to "tip" toward the xy plane. The component of the nuclear magnetic moment in the x–y plane generates ("induces") a radiofrequency signal, which is detected by the instrument. As nuclei relax to their ground states this signal decays over time; this time-dependent signal is called a "Free Induction Decay" (FID) curve. A mathematical operation (a Fourier transform) converts time-dependent data into frequency-dependent data–the NMR signal.

Fragmentation (Section 9.16): Cleavage of a chemical species by the breaking of covalent bonds, as in the formation of fragments during mass spectrometric analysis.

Free energy of activation, $\Delta G^{\ddagger}$ (Section 6.7): The difference in free energy between the transition state and the reactants.

Free-energy change (Section 3.9): The *standard free-energy change*, $\Delta G°$, is the change in free energy between two systems in their standard states. At constant temperature, $\Delta G° = \Delta H° - T\Delta S° = -RT \ln K_{eq}$, where $\Delta H°$ is the standard enthalpy change, $\delta S°$ is the standard entropy change, and K_{eq} is the equilibrium constant. A negative value of $\Delta G°$ for a reaction means that the formation of products is favored when the reaction reaches equilibrium.

Free-energy diagram (Section 6.7): A plot of free-energy changes that take place during a reaction versus the reaction coordinate. It displays free-energy changes as a function of changes in bond orders and distances as reactants proceed through the transition state to become products.

Freon (Section 10.12D): A chlorofluorocarbon or CFC.

Frequency, ν (Sections 2.15 and 13.8A): The number of full cycles of a wave that pass a given point in each second.

Friedel-Crafts acylation (Sections 15.6 and 15.7): Installation of an acyl group on a benzene ring by electrophilic aromatic substitution using an acylium ion as the electrophile (generated in situ using a Lewis acid).

Friedel-Crafts alkylation (Section 15.6): Installation of an alkyl group on a benzene ring by electrophilic aromatic substitution using an alkyl carbocation as the electrophile (generated in situ using a Lewis acid).

Fullerenes (Section 14.8C): Cagelike aromatic molecules with the geometry of a truncated icosahedron (or geodesic dome). The structures are composed of a network of pentagons and hexagons. Each carbon is sp^2 hybridized; the remaining electron at each carbon is delocalized into a system of molecular orbitals that gives the *whole molecule* aromatic character.

Functional class nomenclature (Section 4.3E): A system for naming compounds that uses two or more words to describe the compound. The final word corresponds to the functional group present; the preceding words, usually listed in alphabetical order, describe the remainder of the molecule. Examples are methyl alcohol, ethyl methyl ether, and ethyl bromide.

Functional group (Sections 2.2 and 2.4): The particular group of atoms in a molecule that primarily determines how the molecule reacts.

Functional group interconversion (Section 6.14): A process that converts one functional group into another.

Furanose (Section 22.2C): A sugar in which the cyclic acetal or hemiacetal ring is five membered.

G

Gauche conformation (Section 4.9): A gauche conformation of butane, for example, has the methyl groups at an angle of 60° to each other:

CH₃

CH₃

**A gauche
conformation
of butane**

GC/MS analysis (Section 9.18): An analytical method that couples a gas chromatograph (GC) with a mass spectrometer (MS). The GC separates the components of a mixture to be analyzed by sweeping the compounds, in the gas phase, through a column containing an adsorbant called a *stationary phase*. The gaseous molecules will cling to the surface of the stationary phase (be *adsorbed*) with different strengths. Those molecules that cling (adsorb) weakly will pass through the column quickly; those that *adsorb* more strongly will pass through the column more slowly. The separated components of the mixture are then introduced into the mass spectrometer, where they are analyzed.

gem-**Dihalide** (Section 7.10A): A general term for a molecule or group containing two halogen atoms bonded to the same carbon.

Geminal (*gem*-) substituents (Section 7.10A): Substituents that are on the same atom.

Gene (Section 25.1): A section of DNA that codes for a given protein.

Genetic code (Sections 25.5C and 25.5D): The correspondence of specific three-base sequences in mRNA (codons) that each code for a specific amino acid. Each codon pairs with the anticodon of a specific tRNA, which in turn carries the corresponding amino acid.

Genome (Sections 25.1 and 25.9): The set of all genetic information coded by DNA in an organism.

Genomics (Section 24.14): The study of the complete set of genetic instructions in an organism.

Glycan (See **Polysaccharide** and Section 22.13): An alternate term for a polysaccharide; monosaccharies joined together by glycosidic linkages.

Glycol (Sections 4.3F and 8.15): A diol.

Glycolipids (Section 22.16): Carbohydrates joined through glycosidic linkages to lipids.

Glycoproteins (Section 22.16): Carbohydrates joined through glycosidic linkages to proteins.

Glycoside (Section 22.4): A cyclic mixed acetal of a sugar with an alcohol.

Grignard reagent (Section 12.6B): An organomagnesium halide, usually written RMgX.

Ground state (Section 1.12): The lowest electronic energy state of an atom or molecule.

H

¹H — ¹H correlation spectroscopy (COSY) (Section 9.12): A two-dimensional NMR method used to display the coupling between hydrogen atoms.

Haloform reaction (Section 18.3C): A reaction specific to methyl ketones. In the presence of base multiple halogenations occur at the carbon of the methyl group; excess base leads to acyl substitution of the trihalomethyl group, resulting in a carboxylate anion and a *haloform* (CHX_3).

Halogenation (Sections 10.3–10.5 and 10.8A): A reaction in which one or more halogen atoms are introduced into a molecule.

Halohydrin (Section 8.13): A compound bearing a halogen atom and a hydroxyl group on adjacent (vicinal) carbons.

Halonium ion (Section 8.11A): An ion containing a positive halogen atom bonded to two carbon atoms.

Hammond–Leffler postulate (Section 6.13A): A postulate stating that the structure and geometry of the transition state of a given step will show a greater resemblance to the reactants or products of that step depending on which is closer to the transition state in energy. This means that the transition state of an endothermic step will resemble the products of that step more than the reactants, whereas the transition state of an exothermic step will resemble the reactants of that step more than the products.

Heat of hydrogenation (Section 7.3A): The standard enthalpy change that accompanies the hydrogenation of 1 mol of a compound to form a particular product.

Heisenberg uncertainty principle (Section 1.11): A fundamental principle that states that both the position and momentum of an electron (or of any object) cannot be exactly measured simultaneously.

Hemiacetal (Sections 16.7A and 22.2C): A functional group, consisting of an sp^3 carbon atom bearing both an alkoxyl group and a hydroxyl group [i.e., RCH(OH)(OR′) or R₂C(OH)(OR′)].

Hemiketal (See **Hemiacetal** and Section 16.7A)

Henderson-Hasselbalch equation (Sect. 24.2C): The Henderson-Hasselbalch equation ($pK_a = pH + log[HA]/[A^-]$) shows that when the concentration of an acid and its conjugate base are equal, the pH of the solution equals the pK_a of the acid.

Hertz (Hz) (Sections 9.6A, 9.9C, and 13.8A): The frequency of a wave. Now used instead of the equivalent cycles per second (cps).

Heteroatom (Section 2.1): Atoms such as oxygen, nitrogen, sulfur and the halogens that form bonds to carbon and have unshared pairs of electrons.

Heterocyclic amines (Section 20.1B): A secondary or tertiary amine in which the nitrogen group is part of a carbon-based ring.

Heterocyclic compound (Sections 14.9): A compound whose molecules have a ring containing an element other than carbon.

Heterogeneous catalysis (Sections 7.12 and 7.14A): Catalytic reactions in which the catalyst is insoluble in the reaction mixture.

Heterolysis (Section 3.4): The cleavage of a covalent bond so that one fragment departs with both of the electrons of the covalent bond that joined them. Heterolysis of a bond normally produces positive and negative ions.

Heteronuclear correlation spectroscopy (HETCOR or C-H HETCOR) (Section 9.12): A two-dimensional NMR method used to display the coupling between hydrogens and the carbons to which they are attached.

Heterotopic (chemically nonequivalent atoms) (Section 9.8A): Atoms in a molecule where replacement of one or the other leads to a new compound. Heterotopic atoms are not chemical shift equivalent in NMR spectroscopy.

Hofmann rule (Sections 7.6C and 20.12A): When an elimination yields the alkene with the less substituted double bond, it is said to follow the Hofmann rule.

HOMO (Sections 3.3A, 6.6, and 13.8C): The highest occupied molecular orbital.

Homogeneous catalysis (Section 7.12): Catalytic reactions in which the catalyst is soluble in the reaction mixture.

Homologous series (Section 4.7): A series of compounds in which each member differs from the next member by a constant unit.

Homolysis (Section 10.1): The cleavage of a covalent bond so that each fragment departs with one of the electrons of the covalent bond that joined them.

Homolytic bond dissociation energy, *DH*° (Section 10.2): The enthalpy change that accompanies the homolytic cleavage of a covalent bond.

Homotopic (chemically equivalent) atoms (Section 9.8A): Atoms in a molecule where replacement of one or another results in the same compound. Homotopic atoms are chemical shift equivalent in NMR spectroscopy.

Hückel's rule (Section 14.7): A rule stating that planar monocyclic rings with $(4n + 2)$ delocalized π electrons (i.e., with 2, 6, 10, 14,..., delocalized π electrons) will be aromatic.

Hund's rule (Section 1.10A): A rule used in applying the aufbau principle. When orbitals are of equal energy (i.e., when they are degenerate), electrons are added to each orbital with their spins unpaired, until each degenerate orbital contains one electron. Then electrons are added to the orbitals so that the spins are paired.

Hybrid atomic orbitals (Sections 1.12 and 1.15): An orbital that results from the mathematical combination of pure atomic orbitals, such as the combination of pure *s* and *p* orbitals in varying proportions to form hybrids such as sp^3, sp^2, and sp orbitals.

Hydration (Sections 8.4–8.9 and 11.4): The addition of water to a molecule, such as the addition of water to an alkene to form an alcohol.

Hydrazone (Section 16.8B): An imine in which an amino group ($-NH_2$, $-NHR$, $-NR_2$) is bonded to the nitrogen atom.

Hydride (Section 7.8A): A hydrogen anion, $H:^-$ Hydrogen with a filled 1s shell (containing two electrons) and negative charge.

Hydride ion (Section 12.1A): The anionic form of hydrogen; a proton with two electrons.

Hydroboration (Sections 8.6, 8.7, and 11.4): The addition of a boron hydride (either BH_3 or an alkylborane) to a multiple bond.

Hydrocarbon (Section 2.2): A molecular containing only carbon and hydrogen atoms.

Hydrogen abstraction (Section 10.1B): The process by which a species with an unshared electron (a radical) removes a hydrogen atom from another species, breaking the bond to the hydrogen homolytically.

Hydrogenation (Sections 4.16, 7.3A, and 7.13–7.15): A reaction in which hydrogen adds to a double or triple bond. Hydrogenation is often accomplished through the use of a metal catalyst such as platinum, palladium, rhodium, or ruthenium.

Hydrogen bond (Sections 2.13B, 2.13E, 2.13F, and 2.14): A strong dipole–dipole interaction (4–38 kJ mol^{-1}) that occurs between hydrogen atoms bonded to small strongly electronegative atoms (O, N, or F) and the nonbonding electron pairs on other such electronegative atoms.

Hydrophilic group (Sections 2.13D and 23.2C): A polar group that seeks an aqueous environment.

Hydrophobic group (See also **Lipophilic group**) (Sections 2.13D and 23.2C): A nonpolar group that avoids an aqueous surrounding and seeks a nonpolar environment.

Hyperconjugation (Sections 4.8B and 6.11B): Electron delocalization (via orbital overlap) from a filled bonding orbital to an adjacent unfilled orbital. Hyperconjugation generally has a stabilizing effect.

Imines (Section 16.8): A structure with a carbon-nitrogen double bond. If the groups bonded to carbon are not the same, (*E*) and (*Z*) isomers are possible.

Index of hydrogen deficiency (Section 4.17): The index of hydrogen deficiency (or IHD) equals the number of pairs of hydrogen atoms that must be subtracted from the molecular formula of the corresponding alkane to give the molecular formula of the compound under consideration.

Induced fit hypothesis (Section 24.9): An hypothesis regarding enzyme reactivity whereby formation of the enzyme-substrate complex causes conformational changes in the enzyme that facilitate conversion of the substrate to product.

Inductive effect (Sections 3.7B, 3.10B, and 15.11B): An intrinsic electron-attracting or -releasing effect that results from a nearby dipole in the molecule and that is transmitted through space and through the bonds of a molecule.

Infrared (IR) spectroscopy (Section 2.15): A type of optical spectroscopy that measures the absorption of infrared radiation. Infrared spectroscopy provides structural information about functional groups present in the compound being analyzed.

Inhibitor (Section 24.9): A compound that can negatively alter the activity of an enzyme.

Integration (Section 9.2B): A numerical value representing the relative area under a signal in an NMR spectrum. In ^{1}H NMR, the integration value is proportional to the number of hydrogens producing a given signal.

Intermediate (Sections 3 intro, 6.10, and 6.11): A transient species that exists between reactants and products in a state corresponding to a local energy minimum on a potential energy diagram.

Intermolecular forces (Sections 2.13B and 2.13F): Also known as van der Waals forces. Forces that act between molecules because of permanent (or temporary) electron distributions. Intermolecular forces can be attractive or repulsive. Dipole-dipole forces (including hydrogen bonds) and dispersion forces (also called London forces), are intermolecular forces of the van der Waal type.

Intron (Section 25.5A): Short for "intervening sequence," an intron is a segments of DNA that is not actually used when a protein is expressed, even though it is transcribed into the initial mRNA.

Inversion of configuration (Sections 6.6 and 6.14): At a tetrahedral atom, the process whereby one group is replaced by another bonded 180° opposite to the original group. The other groups at the tetrahedral atom "turn inside out" (shift) in the same way that an umbrella "turns inside out." When a chirality center undergoes configuration inversion, its (R,S) designation may switch, depending on the relative Cahn-Ingold-Prelog priorities of the groups before and after the reaction.

Ion (Sections 1.3A and 3.1A): A chemical species that bears an electrical charge.

Ion–dipole force (Section 2.13D): The interaction of an ion with a permanent dipole. Such interactions (resulting in solvation) occur between ions and the molecules of polar solvents.

Ionic bond (Section 1.3A): A bond formed by the transfer of electrons from one atom to another resulting in the creation of oppositely charged ions.

Ionic reaction (Sections 3.1B and 10.1): A reaction involving ions as reactants, intermediates, or products. Ionic reactions occur through the heterolysis of covalent bonds.

Ion-ion forces (Section 2.13A): Strong electrostatic forces of attraction between ions of opposite charges. These forces hold ions together in a crystal lattice.

Ionization (Section 9.14): Conversion of neutral molecules to ions (charged species).

Isoelectric point (pI) (Section 24.2C): The pH at which the number of positive and negative charges on an amino acid or protein are equal.

Isomers (Sections 1.6 and 5.2A): Different molecules that have the same molecular formula.

Isoprene unit (Section 23.3): A name for the structural unit found in all terpenes:

Isotactic polymer (Special Topic B.1 in *WileyPLUS*): A polymer in which the configuration at each stereogenic center along the chain is the same.

Isotopes (Section 1.2A): Atoms that have the same number of protons in their nuclei but have differing atomic masses because their nuclei have different numbers of neutrons.

IUPAC system (Section 4.3): (also called the "systematic nomenclature") A set of nomenclature rules overseen by the International Union of Pure and Applied Chemistry (IUPAC) that allows every compound to be assigned an unambiguous name.

K

Karplus correlation (Section 9.9D): An empirical correlation between the magnitude of an NMR coupling constant and the dihedral angle between two coupled protons. The dihedral angles derived in this manner can provide information about molecular geometries.

Kekulé structure (Sections 2.1D and 14.4): A structure in which lines are used to represent bonds. The Kekulé structure for benzene is a hexagon of carbon atoms with alternating single and double

bonds around the ring, and with one hydrogen atom attached to each carbon.

Ketal (See **Acetal** and Section 16.7B)

Keto and enol forms (Sections 18.1–18.3): Tautomeric forms of a compound related by a common resonance-stabilized intermediate. An *enol* structure consists of an alcohol functionality bonded to the sp^2 carbon of an alkene. Shifting the hydroxyl proton to the alkene and creation of a carbon-oxygen π-bond results in the *keto* form of the species.

Ketose (Section 22.2A): A monosaccharide containing a ketone group or a hemiacetal or acetal derived from it.

Kinetic control (Sections 7.6B, 13.9A, and 18.4A): A principle stating that when the ratio of products of a reaction is determined by relative rates of reaction, the most abundant product will be the one that is formed fastest. Also called rate control.

Kinetic energy (Section 3.8): Energy that results from the motion of an object. Kinetic energy $(KE) = \frac{1}{2}mv^2$, where m is the mass of the object and v is its velocity.

Kinetic enolate (Section 18.4A): In a situation in which more than one enolate anion can be formed, the *kinetic enolate anion* is that which is formed most rapidly. This is usually the enolate anion with the less substituted double bond; the decrease in steric hindrance permits more rapid deprotonation by the base. A kinetic enolate anion is formed predominantly under conditions that do not permit the establishment of an equilibrium.

Kinetic product (Section 13.9): The product formed fastest when multiple products are possible; the product formed via the lowest energy of activation pathway.

Kinetic resolution (Section 5.10B): A process in which the rate of a reaction with one enantiomer is different than with the other, leading to a preponderance of one product stereoisomer. This process is said to be "stereoselective" in that it leads to the preferential formation of one stereoisomer over other stereoisomers that could possibly be formed.

Kinetics (Section 6.5): A term that refers to rates of reactions.

L

Lactam (Section 17.8I): A cyclic amide.

Lactone (Section 17.7C): A cyclic ester.

LCAO (linear combination of atomic orbitals, Section 1.11): A mathematical method for arriving at wave functions for molecular obitals that involves adding or subtracting wave functions for atomic orbitals.

Leaving group (Sections 6.2, 6.4, and 6.13E): The substituent that departs from the substrate in a nucleophilic substitution reaction.

Leveling effect of a solvent (Section 3.14): An effect that restricts the use of certain solvents with strong acids and bases. In principle, no acid stronger than the conjugate acid of a particular solvent can exist to an appreciable extent in that solvent, and no base stronger than the conjugate base of the solvent can exist to an appreciable extent in that solvent.

Levorotatory (Section 5.8B): A compound that rotates plane-polarized light in a counterclockwise direction.

Lewis acid–base theory (Section 3.3): An acid is an electron pair acceptor, and a base is an electron pair donor.

Lewis structure (or *electron-dot structure*) (Sections 1.3B, 1.4, and 1.5): A representation of a molecule showing electron pairs as a pair of dots or as a dash.

Lipid (Section 23.1): A substance of biological origin that is soluble in nonpolar solvents. Lipids include fatty acids, triacylglycerols (fats and oils), steroids, prostaglandins, terpenes and terpenoids, and waxes.

Lipid bilayers (Section 23.6A): A two-layer noncovalent molecular assembly comprised primarily of phospholipids. The hydrophobic phospholipid "tail" groups of each layer orient toward each other in the center of the two-layered structure due to attractive dispersion forces. The hydrophilic "head" groups of the lipids orient toward the aqueous exterior of the bilayer. Lipid bilayers are important in biological systems such as cell membranes.

Lipophilic group (See also **Hydrophobic group**) (Sections 2.13D and 23.2C): A nonpolar group that avoids an aqueous surrounding and seeks a nonpolar environment.

Lithium diisopropylamide (LDA) (Section 18.4): $(i\text{-}C_3H_7)_2N^-Li^+$ The lithium salt of diisopropylamine. A strong base used to form *lithium enolates* from carbonyl compounds.

Lock-and-key hypothesis (Section 24.9): An hypothesis that explains enzyme specificity on the basis of complementary geometry between the enzyme (the "lock") and the substrate (the "key"), such that their shapes "fit together" correctly for a reaction to occur.

LUMO (Sections 3.3A and 13.8C): The lowest unoccupied molecular orbital.

M

Macromolecule (Section 10.11): A very large molecule.

Magnetic resonance imaging (MRI) (Section 9.12B): A technique based on NMR spectroscopy that is used in medicine.

Malonic ester synthesis (Section 18.7): A reaction in which the α-hydrogen of diethyl propanedioate (diethyl malonate, also called "malonic ester") is removed, creating a resonance-stabilized anion which can serve as a nucleophile in an S_N2 reaction. The α-carbon can be substituted twice; the ester functionalities can be converted into a carboxylic acid which, after decarboxylation, will yield a substituted ketone.

Mannich reaction (Section 19.8): The reaction of an enol with an iminium cation (formed from the reaction of a primary or secondary amine with formaldehyde) to yield a β-aminoalkyl carbonyl compound.

Markovnikov's rule (Sections 8.2B and 8.18): A rule for predicting the regiochemistry of electrophilic additions to alkenes and alkynes that can be stated in various ways. As originally stated (in 1870) by Vladimir Markovnikov, the rule provides that "if an unsymmetrical alkene combines with a hydrogen halide, the halide ion adds to the carbon with the fewer hydrogen atoms." More commonly the rule has been stated in reverse: that in the addition of HX to an alkene or alkyne the hydrogen atom adds to the carbon atom that already has the greater number of hydrogen atoms. A modern expression of Markovnikov's rule is: *In the ionic addition of an unsymmetrical reagent to a multiple bond, the positive portion of the reagent (the electrophile) attaches itself to a carbon atom of the reagent in the way that leads to the formation of the more stable intermediate carbocation.*

Mass spectrometry (MS) (Section 9.13): A technique, useful in structure elucidation, that involves the generation of ions from a molecule, the sorting and detecting of the ions, and the display of the result in terms of the mass/charge ratio and relative amount of each ion.

Matrix-assisted laser desorption-ionization (MALDI) (Section 9.19): A method in mass spectrometry for ionizing analytes that do not ionize well by electrospray ionization. The analyte is mixed with low molecular weight organic molecules that can absorb energy from a laser and then transfer this energy to the analyte, producing +1 ions which are then analyzed by the mass spectrometer.

Mechanism (See **Reaction mechanism**)

Melting Point (Section 2.13A): The temperature at which an equilibrium exists between a well-ordered crystalline substance and the more random liquid state. It reflects the energy needed to overcome the attractive forces between the units (ions, molecules) that comprise the crystal lattice.

Meso compound (Section 5.12B): An optically inactive compound whose molecules are achiral even though they contain tetrahedral atoms with four different attached groups.

Mesylate (Section 11.10): A methanesulfonate ester. Methanesulfonate esters are compounds that contain the CH_3SO_3— group, i.e., CH_3SO_3R.

Meta directors (Section 15.10B): An electron-withdrawing group on an aromatic ring. The major product of electrophilic aromatic substitution on a ring bearing a meta-directing group will have the newly substituted electrophile located meta to the substituent.

Methanide (Section 7.8A): A methyl anion, $-:CH3$, or methyl species that reacts as though it were a methyl anion.

Methylene (Section 8.14A): The carbene with the formula $:CH_2$.

Methylene group (Section 2.4B): The —CH_2— group.

Micelle (Section 23.2C): A spherical cluster of ions in aqueous solution (such as those from a soap) in which the nonpolar groups are in the interior and the ionic (or polar) groups are at the surface.

Michael addition (See **Conjugate addition** and Sections 18.9 and 19.7): A reaction between an active hydrogen compound and an α,β-unsaturated carbonyl compound. The attack by the anion of the active hydrogen compound takes place at the β-carbon of the α,β-unsaturated carbonyl compound. A Michael addition is a type of conjugate addition.

Molar absorptivity, ε (Section 13.8B): A proportionality constant that relates the observed absorbance (A) at a particular wavelength (λ) to the molar concentration of the sample (C) and the length (l) (in centimeters) of the path of the light beam through the sample cell:

$$\varepsilon = A/C \times l$$

Molecular formula (Section 1.6): A formula that gives the total number of each kind of atom in a molecule. The molecular formula is a whole number multiple of the empirical formula. For example the molecular formula for benzene is C_6H_6; the empirical formula is CH.

Molecular ion (Sections 9.14, 9.15, and 9.17): The cation produced in a mass spectrometer when one electron is dislodged from the parent molecule, symbolized $M^{+\cdot}$.

Molecularity (Section 6.5B): The number of species involved in a single step of a reaction (usually the rate-determining step).

Molecular orbital (MO) (Sections 1.11 and 1.15): Orbitals that encompass more than one atom of a molecule. When atomic orbitals combine to form molecular orbitals, the number of molecular orbitals that results always equals the number of atomic orbitals that combine.

Molecule (Section 1.3B): An electrically neutral chemical entity that consists of two or more bonded atoms.

Monomer (Section 10.11): The simple starting compound from which a polymer is made. For example, the polymer polyethylene is made from the monomer ethylene.

Monosaccharide (Sections 22.1A and 22.2): The simplest type of carbohydrate, one that does not undergo hydrolytic cleavage to a simpler carbohydrate.

Mutarotation (Section 22.3): The spontaneous change that takes place in the optical rotation of α and β anomers of a sugar when they are dissolved in water. The optical rotations of the sugars change until they reach the same value.

N

Nanotube (Section 14.8C): A tubular structure with walls resembling fused benzene rings, capped by half of a "buckyball" (buckminsterfullerene) at each end. The entire structure exhibits aromatic character.

Newman projection formula (Section 4.8A): A means of representing the spatial relationships of groups attached to two atoms of a molecule. In writing a Newman projection formula we imagine ourselves viewing the molecule from one end directly along the bond axis joining the two atoms. Bonds that are attached to the front atom are shown as radiating from the center of a circle; those attached to the rear atom are shown as radiating from the edge of the circle:

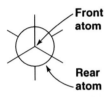

_N_-nitrosoamines (Section 20.6C): Amines bearing an N=O on the nitrogen, such as R—NH—N=O or Ar—NH—N=O. Often referred to as "nitrosamines" in the popular press. N-nitrosoamines are very powerful carcinogens.

Node (Section 1.15): A place where a wave function (ψ) is equal to zero. The greater the number of nodes in an orbital, the greater is the energy of the orbital.

Nonbenzenoid aromatic compound (Section 14.8B): An aromatic compound, such as azulene, that does not contain benzene rings.

Nuclear magnetic resonance (NMR) spectroscopy (Sections 9.2 and 9.11A): A spectroscopic method for measuring the absorption of radio frequency radiation by certain nuclei when the nuclei are in a strong magnetic field. The most important NMR spectra for organic chemists are ^{1}H NMR spectra and ^{13}C NMR spectra. These two types of spectra provide structural information about the carbon framework of the molecule, and about the number and environment of hydrogen atoms attached to each carbon atom.

Nucleic acids (Sections 25.1 and 25.4A): Biological polymers of nucleotides. DNA and RNA are, respectively, nucleic acids that preserve and transcribe hereditary information within cells.

Nucleophile (Sections 3.4A, 6.2, 6.3, and 6.13B): A Lewis base, an electron pair donor that seeks a positive center in a molecule.

Nucleophilic addition-elimination (Section 17.4): Addition of a nucleophile to a carbonyl (or other trigonal) carbon, yielding a tetrahedral intermediate, followed by elimination of a leaving group to yield a trigonal planar product.

Nucleophilic addition to the carbonyl carbon (Sections 12.1A and 16.6): A reaction in which a _nucleophile_ (an electron-pair donor) forms a bond to the carbon of a _carbonyl_ (C=O) group. To avoid violating the octet rule, the electrons of the carbon-oxygen π-bond shift to the oxygen, resulting in a four-coordinate (tetrahedral) carbon.

Nucleophilic aromatic substitution (Section 21.11A): A substitution reaction in which a nucleophile attacks an aromatic ring bearing strongly electron-withdrawing groups in ortho and/or para positions relative to the site of attack and the leaving group. This step is an addition reaction that yields and aryl carbanion (called a Meisenheimer Complex) which is stabilized by the electron-withdrawing groups on the ring. Loss of the leaving group in an elimination step regenerates the aromatic system, yielding a substituted aromatic compound by what was, overall, an addition-elimination process.

Nucleophilicity (Section 6.13B): The relative reactivity of a nucleophile in an S_N2 reaction as measured by relative rates of reaction.

Nucleophilic substitution reaction (Section 6.2): A reaction initiated by a nucleophile (a neutral or negative species with an unshared electron pair) in which the nucleophile reacts with a substrate to replace a substituent (called the leaving group) that departs with an unshared electron pair.

Nucleoside (Sections 22.15A, 25.2, and 25.3): A five-carbon monosaccharide bonded at the 1$'$ position to a purine or pyrimidine.

Nucleotide (Sections 25.2 and 25.3): A five-carbon monosaccharide bonded at the 1$'$ position to a purine or pyrimidine and at the 3$'$ or 5$'$ position to a phosphate group.

O

Octet rule (Sections 1.3 and 1.4A): An empirical rule stating that atoms not having the electronic configuration of a noble gas tend to react by either transferring electrons or sharing electrons so as to achieve the valence electron configuration (i. e., eight electrons) of a noble gas.

Oil (Section 23.2): A triacylglycerol (see below) that is liquid at room temperature.

Olefin (Section 7.1): An old name for an alkene.

Oligonucleotide synthesis (Section 25.7): Synthesis of specific sequence of nucleotides, often by automated solid-phase techniques, in which the nucleotide chain is built up by adding a protected nucleotide in the form of a phosphoramidite to a protected nucleotide linked to a solid phase, (usually a "controlled pore glass") in the presence of a coupling agent. The phosphite triester product is oxidized to a phosphate triester with iodine, producing a chain that has been lengthened by one nucleotide. The protecting group is then removed, and the steps (coupling, oxidation, deprotection) are repeated. After the desired oligonucleotide has been synthesized it is cleaved from the solid support and the remaining protecting groups removed.

Oligopeptide (Section 24.4): A peptide comprised of 3–10 amino acids.

Oligosaccharides (Section 22.1A): A carbohydrate that hydrolyzes to yield 2–10 monosaccharide molecules.

Optically active compound (Sections 5.8 and 5.9): A compound that rotates the plane of polarization of plane-polarized light.

Optical purity (Section 5.9B): A percentage calculated for a mixture of enantiomers by dividing the observed specific rotation for the mixture by the specific rotation of the pure enantiomer and multiplying by 100. The optical purity equals the enantiomeric purity or enantiomeric excess.

Orbital (Section 1.10): A volume of space in which there is a high probability of finding an electron. Orbitals are described mathematically by the squaring of wave functions, and each orbital has a characteristic energy. An orbital can hold two electrons when their spins are paired.

Orbital hybridization (Section 1.12): A mathematical (and theoretical) mixing of two or more atomic orbitals to give the same number of new orbitals, called *hybrid orbitals*, each of which has some of the character of the original atomic orbitals.

Organometallic compound (Section 12.5): A compound that contains a carbon–metal bond.

Orthogonal protecting groups (Section 24.7D): Protecting groups in which one set of protecting groups is stable under conditions for removal of the other, and vice versa.

Ortho-para directors (Section 15.10B): An electron-donating group on an aromatic ring. The major product of electrophilic aromatic substitution on a ring bearing such a group will have the newly substituted electrophile located ortho and/or para to the ortho-para-directing group.

Osazone (Section 22.8): A 1,2-bisarylhydrazone formed by reaction of an aldose or ketose with three molar equivalents of an arylhydrazone. Most common are phenylosazones, formed by reaction with phenylhydrazine, and 2,4-dinitrophenylhydrazones.

Oxidation (Sections 12.2 and 12.4): A reaction that increases the oxidation state of atoms in a molecule or ion. For an organic substrate, oxidation usually involves increasing its oxygen content or decreasing its hydrogen content. Oxidation also accompanies any reaction in which a less electronegative substituent is replaced by a more electronegative one.

Oxidative cleavage (Sections 8.16 and 8.19): A reaction in which the carbon-carbon double bond of an alkene or alkyne is both cleaved and oxidized, yielding compounds with carbon-oxygen double bonds.

Oxidizing agent (Section 12.2): A chemical species that causes another chemical species to become oxidized (lose electrons, or gain bonds to more electronegative elements, often losing bonds to hydrogen in the process). The oxidizing agent is reduced in this process.

Oxime (Section 16.8B): An imine in which a hydroxyl group is bonded to the nitrogen atom.

Oxirane (See **Epoxide** and Section 11.13)

Oxonium ion (Sections 3.12 and 11.12): A chemical species with an oxygen atom that bears a formal positive charge.

Oxonium salt (Section 11.12): A salt in which the cation is a species containing a positively charged oxygen.

Oxymercuration (Sections 8.5 and 11.4): The addition of —OH and —HgO_2CR to a multiple bond.

Oxymercuration-demercuration (Sections 8.5 and 11.4): A two-step process for adding the elements of water (H and OH) to a double bond in a Markovnikov orientation without rearrangements. An alkene reacts with mercuric acetate (or trifluoroacetate), forming a bridged mercurinium ion. Water preferentially attacks the more substituted side of the bridged ion, breaking the bridge and resulting, after loss of a proton, in an alcohol. Reduction with $NaBH_4$ replaces the mercury group with a hydrogen atom, yielding the final product.

Ozonolysis (Sections 8.16B and 8.19): The oxidative cleavage of a multiple bond using O_3 (ozone). The reaction leads to the formation of a cyclic compound called an *ozonide*, which is then reduced to carbonyl compounds by treatment with dimethyl sulfide (Me_2S) or zinc and acetic acid.

P

***p* orbitals** (Section 1.10): A set of three degenerate (equal energy) atomic orbitals shaped like two tangent spheres with a nodal plane at the nucleus. For *p* orbitals of second row elements, the principal quantum number, *n* (see **Atomic orbital**), is 2; the azimuthal quantum number, *l*, is 1; and the magnetic quantum numbers, *m*, are +1, 0, or −1.

Paraffin (Section 4.15): An old name for an alkane.

Partial hydrolysis (Section 24.5D): Random cleavage of a polypeptide with dilute acid, resulting in a family of peptides of varying lengths that can be more easily sequenced than the parent polypeptide. Once each fragment peptide is sequenced, the areas of overlap indicate the sequence of the initial peptide.

Pauli exclusion principle (Section 1.10A): A principle that states that no two electrons of an atom or molecule may have the same set of four quantum numbers. It means that only two electrons can occupy the same orbital, and then only when their spin quantum numbers are opposite. When this is true, we say that the spins of the electrons are paired.

Peptide (Section 24.4): A molecule comprised of amino acids bonded via amide linkages.

Peptide bond, peptide linkage (Section 24.4): The amide linkage between amino acids in a peptide.

Peracid (See **Peroxy acid**, Section 11.13A)

Periplanar (See **Coplanar**, Section 7.6D)

Peroxide (Section 10.1A): A compound with an oxygen–oxygen single bond.

Peroxy acid (Section 11.13A): An acid with the general formula RCO_3H, containing an oxygen–oxygen single bond.

Phase sign (Section 1.9): Signs, either + or −, that are characteristic of all equations that describe the amplitudes of waves.

Phase transfer catalysis (Section 11.16): A reaction using a reagent that transports an ion from an aqueous phase into a nonpolar phase where reaction takes place more rapidly. Tetraalkylammonium ions and crown ethers are phase-transfer catalysts.

Phenyl halide (Section 6.1): An organic halide in which the halogen atom is bonded to a benzene ring. A phenyl halide is a specific type of aryl halide (Section 6.1).

Phospholipid (Section 23.6): Compound that is structurally derived from *phosphatidic acid*. Phosphatidic acids are derivatives of glycerol in which two hydroxyl groups are joined to fatty acids, and one terminal hydroxyl group is joined in an ester linkage to phosphoric acid. In a phospholipid the phosphate group of the phosphatidic acid is joined in ester linkage to a nitrogen-containing compound such as choline, 2-aminoethanol, or L-serine.

Physical property (Section 2.13): Properties of a substance, such as melting point and boiling point, that relate to physical (as opposed to chemical) changes in the substance.

Pi (π) bond (Section 1.13): A bond formed when electrons occupy a bonding π molecular orbital (i.e., the lower energy molecular orbital that results from overlap of parallel *p* orbitals on adjacent atoms).

Pi (π) molecular orbital (Section 1.13): A molecular orbital formed when parallel p orbitals on adjacent atoms overlap. Pi molecular orbitals may be *bonding* (p lobes of the same phase sign overlap) or *antibonding* (p orbitals of opposite phase sign overlap).

pKa (Section 3.5B): The pK_a is the negative logarithm of the acidity constant, K_a. p$K_a = -\log K_a$.

Plane-polarized light (Section 5.8A): Light in which the oscillations of the electrical field occur only in one plane.

Plane of symmetry (Sections 5.6 and 5.12A): An imaginary plane that bisects a molecule in a way such that the two halves of the molecule are mirror images of each other. Any molecule with a plane of symmetry will be achiral.

Polar aprotic solvent (Section 6.13C): A polar solvent that does not have a hydrogen atom attached to an electronegative element. Polar aprotic solvents do *not* hydrogen bond with a Lewis base (e.g., a nucleophile).

Polar covalent bond (Section 2.2): A covalent bond in which the electrons are not equally shared because of differing electronegativities of the bonded atoms.

Polarimeter (Section 5.8B): A device used for measuring optical activity.

Polarizability (Section 6.13C): The susceptibility of the electron cloud of an uncharged molecule to distortion by the influence of an electric charge.

Polar molecule (Section 2.3): A molecule with a dipole moment.

Polar protic solvent (Section 6.13D): A polar solvent that has at least one hydrogen atom bonded to an electronegative element. These hydrogen atoms of the solvent can form hydrogen bonds with a Lewis base (e.g., a nucleophile).

Polymer (Section 10.11): A large molecule made up of many repeating subunits. For example, the polymer polyethylene is made up of the repeating subunit $-(CH_2CH_2)_n-$.

Polymerase chain reaction (PCR) (Section 25.8): A method for multiplying (amplifying) the number of copies of a DNA molecule. The reaction uses DNA polymerase enzymes to attach additional nucleotides to a short oligonucleotide "primer" that is bound to a complementary strand of DNA called a "template." The nucleotide that the polymerases attach are those that are complementary to the base in the adjacent position on the template strand. Each cycle doubles the amount of target DNA that existed prior to the reaction step, yielding an exponential increase in the amount of DNA over time.

Polymerizations (Section 10.11): Reactions in which individual subunits (called *monomers*) are joined together to form long-chain macromolecules.

Polypeptide (Section 24.4): A peptide comprised of many (>10) amino acids.

Polysaccharide (Sections 22.1A and 22.13): A carbohydrate that, on a molecular basis, undergoes hydrolytic cleavage to yield many molecules of a monosaccharide. Also called a glycan.

Polyunsaturated fatty acid/ester (Section 23.2): A fatty acid or ester of a fatty acid whose carbon chain contain two or more double bonds.

Potential energy (Section 3.8): Potential energy is stored energy; it exists when attractive or repulsive forces exist between objects.

Potential energy diagram (Section 4.8B); A graphical plot of the potential energy changes that occurs as molecules (or atoms) react

(or interact). Potential energy is plotted on the vertical axis, and the progress of the reaction on the horizontal axis

Primary carbon atom (Section 2.5): A carbon atom that has only one other carbon atom attached to it.

Primary structure (Sections 24.1, 24.5, and 24.6): The covalent structure of a polypeptide or protein. This structure is determined, in large part, by determining the sequence of amino acids in the protein.

Prochiral center (Section 12.3D): A group is prochiral if replacement of one of two identical groups at a tetrahedral atom, or if addition of a group to a trigonal planar atom, leads to a new chirality center. At a tetrahedral atom where there are two identical groups, the identical groups can be designated pro-R and pro-S depending on what configuration would result when it is imagined that each is replaced by a group of next higher priority (but not higher than another existing group).

Prostaglandins (Section 23.5): Natural C_{20} carboxylic acids that contain a five-membered ring, at least one double bond, and several oxygen-containing functional groups. Prostaglandins mediate a variety of physiological processes.

Prosthetic group (Sections 24.9 and 24.12): An enzyme cofactor that is permanently bound to the enzyme.

Protecting group (Sections 11.11D, 11.11E, 12.9, 15.5, 16.7C, and 24.7A): A group that is introduced into a molecule to protect a sensitive group from reaction while a reaction is carried out at some other location in the molecule. Later, the protecting group is removed. Also called blocking group. (See also **Orthogonal protecting group.**)

Protein (Section 24.4): A large biological polymer of α-amino acids joined by amide linkages.

Proteome Proteome (Sections 25.1 and 25.9): The set of all proteins encoded within the genome of an organism and expressed at any given time.

Proteomics (Section 24.14): The study of all proteins that are expressed in a cell at a given time.

Protic solvent (Sections 3.11, 6.13C, and 6.13D): A solvent whose molecules have a hydrogen atom attached to a strongly electronegative element such as oxygen or nitrogen. Molecules of a protic solvent can therefore form hydrogen bonds to unshared electron pairs of oxygen or nitrogen atoms of solute molecules or ions, thereby stabilizing them. Water, methanol, ethanol, formic acid, and acetic acid are typical protic solvents.

Proton decoupling (Section 9.11B): An electronic technique used in ^{13}C NMR spectroscopy that allows decoupling of spin–spin interactions between ^{13}C nuclei and ^1H nuclei. In spectra obtained in this mode of operation all carbon resonances appear as singlets.

Psi (ψ) function (See **Wave function** and Section 1.9)

Pyranose (Section 22.2C): A sugar in which the cyclic acetal or hemiacetal ring is six membered.

Q

Quartet (Section 9.2): An NMR signal comprised of four peaks in a 1:3:3:1 area ratio, caused by signal splitting from three neighboring NMR-active spin 1/2 nuclei.

Quaternary ammonium salt (Sections 20.2B and 20.3D): Ionic compounds in which a nitrogen bears four organic groups and a positive charge, paired with a counterion.

Quaternary structure (Sections 24.1 and 24.8C): The overall structure of a protein having multiple subunits (non-covalent aggregates of more than one polypeptide chain). Each subunit has a primary, secondary, and tertiary structure of its own.

R

R (Section 2.4A): A symbol used to designate an alkyl group. Oftentimes it is taken to symbolize any organic group.

R,S-System (Section 5.7): A method for designating the configuration of tetrahedral chirality centers.

Racemic form (*racemate* or *racemic mixture*) (Sections 5.9A, 5.9B, and 5.10A): An equimolar mixture of enantiomers. A racemic form is optically inactive.

Racemization (Section 6.12A): A reaction that transforms an optically active compound into a racemic form is said to proceed with racemization. Racemization takes place whenever a reaction causes chiral molecules to be converted to an achiral intermediate.

Radical addition to alkenes (Section 10.10): A process by which an atom with an unshared electron, such as a bromine atom, adds to an alkene with homolytic cleavage of the π-bond and formation of a σ-bond from the radical to the carbon; the resulting carbon radical then continues the chain reaction to product the final product plus another species with an unshared electron.

Radical cation (Section 9.14): A chemical species containing an unshared electron and a positive charge.

Radical (or *free radical*) (Sections 10.1, 10.6, and 10.7): An uncharged chemical species that contains an unpaired electron.

Radical halogenation (Section 10.3): Substitution of a hydrogen by a halogen through a radical reaction mechanism.

Radical reaction (Section 10.1B): A reaction involving radicals. Homolysis of covalent bonds occurs in radical reactions.

Random coil arrangement (Section 24.8): A type of protein secondary structure that is flexible, changing, and statistically random in its conformations.

Rate control (See **Kinetic control**)

Rate-determining step (Section 6.9A): If a reaction takes place in a series of steps, and if the first step is intrinsically slower than all of the others, then the rate of the overall reaction will be the same as (will be determined by) the rate of this slow step.

Reaction coordinate (Section 6.7): The abscissa in a potential energy diagram that represents the progress of the reaction. It represents the changes in bond orders and bond distances that must take place as reactants are converted to products.

Reaction mechanism (Sections 3 intro and 3.13): A step-by-step description of the events that are postulated to take place at the molecular level as reactants are converted to products. A mechanism will include a description of all intermediates and transition states. Any mechanism proposed for a reaction must be consistent with all experimental data obtained for the reaction.

Rearrangement (Sections 3.1, 7.8A, and 7.8B): A reaction that results in a product with the same atoms present but a different carbon skeleton from the reactant. The type of rearrangement called a 1,2 shift involves the migration of an organic group (with its electrons) from one atom to the atom next to it.

Reducing agent (Sections 12.2 and 12.3A): A chemical species that causes another chemical species to become reduced (to gain electrons, or to lose bonds to electronegative elements, often

gaining bonds to hydrogen in the process). The reducing agent is oxidized in this process.

Reducing sugar (Section 22.6A): Sugars that reduce Tollens' or Benedict's reagents. All sugars that contain hemiacetal or hemiketal groups (and therefore are in equilibrium with aldehydes or α-hydroxyketones) are reducing sugars. Sugars in which only acetal or ketal groups are present are nonreducing sugars.

Reduction (Sections 12.2 and 12.3): A reaction that lowers the oxidation state of atoms in a molecule or ion. Reduction of an organic compound usually involves increasing its hydrogen content or decreasing its oxygen content. Reduction also accompanies any reaction that results in replacement of a more electronegative substituent by a less electronegative one.

Reductive amination (Section 20.4C): A method for synthesizing primary, secondary, or tertiary amines in which an aldehyde or ketone is treated with a primary or secondary amine to produce an imine (when primary amines are used) or an iminium ion (when secondary amines are used), followed by reduction to produce an amine product.

Regioselective reaction (Sections 8.2C and 8.18): A reaction that yields only one (or a predominance of one) constitutional isomer as the product when two or more constitutional isomers are possible products.

Relative configuration (Section 5.15A): The relationship between the configurations of two chiral molecules. Molecules are said to have the same relative configuration when similar or identical groups in each occupy the same position in space. The configurations of molecules can be related to each other through reactions of known stereochemistry, for example, through reactions that cause no bonds to a stereogenic center to be broken.

Replication (Section 25.4C): A process in which DNA unwinds, allowing each chain to act as a template for the formation of its complement, producing two identical DNA molecules from one original molecule.

Resolution (Sections 5.16B and 20.3F): The process by which the enantiomers of a racemic form are separated.

Resonance (Sections 3.10A, 13.4, and 15.11B): An effect by which a substituent exerts either an electron-releasing or electron-withdrawing effect through the π system of the molecule.

Resonance energy (Section 14.5): An energy of stabilization that represents the difference in energy between the actual compound and that calculated for a single resonance structure. The resonance energy arises from delocalization of electrons in a conjugated system.

Resonance structures (or *resonance contributors*) (Sections 1.8, 1.8A, 13.2B, and 13.4A): Lewis structures that differ from one another only in the position of their electrons. A single resonance structure will not adequately represent a molecule. The molecule is better represented as a *hybrid* of all of the resonance structures.

Restriction endonucleases (Section 25.6): Enzymes that cleave double-stranded DNA at specific base sequences.

Retro-aldol reaction (Section 19.4B): Aldol reactions are reversible; under certain conditions an aldol product will revert to its aldol reaction precursors. This process is called a *retro-aldol reaction.*

Retrosynthetic analysis (Section 7.15B): A method for planning syntheses that involves reasoning backward from the target molecule through various levels of precursors and thus finally to the starting materials.

Ribonucleic acid (RNA) (Sections 25.1 and 25.5): One of the two classes of molecules (the other is DNA) that carry genetic information in cells. RNA molecules transcribe and translate the information from DNA for the mechanics of protein synthesis.

Ribozyme (Section 25.5B): A ribonucleic acid that acts as a reaction catalyst.

Ring flip (Section 4.12): The change in a cyclohexane ring (resulting from partial bond rotations) that converts one ring conformation to another. A chair–chair ring flip converts any equatorial substitutent to an axial substituent and vice versa.

Ring strain (Section 4.10): The increased potential energy of the cyclic form of a molecule (usually measured by heats of combustion) when compared to its acyclic form.

S

1,2 Shift (Section 7.8A): The migration of a chemical bond with its attached group from one atom to an adjacent atom.

S_N1 reaction (Sections 6.9, 6.10, 6.12, 6.13, and 6.18B): Literally, substitution nucleophilic unimolecular. A multistep nucleophilic substitution in which the leaving group departs in a unimolecular step before the attack of the nucleophile. The rate equation is first order in substrate but zero order in the attacking nucleophile.

S_N2 reaction (Sections 6.5B, 6.6–6.8, 6.13, and 6.18A): Literally, substitution nucleophilic bimolecular. A bimolecular nucleophilic substitution reaction that takes place in a single step. A nucleophile attacks a carbon bearing a leaving group from the back side, causing an inversion of configuration at this carbon and displacement of the leaving group.

Salt (Section 1.3A): The product of a reaction between an acid and a base. Salts are ionic compounds composed of oppositely charged ions.

Sanger *N*-terminal analysis (Section 24.5B): A method for determining the *N*-terminal amino acid residue of a peptide by its S_NAr (nucleophilic aromatic substitution) reaction with dinitrofluorobenzene, followed by peptide hydrolysis and comparison of the product with known standards.

Saponification (Sections 17.7B and 23.2C): Base-promoted hydrolysis of an ester.

Saturated compound (Sections 2.1, 7.12, and 23.2): A compound that does not contain any multiple bonds.

Saturated fatty acids (Section 23.2): Fatty acids that contain no carbon-carbon double bonds.

Sawhorse formula (Section 4.8A): A chemical formula that depicts the spatial relationships of groups in a molecule in a way similar to dash-wedge formulas.

Secondary amine (Section 20.1): A derivative of ammonia in which there are two carbons bonded to a nitrogen atom. Secondary amines have a formula R_2NH, where the R groups can be the same or different.

Secondary carbon (Section 2.5): A carbon atom that has two other carbon atoms attached to it.

Secondary structure (Sections 24.1 and 24.8A): The local conformation of a polypeptide backbone. These local conformations are specified in terms of regular folding patterns such as pleated sheets, α helixes, and turns.

Shielding and deshielding (Section 9.7): Effects observed in NMR spectra caused by the circulation of sigma and pi electrons within the molecule. Shielding causes signals to appear at lower frequencies (upfield), deshielding causes signals to appear at higher frequencies (downfield).

Sigma (σ) bond (Section 1.12A): A single bond. A bond formed when electrons occupy the bonding σ orbital formed by the end-on overlap of atomic orbitals (or hybrid orbitals) on adjacent atoms. In a sigma bond the electron density has circular symmetry when viewed along the bond axis.

Sigma (σ) orbital (Section 1.13): A molecular orbital formed by end-on overlap of orbitals (or lobes of orbitals) on adjacent atoms. Sigma orbitals may be *bonding* (orbitals or lobes of the same phase sign overlap) or *antibonding* (orbitals or lobes of opposite phase sign overlap).

Signal splitting (Sections 9.2C and 9.9): Splitting of an NMR signal into multiple peaks, in patterns such as doublets, triplets, quartets, etc., caused by interactions of the energy levels of the magnetic nucleus under observation with the energy levels of nearby magnetic nuclei.

Silyl ether (silylation) (Section 11.11E): Conversion of an alcohol, R—OH, to a silyl ether (usually of the form R—O—SiR′$_3$, where the groups on silicon may be the same or different). Silyl ethers are used as protecting groups for the alcohol functionality.

Single bond (Section 1.12A): A bond between two atoms comprised of two electrons shared in a sigma bond.

Singlet (Section 9.2C): An NMR signal with only a single, unsplit peak.

Site-specific cleavage (Section 24.5D): A method of cleaving peptides at specific, known sites using enzymes and specialized reagents. For example, the enzyme trypsin preferentially catalyzes hydrolysis of peptide bonds on the C-terminal side of arginine and lysine. Other bonds in the peptide are not cleaved by this reagent.

Solid-phase peptide synthesis (SPPS) (Section 24.7D): A method of peptide synthesis in which the peptide is synthesized on a solid support, one amino acid residue at a time. The first amino acid of the peptide is bonded as an ester between its carboxylic acid group and a hydroxyl of the solid support (a polymer bead). This is then treated with a solution of the second amino acid and appropriate coupling reagents, creating a dipeptide. Excess reagents, byproducts, etc. are washed away. Further linkages are synthesized in the same manner. The last step of the synthesis is cleavage of the peptide from the solid support and purification.

Solubility (Section 2.13D): The extent to which a given solute dissolves in a given solvent, usually expressed as a weight per unit volume (e.g., grams per 100 mL).

Solvent effect (Sections 6.13C and 6.13D): An effect on relative rates of reaction caused by the solvent. For example, the use of a polar solvent will increase the rate of reaction of an alkyl halide in an S_N1 reaction.

Solvolysis (Section 6.12B): Literally, cleavage by the solvent. A nucleophilic substitution reaction in which the nucleophile is a molecule of the solvent.

s orbital (Section 1.10): A spherical atomic orbital. For s orbitals the azimuthal quantum number $l = 0$ (See **Atomic orbital**).

Specific rotation (Section 5.8C): A physical constant calculated from the observed rotation of a compound using the following equation:

$$[\alpha]_D = \frac{\alpha}{c \times l}$$

where α is the observed rotation using the D line of a sodium lamp, c is the concentration of the solution or the density of a neat liquid in grams per milliliter, and l is the length of the tube in decimeters.

Spectroscopy (Section 9.1): The study of the interaction of energy with matter. Energy can be absorbed, transmitted, emitted or cause a chemical change (break bonds) when applied to matter. Among other uses, spectroscopy can be used to probe molecular structure.

Spin decoupling (Section 9.10): An effect that causes spin–spin splitting not to be observed in NMR spectra.

Spin–spin splitting (Section 9.9): An effect observed in NMR spectra. Spin–spin splittings result in a signal appearing as a multiplet (i.e., doublet, triplet, quartet, etc.) and are caused by magnetic couplings of the nucleus being observed with nuclei of nearby atoms.

Splitting tree diagrams (Section 9.9B): A method of illustrating the NMR signal splittings in a molecule by drawing "branches" from the original signal. The distance between the branches is proportional to the magnitude of the coupling constant. This type of analysis is especially useful when multiple splittings (splitting of already split signals) occur due to coupling with non-equivalent protons.

***sp* orbital** (Section 1.14): A hybrid orbital that is derived by mathematically combining one *s* atomic orbital and one *p* atomic orbital. Two *sp* hybrid orbitals are obtained by this process, and they are oriented in opposite directions with an angle of 180° between them.

***sp²* orbital** (Section 1.13): A hybrid orbital that is derived by mathematically combining one *s* atomic orbital and two *p* atomic orbitals. Three *sp²* hybrid orbitals are obtained by this process, and they are directed toward the corners of an equilateral triangle with angles of 120° between them.

***sp³* orbital** (Section 1.12A): A hybrid orbital that is derived by mathematically combining one *s* atomic orbital and three *p* atomic orbitals. Four *sp³* hybrid orbitals are obtained by this process, and they are directed toward the corners of a regular tetrahedron with angles of 109.5° between them.

Staggered conformation (Section 4.8A): A temporary orientation of groups around two atoms joined by a single bond such that the bonds of the back atom exactly bisect the angles formed by the bonds of the front atom when shown in a Newman projection formula:

Front atom

Rear atom

A staggered conformation

Step-growth polymer (See also **Condendsation polymer**, Section 17.12 and Special Topic C in *WileyPLUS*): A polymer produced when bifunctional monomers (or potentially bifunctional monomers) react with each other through the intermolecular elimination of water or an alcohol. Polyesters, polyamides, and polyurethanes are all step-growth (condensation) polymers

Stereochemistry (Sections 5.2B, 6.8, and 6.14): Chemical studies that take into account the spatial aspects of molecules.

Stereogenic carbon (Section 5.4): A single tetrahedral carbon with four different groups attached to it. Also called an *asymmetric carbon*, *a stereocenter*, or *a chirality center*. The last usage is preferred.

Stereogenic center (Section 5.4): When the exchange of two groups bonded to the same atom produces stereoisomers, the atom is said to be a stereogenic atom, or stereogenic center.

Stereoisomers (Sections 1.13B, 4.9A, 4.13, 5.2B, and 5.14): Compounds with the same molecular formula that differ only in the arrangement of their atoms in space. Stereoisomers have the same connectivity and, therefore, are not constitutional isomers. Stereoisomers are classified further as being either enantiomers or diastereomers.

Stereoselective reaction (Sections 5.10B, 8.21C, and 12.3D): In reactions where chirality centers are altered or created, a stereoselective reaction produces a preponderance of one stereoisomer. Furthermore, a stereoselective reaction can be either enantioselective, in which case the reaction produces a preponderance of one enantiomer, or diastereoselective, in which case the reaction produces a preponderance of one diastereomer.

Stereospecific reaction (Sections 8.12 and 8.20C): A reaction in which a particular stereoisomeric form of the reactant reacts in such a way that it leads to a specific stereoisomeric form of the product.

Steric effect (Section 6.13A): An effect on relative reaction rates caused by the space-filling properties of those parts of a molecule attached at or near the reacting site.

Steric hindrance (Sections 4.8B and 6.13A): An effect on relative reaction rates caused when the spatial arrangement of atoms or groups at or near the reacting site hinders or retards a reaction.

Steroid (Section 23.4): Steroids are lipids that are derived from the following perhydrocyclopentanophenanthrene ring system:

Structural formula (Section 1.7): A formula that shows how the atoms of a molecule are attached to each other.

Substituent effect (Sections 3.10D and 15.11F): An effect on the rate of reaction (or on the equilibrium constant) caused by the replacement of a hydrogen atom by another atom or group. Substituent effects include those effects caused by the size of the atom or group, called steric effects, and those effects caused by the ability of the group to release or withdraw electrons, called electronic effects. Electronic effects are further classified as being inductive effects or resonance effects.

Substitution reaction (Sections 3.13, 6.2, 10.3, 15.1, and 17.4): A reaction in which one group replaces another in a molecule.

Substitutive nomenclature (Section 4.3F): A system for naming compounds in which each atom or group, called a substituent, is cited as a prefix or suffix to a parent compound. In the IUPAC system only one group may be cited as a suffix. Locants (usually numbers) are used to tell where the group occurs.

Substrate (Sections 6.2 and 24.9): The molecule or ion that undergoes reaction.

Sugar (Section 22.12A): A carbohydrate.

Sulfa drugs (Section 20.10): Sulfonamide antibacterial agents, most of which have the general structure p-$H_2NC_6H_4SO_2NHR$. Sulfa drugs act as *antimetabolites* (they inhibit the growth of microbes) by inhibiting the enzymatic steps that are involved in the synthesis of folic acid; when deprived of folic acid, the microorganism dies.

Sulfonamides (Section 20.9): An amide derivative of a sulfonic acid, usually made by the reaction of ammonia, or a primary or secondary amine, with a sulfonyl chloride, resulting in compounds having the general formulas $R'SO_2NH_2$, $R'SO_2NHR$, or $R'SO_2NR_2$, respectively.

Sulfonate ester (Section 11.10): A compound with the formula $ROSO_2R'$ and considered to be derivatives of sulfonic acids, $HOSO_2R'$. Sulfonate esters are used in organic synthesis because of the excellent leaving group ability of the fragment $^-OSO_2R'$.

Superposable (Sections 1.13B and 5.1): Two objects are superposable if, when one object is placed on top of the other, all parts of each coincide. To be superposable is different than to be superimposable. Any two objects can be superimposed simply by putting one object on top of the other, whether or not all parts coincide. The condition of superposability must be met for two things to be identical.

Syn addition (Sections 7.13A and 8.15A): An addition that places both parts of the adding reagent on the same face of the reactant.

Syn coplanar (Section 7.6D): The relative position of two groups that have a 0° degree dihedral angle between them.

Syn dihydroxylation (Section 8.16A): An oxidation reaction in which an alkene reacts to become a 1,2-diol (also called a *glycol*) with the newly bonded hydroxyl groups added to the same face of the alkene.

Syndiotactic polymer (Special Topic B.1 in *WileyPLUS*): A polymer in which the configuration at the stereogenic centers along the chain alternate regularly: (R), (S), (R), (S), etc.

Synthetic equivalent (Sections 8.20B, 18.6, and 18.7): A compound that functions as the equivalent of a molecular fragment needed in a synthesis.

Synthon (Section 8.20B): The fragments that result (on paper) from the disconnection of a bond. The actual reagent that will, in a synthetic step, provide the synthon is called the *synthetic equivalent*.

T

Tautomerization (Section 18.2): An isomerization by which tautomers are rapidly interconverted, as in keto-enol tautomerization.

Tautomers (Section 18.2): Constitutional isomers that are easily interconverted. Keto and enol tautomers, for example, are rapidly interconverted in the presence of acids and bases.

Terminal residue analysis (Section 24.5): Methods used to determine the sequence of amino acids in a peptide by reactions involving the *N*- and *C*-terminal residues.

Terpene (Section 23.3): Terpenes are lipids that have a structure that can be derived on paper by linking isoprene units.

Terpenoids (Section 23.3): Oxygen-containing derivatives of terpenes.

Tertiary amine (Section 20.1): A derivative of ammonia in which there are three carbons bonded to a nitrogen atom. Tertiary amines have a formula R_3N where the R groups can be the same or different.

Tertiary carbon (Section 2.5): A carbon atom that has three other carbon atoms attached to it.

Tertiary structure (Sections 24.1 and 24.8B): The three dimensional shape of a protein that arises from folding of its polypeptide chains superimposed on its α helixes and pleated sheets.

Tetrahedral intermediate (Section 17.4): A species created by the attack of a nucleophile on a trigonal carbon atom. In the case of a carbonyl group, as the electrons of the nucleophile form a bond to the carbonyl carbon the electrons of the carbon-oxygen π-bond shift to the oxygen. The carbon of the carbonyl group becomes four-coordinate (tetrahedral), while the oxygen gains an electron-pair and becomes negatively charged.

Thermodynamic control (Section 18.4A): A principle stating that the ratio of products of a reaction that reaches equilibrium is determined by the relative stabilities of the products (as measured by their standard free energies, $\Delta G°$). The most abundant product will be the one that is the most stable. Also called equilibrium control.

Thermodynamic enolate (Section 18.4A): In a situation in which more than one enolate anion can be formed, the *thermodynamic enolate* is the more stable of the possible enolate anions—usually the enolate with the more substituted double bond. A thermodynamic enolate is formed predominantly under conditions that permit the establishment of an equilibrium.

Thermodynamic or equilibrium product (Section 13.9A): When multiple products are possible, the product formed that is most stable; sometimes formed via a reversible, equilibrium process.

Torsional barrier (Section 4.8B): The barrier to rotation of groups joined by a single bond caused by repulsions between the aligned electron pairs in the eclipsed form.

Torsional strain (Sections 4.9 and 4.10): The strain associated with an eclipsed conformation of a molecule; it is caused by repulsions between the aligned electron pairs of the eclipsed bonds.

Tosylate (Section 11.10): A *p*-toluenesulfonate ester, which is a compound that contains the p-$CH_3C_6H_4SO_3$— group, i.e., p-$CH_3C_6H_4SO_3R$

Transcription (Section 25.5): Synthesis of a messenger RNA (mRNA) molecule that is complimentary to a section of DNA that carries genetic information.

Transesterification (Section 17.7A): A reaction involving the exchange of the alkoxyl portion of an ester for a different alkoxyl group, resulting in a new ester.

Transition state (Sections 6.6, 6.7, and 6.10): A state on a potential energy diagram corresponding to an energy maximum (i.e., characterized by having higher potential energy than immediately adjacent states). The term transition state is also used to refer to the species that occurs at this state of maximum potential energy; another term used for this species is *the activated complex*.

Translation (Section 25.5E): The ribosomal synthesis of a polypeptide using an mRNA template.

Triacylglycerols (Section 23.2): An ester of glycerol (glycerin) in which all three of the hydroxyl groups are esterified.

Triflate (Section 11.10): A methanesulfonate ester, which is a compound that contains the CH_3SO_3— group, i.e., p-CH_3SO_3R

Tripeptide (Section 24.4): A peptide comprised of three amino acids.

Triple bonds (Section 1.3B): Bonds comprised of one sigma (σ) bond and two pi (π) bonds.

Triplet (Section 9.2C): An NMR signal comprised of three peaks in a 1:2:1 area ratio, caused by signal splitting from two neighboring NMR-active spin 1/2 nuclei.

Trisaccharides (Section 22.1A): A carbohydrate that, when hydrolyzed, yields three monosaccharide molecules.

Two-dimensional (2D) NMR (Section 9.12): NMR techniques such as COSY and HETCOR that correlate one property (e.g., coupling), or type of nucleus, with another. (See **COSY** and **HETCOR**.)

U

Ultraviolet–visible (UV–Vis) spectroscopy (Section 13.8): A type of optical spectroscopy that measures the absorption of light in the visible and ultraviolet regions of the spectrum. Visible–UV spectra primarily provide structural information about the kind and extent of conjugation of multiple bonds in the compound being analyzed.

Unimolecular reaction (Section 6.9): A reaction whose rate-determining step involves only one species.

Unsaturated compound (Sections 2.1, 7.13, and 23.2): A compound that contains multiple bonds.

Unsaturated fatty acids (Section 23.2): Fatty acids that contain at least one carbon-carbon double bond.

Upfield (Section 9.3): Any area or signal in an NMR spectrum that is to the right relative to another. (See **Downfield** for comparison.) A signal that is upfield of another occurs at lower frequency (and lower δ and ppm values) than the other signal.

V

Valence shell (Section 1.3): The outermost shell of electrons in an atom.

***vic*-Dihalide** (Section 7.10): A general term for a molecule having halogen atoms bonded to each of two adjacent carbons.

Vicinal coupling (Sections 9.9 and 9.12A): The splitting of an NMR signal caused by hydrogen atoms on adjacent carbons. (See also **Coupling** and **Signal Splitting**.)

Vicinal (*vic-*) substituents (Section 7.10): Substituents that are on adjacent atoms.

Vinyl group (Sections 4.5 and 6.1): The CH_2—CH— group.

VSEPR model (valence shell electron pair repulsion) (Section 1.16): A method of predicting the geometry at a covalently bonded atom by considering the optimum geometric separation between groups of bonding and non-bonding electrons around the atom

W

Wave function (or ψ **function**) (Section 1.9): A mathematical expression derived from *quantum mechanics* corresponding to an energy state for an electron, i.e., for an orbital. The square of the ψ function, ψ^2, gives the probability of finding the electron in a particular place in space.

Wavelength, λ (Sections 2.15 and 13.8A): The distance between consecutive crests (or troughs) of a wave.

Wavenumber, $\bar{v}$ (Section 2.15): A way to express the frequency of a wave. The wavenumber is the number of waves per centimeter, expressed as cm^{-1}.

Waxes (Section 23.7): Esters of long-chain fatty acids and long-chain alcohols.

Williamson ether synthesis (Section 11.11B): The synthesis of an ether by the S_N2 reaction of an alkoxide ion with a substrate bearing a suitable leaving group (often a halide, sulfonate, or sulfate).

Y

Ylide (Section 16.10): An electrically neutral molecule that has a negative carbon with an unshared electron pair adjacent to a positive heteroatom.

Z

Zaitsev's rule (Sections 7.6B and 7.8A): A rule stating that an elimination will give as the major product the most stable alkene (i.e., the alkene with the most highly substituted double bond).

Zwitterion (See **Dipolar ion** and Section 24.2C): Another name for a dipolar ion.

[INDEX]